COMPUTER TOOLS promote flexibility and meet ABET requir

- *PSpice* is introduced in Chapter 3 and appears in special sections througho Appendix D serves as a tutorial on *PSpice* for Windows for readers not fami use. The special sections contain examples and practice problems using *PSpice*. Additional homework problems at the end of each chapter also provide an opportunity to use *Pspice*.

- *MATLAB®* is introduced through a tutorial in Appendix E to show its usage in circuit analysis. A number of examples and practice problems are presented throughout the book in a manner that will allow the student to develop a facility with this powerful tool. A number of end-of-chapter problems will aid in understanding how to effectively use *MATLAB*.

- Multisim 2001 Textbook Edition from Electronics Workbench and more than 125 circuit files from the book presented in the *MultiSim* software are included on a CD-ROM with the book. Multisim 2001, the latest release of the Electronics Workbench flagship product, delivers intuitive schematic capture, accurate simulation and analysis, along with programmable logic. It provides industry-leading power with all of the features and functionality instructors demand in an easy-to-learn and easy-to-use package. Students can create circuits, analyze pre-built circuits, work through virtual laboratory assignments, simulate circuit behavior and troubleshoot for faults. Teachers can customize their circuits using Multisim's powerful "Teacher Features" including the ability to build faulted components into a circuit and to password protect access to components, instruments, and analyses.

CAREERS AND HISTORY of electrical engineering pioneers

Since a course in circuit analysis maybe a student's first exposure to electrical engineering, each chapter opens with either an historical sketch of an electrical engineering pioneer or a career-oriented talk on a sub-discipline of electrical engineering. The chapter openers are intended to help students grasp the scope of electrical engineering and give thought to the various careers available to EE graduates. The opening boxes include information on careers in electronics, instrumentation, electromagnetics, control systems, engineering education, the importance of good communication skills, and profiles such engineering pioneers as Faraday, Ampere, Edison, Henry, Fourier, Volta, and Bell.

Fundamentals of

ELECTRIC CIRCUITS

Second Edition

CHARLES K. ALEXANDER
Dean, Fenn College of Engineering

Cleveland State University

MATTHEW N. O. SADIKU
Department of
Electrical Engineering

Prairie View A&M University

Boston   Burr Ridge, IL   Dubuque, IA   Madison, WI   New York   San Francisco   St. Louis
Bangkok   Bogotá   Caracas   Kuala Lumpur   Lisbon   London   Madrid   Mexico City
Milan   Montreal   New Delhi   Santiago   Seoul   Singapore   Sydney   Taipei   Toronto

The McGraw·Hill Companies

FUNDAMENTALS OF ELECTRIC CIRCUITS, SECOND EDITION

Published by McGraw-Hill, a business unit of The McGraw-Hill Companies, Inc.,
1221 Avenue of the Americas, New York, NY 10020. Copyright © 2004, 2000 by
The McGraw-Hill Companies, Inc. All rights reserved. No part of this publication may be
reproduced or distributed in any form or by any means, or stored in a database or retrieval
system, without the prior written consent of The McGraw-Hill Companies, Inc., including,
but not limited to, in any network or other electronic storage or transmission, or broadcast
for distance learning.

Some ancillaries, including electronic and print components, may not be available to
customers outside the United States.

This book is printed on acid-free paper.

2 3 4 5 6 7 8 9 0 VNH/VNH 0 9 8 7 6 5

ISBN 0-07-304718-X

Publisher: *Elizabeth A. Jones*
Senior sponsoring editor: *Carlise Paulson*
Developmental editor: *Michelle L. Flomenhoft*
Executive marketing manager: *John Wannemacher*
Marketing coordinator: *Courtney Cooney*
Project manager: *Jane Mohr*
Production supervisor: *Sherry L. Kane*
Media project manager: *Jodi K. Banowetz*
Senior media technology producer: *Phillip Meek*
Coordinator of freelance design: *Rick D. Noel*
Cover/interior designer: *Maureen McCutcheon*
Cover image: *© Getty Images/PhotoDisc, Close-up view of circuit board, Lawrence Lawry*
Lead photo research coordinator: *Carrie K. Burger*
Photo research: *David A. Tietz*
Compositor: *UG / GGS Information Services, Inc.*
Typeface: *10/12 Times Roman*
Printer: *Von Hoffmann Corporation*

Library of Congress Cataloging-in-Publication Data
Alexander, Charles K.
    Fundamentals of electric circuits / Charles K. Alexander, Matthew N. O. Sadiku. —
2nd ed.
        p.   cm.
    Includes bibliographical references and index.
    ISBN 0-07-304718-X
    1. Electric circuits.   I. Sadiku, Matthew N. O.   II. Title.

TK454 .A452   2004
621.319′24—dc21   2002030941
                                                                    CIP

www.mhhe.com

Dedicated to our families, especially

Chris
2002

Contents

Preface   x

Acknowledgments   xii

Guided Tour   xiv

A Note to the Student   xvi

About the Authors   xvii

PART I   DC Circuits   I

Chapter I   Basic Concepts   3

1.1   Introduction   4
1.2   Systems of Units   4
1.3   Charge and Current   6
1.4   Voltage   9
1.5   Power and Energy   10
1.6   Circuit Elements   13
†1.7   Applications   15
    1.7.1   TV Picture Tube
    1.7.2   Electricity Bills
†1.8   Problem Solving   18
1.9   Summary   21
Review Questions   22
Problems   23
Comprehensive Problems   25

Chapter 2   Basic Laws   27

2.1   Introduction   28
2.2   Ohm's Law   28
†2.3   Nodes, Branches, and Loops   33
2.4   Kirchhoff's Laws   35
2.5   Series Resistors and Voltage Division   42
2.6   Parallel Resistors and Current Division   43
†2.7   Wye-Delta Transformations   51
†2.8   Applications   55
    2.8.1   Lighting Systems
    2.8.2   Design of DC Meters
2.9   Summary   61
Review Questions   62
Problems   64
Comprehensive Problems   74

Chapter 3   Methods of Analysis   77

3.1   Introduction   78
3.2   Nodal Analysis   78
3.3   Nodal Analysis with Voltage Sources   85
3.4   Mesh Analysis   90
3.5   Mesh Analysis with Current Sources   95
†3.6   Nodal and Mesh Analyses by Inspection   98
3.7   Nodal Versus Mesh Analysis   102
3.8   Circuit Analysis with *PSpice*   103
†3.9   Applications: DC Transistor Circuits   106
3.10   Summary   110
Review Questions   111
Problems   112
Comprehensive Problem   124

Chapter 4   Circuit Theorems   125

4.1   Introduction   126
4.2   Linearity Property   126
4.3   Superposition   128
4.4   Source Transformation   133
4.5   Thevenin's Theorem   137
4.6   Norton's Theorem   143
†4.7   Derivations of Thevenin's and Norton's Theorems   146
4.8   Maximum Power Transfer   148
4.9   Verifying Circuit Theorems with *PSpice*   150
†4.10   Applications   153
    4.10.1   Source Modeling
    4.10.2   Resistance Measurement
4.11   Summary   159
Review Questions   159
Problems   160
Comprehensive Problems   170

Chapter 5   Operational Amplifiers   173

5.1   Introduction   174
5.2   Operational Amplifiers   174
5.3   Ideal Op Amp   178
5.4   Inverting Amplifier   179
5.5   Noninverting Amplifier   182
5.6   Summing Amplifier   184
5.7   Difference Amplifier   185
5.8   Cascaded Op Amp Circuits   189
5.9   Op Amp Circuit Analysis with *PSpice*   191

†**5.10** Applications   193

5.10.1 Digital-to-Analog Converter
5.10.2 Instrumentation Amplifiers

5.11 Summary   196

Review Questions   198
Problems   199
Comprehensive Problems   210

Chapter 6 Capacitors and Inductors   211

6.1 Introduction   212
6.2 Capacitors   212
6.3 Series and Parallel Capacitors   218
6.4 Inductors   222
6.5 Series and Parallel Inductors   226
†**6.6** Applications   230

6.6.1 Integrator
6.6.2 Differentiator
6.6.3 Analog Computer

6.7 Summary   236

Review Questions   237
Problems   238
Comprehensive Problems   247

Chapter 7 First-Order Circuits   249

7.1 Introduction   250
7.2 The Source-Free *RC* Circuit   250
7.3 The Source-Free *RL* Circuit   255
7.4 Singularity Functions   261
7.5 Step Response of an *RC* Circuit   269
7.6 Step Response of an *RL* Circuit   276
†**7.7** First-Order Op Amp Circuits   280
7.8 Transient Analysis with *PSpice*   285
†**7.9** Applications   288

7.9.1 Delay Circuits
7.9.2 Photoflash Unit
7.9.3 Relay Circuits
7.9.4 Automobile Ignition Circuit

7.10 Summary   294

Review Questions   296
Problems   297
Comprehensive Problems   307

Chapter 8 Second-Order Circuits   309

8.1 Introduction   310
8.2 Finding Initial and Final Values   310
8.3 The Source-Free Series *RLC* Circuit   315

8.4 The Source-Free Parallel *RLC* Circuit   322
8.5 Step Response of a Series *RLC* Circuit   328
8.6 Step Response of a Parallel *RLC* Circuit   333
8.7 General Second-Order Circuits   336
8.8 Second-Order Op Amp Circuits   341
8.9 *PSpice* Analysis of *RLC* Circuits   344
†**8.10** Duality   346
†**8.11** Applications   350

8.11.1 Automobile Ignition System
8.11.2 Smoothing Circuits

8.12 Summary   354

Review Questions   354
Problems   355
Comprehensive Problems   364

PART 2 AC Circuits   367

Chapter 9 Sinusoids and Phasors   369

9.1 Introduction   370
9.2 Sinusoids   371
9.3 Phasors   375
9.4 Phasor Relationships for Circuit Elements   383
9.5 Impedance and Admittance   385
†**9.6** Kirchhoff's Laws in the Frequency Domain   388
9.7 Impedance Combinations   389
†**9.8** Applications   395

9.8.1 Phase-Shifters
9.8.2 AC Bridges

9.9 Summary   400

Review Questions   401
Problems   402
Comprehensive Problems   410

Chapter 10 Sinusoidal Steady-State Analysis   413

10.1 Introduction   414
10.2 Nodal Analysis   414
10.3 Mesh Analysis   417
10.4 Superposition Theorem   421
10.5 Source Transformation   425
10.6 Thevenin and Norton Equivalent Circuits   426
10.7 Op amp AC Circuits   431
10.8 AC Analysis Using *PSpice*   434

†10.9   Applications   437

    10.9.1   Capacitance Multiplier
    10.9.2   Oscillators

10.10   Summary   441

Review Questions   442
Problems   443

Chapter 11   AC Power Analysis   457

11.1   Introduction   458
11.2   Instantaneous and Average
    Power   458
11.3   Maximum Average Power
    Transfer   464
11.4   Effective or RMS Value   468
11.5   Apparent Power and Power
    Factor   471
11.6   Complex Power   473
†11.7   Conservation of AC Power   478
11.8   Power Factor Correction   481
†11.9   Applications   484

    11.9.1   Power Measurement
    11.9.2   Electricity Consumption Cost

11.10   Summary   488

Review Questions   489
Problems   490
Comprehensive Problems   500

Chapter 12   Three-Phase Circuits   503

12.1   Introduction   504
12.2   Balanced Three-Phase Voltages   505
12.3   Balanced Wye-Wye Connection   508
12.4   Balanced Wye-Delta
    Connection   512
12.5   Balanced Delta-Delta
    Connection   514
12.6   Balanced Delta-Wye
    Connection   516
12.7   Power in a Balanced System   520
†12.8   Unbalanced Three-Phase
    Systems   526
12.9   *PSpice* for Three-Phase Circuits   530
†12.10   Applications   534

    12.10.1   Three-Phase Power Measurement
    12.10.2   Residential Wiring

12.11   Summary   543

Review Questions   543
Problems   544
Comprehensive Problems   553

Chapter 13   Magnetically Coupled Circuits   555

13.1   Introduction   556
13.2   Mutual Inductance   556
13.3   Energy in a Coupled Circuit   563
13.4   Linear Transformers   567
13.5   Ideal Transformers   573
13.6   Ideal Autotransformers   580
†13.7   Three-Phase Transformers   584
13.8   *PSpice* Analysis of Magnetically
    Coupled Circuits   587
†13.9   Applications   591

    13.9.1   Transformer as an Isolation Device
    13.9.2   Transformer as a Matching Device
    13.9.3   Power Distribution

13.10   Summary   597

Review Questions   598
Problems   599
Comprehensive Problems   612

Chapter 14   Frequency Response   613

14.1   Introduction   614
14.2   Transfer Function   614
†14.3   The Decibel Scale   618
14.4   Bode Plots   619
14.5   Series Resonance   630
14.6   Parallel Resonance   635
14.7   Passive Filters   638
    14.7.1   Lowpass Filter
    14.7.2   Highpass Filter
    14.7.3   Bandpass Filter
    14.7.4   Bandstop Filter
14.8   Active Filters   643
    14.8.1   First-Order Lowpass Filter
    14.8.2   First-Order Highpass Filter
    14.8.3   Bandpass Filter
    14.8.4   Bandreject (or Notch) Filter
†14.9   Scaling   649
    14.9.1   Magnitude Scaling
    14.9.2   Frequency Scaling
    14.9.3   Magnitude and Frequency Scaling
14.10   Frequency Response Using
    PSpice   652
†14.11   Applications   656

    14.11.1   Radio Receiver
    14.11.2   Touch-Tone Telephone
    14.11.3   Crossover Network

14.12   Summary   661

Review Questions   663
Problems   663
Comprehensive Problems   672

PART 3 | Advanced Circuit Analysis   673

Chapter 15 Introduction to Laplace Transforms   675

15.1   Introduction   676
15.2   Definition of the Laplace Transform   676
15.3   Properties of the Laplace Transform   679
15.4   The Inverse Laplace Transform   689
    15.4.1   Simple Poles
    15.4.2   Repeated Poles
    15.4.3   Complex Poles
15.5   The Convolution Integral   697
†15.6   Application to Integrodifferential Equations   706
15.7   Summary   708
Review Questions   709
Problems   709

Chapter 16 Applications of Laplace Transforms   715

16.1   Introduction   716
16.2   Circuit Element Models   716
16.3   Circuit Analysis   722
16.4   Transfer Functions   726
16.5   State Variables   731
†16.6   Applications   738
    16.6.1   Network Stability
    16.6.2   Network Synthesis
16.7   Computation Using *MATLAB*   745
16.8   Summary   747
Review Questions   748
Problems   749
Comprehensive Problems   756

Chapter 17 The Fourier Series   757

17.1   Introduction   758
17.2   Trigonometric Fourier Series   758
17.3   Symmetry Considerations   767
    17.3.1   Even Symmetry
    17.3.2   Odd Symmetry
    17.3.3   Half-Wave Symmetry
17.4   Circuit Applications   777
17.5   Average Power and RMS Values   780
17.6   Exponential Fourier Series   784

17.7   Fourier Analysis with *PSpice*   790
    17.7.1   Discrete Fourier Transform
    17.7.2   Fast Fourier Transform
†17.8   Applications   796
    17.8.1   Spectrum Analyzers
    17.8.2   Filters
17.9   Summary   799
Review Questions   801
Problems   801
Comprehensive Problems   811

Chapter 18 Fourier Transform   813

18.1   Introduction   814
18.2   Definition of the Fourier Transform   814
18.3   Properties of the Fourier Transform   820
18.4   Circuit Applications   833
18.5   Parseval's Theorem   835
18.6   Comparing the Fourier and Laplace Transforms   838
†18.7   Applications   839
    18.7.1   Amplitude Modulation
    18.7.2   Sampling
18.8   Summary   843
Review Questions   844
Problems   844
Comprehensive Problems   851

Chapter 19 Two-Port Networks   853

19.1   Introduction   854
19.2   Impedance Parameters   854
19.3   Admittance Parameters   859
19.4   Hybrid Parameters   862
19.5   Transmission Parameters   867
†19.6   Relationships Between Parameters   871
19.7   Interconnection of Networks   875
19.8   Computing Two-Port Parameters Using *PSpice*   881
†19.9   Applications   884
    19.9.1   Transistor Circuits
    19.9.2   Ladder Network Synthesis
19.10   Summary   891
Review Questions   892
Problems   893
Comprehensive Problems   904

Appendix A   Simultaneous Equations and Matrix
    Inversion   A-1

Appendix B   Complex Numbers   A-11

Appendix C   Mathematical Formulas   A-19

Appendix D   *PSpice* for Windows   A-25

Appendix E   *MATLAB*   A-53

Appendix F   Answers to Odd-Numbered
    Problems   A-73

Selected Bibliography   B-1

Index   I-1

PREFACE |

Features

The main objectives of the second edition of this book remain the same as in the first edition—to present circuit analysis in a manner that is clearer, more interesting, and easier to understand than earlier texts. This objective is achieved in the following ways:

- A course in circuit analysis is perhaps the first exposure students have to electrical engineering. We have included several features to help students feel at home with the subject. Each chapter opens with either historical sketches of some electrical engineering pioneers to be mentioned in the chapter or a career talk on a subdiscipline of electrical engineering. This is followed by an introduction that links the chapter with the previous chapters and states the chapter objectives. The chapter ends with a summary of the key points and formulas.

- Problem solving is discussed in Chapter 1 to promote sound, step-by-step problem-solving practices. A bookmark is included with each copy of the book to remind students of the solution steps (and to mark their place).

- All principles are presented in a lucid, logical, step-by-step manner. As much as possible, we avoid wordiness and giving too much detail that could hide concepts and impede overall understanding of the material.

- Important formulas are boxed as a means of helping students sort out what is essential from what is not. Also, to ensure that students clearly get the gist of the matter, key terms are defined and highlighted.

- Marginal notes are used as a pedagogical aid. They serve multiple uses such as hints, cross-references, more exposition, warnings, reminders not to make some particular common mistakes, and problem-solving insights.

- Thoroughly worked examples are liberally given at the end of every section. The examples are regarded as part of the text and are clearly explained without asking the reader to fill in missing steps. Thoroughly worked examples give students a good understanding of the solution and the confidence to solve problems themselves. Some of the problems are solved in two or three ways to facilitate an understanding and comparison of different approaches.

- To give students practice opportunity, each illustrative example is immediately followed by a practice problem with the answer. The students can follow the example step by step to solve the practice problem without flipping pages or looking at the end of the book for answers. The practice problem is also intended to test if students understand the preceding example. It will reinforce their grasp of the material before they move on to the next section.

- The last section in each chapter is devoted to application aspects of the concepts covered in the chapter. The material covered in the chapter is applied to at least one or two practical problems or devices. This helps the students see how the concepts are applied to real-life situations.

- Ten review questions in the form of multiple-choice objective items are provided at the end of each chapter with answers. The review questions are intended to cover the little "tricks" which the examples and end-of-chapter problems may not cover. They serve as a self-test device and help students determine how well they have mastered the chapter.

- The end-of-chapter homework problems (as well as the solutions available at the website for instructors only) have been thoroughly checked for accuracy. There are approximately 25 percent new problems in this edition.

- In recognition of the requirement by ABET® (Accreditation Board for Engineering and Technology) on integrating computer tools, the use of *PSpice* is encouraged in a student-friendly manner. Since the Windows version of *PSpice* is becoming popular, it is used instead of the MS-DOS version of *PSpice*. *PSpice* is covered early in the text so that students can become familiar and use it throughout the text. Appendix D serves as a tutorial on *PSpice* for Windows.

- The operational amplifier (op amp) as a basic element is introduced early in the text.

- To ease the transition between the circuit course and signals and systems courses, Fourier and Laplace transforms are covered lucidly and thoroughly.

Organization

This book was written for a two-semester or three-quarter course in linear circuit analysis. The book may also be used for a one-semester course by a proper selection of chapters and sections by the instructor. It is broadly divided into three parts.

- Part 1, consisting of Chapters 1 to 8, is devoted to dc circuits. It covers the fundamental laws and theorems, circuit techniques, and passive and active elements.

- Part 2, which contains Chapters 9 to 14, deals with ac circuits. It introduces phasors, sinusoidal steady-state analysis, ac power, rms values, three-phase systems, and frequency response.

- Part 3, consisting of Chapters 15 to 19, is devoted to advanced techniques for network analysis. It provides students with a solid introduction to the Laplace transform, Fourier series, Fourier transform, and two-port network analysis. The material in three parts is more than sufficient for a two-semester course, so the instructor must select which chapters or sections to cover. Sections marked with the dagger sign (†) may be skipped, explained briefly, or assigned as homework. They can be omitted without loss of continuity. Each chapter has plenty of problems grouped according to the sections of the related material and diverse enough that the instructor can choose some as examples and assign some as homework. More difficult problems are marked with an asterisk (*). Comprehensive problems follow the end-of-chapter problems. They are mostly applications problems which require skills learned from that particular chapter.

In this edition, a new chapter (Chapter 16) has been added to augment Chapter 15 on the Laplace transform. This expansion of analysis in the s domain reflects the importance of the frequency domain in helping the student to fully understand circuits. A new appendix (Appendix E) has been added to provide a tutorial on *MATLAB* and encourage its usage in circuit analysis. In addition, several chapters now include problems to be solved using *MATLAB*. Appendix D on *PSpice* has been upgraded. All the errors in the first edition have been corrected, and every effort has been made to make this edition as error-free as possible.

Prerequisites

As with most introductory circuit courses, the main prerequisites, for a course using the text, are physics and calculus. Although familiarity with complex numbers is helpful in the later part of the book, it is not required.

Supplements

Student CD-ROM. The CD-ROM from the first edition has been upgraded to include the following: Multisim 2001 Textbook Edition from Electronics Workbench and more than 125 circuit files from the book presented in the *Multisim* software. *Multisim 2001*, the latest release of the Electronics Workbench flagship product, delivers intuitive schematic capture, accurate simulation and analysis, along with programmable logic. It provides industry-leading power with all the features and functionality instructors demand in an easy-to-learn and easy-to-use package. Students can create circuits, analyze prebuilt circuits, work through virtual laboratory assignments, simulate circuit behavior, and troubleshoot for faults. Teachers can customize their circuits using *Multisim*'s powerful Teacher Features including the ability to build faulted components into a circuit and to password protect access to components, instruments, and analyses.

Problem Solving Made *Almost* Easy. The workbook, *A Companion to Alexander/Sadiku's Fundamentals of Electric Circuits*, is for sale to students who wish to practice their problem-solving techniques. The workbook contains a discussion of problem-solving strategies and 150 additional problems with complete solutions provided.

Online Learning Center (OLC). The Online Learning Center, which provides material for students and instructors, has been upgraded to include the following: updated solutions manual for instructors only, updated and new PowerPoint slides, updated web links, updated network analysis tutorials, sample pages from the companion workbook, quizzes, learning objectives, and flashcards. More information can be found at www.mhhe.com/alexander2.

Although the textbook is meant to be self-explanatory and act as a tutor for the student, the personal contact in teaching is not forgotten. It is hoped that the book supplies the instructor with all the pedagogical tools necessary to effectively present the material.

Personal Note

Matthew and I would like to express our appreciation for the loving support we have received from our wives (Chris and Hannah), daughters (Ann, Joyce, Christina, Tamara, and Jennifer), son (Baixi), our parents (Ayisat and Solomon Sadiku and Ken and June Alexander), and our extended families.

Unfortunately, Matthew's loving and supportive wife, Chris, passed away during the spring of 2002. It was a tragic loss of a wife, mother of Ann and Joyce, friend, valued companion, and blessed person. She will be missed. On behalf of Matthew, I would like to extend our appreciation for the care and support he and his daughters have received during a very difficult period.

ACKNOWLEDGMENTS

We would like to thank the editorial and production staff of McGraw-Hill for being one of the most professional staffs with whom we have worked! In particular, Kelly Butcher, Senior Developmental Editor; Carlise Paulson, Sponsoring Editor; Michelle Flomenhoft, Developmental Editor II; and Jane Mohr, Project Manager, have been very helpful and patient.

Thanks also to the following: Publisher, Betsy Jones; Marketing Manager, John Wannemacher; Media Producer, Phillip Meek; Production Supervisor, Sherry Kane; Designer, Rick Noel; Photo Research, Carrie Burger; Media Project Manager, Jodi Banowetz.

This edition has benefited from the insightful comments of the following reviewers (in alphabetical order):

Edward W. Chandler, Milwaukee School of Engineering

Mohamed K. Darwish, Brunel University (United Kingdom)

Kevin D. Donohue, University of Kentucky

Gary K. Fedder, Carnegie Mellon University

Cynthia J. Finelli, Kettering University

William K. Kennedy, University of Canterbury (New Zealand)

Bin-Da Liu, National Cheng Kung University (Taiwan)

Damon Miller, Western Michigan University

Ahmad Nafisi, California Polytechnic State University, San Luis Obispo

Hadi Saadat, Milwaukee School of Engineering

Fred Terry, Christian Brother University

Promod Vohra, Northern Illinois University

We would also like to thank the following reviewers for their feedback regarding Chapter 5 and additional resources for their circuits course:

Bogdan Adamczyk, Grand Valley State University

Dr. Keyvan Ahdut, University of the District of Columbia

Hamid Allamehzadeh, Eastern New Mexico University

Jorge L. Aravena, Louisiana State University

Dr. Idir Azouz, Southern Utah University

John A. Bloom, Biola University

Dr. Kiron C. Bordoloi, University of Louisville

James H. Burghart, Cleveland State University

Phil Burton, University of Limerick

Michael Casey, Institute of Technology, Sligo Ballinode Sligo Republic of Ireland

Amit Chatterjea, Purdue University, Fort Wayne

Erik Cheever, Swarthmore College

Fow-Sen Choa, University of Maryland, Baltimore County

Dr. Chiu H. Choi, University of North Florida

Dr. Thomas G. Cleaver, University of Louisville

Michael J. Cloud, Lawrence Technological University

Mehmet Cultu, Gannon University

Dr. Saswati Datta, University of Maryland, Baltimore County

Shirshak Dhali, Southern Illinois University

Fred Dreyfus, Pace University

Amelito G. Enriquez, Cañada College

Dr. Ali Eydgahi, University of Maryland Eastern Shore

Rob Frohne, Walla Walla College

Andreas Fuchs, Pennsylvania State University Erie

Tayeb A. Giuma, University of North Florida

Chandrakanth H. Gowda, Tuskegee University

Duane Hanselman, University of Maine

Reza Hashemian, Northern Illinois University

Dr. Hassan Hassan, Lawrence Technological University

Dr. Rod Heisler, Walla Walla College

Amelito G. Henriquez, University of New Orleans

H. Randolph Holt, Northern Kentucky University

Reza Iravani, University of Toronto

Richard Johnston, Lawrence Technological University

Albert M. Knebel, Monroe Community College

William B. Kolasa, Lawrence Technological University

Roger A. Kuntz, Penn State Erie, The Behrend College

Sharad R. Laxpati, University of Illinois at Chicago

Choon Sae Lee, Southern Methodist University

Venus Limcharoen, Thammasat University

Bin-Da Liu, National Cheng Kung University

Joseph L. LoCicero, Illinois Institute of Technology

Dr. Emeka V. Maduike Maduike, New York Institute of Technology

Md Mahfudz Md Zan, Universiti Teknologi MARA

Dr. Claire L. McCullough, University of Tennessee at Chattanooga

José Medina, State University of New York, College of Technology at Delhi

Martin Mintchev, University of Calgary

Philip C. Munro, Youngstown State University

Sarhan M. Musa, Prairie View A&M University

Nader Namazi, The Catholic University of America

Sudarshan Rao Nelatury, Villanova University

S. Puthusserypady, National University of Singapore

Dr. Habib Rahman, Saint Louis University

Dr. V. Rajaravivarma, Central Connecticut State University

Robert W. Sherwood, Germanna Community College

Elisa H. Barney Smith, Boise State University

Terry L. Speicher, Pennsylvania State University

James C. Squire, Virginia Military Institute

David W. Sukow, Washington and Lee University

Les Thede, Ohio Northern University

Constantine Vassiliadis, Ohio University

Sam Villareal, The University of Texas at Dallas

Chia-Jiu Wang, University of Colorado at Colorado Springs

Dr. Xingwu Wang, Alfred University

Sandra A. Yost, University of Detroit, Mercy

Dr. Hewlon Zimmer, U.S. Merchant Marine Academy

Finally, we are particularly indebted to those instructors and students who used the first edition and took the time to point out errors in that edition. We wish to continue this important spirit, so please keep sending us those e-mails (or direct them to the publisher). We can be reached at c.alexander@ieee.org for Charles Alexander and sadiku@ieee.org for Matthew Sadiku.

C. K. Alexander and M. N. O. Sadiku

GUIDED TOUR

The main objective of this book is to present circuit analysis in a manner that is clearer, more interesting, and easier to understand. For you, the student, here are some features to help you study and be successful in this course.

Each chapter opens with either a historical sketch of an electrical engineering pioneer or a career-oriented talk on a subdiscipline of electrical engineering to give students a sense of the real-world applications of electrical engineering.

Each illustrative example is immediately followed by a practice problem and answer to test understanding of the preceding example.

CHAPTER 5

OPERATIONAL AMPLIFIERS

The purpose of computing is insight, not numbers.
—Richard W. Hamming

Enhancing Your Career

Career in Electronic Instrumentation Engineering involves applying physical principles to design devices for the benefit of humanity. But physical principles cannot be understood without measurement. In fact, physicists often say that physics is the science that measures reality. Just as measurements are a tool for understanding the physical world, instruments are tools for measurement. The operational amplifier introduced in this chapter is a building block of modern electronic instrumentation. Therefore, mastery of operational amplifier fundamentals is paramount to any practical application of electronic circuits.

Electronic instruments are used in all fields of science and engineering. They have proliferated in science and technology to the extent that it would be ridiculous to have a scientific or technical education without exposure to electronic instruments. For example, physicists, physiologists, chemists, and biologists must learn to use electronic instruments. For electrical engineering students in particular, the skill in operating digital and analog electronic instruments is crucial. Such instruments include ammeters, voltmeters, ohmmeters, oscilloscopes, spectrum analyzers, and signal generators.

Beyond developing the skill for operating the instruments, some electrical engineers specialize in designing and constructing electronic instruments. These engineers derive pleasure in building their own instruments. Most

*Electronic Instrumentation used in medical research.
Source: Photo Researchers/Geoff Tompkinson/Science Photo Library/.*

of them invent and patent their inventions. Specialists in electronic instruments find employment in medical schools, hospitals, research laboratories, aircraft industries, and thousands of other industries where electronic instruments are routinely used.

173

CHAPTER 3   Methods of Analysis   93

EXAMPLE 3.5

For the circuit in Fig. 3.18, find the branch currents I_1, I_2, and I_3 using mesh analysis.

Solution:

We first obtain the mesh currents using KVL. For mesh 1,

$$-15 + 5i_1 + 10(i_1 - i_2) + 10 = 0$$

or

$$3i_1 - 2i_2 = 1 \qquad (3.5.1)$$

For mesh 2,

$$6i_2 + 4i_2 + 10(i_2 - i_1) - 10 = 0$$

or

$$i_1 = 2i_2 - 1 \qquad (3.5.2)$$

METHOD 1 Using the substitution method, we substitute Eq. (3.5.2) into Eq. (3.5.1), and write

$$6i_2 - 3 - 2i_2 = 1 \implies i_2 = 1 \text{ A}$$

From Eq. (3.5.2), $i_1 = 2i_2 - 1 = 2 - 1 = 1$ A. Thus,

$$I_1 = i_1 = 1 \text{ A}, \qquad I_2 = i_2 = 1 \text{ A}, \qquad I_3 = i_1 - i_2 = 0$$

METHOD 2 To use Cramer's rule, we cast Eqs. (3.5.1) and (3.5.2) in matrix form as

$$\begin{bmatrix} 3 & -2 \\ -1 & 2 \end{bmatrix} \begin{bmatrix} i_1 \\ i_2 \end{bmatrix} = \begin{bmatrix} 1 \\ 1 \end{bmatrix}$$

We obtain the determinants

$$\Delta = \begin{vmatrix} 3 & -2 \\ -1 & 2 \end{vmatrix} = 6 - 2 = 4$$

$$\Delta_1 = \begin{vmatrix} 1 & -2 \\ 1 & 2 \end{vmatrix} = 2 + 2 = 4, \qquad \Delta_2 = \begin{vmatrix} 3 & 1 \\ -1 & 1 \end{vmatrix} = 3 + 1 = 4$$

Thus,

$$i_1 = \frac{\Delta_1}{\Delta} = 1 \text{ A}, \qquad i_2 = \frac{\Delta_2}{\Delta} = 1 \text{ A}$$

as before.

Figure 3.18   For Example 3.5.

---

94   PART 1   DC Circuits

PRACTICE PROBLEM 3.5

Calculate the mesh currents i_1 and i_2 in the circuit of Fig. 3.19.

Answer: $i_1 = \frac{2}{3}$ A, $i_2 = 0$ A.

Figure 3.19   For Practice Prob. 3.5.

EXAMPLE 3.6

Use mesh analysis to find the current I_o in the circuit in Fig. 3.20.

Solution:

We apply KVL to the three meshes in turn. For mesh 1,

$$-24 + 10(i_1 - i_2) + 12(i_1 - i_3) = 0$$

or

$$11i_1 - 5i_2 - 6i_3 = 12 \qquad (3.6.1)$$

For mesh 2,

$$24i_2 + 4(i_2 - i_3) + 10(i_2 - i_1) = 0$$

or

$$-5i_1 + 19i_2 - 2i_3 = 0 \qquad (3.6.2)$$

For mesh 3,

$$4I_o + 12(i_3 - i_1) + 4(i_3 - i_2) = 0$$

But at node A, $I_o = i_1 - i_2$, so that

$$4(i_1 - i_2) + 12(i_3 - i_1) + 4(i_3 - i_2) = 0$$

or

$$-i_1 - i_2 + 2i_3 = 0 \qquad (3.6.3)$$

In matrix form, Eqs. (3.6.1) to (3.6.3) become

$$\begin{bmatrix} 11 & -5 & -6 \\ -5 & 19 & -2 \\ -1 & -1 & 2 \end{bmatrix} \begin{bmatrix} i_1 \\ i_2 \\ i_3 \end{bmatrix} = \begin{bmatrix} 12 \\ 0 \\ 0 \end{bmatrix}$$

We obtain the determinants as

$$\Delta = \begin{vmatrix} 11 & -5 & -6 \\ -5 & 19 & -2 \\ -1 & -1 & 2 \end{vmatrix}$$

$$= 418 - 30 - 10 - 114 - 22 - 50 = 192$$

Figure 3.20   For Example 3.6.

ce® for Windows is a student-friendly tool introduced to
nts early in the text and used throughout, with discussions
xamples at the end of each appropriate chapter.

The last section in each chapter is
devoted to applications of the
concepts covered in the chapter to
help students apply the concepts to
real-life situations.

The Online Learning Center includes resources for instructors and
students:

For Instructors:
– Solutions Manual
– PowerPoint Slides
– COSMOS (The Complete
  Online Solutions Manual
  Organization System)

For Students:
– Network Analysis
  Tutorials
– FE Interactive Exam
  Review Questions
– Quizzes
– Learning Objectives
– Flashcards
– Web Links

A NOTE TO THE STUDENT

This may be your first course in electrical engineering. Although electrical engineering is an exciting and challenging discipline, the course may intimidate you. This book was written to prevent that. A good textbook and a good professor are an advantage—but you are the one who does the learning. If you keep the following ideas in mind, you will do very well in this course.

- This course is the foundation on which most other courses in the electrical engineering curriculum rest. For this reason, put in as much effort as you can. Study the course regularly.

- Problem solving is an essential part of the learning process. Solve as many problems as you can. Begin by solving the practice problem following each example, and then proceed to the end-of-chapter problems. The best way to learn is to solve a lot of problems. An asterisk in front of a problem indicates a challenging problem.

- *Spice*, a computer circuit analysis program, is used throughout the textbook. *Pspice*, the personal computer version of *Spice*, is the popular standard circuit analysis program at most universities, *Pspice for Windows* is described in Appendix D. Make an effort to learn *Pspice*, because you can check any circuit problem with *Pspice* and be sure you are handing in a correct problem solution.

- *MATLAB* is another software that is very useful in circuit analysis and other courses you will be taking. A brief tutorial on *MATLAB* is given in Appendix E to get you started. The best way to learn *MATLAB* is to start working with it once you know a few commands.

- Each chapter ends with a section on how the material covered in the chapter can be applied to real-life situations. The concepts in this section may be new and advanced to you. No doubt, you will learn more of the details in other courses. We are mainly interested in gaining a general familiarity with these ideas.

- Attempt the review questions at the end of each chapter. They will help you discover some "tricks" not revealed in class or in the textbook.

A short review on finding determinants is covered in Appendix A, complex numbers in Appendix B, and mathematical formulas in Appendix C. Answers to odd-numbered problems are given in Appendix F.

Have fun!

C. K. A. and M. N. O. S.

ABOUT THE AUTHORS

Charles K. Alexander is dean and professor of electrical and computer engineering of the Fenn College of Engineering at Cleveland State University, Cleveland, Ohio. From 1998 until 2002, he was interim director (2000 and 2001) of the Institute for Corrosion and Multiphase Technologies and Stocker Visiting Professor of electrical engineering and computer science at Ohio University. From 1994–1996 he was dean of engineering and computer science at California State University, Northridge. From 1989–1994 he was acting dean of the college of engineering at Temple University, and from 1986–1989 he was professor and chairman of the department of electrical engineering at Temple. From 1980–1986 he held the same positions at Tennessee Technological University. He was an associate professor and a professor of electrical engineering at Youngstown State University from 1972–1980, where he was named Distinguished Professor in 1977 in recognition of "outstanding teaching and research." He was assistant professor of electrical engineering at Ohio University in 1971–1972. He received the Ph.D. (1971) and M.S.E.E. (1967) from Ohio University and the B.S.E.E. (1965) from Ohio Northern University.

Charles K. Alexander

Dr. Alexander has been a consultant to 23 companies and governmental organizations, including the Air Force and Navy and several law firms. He has received over $6 million in research and development funds for projects ranging from solar energy to software engineering. He has authored 40 publications, including a workbook and a videotape lecture series, and is coauthor of *Fundamentals of Electric Circuits* and *Problem Solving Made Almost Easy*, both with McGraw-Hill. He has made more than 500 paper, professional, and technical presentations.

Dr. Alexander is a fellow of the IEEE and served as its president and CEO in 1997. In 1993 and 1994 he was IEEE vice president, professional activities, and chair of the United States Activities Board (USAB). In 1991–1992 he was region 2 director, serving on the Regional Activities Board (RAB) and USAB. He has also been a member of the Educational Activities Board. He served as chair of the USAB Member Activities Council and vice chair of the USAB Professional Activities Council for Engineers, and he chaired the RAB Student Activities Committee and the USAB Student Professional Awareness Committee. In 1998 he received the Distinguished Engineering Education Achievement Award from the Engineering Council, and in 1996 he received the Distinguished Engineering Education Leadership Award from the same group. When he became a fellow of the IEEE in 1994, the citation read "for leadership in the field of engineering education and the professional development of engineering students." In 1984 he received the IEEE Centennial Medal, and in 1983 he received the IEEE/RAB Innovation Award, given to the IEEE member who best contributes to RAB's goals and objectives.

Matthew N. O. Sadiku

Matthew N. O. Sadiku is presently a professor at Prairie View A&M University. Prior to joining Prairie View, he taught at Florida Atlantic University, Boca Raton, and Temple University, Philadelphia. He has also worked for Lucent/Avaya and and Boeing Satellite Systems.

Dr. Sadiku is the author of over 120 professional papers and over 20 books including *Elements of Electromagnetics* (Oxford University Press, 3rd ed., 2001), *Numerical Techniques in Electromagnetics* (2nd ed., CRC Press, 2000), *Simulation of Local Area Networks* (with M. Ilyas, CRC Press, 1994), *Metropolitan Area Networks* (CRC Press, 1994), and *Fundamentals of Electric Circuits* (with A. K. Alexander, McGraw-Hill, 2nd ed., 2004). His books are used worldwide, and some of them have been translated into Korean, Chinese, Italian, and Spanish. He was the recipient of the 2000 McGraw-Hill/Jacob Millman Award for outstanding contributions in the field of electrical engineering. He was the IEEE region 2 Student Activities Committee chairman and is an associate editor for IEEE Transactions on Education. He received his Ph.D. at Tennessee Technological University, Cookeville.

DC CIRCUITS

Chapter **1** *Basic Concepts*

Chapter **2** *Basic Laws*

Chapter **3** *Methods of Analysis*

Chapter **4** *Circuit Theorems*

Chapter **5** *Operational Amplifiers*

Chapter **6** *Capacitors and Inductors*

Chapter **7** *First-Order Circuits*

Chapter **8** *Second-Order Circuits*

C H A P T E R   1

BASIC CONCEPTS

*Engineering refers to the practice of organizing the design and construc-
tion [and, I would add operation] of any artifice which transforms the
physical world around us to meet some recognized need.*

—G. F. C. Rogers

Historical Profiles

Alessandro Antonio Volta (1745–1827), an Italian physicist, invented the electric
battery—which provided the first continuous flow of electricity—and the capacitor.

Born into a noble family in Como, Italy, Volta was performing electrical
experiments at age 18. His invention of the battery in 1796 revolutionized the use of
electricity. The publication of his work in 1800 marked the beginning of electric circuit
theory. Volta received many honors during his lifetime. The unit of voltage or potential
difference, the volt, was named in his honor.

Andre-Marie Ampere (1775–1836), a French mathematician and physicist, laid the
foundation of electrodynamics. He defined the electric current and developed a way to
measure it in the 1820s.

Born in Lyons, France, Ampere at age 12 mastered Latin in a few weeks, as he
was intensely interested in mathematics and many of the best mathematical works were
in Latin. He was a brilliant scientist and a prolific writer. He formulated the laws of
electromagnetics. He invented the electromagnet and the ammeter. The unit of electric
current, the ampere, was named after him.

1.1 INTRODUCTION

Electric circuit theory and electromagnetic theory are the two fundamental theories upon which all branches of electrical engineering are
built. Many branches of electrical engineering, such as power, electric
machines, control, electronics, communications, and instrumentation, are
based on electric circuit theory. Therefore, the basic electric circuit theory
course is the most important course for an electrical engineering student,
and always an excellent starting point for a beginning student in electrical engineering education. Circuit theory is also valuable to students
specializing in other branches of the physical sciences because circuits
are a good model for the study of energy systems in general, and because
of the applied mathematics, physics, and topology involved.

In electrical engineering, we are often interested in communicating
or transferring energy from one point to another. To do this requires an
interconnection of electrical devices. Such interconnection is referred to
as an *electric circuit*, and each component of the circuit is known as an
element.

An electric circuit is an interconnection of electrical elements.

A simple electric circuit is shown in Fig. 1.1. It consists of three
basic elements: a battery, a lamp, and connecting wires. Such a simple
circuit can exist by itself; it has several applications, such as a torch light,
a search light, and so forth.

A complicated real circuit is displayed in Fig. 1.2, representing the
schematic diagram for a radio receiver. Although it seems complicated,
this circuit can be analyzed using the techniques we cover in this book.
Our goal in this text is to learn various analytical techniques and computer
software applications for describing the behavior of a circuit like this.

Electric circuits are used in numerous electrical systems to accomplish different tasks. Our objective in this book is not the study of various
uses and applications of circuits. Rather our major concern is the analysis of the circuits. By the analysis of a circuit, we mean a study of the
behavior of the circuit: How does it respond to a given input? How do the
interconnected elements and devices in the circuit interact?

We commence our study by defining some basic concepts. These
concepts include charge, current, voltage, circuit elements, power, and
energy. Before defining these concepts, we must first establish a system
of units that we will use throughout the text.

Figure 1.1   A simple electric circuit.

1.2 SYSTEMS OF UNITS

As electrical engineers, we deal with measurable quantities. Our measurement, however, must be communicated in a standard language that
virtually all professionals can understand, irrespective of the country
where the measurement is conducted. Such an international measurement language is the International System of Units (SI), adopted by the
General Conference on Weights and Measures in 1960. In this system,

Figure I.2   Electric circuit of a radio receiver.
(Reproduced with permission from QST, August 1995, p. 23.)

there are six principal units from which the units of all other physical quantities can be derived. Table 1.1 shows the six units, their symbols, and the physical quantities they represent. The SI units are used throughout this text.

One great advantage of the SI unit is that it uses prefixes based on the power of 10 to relate larger and smaller units to the basic unit. Table 1.2 shows the SI prefixes and their symbols. For example, the following are expressions of the same distance in meters (m):

$$600{,}000{,}000 \text{ mm} \qquad 600{,}000 \text{ m} \qquad 600 \text{ km}$$

TABLE I.1   The six basic SI units.

Quantity	Basic unit	Symbol
Length	meter	m
Mass	kilogram	kg
Time	second	s
Electric current	ampere	A
Thermodynamic temperature	kelvin	K
Luminous intensity	candela	cd

TABLE I.2   The SI prefixes.

Multiplier	Prefix	Symbol
10^{18}	exa	E
10^{15}	peta	P
10^{12}	tera	T
10^{9}	giga	G
10^{6}	mega	M
10^{3}	kilo	k
10^{2}	hecto	h
10	deka	da
10^{-1}	deci	d
10^{-2}	centi	c
10^{-3}	milli	m
10^{-6}	micro	μ
10^{-9}	nano	n
10^{-12}	pico	p
10^{-15}	femto	f
10^{-18}	atto	a

1.3   CHARGE AND CURRENT

The concept of electric charge is the underlying principle for explaining all electrical phenomena. Also, the most basic quantity in an electric circuit is the *electric charge*. We all experience the effect of electric charge when we try to remove our wool sweater and have it stick to our body or walk across a carpet and receive a shock.

> Charge is an electrical property of the atomic particles of which matter consists, measured in coulombs (C).

We know from elementary physics that all matter is made of fundamental building blocks known as atoms and that each atom consists of electrons, protons, and neutrons. We also know that the charge e on an electron is negative and equal in magnitude to 1.602×10^{-19} C, while a proton carries a positive charge of the same magnitude as the electron. The presence of equal numbers of protons and electrons leaves an atom neutrally charged.

The following points should be noted about electric charge:

1. The coulomb is a large unit for charges. In 1 C of charge, there are $1/(1.602 \times 10^{-19}) = 6.24 \times 10^{18}$ electrons. Thus realistic or laboratory values of charges are on the order of pC, nC, or μC.[1]

2. According to experimental observations, the only charges that occur in nature are integral multiples of the electronic charge $e = -1.602 \times 10^{-19}$ C.

3. The *law of conservation of charge* states that charge can neither be created nor destroyed, only transferred. Thus the algebraic sum of the electric charges in a system does not change.

We now consider the flow of electric charges. A unique feature of electric charge or electricity is the fact that it is mobile; that is, it can be transferred from one place to another, where it can be converted to another form of energy.

When a conducting wire (consisting of several atoms) is connected to a battery (a source of electromotive force), the charges are compelled to move; positive charges move in one direction while negative charges move in the opposite direction. This motion of charges creates electric current. It is conventional to take the current flow as the movement of positive charges, that is, opposite to the flow of negative charges, as Fig. 1.3 illustrates. This convention was introduced by Benjamin Franklin (1706–1790), the American scientist and inventor. Although we now know that current in metallic conductors is due to negatively charged electrons, we will follow the universally accepted convention that current is the net flow of positive charges. Thus,

Battery

Figure 1.3   Electric current due to flow of electronic charge in a conductor.

A convention is a standard way of describing something so that others in the profession can understand what we mean. We will be using IEEE conventions throughout this book.

---

[1] However, a large power supply capacitor can store up to 0.5 C of charge.

Electric current is the time rate of change of charge, measured in amperes (A).

Mathematically, the relationship between current i, charge q, and time t is

$$i \overset{\Delta}{=} \frac{dq}{dt} \qquad (1.1)$$

where current is measured in amperes (A), and

1 ampere = 1 coulomb/second

The charge transferred between time t_0 and t is obtained by integrating both sides of Eq. (1.1). We obtain

$$q \overset{\Delta}{=} \int_{t_0}^{t} i \, dt \qquad (1.2)$$

The way we define current as i in Eq. (1.1) suggests that current need not be a constant-valued function. As many of the examples and problems in this chapter and subsequent chapters suggest, there can be several types of current; that is, charge can vary with time in several ways.

If the current does not change with time, but remains constant, we call it a *direct current* (dc).

A direct current (dc) is a current that remains constant with time.

By convention the symbol I is used to represent such a constant current.

A time-varying current is represented by the symbol i. A common form of time-varying current is the sinusoidal current or *alternating current* (ac).

An alternating current (ac) is a current that varies sinusoidally with time.

Such current is used in your household, to run the air conditioner, refrigerator, washing machine, and other electric appliances. Figure 1.4 shows direct current and alternating current; these are the two most common types of current. We will consider other types later in the book.

Once we define current as the movement of charge, we expect current to have an associated direction of flow. As mentioned earlier, the direction of current flow is conventionally taken as the direction of positive charge movement. Based on this convention, a current of 5 A may be represented positively or negatively as shown in Fig. 1.5. In other words, a negative current of -5 A flowing in one direction as shown in Fig. 1.5(b) is the same as a current of $+5$ A flowing in the opposite direction.

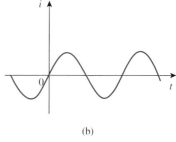

Figure 1.4 Two common types of current: (a) direct current (dc), (b) alternating current (ac).

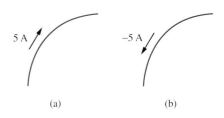

Figure 1.5 Conventional current flow: (a) positive current flow, (b) negative current flow.

EXAMPLE 1.1

How much charge is represented by 4,600 electrons?

Solution:

Each electron has -1.602×10^{-19} C. Hence 4,600 electrons will have

$$-1.602 \times 10^{-19} \text{ C/electron} \times 4,600 \text{ electrons} = -7.369 \times 10^{-16} \text{ C}$$

PRACTICE PROBLEM 1.1

Calculate the amount of charge represented by two million protons.

Answer: $+3.204 \times 10^{-13}$ C.

EXAMPLE 1.2

The total charge entering a terminal is given by $q = 5t \sin 4\pi t$ mC. Calculate the current at $t = 0.5$ s.

Solution:

$$i = \frac{dq}{dt} = \frac{d}{dt}(5t \sin 4\pi t) \text{ mC/s} = (5 \sin 4\pi t + 20\pi t \cos 4\pi t) \text{ mA}$$

At $t = 0.5$,

$$i = 5 \sin 2\pi + 10\pi \cos 2\pi = 0 + 10\pi = 31.42 \text{ mA}$$

PRACTICE PROBLEM 1.2

If in Example 1.2, $q = (10 - 10e^{-2t})$ mC, find the current at $t = 0.5$ s.

Answer: 7.36 mA.

EXAMPLE 1.3

Determine the total charge entering a terminal between $t = 1$ s and $t = 2$ s if the current passing the terminal is $i = (3t^2 - t)$ A.

Solution:

$$q = \int_{t=1}^{2} i \, dt = \int_{1}^{2} (3t^2 - t) \, dt$$

$$= \left(t^3 - \frac{t^2}{2} \right) \Big|_{1}^{2} = (8 - 2) - \left(1 - \frac{1}{2} \right) = 5.5 \text{ C}$$

PRACTICE PROBLEM 1.3

The current flowing through an element is

$$i = \begin{cases} 2 \text{ A}, & 0 < t < 1 \\ 2t^2 \text{ A}, & t > 1 \end{cases}$$

Calculate the charge entering the element from $t = 0$ to $t = 2$ s.

Answer: 6.667 C.

1.4 VOLTAGE

As explained briefly in the previous section, to move the electron in a conductor in a particular direction requires some work or energy transfer. This work is performed by an external electromotive force (emf), typically represented by the battery in Fig. 1.3. This emf is also known as *voltage* or *potential difference*. The voltage v_{ab} between two points a and b in an electric circuit is the energy (or work) needed to move a unit charge from a to b; mathematically,

$$v_{ab} \triangleq \frac{dw}{dq} \tag{1.3}$$

where w is energy in joules (J) and q is charge in coulombs (C). The voltage v_{ab} or simply v is measured in volts (V), named in honor of the Italian physicist Alessandro Antonio Volta (1745–1827), who invented the first voltaic battery. From Eq. (1.3), it is evident that

1 volt = 1 joule/coulomb = 1 newton meter/coulomb

Thus,

> Voltage (or potential difference) is the energy required to move a unit charge through an element, measured in volts (V).

Figure 1.6 shows the voltage across an element (represented by a rectangular block) connected to points a and b. The plus (+) and minus (−) signs are used to define reference direction or voltage polarity. The v_{ab} can be interpreted in two ways: (1) point a is at a potential of v_{ab} volts higher than point b, or (2) the potential at point a with respect to point b is v_{ab}. It follows logically that in general

$$v_{ab} = -v_{ba} \tag{1.4}$$

For example, in Fig. 1.7, we have two representations of the same voltage. In Fig. 1.7(a), point a is +9 V above point b; in Fig. 1.7(b), point b is −9 V above point a. We may say that in Fig. 1.7(a), there is a 9-V *voltage drop* from a to b or equivalently a 9-V *voltage rise* from b to a. In other words, a voltage drop from a to b is equivalent to a voltage rise from b to a.

Current and voltage are the two basic variables in electric circuits. The common term *signal* is used for an electric quantity such as a current or a voltage (or even electromagnetic wave) when it is used for conveying information. Engineers prefer to call such variables signals rather than mathematical functions of time because of their importance in communications and other disciplines. Like electric current, a constant voltage is called a *dc voltage* and is represented by V, whereas a sinusoidally time-varying voltage is called an *ac voltage* and is represented by v. A dc voltage is commonly produced by a battery; ac voltage is produced by an electric generator.

Figure 1.6   Polarity of voltage v_{ab}.

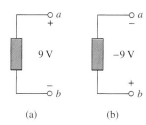

Figure 1.7   Two equivalent representations of the same voltage v_{ab}: (a) point a is 9 V above point b, (b) point b is −9 V above point a.

Keep in mind that electric current is always *through* an element and that electric voltage is always *across* the element or between two points.

1.5   POWER AND ENERGY

Although current and voltage are the two basic variables in an electric circuit, they are not sufficient by themselves. For practical purposes, we need to know how much *power* an electric device can handle. We all know from experience that a 100-watt bulb gives more light than a 60-watt bulb. We also know that when we pay our bills to the electric utility companies, we are paying for the electric *energy* consumed over a certain period of time. Thus power and energy calculations are important in circuit analysis.

To relate power and energy to voltage and current, we recall from physics that:

> Power is the time rate of expending or absorbing energy, measured in watts (W).

We write this relationship as

$$p \overset{\Delta}{=} \frac{dw}{dt} \tag{1.5}$$

where p is power in watts (W), w is energy in joules (J), and t is time in seconds (s). From Eqs. (1.1), (1.3), and (1.5), it follows that

$$p = \frac{dw}{dt} = \frac{dw}{dq} \cdot \frac{dq}{dt} = vi \tag{1.6}$$

or

$$p = vi \tag{1.7}$$

The power p in Eq. (1.7) is a time-varying quantity and is called the *instantaneous power*. Thus, the power absorbed or supplied by an element is the product of the voltage across the element and the current through it. If the power has a + sign, power is being delivered to or absorbed by the element. If, on the other hand, the power has a − sign, power is being supplied by the element. But how do we know when the power has a negative or a positive sign?

Current direction and voltage polarity play a major role in determining the sign of power. It is therefore important that we pay attention to the relationship between current i and voltage v in Fig. 1.8(a). The voltage polarity and current direction must conform with those shown in Fig. 1.8(a) in order for the power to have a positive sign. This is known as the *passive sign convention*. By the passive sign convention, current enters through the positive polarity of the voltage. In this case, $p = +vi$ or $vi > 0$ implies that the element is absorbing power. However, if $p = -vi$ or $vi < 0$, as in Fig. 1.8(b), the element is releasing or supplying power.

Figure 1.8   Reference polarities for power using the passive sign convention: (a) absorbing power, (b) supplying power.

$$p = +vi$$

(a)

$$p = -vi$$

(b)

> Passive sign convention is satisfied when the current enters through the positive terminal of an element and $p = +vi$. If the current enters through the negative terminal, $p = -vi$.

Unless otherwise stated, we will follow the passive sign convention throughout this text. For example, the element in both circuits of Fig. 1.9 has an absorbing power of +12 W because a positive current enters the positive terminal in both cases. In Fig. 1.10, however, the element is supplying power of +12 W because a positive current enters the negative terminal. Of course, an absorbing power of −12 W is equivalent to a supplying power of +12 W. In general,

When the voltage and current directions conform to Fig. 1.8(b), we have the active sign convention and $p = +vi$.

+Power absorbed = −Power supplied

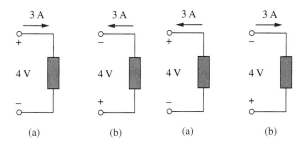

Figure 1.9 Two cases of an element with an absorbing power of 12 W:
(a) $p = 4 \times 3 = 12$ W,
(b) $p = 4 \times 3 = 12$ W.

Figure 1.10 Two cases of an element with a supplying power of 12 W:
(a) $p = 4 \times (-3) = -12$ W,
(b) $p = 4 \times (-3) = -12$ W.

In fact, the *law of conservation of energy* must be obeyed in any electric circuit. For this reason, the algebraic sum of power in a circuit, at any instant of time, must be zero:

$$\sum p = 0 \qquad (1.8)$$

This again confirms the fact that the total power supplied to the circuit must balance the total power absorbed.

From Eq. (1.6), the energy absorbed or supplied by an element from time t_0 to time t is

$$w = \int_{t_0}^{t} p \, dt = \int_{t_0}^{t} vi \, dt \qquad (1.9)$$

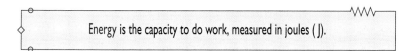

Energy is the capacity to do work, measured in joules (J).

The electric power utility companies measure energy in watt-hours (Wh), where

1 Wh = 3,600 J

EXAMPLE 1.4

An energy source forces a constant current of 2 A for 10 s to flow through a lightbulb. If 2.3 kJ is given off in the form of light and heat energy, calculate the voltage drop across the bulb.

Solution:

The total charge is

$$\Delta q = i\,\Delta t = 2 \times 10 = 20 \text{ C}$$

The voltage drop is

$$v = \frac{\Delta w}{\Delta q} = \frac{2.3 \times 10^3}{20} = 115 \text{ V}$$

PRACTICE PROBLEM 1.4

To move charge q from point a to point b requires -30 J. Find the voltage drop v_{ab} if: (a) $q = 2$ C, (b) $q = -6$ C.

Answer: (a) -15 V, (b) 5 V.

EXAMPLE 1.5

Find the power delivered to an element at $t = 3$ ms if the current entering its positive terminal is

$$i = 5 \cos 60\pi t \text{ A}$$

and the voltage is: (a) $v = 3i$, (b) $v = 3\,di/dt$.

Solution:

(a) The voltage is $v = 3i = 15 \cos 60\pi t$; hence, the power is

$$p = vi = 75 \cos^2 60\pi t \text{ W}$$

At $t = 3$ ms,

$$p = 75 \cos^2(60\pi \times 3 \times 10^{-3}) = 75 \cos^2 0.18\pi = 53.48 \text{ W}$$

(b) We find the voltage and the power as

$$v = 3\frac{di}{dt} = 3(-60\pi)5 \sin 60\pi t = -900\pi \sin 60\pi t \text{ V}$$

$$p = vi = -4500\pi \sin 60\pi t \cos 60\pi t \text{ W}$$

At $t = 3$ ms,

$$p = -4500\pi \sin 0.18\pi \cos 0.18\pi \text{ W}$$

$$= -14137.167 \sin 32.4° \cos 32.4° = -6.396 \text{ kW}$$

PRACTICE PROBLEM 1.5

Find the power delivered to the element in Example 1.5 at $t = 5$ ms if the current remains the same but the voltage is: (a) $v = 2i$ V, (b) $v = \left(10 + 5\int_0^t i\,dt\right)$ V.

Answer: (a) 17.27 W, (b) 29.7 W.

EXAMPLE 1.6

How much energy does a 100-W electric bulb consume in two hours?

Solution:

$$w = pt = 100 \ (\text{W}) \times 2 \ (\text{h}) \times 60 \ (\text{min/h}) \times 60 \ (\text{s/min})$$
$$= 720{,}000 \ \text{J} = 720 \ \text{kJ}$$

This is the same as

$$w = pt = 100 \ \text{W} \times 2 \ \text{h} = 200 \ \text{Wh}$$

PRACTICE PROBLEM 1.6

A stove element draws 15 A when connected to a 120-V line. How long does it take to consume 30 kJ?

Answer: 16.67 s.

1.6   CIRCUIT ELEMENTS

As we discussed in Section 1.1, an element is the basic building block of a circuit. An electric circuit is simply an interconnection of the elements. Circuit analysis is the process of determining voltages across (or the currents through) the elements of the circuit.

There are two types of elements found in electric circuits: *passive* elements and *active* elements. An active element is capable of generating energy while a passive element is not. Examples of passive elements are resistors, capacitors, and inductors. Typical active elements include generators, batteries, and operational amplifiers. Our aim in this section is to gain familiarity with some important active elements.

The most important active elements are voltage or current sources that generally deliver power to the circuit connected to them. There are two kinds of sources: independent and dependent sources.

> An ideal independent source is an active element that provides a specified voltage or current that is completely independent of other circuit elements.

In other words, an ideal independent voltage source delivers to the circuit whatever current is necessary to maintain its terminal voltage. Physical sources such as batteries and generators may be regarded as approximations to ideal voltage sources. Figure 1.11 shows the symbols for independent voltage sources. Notice that both symbols in Fig. 1.11(a) and (b) can be used to represent a dc voltage source, but only the symbol in Fig. 1.11(a) can be used for a time-varying voltage source. Similarly, an ideal independent current source is an active element that provides a specified current completely independent of the voltage across the source. That is, the current source delivers to the circuit whatever voltage is necessary

Figure 1.11   Symbols for independent voltage sources: (a) used for constant or time-varying voltage, (b) used for constant voltage (dc).

Figure 1.12 Symbol for independent current source.

to maintain the designated current. The symbol for an independent current source is displayed in Fig. 1.12, where the arrow indicates the direction of current i.

> An ideal dependent (or controlled) source is an active element in which the source quantity is controlled by another voltage or current.

Dependent sources are usually designated by diamond-shaped symbols, as shown in Fig. 1.13. Since the control of the dependent source is achieved by a voltage or current of some other element in the circuit, and the source can be voltage or current, it follows that there are four possible types of dependent sources, namely:

1. A voltage-controlled voltage source (VCVS).
2. A current-controlled voltage source (CCVS).
3. A voltage-controlled current source (VCCS).
4. A current-controlled current source (CCCS).

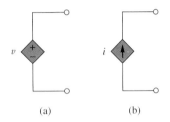

(a)   (b)

Figure 1.13 Symbols for: (a) dependent voltage source, (b) dependent current source.

Dependent sources are useful in modeling elements such as transistors, operational amplifiers and integrated circuits. An example of a current-controlled voltage source is shown on the right-hand side of Fig. 1.14, where the voltage $10i$ of the voltage source depends on the current i through element C. Students might be surprised that the value of the dependent voltage source is $10i$ V (and not $10i$ A) because it is a voltage source. The key idea to keep in mind is that a voltage source comes with polarities $(+\ -)$ in its symbol, while a current source comes with an arrow, irrespective of what it depends on.

It should be noted that an ideal voltage source (dependent or independent) will produce any current required to ensure that the terminal voltage is as stated, whereas an ideal current source will produce the necessary voltage to ensure the stated current flow. Thus an ideal source could in theory supply an infinite amount of energy. It should also be noted that not only do sources supply power to a circuit, they can absorb power from a circuit too. For a voltage source, we know the voltage but not the current supplied or drawn by it. By the same token, we know the current supplied by a current source but not the voltage across it.

Figure 1.14 The source on the right-hand side is a current-controlled voltage source.

EXAMPLE 1.7

Figure 1.15 For Example 1.7.

Calculate the power supplied or absorbed by each element in Fig. 1.15.

Solution:

We apply the sign convention for power shown in Figs. 1.8 and 1.9. For p_1, the 5-A current is out of the positive terminal (or into the negative terminal); hence,

$$p_1 = 20(-5) = -100 \text{ W} \qquad \text{Supplied power}$$

For p_2 and p_3, the current flows into the positive terminal of the element in each case.

$$p_2 = 12(5) = 60 \text{ W} \qquad \text{Absorbed power}$$
$$p_3 = 8(6) = 48 \text{ W} \qquad \text{Absorbed power}$$

For p_4, we should note that the voltage is 8 V (positive at the top), the same as the voltage for p_3, since both the passive element and the dependent source are connected to the same terminals. (Remember that voltage is always measured across an element in a circuit.) Since the current flows out of the positive terminal,

$$p_4 = 8(-0.2 \, I) = 8(-0.2 \times 5) = -8 \text{ W} \qquad \text{Supplied power}$$

We should observe that the 20-V independent voltage source and 0.2 I dependent current source are supplying power to the rest of the network, while the two passive elements are absorbing power. Also,

$$p_1 + p_2 + p_3 + p_4 = -100 + 60 + 48 - 8 = 0$$

In agreement with Eq. (1.8), the total power supplied equals the total power absorbed.

PRACTICE PROBLEM 1.7

Compute the power absorbed or supplied by each component of the circuit in Fig. 1.16.

Answer: $p_1 = -40$ W, $p_2 = 16$ W, $p_3 = 9$ W, $p_4 = 15$ W.

Figure 1.16   For Practice Prob. 1.7.

†1.7 APPLICATIONS[2]

In this section, we will consider two practical applications of the concepts developed in this chapter. The first one deals with the TV picture tube and the other with how electric utilities determine your electric bill.

1.7.1 TV Picture Tube
One important application of the motion of electrons is found in both the transmission and reception of TV signals. At the transmission end, a TV camera reduces a scene from an optical image to an electrical signal. Scanning is accomplished with a thin beam of electrons in an iconoscope camera tube.

At the receiving end, the image is reconstructed by using a cathode-ray tube (CRT) located in the TV receiver.[3] The CRT is depicted in

---

[2]The dagger sign preceding a section heading indicates a section that may be skipped, explained briefly, or assigned as homework.

[3]Modern TV tubes use a different technology.

Fig. 1.17. Unlike the iconoscope tube, which produces an electron beam of constant intensity, the CRT beam varies in intensity according to the incoming signal. The electron gun, maintained at a high potential, fires the electron beam. The beam passes through two sets of plates for vertical and horizontal deflections so that the spot on the screen where the beam strikes can move right and left and up and down. When the electron beam strikes the fluorescent screen, it gives off light at that spot. Thus the beam can be made to "paint" a picture on the TV screen.

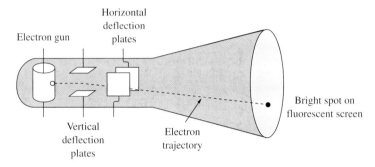

Figure 1.17   Cathode-ray tube.
(Source: D. E. Tilley, Contemporary College Physics [Menlo Park, CA: Benjamin/Cummings, 1979], p. 319.)

EXAMPLE 1.8

The electron beam in a TV picture tube carries 10^{15} electrons per second. As a design engineer, determine the voltage V_o needed to accelerate the electron beam to achieve 4 W.

Solution:

The charge on an electron is

$$e = -1.6 \times 10^{-19} \text{ C}$$

If the number of electrons is n, then $q = ne$ and

$$i = \frac{dq}{dt} = e\frac{dn}{dt} = (-1.6 \times 10^{-19})(10^{15}) = -1.6 \times 10^{-4} \text{ A}$$

The negative sign indicates that the electron flows in a direction opposite to electron flow as shown in Fig. 1.18, which is a simplified diagram of the CRT for the case when the vertical deflection plates carry no charge. The beam power is

$$p = V_o i \qquad \text{or} \qquad V_o = \frac{p}{i} = \frac{4}{1.6 \times 10^{-4}} = 25{,}000 \text{ V}$$

Thus the required voltage is 25 kV.

Figure 1.18   A simplified diagram of the cathode-ray tube; for Example 1.8.

PRACTICE PROBLEM 1.8

If an electron beam in a TV picture tube carries 10^{13} electrons/second and is passing through plates maintained at a potential difference of 30 kV, calculate the power in the beam.

Answer: 48 mW.

1.7.2 Electricity Bills

The second application deals with how an electric utility company charges their customers. The cost of electricity depends upon the amount of energy consumed in kilowatt-hours (kWh). (Other factors that affect the cost include demand and power factors; we will ignore these for now.) However, even if a consumer uses no energy at all, there is a minimum service charge the customer must pay because it costs money to stay connected to the power line. As energy consumption increases, the cost per kWh drops. It is interesting to note the average monthly consumption of household appliances for a family of five, shown in Table 1.3.

TABLE 1.3   Typical average monthly consumption of household appliances.

Appliance	kWh consumed	Appliance	kWh consumed
Water heater	500	Washing machine	120
Freezer	100	Stove	100
Lighting	100	Dryer	80
Dishwasher	35	Microwave oven	25
Electric iron	15	Personal computer	12
TV	10	Radio	8
Toaster	4	Clock	2

EXAMPLE 1.9

A homeowner consumes 700 kWh in January. Determine the electricity bill for the month using the following residential rate schedule:

Base monthly charge of $12.00.

First 100 kWh per month at 16 cents/kWh.

Next 200 kWh per month at 10 cents/kWh.

Over 200 kWh per month at 6 cents/kWh.

Solution:

We calculate the electricity bill as follows.

$$\text{Base monthly charge} = \$12.00$$

$$\text{First 100 kWh @ \$0.16/kWh} = \$16.00$$

$$\text{Next 200 kWh @ \$0.10/kWh} = \$20.00$$

$$\text{Remaining 400 kWh @ \$0.06/kWh} = \$24.00$$

$$\text{Total Charge} = \$72.00$$

$$\text{Average cost} = \frac{\$72}{100 + 200 + 400} = 10.2 \text{ cents/kWh}$$

PRACTICE PROBLEM 1.9

Referring to the residential rate schedule in Example 1.9, calculate the average cost per kWh if only 400 kWh are consumed in July when the family is on vacation most of the time.

Answer: 13.5 cents/kWh.

†1.8   PROBLEM SOLVING

Although the problems to be solved during one's career will vary in complexity and magnitude, the basic principles to be followed remain the same. The process outlined here is the one developed by the authors over many years of problem solving with students, for the solution of engineering problems in industry, and for problem solving in research.

We will list the steps simply and then elaborate on them.

1. Carefully **Define** the problem.
2. **Present** everything you know about the problem.
3. Establish a set of **Alternative** solutions and determine the one that promises the greatest likelihood of success.
4. **Attempt** a problem solution.
5. **Evaluate** the solution and check for accuracy.
6. Has the problem been solved **Satisfactorily**? If so, present the solution; if not, then return to step 3 and continue through the process again.

1. *Carefully **Define** the problem*. This may be the most important part of the process, because it becomes the foundation for all the rest of the steps. In general, the presentation of engineering problems is somewhat incomplete. You must do all you can to make sure you understand the problem as thoroughly as the presenter of the problem understands it. Time spent at this point clearly identifying the problem will save you considerable time and frustration later. As a student, you can clarify a problem statement in a textbook by asking your professor to help you understand it better. A problem presented to you in industry may require that you consult several individuals. At this step, it is important to develop questions that need to be addressed before continuing the solution process. If you have such questions, you need to consult with the appropriate individuals or resources to obtain the answers to those questions. With those answers, you can now refine the problem, and use that refinement as the problem statement for the rest of the solution process.

2. ***Present** everything you know about the problem*. You are now ready to write down everything you know about the problem and its possible solutions. This important step will save you time and frustration later.

3. *Establish a set of **Alternative** solutions and determine the one that promises the greatest likelihood of success*. Almost every problem will have a number of possible paths that can lead to a solution. It is

highly desirable to identify as many of those paths as possible. At this point, you also need to determine what tools are available to you, such as *PSpice* and *MATLAB* and other software packages that can greatly reduce effort and increase accuracy. Again, we want to stress that time spent carefully defining the problem and investigating alternative approaches to its solution will pay big dividends later. Evaluating the alternatives and determining which promises the greatest likelihood of success may be difficult but will be well worth the effort. Document this process well since you will want to come back to it if the first approach does not work.

4. ***Attempt*** *a problem solution*. Now is the time to actually begin solving the problem. The process you follow must be well documented in order to present a detailed solution if successful, and to evaluate the process if you are not successful. This detailed evaluation may lead to corrections that can then lead to a successful solution. It can also lead to new alternatives to try. Many times, it is wise to fully set up a solution before putting numbers into equations. This will help in checking your results.

5. ***Evaluate*** *the solution and check for accuracy*. You now thoroughly evaluate what you have accomplished. Decide if you have an acceptable solution, one that you want to present to your team, boss, or professor.

6. *Has the problem been solved* ***Satisfactorily****? If so, present the solution; if not, then return to step 3 and continue through the process again.* Now you need to present your solution or try another alternative. At this point, presenting your solution may bring closure to the process. Often, however, presentation of a solution leads to further refinement of the problem definition, and the process continues. Following this process will eventually lead to a satisfactory conclusion.

Now let us look at this process for a student taking an electrical and computer engineering foundations course. (The basic process also applies to almost every engineering course.) Keep in mind that although the steps have been simplified to apply to academic types of problems, the process as stated always needs to be followed. We consider a simple example.

Assume that we have been given the circuit shown in Fig. 1.19. The instructor asks us to solve for the current flowing through the 8-ohm resistor.

Figure 1.19   Illustrative example.

1. *Carefully* ***Define*** *the problem*. This is only a simple example, but we can already see that we do not know the polarity on the 3-V source. We have the following options. We can ask the professor what the polarity should be. If we cannot ask, then we need to make a decision on what to do

next. If we have time to work the problem both ways, we can solve for the current when the 3-V source is plus on top and then plus on the bottom. If we do not have the time to work it both ways, assume a polarity and then carefully document your decision. Let us assume that the professor tells us that the source is plus on the bottom as shown in Fig. 1.20.

2. **Present** *everything you know about the problem*. Presenting all that we know about the problem involves labeling the circuit clearly so that we define what we seek.

Given the following circuit, solve for $i_{8\Omega}$.

Figure 1.20   Problem defintion.

We now check with the professor, if reasonable, to see if the problem is properly defined.

3. *Establish a set of* **Alternative** *solutions and determine the one that promises the greatest likelihood of success.* There are essentially three techniques that can be used to solve this problem. Later in the text you will see that you can use circuit analysis (using Kirchoff's laws and Ohm's law), nodal analysis, and mesh analysis.

To solve for $i_{8\Omega}$ using circuit analysis will eventually lead to a solution, but it will likely take more work than either nodal or mesh analysis. To solve for $i_{8\Omega}$ using mesh analysis will require writing two simultaneous equations to find the two loop currents indicated in Fig. 1.21. Using nodal analysis requires solving for only one unknown. This is the easiest approach.

Figure 1.21   Using nodal analysis.

Therefore, we will solve for $i_{8\Omega}$ using nodal analysis.

4. **Attempt** *a problem solution.* We first write down all of the equations we will need in order to find $i_{8\Omega}$.

$$i_{8\Omega} = i_2, \qquad i_2 = \frac{v_1}{8}, \qquad i_{8\Omega} = \frac{v_1}{8}$$

$$\frac{v_1 - 5}{2} + \frac{v_1 - 0}{8} + \frac{v_1 + 3}{4} = 0$$

Now we can solve for v_1.

$$8\left[\frac{v_1 - 5}{2} + \frac{v_1 - 0}{8} + \frac{v_1 + 3}{4}\right] = 0$$

leads to $(4v_1 - 20) + (v_1) + (2v_1 + 6) = 0$

$$7v_1 = +14, \qquad v_1 = +2 \text{ V}, \qquad i_{8\Omega} = \frac{v_1}{8} = \frac{2}{8} = \mathbf{0.25\ A}$$

5. ***Evaluate*** *the solution and check for accuracy.* We can now use Kirchoff's voltage law to check the results.

$$i_1 = \frac{v_1 - 5}{2} = \frac{2 - 5}{2} = -\frac{3}{2} = -1.5 \text{ A}$$

$$i_2 = i_{8\Omega} = 0.25 \text{ A}$$

$$i_3 = \frac{v_1 + 3}{4} = \frac{2 + 3}{4} = \frac{5}{4} = 1.25 \text{ A}$$

$$i_1 + i_2 + i_3 = \underline{-1.5 + 0.25 + 1.25 = 0} \qquad \text{(Checks.)}$$

Applying KVL to loop 1,

$$\begin{aligned}
-5 + v_{2\Omega} + v_{8\Omega} &= -5 + (-i_1 \times 2) + (i_2 \times 8) \\
&= -5 + (-(-1.5)2) + (0.25 \times 8) \\
&= \underline{-5 + 3 + 2 = 0} \qquad \text{(Checks.)}
\end{aligned}$$

Applying KVL to loop 2,

$$\begin{aligned}
-v_{8\Omega} + v_{4\Omega} - 3 &= -(i_2 \times 8) + (i_3 \times 4) - 3 \\
&= -(0.25 \times 8) + (1.25 \times 4) - 3 \\
&= \underline{-2 + 5 - 3 = 0} \qquad \text{(Checks.)}
\end{aligned}$$

So we now have a very high degree of confidence in the accuracy of our answer.

6. Has the problem been solved **Satisfactorily**? If so, present the solution; if not, then return to step 3 and continue through the process again. This problem has been solved satisfactorily.

The current through the 8-ohm resistor is 0.25 amp flowing down through the 8-ohm resistor.

1.9   SUMMARY

1. An electric circuit consists of electrical elements connected together.

2. The International System of Units (SI) is the international measurement language, which enables engineers to communicate their results. From the six principal units, the units of other physical quantities can be derived.

3. Current is the rate of charge flow.

$$i = \frac{dq}{dt}$$

4. Voltage is the energy required to move 1 C of charge through an element.

$$v = \frac{dw}{dq}$$

5. Power is the energy supplied or absorbed per unit time. It is also the product of voltage and current.

$$p = \frac{dw}{dt} = vi$$

6. According to the passive sign convention, power assumes a positive sign when the current enters the positive polarity of the voltage across an element.

7. An ideal voltage source produces a specific potential difference across its terminals regardless of what is connected to it. An ideal current source produces a specific current through its terminals regardless of what is connected to it.

8. Voltage and current sources can be dependent or independent. A dependent source is one whose value depends on some other circuit variable.

9. Two areas of application of the concepts covered in this chapter are the TV picture tube and electricity billing procedure.

REVIEW QUESTIONS

1.1 One millivolt is one millionth of a volt.

  (a) True   (b) False

1.2 The prefix *micro* stands for:

  (a) 10^6 (b) 10^3 (c) 10^{-3} (d) 10^{-6}

1.3 The voltage 2,000,000 V can be expressed in powers of 10 as:

  (a) 2 mV   (b) 2 kV   (c) 2 MV   (d) 2 GV

1.4 A charge of 2 C flowing past a given point each second is a current of 2 A.

  (a) True   (b) False

1.5 The unit of current is:

  (a) Coulomb   (b) Ampere
  (c) Volt   (d) Joule

1.6 Voltage is measured in:

  (a) Watts   (b) Amperes
  (c) Volts   (d) Joules per second

1.7 A 4-A current charging a dielectric material will accumulate a charge of 24 C after 6 s.

  (a) True   (b) False

1.8 The voltage across a 1.1 kW toaster that produces a current of 10 A is:

  (a) 11 kV   (b) 1100 V (c) 110 V   (d) 11 V

1.9 Which of these is not an electrical quantity?

  (a) charge   (b) time   (c) voltage
  (d) current   (e) power

1.10 The dependent source in Fig. 1.22 is:

  (a) voltage-controlled current source
  (b) voltage-controlled voltage source
  (c) current-controlled voltage source
  (d) current-controlled current source

Figure 1.22   For Review Question 1.10.

Answers: 1.1b, 1.2d, 1.3c, 1.4a, 1.5b, 1.6c, 1.7a, 1.8c, 1.9b, 1.10d.

PROBLEMS

Section 1.3   Charge and Current

1.1   How many coulombs are represented by these amounts of electrons:

(a) 6.482×10^{17} (b) 1.24×10^{18}
(c) 2.46×10^{19} (d) 1.628×10^{20}

1.2   Determine the current flowing through an element if the charge flow is given by

(a) $q(t) = (3t + 8)$ mC
(b) $q(t) = (8t^2 + 4t - 2)$ C
(c) $q(t) = 3e^{-t} - 5e^{-2t}$ nC
(d) $q(t) = 10 \sin 120\pi t$ pC
(e) $q(t) = 20e^{-4t} \cos 50t \, \mu$C

1.3   Find the charge $q(t)$ flowing through a device if the current is:

(a) $i(t) = 3$ A, $q(0) = 1$ C
(b) $i(t) = (2t + 5)$ mA, $q(0) = 0$
(c) $i(t) = 20 \cos(10t + \pi/6) \, \mu$A, $q(0) = 2 \, \mu$C
(d) $i(t) = 10e^{-30t} \sin 40t$ A, $q(0) = 0$

1.4   The current flowing through a device is $i(t) = 5 \sin 6\pi t$ A. Calculate the total charge flow through the device from $t = 0$ to $t = 10$ ms.

1.5   Determine the total charge flowing into an element for $0 < t < 2$ s when the current entering its positive terminal is $i(t) = e^{-2t}$ mA.

1.6   The charge entering a certain element is shown in Fig. 1.23. Find the current at:

(a) $t = 1$ ms   (b) $t = 6$ ms   (c) $t = 10$ ms

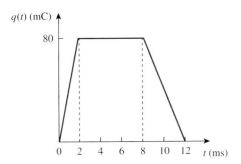

Figure 1.23   For Prob. 1.6.

1.7   The charge flowing in a wire is plotted in Fig. 1.24. Sketch the corresponding current.

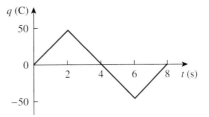

Figure 1.24   For Prob. 1.7.

1.8   The current flowing past a point in a device is shown in Fig. 1.25. Calculate the total charge through the point.

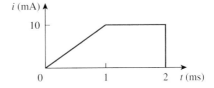

Figure 1.25   For Prob. 1.8.

1.9   The current through an element is shown in Fig. 1.26. Determine the total charge that passed through the element at:

(a) $t = 1$ s   (b) $t = 3$ s   (c) $t = 5$ s

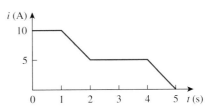

Figure 1.26   For Prob. 1.9.

Sections 1.4 and 1.5   Voltage, Power, and Energy

1.10   A lightning bolt with 8 kA strikes an object for 15μs. How much charge is deposited on the object?

1.11   A rechargeable flashlight battery is capable of delivering 85 mA for about 12 h. How much charge can it release at that rate? If its terminal voltage is 1.2 V, how much energy can the battery deliver?

1.12   If the current flowing through an element is given by

$$i(t) = \begin{cases} 3t\,\text{A}, & 0 \leq t < 6\,\text{s} \\ 18\,\text{A}, & 6 \leq t < 10\,\text{s} \\ -12\,\text{A}, & 10 \leq t < 15\,\text{s} \\ 0, & t \geq 15\,\text{s} \end{cases}$$

Plot the charge stored in the element over $0 < t < 20$ s.

1.13   A certain electrical element draws the current $i(t) = 10\cos 4t$ A at a voltage $v(t) = 120\cos 4t$ V. Find the energy absorbed by the element in 2 s.

1.14   The voltage v across a device and the current i through it are

$$v(t) = 5\cos 2t \text{ V}, \qquad i(t) = 10(1 - e^{-0.5t})\text{ A}$$

Calculate:

(a)   the total charge in the device at $t = 1$ s.
(b)   the power consumed by the device at $t = 1$ s.

1.15   The current entering the positive terminal of a device is $i(t) = 3e^{-2t}$ A and the voltage across the device is $v(t) = 5\,di/dt$ V.

(a)   Find the charge delivered to the device between $t = 0$ and $t = 2$ s.
(b)   Calculate the power absorbed.
(c)   Determine the energy absorbed in 3 s.

1.16   Figure 1.27 shows the current through and the voltage across a device. Find the total energy absorbed by the device for the period of $0 < t < 4$ s.

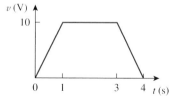

Figure 1.27   For Prob. 1.16.

Section 1.6   Circuit Elements

1.17   Figure 1.28 shows a circuit with five elements. If $p_1 = -205$ W, $p_2 = 60$ W, $p_4 = 45$ W, $p_5 = 30$ W, calculate the power p_3 received or delivered by element 3.

Figure 1.28   For Prob. 1.17.

1.18   Find the power absorbed by each of the elements in Fig. 1.29.

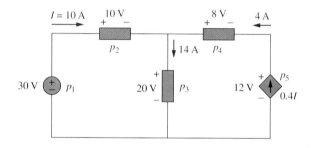

Figure 1.29   For Prob. 1.18.

1.19   Determine I_s in the circuit of Fig. 1.30.

Figure 1.30   For Prob. 1.19.

1.20   Find V_o in the circuit of Fig. 1.31.

Figure 1.31   For Prob. 1.20.

Section 1.7   Applications

1.21 It takes eight photons to strike the surface of a photodetector in order to emit one electron. If 4×10^{11} photons/second strike the surface of the photodetector, calculate the amount of current flow.

1.22 Find the power rating of the following electrical appliances in your household:

(a) Lightbulb   (b) Radio set
(c) TV set   (d) Refrigerator
(e) Personal computer   (f) PC printer
(g) Microwave oven   (h) Blender

1.23 A 1.5-kW electric heater is connected to a 120-V source.

(a) How much current does the heater draw?
(b) If the heater is on for 45 minutes, how much energy is consumed in kilowatt-hours (kWh)?
(c) Calculate the cost of operating the heater for 45 minutes if energy costs 10 cents/kWh.

1.24 When connected to 110-V lines, a stove element takes 8 A. Calculate how much power the element is consuming.

1.25 A 1.2-kW toaster takes roughly 4 minutes to heat four slices of bread. Find the cost of operating the toaster once per day for 1 month (30 days). Assume energy costs 9 cents/kWh.

1.26 A flashlight battery has a rating of 0.8 ampere-hours (Ah) and a lifetime of 10 hours.

(a) How much current can it deliver?
(b) How much power can it give if its terminal voltage is 6 V?
(c) How much energy is stored in the battery in kWh?

1.27 A constant current of 3 A for 4 hours is required to charge an automotive battery. If the terminal voltage is $10 + t/2$ V, where t is in hours,

(a) how much charge is transported as a result of the charging?
(b) how much energy is expended?
(c) how much does the charging cost? Assume electricity costs 9 cents/kWh.

1.28 A 30-W incandescent lamp is connected to a 120-V source and is left burning continuously in an otherwise dark staircase. Determine:

(a) the current through the lamp,
(b) the cost of operating the light for one non-leap year if electricity costs 12 cents per kWh.

1.29 An electric stove with four burners and an oven is used in preparing a meal as follows.

Burner 1: 20 minutes   Burner 2: 40 minutes
Burner 3: 15 minutes   Burner 4: 45 minutes
Oven: 30 minutes

If each burner is rated at 1.2 kW and the oven at 1.8 kW, and electricity costs 12 cents per kWh, calculate the cost of electricity used in preparing the meal.

1.30 GPU Energy (the electric power company in New Jersey) charged a consumer $52.75 one month. If the basic service charge is $5.23 and the company charges $0.11 per kWh, how much energy in kWh was used by the consumer?

1.31 In a household, a 120-W personal computer (PC) is run for 4 h/day, while a 60-W bulb runs for 8 h/day. If the utility company charges $0.12/kWh, calculate how much the household pays per year on the PC and the bulb.

COMPREHENSIVE PROBLEMS

1.32 A telephone wire has a current of 20 μA flowing through it. How long does it take for a charge of 15 C to pass through the wire?

1.33 A lightning bolt carried a current of 2 kA and lasted for 3 ms. How many coulombs of charge were contained in the lightning bolt?

1.34 Figure 1.32 shows the power consumption of a certain household in 1 day. Calculate: (a) the total energy consumed in kWh, (b) the average power per hour.

Figure I.32   For Prob. 1.34.

1.35 The graph in Fig. 1.33 represents the power drawn by
an industrial plant between 8:00 and 8:30 A.M.
Calculate the total energy in MWh consumed by the
plant.

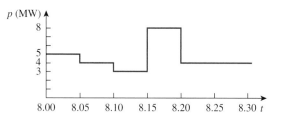

Figure 1.33   For Prob. 1.35.

1.36 A battery may be rated in ampere-hours (Ah). An
lead-acid battery is rated at 160 Ah.

(a) What is the maximum current it can supply for
40 h?

(b) How many days will it last if it is discharged at
1 mA?

1.37 How much work is done by a 12-V automobile
battery in moving 5×10^{20} electrons from the
positive terminal to the negative terminal?

1.38 How much energy does a 10-hp motor deliver in
30 minutes? Assume that 1 horsepower = 746 W.

1.39 A 2-kW electric iron is connected to a 120-V line.
Calculate the current drawn by the iron.

BASIC LAWS

Science is knowledge arranged and classified according to truth, facts, and the general laws of nature.

—Luther Burbank

Historical Profiles

Georg Simon Ohm (1787–1854), a German physicist, in 1826 experimentally determined the most basic law relating voltage and current for a resistor. Ohm's work was initially denied by critics.

Born of humble beginnings in Erlangen, Bavaria, Ohm threw himself into electrical research. His efforts resulted in his famous law. He was awarded the Copley Medal in 1841 by the Royal Society of London. In 1849, he was given the Professor of Physics chair by the University of Munich. To honor him, the unit of resistance was named the ohm.

Gustav Robert Kirchhoff (1824–1887), a German physicist, stated two basic laws in 1847 concerning the relationship between the currents and voltages in an electrical network. Kirchhoff's laws, along with Ohm's law, form the basis of circuit theory.

Born the son of a lawyer in Konigsberg, East Prussia, Kirchhoff entered the University of Konigsberg at age 18 and later became a lecturer in Berlin. His collaborative work in spectroscopy with German chemist Robert Bunsen led to the discovery of cesium in 1860 and rubidium in 1861. Kirchhoff was also credited with the Kirchhoff law of radiation. Thus Kirchhoff is famous among engineers, chemists, and physicists.

2.1   INTRODUCTION

Chapter 1 introduced basic concepts such as current, voltage, and power in an electric circuit. To actually determine the values of these variables in a given circuit requires that we understand some fundamental laws that govern electric circuits. These laws, known as Ohm's law and Kirchhoff's laws, form the foundation upon which electric circuit analysis is built.

In this chapter, in addition to these laws, we shall discuss some techniques commonly applied in circuit design and analysis. These techniques include combining resistors in series or parallel, voltage division, current division, and delta-to-wye and wye-to-delta transformations. The application of these laws and techniques will be restricted to resistive circuits in this chapter. We will finally apply the laws and techniques to real-life problems of electrical lighting and the design of dc meters.

2.2   OHM'S LAW

Materials in general have a characteristic behavior of resisting the flow of electric charge. This physical property, or ability to resist current, is known as *resistance* and is represented by the symbol R. The resistance of any material with a uniform cross-sectional area A depends on A and its length ℓ, as shown in Fig. 2.1(a). We can represent resistance (as measured in the laboratory), in mathematical form,

$$R = \rho \frac{\ell}{A} \tag{2.1}$$

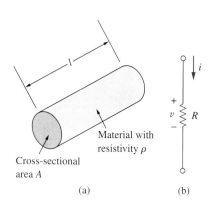

Figure 2.1   (a) Resistor, (b) Circuit symbol for resistance.

where ρ is known as the *resistivity* of the material in ohm-meters. Good conductors, such as copper and aluminum, have low resistivities, while insulators, such as mica and paper, have high resistivities. Table 2.1 presents the values of ρ for some common materials and shows which materials are used for conductors, insulators, and semiconductors.

TABLE 2.1	Resistivities of common materials.	
Material	Resistivity (Ω·m)	Usage
Silver	1.64×10^{-8}	Conductor
Copper	1.72×10^{-8}	Conductor
Aluminum	2.8×10^{-8}	Conductor
Gold	2.45×10^{-8}	Conductor
Carbon	4×10^{-5}	Semiconductor
Germanium	47×10^{-2}	Semiconductor
Silicon	6.4×10^{2}	Semiconductor
Paper	10^{10}	Insulator
Mica	5×10^{11}	Insulator
Glass	10^{12}	Insulator
Teflon	3×10^{12}	Insulator

The circuit element used to model the current-resisting behavior of a material is the *resistor*. For the purpose of constructing circuits, resistors are usually made from metallic alloys and carbon compounds. The circuit symbol for the resistor is shown in Fig. 2.1(b), where R stands for the resistance of the resistor. The resistor is the simplest passive element.

Georg Simon Ohm (1787–1854), a German physicist, is credited with finding the relationship between current and voltage for a resistor. This relationship is known as *Ohm's law*.

> Ohm's law states that the voltage v across a resistor is directly proportional to the current i flowing through the resistor.

That is,

$$v \propto i \tag{2.2}$$

Ohm defined the constant of proportionality for a resistor to be the resistance, R. (The resistance is a material property which can change if the internal or external conditions of the element are altered, e.g., if there are changes in the temperature.) Thus, Eq. (2.2) becomes

$$\boxed{v = iR} \tag{2.3}$$

which is the mathematical form of Ohm's law. R in Eq. (2.3) is measured in the unit of ohms, designated Ω. Thus,

> The resistance R of an element denotes its ability to resist the flow of electric current; it is measured in ohms (Ω).

We may deduce from Eq. (2.3) that

$$R = \frac{v}{i} \tag{2.4}$$

so that

$$1 \ \Omega = 1 \ \text{V/A}$$

To apply Ohm's law as stated in Eq. (2.3), we must pay careful attention to the current direction and voltage polarity. The direction of current i and the polarity of voltage v must conform with the passive sign convention, as shown in Fig. 2.1(b). This implies that current flows from a higher potential to a lower potential in order for $v = iR$. If current flows from a lower potential to a higher potential, $v = -iR$.

Since the value of R can range from zero to infinity, it is important that we consider the two extreme possible values of R. An element with $R = 0$ is called a *short circuit*, as shown in Fig. 2.2(a). For a short circuit,

$$v = iR = 0 \tag{2.5}$$

showing that the voltage is zero but the current could be anything. In practice, a short circuit is usually a connecting wire assumed to be a perfect conductor. Thus,

(a)

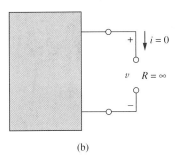

(b)

Figure 2.2 (a) Short circuit ($R = 0$), (b) Open circuit ($R = \infty$).

Figure 2.3   Fixed resistors: (a) wire-wound type, (b) carbon film type. *(Courtesy of Tech America.)*

(a)   (b)

Figure 2.4   Circuit symbol for: (a) a variable resistor in general, (b) a potentiometer.

Figure 2.6   Resistors in a thick-film circuit. *(Source: G. Daryanani, Principles of Active Network Synthesis and Design [New York: John Wiley, 1976], p. 461c.)*

A short circuit is a circuit element with resistance approaching zero.

Similarly, an element with $R = \infty$ is known as an *open circuit*, as shown in Fig. 2.2(b). For an open circuit,

$$i = \lim_{R \to \infty} \frac{v}{R} = 0 \tag{2.6}$$

indicating that the current is zero though the voltage could be anything. Thus,

An open circuit is a circuit element with resistance approaching infinity.

A resistor is either fixed or variable. Most resistors are of the fixed type, meaning their resistance remains constant. The two common types of fixed resistors (wirewound and composition) are shown in Fig. 2.3. The composition resistors are used when large resistance is needed. The circuit symbol in Fig. 2.1(b) is for a fixed resistor. Variable resistors have adjustable resistance. The symbol for a variable resistor is shown in Fig. 2.4(a). A common variable resistor is known as a *potentiometer* or *pot* for short, with the symbol shown in Fig. 2.4(b). The pot is a three-terminal element with a sliding contact or wiper. By sliding the wiper, the resistances between the wiper terminal and the fixed terminals vary. Like fixed resistors, variable resistors can either be of wirewound or composition type, as shown in Fig. 2.5. Although resistors like those in Figs. 2.3 and 2.5 are used in circuit designs, today most circuit components including resistors are either surface mounted or integrated, as typically shown in Fig. 2.6.

Figure 2.5   Variable resistors: (a) composition type, (b) slider pot. *(Courtesy of Tech America.)*

It should be pointed out that not all resistors obey Ohm's law. A resistor that obeys Ohm's law is known as a *linear* resistor. It has a constant resistance and thus its current-voltage characteristic is as illustrated in Fig. 2.7(a): its *i-v* graph is a straight line passing through the origin. A *nonlinear* resistor does not obey Ohm's law. Its resistance varies with current and its *i-v* characteristic is typically shown in Fig. 2.7(b).

Examples of devices with nonlinear resistance are the lightbulb and the diode. Although all practical resistors may exhibit nonlinear behavior under certain conditions, we will assume in this book that all elements actually designated as resistors are linear.

A useful quantity in circuit analysis is the reciprocal of resistance R, known as *conductance* and denoted by G:

$$G = \frac{1}{R} = \frac{i}{v} \qquad (2.7)$$

The conductance is a measure of how well an element will conduct electric current. The unit of conductance is the *mho* (ohm spelled backward) or reciprocal ohm, with symbol ℧, the inverted omega. Although engineers often use the mhos, in this book we prefer to use the siemens (S), the SI unit of conductance:

$$1 \text{ S} = 1 \text{ ℧} = 1 \text{ A/V} \qquad (2.8)$$

Thus,

> Conductance is the ability of an element to conduct electric current; it is measured in mhos (℧) or siemens (S).

The same resistance can be expressed in ohms or siemens. For example, 10 Ω is the same as 0.1 S. From Eq. (2.7), we may write

$$i = Gv \qquad (2.9)$$

The power dissipated by a resistor can be expressed in terms of R. Using Eqs. (1.7) and (2.3),

$$p = vi = i^2R = \frac{v^2}{R} \qquad (2.10)$$

The power dissipated by a resistor may also be expressed in terms of G as

$$p = vi = v^2G = \frac{i^2}{G} \qquad (2.11)$$

We should note two things from Eqs. (2.10) and (2.11):

1. The power dissipated in a resistor is a nonlinear function of either current or voltage.

2. Since R and G are positive quantities, the power dissipated in a resistor is always positive. Thus, a resistor always absorbs power from the circuit. This confirms the idea that a resistor is a passive element, incapable of generating energy.

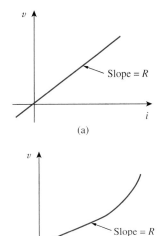

Figure 2.7   The i-v characteristic of: (a) a linear resistor, (b) a nonlinear resistor.

EXAMPLE 2.1

An electric iron draws 2 A at 120 V. Find its resistance.

Solution:

From Ohm's law,

$$R = \frac{v}{i} = \frac{120}{2} = 60 \ \Omega$$

PRACTICE PROBLEM 2.1

The essential component of a toaster is an electrical element (a resistor) that converts electrical energy to heat energy. How much current is drawn by a toaster with resistance 12 Ω at 110 V?

Answer: 9.167 A.

EXAMPLE 2.2

Figure 2.8　For Example 2.2.

In the circuit shown in Fig. 2.8, calculate the current i, the conductance G, and the power p.

Solution:

The voltage across the resistor is the same as the source voltage (30 V) because the resistor and the voltage source are connected to the same pair of terminals. Hence, the current is

$$i = \frac{v}{R} = \frac{30}{5 \times 10^3} = 6 \text{ mA}$$

The conductance is

$$G = \frac{1}{R} = \frac{1}{5 \times 10^3} = 0.2 \text{ mS}$$

We can calculate the power in various ways using either Eqs. (1.7), (2.10), or (2.11).

$$p = vi = 30(6 \times 10^{-3}) = 180 \text{ mW}$$

or

$$p = i^2R = (6 \times 10^{-3})^2 5 \times 10^3 = 180 \text{ mW}$$

or

$$p = v^2G = (30)^2 0.2 \times 10^{-3} = 180 \text{ mW}$$

PRACTICE PROBLEM 2.2

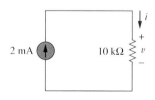

Figure 2.9　For Practice Prob. 2.2

For the circuit shown in Fig. 2.9, calculate the voltage v, the conductance G, and the power p.

Answer: 20 V, 100 μS, 40 mW.

EXAMPLE 2.3

A voltage source of $20 \sin \pi t$ V is connected across a 5-kΩ resistor. Find the current through the resistor and the power dissipated.

Solution:

$$i = \frac{v}{R} = \frac{20 \sin \pi t}{5 \times 10^3} = 4 \sin \pi t \text{ mA}$$

Hence,

$$p = vi = 80 \sin^2 \pi t \text{ mW}$$

PRACTICE PROBLEM 2.3

A resistor absorbs an instantaneous power of $20 \cos^2 t$ mW when connected to a voltage source $v = 10 \cos t$ V. Find i and R.

Answer: $2 \cos t$ mA, 5 kΩ.

†2.3 NODES, BRANCHES, AND LOOPS

Since the elements of an electric circuit can be interconnected in several ways, we need to understand some basic concepts of network topology. To differentiate between a circuit and a network, we may regard a network as an interconnection of elements or devices, whereas a circuit is a network providing one or more closed paths. The convention, when addressing network topology, is to use the word network rather than circuit. We do this even though the words network and circuit mean the same thing when used in this context. In network topology, we study the properties relating to the placement of elements in the network and the geometric configuration of the network. Such elements include branches, nodes, and loops.

> A branch represents a single element such as a voltage source or a resistor.

In other words, a branch represents any two-terminal element. The circuit in Fig. 2.10 has five branches, namely, the 10-V voltage source, the 2-A current source, and the three resistors.

> A node is the point of connection between two or more branches.

A node is usually indicated by a dot in a circuit. If a short circuit (a connecting wire) connects two nodes, the two nodes constitute a single node. The circuit in Fig. 2.10 has three nodes a, b, and c. Notice that the three points that form node b are connected by perfectly conducting wires and therefore constitute a single point. The same is true of the four points forming node c. We demonstrate that the circuit in Fig. 2.10 has only three nodes by redrawing the circuit in Fig. 2.11. The two circuits in

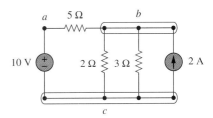

Figure 2.10   Nodes, branches, and loops.

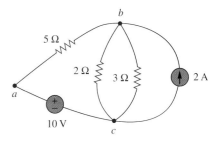

Figure 2.11   The three-node circuit of Fig. 2.10 is redrawn.

Figs. 2.10 and 2.11 are identical. However, for the sake of clarity, nodes b and c are spread out with perfect conductors as in Fig. 2.10.

A loop is any closed path in a circuit.

A loop is a closed path formed by starting at a node, passing through a set of nodes, and returning to the starting node without passing through any node more than once. A loop is said to be *independent* if it contains at least one branch which is not a part of any other independent loop. Independent loops or paths result in independent sets of equations.

For example, the closed path *abca* containing the 2-Ω resistor in Fig. 2.11 is a loop. Another loop is the closed path *bcb* containing the 3-Ω resistor and the current source. Although one can identify six loops in Fig. 2.11, only three of them are independent.

A network with b branches, n nodes, and l independent loops will satisfy the fundamental theorem of network topology:

$$b = l + n - 1 \qquad (2.12)$$

As the next two definitions show, circuit topology is of great value to the study of voltages and currents in an electric circuit.

Two or more elements are in series if they exclusively share a single node and consequently carry the same current.
Two or more elements are in parallel if they are connected to the same two nodes and consequently have the same voltage across them.

Elements are in series when they are chain-connected or connected sequentially, end to end. For example, two elements are in series if they share one common node and no other element is connected to that common node. Elements in parallel are connected to the same pair of terminals. Elements may be connected in a way that they are neither in series nor in parallel. In the circuit shown in Fig. 2.10, the voltage source and the 5-Ω resistor are in series because the same current will flow through them. The 2-Ω resistor, the 3-Ω resistor, and the current source are in parallel because they are connected to the same two nodes (b and c) and consequently have the same voltage across them. The 5-Ω and 2-Ω resistors are neither in series nor in parallel with each other.

E X A M P L E 2 . 4

Determine the number of branches and nodes in the circuit shown in Fig. 2.12. Identify which elements are in series and which are in parallel.

Solution:

Since there are four elements in the circuit, the circuit has four branches: 10 V, 5 Ω, 6 Ω, and 2 A. The circuit has three nodes as identified in

Fig. 2.13. The 5-Ω resistor is in series with the 10-V voltage source because the same current would flow in both. The 6-Ω resistor is in parallel with the 2-A current source because both are connected to the same nodes 2 and 3.

Figure 2.12   For Example 2.4.

Figure 2.13   The three nodes in the circuit of Fig. 2.12.

PRACTICE PROBLEM 2.4

How many branches and nodes does the circuit in Fig. 2.14 have? Identify the elements that are in series and in parallel.

Answer: Five branches and three nodes are identified in Fig. 2.15. The 1-Ω and 2-Ω resistors are in parallel. The 4-Ω resistor and 10-V source are also in parallel.

Figure 2.14   For Practice Prob. 2.4.

Figure 2.15   Answer for Practice Prob. 2.4.

2.4   KIRCHHOFF'S LAWS

Ohm's law by itself is not sufficient to analyze circuits. However, when it is coupled with Kirchhoff's two laws, we have a sufficient, powerful set of tools for analyzing a large variety of electric circuits. Kirchhoff's laws were first introduced in 1847 by the German physicist Gustav Robert Kirchhoff (1824–1887). These laws are formally known as Kirchhoff's current law (KCL) and Kirchhoff's voltage law (KVL).

Kirchhoff's first law is based on the law of conservation of charge, which requires that the algebraic sum of charges within a system cannot change.

Kirchhoff's current law (KCL) states that the algebraic sum of currents entering a node (or a closed boundary) is zero.

Mathematically, KCL implies that

$$\sum_{n=1}^{N} i_n = 0 \qquad (2.13)$$

where N is the number of branches connected to the node and i_n is the nth current entering (or leaving) the node. By this law, currents entering a node may be regarded as positive, while currents leaving the node may be taken as negative or vice versa.

To prove KCL, assume a set of currents $i_k(t), k = 1, 2, \ldots,$ flow into a node. The algebraic sum of currents at the node is

$$i_T(t) = i_1(t) + i_2(t) + i_3(t) + \cdots \qquad (2.14)$$

Integrating both sides of Eq. (2.14) gives

$$q_T(t) = q_1(t) + q_2(t) + q_3(t) + \cdots \qquad (2.15)$$

where $q_k(t) = \int i_k(t)\, dt$ and $q_T(t) = \int i_T(t)\, dt$. But the law of conservation of electric charge requires that the algebraic sum of electric charges at the node must not change; that is, the node stores no net charge. Thus $q_T(t) = 0 \rightarrow i_T(t) = 0$, confirming the validity of KCL.

Consider the node in Fig. 2.16. Applying KCL gives

$$i_1 + (-i_2) + i_3 + i_4 + (-i_5) = 0 \qquad (2.16)$$

since currents i_1, i_3, and i_4 are entering the node, while currents i_2 and i_5 are leaving it. By rearranging the terms, we get

$$i_1 + i_3 + i_4 = i_2 + i_5 \qquad (2.17)$$

Equation (2.17) is an alternative form of KCL:

Figure 2.16   Currents at a node illustrating KCL.

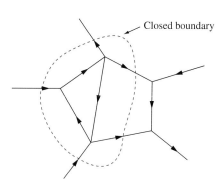

Closed boundary

Figure 2.17   Applying KCL to a closed boundary.

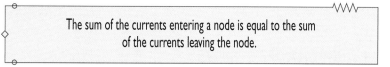

The sum of the currents entering a node is equal to the sum of the currents leaving the node.

Note that KCL also applies to a closed boundary. This may be regarded as a generalized case, because a node may be regarded as a closed surface shrunk to a point. In two dimensions, a closed boundary is the same as a closed path. As typically illustrated in the circuit of Fig. 2.17, the total current entering the closed surface is equal to the total current leaving the surface.

A simple application of KCL is combining current sources in parallel. The combined current is the algebraic sum of the current supplied by the individual sources. For example, the current sources shown

Two sources (or circuits in general) are said to be equivalent if they have the same i-v relationship at a pair of terminals.

in Fig. 2.18(a) can be combined as in Fig. 2.18(b). The combined or equivalent current source can be found by applying KCL to node a.

$$I_T + I_2 = I_1 + I_3$$

or

$$I_T = I_1 - I_2 + I_3 \qquad (2.18)$$

A circuit cannot contain two different currents, I_1 and I_2, in series, unless $I_1 = I_2$; otherwise KCL will be violated.

Kirchhoff's second law is based on the principle of conservation of energy:

Kirchhoff's voltage law (KVL) states that the algebraic sum of all voltages around a closed path (or loop) is zero.

Expressed mathematically, KVL states that

$$\sum_{m=1}^{M} v_m = 0 \qquad (2.19)$$

where M is the number of voltages in the loop (or the number of branches in the loop) and v_m is the mth voltage.

To illustrate KVL, consider the circuit in Fig. 2.19. The sign on each voltage is the polarity of the terminal encountered first as we travel around the loop. We can start with any branch and go around the loop either clockwise or counterclockwise. Suppose we start with the voltage source and go clockwise around the loop as shown; then voltages would be $-v_1, +v_2, +v_3, -v_4,$ and $+v_5$, in that order. For example, as we reach branch 3, the positive terminal is met first; hence we have $+v_3$. For branch 4, we reach the negative terminal first; hence, $-v_4$. Thus, KVL yields

$$-v_1 + v_2 + v_3 - v_4 + v_5 = 0 \qquad (2.20)$$

Rearranging terms gives

$$v_2 + v_3 + v_5 = v_1 + v_4 \qquad (2.21)$$

which may be interpreted as

Sum of voltage drops = Sum of voltage rises $\qquad (2.22)$

This is an alternative form of KVL. Notice that if we had traveled counterclockwise, the result would have been $+v_1, -v_5, +v_4, -v_3,$ and $-v_2$, which is the same as before except that the signs are reversed. Hence, Eqs. (2.20) and (2.21) remain the same.

When voltage sources are connected in series, KVL can be applied to obtain the total voltage. The combined voltage is the algebraic sum of the voltages of the individual sources. For example, for the voltage

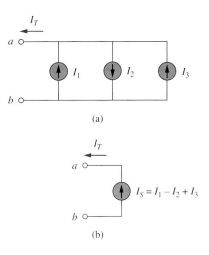

(a)

(b)

Figure 2.18   Current sources in parallel: (a) original circuit, (b) equivalent circuit.

KVL can be applied in two ways: by taking either a clockwise or a counterclockwise trip around the loop. Either way, the algebraic sum of voltages around the loop is zero.

Figure 2.19   A single-loop circuit illustrating KVL.

sources shown in Fig. 2.20(a), the combined or equivalent voltage source in Fig. 2.20(b) is obtained by applying KVL.

$$-V_{ab} + V_1 + V_2 - V_3 = 0$$

or

$$V_{ab} = V_1 + V_2 - V_3 \tag{2.23}$$

To avoid violating KVL, a circuit cannot contain two different voltages V_1 and V_2 in parallel unless $V_1 = V_2$.

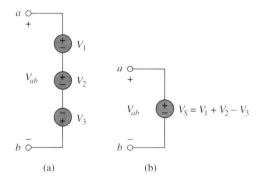

Figure 2.20   Voltage sources in series: (a) original circuit, (b) equivalent circuit.

EXAMPLE 2.5

For the circuit in Fig. 2.21(a), find voltages v_1 and v_2.

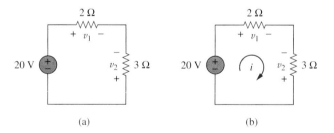

Figure 2.21   For Example 2.5.

Solution:

To find v_1 and v_2, we apply Ohm's law and Kirchhoff's voltage law. Assume that current i flows through the loop as shown in Fig. 2.21(b). From Ohm's law,

$$v_1 = 2i, \qquad v_2 = -3i \tag{2.5.1}$$

Applying KVL around the loop gives

$$-20 + v_1 - v_2 = 0 \tag{2.5.2}$$

Substituting Eq. (2.5.1) into Eq. (2.5.2), we obtain

$$-20 + 2i + 3i = 0 \quad \text{or} \quad 5i = 20 \quad \Longrightarrow \quad i = 4 \text{ A}$$

Substituting i in Eq. (2.5.1) finally gives

$$v_1 = 8 \text{ V}, \qquad v_2 = -12 \text{ V}$$

PRACTICE PROBLEM 2.5

Find v_1 and v_2 in the circuit of Fig. 2.22.

Answer: 12 V, −6 V.

Figure 2.22   For Practice Prob. 2.5

EXAMPLE 2.6

Determine v_o and i in the circuit shown in Fig. 2.23(a).

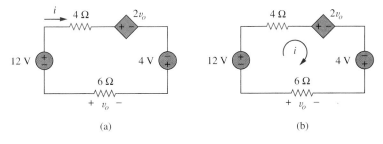

(a)   (b)

Figure 2.23   For Example 2.6.

Solution:

We apply KVL around the loop as shown in Fig. 2.23(b). The result is

$$-12 + 4i + 2v_o - 4 + 6i = 0 \qquad (2.6.1)$$

Applying Ohm's law to the 6-Ω resistor gives

$$v_o = -6i \qquad (2.6.2)$$

Substituting Eq. (2.6.2) into Eq. (2.6.1) yields

$$-16 + 10i - 12i = 0 \quad \Longrightarrow \quad i = -8 \text{ A}$$

and $v_o = 48$ V.

PRACTICE PROBLEM 2.6

35 V $10\,\Omega$ $+\ v_x\ -$ $2v_x$
$5\,\Omega$ $+\ v_o\ -$

Figure 2.24   For Practice Prob. 2.6.

Find v_x and v_o in the circuit of Fig. 2.24.

Answer: 10 V, -5 V.

EXAMPLE 2.7

Figure 2.25   For Example 2.7.

Find current i_o and voltage v_o in the circuit shown in Fig. 2.25.

Solution:

Applying KCL to node a, we obtain

$$3 + 0.5i_o = i_o \quad \Longrightarrow \quad i_o = 6\text{ A}$$

For the 4-Ω resistor, Ohm's law gives

$$v_o = 4i_o = 24\text{ V}$$

PRACTICE PROBLEM 2.7

Figure 2.26   For Practice Prob. 2.7.

Find v_o and i_o in the circuit of Fig. 2.26.

Answer: 8 V, 4 A.

EXAMPLE 2.8

Find the currents and voltages in the circuit shown in Fig. 2.27(a).

(a)   (b)

Figure 2.27   For Example 2.8.

Solution:

We apply Ohm's law and Kirchhoff's laws. By Ohm's law,

$$v_1 = 8i_1, \qquad v_2 = 3i_2, \qquad v_3 = 6i_3 \qquad (2.8.1)$$

Since the voltage and current of each resistor are related by Ohm's law as shown, we are really looking for three things: (v_1, v_2, v_3) or

(i_1, i_2, i_3). At node a, KCL gives

$$i_1 - i_2 - i_3 = 0 \qquad (2.8.2)$$

Applying KVL to loop 1 as in Fig. 2.27(b),

$$-30 + v_1 + v_2 = 0$$

We express this in terms of i_1 and i_2 as in Eq. (2.8.1) to obtain

$$-30 + 8i_1 + 3i_2 = 0$$

or

$$i_1 = \frac{(30 - 3i_2)}{8} \qquad (2.8.3)$$

Applying KVL to loop 2,

$$-v_2 + v_3 = 0 \qquad \Longrightarrow \qquad v_3 = v_2 \qquad (2.8.4)$$

as expected since the two resistors are in parallel. We express v_1 and v_2 in terms of i_1 and i_2 as in Eq. (2.8.1). Equation (2.8.4) becomes

$$6i_3 = 3i_2 \qquad \Longrightarrow \qquad i_3 = \frac{i_2}{2} \qquad (2.8.5)$$

Substituting Eqs. (2.8.3) and (2.8.5) into (2.8.2) gives

$$\frac{30 - 3i_2}{8} - i_2 - \frac{i_2}{2} = 0$$

or $i_2 = 2$ A. From the value of i_2, we now use Eqs. (2.8.1) to (2.8.5) to obtain

$$i_1 = 3 \text{ A}, \qquad i_3 = 1 \text{ A}, \qquad v_1 = 24 \text{ V}, \qquad v_2 = 6 \text{ V}, \qquad v_3 = 6 \text{ V}$$

PRACTICE PROBLEM 2.8

Find the currents and voltages in the circuit shown in Fig. 2.28.

Answer: $v_1 = 3$ V, $v_2 = 2$ V, $v_3 = 5$ V, $i_1 = 1.5$ A, $i_2 = 0.25$ A, $i_3 = 1.25$ A.

Figure 2.28   For Practice Prob. 2.8.

Figure 2.29   A single-loop circuit with two resistors in series.

Figure 2.30   Equivalent circuit of the Fig. 2.29 circuit.

Resistors in series behave as a single resistor whose resistance is equal to the sum of the resistances of the individual resistors.

2.5   SERIES RESISTORS AND VOLTAGE DIVISION

The need to combine resistors in series or in parallel occurs so frequently that it warrants special attention. The process of combining the resistors is facilitated by combining two of them at a time. With this in mind, consider the single-loop circuit of Fig. 2.29. The two resistors are in series, since the same current i flows in both of them. Applying Ohm's law to each of the resistors, we obtain

$$v_1 = i R_1, \qquad v_2 = i R_2 \qquad (2.24)$$

If we apply KVL to the loop (moving in the clockwise direction), we have

$$-v + v_1 + v_2 = 0 \qquad (2.25)$$

Combining Eqs. (2.24) and (2.25), we get

$$v = v_1 + v_2 = i(R_1 + R_2) \qquad (2.26)$$

or

$$i = \frac{v}{R_1 + R_2} \qquad (2.27)$$

Notice that Eq. (2.26) can be written as

$$v = i R_{eq} \qquad (2.28)$$

implying that the two resistors can be replaced by an equivalent resistor R_{eq}; that is,

$$R_{eq} = R_1 + R_2 \qquad (2.29)$$

Thus, Fig. 2.29 can be replaced by the equivalent circuit in Fig. 2.30. The two circuits in Figs. 2.29 and 2.30 are equivalent because they exhibit the same voltage-current relationships at the terminals a-b. An equivalent circuit such as the one in Fig. 2.30 is useful in simplifying the analysis of a circuit. In general,

> The equivalent resistance of any number of resistors connected in series is the sum of the individual resistances.

For N resistors in series then,

$$R_{eq} = R_1 + R_2 + \cdots + R_N = \sum_{n=1}^{N} R_n \qquad (2.30)$$

To determine the voltage across each resistor in Fig. 2.29, we substitute Eq. (2.26) into Eq. (2.24) and obtain

$$v_1 = \frac{R_1}{R_1 + R_2} v, \qquad v_2 = \frac{R_2}{R_1 + R_2} v \qquad (2.31)$$

Notice that the source voltage v is divided among the resistors in direct proportion to their resistances; the larger the resistance, the larger the voltage drop. This is called the *principle of voltage division*, and the circuit in Fig. 2.29 is called a *voltage divider*. In general, if a voltage divider has N resistors ($R_1, R_2, \ldots, R_N$) in series with the source voltage v, the nth resistor (R_n) will have a voltage drop of

$$v_n = \frac{R_n}{R_1 + R_2 + \cdots + R_N} v \qquad (2.32)$$

2.6 PARALLEL RESISTORS AND CURRENT DIVISION

Consider the circuit in Fig. 2.31, where two resistors are connected in parallel and therefore have the same voltage across them. From Ohm's law,

$$v = i_1 R_1 = i_2 R_2$$

or

$$i_1 = \frac{v}{R_1}, \qquad i_2 = \frac{v}{R_2} \qquad (2.33)$$

Applying KCL at node a gives the total current i as

$$i = i_1 + i_2 \qquad (2.34)$$

Substituting Eq. (2.33) into Eq. (2.34), we get

$$i = \frac{v}{R_1} + \frac{v}{R_2} = v\left(\frac{1}{R_1} + \frac{1}{R_2}\right) = \frac{v}{R_{eq}} \qquad (2.35)$$

where R_{eq} is the equivalent resistance of the resistors in parallel:

$$\frac{1}{R_{eq}} = \frac{1}{R_1} + \frac{1}{R_2} \qquad (2.36)$$

or

$$\frac{1}{R_{eq}} = \frac{R_1 + R_2}{R_1 R_2}$$

or

$$\boxed{R_{eq} = \frac{R_1 R_2}{R_1 + R_2}} \qquad (2.37)$$

Thus,

The equivalent resistance of two parallel resistors is equal to the product of their resistances divided by their sum.

It must be emphasized that this applies only to two resistors in parallel. From Eq. (2.37), if $R_1 = R_2$, then $R_{eq} = R_1/2$.

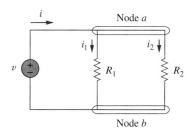

Figure 2.31   Two resistors in parallel.

We can extend the result in Eq. (2.36) to the general case of a circuit with N resistors in parallel. The equivalent resistance is

$$\frac{1}{R_{eq}} = \frac{1}{R_1} + \frac{1}{R_2} + \cdots + \frac{1}{R_N} \tag{2.38}$$

Note that R_{eq} is always smaller than the resistance of the smallest resistor in the parallel combination. If $R_1 = R_2 = \cdots = R_N = R$, then

$$R_{eq} = \frac{R}{N} \tag{2.39}$$

For example, if four 100-Ω resistors are connected in parallel, their equivalent resistance is 25 Ω.

It is often more convenient to use conductance rather than resistance when dealing with resistors in parallel. From Eq. (2.38), the equivalent conductance for N resistors in parallel is

Conductances in parallel behave as a single conductance whose value is equal to the sum of the individual conductances.

$$G_{eq} = G_1 + G_2 + G_3 + \cdots + G_N \tag{2.40}$$

where $G_{eq} = 1/R_{eq}$, $G_1 = 1/R_1$, $G_2 = 1/R_2$, $G_3 = 1/R_3, \ldots, G_N = 1/R_N$. Equation (2.40) states:

The equivalent conductance of resistors connected in parallel is the sum of their individual conductances.

This means that we may replace the circuit in Fig. 2.31 with that in Fig. 2.32. Notice the similarity between Eqs. (2.30) and (2.40). The equivalent conductance of parallel resistors is obtained the same way as the equivalent resistance of series resistors. In the same manner, the equivalent conductance of resistors in series is obtained just the same way as the resistance of resistors in parallel. Thus the equivalent conductance G_{eq} of N resistors in series (such as shown in Fig. 2.29) is

$$\frac{1}{G_{eq}} = \frac{1}{G_1} + \frac{1}{G_2} + \frac{1}{G_3} + \cdots + \frac{1}{G_N} \tag{2.41}$$

Figure 2.32 Equivalent circuit to Fig. 2.31.

Given the total current i entering node a in Fig. 2.31, how do we obtain current i_1 and i_2? We know that the equivalent resistor has the same voltage, or

$$v = i R_{eq} = \frac{i R_1 R_2}{R_1 + R_2} \tag{2.42}$$

Combining Eqs. (2.33) and (2.42) results in

$$i_1 = \frac{R_2\, i}{R_1 + R_2}, \qquad i_2 = \frac{R_1\, i}{R_1 + R_2} \tag{2.43}$$

which shows that the total current i is shared by the resistors in inverse proportion to their resistances. This is known as the *principle of current division*, and the circuit in Fig. 2.31 is known as a *current divider*. Notice that the larger current flows through the smaller resistance.

As an extreme case, suppose one of the resistors in Fig. 2.31 is zero, say $R_2 = 0$; that is, R_2 is a short circuit, as shown in Fig. 2.33(a). From Eq. (2.43), $R_2 = 0$ implies that $i_1 = 0$, $i_2 = i$. This means that the entire current i bypasses R_1 and flows through the short circuit $R_2 = 0$, the path of least resistance. Thus when a circuit is short circuited, as shown in Fig. 2.33(a), two things should be kept in mind:

1. The equivalent resistance $R_{eq} = 0$. [See what happens when $R_2 = 0$ in Eq. (2.37).]

2. The entire current flows through the short circuit.

As another extreme case, suppose $R_2 = \infty$, that is, R_2 is an open circuit, as shown in Fig. 2.33(b). The current still flows through the path of least resistance, R_1. By taking the limit of Eq. (2.37) as $R_2 \to \infty$, we obtain $R_{eq} = R_1$ in this case.

If we divide both the numerator and denominator by $R_1 R_2$, Eq. (2.43) becomes

$$i_1 = \frac{G_1}{G_1 + G_2} i \qquad (2.44a)$$

$$i_2 = \frac{G_2}{G_1 + G_2} i \qquad (2.44b)$$

(a)

(b)

Figure 2.33   (a) A shorted circuit, (b) an open circuit.

Thus, in general, if a current divider has N conductors ($G_1, G_2, \ldots, G_N$) in parallel with the source current i, the nth conductor (G_n) will have current

$$i_n = \frac{G_n}{G_1 + G_2 + \cdots + G_N} i \qquad (2.45)$$

In general, it is often convenient and possible to combine resistors in series and parallel and reduce a resistive network to a single *equivalent resistance* R_{eq}. Such an equivalent resistance is the resistance between the designated terminals of the network and must exhibit the same i-v characteristics as the original network at the terminals.

EXAMPLE 2.9

Find R_{eq} for the circuit shown in Fig. 2.34.

Solution:

To get R_{eq}, we combine resistors in series and in parallel. The 6-Ω and 3-Ω resistors are in parallel, so their equivalent resistance is

$$6\,\Omega \parallel 3\,\Omega = \frac{6 \times 3}{6 + 3} = 2\,\Omega$$

(The symbol $\parallel$ is used to indicate a parallel combination.) Also, the 1-Ω and 5-Ω resistors are in series; hence their equivalent resistance is

$$1\,\Omega + 5\,\Omega = 6\,\Omega$$

Figure 2.34   For Example 2.9.

(a)

(b)

Figure 2.35   Equivalent circuits for Example 2.9.

Thus the circuit in Fig. 2.34 is reduced to that in Fig. 2.35(a). In Fig. 2.35(a), we notice that the two 2-Ω resistors are in series, so the equivalent resistance is

$$2\,\Omega + 2\,\Omega = 4\,\Omega$$

This 4-Ω resistor is now in parallel with the 6-Ω resistor in Fig. 2.35(a); their equivalent resistance is

$$4\,\Omega \parallel 6\,\Omega = \frac{4 \times 6}{4 + 6} = 2.4\,\Omega$$

The circuit in Fig. 2.35(a) is now replaced with that in Fig. 2.35(b). In Fig. 2.35(b), the three resistors are in series. Hence, the equivalent resistance for the circuit is

$$R_{\text{eq}} = 4\,\Omega + 2.4\,\Omega + 8\,\Omega = 14.4\,\Omega$$

PRACTICE PROBLEM 2.9

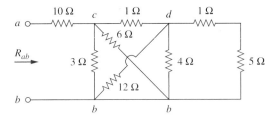

Figure 2.36   For Practice Prob. 2.9.

By combining the resistors in Fig. 2.36, find R_{eq}.

Answer: 6 Ω.

EXAMPLE 2.10

Calculate the equivalent resistance R_{ab} in the circuit in Fig. 2.37.

Figure 2.37   For Example 2.10.

Solution:

The 3-Ω and 6-Ω resistors are in parallel because they are connected to the same two nodes c and b. Their combined resistance is

$$3\,\Omega \parallel 6\,\Omega = \frac{3 \times 6}{3 + 6} = 2\,\Omega \qquad (2.10.1)$$

Similarly, the 12-Ω and 4-Ω resistors are in parallel since they are connected to the same two nodes d and b. Hence

$$12\ \Omega\ \|\ 4\ \Omega = \frac{12 \times 4}{12 + 4} = 3\ \Omega \qquad (2.10.2)$$

Also the 1-Ω and 5-Ω resistors are in series; hence, their equivalent resistance is

$$1\ \Omega + 5\ \Omega = 6\ \Omega \qquad (2.10.3)$$

With these three combinations, we can replace the circuit in Fig. 2.37 with that in Fig. 2.38(a). In Fig. 2.38(a), 3-Ω in parallel with 6-Ω gives 2-Ω, as calculated in Eq. (2.10.1). This 2-Ω equivalent resistance is now in series with the 1-Ω resistance to give a combined resistance of $1\ \Omega + 2\ \Omega = 3\ \Omega$. Thus, we replace the circuit in Fig. 2.38(a) with that in Fig. 2.38(b). In Fig. 2.38(b), we combine the 2-Ω and 3-Ω resistors in parallel to get

$$2\ \Omega\ \|\ 3\ \Omega = \frac{2 \times 3}{2 + 3} = 1.2\ \Omega$$

This 1.2-Ω resistor is in series with the 10-Ω resistor, so that

$$R_{ab} = 10 + 1.2 = 11.2\ \Omega$$

(a)

(b)

Figure 2.38   Equivalent circuits for Example 2.10.

PRACTICE PROBLEM 2.10

Find R_{ab} for the circuit in Fig. 2.39.

Answer: 11 Ω.

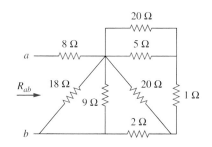

Figure 2.39   For Practice Prob. 2.10.

EXAMPLE 2.11

Find the equivalent conductance G_{eq} for the circuit in Fig. 2.40(a).

Solution:

The 8-S and 12-S resistors are in parallel, so their conductance is

$$8\ S + 12\ S = 20\ S$$

This 20-S resistor is now in series with 5 S as shown in Fig. 2.40(b) so that the combined conductance is

$$\frac{20 \times 5}{20 + 5} = 4\ S$$

This is in parallel with the 6-S resistor. Hence

$$G_{eq} = 6 + 4 = 10\ S$$

We should note that the circuit in Fig. 2.40(a) is the same as that in Fig. 2.40(c). While the resistors in Fig. 2.40(a) are expressed in siemens,

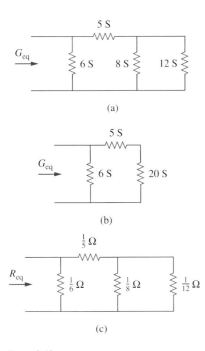

(a)

(b)

(c)

Figure 2.40   For Example 2.11: (a) original circuit, (b) its equivalent circuit, (c) same circuit as in (a) but resistors are expressed in ohms.

those in Fig. 2.40(c) are expressed in ohms. To show that the circuits are the same, we find R_{eq} for the circuit in Fig. 2.40(c).

$$R_{eq} = \frac{1}{6} \,\|\, \left(\frac{1}{5} + \frac{1}{8} \,\|\, \frac{1}{12} \right) = \frac{1}{6} \,\|\, \left(\frac{1}{5} + \frac{1}{20} \right) = \frac{1}{6} \,\|\, \frac{1}{4}$$

$$= \frac{\frac{1}{6} \times \frac{1}{4}}{\frac{1}{6} + \frac{1}{4}} = \frac{1}{10} \; \Omega$$

$$G_{eq} = \frac{1}{R_{eq}} = 10 \text{ S}$$

This is the same as we obtained previously.

PRACTICE PROBLEM 2.11

Figure 2.41   For Practice Prob. 2.11.

Calculate G_{eq} in the circuit of Fig. 2.41.

Answer: 4 S.

EXAMPLE 2.12

Find i_o and v_o in the circuit shown in Fig. 2.42(a). Calculate the power dissipated in the 3-Ω resistor.

Solution:

The 6-Ω and 3-Ω resistors are in parallel, so their combined resistance is

$$6 \; \Omega \,\|\, 3 \; \Omega = \frac{6 \times 3}{6 + 3} = 2 \; \Omega$$

Thus our circuit reduces to that shown in Fig. 2.42(b). Notice that v_o is not affected by the combination of the resistors because the resistors are in parallel and therefore have the same voltage v_o. From Fig. 2.42(b), we can obtain v_o in two ways. One way is to apply Ohm's law to get

$$i = \frac{12}{4+2} = 2 \text{ A}$$

and hence, $v_o = 2i = 2 \times 2 = 4$ V. Another way is to apply voltage division, since the 12 V in Fig. 2.42(b) is divided between the 4-Ω and 2-Ω resistors. Hence,

$$v_o = \frac{2}{2+4}(12 \text{ V}) = 4 \text{ V}$$

Similarly, i_o can be obtained in two ways. One approach is to apply Ohm's law to the 3-Ω resistor in Fig. 2.42(a) now that we know v_o; thus,

$$v_o = 3i_o = 4 \quad \Longrightarrow \quad i_o = \frac{4}{3} \text{ A}$$

Another approach is to apply current division to the circuit in Fig. 2.42(a) now that we know i, by writing

$$i_o = \frac{6}{6+3}i = \frac{2}{3}(2 \text{ A}) = \frac{4}{3} \text{ A}$$

The power dissipated in the 3-Ω resistor is

$$p_o = v_o i_o = 4\left(\frac{4}{3}\right) = 5.333 \text{ W}$$

(a)

(b)

Figure 2.42   For Example 2.12: (a) original circuit, (b) its equivalent circuit.

PRACTICE PROBLEM 2.12

Find v_1 and v_2 in the circuit shown in Fig. 2.43. Also calculate i_1 and i_2 and the power dissipated in the 12-Ω and 40-Ω resistors.

Answer: $v_1 = 5$ V, $i_1 = 416.7$ mA, $p_1 = 2.083$ W, $v_2 = 10$ V, $i_2 = 250$ mA, $p_2 = 2.5$ W.

Figure 2.43   For Practice Prob. 2.12.

EXAMPLE 2.13

For the circuit shown in Fig. 2.44(a), determine: (a) the voltage v_o, (b) the power supplied by the current source, (c) the power absorbed by each resistor.

Solution:

(a) The 6-kΩ and 12-kΩ resistors are in series so that their combined value is $6 + 12 = 18$ kΩ. Thus the circuit in Fig. 2.44(a) reduces to that

(a)

(b)

Figure 2.44   For Example 2.13: (a) original circuit, (b) its equivalent circuit.

shown in Fig. 2.44(b). We now apply the current division technique to find i_1 and i_2.

$$i_1 = \frac{18,000}{9,000 + 18,000}(30 \text{ mA}) = 20 \text{ mA}$$

$$i_2 = \frac{9000}{9,000 + 18,000}(30 \text{ mA}) = 10 \text{ mA}$$

Notice that the voltage across the 9-kΩ and 18-kΩ resistors is the same, and $v_o = 9,000i_1 = 18,000i_2 = 180$ V, as expected.

(b) Power supplied by the source is

$$p_o = v_o i_o = 180(30) \text{ mW} = 5.4 \text{ W}$$

(c) Power absorbed by the 12-kΩ resistor is

$$p = iv = i_2(i_2 R) = i_2^2 R = (10 \times 10^{-3})^2(12,000) = 1.2 \text{ W}$$

Power absorbed by the 6-kΩ resistor is

$$p = i_2^2 R = (10 \times 10^{-3})^2(6,000) = 0.6 \text{ W}$$

Power absorbed by the 9-kΩ resistor is

$$p = \frac{v_o^2}{R} = \frac{(180)^2}{9,000} = 3.6 \text{ W}$$

or

$$p = v_o i_1 = 180(20) \text{ mW} = 3.6 \text{ W}$$

Notice that the power supplied (5.4 W) equals the power absorbed (1.2 + 0.6 + 3.6 = 5.4 W). This is one way of checking results.

PRACTICE PROBLEM 2.13

For the circuit shown in Fig. 2.45, find: (a) v_1 and v_2, (b) the power dissipated in the 3-kΩ and 20-kΩ resistors, and (c) the power supplied by the current source.

Figure 2.45   For Practice Prob. 2.13.

Answer: (a) 15 V, 20 V, (b) 75 mW, 20 mW, (c) 200 mW.

†2.7 WYE-DELTA TRANSFORMATIONS

Situations often arise in circuit analysis when the resistors are neither in parallel nor in series. For example, consider the bridge circuit in Fig. 2.46. How do we combine resistors R_1 through R_6 when the resistors are neither in series nor in parallel? Many circuits of the type shown in Fig. 2.46 can be simplified by using three-terminal equivalent networks. These are the wye (Y) or tee (T) network shown in Fig. 2.47 and the delta (Δ) or pi (Π) network shown in Fig. 2.48. These networks occur by themselves or as part of a larger network. They are used in three-phase networks, electrical filters, and matching networks. Our main interest here is in how to identify them when they occur as part of a network and how to apply wye-delta transformation in the analysis of that network.

Figure 2.46   The bridge network.

(a)   (b)

Figure 2.47   Two forms of the same network: (a) Y, (b) T.

Delta to Wye Conversion

Suppose it is more convenient to work with a wye network in a place where the circuit contains a delta configuration. We superimpose a wye network on the existing delta network and find the equivalent resistances in the wye network. To obtain the equivalent resistances in the wye network, we compare the two networks and make sure that the resistance between each pair of nodes in the Δ (or Π) network is the same as the resistance between the same pair of nodes in the Y (or T) network. For terminals 1 and 2 in Figs. 2.47 and 2.48, for example,

$$R_{12}(Y) = R_1 + R_3$$
$$R_{12}(\Delta) = R_b \parallel (R_a + R_c) \tag{2.46}$$

Setting $R_{12}(Y) = R_{12}(\Delta)$ gives

$$R_{12} = R_1 + R_3 = \frac{R_b(R_a + R_c)}{R_a + R_b + R_c} \tag{2.47a}$$

Similarly,

$$R_{13} = R_1 + R_2 = \frac{R_c(R_a + R_b)}{R_a + R_b + R_c} \tag{2.47b}$$

$$R_{34} = R_2 + R_3 = \frac{R_a(R_b + R_c)}{R_a + R_b + R_c} \tag{2.47c}$$

Subtracting Eq. (2.47c) from Eq. (2.47a), we get

$$R_1 - R_2 = \frac{R_c(R_b - R_a)}{R_a + R_b + R_c} \tag{2.48}$$

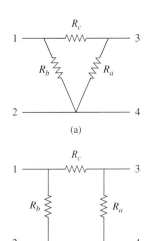

(a)

(b)

Figure 2.48   Two forms of the same network: (a) Δ, (b) Π.

Adding Eqs. (2.47b) and (2.48) gives

$$R_1 = \frac{R_b R_c}{R_a + R_b + R_c} \qquad (2.49)$$

and subtracting Eq. (2.48) from Eq. (2.47b) yields

$$R_2 = \frac{R_c R_a}{R_a + R_b + R_c} \qquad (2.50)$$

Subtracting Eq. (2.49) from Eq. (2.47a), we obtain

$$R_3 = \frac{R_a R_b}{R_a + R_b + R_c} \qquad (2.51)$$

We do not need to memorize Eqs. (2.49) to (2.51). To transform a Δ network to Y, we create an extra node n as shown in Fig. 2.49 and follow this conversion rule:

Each resistor in the Y network is the product of the resistors in the two adjacent Δ branches, divided by the sum of the three Δ resistors.

One can follow this rule and obtain Eqs (2.49) to (2.51) from Fig 2.49.

Wye to Delta Conversion

To obtain the conversion formulas for transforming a wye network to an equivalent delta network, we note from Eqs. (2.49) to (2.51) that

$$
\begin{aligned}
R_1 R_2 + R_2 R_3 + R_3 R_1 &= \frac{R_a R_b R_c (R_a + R_b + R_c)}{(R_a + R_b + R_c)^2} \\
&= \frac{R_a R_b R_c}{R_a + R_b + R_c}
\end{aligned}
\qquad (2.52)
$$

Dividing Eq. (2.52) by each of Eqs. (2.49) to (2.51) leads to the following equations:

$$R_a = \frac{R_1 R_2 + R_2 R_3 + R_3 R_1}{R_1} \qquad (2.53)$$

$$R_b = \frac{R_1 R_2 + R_2 R_3 + R_3 R_1}{R_2} \qquad (2.54)$$

$$R_c = \frac{R_1 R_2 + R_2 R_3 + R_3 R_1}{R_3} \qquad (2.55)$$

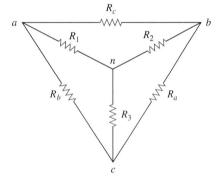

Figure 2.49   Superposition of Y and Δ networks as an aid in transforming one to the other.

From Eqs. (2.53) to (2.55) and Fig. 2.49, the conversion rule for Y to Δ is as follows:

> Each resistor in the Δ network is the sum of all possible products of Y resistors taken two at a time, divided by the opposite Y resistor.

The Y and Δ networks are said to be *balanced* when

$$R_1 = R_2 = R_3 = R_Y, \qquad R_a = R_b = R_c = R_\Delta \qquad (2.56)$$

Under these conditions, conversion formulas become

$$R_Y = \frac{R_\Delta}{3} \qquad \text{or} \qquad R_\Delta = 3R_Y \qquad (2.57)$$

One may wonder why R_Y is less than R_Δ. Well, we notice that the Y-connection is like a "series" connection while the Δ-connection is like a "parallel" connection.

Note that in making the transformation, we do not take anything out of the circuit or put in anything new. We are merely substituting different but mathematically equivalent three-terminal network patterns to create a circuit in which resistors are either in series or in parallel, allowing us to calculate R_{eq} if necessary.

EXAMPLE 2.14

Convert the Δ network in Fig. 2.50(a) to an equivalent Y network.

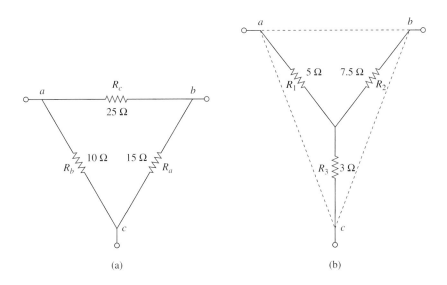

Figure 2.50   For Example 2.14: (a) original Δ network, (b) Y equivalent network.

Solution:

Using Eqs. (2.49) to (2.51), we obtain

$$R_1 = \frac{R_b R_c}{R_a + R_b + R_c} = \frac{25 \times 10}{25 + 10 + 15} = \frac{250}{50} = 5 \, \Omega$$

$$R_2 = \frac{R_c R_a}{R_a + R_b + R_c} = \frac{25 \times 15}{50} = 7.5 \, \Omega$$

$$R_3 = \frac{R_a R_b}{R_a + R_b + R_c} = \frac{15 \times 10}{50} = 3 \, \Omega$$

The equivalent Y network is shown in Fig. 2.50(b).

PRACTICE PROBLEM 2.14

Figure 2.51   For Practice Prob. 2.14.

Transform the wye network in Fig. 2.51 to a delta network.

Answer: $R_a = 140 \, \Omega$, $R_b = 70 \, \Omega$, $R_c = 35 \, \Omega$.

EXAMPLE 2.15

Figure 2.52   For Example 2.15.

Obtain the equivalent resistance R_{ab} for the circuit in Fig. 2.52 and use it to find current i.

Solution:

In this circuit, there are two Y networks and one △ network. Transforming just one of these will simplify the circuit. If we convert the Y network comprising the 5-Ω, 10-Ω, and 20-Ω resistors, we may select

$$R_1 = 10 \, \Omega, \qquad R_2 = 20 \, \Omega, \qquad R_3 = 5 \, \Omega$$

Thus from Eqs. (2.53) to (2.55) we have

$$R_a = \frac{R_1 R_2 + R_2 R_3 + R_3 R_1}{R_1} = \frac{10 \times 20 + 20 \times 5 + 5 \times 10}{10}$$

$$= \frac{350}{10} = 35 \, \Omega$$

$$R_b = \frac{R_1 R_2 + R_2 R_3 + R_3 R_1}{R_2} = \frac{350}{20} = 17.5 \, \Omega$$

$$R_c = \frac{R_1 R_2 + R_2 R_3 + R_3 R_1}{R_3} = \frac{350}{5} = 70 \, \Omega$$

With the Y converted to △, the equivalent circuit (with the voltage source removed for now) is shown in Fig. 2.53(a). Combining the three pairs of resistors in parallel, we obtain

$$70 \parallel 30 = \frac{70 \times 30}{70 + 30} = 21\ \Omega$$

$$12.5 \parallel 17.5 = \frac{12.5 \times 17.5}{12.5 + 17.5} = 7.2917\ \Omega$$

$$15 \parallel 35 = \frac{15 \times 35}{15 + 35} = 10.5\ \Omega$$

so that the equivalent circuit is shown in Fig. 2.53(b). Hence, we find

$$R_{ab} = (7.292 + 10.5) \parallel 21 = \frac{17.792 \times 21}{17.792 + 21} = 9.632\ \Omega$$

Then

$$i = \frac{v_s}{R_{ab}} = \frac{120}{9.632} = 12.458\ \text{A}$$

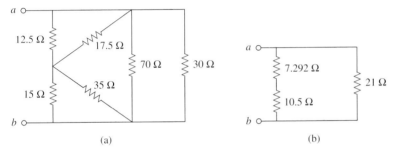

Figure 2.53   Equivalent circuits to Fig. 2.52, with the voltage removed.

PRACTICE PROBLEM 2.15

For the bridge network in Fig. 2.54, find R_{ab} and i.

Answer: $40\ \Omega$, 2.5 A.

Figure 2.54   For Practice Prob. 2.15.

†2.8   APPLICATIONS

Resistors are often used to model devices that convert electrical energy into heat or other forms of energy. Such devices include conducting wire, lightbulbs, electric heaters, stoves, ovens, and loudspeakers. In this

So far, we have assumed that connecting wires are perfect conductors (i.e., conductors of zero resistance). In real physical systems, however, the resistance of the connecting wire may be appreciably large, and the modeling of the system must include that resistance.

section, we will consider two real-life problems that apply the concepts developed in this chapter: electrical lighting systems and design of dc meters.

2.8.1 Lighting Systems

Lighting systems, such as in a house or on a Christmas tree, often consist of N lamps connected either in parallel or in series, as shown in Fig. 2.55. Each lamp is modeled as a resistor. Assuming that all the lamps are identical and V_o is the power-line voltage, the voltage across each lamp is V_o for the parallel connection and V_o/N for the series connection. The series connection is easy to manufacture but is seldom used in practice, for at least two reasons. First, it is less reliable; when a lamp fails, all the lamps go out. Second, it is harder to maintain; when a lamp is bad, one must test all the lamps one by one to detect the faulty one.

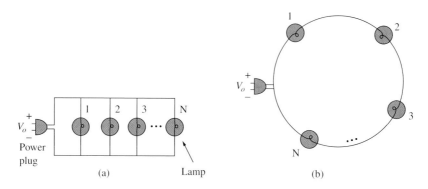

Figure 2.55   (a) Parallel connection of lightbulbs, (b) series connection of lightbulbs.

E X A M P L E 2 . 1 6

Three lightbulbs are connected to a 9-V battery as shown in Fig. 2.56(a). Calculate: (a) the total current supplied by the battery, (b) the current through each bulb, (c) the resistance of each bulb.

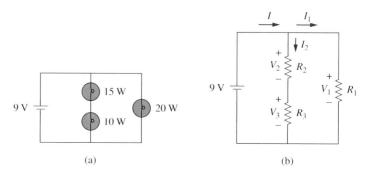

Figure 2.56   (a) Lighting system with three bulbs, (b) resistive circuit equivalent model.

Solution:

(a) The total power supplied by the battery is equal to the total power absorbed by the bulbs, that is,

$$p = 15 + 10 + 20 = 45 \text{ W}$$

Since $p = VI$, then the total current supplied by the battery is

$$I = \frac{p}{V} = \frac{45}{9} = 5 \text{ A}$$

(b) The bulbs can be modeled as resistors as shown in Fig. 2.56(b). Since R_1 (20-W bulb) is in parallel with the battery as well as the series combination of R_2 and R_3,

$$V_1 = V_2 + V_3 = 9 \text{ V}$$

The current through R_1 is

$$I_1 = \frac{p_1}{V_1} = \frac{20}{9} = 2.222 \text{ A}$$

By KCL, the current through the series combination of R_2 and R_3 is

$$I_2 = I - I_1 = 5 - 2.222 = 2.778 \text{ A}$$

(c) Since $p = I^2 R$,

$$R_1 = \frac{p_1}{I_1^2} = \frac{20}{2.222^2} = 4.05 \ \Omega$$

$$R_2 = \frac{p_2}{I_2^2} = \frac{15}{2.777^2} = 1.945 \ \Omega$$

$$R_3 = \frac{p_3}{I_3^2} = \frac{10}{2.777^2} = 1.297 \ \Omega$$

PRACTICE PROBLEM 2.16

Refer to Fig. 2.55 and assume there are 10 lightbulbs, each with a power rating of 40 W. If the voltage at the plug is 110 V for the parallel and series connections, calculate the current through each bulb for both cases.

Answer: 0.364 A (parallel), 3.64 A (series).

2.8.2 Design of DC Meters

By their nature, resistors are used to control the flow of current. We take advantage of this property in several applications, such as in a potentiometer (Fig. 2.57). The word *potentiometer*, derived from the words *potential* and *meter*, implies that potential can be metered out. The potentiometer (or pot for short) is a three-terminal device that operates on the principle of voltage division. It is essentially an adjustable voltage divider. As a voltage regulator, it is used as a volume or level control on radios, TVs, and other devices. In Fig. 2.57,

$$V_{\text{out}} = V_{bc} = \frac{R_{bc}}{R_{ac}} V_{\text{in}} \tag{2.58}$$

where $R_{ac} = R_{ab} + R_{bc}$. Thus, V_{out} decreases or increases as the sliding contact of the pot moves toward c or a, respectively.

Figure 2.57   The potentiometer controlling potential levels.

Another application where resistors are used to control current flow is in the analog dc meters—the ammeter, voltmeter, and ohmmeter, which measure current, voltage, and resistance, respectively. Each of these meters employs the d'Arsonval meter movement, shown in Fig. 2.58. The movement consists essentially of a movable iron-core coil mounted on a pivot between the poles of a permanent magnet. When current flows through the coil, it creates a torque which causes the pointer to deflect. The amount of current through the coil determines the deflection of the pointer, which is registered on a scale attached to the meter movement. For example, if the meter movement is rated 1 mA, 50 Ω, it would take 1 mA to cause a full-scale deflection of the meter movement. By introducing additional circuitry to the d'Arsonval meter movement, an ammeter, voltmeter, or ohmmeter can be constructed.

Consider Fig. 2.59, where an analog voltmeter and ammeter are connected to an element. The voltmeter measures the voltage across a *load* and is therefore connected in parallel with the element. As shown in Fig. 2.60(a), the voltmeter consists of a d'Arsonval movement in series with a resistor whose resistance R_m is deliberately made very large (theoretically, infinite), to minimize the current drawn from the circuit. To extend the range of voltage that the meter can measure, series multiplier resistors are often connected with the voltmeters, as shown in Fig. 2.60(b). The multiple-range voltmeter in Fig. 2.60(b) can measure voltage from 0 to 1 V, 0 to 10 V, or 0 to 100 V, depending on whether the switch is connected to R_1, R_2, or R_3, respectively.

Let us calculate the multiplier resistor R_n for the single-range voltmeter in Fig. 2.60(a), or $R_n = R_1$, R_2, or R_3 for the multiple-range voltmeter in Fig. 2.60(b). We need to determine the value of R_n to be connected in series with the internal resistance R_m of the voltmeter. In any design, we consider the worst-case condition. In this case, the worst case occurs when the full-scale current $I_{fs} = I_m$ flows through the meter. This should also correspond to the maximum voltage reading or the full-scale voltage V_{fs}. Since the multiplier resistance R_n is in series with the

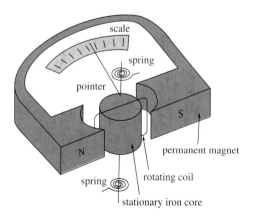

Figure 2.58   A d'Arsonval meter movement.

Figure 2.59   Connection of a voltmeter and an ammeter to an element.

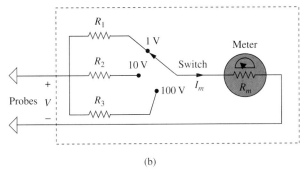

(b)

Figure 2.60   Voltmeters: (a) single-range type, (b) multiple-range type.

internal resistance R_m,

$$V_{\text{fs}} = I_{\text{fs}}(R_n + R_m) \tag{2.59}$$

From this, we obtain

$$R_n = \frac{V_{\text{fs}}}{I_{\text{fs}}} - R_m \tag{2.60}$$

Similarly, the ammeter measures the current through the load and is connected in series with it. As shown in Fig. 2.61(a), the ammeter consists of a d'Arsonval movement in parallel with a resistor whose resistance R_m is deliberately made very small (theoretically, zero) to minimize the voltage drop across it. To allow multiple range, shunt resistors are often connected in parallel with R_m as shown in Fig. 2.61(b). The shunt resistors allow the meter to measure in the range 0–10 mA, 0–100 mA, or 0–1 A, depending on whether the switch is connected to R_1, R_2, or R_3, respectively.

Now our objective is to obtain the multiplier shunt R_n for the single-range ammeter in Fig. 2.61(a), or $R_n = R_1$, R_2, or R_3 for the multiple-range ammeter in Fig. 2.61(b). We notice that R_m and R_n are in parallel and that at full-scale reading $I = I_{\text{fs}} = I_m + I_n$, where I_n is the current through the shunt resistor R_n. Applying the current division principle yields

$$I_m = \frac{R_n}{R_n + R_m} I_{\text{fs}}$$

or

$$R_n = \frac{I_m}{I_{\text{fs}} - I_m} R_m \tag{2.61}$$

(a)

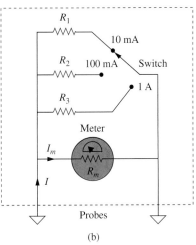

(b)

Figure 2.61   Ammeters: (a) single-range type, (b) multiple-range type.

The resistance R_x of a linear resistor can be measured in two ways. An indirect way is to measure the current I that flows through it by connecting an ammeter in series with it and the voltage V across it by connecting a voltmeter in parallel with it, as shown in Fig. 2.62(a). Then

$$R_x = \frac{V}{I} \tag{2.62}$$

The direct method of measuring resistance is to use an ohmmeter. An ohmmeter consists basically of a d'Arsonval movement, a variable resistor or potentiometer, and a battery, as shown in Fig. 2.62(b). Applying KVL to the circuit in Fig. 2.62(b) gives

$$E = (R + R_m + R_x)I_m$$

or

$$R_x = \frac{E}{I_m} - (R + R_m) \tag{2.63}$$

The resistor R is selected such that the meter gives a full-scale deflection, that is, $I_m = I_{fs}$ when $R_x = 0$. This implies that

$$E = (R + R_m)I_{fs} \tag{2.64}$$

Substituting Eq. (2.64) into Eq. (2.63) leads to

$$R_x = \left(\frac{I_{fs}}{I_m} - 1\right)(R + R_m) \tag{2.65}$$

As mentioned, the types of meters we have discussed are known as *analog* meters and are based on the d'Arsonval meter movement. Another type of meter, called a *digital meter*, is based on active circuit elements such as op amps. For example, a digital multimeter displays measurements of dc or ac voltage, current, and resistance as discrete numbers, instead of using a pointer deflection on a continuous scale as in an analog multimeter. Digital meters are what you would most likely use in a modern lab. However, the design of digital meters is beyond the scope of this book.

(a)

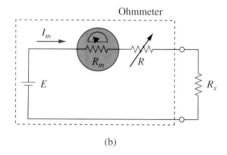

(b)

Figure 2.62   Two ways of measuring resistance: (a) using an ammeter and a voltmeter, (b) using an ohmmeter.

EXAMPLE 2.17

Following the voltmeter setup of Fig. 2.60, design a voltmeter for the following multiple ranges:
(a) 0–1 V   (b) 0–5 V   (c) 0–50 V   (d) 0–100 V
Assume that the internal resistance $R_m = 2\ k\Omega$ and the full-scale current $I_{fs} = 100\ \mu A$.

Solution:

We apply Eq. (2.60) and assume that R_1, R_2, R_3, and R_4 correspond with ranges 0–1 V, 0–5 V, 0–50 V, and 0–100 V, respectively.
(a) For range 0–1 V,

$$R_1 = \frac{1}{100 \times 10^{-6}} - 2000 = 10{,}000 - 2000 = 8\ k\Omega$$

(b) For range 0–5 V,

$$R_2 = \frac{5}{100 \times 10^{-6}} - 2000 = 50{,}000 - 2000 = 48 \text{ k}\Omega$$

(c) For range 0–50 V,

$$R_3 = \frac{50}{100 \times 10^{-6}} - 2000 = 500{,}000 - 2000 = 498 \text{ k}\Omega$$

(d) For range 0–100 V,

$$R_4 = \frac{100 \text{ V}}{100 \times 10^{-6}} - 2000 = 1{,}000{,}000 - 2000 = 998 \text{ k}\Omega$$

Note that the ratio of the total resistance $(R_n + R_m)$ to the full-scale voltage V_{fs} is constant and equal to $1/I_{fs}$ for the four ranges. This ratio (given in ohms per volt, or Ω/V) is known as the *sensitivity* of the voltmeter. The larger the sensitivity, the better the voltmeter.

PRACTICE PROBLEM 2.17

Following the ammeter setup of Fig. 2.61, design an ammeter for the following multiple ranges:
(a) 0–1 A   (b) 0–100 mA   (c) 0–10 mA
Take the full-scale meter current as $I_m = 1$ mA and the internal resistance of the ammeter as $R_m = 50 \,\Omega$.

Answer: Shunt resistors: 0.05 Ω, 0.505 Ω, 5.556 Ω.

2.9   SUMMARY

1. A resistor is a passive element in which the voltage v across it is directly proportional to the current i through it. That is, a resistor is a device that obeys Ohm's law,

$$v = iR$$

where R is the resistance of the resistor.

2. A short circuit is a resistor (a perfectly conducting wire) with zero resistance ($R = 0$). An open circuit is a resistor with infinite resistance ($R = \infty$).

3. The conductance G of a resistor is the reciprocal of its resistance:

$$G = \frac{1}{R}$$

4. A branch is a single two-terminal element in an electric circuit. A node is the point of connection between two or more branches. A loop is a closed path in a circuit. The number of branches b, the number of nodes n, and the number of independent loops l in a network are related as

$$b = l + n - 1$$

5. Kirchhoff's current law (KCL) states that the currents at any node algebraically sum to zero. In other words, the sum of the currents entering a node equals the sum of currents leaving the node.

6. Kirchhoff's voltage law (KVL) states that the voltages around a closed path algebraically sum to zero. In other words, the sum of voltage rises equals the sum of voltage drops.

7. Two elements are in series when they are connected sequentially, end to end. When elements are in series, the same current flows through them ($i_1 = i_2$). They are in parallel if they are connected to the same two nodes. Elements in parallel always have the same voltage across them ($v_1 = v_2$).

8. When two resistors R_1 ($=1/G_1$) and R_2 ($=1/G_2$) are in series, their equivalent resistance R_{eq} and equivalent conductance G_{eq} are

$$R_{eq} = R_1 + R_2, \qquad G_{eq} = \frac{G_1 G_2}{G_1 + G_2}$$

9. When two resistors R_1 ($=1/G_1$) and R_2 ($=1/G_2$) are in parallel, their equivalent resistance R_{eq} and equivalent conductance G_{eq} are

$$R_{eq} = \frac{R_1 R_2}{R_1 + R_2}, \qquad G_{eq} = G_1 + G_2$$

10. The voltage division principle for two resistors in series is

$$v_1 = \frac{R_1}{R_1 + R_2} v, \qquad v_2 = \frac{R_2}{R_1 + R_2} v$$

11. The current division principle for two resistors in parallel is

$$i_1 = \frac{R_2}{R_1 + R_2} i, \qquad i_2 = \frac{R_1}{R_1 + R_2} i$$

12. The formulas for a delta-to-wye transformation are

$$R_1 = \frac{R_b R_c}{R_a + R_b + R_c}, \qquad R_2 = \frac{R_c R_a}{R_a + R_b + R_c}$$

$$R_3 = \frac{R_a R_b}{R_a + R_b + R_c}$$

13. The formulas for a wye-to-delta transformation are

$$R_a = \frac{R_1 R_2 + R_2 R_3 + R_3 R_1}{R_1}, \qquad R_b = \frac{R_1 R_2 + R_2 R_3 + R_3 R_1}{R_2}$$

$$R_c = \frac{R_1 R_2 + R_2 R_3 + R_3 R_1}{R_3}$$

14. The basic laws covered in this chapter can be applied to the problems of electrical lighting and design of dc meters.

REVIEW QUESTIONS

2.1   The reciprocal of resistance is:

(a) voltage   (b) current
(c) conductance   (d) coulombs

2.2   An electric heater draws 10 A from a 120-V line. The resistance of the heater is:

(a) 1200 Ω   (b) 120 Ω
(c) 12 Ω   (d) 1.2 Ω

2.3 The voltage drop across a 1.5-kW toaster that draws 12 A of current is:

(a) 18 kV   (b) 125 V
(c) 120 V   (d) 10.42 V

2.4 The maximum current that a 2W, 80 kΩ resistor can safely conduct is:

(a) 160 kA   (b) 40 kA
(c) 5 mA   (d) 25 μA

2.5 A network has 12 branches and 8 independent loops. How many nodes are there in the network?

(a) 19   (b) 17   (c) 5   (d) 4

2.6 The current I in the circuit in Fig. 2.63 is:

(a) −0.8 A   (b) −0.2 A
(c) 0.2 A   (d) 0.8 A

Figure 2.63   For Review Question 2.6.

2.7 The current I_o in Fig. 2.64 is:

(a) −4 A   (b) −2 A   (c) 4 A   (d) 16 A

Figure 2.64   For Review Question 2.7.

2.8 In the circuit in Fig. 2.65, V is:

(a) 30 V   (b) 14 V   (c) 10 V   (d) 6 V

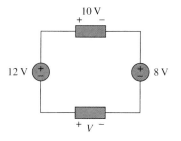

Figure 2.65   For Review Question 2.8.

2.9 Which of the circuits in Fig. 2.66 will give you $V_{ab} = 7$ V?

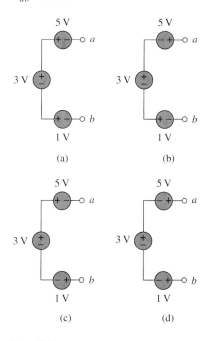

Figure 2.66   For Review Question 2.9.

2.10 In the circuit in Fig. 2.67, a decrease in R_3 leads to a decrease of:

(a) current through R_3
(b) voltage through R_3
(c) voltage across R_1
(d) power dissipated in R_2
(e) none of the above

Figure 2.67   For Review Question 2.10

Answers: 2.1c, 2.2c, 2.3b, 2.4c, 2.5c, 2.6b, 2.7a, 2.8d, 2.9d, 2.10b.

PROBLEMS

Section 2.2   Ohm's Law

2.1   The voltage across a 5-kΩ resistor is 16 V. Find the current through the resistor.

2.2   Find the hot resistance of a lightbulb rated 60 W, 120 V.

2.3   When the voltage across a resistor is 120 V, the current through it is 2.5 mA. Calculate its conductance.

2.4   (a) Calculate current i in Fig. 2.68 when the switch is in position 1.
         (b) Find the current when the switch is in position 2.

Figure 2.68   For Prob. 2.4.

Section 2.3   Nodes, Branches, and Loops

2.5   For the network graph in Fig. 2.69, find the number of nodes, branches, and loops.

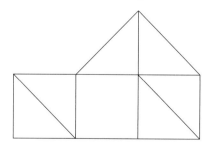

Figure 2.69   For Prob. 2.5.

2.6   In the network graph shown in Fig. 2.70, determine the number of branches and nodes.

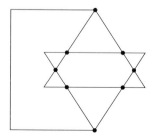

Figure 2.70   For Prob. 2.6.

2.7   Determine the number of branches and nodes in the circuit in Fig. 2.71.

Figure 2.71   For Prob. 2.7.

Section 2.4   Kirchhoff's Laws

2.8   Use KCL to obtain currents i_1, i_2, and i_3 in the circuit shown in Fig. 2.72.

Figure 2.72   For Prob. 2.8.

2.9   Find i_1, i_2, and i_3 in the circuit in Fig. 2.73.

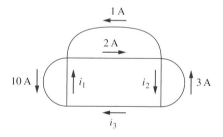

Figure 2.73   For Prob. 2.9.

2.10   Determine i_1 and i_2 in the circuit in Fig. 2.74.

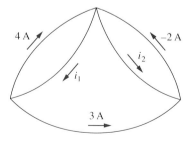

Figure 2.74   For Prob. 2.10.

2.11   Determine v_1 through v_4 in the circuit in Fig. 2.75.

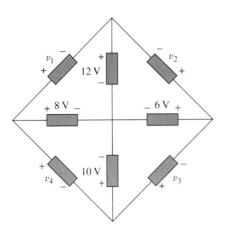

Figure 2.75   For Prob. 2.11.

2.12   In the circuit in Fig. 2.76, obtain v_1, v_2, and v_3.

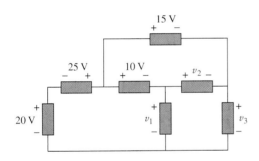

Figure 2.76   For Prob. 2.12.

2.13   For the circuit in Fig. 2.77, use KCL to find the branch currents I_1 to I_4.

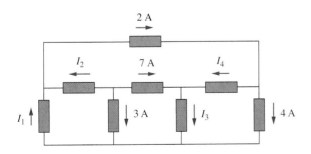

Figure 2.77   For Prob. 2.13

2.14   Given the circuit in Fig. 2.78, use KVL to find the branch voltages V_1 to V_4.

Figure 2.78   For Prob. 2.14

2.15   Find v_1, v_2, and v_3 in the circuit in Fig. 2.79.

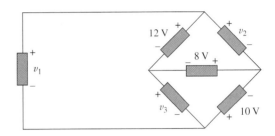

Figure 2.79   For Prob. 2.15

2.16   Find v_1 and v_2 in the circuit in Fig. 2.80.

Figure 2.80   For Prob. 2.16.

2.17   Obtain v_1 through v_3 in the circuit of Fig. 2.81.

Figure 2.81   For Prob. 2.17.

2.18 Find I and V_{ab} in the circuit of Fig. 2.82.

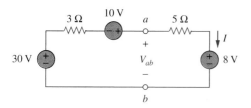

Figure 2.82   For Prob. 2.18.

2.19 From the circuit in Fig. 2.83, find I, the power dissipated by the resistor, and the power supplied by each source.

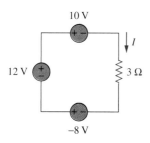

Figure 2.83   For Prob. 2.19.

2.20 Determine i_o in the circuit of Fig. 2.84.

Figure 2.84   For Prob. 2.20.

2.21 Calculate the power dissipated in the 5-Ω resistor in the circuit of Fig. 2.85.

Figure 2.85   For Prob. 2.21.

2.22 Find V_o in the circuit in Fig. 2.86 and the power dissipated by the controlled source.

Figure 2.86   For Prob. 2.22.

2.23 In the circuit shown in Fig. 2.87, determine v_x and the power absorbed by the 12-Ω resistor.

Figure 2.87   For Prob. 2.23.

2.24 For the circuit in Fig. 2.88, find V_o/V_s in terms of α, R_1, R_2, R_3, and R_4. If $R_1 = R_2 = R_3 = R_4$, what value of α will produce $|V_o/V_s| = 10$?

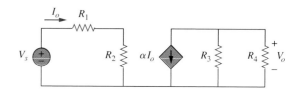

Figure 2.88   For Prob. 2.24.

2.25 For the network in Fig. 2.89, find the current, voltage, and power associated with the 20-kΩ resistor.

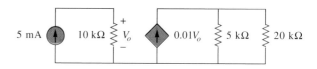

Figure 2.89   For Prob. 2.25.

Sections 2.5 and 2.6   Series and Parallel Resistors

2.26   For the circuit in Fig. 2.90, find i_1 and i_2.

Figure 2.90   For Prob. 2.26.

2.27   Find v_1 and v_2 in the circuit in Fig. 2.91.

Figure 2.91   For Prob. 2.27.

2.28   Find v_1, v_2, and v_3 in the circuit in Fig. 2.92.

Figure 2.92   For Prob. 2.28.

2.29   Calculate v_1, i_1, v_2, and i_2 in the circuit of Fig. 2.93.

Figure 2.93   For Prob. 2.29.

2.30   Find i, v, and the power dissipated in the 6-Ω resistor in Fig. 2.94.

Figure 2.94   For Prob. 2.30.

2.31   In the circuit in Fig. 2.95, find v, i, and the power absorbed by the 4-Ω resistor.

Figure 2.95   For Prob. 2.31.

2.32   Find i_1 through i_4 in the circuit in Fig. 2.96.

Figure 2.96   For Prob. 2.32.

2.33   Obtain v and i in the circuit in Fig. 2.97.

Figure 2.97   For Prob. 2.33.

2.34   Determine i_1, i_2, v_1, and v_2 in the ladder network in Fig. 2.98. Calculate the power dissipated in the 2-Ω resistor.

Figure 2.98   For Prob. 2.34.

2.35   Calculate V_o and I_o in the circuit of Fig. 2.99.

Figure 2.99   For Prob. 2.35.

2.36   Find V_o and I_o in the circuit of Fig. 2.100.

Figure 2.100   For Prob. 2.36.

2.37   In the circuit of Fig. 2.101, find R if $V_o = 4V$.

Figure 2.101   For Prob. 2.37.

2.38   Find I and V_s in the circuit of Fig. 2.102 if the current through the 3-Ω resistor is 2 A.

Figure 2.102   For Prob. 2.38.

2.39   Find the equivalent resistance at terminals a-b for each of the networks in Fig. 2.103.

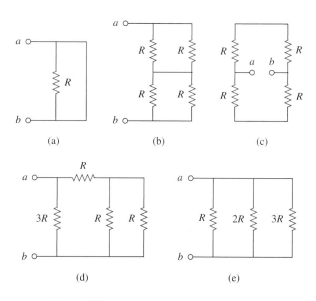

Figure 2.103   For Prob. 2.39.

2.40   For the ladder network in Fig. 2.104, find I and R_{eq}.

Figure 2.104   For Prob. 2.40.

2.41 If $R_{eq} = 50\ \Omega$ in the circuit in Fig. 2.105, find R.

Figure 2.105   For Prob. 2.41.

2.42 Reduce each of the circuits in Fig. 2.106 to a single resistor at terminals a-b.

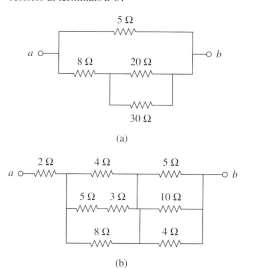

(a)

(b)

Figure 2.106   For Prob. 2.42.

2.43 Calculate the equivalent resistance R_{ab} at terminals a-b for each of the circuits in Fig. 2.107.

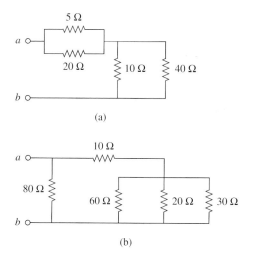

(a)

(b)

Figure 2.107   For Prob. 2.43.

2.44 For the circuit in Fig. 2.108, obtain the equivalent resistance at terminals a-b.

Figure 2.108   For Prob. 2.44.

2.45 Find the equivalent resistance at terminals a-b of each circuit in Fig. 2.109.

(a)

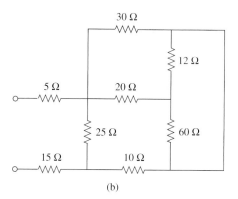

(b)

Figure 2.109   For Prob. 2.45.

2.46   Find R_{eq} at terminals a-b for each of the circuits in Fig. 2.110.

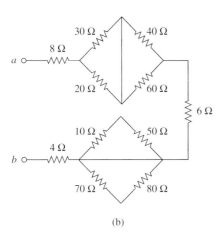

(b)

Figure 2.110   For Prob. 2.46.

2.47   Find the equivalent resistance R_{ab} in the circuit of Fig. 2.111.

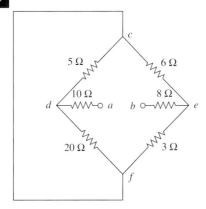

Figure 2.111   For Prob. 2.47.

Section 2.7   Wye-Delta Transformations

2.48   Convert the circuits in Fig. 2.112 from Y to Δ.

(a)   (b)

Figure 2.112   For Prob. 2.48.

2.49   Transform the circuits in Fig. 2.113 from Δ to Y.

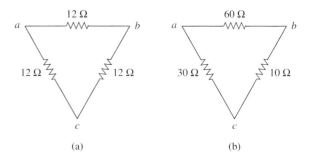

(a)   (b)

Figure 2.113   For Prob. 2.49.

2.50   What value of R in the circuit of Fig. 2.114 would cause the current source to deliver 800 mW to the resistors?

Figure 2.114   For Prob. 2.50.

2.51   Obtain the equivalent resistance at the terminals a-b for each of the circuits in Fig. 2.115.

(a)

Figure 2.115   For Prob. 2.51.

(b)

Figure 2.115   continued

*2.52 Find the equivalent resistance R_{ab} in each of the circuits of Fig. 2.116. Each resistor is 100 Ω.

(a)

(b)

Figure 2.116   For Prob. 2.52.

*2.53 Obtain the equivalent resistance R_{ab} in each of the circuits of Fig. 2.117. In (b), all resistors have a value of 30 Ω.

(a)

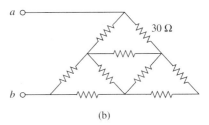

(b)

Figure 2.117   For Prob. 2.53.

2.54 Consider the circuit in Fig. 2.118. Find the equivalent resistance at terminals: (a) a-b, (b) c-d.

Figure 2.118   For Prob. 2.54

2.55 Calculate I_o in the circuit of Fig. 2.119.

Figure 2.119   For Prob. 2.55.

2.56 Determine V in the circuit of Fig. 2.120.

Figure 2.120   For Prob. 2.56.

*An asterisk indicates a challenging problem.

*2.57   Find R_{eq} and I in the circuit of Fig. 2.121.

Figure 2.121   For Prob. 2.57.

Section 2.8   Applications

2.58   The lightbulb in Fig. 2.122 is rated 120 V, 0.75 A.
        Calculate V_s to make the lightbulb operate at the
        rated conditions.

Figure 2.122   For Prob. 2.58.

2.59   Three lightbulbs are connected in series to a 100-V
        battery as shown in Fig. 2.123. Find the current I
        through the bulbs.

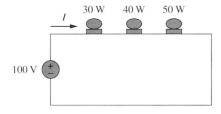

Figure 2.123   For Prob. 2.59.

2.60   If the three bulbs of Prob. 2.59 are connected in
        parallel to the 100-V battery, calculate the current
        through each bulb.

2.61   As a design engineer, you are asked to design a
        lighting system consisting of a 70-W power supply
        and two lightbulbs as shown in Fig. 2.124. You must
        select the two bulbs from the following three
        available bulbs.

$R_1 = 80\ \Omega$, cost = \$0.60 (standard size)
$R_2 = 90\ \Omega$, cost = \$0.90 (standard size)
$R_3 = 100\ \Omega$, cost = \$0.75 (nonstandard size)

The system should be designed for minimum cost
such that $I = 1.2\ \text{A} \pm 5$ percent.

Figure 2.124   For Prob. 2.61.

2.62   A three-wire system supplies two loads A and B as
        shown in Fig. 2.125. Load A consists of a motor
        drawing a current of 8 A, while load B is a PC
        drawing 2 A. Assuming 10 h/day of use for 365 days
        and 6 cents/kWh, calculate the annual energy cost of
        the system.

Figure 2.125   For Prob. 2.62.

2.63   If an ammeter with an internal resistance of 100 Ω
        and a current capacity of 2 mA is to measure 5 A,
        determine the value of the resistance needed.
        Calculate the power dissipated in the shunt resistor.

2.64   The potentiometer (adjustable resistor) R_x in
        Fig. 2.126 is to be designed to adjust current i_x from
        1 A to 10 A. Calculate the values of R and R_x to
        achieve this.

Figure 2.126   For Prob. 2.64.

2.65   A d'Arsonval meter with an internal resistance of
        1 kΩ requires 10 mA to produce full-scale deflection.
        Calculate the value of a series resistance needed to
        measure 50 V of full scale.

2.66   A 20-kΩ/V voltmeter reads 10 V full scale.

    (a)   What series resistance is required to make the meter read 50 V full scale?

    (b)   What power will the series resistor dissipate when the meter reads full scale?

2.67   (a)   Obtain the voltage V_o in the circuit of Fig. 2.127 (a).

    (b)   Determine the voltage V_o' measured when a voltmeter with 6-kΩ internal resistance is connected as shown in Fig. 2.127(b).

    (c)   The finite resistance of the meter introduces an error into the measurement. Calculate the percent error as

$$\left| \frac{V_o - V_o'}{V_o} \right| \times 100\%$$

    (d)   Find the percent error if the internal resistance were 36 kΩ.

(a)

(b)

Figure 2.127   For Prob. 2.67.

2.68   (a)   Find the current I in the circuit of Fig. 2.128(a).

    (b)   An ammeter with an internal resistance of 1 Ω is inserted in the network to measure I' as shown in Fig. 2.128(b). What is I'?

    (c)   Calculate the percent error introduced by the meter as

$$\left| \frac{I - I'}{I} \right| \times 100\%$$

(a)

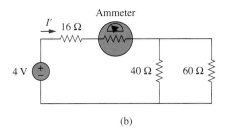

(b)

Figure 2.128   For Prob. 2.68.

2.69   A voltmeter is used to measure V_o in the circuit in Fig. 2.129. The voltmeter model consists of an ideal voltmeter in parallel with a 100-kΩ resistor. Let $V_s = 40$ V, $R_s = 10$ kΩ, and $R_1 = 20$ kΩ. Calculate V_o with and without the voltmeter when

    (a) $R_2 = 1$ kΩ   (b) $R_2 = 10$ kΩ

    (c) $R_2 = 100$ kΩ

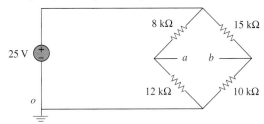

Figure 2.129   For Prob. 2.69.

2.70   (a) Consider the Wheatstone bridge shown in Fig. 2.130. Calculate v_a, v_b, and v_{ab}. (b) Rework part (a) if the ground is placed at a instead of o.

Figure 2.130   For Prob. 2.70.

2.71   Figure 2.131 represents a model of a solar photovoltaic panel. Given that $V_s = 30$ V, $R_1 = 20$ Ω, and $i_L = 1$ A, find R_L.

Figure 2.131   For Prob. 2.71.

2.72 A 9-V battery can supply 12 A for a parallel set of Christmas tree lights. If each lightbulb is 15 Ω, calculate the maximum number of lights that can be supplied.

2.73 An ammeter model consists of an ideal ammeter in series with a 20-Ω resistor. It is connected with a current source and an unknown resistor R_x as shown in Fig. 2.132. The ammeter reading is noted. When a potentiometer R is added and adjusted until the ammeter reading drops to one half its previous reading, then $R = 65\ \Omega$. What is the value of R_x?

Figure 2.132   For Prob. 2.73.

2.74 The circuit in Fig. 2.133 is to control the speed of a motor such that the motor draws currents 5 A, 3 A, and 1 A when the switch is at high, medium, and low

positions, respectively. The motor can be modeled as a load resistance of 20 mΩ. Determine the series dropping resistances R_1, R_2, and R_3.

Figure 2.133   For Prob. 2.74.

2.75 An ohmmeter is constructed with a 2-V battery and 0.1-mA (full-scale) meter with 100-Ω internal resistance.

(a) Calculate the resistance of the (variable) resistor required to be in series with the meter and the battery.

(b) Determine the unknown resistance across the terminals of the ohmmeter that will cause the meter to deflect half scale.

COMPREHENSIVE PROBLEMS

2.76 An electric heater connected to a 120-V source consists of two identical 0.4-Ω elements made of Nichrome wire. The elements provide low heat when connected in series and high heat when connected in parallel. Find the power at low and high heat settings.

2.77 Suppose your circuit laboratory has the following standard commercially available resistors in large quantities:

    1.8 Ω 20 Ω 300 Ω 24 kΩ 56 kΩ

Using series and parallel combinations and a minimum number of available resistors, how would you obtain the following resistances for an electronic circuit design?

(a) 5 Ω (b) 311.8 Ω
(c) 40 kΩ (d) 52.32 kΩ

2.78 In the circuit in Fig. 2.134, the wiper divides the potentiometer resistance between αR and $(1 - \alpha)R$, $0 \le \alpha \le 1$. Find v_o/v_s.

Figure 2.134   For Prob. 2.78.

2.79 An electric pencil sharpener rated 240 mW, 6 V is connected to a 9-V battery as shown in Fig. 2.135. Calculate the value of the series-dropping resistor R_x needed to power the sharpener.

Figure 2.135   For Prob. 2.79.

2.80 A loudspeaker is connected to an amplifier as shown in Fig. 2.136. If a 10-Ω loudspeaker draws the maximum power of 12 W from the amplifier, determine the maximum power a 4-Ω loudspeaker will draw.

Figure 2.136   For Prob. 2.80.

2.81 In a certain application, the circuit in Fig. 2.137 must be designed to meet these two criteria:

(a) $V_o/V_s = 0.05$ (b) $R_{eq} = 40\ k\Omega$

If the load resistor 5 kΩ is fixed, find R_1 and R_2 to meet the criteria.

Figure 2.137   For Prob. 2.81.

2.82 The pin diagram of a resistance array is shown in Fig. 2.138. Find the equivalent resistance between the following:

(a) 1 and 2   (b) 1 and 3   (c) 1 and 4

Figure 2.138   For Prob. 2.82.

2.83 Two delicate devices are rated as shown in Fig. 2.139. Find the values of the resistors R_1 and R_2 needed to power the devices using a 24-V battery.

Figure 2.139   For Prob. 2.83.

C H A P T E R   3

METHODS OF ANALYSIS

The mere formulation of a problem is far more often essential than its solution, which may be merely a matter of mathematical or experimental skill.

—Albert Einstein

Enhancing Your Career

Career in Electronics   One area of application for electric circuit analysis is electronics. The term *electronics* was originally used to distinguish circuits of very low current levels. This distinction no longer holds, as power semiconductor devices operate at high levels of current. Today, electronics is regarded as the science of the motion of charges in a gas, vacuum, or semiconductor. Modern electronics involves transistors and transistor circuits. The earlier electronic circuits were assembled from components. Many electronic circuits are now produced as integrated circuits, fabricated in a semiconductor substrate or chip.

     Electronic circuits find applications in many areas, such as automation, broadcasting, computers, and instrumentation. The range of devices that use electronic circuits is enormous and is limited only by our imagination. Radio, television, computers, and stereo systems are but a few.

     An electrical engineer usually performs diverse functions and is likely to use, design, or construct systems that incorporate some form of electronic circuits. Therefore, an understanding of the operation and analysis of electronics is essential to the electrical engineer. Electronics has become a specialty distinct from other disciplines within electrical engineering. Because the field of electronics is ever advancing, an electronics engineer must update his/her knowledge from time to time. The best way to do this is by being a member of a professional organization such as the Institute of Electrical and Electronics Engineers (IEEE).

Troubleshooting an electronic circuit board.
© Michael Rosenfeld/Getty Images

With a membership of over 300,000, the IEEE is the largest professional organization in the world. Members benefit immensely from the numerous magazines, journals, transactions, and conference/symposium proceedings published yearly by IEEE. You should consider becoming an IEEE member.

3.1   INTRODUCTION

Having understood the fundamental laws of circuit theory (Ohm's law and Kirchhoff's laws), we are now prepared to apply these laws to develop two powerful techniques for circuit analysis: nodal analysis, which is based on a systematic application of Kirchhoff's current law (KCL), and mesh analysis, which is based on a systematic application of Kirchhoff's voltage law (KVL). The two techniques are so important that this chapter should be regarded as the most important in the book. Students are therefore encouraged to pay careful attention.

With the two techniques to be developed in this chapter, we can analyze any linear circuit by obtaining a set of simultaneous equations that are then solved to obtain the required values of current or voltage. One method of solving simultaneous equations involves Cramer's rule, which allows us to calculate circuit variables as a quotient of determinants. The examples in the chapter will illustrate this method; Appendix A also briefly summarizes the essentials the reader needs to know for applying Cramer's rule. Another method of solving simultaneous equations is to use *MATLAB*, a computer software discussed in Appendix E.

Also in this chapter, we introduce the use of *PSpice for Windows*, a circuit simulation computer software program that we will use throughout the text. Finally, we apply the techniques learned in this chapter to analyze transistor circuits.

3.2   NODAL ANALYSIS

Nodal analysis is also known as the *node-voltage method*.

Nodal analysis provides a general procedure for analyzing circuits using node voltages as the circuit variables. Choosing node voltages instead of element voltages as circuit variables is convenient and reduces the number of equations one must solve simultaneously.

To simplify matters, we shall assume in this section that circuits do not contain voltage sources. Circuits that contain voltage sources will be analyzed in the next section.

In *nodal analysis*, we are interested in finding the node voltages. Given a circuit with n nodes without voltage sources, the nodal analysis of the circuit involves taking the following three steps.

S t e p s   t o   D e t e r m i n e   N o d e   V o l t a g e s :

1. Select a node as the reference node. Assign voltages $v_1, v_2, \ldots, v_{n-1}$ to the remaining $n - 1$ nodes. The voltages are referenced with respect to the reference node.

2. Apply KCL to each of the $n - 1$ nonreference nodes. Use Ohm's law to express the branch currents in terms of node voltages.

3. Solve the resulting simultaneous equations to obtain the unknown node voltages.

We shall now explain and apply these three steps.

The first step in nodal analysis is selecting a node as the *reference* or *datum node*. The reference node is commonly called the *ground* since it is assumed to have zero potential. A reference node is indicated by any of the three symbols in Fig. 3.1. The type of ground in Fig. 3.1(b) is called a *chassis ground* and is used in devices where the case, enclosure, or chassis acts as a reference point for all circuits. When the potential of the earth is used as reference, we use the *earth ground* in Fig. 3.1(a) or (c). We shall always use the symbol in Fig. 3.1(b).

Once we have selected a reference node, we assign voltage designations to nonreference nodes. Consider, for example, the circuit in Fig. 3.2(a). Node 0 is the reference node ($v = 0$), while nodes 1 and 2 are assigned voltages v_1 and v_2, respectively. Keep in mind that the node voltages are defined with respect to the reference node. As illustrated in Fig. 3.2(a), each node voltage is the voltage rise from the reference node to the corresponding nonreference node or simply the voltage of that node with respect to the reference node.

As the second step, we apply KCL to each nonreference node in the circuit. To avoid putting too much information on the same circuit, the circuit in Fig. 3.2(a) is redrawn in Fig. 3.2(b), where we now add i_1, i_2, and i_3 as the currents through resistors R_1, R_2, and R_3, respectively. At node 1, applying KCL gives

$$I_1 = I_2 + i_1 + i_2 \tag{3.1}$$

At node 2,

$$I_2 + i_2 = i_3 \tag{3.2}$$

We now apply Ohm's law to express the unknown currents i_1, i_2, and i_3 in terms of node voltages. The key idea to bear in mind is that, since resistance is a passive element, by the passive sign convention, current must always flow from a higher potential to a lower potential.

> Current flows from a higher potential to a lower potential in a resistor.

We can express this principle as

$$\boxed{i = \frac{v_{\text{higher}} - v_{\text{lower}}}{R}} \tag{3.3}$$

Note that this principle is in agreement with the way we defined resistance in Chapter 2 (see Fig. 2.1). With this in mind, we obtain from Fig. 3.2(b),

$$i_1 = \frac{v_1 - 0}{R_1} \qquad \text{or} \qquad i_1 = G_1 v_1$$

$$i_2 = \frac{v_1 - v_2}{R_2} \qquad \text{or} \qquad i_2 = G_2(v_1 - v_2) \tag{3.4}$$

$$i_3 = \frac{v_2 - 0}{R_3} \qquad \text{or} \qquad i_3 = G_3 v_2$$

Substituting Eq. (3.4) in Eqs. (3.1) and (3.2) results, respectively, in

$$I_1 = I_2 + \frac{v_1}{R_1} + \frac{v_1 - v_2}{R_2} \tag{3.5}$$

$$I_2 + \frac{v_1 - v_2}{R_2} = \frac{v_2}{R_3} \tag{3.6}$$

The number of nonreference nodes is equal to the number of independent equations that we will derive.

(a)   (b)   (c)

Figure 3.1   Common symbols for indicating a reference node, (a) common ground, (b) ground, (c) chassis ground.

(a)

(b)

Figure 3.2   Typical circuit for nodal analysis.

In terms of the conductances, Eqs. (3.5) and (3.6) become

$$I_1 = I_2 + G_1 v_1 + G_2(v_1 - v_2) \tag{3.7}$$

$$I_2 + G_2(v_1 - v_2) = G_3 v_2 \tag{3.8}$$

The third step in nodal analysis is to solve for the node voltages. If we apply KCL to $n - 1$ nonreference nodes, we obtain $n - 1$ simultaneous equations such as Eqs. (3.5) and (3.6) or (3.7) and (3.8). For the circuit of Fig. 3.2, we solve Eqs. (3.5) and (3.6) or (3.7) and (3.8) to obtain the node voltages v_1 and v_2 using any standard method, such as the substitution method, the elimination method, Cramer's rule, or matrix inversion. To use either of the last two methods, one must cast the simultaneous equations in matrix form. For example, Eqs. (3.7) and (3.8) can be cast in matrix form as

| Appendix A discusses how to use Cramer's rule.

$$\begin{bmatrix} G_1 + G_2 & -G_2 \\ -G_2 & G_2 + G_3 \end{bmatrix} \begin{bmatrix} v_1 \\ v_2 \end{bmatrix} = \begin{bmatrix} I_1 - I_2 \\ I_2 \end{bmatrix} \tag{3.9}$$

which can be solved to get v_1 and v_2. Equation 3.9 will be generalized in Section 3.6. The simultaneous equations may also be solved using calculators or with software packages such as *MATLAB, Mathcad, Maple,* and *Quattro Pro.*

EXAMPLE 3.1

Calculate the node voltages in the circuit shown in Fig. 3.3(a).

Solution:

Consider Fig. 3.3(b), where the circuit in Fig. 3.3(a) has been prepared for nodal analysis. Notice how the currents are selected for the application of KCL. Except for the branches with current sources, the labeling of the currents is arbitrary but consistent. (By consistent, we mean that if, for example, we assume that i_2 enters the 4 Ω resistor from the left-hand side, i_2 must leave the resistor from the right-hand side.) The reference node is selected, and the node voltages v_1 and v_2 are now to be determined.

At node 1, applying KCL and Ohm's law gives

$$i_1 = i_2 + i_3 \quad \Longrightarrow \quad 5 = \frac{v_1 - v_2}{4} + \frac{v_1 - 0}{2}$$

Multiplying each term in the last equation by 4, we obtain

$$20 = v_1 - v_2 + 2v_1$$

or

$$3v_1 - v_2 = 20 \tag{3.1.1}$$

At node 2, we do the same thing and get

$$i_2 + i_4 = i_1 + i_5 \quad \Longrightarrow \quad \frac{v_1 - v_2}{4} + 10 = 5 + \frac{v_2 - 0}{6}$$

Multiplying each term by 12 results in

$$3v_1 - 3v_2 + 120 = 60 + 2v_2$$

(a)

(b)

Figure 3.3   For Example 3.1: (a) original circuit, (b) circuit for analysis.

or

$$-3v_1 + 5v_2 = 60 \qquad\qquad (3.1.2)$$

Now we have two simultaneous Eqs. (3.1.1) and (3.1.2). We can solve the equations using any method and obtain the values of v_1 and v_2.

METHOD **1** Using the elimination technique, we add Eqs. (3.1.1) and (3.1.2).

$$4v_2 = 80 \qquad\Longrightarrow\qquad v_2 = 20 \text{ V}$$

Substituting $v_2 = 20$ in Eq. (3.1.1) gives

$$3v_1 - 20 = 20 \qquad\Longrightarrow\qquad v_1 = \frac{40}{3} = 13.33 \text{ V}$$

METHOD **2** To use Cramer's rule, we need to put Eqs. (3.1.1) and (3.1.2) in matrix form as

$$\begin{bmatrix} 3 & -1 \\ -3 & 5 \end{bmatrix} \begin{bmatrix} v_1 \\ v_2 \end{bmatrix} = \begin{bmatrix} 20 \\ 60 \end{bmatrix} \qquad\qquad (3.1.3)$$

The determinant of the matrix is

$$\Delta = \begin{vmatrix} 3 & -1 \\ -3 & 5 \end{vmatrix} = 15 - 3 = 12$$

We now obtain v_1 and v_2 as

$$v_1 = \frac{\Delta_1}{\Delta} = \frac{\begin{vmatrix} 20 & -1 \\ 60 & 5 \end{vmatrix}}{\Delta} = \frac{100 + 60}{12} = 13.33 \text{ V}$$

$$v_2 = \frac{\Delta_2}{\Delta} = \frac{\begin{vmatrix} 3 & 20 \\ -3 & 60 \end{vmatrix}}{\Delta} = \frac{180 + 60}{12} = 20 \text{ V}$$

giving us the same result as did the elimination method.

If we need the currents, we can easily calculate them from the values of the nodal voltages.

$$i_1 = 5 \text{ A}, \qquad i_2 = \frac{v_1 - v_2}{4} = -1.6667 \text{ A}, \qquad i_3 = \frac{v_1}{2} = 6.666 \text{ A}$$

$$i_4 = 10 \text{ A}, \qquad i_5 = \frac{v_2}{6} = 3.333 \text{ A}$$

The fact that i_2 is negative shows that the current flows in the direction opposite to the one assumed.

PRACTICE PROBLEM 3.1

Obtain the node voltages in the circuit in Fig. 3.4.

Answer: $v_1 = -2$ V, $v_2 = -14$ V.

Figure 3.4   For Practice Prob. 3.1.

EXAMPLE 3.2

Determine the voltages at the nodes in Fig. 3.5(a).

Solution:

The circuit in this example has three nonreference nodes, unlike the previous example which has two nonreference nodes. We assign voltages to the three nodes as shown in Fig. 3.5(b) and label the currents.

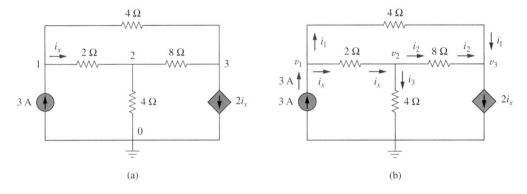

Figure 3.5   For Example 3.2: (a) original circuit, (b) circuit for analysis.

At node 1,

$$3 = i_1 + i_x \qquad \Longrightarrow \qquad 3 = \frac{v_1 - v_3}{4} + \frac{v_1 - v_2}{2}$$

Multiplying by 4 and rearranging terms, we get

$$3v_1 - 2v_2 - v_3 = 12 \qquad\qquad (3.2.1)$$

At node 2,

$$i_x = i_2 + i_3 \qquad \Longrightarrow \qquad \frac{v_1 - v_2}{2} = \frac{v_2 - v_3}{8} + \frac{v_2 - 0}{4}$$

Multiplying by 8 and rearranging terms, we get

$$-4v_1 + 7v_2 - v_3 = 0 \qquad\qquad (3.2.2)$$

At node 3,

$$i_1 + i_2 = 2i_x \qquad \Longrightarrow \qquad \frac{v_1 - v_3}{4} + \frac{v_2 - v_3}{8} = \frac{2(v_1 - v_2)}{2}$$

Multiplying by 8, rearranging terms, and dividing by 3, we get

$$2v_1 - 3v_2 + v_3 = 0 \qquad (3.2.3)$$

We have three simultaneous equations to solve to get the node voltages v_1, v_2, and v_3. We shall solve the equations in three ways.

METHOD **1**   Using the elimination technique, we add Eqs. (3.2.1) and (3.2.3).

$$5v_1 - 5v_2 = 12$$

or

$$v_1 - v_2 = \frac{12}{5} = 2.4 \qquad (3.2.4)$$

Adding Eqs. (3.2.2) and (3.2.3) gives

$$-2v_1 + 4v_2 = 0 \qquad \Longrightarrow \qquad v_1 = 2v_2 \qquad (3.2.5)$$

Substituting Eq. (3.2.5) into Eq. (3.2.4) yields

$$2v_2 - v_2 = 2.4 \qquad \Longrightarrow \qquad v_2 = 2.4, \qquad v_1 = 2v_2 = 4.8 \text{ V}$$

From Eq. (3.2.3), we get

$$v_3 = 3v_2 - 2v_1 = 3v_2 - 4v_2 = -v_2 = -2.4 \text{ V}$$

Thus,

$$v_1 = 4.8 \text{ V}, \qquad v_2 = 2.4 \text{ V}, \qquad v_3 = -2.4 \text{ V}$$

METHOD **2**   To use Cramer's rule, we put Eqs. (3.2.1) to (3.2.3) in matrix form.

$$\begin{bmatrix} 3 & -2 & -1 \\ -4 & 7 & -1 \\ 2 & -3 & 1 \end{bmatrix} \begin{bmatrix} v_1 \\ v_2 \\ v_3 \end{bmatrix} = \begin{bmatrix} 12 \\ 0 \\ 0 \end{bmatrix} \qquad (3.2.6)$$

From this, we obtain

$$v_1 = \frac{\Delta_1}{\Delta}, \qquad v_2 = \frac{\Delta_2}{\Delta}, \qquad v_3 = \frac{\Delta_3}{\Delta}$$

where Δ, Δ_1, Δ_2, and Δ_3 are the determinants to be calculated as follows. As explained in Appendix A, to calculate the determinant of a 3 by 3 matrix, we repeat the first two rows and cross multiply.

$$\Delta = \begin{vmatrix} 3 & -2 & -1 \\ -4 & 7 & -1 \\ 2 & -3 & 1 \end{vmatrix} =$$

$$= 21 - 12 + 4 + 14 - 9 - 8 = 10$$

Similarly, we obtain

$$\Delta_1 = \qquad\qquad = 84 + 0 + 0 - 0 - 36 - 0 = 48$$

$$\Delta_2 = \qquad\qquad = 0 + 0 - 24 - 0 - 0 + 48 = 24$$

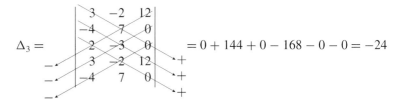

$$\Delta_3 = \qquad\qquad = 0 + 144 + 0 - 168 - 0 - 0 = -24$$

Thus, we find

$$v_1 = \frac{\Delta_1}{\Delta} = \frac{48}{10} = 4.8 \text{ V}, \qquad v_2 = \frac{\Delta_2}{\Delta} = \frac{24}{10} = 2.4 \text{ V}$$

$$v_3 = \frac{\Delta_3}{\Delta} = \frac{-24}{10} = -2.4 \text{ V}$$

as we obtained with Method 1.

METHOD **3** We now use *MATLAB* to solve the matrix. Equation (3.2.6) can be written as

$$\mathbf{AV} = \mathbf{B} \qquad \Longrightarrow \qquad \mathbf{V} = \mathbf{A}^{-1}\mathbf{B}$$

where $\mathbf{A}$ is the 3 by 3 square matrix, $\mathbf{B}$ is the column vector, and $\mathbf{V}$ is a column vector comprised of v_1, v_2, and v_3 that we want to determine.

We use *MATLAB* to determine **V** as follows:

$$>>A = \begin{bmatrix} 3 & -2 & -1; & -4 & 7 & -1; & 2 & -3 & 1 \end{bmatrix};$$

$$>>B = \begin{bmatrix} 12 & 0 & 0 \end{bmatrix};$$

$$>>V = inv(A) * B$$

$$V = \begin{matrix} 4.8000 \\ 2.4000 \\ -2.4000 \end{matrix}$$

Thus, $v_1 = 4.8$ V, $v_2 = 2.4$ V, and $v_3 = -2.4$ V, as obtained previously.

PRACTICE PROBLEM 3.2

Find the voltages at the three nonreference nodes in the circuit of Fig. 3.6.

Answer: $v_1 = 80$ V, $v_2 = -64$ V, $v_3 = 156$ V.

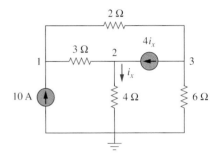

Figure 3.6   For Practice Prob. 3.2.

3.3   NODAL ANALYSIS WITH VOLTAGE SOURCES

We now consider how voltage sources affect nodal analysis. We use the circuit in Fig. 3.7 for illustration. Consider the following two possibilities.

CASE **1** If a voltage source is connected between the reference node and a nonreference node, we simply set the voltage at the nonreference node equal to the voltage of the voltage source. In Fig. 3.7, for example,

$$v_1 = 10 \text{ V} \tag{3.10}$$

Thus our analysis is somewhat simplified by this knowledge of the voltage at this node.

CASE **2** If the voltage source (dependent or independent) is connected between two nonreference nodes, the two nonreference nodes form a *generalized node* or *supernode*; we apply both KCL and KVL to determine the node voltages.

A supernode may be regarded as a closed surface enclosing the voltage source and its two nodes.

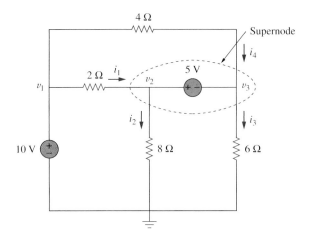

Figure 3.7   A circuit with a supernode.

A supernode is formed by enclosing a (dependent or independent) voltage source connected between two nonreference nodes and any elements connected in parallel with it.

In Fig. 3.7, nodes 2 and 3 form a supernode. (We could have more than two nodes forming a single supernode. For example, see the circuit in Fig. 3.14.) We analyze a circuit with supernodes using the same three steps mentioned in the previous section except that the supernodes are treated differently. Why? Because an essential component of nodal analysis is applying KCL, which requires knowing the current through each element. There is no way of knowing the current through a voltage source in advance. However, KCL must be satisfied at a supernode like any other node. Hence, at the supernode in Fig. 3.7,

$$i_1 + i_4 = i_2 + i_3 \tag{3.11a}$$

or

$$\frac{v_1 - v_2}{2} + \frac{v_1 - v_3}{4} = \frac{v_2 - 0}{8} + \frac{v_3 - 0}{6} \tag{3.11b}$$

To apply Kirchhoff's voltage law to the supernode in Fig. 3.7, we redraw the circuit as shown in Fig. 3.8. Going around the loop in the clockwise direction gives

$$-v_2 + 5 + v_3 = 0 \quad \Longrightarrow \quad v_2 - v_3 = 5 \tag{3.12}$$

From Eqs. (3.10), (3.11b), and (3.12), we obtain the node voltages.

Note the following properties of a supernode:

1. The voltage source inside the supernode provides a constraint equation needed to solve for the node voltages.

2. A supernode has no voltage of its own.

3. A supernode requires the application of both KCL and KVL.

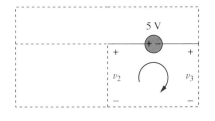

Figure 3.8   Applying KVL to a supernode.

EXAMPLE 3.3

For the circuit shown in Fig. 3.9, find the node voltages.

Solution:

The supernode contains the 2-V source, nodes 1 and 2, and the 10-Ω resistor. Applying KCL to the supernode as shown in Fig. 3.10(a) gives

$$2 = i_1 + i_2 + 7$$

Expressing i_1 and i_2 in terms of the node voltages

$$2 = \frac{v_1 - 0}{2} + \frac{v_2 - 0}{4} + 7 \quad \Longrightarrow \quad 8 = 2v_1 + v_2 + 28$$

or

$$v_2 = -20 - 2v_1 \qquad\qquad (3.3.1)$$

To get the relationship between v_1 and v_2, we apply KVL to the circuit in Fig. 3.10(b). Going around the loop, we obtain

$$-v_1 - 2 + v_2 = 0 \quad \Longrightarrow \quad v_2 = v_1 + 2 \qquad (3.3.2)$$

From Eqs. (3.3.1) and (3.3.2), we write

$$v_2 = v_1 + 2 = -20 - 2v_1$$

or

$$3v_1 = -22 \quad \Longrightarrow \quad v_1 = -7.333 \text{ V}$$

and $v_2 = v_1 + 2 = -5.333$ V. Note that the 10-Ω resistor does not make any difference because it is connected across the supernode.

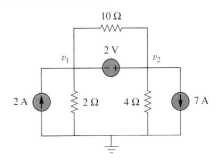

Figure 3.9   For Example 3.3.

(a)

(b)

Figure 3.10   Applying: (a) KCL to the supernode, (b) KVL to the loop.

PRACTICE PROBLEM 3.3

Find v and i in the circuit in Fig. 3.11.

Answer: -0.2 V, 1.4 A.

Figure 3.11   For Practice Prob. 3.3.

EXAMPLE 3.4

Find the node voltages in the circuit of Fig. 3.12.

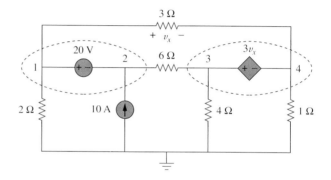

Figure 3.12   For Example 3.4.

Solution:

Nodes 1 and 2 form a supernode; so do nodes 3 and 4. We apply KCL to the two supernodes as in Fig. 3.13(a). At supernode 1-2,

$$i_3 + 10 = i_1 + i_2$$

Expressing this in terms of the node voltages,

$$\frac{v_3 - v_2}{6} + 10 = \frac{v_1 - v_4}{3} + \frac{v_1}{2}$$

or

$$5v_1 + v_2 - v_3 - 2v_4 = 60 \qquad\qquad (3.4.1)$$

At supernode 3-4,

$$i_1 = i_3 + i_4 + i_5 \qquad\Longrightarrow\qquad \frac{v_1 - v_4}{3} = \frac{v_3 - v_2}{6} + \frac{v_4}{1} + \frac{v_3}{4}$$

or

$$4v_1 + 2v_2 - 5v_3 - 16v_4 = 0 \qquad\qquad (3.4.2)$$

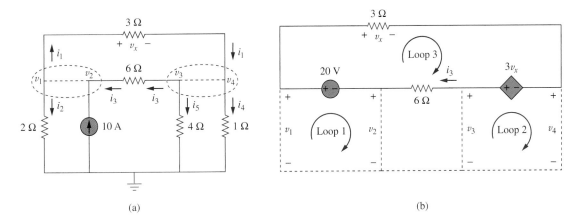

(a)   (b)

Figure 3.13   Applying: (a) KCL to the two supernodes, (b) KVL to the loops.

We now apply KVL to the branches involving the voltage sources as shown in Fig. 3.13(b). For loop 1,

$$-v_1 + 20 + v_2 = 0 \qquad \Longrightarrow \qquad v_1 - v_2 = 20 \qquad (3.4.3)$$

For loop 2,

$$-v_3 + 3v_x + v_4 = 0$$

But $v_x = v_1 - v_4$ so that

$$3v_1 - v_3 - 2v_4 = 0 \qquad (3.4.4)$$

For loop 3,

$$v_x - 3v_x + 6i_3 - 20 = 0$$

But $6i_3 = v_3 - v_2$ and $v_x = v_1 - v_4$. Hence

$$-2v_1 - v_2 + v_3 + 2v_4 = 20 \qquad (3.4.5)$$

We need four node voltages, v_1, v_2, v_3, and v_4, and it requires only four out of the five Eqs. (3.4.1) to (3.4.5) to find them. Although the fifth equation is redundant, it can be used to check results. We can solve Eqs. (3.4.1) to (3.4.4) directly using *MATLAB*. We can eliminate one node voltage so that we solve three simultaneous equations instead of four. From Eq. (3.4.3), $v_2 = v_1 - 20$. Substituting this into Eqs. (3.4.1) and (3.4.2), respectively, gives

$$6v_1 - v_3 - 2v_4 = 80 \qquad (3.4.6)$$

and

$$6v_1 - 5v_3 - 16v_4 = 40 \qquad (3.4.7)$$

Equations (3.4.4), (3.4.6), and (3.4.7) can be cast in matrix form as

$$\begin{bmatrix} 3 & -1 & -2 \\ 6 & -1 & -2 \\ 6 & -5 & -16 \end{bmatrix} \begin{bmatrix} v_1 \\ v_3 \\ v_4 \end{bmatrix} = \begin{bmatrix} 0 \\ 80 \\ 40 \end{bmatrix}$$

Using Cramer's rule,

$$\Delta = \begin{vmatrix} 3 & -1 & -2 \\ 6 & -1 & -2 \\ 6 & -5 & -16 \end{vmatrix} = -18, \qquad \Delta_1 = \begin{vmatrix} 0 & -1 & -2 \\ 80 & -1 & -2 \\ 40 & -5 & -16 \end{vmatrix} = -480$$

$$\Delta_3 = \begin{vmatrix} 3 & 0 & -2 \\ 6 & 80 & -2 \\ 6 & 40 & -16 \end{vmatrix} = -3120, \qquad \Delta_4 = \begin{vmatrix} 3 & -1 & 0 \\ 6 & -1 & 80 \\ 6 & -5 & 40 \end{vmatrix} = 840$$

Thus, we arrive at the node voltages as

$$v_1 = \frac{\Delta_1}{\Delta} = \frac{-480}{-18} = 26.667 \text{ V}, \qquad v_3 = \frac{\Delta_3}{\Delta} = \frac{-3120}{-18} = 173.333 \text{ V}$$

$$v_4 = \frac{\Delta_4}{\Delta} = \frac{840}{-18} = -46.667 \text{ V}$$

and $v_2 = v_1 - 20 = 6.667$ V. We have not used Eq. (3.4.5); it can be used to cross check results.

PRACTICE PROBLEM 3.4

Find v_1, v_2, and v_3 in the circuit in Fig. 3.14 using nodal analysis.

Answer: $v_1 = 3.043$ V, $v_2 = -6.956$ V, $v_3 = 0.6522$ V.

Figure 3.14   For Practice Prob. 3.4.

3.4 MESH ANALYSIS

Mesh analysis provides another general procedure for analyzing circuits, using mesh currents as the circuit variables. Using mesh currents instead of element currents as circuit variables is convenient and reduces the number of equations that must be solved simultaneously. Recall that a loop is a closed path with no node passed more than once. A mesh is a loop that does not contain any other loop within it.

Nodal analysis applies KCL to find unknown voltages in a given circuit, while mesh analysis applies KVL to find unknown currents. Mesh analysis is not quite as general as nodal analysis because it is only applicable to a circuit that is *planar*. A planar circuit is one that can be drawn in a plane with no branches crossing one another; otherwise it is *nonplanar*. A circuit may have crossing branches and still be planar if it can be redrawn such that it has no crossing branches. For example, the circuit in Fig. 3.15(a) has two crossing branches, but it can be redrawn as in Fig. 3.15(b). Hence, the circuit in Fig. 3.15(a) is planar. However, the circuit in Fig. 3.16 is nonplanar, because there is no way to redraw it

Mesh analysis is also known as *loop analysis* or the *mesh-current method*.

and avoid the branches crossing. Nonplanar circuits can be handled using nodal analysis, but they will not be considered in this text.

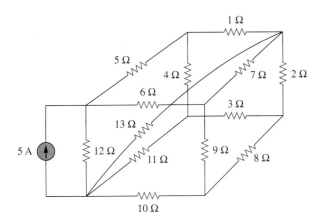

Figure 3.16   A nonplanar circuit.

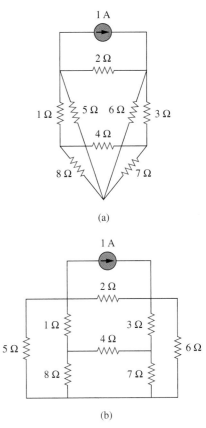

(a)

(b)

Figure 3.15   (a) A planar circuit with crossing branches, (b) the same circuit redrawn with no crossing branches.

To understand mesh analysis, we should first explain more about what we mean by a mesh.

A mesh is a loop which does not contain any other loops within it.

In Fig. 3.17, for example, paths *abefa* and *bcdeb* are meshes, but path *abcdefa* is not a mesh. The current through a mesh is known as *mesh current*. In mesh analysis, we are interested in applying KVL to find the mesh currents in a given circuit.

Although path *abcdefa* is a loop and not a mesh, KVL still holds. This is the reason for loosely using the terms *loop analysis* and *mesh analysis* to mean the same thing.

Figure 3.17   A circuit with two meshes.

In this section, we will apply mesh analysis to planar circuits that do not contain current sources. In the next sections, we will consider circuits with current sources. In the mesh analysis of a circuit with n meshes, we take the following three steps.

Steps to Determine Mesh Currents:

1. Assign mesh currents $i_1, i_2, \ldots, i_n$ to the n meshes.
2. Apply KVL to each of the n meshes. Use Ohm's law to express the voltages in terms of the mesh currents.
3. Solve the resulting n simultaneous equations to get the mesh currents.

To illustrate the steps, consider the circuit in Fig. 3.17. The first step requires that mesh currents i_1 and i_2 are assigned to meshes 1 and 2. Although a mesh current may be assigned to each mesh in an arbitrary direction, it is conventional to assume that each mesh current flows clockwise.

As the second step, we apply KVL to each mesh. Applying KVL to mesh 1, we obtain

$$-V_1 + R_1 i_1 + R_3(i_1 - i_2) = 0$$

or

$$(R_1 + R_3)i_1 - R_3 i_2 = V_1 \qquad (3.13)$$

For mesh 2, applying KVL gives

$$R_2 i_2 + V_2 + R_3(i_2 - i_1) = 0$$

or

$$-R_3 i_1 + (R_2 + R_3)i_2 = -V_2 \qquad (3.14)$$

Note in Eq. (3.13) that the coefficient of i_1 is the sum of the resistances in the first mesh, while the coefficient of i_2 is the negative of the resistance common to meshes 1 and 2. Now observe that the same is true in Eq. (3.14). This can serve as a shortcut way of writing the mesh equations. We will exploit this idea in Section 3.6.

The third step is to solve for the mesh currents. Putting Eqs. (3.13) and (3.14) in matrix form yields

$$\begin{bmatrix} R_1 + R_3 & -R_3 \\ -R_3 & R_2 + R_3 \end{bmatrix} \begin{bmatrix} i_1 \\ i_2 \end{bmatrix} = \begin{bmatrix} V_1 \\ -V_2 \end{bmatrix} \qquad (3.15)$$

which can be solved to obtain the mesh currents i_1 and i_2. We are at liberty to use any technique for solving the simultaneous equations. According to Eq. (2.12), if a circuit has n nodes, b branches, and l independent loops or meshes, then $l = b - n + 1$. Hence, l independent simultaneous equations are required to solve the circuit using mesh analysis.

Notice that the branch currents are different from the mesh currents unless the mesh is isolated. To distinguish between the two types of currents, we use i for a mesh current and I for a branch current. The current elements I_1, I_2, and I_3 are algebraic sums of the mesh currents. It is evident from Fig. 3.17 that

$$I_1 = i_1, \qquad I_2 = i_2, \qquad I_3 = i_1 - i_2 \qquad (3.16)$$

The direction of the mesh current is arbitrary—(clockwise or counterclockwise)—and does not affect the validity of the solution.

The shortcut way will not apply if one mesh current is assumed clockwise and the other assumed anticlockwise, although this is permissible.

EXAMPLE 3.5

For the circuit in Fig. 3.18, find the branch currents I_1, I_2, and I_3 using mesh analysis.

Solution:

We first obtain the mesh currents using KVL. For mesh 1,

$$-15 + 5i_1 + 10(i_1 - i_2) + 10 = 0$$

or

$$3i_1 - 2i_2 = 1 \qquad (3.5.1)$$

For mesh 2,

$$6i_2 + 4i_2 + 10(i_2 - i_1) - 10 = 0$$

or

$$i_1 = 2i_2 - 1 \qquad (3.5.2)$$

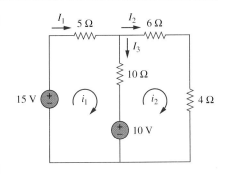

Figure 3.18   For Example 3.5.

METHOD 1   Using the substitution method, we substitute Eq. (3.5.2) into Eq. (3.5.1), and write

$$6i_2 - 3 - 2i_2 = 1 \qquad \Longrightarrow \qquad i_2 = 1 \text{ A}$$

From Eq. (3.5.2), $i_1 = 2i_2 - 1 = 2 - 1 = 1$ A. Thus,

$$I_1 = i_1 = 1 \text{ A}, \qquad I_2 = i_2 = 1 \text{ A}, \qquad I_3 = i_1 - i_2 = 0$$

METHOD 2   To use Cramer's rule, we cast Eqs. (3.5.1) and (3.5.2) in matrix form as

$$\begin{bmatrix} 3 & -2 \\ -1 & 2 \end{bmatrix} \begin{bmatrix} i_1 \\ i_2 \end{bmatrix} = \begin{bmatrix} 1 \\ 1 \end{bmatrix}$$

We obtain the determinants

$$\Delta = \begin{vmatrix} 3 & -2 \\ -1 & 2 \end{vmatrix} = 6 - 2 = 4$$

$$\Delta_1 = \begin{vmatrix} 1 & -2 \\ 1 & 2 \end{vmatrix} = 2 + 2 = 4, \qquad \Delta_2 = \begin{vmatrix} 3 & 1 \\ -1 & 1 \end{vmatrix} = 3 + 1 = 4$$

Thus,

$$i_1 = \frac{\Delta_1}{\Delta} = 1 \text{ A}, \qquad i_2 = \frac{\Delta_2}{\Delta} = 1 \text{ A}$$

as before.

PRACTICE PROBLEM 3.5

2 Ω   9 Ω
12 Ω
12 V i_1
i_2 8 V
4 Ω   3 Ω

Figure 3.19   For Practice Prob. 3.5.

Calculate the mesh currents i_1 and i_2 in the circuit of Fig. 3.19.

Answer: $i_1 = \frac{2}{3}$ A, $i_2 = 0$ A.

EXAMPLE 3.6

i_1 A i_2
I_o
10 Ω i_2 24 Ω
24 V i_1 4 Ω
12 Ω i_3 $4I_o$

Figure 3.20   For Example 3.6.

Use mesh analysis to find the current I_o in the circuit in Fig. 3.20.

Solution:

We apply KVL to the three meshes in turn. For mesh 1,

$$-24 + 10(i_1 - i_2) + 12(i_1 - i_3) = 0$$

or

$$11i_1 - 5i_2 - 6i_3 = 12 \qquad (3.6.1)$$

For mesh 2,

$$24i_2 + 4(i_2 - i_3) + 10(i_2 - i_1) = 0$$

or

$$-5i_1 + 19i_2 - 2i_3 = 0 \qquad (3.6.2)$$

For mesh 3,

$$4I_o + 12(i_3 - i_1) + 4(i_3 - i_2) = 0$$

But at node A, $I_o = i_1 - i_2$, so that

$$4(i_1 - i_2) + 12(i_3 - i_1) + 4(i_3 - i_2) = 0$$

or

$$-i_1 - i_2 + 2i_3 = 0 \qquad (3.6.3)$$

In matrix form, Eqs. (3.6.1) to (3.6.3) become

$$\begin{bmatrix} 11 & -5 & -6 \\ -5 & 19 & -2 \\ -1 & -1 & 2 \end{bmatrix} \begin{bmatrix} i_1 \\ i_2 \\ i_3 \end{bmatrix} = \begin{bmatrix} 12 \\ 0 \\ 0 \end{bmatrix}$$

We obtain the determinants as

$$\Delta = \begin{vmatrix} 11 & -5 & -6 \\ -5 & 19 & -2 \\ -1 & -1 & 2 \\ 11 & -5 & -6 \\ -5 & 19 & -2 \end{vmatrix}$$

$$= 418 - 30 - 10 - 114 - 22 - 50 = 192$$

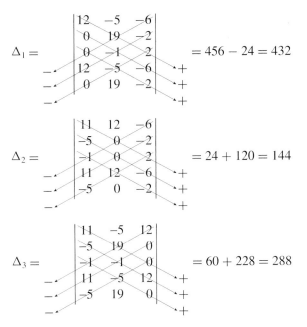

$$\Delta_1 = \begin{vmatrix} 12 & -5 & -6 \\ 0 & 19 & -2 \\ 0 & -1 & 2 \end{vmatrix} = 456 - 24 = 432$$

$$\Delta_2 = \begin{vmatrix} 11 & 12 & -6 \\ -5 & 0 & -2 \\ -1 & 0 & 2 \end{vmatrix} = 24 + 120 = 144$$

$$\Delta_3 = \begin{vmatrix} 11 & -5 & 12 \\ -5 & 19 & 0 \\ -1 & -1 & 0 \end{vmatrix} = 60 + 228 = 288$$

We calculate the mesh currents using Cramer's rule as

$$i_1 = \frac{\Delta_1}{\Delta} = \frac{432}{192} = 2.25 \text{ A}, \qquad i_2 = \frac{\Delta_2}{\Delta} = \frac{144}{192} = 0.75 \text{ A}$$

$$i_3 = \frac{\Delta_3}{\Delta} = \frac{288}{192} = 1.5 \text{ A}$$

Thus, $I_o = i_1 - i_2 = 1.5$ A.

PRACTICE PROBLEM 3.6

Using mesh analysis, find I_o in the circuit in Fig. 3.21.

Answer: −5 A.

Figure 3.21   For Practice Prob. 3.6.

3.5 MESH ANALYSIS WITH CURRENT SOURCES

Applying mesh analysis to circuits containing current sources (dependent or independent) may appear complicated. But it is actually much easier than what we encountered in the previous section, because the presence of the current sources reduces the number of equations. Consider the following two possible cases.

Figure 3.22   A circuit with a current source.

CASE **1**   When a current source exists only in one mesh: Consider the circuit in Fig. 3.22, for example. We set $i_2 = -5$ A and write a mesh equation for the other mesh in the usual way, that is,

$$-10 + 4i_1 + 6(i_1 - i_2) = 0 \quad \Longrightarrow \quad i_1 = -2 \text{ A} \qquad (3.17)$$

CASE **2**   When a current source exists between two meshes: Consider the circuit in Fig. 3.23(a), for example. We create a *supermesh* by excluding the current source and any elements connected in series with it, as shown in Fig. 3.23(b). Thus,

> A supermesh results when two meshes have a (dependent or independent) current source in common.

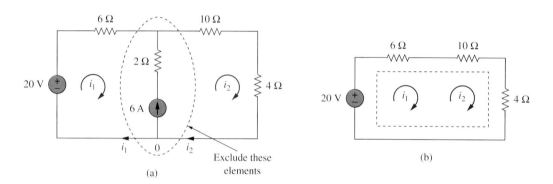

Figure 3.23   (a) Two meshes having a current source in common, (b) a supermesh, created by excluding the current source.

As shown in Fig. 3.23(b), we create a supermesh as the periphery of the two meshes and treat it differently. (If a circuit has two or more supermeshes that intersect, they should be combined to form a larger supermesh.) Why treat the supermesh differently? Because mesh analysis applies KVL—which requires that we know the voltage across each branch—and we do not know the voltage across a current source in advance. However, a supermesh must satisfy KVL like any other mesh. Therefore, applying KVL to the supermesh in Fig. 3.23(b) gives

$$-20 + 6i_1 + 10i_2 + 4i_2 = 0$$

or

$$6i_1 + 14i_2 = 20 \qquad (3.18)$$

We apply KCL to a node in the branch where the two meshes intersect. Applying KCL to node 0 in Fig. 3.23(a) gives

$$i_2 = i_1 + 6 \qquad (3.19)$$

Solving Eqs. (3.18) and (3.19), we get

$$i_1 = -3.2 \text{ A}, \qquad i_2 = 2.8 \text{ A} \qquad (3.20)$$

Note the following properties of a supermesh:

1. The current source in the supermesh provides the constraint equation necessary to solve for the mesh currents.

2. A supermesh has no current of its own.

3. A supermesh requires the application of both KVL and KCL.

EXAMPLE 3.7

For the circuit in Fig. 3.24, find i_1 to i_4 using mesh analysis.

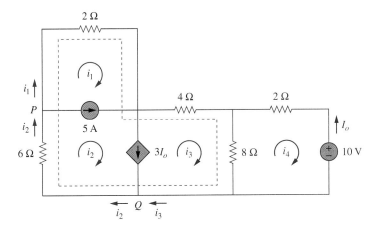

Figure 3.24   For Example 3.7.

Solution:

Note that meshes 1 and 2 form a supermesh since they have an independent current source in common. Also, meshes 2 and 3 form another supermesh because they have a dependent current source in common. The two supermeshes intersect and form a larger supermesh as shown. Applying KVL to the larger supermesh,

$$2i_1 + 4i_3 + 8(i_3 - i_4) + 6i_2 = 0$$

or

$$i_1 + 3i_2 + 6i_3 - 4i_4 = 0 \qquad (3.7.1)$$

For the independent current source, we apply KCL to node P:

$$i_2 = i_1 + 5 \qquad (3.7.2)$$

For the dependent current source, we apply KCL to node Q:

$$i_2 = i_3 + 3i_o$$

But $i_o = -i_4$, hence,

$$i_2 = i_3 - 3i_4 \qquad (3.7.3)$$

Applying KVL in mesh 4,

$$2i_4 + 8(i_4 - i_3) + 10 = 0$$

or

$$5i_4 - 4i_3 = -5 \qquad (3.7.4)$$

From Eqs. (3.7.1) to (3.7.4),

$$i_1 = -7.5 \text{ A}, \qquad i_2 = -2.5 \text{ A}, \qquad i_3 = 3.93 \text{ A}, \qquad i_4 = 2.143 \text{ A}$$

PRACTICE PROBLEM 3.7

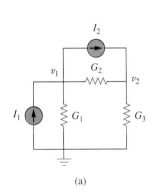

Use mesh analysis to determine i_1, i_2, and i_3 in Fig. 3.25.

Answer: $i_1 = 3.474 \text{ A}, i_2 = 0.4737 \text{ A}, i_3 = 1.1052 \text{ A}.$

Figure 3.25   For Practice Prob. 3.7.

†3.6   NODAL AND MESH ANALYSES BY INSPECTION

This section presents a generalized procedure for nodal or mesh analysis. It is a shortcut approach based on mere inspection of a circuit.

When all sources in a circuit are independent current sources, we do not need to apply KCL to each node to obtain the node-voltage equations as we did in Section 3.2. We can obtain the equations by mere inspection of the circuit. As an example, let us reexamine the circuit in Fig. 3.2, shown again in Fig. 3.26(a) for convenience. The circuit has two nonreference nodes and the node equations were derived in Section 3.2 as

$$\begin{bmatrix} G_1 + G_2 & -G_2 \\ -G_2 & G_2 + G_3 \end{bmatrix} \begin{bmatrix} v_1 \\ v_2 \end{bmatrix} = \begin{bmatrix} I_1 - I_2 \\ I_2 \end{bmatrix} \qquad (3.21)$$

Observe that each of the diagonal terms is the sum of the conductances connected directly to node 1 or 2, while the off-diagonal terms are the negatives of the conductances connected between the nodes. Also, each term on the right-hand side of Eq. (3.21) is the algebraic sum of the currents entering the node.

In general, if a circuit with independent current sources has N nonreference nodes, the node-voltage equations can be written in terms of the conductances as

$$\begin{bmatrix} G_{11} & G_{12} & \cdots & G_{1N} \\ G_{21} & G_{22} & \cdots & G_{2N} \\ \vdots & \vdots & \vdots & \vdots \\ G_{N1} & G_{N2} & \cdots & G_{NN} \end{bmatrix} \begin{bmatrix} v_1 \\ v_2 \\ \vdots \\ v_N \end{bmatrix} = \begin{bmatrix} i_1 \\ i_2 \\ \vdots \\ i_N \end{bmatrix} \qquad (3.22)$$

or simply

$$\mathbf{Gv} = \mathbf{i} \qquad (3.23)$$

Figure 3.26   (a) The circuit in Fig. 3.2, (b) the circuit in Fig. 3.17.

where

G_{kk} = Sum of the conductances connected to node k

$G_{kj} = G_{jk}$ = Negative of the sum of the conductances directly connecting nodes k and $j, k \neq j$

v_k = Unknown voltage at node k

i_k = Sum of all independent current sources directly connected to node k, with currents entering the node treated as positive

G is called the *conductance matrix*; **v** is the output vector; and **i** is the input vector. Equation (3.22) can be solved to obtain the unknown node voltages. Keep in mind that this is valid for circuits with only independent current sources and linear resistors.

Similarly, we can obtain mesh-current equations by inspection when a linear resistive circuit has only independent voltage sources. Consider the circuit in Fig. 3.17, shown again in Fig. 3.26(b) for convenience. The circuit has two nonreference nodes and the node equations were derived in Section 3.4 as

$$\begin{bmatrix} R_1 + R_3 & -R_3 \\ -R_3 & R_2 + R_3 \end{bmatrix} \begin{bmatrix} i_1 \\ i_2 \end{bmatrix} = \begin{bmatrix} v_1 \\ -v_2 \end{bmatrix} \tag{3.24}$$

We notice that each of the diagonal terms is the sum of the resistances in the related mesh, while each of the off-diagonal terms is the negative of the resistance common to meshes 1 and 2. Each term on the right-hand side of Eq. (3.24) is the algebraic sum taken clockwise of all independent voltage sources in the related mesh.

In general, if the circuit has N meshes, the mesh-current equations can be expressed in terms of the resistances as

$$\begin{bmatrix} R_{11} & R_{12} & \dots & R_{1N} \\ R_{21} & R_{22} & \dots & R_{2N} \\ \vdots & \vdots & \vdots & \vdots \\ R_{N1} & R_{N2} & \dots & R_{NN} \end{bmatrix} \begin{bmatrix} i_1 \\ i_2 \\ \vdots \\ i_N \end{bmatrix} = \begin{bmatrix} v_1 \\ v_2 \\ \vdots \\ v_N \end{bmatrix} \tag{3.25}$$

or simply

$$\mathbf{Ri} = \mathbf{v} \tag{3.26}$$

where

R_{kk} = Sum of the resistances in mesh k

$R_{kj} = R_{jk}$ = Negative of the sum of the resistances in common with meshes k and $j, k \neq j$

i_k = Unknown mesh current for mesh k in the clockwise direction

v_k = Sum taken clockwise of all independent voltage sources in mesh k, with voltage rise treated as positive

R is called the *resistance matrix*; **i** is the output vector; and **v** is the input vector. We can solve Eq. (3.25) to obtain the unknown mesh currents.

EXAMPLE 3.8

Write the node-voltage matrix equations for the circuit in Fig. 3.27 by inspection.

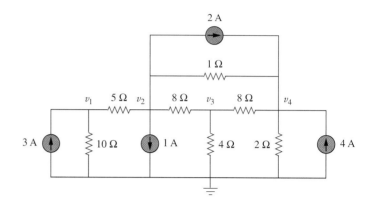

Figure 3.27   For Example 3.8.

Solution:

The circuit in Fig. 3.27 has four nonreference nodes, so we need four node equations. This implies that the size of the conductance matrix $\mathbf{G}$, is 4 by 4. The diagonal terms of $\mathbf{G}$, in siemens, are

$$G_{11} = \frac{1}{5} + \frac{1}{10} = 0.3, \qquad G_{22} = \frac{1}{5} + \frac{1}{8} + \frac{1}{1} = 1.325$$

$$G_{33} = \frac{1}{8} + \frac{1}{8} + \frac{1}{4} = 0.5, \qquad G_{44} = \frac{1}{8} + \frac{1}{2} + \frac{1}{1} = 1.625$$

The off-diagonal terms are

$$G_{12} = -\frac{1}{5} = -0.2, \qquad G_{13} = G_{14} = 0$$

$$G_{21} = -0.2, \qquad G_{23} = -\frac{1}{8} = -0.125, \qquad G_{24} = -\frac{1}{1} = -1$$

$$G_{31} = 0, \qquad G_{32} = -0.125, \qquad G_{34} = -\frac{1}{8} = -0.125$$

$$G_{41} = 0, \qquad G_{42} = -1, \qquad G_{43} = -0.125$$

The input current vector $\mathbf{i}$ has the following terms, in amperes:

$$i_1 = 3, \qquad i_2 = -1 - 2 = -3, \qquad i_3 = 0, \qquad i_4 = 2 + 4 = 6$$

Thus the node-voltage equations are

$$\begin{bmatrix} 0.3 & -0.2 & 0 & 0 \\ -0.2 & 1.325 & -0.125 & -1 \\ 0 & -0.125 & 0.5 & -0.125 \\ 0 & -1 & -0.125 & 1.625 \end{bmatrix} \begin{bmatrix} v_1 \\ v_2 \\ v_3 \\ v_4 \end{bmatrix} = \begin{bmatrix} 3 \\ -3 \\ 0 \\ 6 \end{bmatrix}$$

which can be solved using *MATLAB* to obtain the node voltages v_1, v_2, v_3, and v_4.

PRACTICE PROBLEM 3.8

By inspection, obtain the node-voltage equations for the circuit in Fig. 3.28.

Answer:

$$\begin{bmatrix} 1.3 & -0.2 & -1 & 0 \\ -0.2 & 0.2 & 0 & 0 \\ -1 & 0 & 1.25 & -0.25 \\ 0 & 0 & -0.25 & 0.75 \end{bmatrix} \begin{bmatrix} v_1 \\ v_2 \\ v_3 \\ v_4 \end{bmatrix} = \begin{bmatrix} 0 \\ 3 \\ -1 \\ 3 \end{bmatrix}$$

Figure 3.28   For Practice Prob. 3.8.

EXAMPLE 3.9

By inspection, write the mesh-current equations for the circuit in Fig. 3.29.

Figure 3.29   For Example 3.9.

Solution:

We have five meshes, so the resistance matrix is 5 by 5. The diagonal terms, in ohms, are:

$$R_{11} = 5 + 2 + 2 = 9, \qquad R_{22} = 2 + 4 + 1 + 1 + 2 = 10$$
$$R_{33} = 2 + 3 + 4 = 9, \qquad R_{44} = 1 + 3 + 4 = 8, \qquad R_{55} = 1 + 3 = 4$$

The off-diagonal terms are:

$$R_{12} = -2, \qquad R_{13} = -2, \qquad R_{14} = 0 = R_{15}$$
$$R_{21} = -2, \qquad R_{23} = -4, \qquad R_{24} = -1, \qquad R_{25} = -1$$
$$R_{31} = -2, \qquad R_{32} = -4, \qquad R_{34} = 0 = R_{35}$$
$$R_{41} = 0, \qquad R_{42} = -1, \qquad R_{43} = 0, \qquad R_{45} = -3$$
$$R_{51} = 0, \qquad R_{52} = -1, \qquad R_{53} = 0, \qquad R_{54} = -3$$

The input voltage vector **v** has the following terms in volts:

$$v_1 = 4, \qquad v_2 = 10 - 4 = 6$$
$$v_3 = -12 + 6 = -6, \qquad v_4 = 0, \qquad v_5 = -6$$

Thus the mesh-current equations are:

$$
\begin{bmatrix}
9 & -2 & -2 & 0 & 0 \\
-2 & 10 & -4 & -1 & -1 \\
-2 & -4 & 9 & 0 & 0 \\
0 & -1 & 0 & 8 & -3 \\
0 & -1 & 0 & -3 & 4
\end{bmatrix}
\begin{bmatrix}
i_1 \\ i_2 \\ i_3 \\ i_4 \\ i_5
\end{bmatrix}
=
\begin{bmatrix}
4 \\ 6 \\ -6 \\ 0 \\ -6
\end{bmatrix}
$$

From this, we can use *MATLAB* to obtain mesh currents i_1, i_2, i_3, i_4, and i_5.

PRACTICE PROBLEM 3.9

By inspection, obtain the mesh-current equations for the circuit in Fig. 3.30.

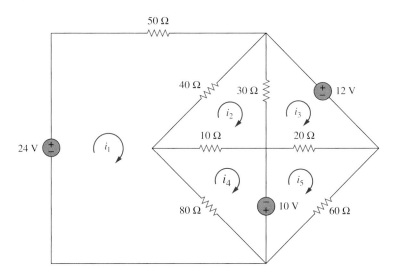

Figure 3.30   For Practice Prob. 3.9.

Answer:

$$
\begin{bmatrix}
170 & -40 & 0 & -80 & 0 \\
-40 & 80 & -30 & -10 & 0 \\
0 & -30 & 50 & 0 & -20 \\
-80 & -10 & 0 & 90 & 0 \\
0 & 0 & -20 & 0 & 80
\end{bmatrix}
\begin{bmatrix}
i_1 \\ i_2 \\ i_3 \\ i_4 \\ i_5
\end{bmatrix}
=
\begin{bmatrix}
24 \\ 0 \\ -12 \\ 10 \\ -10
\end{bmatrix}
$$

3.7 NODAL VERSUS MESH ANALYSIS

Both nodal and mesh analyses provide a systematic way of analyzing a complex network. Someone may ask: Given a network to be analyzed, how do we know which method is better or more efficient? The choice of the better method is dictated by two factors.

The first factor is the nature of the particular network. Networks that contain many series-connected elements, voltage sources, or supermeshes are more suitable for mesh analysis, whereas networks with parallel-connected elements, current sources, or supernodes are more suitable for nodal analysis. Also, a circuit with fewer nodes than meshes is better analyzed using nodal analysis, while a circuit with fewer meshes than nodes is better analyzed using mesh analysis. The key is to select the method that results in the smaller number of equations.

The second factor is the information required. If node voltages are required, it may be expedient to apply nodal analysis. If branch or mesh currents are required, it may be better to use mesh analysis.

It is helpful to be familiar with both methods of analysis, for at least two reasons. First, one method can be used to check the results from the other method, if possible. Second, since each method has its limitations, only one method may be suitable for a particular problem. For example, mesh analysis is the only method to use in analyzing transistor circuits, as we shall see in Section 3.9. But mesh analysis cannot easily be used to solve an op amp circuit, as we shall see in Chapter 5, because there is no direct way to obtain the voltage across the op amp itself. For nonplanar networks, nodal analysis is the only option, because mesh analysis only applies to planar networks. Also, nodal analysis is more amenable to solution by computer, as it is easy to program. This allows one to analyze complicated circuits that defy hand calculation. A computer software package based on nodal analysis is introduced next.

3.8   CIRCUIT ANALYSIS WITH *PSPICE*

PSpice is a computer software circuit analysis program that we will gradually learn to use throughout the course of this text. This section illustrates how to use *PSpice for Windows* to analyze the dc circuits we have studied so far.

The reader is expected to review Sections D.1 through D.3 of Appendix D before proceeding in this section. It should be noted that *PSpice* is only helpful in determining branch voltages and currents when the numerical values of all the circuit components are known.

Appendix D provides a tutorial on using *PSpice* for Windows.

EXAMPLE 3.10

Use *PSpice* to find the node voltages in the circuit of Fig. 3.31.

Solution:

The first step is to draw the given circuit using Schematics. If one follows the instructions given in Appendix sections D.2 and D.3, the schematic in Fig. 3.32 is produced. Since this is a dc analysis, we use voltage source VDC and current source IDC. The pseudocomponent VIEWPOINTS are added to display the required node voltages. Once the circuit is drawn and saved as *exam310.sch*, we run *PSpice* by selecting **Analysis/Simulate**. The circuit is simulated and the results are displayed on VIEWPOINTS

Figure 3.31   For Example 3.10.

Figure 3.32   For Example 3.10; the schematic of the circuit in Fig. 3.31.

and also saved in output file *exam310.out*. The output file includes the following:

NODE	VOLTAGE	NODE	VOLTAGE	NODE	VOLTAGE
(1)	120.0000	(2)	81.2900	(3)	89.0320

indicating that $V_1 = 120$ V, $V_2 = 81.29$ V, $V_3 = 89.032$ V.

PRACTICE PROBLEM 3.10

For the circuit in Fig. 3.33, use *PSpice* to find the node voltages.

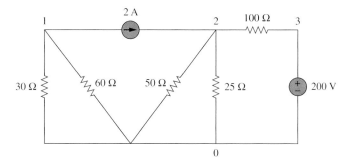

Figure 3.33   For Practice Prob. 3.10.

Answer: $V_1 = -40$ V, $V_2 = 57.14$ V, $V_3 = 200$ V.

EXAMPLE 3.11

In the circuit in Fig. 3.34, determine the currents i_1, i_2, and i_3.

Solution:

The schematic is shown in Fig. 3.35. (The schematic in Fig. 3.35 includes the output results, implying that it is the schematic displayed on the screen *after* the simulation.) Notice that the voltage-controlled voltage source E1 in Fig. 3.35 is connected so that its input is the voltage across the 4-Ω resistor; its gain is set equal to 3. In order to display the required currents, we insert pseudocomponent IPROBES in the appropriate branches. The schematic is saved as *exam311.sch* and simulated by

Figure 3.34   For Example 3.11.

Figure 3.35   The schematic of the circuit in Fig. 3.34.

selecting **Analysis/Simulate**. The results are displayed on IPROBES as shown in Fig. 3.35 and saved in output file *exam311.out*. From the output file or the IPROBES, we obtain $i_1 = i_2 = 1.333$ A and $i_3 = 2.667$ A.

PRACTICE PROBLEM 3.11

Use *PSpice* to determine currents i_1, i_2, and i_3 in the circuit of Fig. 3.36.

Answer: $i_1 = -0.4286$ A, $i_2 = 2.286$ A, $i_3 = 2$ A.

Figure 3.36   For Practice Prob. 3.11.

†3.9 APPLICATIONS: DC TRANSISTOR CIRCUITS

Most of us deal with electronic products on a routine basis and have some experience with personal computers. A basic component for the integrated circuits found in these electronics and computers is the active, three-terminal device known as the *transistor.* Understanding the transistor is essential before an engineer can start an electronic circuit design.

Figure 3.37 depicts various kinds of transistors commercially available. There are two basic types of transistors: *bipolar junction transistors* (BJTs) and *field-effect transistors* (FETs). Here, we consider only the BJTs, which were the first of the two and are still used today. Our objective is to present enough detail about the BJT to enable us to apply the techniques developed in this chapter to analyze dc transistor circuits.

Figure 3.37   Various types of transistors. *(Courtesy of Tech America.)*

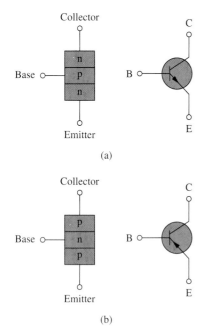

Figure 3.38   Two types of BJTs and their circuit symbols: (a) *npn*, (b) *pnp*.

There are two types of BJTs: *npn* and *pnp*, with their circuit symbols as shown in Fig. 3.38. Each type has three terminals, designated as emitter (E), base (B), and collector (C). For the *npn* transistor, the currents and voltages of the transistor are specified as in Fig. 3.39. Applying KCL to Fig. 3.39(a) gives

$$I_E = I_B + I_C \tag{3.27}$$

where I_E, I_C, and I_B are emitter, collector, and base currents, respectively. Similarly, applying KVL to Fig. 3.39(b) gives

$$V_{CE} + V_{EB} + V_{BC} = 0 \tag{3.28}$$

where V_{CE}, V_{EB}, and V_{BC} are collector-emitter, emitter-base, and base-collector voltages. The BJT can operate in one of three modes: active, cutoff, and saturation. When transistors operate in the active mode, typically $V_{BE} \simeq 0.7$ V,

$$I_C = \alpha I_E \tag{3.29}$$

where α is called the *common-base current gain*. In Eq. (3.29), α denotes the fraction of electrons injected by the emitter that are collected by the collector. Also,

$$I_C = \beta I_B \qquad (3.30)$$

where β is known as the *common-emitter current gain*. The α and β are characteristic properties of a given transistor and assume constant values for that transistor. Typically, α takes values in the range of 0.98 to 0.999, while β takes values in the range 50 to 1000. From Eqs. (3.27) to (3.30), it is evident that

$$I_E = (1 + \beta)I_B \qquad (3.31)$$

and

$$\beta = \frac{\alpha}{1 - \alpha} \qquad (3.32)$$

These equations show that, in the active mode, the BJT can be modeled as a dependent current-controlled current source. Thus, in circuit analysis, the dc equivalent model in Fig. 3.40(b) may be used to replace the *npn* transistor in Fig. 3.40(a). Since β in Eq. (3.32) is large, a small base current controls large currents in the output circuit. Consequently, the bipolar transistor can serve as an amplifier, producing both current gain and voltage gain. Such amplifiers can be used to furnish a considerable amount of power to transducers such as loudspeakers or control motors.

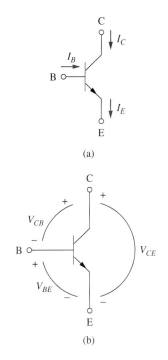

(a)

(b)

Figure 3.39   The terminal variables of an *npn* transistor: (a) currents, (b) voltages.

In fact, transistor circuits provide motivation to study dependent sources.

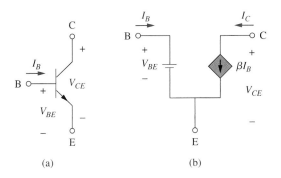

(a)   (b)

Figure 3.40   (a) An *npn* transistor, (b) its dc equivalent model.

It should be observed in the following examples that one cannot directly analyze transistor circuits using nodal analysis because of the potential difference between the terminals of the transistor. Only when the transistor is replaced by its equivalent model can we apply nodal analysis.

EXAMPLE 3.12

Find I_B, I_C, and v_o in the transistor circuit of Fig. 3.41. Assume that the transistor operates in the active mode and that $\beta = 50$.

Figure 3.41   For Example 3.12.

Solution:

For the input loop, KVL gives

$$-4 + I_B(20 \times 10^3) + V_{BE} = 0$$

Since $V_{BE} = 0.7$ V in the active mode,

$$I_B = \frac{4 - 0.7}{20 \times 10^3} = 165 \ \mu A$$

But

$$I_C = \beta I_B = 50 \times 165 \ \mu A = 8.25 \text{ mA}$$

For the output loop, KVL gives

$$-v_o - 100 I_C + 6 = 0$$

or

$$v_o = 6 - 100 I_C = 6 - 0.825 = 5.175 \text{ V}$$

Note that $v_o = V_{CE}$ in this case.

PRACTICE PROBLEM 3.12

For the transistor circuit in Fig. 3.42, let $\beta = 100$ and $V_{BE} = 0.7$ V. Determine v_o and V_{CE}.

Answer: 2.876 V, 1.984 V.

Figure 3.42   For Practice Prob. 3.12.

EXAMPLE 3.13

For the BJT circuit in Fig. 3.43, $\beta = 150$ and $V_{BE} = 0.7$ V. Find v_o.

Solution:

We can solve this problem in two ways. One way is by direct analysis of the circuit in Fig. 3.43. Another way is by replacing the transistor with its equivalent circuit.

Figure 3.43   For Example 3.13.

METHOD 1 We can solve the problem as we solved the problem in the previous example. We apply KVL to the input and output loops as shown in Fig. 3.44(a). For loop 1,

$$2 = 100 \times 10^3 I_1 + 200 \times 10^3 I_2 \qquad (3.13.1)$$

For loop 2,

$$V_{BE} = 0.7 = 200 \times 10^3 I_2 \qquad \Longrightarrow \qquad I_2 = 3.5 \ \mu\text{A} \qquad (3.13.2)$$

For loop 3,

$$-v_o - 1000 I_C + 16 = 0$$

or

$$v_o = 16 - 1000 I_C \qquad (3.13.3)$$

From Eqs. (3.13.1) and (3.13.2),

$$I_1 = \frac{2 - 0.7}{100 \times 10^3} = 13 \ \mu\text{A}, \qquad I_B = I_1 - I_2 = 9.5 \ \mu\text{A}$$

$$I_C = \beta I_B = 150 \times 9.5 \ \mu\text{A} = 1.425 \ \text{mA}$$

(a)

(b)

Figure 3.44   Solution of the problem in Example 3.13: (a) method 1, (b) method 2.

Substituting for I_C in Eq. (3.13.3),

$$v_o = 16 - 1.425 = 14.575 \text{ V}$$

METHOD **2**   We can modify the circuit in Fig. 3.43 by replacing the transistor by its equivalent model in Fig. 3.40(b). The result is the circuit shown in Fig. 3.44(b). Notice that the locations of the base (B), emitter (E), and collector (C) remain the same in both the original circuit in Fig. 3.43 and its equivalent circuit in Fig. 3.44(b). From the output loop,

$$v_o = 16 - 1000(150 I_B)$$

But

$$I_B = I_1 - I_2 = \frac{2 - 0.7}{100 \times 10^3} - \frac{0.7}{200 \times 10^3} = (13 - 3.5) \, \mu\text{A} = 9.5 \, \mu\text{A}$$

and so

$$v_o = 16 - 1000(150 \times 9.5 \times 10^{-6}) = 14.575 \text{ V}$$

PRACTICE PROBLEM 3.13

Figure 3.45   For Practice Prob. 3.13.

The transistor circuit in Fig. 3.45 has $\beta = 80$ and $V_{BE} = 0.7$ V. Find v_o and I_o.

Answer: -3 V, $-150 \, \mu\text{A}$.

3.10 SUMMARY

1. Nodal analysis is the application of Kirchhoff's current law at the nonreference nodes. (It is applicable to both planar and nonplanar circuits.) We express the result in terms of the node voltages. Solving the simultaneous equations yields the node voltages.

2. A supernode consists of two nonreference nodes connected by a (dependent or independent) voltage source.

3. Mesh analysis is the application of Kirchhoff's voltage law around meshes in a planar circuit. We express the result in terms of mesh currents. Solving the simultaneous equations yields the mesh currents.

4. A supermesh consists of two meshes that have a (dependent or independent) current source in common.

5. Nodal analysis is normally used when a circuit has fewer node equations than mesh equations. Mesh analysis is normally used when a circuit has fewer mesh equations than node equations.

6. Circuit analysis can be carried out using *PSpice*.

7. DC transistor circuits can be analyzed using the techniques covered in this chapter.

REVIEW QUESTIONS

3.1   At node 1 in the circuit in Fig. 3.46, applying KCL gives:

(a) $2 + \dfrac{12 - v_1}{3} = \dfrac{v_1}{6} + \dfrac{v_1 - v_2}{4}$

(b) $2 + \dfrac{v_1 - 12}{3} = \dfrac{v_1}{6} + \dfrac{v_2 - v_1}{4}$

(c) $2 + \dfrac{12 - v_1}{3} = \dfrac{0 - v_1}{6} + \dfrac{v_1 - v_2}{4}$

(d) $2 + \dfrac{v_1 - 12}{3} = \dfrac{0 - v_1}{6} + \dfrac{v_2 - v_1}{4}$

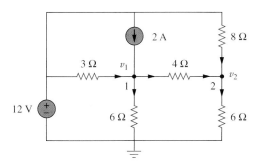

Figure 3.46   For Review Questions 3.1 and 3.2.

3.2   In the circuit in Fig. 3.46, applying KCL at node 2 gives:

(a) $\dfrac{v_2 - v_1}{4} + \dfrac{v_2}{8} = \dfrac{v_2}{6}$

(b) $\dfrac{v_1 - v_2}{4} + \dfrac{v_2}{8} = \dfrac{v_2}{6}$

(c) $\dfrac{v_1 - v_2}{4} + \dfrac{12 - v_2}{8} = \dfrac{v_2}{6}$

(d) $\dfrac{v_2 - v_1}{4} + \dfrac{v_2 - 12}{8} = \dfrac{v_2}{6}$

3.3   For the circuit in Fig. 3.47, v_1 and v_2 are related as:

(a) $v_1 = 6i + 8 + v_2$ (b) $v_1 = 6i - 8 + v_2$

(c) $v_1 = -6i + 8 + v_2$ (d) $v_1 = -6i - 8 + v_2$

Figure 3.47   For Review Questions 3.3 and 3.4.

3.4   In the circuit in Fig. 3.47, the voltage v_2 is:

(a) -8 V   (b) -1.6 V

(c) 1.6 V   (d) 8 V

3.5   The current i in the circuit in Fig. 3.48 is:

(a) -2.667 A   (b) -0.667 A

(c) 0.667 A   (d) 2.667 A

Figure 3.48   For Review Questions 3.5 and 3.6.

3.6   The loop equation for the circuit in Fig. 3.48 is:

(a) $-10 + 4i + 6 + 2i = 0$

(b) $10 + 4i + 6 + 2i = 0$

(c) $10 + 4i - 6 + 2i = 0$

(d) $-10 + 4i - 6 + 2i = 0$

3.7   In the circuit in Fig. 3.49, current i_1 is:

   (a) 4 A   (b) 3 A   (c) 2 A   (d) 1 A

Figure 3.49   For Review Questions 3.7 and 3.8.

3.8   The voltage v across the current source in the circuit of Fig. 3.49 is:

   (a) 20 V   (b) 15 V   (c) 10 V   (d) 5 V

3.9   The *PSpice* part name for a current-controlled voltage source is:

   (a) EX   (b) FX   (c) HX   (d) GX

3.10   Which of the following statements are not true of the pseudocomponent IPROBE:

   (a) It must be connected in series.
   (b) It plots the branch current.
   (c) It displays the current through the branch in which it is connected.
   (d) It can be used to display voltage by connecting it in parallel.
   (e) It is used only for dc analysis.
   (f) It does not correspond to a particular circuit element.

Answers: 3.1a, 3.2c, 3.3b, 3.4d, 3.5c, 3.6a, 3.7d, 3.8b, 3.9c, 3.10b,d.

PROBLEMS

Sections 3.2 and 3.3   **Nodal Analysis**

3.1   Determine v_1, v_2, and the power dissipated in all the resistors in the circuit of Fig. 3.50.

Figure 3.50   For Prob. 3.1.

3.2   For the circuit in Fig. 3.51, obtain v_1 and v_2.

Figure 3.51   For Prob. 3.2.

3.3   Find the currents I_1 through I_4 and the voltage v_o in the circuit in Fig. 3.52.

Figure 3.52   For Prob. 3.3.

3.4   Given the circuit in Fig. 3.53, calculate the currents I_1 through I_4.

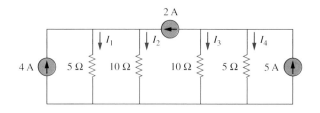

Figure 3.53   For Prob. 3.4.

3.5   Obtain v_o in the circuit of Fig. 3.54.

Figure 3.54   For Prob. 3.5.

3.6   Use nodal analysis to obtain v_o in the circuit in Fig. 3.55.

Figure 3.55   For Prob. 3.6.

3.7   Find the voltages at nodes a and b in Fig. 3.56 using nodal analysis.

Figure 3.56   For Prob. 3.7.

3.8   Using nodal analysis, find v_o in the circuit of Fig. 3.57.

Figure 3.57   For Prob. 3.8.

3.9   Calculate v_o in the circuit in Fig. 3.58.

Figure 3.58   For Prob. 3.9.

3.10   Find I_o in the circuit in Fig. 3.59.

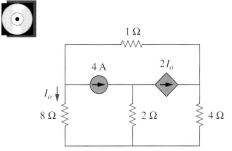

Figure 3.59   For Prob. 3.10.

3.11   Solve for i_1 and i_2 in the circuit in Fig. 3.22 (Section 3.5) using nodal analysis.

3.12   Use nodal analysis to find currents I_1 and I_2 in the circuit of Fig. 3.60.

Figure 3.60   For Prob. 3.12.

3.13   Calculate v_1 and v_2 in the circuit in Fig. 3.61 using nodal analysis.

Figure 3.61   For Prob. 3.13.

3.14   Using nodal analysis, find v_o in the circuit of
           Fig. 3.62.

Figure 3.62   For Prob. 3.14.

3.15   Apply nodal analysis to find i_o and the power
           dissipated in each resistor in the circuit of Fig. 3.63.

Figure 3.63   For Prob. 3.15.

3.16   Determine voltages v_1 through v_3 in the circuit of
           Fig. 3.64 using nodal analysis.

Figure 3.64   For Prob. 3.16.

3.17   Using nodal analysis, find current i_o in the circuit of
           Fig. 3.65.

Figure 3.65   For Prob. 3.17.

3.18   Determine the node voltages in the circuit in
           Fig. 3.66 using nodal analysis.

Figure 3.66   For Prob. 3.18.

3.19   Use nodal analysis to find v_1, v_2, and v_3 in the circuit
           in Fig. 3.67.

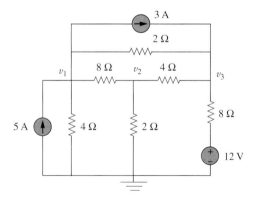

Figure 3.67   For Prob. 3.19.

3.20 For the circuit in Fig. 3.68, find v_1, v_2, and v_3 using nodal analysis.

Figure 3.68   For Prob.3.20.

3.21 For the circuit in Fig. 3.69, find v_1 and v_2 using nodal analysis.

Figure 3.69   For Prob. 3.21.

3.22 Determine v_1 and v_2 in the circuit in Fig. 3.70.

Figure 3.70   For Prob. 3.22.

3.23 Obtain v_1 and v_2 in the circuit of Fig. 3.71.

Figure 3.71   For Prob. 3.23.

3.24 Use nodal analysis to find i_o in the circuit shown in Fig. 3.72.

Figure 3.72   For Prob. 3.24.

3.25 Find v_o and i_o in the circuit in Fig. 3.73.

Figure 3.73   For Prob. 3.25.

3.26 Calculate the node voltages v_1, v_2, and v_3 in the circuit of Fig. 3.74.

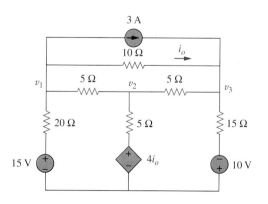

Figure 3.74   For Prob. 3.26.

*3.27   Use nodal analysis to determine voltages v_1, v_2, and v_3 in the circuit in Fig. 3.75.

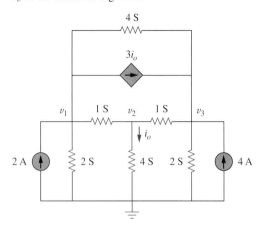

Figure 3.75   For Prob. 3.27.

*3.28   Use *MATLAB* to find the voltages at nodes a, b, c, and d in the circuit of Fig. 3.76.

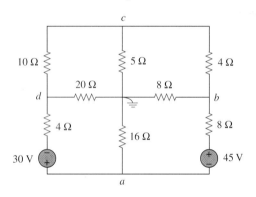

Figure 3.76   For Prob. 3.28.

3.29   Use *MATLAB* to solve for the node voltages in the circuit of Fig. 3.77.

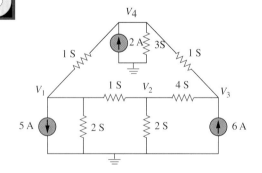

Figure 3.77   For Prob. 3.29.

*An asterisk indicates a challenging problem.

3.30   Using nodal analysis, find v_o and I_o in the circuit of Fig. 3.78.

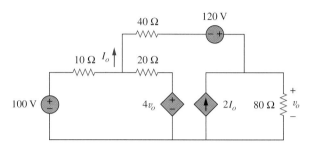

Figure 3.78   For Prob. 3.30.

3.31   Find the node voltages for the circuit in Fig. 3.79.

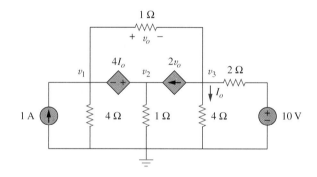

Figure 3.79   For Prob. 3.31.

*3.32   Obtain the node voltages v_1, v_2, and v_3 in the circuit of Fig. 3.80.

Figure 3.80   For Prob. 3.32.

Sections 3.4 and 3.5   **Mesh Analysis**

3.33   Which of the circuits in Fig. 3.81 is planar? For the planar circuit, redraw the circuits with no crossing branches.

(a)

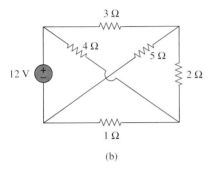

(b)

Figure 3.81   For Prob. 3.33.

3.34   Determine which of the circuits in Fig. 3.82 is planar and redraw it with no crossing branches.

(a)

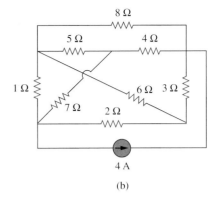

(b)

Figure 3.82   For Prob. 3.34.

3.35   Rework Prob. 3.5 using mesh analysis.

3.36   Rework Prob. 3.6 using mesh analysis.

3.37   Solve Prob. 3.8 using mesh analysis.

3.38   Solve Prob. 3.9 using mesh analysis.

3.39   Determine the mesh currents i_1 and i_2 in the circuit shown in Fig. 3.83.

Figure 3.83   For Prob. 3.39.

3.40   For the bridge network in Fig. 3.84, find i_o using mesh analysis.

Figure 3.84   For Prob. 3.40.

3.41   Apply mesh analysis to find i in Fig. 3.85.

Figure 3.85   For Prob. 3.41.

3.42   Determine the mesh currents in the circuit of Fig. 3.86.

Figure 3.86   For Prob. 3.42.

3.43   Use mesh analysis to find v_{ab} and i_o in the circuit in Fig. 3.87.

Figure 3.87   For Prob. 3.43.

3.44   Use mesh analysis to obtain i_o in the circuit of Fig. 3.88.

Figure 3.88   For Prob. 3.44.

3.45   Find current i in the circuit in Fig. 3.89.

Figure 3.89   For Prob. 3.45.

3.46   Calculate the mesh currents i_1 and i_2 in Fig. 3.90.

Figure 3.90   For Prob. 3.46.

3.47   Rework Prob. 3.19 using mesh analysis.

3.48   Determine the current through the 10-kΩ resistor in the circuit in Fig. 3.91 using mesh analysis.

Figure 3.91   For Prob. 3.48.

3.49 Find v_o and i_o in the circuit of Fig. 3.92.

Figure 3.92   For Prob. 3.49.

3.50 Use mesh analysis to find the current i_o in the circuit in Fig. 3.93.

Figure 3.93   For Prob. 3.50.

3.51 Apply mesh analysis to find v_o in the circuit in Fig. 3.94.

Figure 3.94   For Prob. 3.51.

3.52 Use mesh analysis to find i_1, i_2, and i_3 in the circuit of Fig. 3.95.

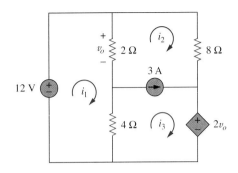

Figure 3.95   For Prob. 3.52.

3.53 Rework Prob. 3.12 using mesh analysis.

3.54 Find the mesh currents i_1, i_2, and i_3 in the circuit in Fig. 3.96.

Figure 3.96   For Prob. 3.54.

*3.55** In the circuit of Fig. 3.97, solve for I_1, I_2, and I_3.

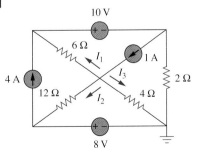

Figure 3.97   For Prob. 3.55.

3.56   Determine v_1 and v_2 in the circuit of Fig. 3.98.

Figure 3.98   For Prob. 3.56.

3.57   In the circuit in Fig. 3.99, find the values of R, V_1, and V_2 given that $i_o = 18$ mA.

Figure 3.99   For Prob. 3.57.

3.58   Find i_1, i_2, and i_3 in the circuit in Fig. 3.100.

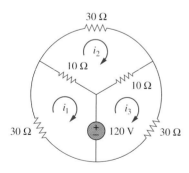

Figure 3.100   For Prob. 3.58.

3.59   Rework Prob. 3.30 using mesh analysis.

3.60   Calculate the power dissipated in each resistor in the circuit in Fig. 3.101.

Figure 3.101   For Prob. 3.60.

3.61   Calculate the current gain i_o/i_s in the circuit of Fig. 3.102.

Figure 3.102   For Prob. 3.61.

3.62   Find the mesh currents i_1, i_2, and i_3 in the network of Fig. 3.103.

Figure 3.103   For Prob. 3.62.

3.63   Find v_x and i_x in the circuit shown in Fig. 3.104.

Figure 3.104   For Prob. 3.63.

3.64   Find v_o and i_o in the circuit of Fig. 3.105.

Figure 3.105   For Prob. 3.64.

3.65   Use *MATLAB* to solve for the mesh currents in the circuit of Fig. 3.106.

Figure 3.106   For Prob. 3.65.

3.66   Find I_o in the circuit in Fig. 3.107 using mesh analysis. You may use *MATLAB*.

Figure 3.107   For Prob. 3.66.

Section 3.6   Nodal and Mesh Analyses by Inspection

3.67   Obtain the node-voltage equations for the circuit in Fig. 3.108 by inspection. Determine the node voltages v_1 and v_2.

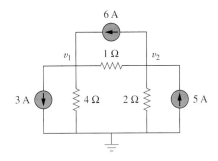

Figure 3.108   For Prob. 3.67.

3.68   By inspection, write the node-voltage equations for the circuit in Fig. 3.109 and obtain the node voltages.

Figure 3.109   For Prob. 3.68.

3.69   For the circuit shown in Fig. 3.110, write the node-voltage equations by inspection.

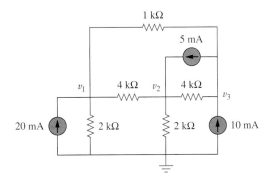

Figure 3.110   For Prob. 3.69.

3.70 Write the node-voltage equations of the circuit in Fig. 3.111 by inspection.

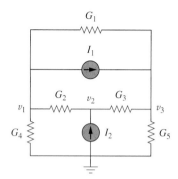

Figure 3.111   For Prob. 3.70.

3.71 Obtain the mesh-current equations for the circuit in Fig. 3.112 by inspection. Calculate the power absorbed by the 8-Ω resistor.

Figure 3.112   For Prob. 3.71.

3.72 By inspection, write the mesh-current equations for the circuit in Fig. 3.113.

Figure 3.113   For Prob. 3.72.

3.73 Write the mesh-current equations for the circuit in Fig. 3.114.

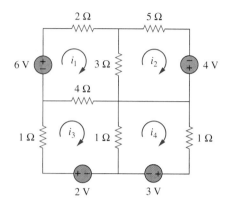

Figure 3.114   For Prob. 3.73.

3.74 By inspection, obtain the mesh-current equations for the circuit in Fig. 3.115.

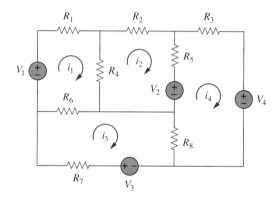

Figure 3.115   For Prob. 3.74.

Section 3.8   Circuit Analysis with *PSpice*

3.75 Use *PSpice* to solve Prob. 3.58.

3.76 Use *PSpice* to solve Prob. 3.27.

3.77 Rework Prob. 3.67 using *PSpice*.

3.78 Solve Prob. 3.20 using *PSpice*.

3.79 Rework Prob. 3.28 using *PSpice*.

3.80 Find the nodal voltages v_1 through v_4 in the circuit in Fig. 3.116 using *PSpice*.

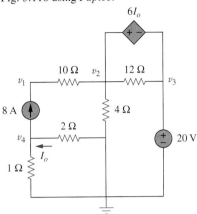

Figure 3.116   For Prob. 3.80.

3.81 Use *PSpice* to solve the problem in Example 3.4.

3.82 If the Schematics Netlist for a network is as follows, draw the network.

```
R_R1    1   2   2K
R_R2    2   0   4K
R_R3    3   0   8K
R_R4    3   4   6K
R_R5    1   3   3K
V_VS    4   0   DC      100
I_IS    0   1   DC      4
F_F1    1   3   VF_F1   2
VF_F1   5   0   0V
E_E1    3   2   1       3    3
```

3.83 The following program is the Schematics Netlist of a particular circuit. Draw the circuit and determine the voltage at node 2.

```
R_R1    1   2   20
R_R2    2   0   50
R_R3    2   3   70
R_R4    3   0   30
V_VS    1   0   20V
I_IS    2   0   DC    2A
```

Section 3.9   Applications

3.84 Calculate v_o and I_o in the circuit of Fig. 3.117.

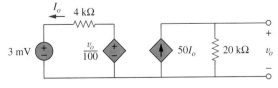

Figure 3.117   For Prob. 3.84.

3.85 An audio amplifier with a resistance of 9 Ω supplies power to a speaker. What should be the resistance of the speaker for maximum power to be delivered?

3.86 For the simplified transistor circuit of Fig. 3.118, calculate the voltage v_o.

Figure 3.118   For Prob. 3.86.

3.87 For the circuit in Fig. 3.119, find the gain v_o/v_s.

Figure 3.119   For Prob. 3.87.

*3.88 Determine the gain v_o/v_s of the transistor amplifier circuit in Fig. 3.120.

Figure 3.120   For Prob. 3.88.

3.89 For the simple transistor circuit of Fig. 3.121, let $\beta = 75$, $V_{BE} = 0.7$ V. What value of v_i is required to give a collector-emitter voltage of 2 V?

Figure 3.121   For Prob. 3.89.

3.90   Calculate v_s for the transistor in Fig. 3.122 given that $v_o = 4$ V, $\beta = 150$, $V_{BE} = 0.7$ V.

Figure 3.122   For Prob. 3.90.

3.91   For the transistor circuit of Fig. 3.123, find I_B, V_{CE}, and v_o. Take $\beta = 200$, $V_{BE} = 0.7$ V.

Figure 3.123   For Prob. 3.91.

3.92   Find I_B and V_C for the circuit in Fig. 3.124. Let $\beta = 100$, $V_{BE} = 0.7$ V.

Figure 3.124   For Prob. 3.92.

COMPREHENSIVE PROBLEM

*3.93   Rework Example 3.11 with hand calculation.

C H A P T E R　4

CIRCUIT THEOREMS

If it can't be expressed in figures, it is not science; it is opinion.

—Lazarus Long

Enhancing Your Career

Enhancing Your Communication Skill　Taking a course in circuit analysis is one step in preparing yourself for a career in electrical engineering. Enhancing your communication skill while in school should also be part of that preparation, as a large part of your time will be spent communicating.

People in industry have complained again and again that graduating engineers are ill-prepared in written and oral communication. An engineer who communicates effectively becomes a valuable asset.

You can probably speak or write easily and quickly. But how *effectively* do you communicate? The art of effective communication is of the utmost importance to your success as an engineer.

For engineers in industry, communication is key to promotability. Consider the result of a survey of U.S. corporations that asked what factors influence managerial promotion. The survey includes a listing of 22 personal qualities and their importance in advancement. You may be surprised to note that "technical skill based on experience" placed fourth from the bottom. Attributes such as self-confidence, ambition, flexibility, maturity, ability to make sound decisions, getting things done with and through people, and capacity for hard work all ranked higher. At the top of the list was "ability to communicate." The higher your professional career progresses, the more you will need to communicate. Therefore, you should regard effective communication as an important tool in your engineering tool chest.

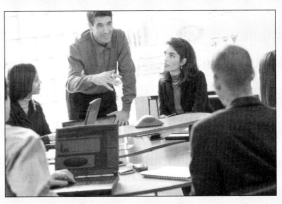

Ability to communicate effectively is regarded by many as the most important step to an executive promotion.
© *Jon Feingersh/CORBIS*

Learning to communicate effectively is a lifelong task you should always work toward. The best time to begin is while still in school. Continually look for opportunities to develop and strengthen your reading, writing, listening, and speaking skills. You can do this through classroom presentations, team projects, active participation in student organizations, and enrollment in communication courses. The risks are less now than later in the workplace.

4.1   INTRODUCTION

A major advantage of analyzing circuits using Kirchhoff's laws as we did in Chapter 3 is that we can analyze a circuit without tampering with its original configuration. A major disadvantage of this approach is that, for a large, complex circuit, tedious computation is involved.

The growth in areas of application of electric circuits has led to an evolution from simple to complex circuits. To handle the complexity, engineers over the years have developed some theorems to simplify circuit analysis. Such theorems include Thevenin's and Norton's theorems. Since these theorems are applicable to *linear* circuits, we first discuss the concept of circuit linearity. In addition to circuit theorems, we discuss the concepts of superposition, source transformation, and maximum power transfer in this chapter. The concepts we develop are applied in the last section to source modeling and resistance measurement.

4.2   LINEARITY PROPERTY

Linearity is the property of an element describing a linear relationship between cause and effect. Although the property applies to many circuit elements, we shall limit its applicability to resistors in this chapter. The property is a combination of both the homogeneity (scaling) property and the additivity property.

The homogeneity property requires that if the input (also called the *excitation*) is multiplied by a constant, then the output (also called the *response*) is multiplied by the same constant. For a resistor, for example, Ohm's law relates the input i to the output v,

$$v = iR \tag{4.1}$$

If the current is increased by a constant k, then the voltage increases correspondingly by k, that is,

$$\boxed{kiR = kv} \tag{4.2}$$

The additivity property requires that the response to a sum of inputs is the sum of the responses to each input applied separately. Using the voltage-current relationship of a resistor, if

$$v_1 = i_1 R \tag{4.3a}$$

and

$$v_2 = i_2 R \tag{4.3b}$$

then applying $(i_1 + i_2)$ gives

$$\boxed{v = (i_1 + i_2)R = i_1 R + i_2 R = v_1 + v_2} \tag{4.4}$$

We say that a resistor is a linear element because the voltage-current relationship satisfies both the homogeneity and the additivity properties.

In general, a circuit is linear if it is both additive and homogeneous. A linear circuit consists of only linear elements, linear dependent sources, and independent sources.

A linear circuit is one whose output is linearly related
(or directly proportional) to its input.

For example, when current i_1 flows through resistor R, the power is $p_1 = Ri_1^2$, and when current i_2 flows through R, the power is $p_2 = Ri_2^2$. If current $i_1 + i_2$ flows through R, the power absorbed is $p_3 = R(i_1 + i_2)^2 = Ri_1^2 + Ri_2^2 + 2Ri_1i_2 \neq p_1 + p_2$. Thus, the power relation is nonlinear.

Throughout this book we consider only linear circuits. Note that since $p = i^2R = v^2/R$ (making it a quadratic function rather than a linear one), the relationship between power and voltage (or current) is nonlinear. Therefore, the theorems covered in this chapter are not applicable to power.

To illustrate the linearity principle, consider the linear circuit shown in Fig. 4.1. The linear circuit has no independent sources inside it. It is excited by a voltage source v_s, which serves as the input. The circuit is terminated by a load R. We may take the current i through R as the output. Suppose $v_s = 10$ V gives $i = 2$ A. According to the linearity principle, $v_s = 1$ V will give $i = 0.2$ A. By the same token, $i = 1$ mA must be due to $v_s = 5$ mV.

Figure 4.1   A linear circuit with input v_s and output i.

EXAMPLE 4.1

For the circuit in Fig. 4.2, find I_o when $v_s = 12$ V and $v_s = 24$ V.

Solution:

Applying KVL to the two loops, we obtain

$$12i_1 - 4i_2 + v_s = 0 \qquad (4.1.1)$$

$$-4i_1 + 16i_2 - 3v_x - v_s = 0 \qquad (4.1.2)$$

But $v_x = 2i_1$. Equation (4.1.2) becomes

$$-10i_1 + 16i_2 - v_s = 0 \qquad (4.1.3)$$

Adding Eqs. (4.1.1) and (4.1.3) yields

$$2i_1 + 12i_2 = 0 \qquad \Longrightarrow \qquad i_1 = -6i_2$$

Substituting this in Eq. (4.1.1), we get

$$-76i_2 + v_s = 0 \qquad \Longrightarrow \qquad i_2 = \frac{v_s}{76}$$

When $v_s = 12$ V,

$$I_o = i_2 = \frac{12}{76} \text{ A}$$

When $v_s = 24$ V,

$$I_o = i_2 = \frac{24}{76} \text{ A}$$

showing that when the source value is doubled, I_o doubles.

Figure 4.2   For Example 4.1.

PRACTICE PROBLEM 4.1

Figure 4.3   For Practice Prob. 4.1.

For the circuit in Fig. 4.3, find v_o when $i_s = 15$ and $i_s = 30$ A.

Answer: 10 V, 20 V.

EXAMPLE 4.2

Assume $I_o = 1$ A and use linearity to find the actual value of I_o in the circuit in Fig. 4.4.

Figure 4.4   For Example 4.2.

Solution:

If $I_o = 1$ A, then $V_1 = (3+5)I_o = 8$ V and $I_1 = V_1/4 = 2$ A. Applying KCL at node 1 gives

$$I_2 = I_1 + I_o = 3 \text{ A}$$

$$V_2 = V_1 + 2I_2 = 8 + 6 = 14 \text{ V}, \qquad I_3 = \frac{V_2}{7} = 2 \text{ A}$$

Applying KCL at node 2 gives

$$I_4 = I_3 + I_2 = 5 \text{ A}$$

Therefore, $I_s = 5$ A. This shows that assuming $I_o = 1$ gives $I_s = 5$ A; the actual source current of 15 A will give $I_o = 3$ A as the actual value.

PRACTICE PROBLEM 4.2

Figure 4.5   For Practice Prob. 4.2.

Assume that $V_o = 1$ V and use linearity to calculate the actual value of V_o in the circuit of Fig. 4.5.

Answer: 4 V.

4.3   SUPERPOSITION

If a circuit has two or more independent sources, one way to determine the value of a specific variable (voltage or current) is to use nodal or mesh analysis as in Chapter 3. Another way is to determine the contribution of each independent source to the variable and then add them up. The latter approach is known as the *superposition*.

The idea of superposition rests on the linearity property.

Superposition is not limited to circuit analysis but is applicable in many fields where cause and effect bear a linear relationship to one another.

> The superposition principle states that the voltage across (or current through) an element in a linear circuit is the algebraic sum of the voltages across (or currents through) that element due to each independent source acting alone.

The principle of superposition helps us to analyze a linear circuit with more than one independent source by calculating the contribution of each independent source separately. However, to apply the superposition principle, we must keep two things in mind:

Other terms such as *killed, made inactive, deadened,* or *set equal to zero* are often used to convey the same idea.

1. We consider one independent source at a time while all other independent sources are *turned off*. This implies that we replace every voltage source by 0 V (or a short circuit), and every current source by 0 A (or an open circuit). This way we obtain a simpler and more manageable circuit.

2. Dependent sources are left intact because they are controlled by circuit variables.

With these in mind, we apply the superposition principle in three steps:

> **Steps to Apply Superposition Principle:**
>
> 1. Turn off all independent sources except one source. Find the output (voltage or current) due to that active source using the techniques covered in Chapters 2 and 3.
> 2. Repeat step 1 for each of the other independent sources.
> 3. Find the total contribution by adding algebraically all the contributions due to the independent sources.

Analyzing a circuit using superposition has one major disadvantage: it may very likely involve more work. If the circuit has three independent sources, we may have to analyze three simpler circuits each providing the contribution due to the respective individual source. However, superposition does help reduce a complex circuit to simpler circuits through replacement of voltage sources by short circuits and of current sources by open circuits.

Keep in mind that superposition is based on linearity. For this reason, it is not applicable to the effect on power due to each source, because the power absorbed by a resistor depends on the square of the voltage or current. If the power value is needed, the current through (or voltage across) the element must be calculated first using superposition.

EXAMPLE 4.3

Use the superposition theorem to find v in the circuit in Fig. 4.6.

Figure 4.6   For Example 4.3.

(a)

(b)

Figure 4.7   For Example 4.3:
(a) calculating v_1, (b) calculating v_2.

Solution:

Since there are two sources, let

$$v = v_1 + v_2$$

where v_1 and v_2 are the contributions due to the 6-V voltage source and the 3-A current source, respectively. To obtain v_1, we set the current source to zero, as shown in Fig. 4.7(a). Applying KVL to the loop in Fig. 4.7(a) gives

$$12i_1 - 6 = 0 \qquad \Longrightarrow \qquad i_1 = 0.5 \text{ A}$$

Thus,

$$v_1 = 4i_1 = 2 \text{ V}$$

We may also use voltage division to get v_1 by writing

$$v_1 = \frac{4}{4 + 8}(6) = 2 \text{ V}$$

To get v_2, we set the voltage source to zero, as in Fig. 4.7(b). Using current division,

$$i_3 = \frac{8}{4 + 8}(3) = 2 \text{ A}$$

Hence,

$$v_2 = 4i_3 = 8 \text{ V}$$

And we find

$$v = v_1 + v_2 = 2 + 8 = 10 \text{ V}$$

PRACTICE PROBLEM 4.3

Figure 4.8   For Practice Prob. 4.3.

Using the superposition theorem, find v_o in the circuit in Fig. 4.8.

Answer: 12 V.

EXAMPLE 4.4

Figure 4.9   For Example 4.4.

Find i_o in the circuit in Fig. 4.9 using superposition.

Solution:

The circuit in Fig. 4.9 involves a dependent source, which must be left intact. We let

$$i_o = i_o' + i_o'' \tag{4.4.1}$$

where i_o' and i_o'' are due to the 4-A current source and 20-V voltage source respectively. To obtain i_o', we turn off the 20-V source so that we have the circuit in Fig. 4.10(a). We apply mesh analysis in order to obtain i_o'. For loop 1,

$$i_1 = 4 \text{ A} \tag{4.4.2}$$

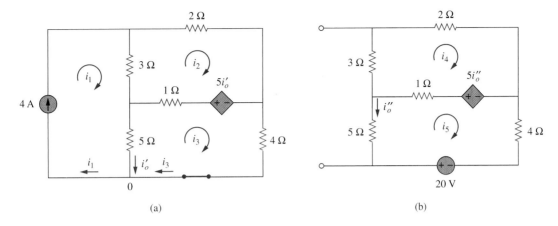

Figure 4.10   For Example 4.4: Applying superposition to (a) obtain i'_0, (b) obtain i''_0.

For loop 2,

$$-3i_1 + 6i_2 - 1i_3 - 5i'_o = 0 \qquad (4.4.3)$$

For loop 3,

$$-5i_1 - 1i_2 + 10i_3 + 5i'_o = 0 \qquad (4.4.4)$$

But at node 0,

$$i_3 = i_1 - i'_o = 4 - i'_o \qquad (4.4.5)$$

Substituting Eqs. (4.4.2) and (4.4.5) into Eqs. (4.4.3) and (4.4.4) gives two simultaneous equations

$$3i_2 - 2i'_o = 8 \qquad (4.4.6)$$

$$i_2 + 5i'_o = 20 \qquad (4.4.7)$$

which can be solved to get

$$i'_o = \frac{52}{17} \text{ A} \qquad (4.4.8)$$

To obtain i''_o, we turn off the 4-A current source so that the circuit becomes that shown in Fig. 4.10(b). For loop 4, KVL gives

$$6i_4 - i_5 - 5i''_o = 0 \qquad (4.4.9)$$

and for loop 5,

$$-i_4 + 10i_5 - 20 + 5i''_o = 0 \qquad (4.4.10)$$

But $i_5 = -i''_o$. Substituting this in Eqs. (4.4.9) and (4.4.10) gives

$$6i_4 - 4i''_o = 0 \qquad (4.4.11)$$

$$i_4 + 5i''_o = -20 \qquad (4.4.12)$$

which we solve to get

$$i''_o = -\frac{60}{17} \text{ A} \qquad (4.4.13)$$

Now substituting Eqs. (4.4.8) and (4.4.13) into Eq. (4.4.1) gives

$$i_o = -\frac{8}{17} = -0.4706 \text{ A}$$

PRACTICE PROBLEM 4.4

Figure 4.11   For Practice Prob. 4.4.

Use superposition to find v_x in the circuit in Fig. 4.11.

Answer: $v_x = 12.5$ V.

EXAMPLE 4.5

Figure 4.12   For Example 4.5.

For the circuit in Fig. 4.12, use the superposition theorem to find i.

Solution:

In this case, we have three sources. Let

$$i = i_1 + i_2 + i_3$$

where i_1, i_2, and i_3 are due to the 12-V, 24-V, and 3-A sources respectively. To get i_1, consider the circuit in Fig. 4.13(a). Combining 4 Ω (on the right-hand side) in series with 8 Ω gives 12 Ω. The 12 Ω in parallel with 4 Ω gives $12 \times 4/16 = 3$ Ω. Thus,

$$i_1 = \frac{12}{6} = 2 \text{ A}$$

To get i_2, consider the circuit in Fig. 4.13(b). Applying mesh analysis,

$$16i_a - 4i_b + 24 = 0 \quad \Longrightarrow \quad 4i_a - i_b = -6 \qquad (4.5.1)$$

$$7i_b - 4i_a = 0 \quad \Longrightarrow \quad i_a = \frac{7}{4}i_b \qquad (4.5.2)$$

Substituting Eq. (4.5.2) into Eq. (4.5.1) gives

$$i_2 = i_b = -1$$

To get i_3, consider the circuit in Fig. 4.13(c). Using nodal analysis,

$$3 = \frac{v_2}{8} + \frac{v_2 - v_1}{4} \quad \Longrightarrow \quad 24 = 3v_2 - 2v_1 \qquad (4.5.3)$$

$$\frac{v_2 - v_1}{4} = \frac{v_1}{4} + \frac{v_1}{3} \quad \Longrightarrow \quad v_2 = \frac{10}{3}v_1 \qquad (4.5.4)$$

Substituting Eq. (4.5.4) into Eq. (4.5.3) leads to $v_1 = 3$ and

$$i_3 = \frac{v_1}{3} = 1 \text{ A}$$

Thus,

$$i = i_1 + i_2 + i_3 = 2 - 1 + 1 = 2 \text{ A}$$

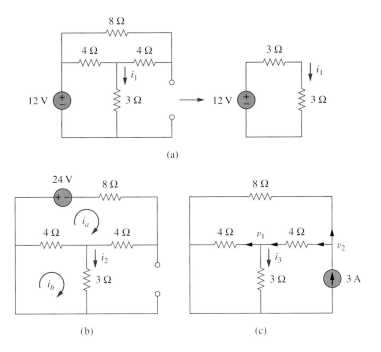

(a)

(b)   (c)

Figure 4.13   For Example 4.5.

4.5

Find I in the circuit in Fig. 4.14 using the superposition principle.

Figure 4.14   For Practice Prob. 4.5.

Answer: 0.75 A.

4.4 SOURCE TRANSFORMATION

We have noticed that series-parallel combination and wye-delta transformation help simplify circuits. *Source transformation* is another tool for simplifying circuits. Basic to these tools is the concept of *equivalence*. We recall that an equivalent circuit is one whose *v-i* characteristics are identical with the original circuit.

In Section 3.6, we saw that node-voltage (or mesh-current) equations can be obtained by mere inspection of a circuit when the sources are all independent current (or all independent voltage) sources. It is therefore expedient in circuit analysis to be able to substitute a voltage source in series with a resistor for a current source in parallel with a resistor, or vice versa, as shown in Fig. 4.15. Either substitution is known as a *source transformation*.

Figure 4.15   Transformation of independent sources.

A source transformation is the process of replacing a voltage source v_s in series with a resistor R by a current source i_s in parallel with a resistor R, or vice versa.

The two circuits in Fig. 4.15 are equivalent—provided they have the same voltage-current relation at terminals *a-b*. It is easy to show that they are indeed equivalent. If the sources are turned off, the equivalent resistance at terminals *a-b* in both circuits is R. Also, when terminals *a-b* are short-circuited, the short-circuit current flowing from *a* to *b* is $i_{sc} = v_s/R$ in the circuit on the left-hand side and $i_{sc} = i_s$ for the circuit on the right-hand side. Thus, $v_s/R = i_s$ in order for the two circuits to be equivalent. Hence, source transformation requires that

$$v_s = i_s R \qquad \text{or} \qquad i_s = \frac{v_s}{R} \qquad (4.5)$$

Source transformation also applies to dependent sources, provided we carefully handle the dependent variable. As shown in Fig. 4.16, a dependent voltage source in series with a resistor can be transformed to a dependent current source in parallel with the resistor or vice versa where we make sure that Eq. (4.5) is satisfied.

Figure 4.16   Transformation of dependent sources.

Like the wye-delta transformation we studied in Chapter 2, a source transformation does not affect the remaining part of the circuit. When applicable, source transformation is a powerful tool that allows circuit manipulations to ease circuit analysis. However, we should keep the following points in mind when dealing with source transformation.

1. Note from Fig. 4.15 (or Fig. 4.16) that the arrow of the current source is directed toward the positive terminal of the voltage source.

2. Note from Eq. (4.5) that source transformation is not possible when $R = 0$, which is the case with an ideal voltage source. However, for a practical, nonideal voltage source, $R \neq 0$. Similarly, an ideal current source with $R = \infty$ cannot be replaced by a finite voltage source. More will be said on ideal and nonideal sources in Section 4.10.1.

EXAMPLE 4.6

Use source transformation to find v_o in the circuit in Fig. 4.17.

Solution:

We first transform the current and voltage sources to obtain the circuit in Fig. 4.18(a). Combining the 4-Ω and 2-Ω resistors in series and transforming the 12-V voltage source gives us Fig. 4.18(b). We now combine the 3-Ω and 6-Ω resistors in parallel to get 2-Ω. We also combine the 2-A and 4-A current sources to get a 2-A source. Thus, by repeatedly applying source transformations, we obtain the circuit in Fig. 4.18(c).

Figure 4.17   For Example 4.6.

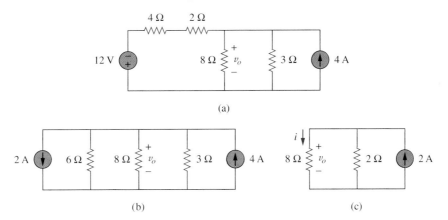

(a)

(b)   (c)

Figure 4.18   For Example 4.6.

We use current division in Fig. 4.18(c) to get

$$i = \frac{2}{2+8}(2) = 0.4$$

and

$$v_o = 8i = 8(0.4) = 3.2 \text{ V}$$

Alternatively, since the 8-Ω and 2-Ω resistors in Fig. 4.18(c) are in parallel, they have the same voltage v_o across them. Hence,

$$v_o = (8 \parallel 2)(2 \text{ A}) = \frac{8 \times 2}{10}(2) = 3.2 \text{ V}$$

PRACTICE PROBLEM 4.6

Find i_o in the circuit of Fig. 4.19 using source transformation.

Figure 4.19   For Practice Prob. 4.6.

Answer: 1.78 A.

EXAMPLE 4.7

Figure 4.20   For Example 4.7.

Find v_x in Fig. 4.20 using source transformation.

Solution:

The circuit in Fig. 4.20 involves a voltage-controlled dependent current source. We transform this dependent current source as well as the 6-V independent voltage source as shown in Fig. 4.21(a). The 18-V voltage source is not transformed because it is not connected in series with any resistor. The two 2-Ω resistors in parallel combine to give a 1-Ω resistor, which is in parallel with the 3-A current source. The current source is transformed to a voltage source as shown in Fig. 4.21(b). Notice that the terminals for v_x are intact. Applying KVL around the loop in Fig. 4.21(b) gives

$$-3 + 5i + v_x + 18 = 0 \tag{4.7.1}$$

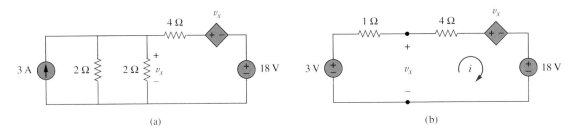

                (a)   (b)

Figure 4.21   For Example 4.7: Applying source transformation to the circuit in Fig. 4.20.

Applying KVL to the loop containing only the 3-V voltage source, the 1-Ω resistor, and v_x yields

$$-3 + 1i + v_x = 0 \qquad \Longrightarrow \qquad v_x = 3 - i \tag{4.7.2}$$

Substituting this into Eq. (4.7.1), we obtain

$$15 + 5i + 3 - i = 0 \qquad \Longrightarrow \qquad i = -4.5 \text{ A}$$

Alternatively, we may apply KVL to the loop containing v_x, the 4-Ω resistor, the voltage-controlled dependent voltage source, and the 18-V voltage source in Fig. 4.21(b). We obtain

$$-v_x + 4i + v_x + 18 = 0 \quad \Longrightarrow \quad i = -4.5 \text{ A}$$

Thus, $v_x = 3 - i = 7.5$ V.

Use source transformation to find i_x in the circuit shown in Fig. 4.22.

Answer: 1.176 A.

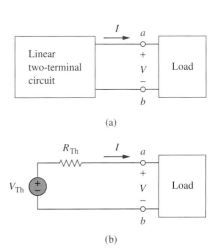

Figure 4.22   For Practice Prob. 4.7.

4.5   THEVENIN'S THEOREM

It often occurs in practice that a particular element in a circuit is variable (usually called the *load*) while other elements are fixed. As a typical example, a household outlet terminal may be connected to different appliances constituting a variable load. Each time the variable element is changed, the entire circuit has to be analyzed all over again. To avoid this problem, Thevenin's theorem provides a technique by which the fixed part of the circuit is replaced by an equivalent circuit.

According to Thevenin's theorem, the linear circuit in Fig. 4.23(a) can be replaced by that in Fig. 4.23(b). (The load in Fig. 4.23 may be a single resistor or another circuit.) The circuit to the left of the terminals *a-b* in Fig. 4.23(b) is known as the *Thevenin equivalent circuit*; it was developed in 1883 by M. Leon Thevenin (1857–1926), a French telegraph engineer.

> Thevenin's theorem states that a linear two-terminal circuit can be replaced by an equivalent circuit consisting of a voltage source V_{Th} in series with a resistor R_{Th}, where V_{Th} is the open-circuit voltage at the terminals and R_{Th} is the input or equivalent resistance at the terminals when the independent sources are turned off.

Figure 4.23   Replacing a linear two-terminal circuit by its Thevenin equivalent: (a) original circuit, (b) the Thevenin equivalent circuit.

The proof of the theorem will be given later, in Section 4.7. Our major concern right now is how to find the Thevenin equivalent voltage V_{Th} and resistance R_{Th}. To do so, suppose the two circuits in Fig. 4.23 are equivalent. Two circuits are said to be *equivalent* if they have the same voltage-current relation at their terminals. Let us find out what will make the two circuits in Fig. 4.23 equivalent. If the terminals *a-b* are made open-circuited (by removing the load), no current flows, so that the open-circuit voltage across the terminals *a-b* in Fig. 4.23(a) must be equal to the voltage source V_{Th} in Fig. 4.23(b), since the two circuits are equivalent. Thus V_{Th} is the open-circuit voltage across the terminals as shown in Fig. 4.24(a); that is,

$$V_{Th} = v_{oc} \tag{4.6}$$

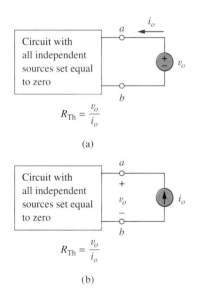

Figure 4.24   Finding V_{Th} and R_{Th}.

Again, with the load disconnected and terminals a-b open-circuited, we turn off all independent sources. The input resistance (or equivalent resistance) of the dead circuit at the terminals a-b in Fig. 4.23(a) must be equal to R_{Th} in Fig. 4.23(b) because the two circuits are equivalent. Thus, R_{Th} is the input resistance at the terminals when the independent sources are turned off, as shown in Fig. 4.24(b); that is,

$$R_{Th} = R_{in} \tag{4.7}$$

To apply this idea in finding the Thevenin resistance R_{Th}, we need to consider two cases.

$\boxed{\text{CASE } \mathbf{1}}$ If the network has no dependent sources, we turn off all independent sources. R_{Th} is the input resistance of the network looking between terminals a and b, as shown in Fig. 4.24(b).

$\boxed{\text{CASE } \mathbf{2}}$ If the network has dependent sources, we turn off all independent sources. As with superposition, dependent sources are not to be turned off because they are controlled by circuit variables. We apply a voltage source v_o at terminals a and b and determine the resulting current i_o. Then $R_{Th} = v_o/i_o$, as shown in Fig. 4.25(a). Alternatively, we may insert a current source i_o at terminals a-b as shown in Fig. 4.25(b) and find the terminal voltage v_o. Again $R_{Th} = v_o/i_o$. Either of the two approaches will give the same result. In either approach we may assume any value of v_o and i_o. For example, we may use $v_o = 1$ V or $i_o = 1$ A, or even use unspecified values of v_o or i_o.

It often occurs that R_{Th} takes a negative value. In this case, the negative resistance ($v = -iR$) implies that the circuit is supplying power. This is possible in a circuit with dependent sources; Example 4.10 will illustrate this.

Thevenin's theorem is very important in circuit analysis. It helps simplify a circuit. A large circuit may be replaced by a single independent voltage source and a single resistor. This replacement technique is a powerful tool in circuit design.

As mentioned earlier, a linear circuit with a variable load can be replaced by the Thevenin equivalent, exclusive of the load. The equivalent

Figure 4.25   Finding R_{Th} when circuit has dependent sources.

Later we will see that an alternative way of finding R_{Th} is $R_{Th} = v_{oc}/i_{sc}$.

network behaves the same way externally as the original circuit. Consider a linear circuit terminated by a load R_L, as shown in Fig. 4.26(a). The current I_L through the load and the voltage V_L across the load are easily determined once the Thevenin equivalent of the circuit at the load's terminals is obtained, as shown in Fig. 4.26(b). From Fig. 4.26(b), we obtain

$$I_L = \frac{V_{Th}}{R_{Th} + R_L} \qquad (4.8a)$$

$$V_L = R_L I_L = \frac{R_L}{R_{Th} + R_L} V_{Th} \qquad (4.8b)$$

Note from Fig. 4.26(b) that the Thevenin equivalent is a simple voltage divider, yielding V_L by mere inspection.

Figure 4.26   A circuit with a load: (a) original circuit, (b) Thevenin equivalent.

EXAMPLE 4.8

Find the Thevenin equivalent circuit of the circuit shown in Fig. 4.27, to the left of the terminals a-b. Then find the current through $R_L = 6, 16,$ and 36 Ω.

Solution:

We find R_{Th} by turning off the 32-V voltage source (replacing it with a short circuit) and the 2-A current source (replacing it with an open circuit). The circuit becomes what is shown in Fig. 4.28(a). Thus,

$$R_{Th} = 4 \parallel 12 + 1 = \frac{4 \times 12}{16} + 1 = 4 \ \Omega$$

Figure 4.27   For Example 4.8.

Figure 4.28   For Example 4.8: (a) finding R_{Th}, (b) finding V_{Th}.

To find V_{Th}, consider the circuit in Fig. 4.28(b). Applying mesh analysis to the two loops, we obtain

$$-32 + 4i_1 + 12(i_1 - i_2) = 0, \qquad i_2 = -2 \ \text{A}$$

Solving for i_1, we get $i_1 = 0.5$ A. Thus,

$$V_{Th} = 12(i_1 - i_2) = 12(0.5 + 2.0) = 30 \ \text{V}$$

Alternatively, it is even easier to use nodal analysis. We ignore the 1-Ω resistor since no current flows through it. At the top node, KCL gives

$$\frac{32 - V_{Th}}{4} + 2 = \frac{V_{Th}}{12}$$

or

$$96 - 3V_{Th} + 24 = V_{Th} \implies V_{Th} = 30 \text{ V}$$

as obtained before. We could also use source transformation to find V_{Th}.

The Thevenin equivalent circuit is shown in Fig. 4.29. The current through R_L is

$$I_L = \frac{V_{Th}}{R_{Th} + R_L} = \frac{30}{4 + R_L}$$

When $R_L = 6$,

$$I_L = \frac{30}{10} = 3 \text{ A}$$

When $R_L = 16$,

$$I_L = \frac{30}{20} = 1.5 \text{ A}$$

When $R_L = 36$,

$$I_L = \frac{30}{40} = 0.75 \text{ A}$$

Figure 4.29 The Thevenin equivalent circuit for Example 4.8.

PRACTICE PROBLEM 4.8

Using Thevenin's theorem, find the equivalent circuit to the left of the terminals in the circuit in Fig. 4.30. Then find I.

Figure 4.30 For Practice Prob. 4.8.

Answer: $V_{Th} = 6$ V, $R_{Th} = 3$ Ω, $I = 1.5$ A.

EXAMPLE 4.9

Find the Thevenin equivalent of the circuit in Fig. 4.31.

Solution:

This circuit contains a dependent source, unlike the circuit in the previous example. To find R_{Th}, we set the independent source equal to zero but leave the dependent source alone. Because of the presence of the dependent source, however, we excite the network with a voltage source v_o connected to the terminals as indicated in Fig. 4.32(a). We may set $v_o = 1$ V to ease calculation, since the circuit is linear. Our goal is to find the current i_o through the terminals, and then obtain $R_{Th} = 1/i_o$. (Alternatively, we may insert a 1-A current source, find the corresponding voltage v_o, and obtain $R_{Th} = v_o/1$.)

Figure 4.31   For Example 4.9.

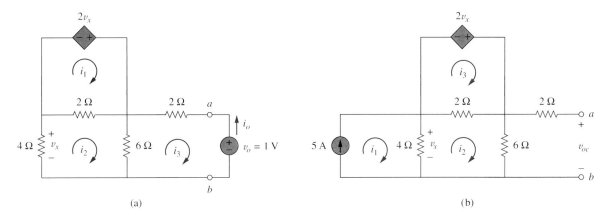

Figure 4.32   Finding R_{Th} and V_{Th} for Example 4.9.

Applying mesh analysis to loop 1 in the circuit in Fig. 4.32(a) results in

$$-2v_x + 2(i_1 - i_2) = 0 \quad \text{or} \quad v_x = i_1 - i_2$$

But $-4i_2 = v_x = i_1 - i_2$; hence,

$$i_1 = -3i_2 \qquad (4.9.1)$$

For loops 2 and 3, applying KVL produces

$$4i_2 + 2(i_2 - i_1) + 6(i_2 - i_3) = 0 \qquad (4.9.2)$$
$$6(i_3 - i_2) + 2i_3 + 1 = 0 \qquad (4.9.3)$$

Solving these equations gives

$$i_3 = -\frac{1}{6} \text{ A}$$

But $i_o = -i_3 = 1/6$ A. Hence,

$$R_{Th} = \frac{1 \text{ V}}{i_o} = 6 \text{ }\Omega$$

To get V_{Th}, we find v_{oc} in the circuit of Fig. 4.32(b). Applying mesh analysis, we get

$$i_1 = 5 \tag{4.9.4}$$

$$-2v_x + 2(i_3 - i_2) = 0 \quad\Longrightarrow\quad v_x = i_3 - i_2 \tag{4.9.5}$$

$$4(i_2 - i_1) + 2(i_2 - i_3) + 6i_2 = 0$$

or

$$12i_2 - 4i_1 - 2i_3 = 0 \tag{4.9.6}$$

But $4(i_1 - i_2) = v_x$. Solving these equations leads to $i_2 = 10/3$. Hence,

$$V_{\text{Th}} = v_{oc} = 6i_2 = 20 \text{ V}$$

The Thevenin equivalent is as shown in Fig. 4.33.

Figure 4.33   The Thevenin equivalent of the circuit in Fig. 4.31.

PRACTICE PROBLEM 4.9

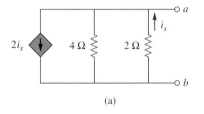

Figure 4.34   For Practice Prob. 4.9.

Find the Thevenin equivalent circuit of the circuit in Fig. 4.34 to the left of the terminals.

Answer: $V_{\text{Th}} = 5.33$ V, $R_{\text{Th}} = 0.44$ Ω.

EXAMPLE 4.10

Figure 4.35   For Example 4.10.

Determine the Thevenin equivalent of the circuit in Fig. 4.35(a).

Solution:

Since the circuit in Fig. 4.35(a) has no independent sources, $V_{\text{Th}} = 0$ V. To find R_{Th}, it is best to apply a current source i_o at the terminals as shown in Fig. 4.35(b). Applying nodal analysis gives

$$i_o + i_x = 2i_x + \frac{v_o}{4} \tag{4.10.1}$$

But

$$i_x = \frac{0 - v_o}{2} = -\frac{v_o}{2} \tag{4.10.2}$$

Substituting Eq. (4.10.2) into Eq. (4.10.1) yields

$$i_o = i_x + \frac{v_o}{4} = -\frac{v_o}{2} + \frac{v_o}{4} = -\frac{v_o}{4} \quad \text{or} \quad v_o = -4i_o$$

Thus,

$$R_{\text{Th}} = \frac{v_o}{i_o} = -4 \ \Omega$$

The negative value of the resistance tells us that, according to the passive sign convention, the circuit in Fig. 4.35(a) is supplying power. Of course, the resistors in Fig. 4.35(a) cannot supply power (they absorb power); it is the dependent source that supplies the power. This is an example of how a dependent source and resistors could be used to simulate negative resistance.

PRACTICE PROBLEM 4.10

Obtain the Thevenin equivalent of the circuit in Fig. 4.36.

Answer: $V_{\text{Th}} = 0$ V, $R_{\text{Th}} = -7.5$ Ω.

Figure 4.36   For Practice Prob. 4.10.

4.6   NORTON'S THEOREM

In 1926, about 43 years after Thevenin published his theorem, E. L. Norton, an American engineer at Bell Telephone Laboratories, proposed a similar theorem.

> **Norton's theorem** states that a linear two-terminal circuit can be replaced by an equivalent circuit consisting of a current source I_N in parallel with a resistor R_N, where I_N is the short-circuit current through the terminals and R_N is the input or equivalent resistance at the terminals when the independent sources are turned off.

Thus, the circuit in Fig. 4.37(a) can be replaced by the one in Fig. 4.37(b).

The proof of Norton's theorem will be given in the next section. For now, we are mainly concerned with how to get R_N and I_N. We find R_N in the same way we find R_{Th}. In fact, from what we know about source transformation, the Thevenin and Norton resistances are equal; that is,

$$R_N = R_{\text{Th}} \tag{4.9}$$

To find the Norton current I_N, we determine the short-circuit current flowing from terminal a to b in both circuits in Fig. 4.37. It is evident that the short-circuit current in Fig. 4.37(b) is I_N. This must be the same short-circuit current from terminal a to b in Fig. 4.37(a), since the two circuits are equivalent. Thus,

$$I_N = i_{sc} \tag{4.10}$$

shown in Fig. 4.38. Dependent and independent sources are treated the same way as in Thevenin's theorem.

Observe the close relationship between Norton's and Thevenin's theorems: $R_N = R_{\text{Th}}$ as in Eq. (4.9), and

$$I_N = \frac{V_{\text{Th}}}{R_{\text{Th}}} \tag{4.11}$$

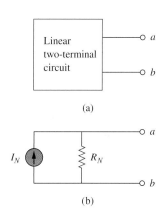

(a)

(b)

Figure 4.37   (a) Original circuit, (b) Norton equivalent circuit.

Figure 4.38   Finding Norton current I_N.

The Thevenin and Norton equivalent circuits are related by a source transformation.

This is essentially source transformation. For this reason, source transformation is often called Thevenin-Norton transformation.

Since V_{Th}, I_N, and R_{Th} are related according to Eq. (4.11), to determine the Thevenin or Norton equivalent circuit requires that we find:

- The open-circuit voltage v_{oc} across terminals a and b.
- The short-circuit current i_{sc} at terminals a and b.
- The equivalent or input resistance R_{in} at terminals a and b when all independent sources are turned off.

We can calculate any two of the three using the method that takes the least effort and use them to get the third using Ohm's law. Example 4.11 will illustrate this. Also, since

$$V_{\text{Th}} = v_{oc} \tag{4.12a}$$

$$I_N = i_{sc} \tag{4.12b}$$

$$R_{\text{Th}} = \frac{v_{oc}}{i_{sc}} = R_N \tag{4.12c}$$

the open-circuit and short-circuit tests are sufficient to find any Thevenin or Norton equivalent.

EXAMPLE 4.11

Figure 4.39   For Example 4.11.

Find the Norton equivalent circuit of the circuit in Fig. 4.39.

Solution:

We find R_N in the same way we find R_{Th} in the Thevenin equivalent circuit. Set the independent sources equal to zero. This leads to the circuit in Fig. 4.40(a), from which we find R_N. Thus,

$$R_N = 5 \parallel (8 + 4 + 8) = 5 \parallel 20 = \frac{20 \times 5}{25} = 4 \; \Omega$$

To find I_N, we short-circuit terminals a and b, as shown in Fig. 4.40(b). We ignore the 5-Ω resistor because it has been short-circuited. Applying mesh analysis, we obtain

$$i_1 = 2 \text{ A}, \qquad 20i_2 - 4i_1 - 12 = 0$$

From these equations, we obtain

$$i_2 = 1 \text{ A} = i_{sc} = I_N$$

Alternatively, we may determine I_N from $V_{\text{Th}}/R_{\text{Th}}$. We obtain V_{Th} as the open-circuit voltage across terminals a and b in Fig. 4.40(c). Using mesh analysis, we obtain

$$i_3 = 2 \text{ A}$$

$$25i_4 - 4i_3 - 12 = 0 \qquad \Longrightarrow \qquad i_4 = 0.8 \text{ A}$$

and

$$v_{oc} = V_{\text{Th}} = 5i_4 = 4 \text{ V}$$

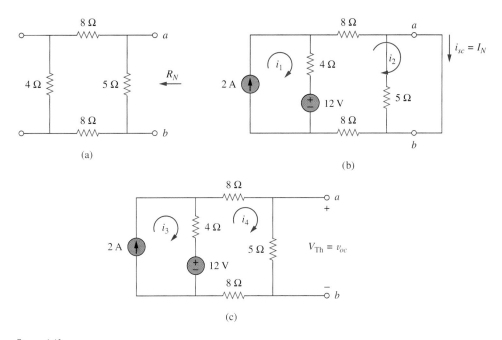

Figure 4.40   For Example 4.11; finding: (a) R_N, (b) $I_N = i_{sc}$, (c) $V_{Th} = v_{oc}$.

Hence,

$$I_N = \frac{V_{Th}}{R_{Th}} = \frac{4}{4} = 1 \text{ A}$$

as obtained previously. This also serves to confirm Eq. (4.12c) that $R_{Th} = v_{oc}/i_{sc} = 4/1 = 4 \ \Omega$. Thus, the Norton equivalent circuit is as shown in Fig. 4.41.

Figure 4.41   Norton equivalent of the circuit in Fig. 4.39.

PRACTICE PROBLEM 4.11

Find the Norton equivalent circuit for the circuit in Fig. 4.42.

Answer: $R_N = 3 \ \Omega$, $I_N = 4.5 \text{ A}$.

Figure 4.42   For Practice Prob. 4.11.

EXAMPLE 4.12

Using Norton's theorem, find R_N and I_N of the circuit in Fig. 4.43 at terminals a-b.

Solution:

To find R_N, we set the independent voltage source equal to zero and connect a voltage source of $v_o = 1$ V (or any unspecified voltage v_o) to

Figure 4.43   For Example 4.12.

the terminals. We obtain the circuit in Fig. 4.44(a). We ignore the 4-Ω resistor because it is short-circuited. Also due to the short circuit, the 5-Ω resistor, the voltage source, and the dependent current source are all in parallel. Hence, $i_x = 0$. At node a, $i_o = \frac{1v}{5\Omega} = 0.2$ A, and

$$R_N = \frac{v_o}{i_o} = \frac{1}{0.2} = 5 \; \Omega$$

To find I_N, we short-circuit terminals a and b and find the current i_{sc}, as indicated in Fig. 4.44(b). Note from this figure that the 4-Ω resistor, the 10-V voltage source, the 5-Ω resistor, and the dependent current source are all in parallel. Hence,

$$i_x = \frac{10}{4} = 2.5 \; A$$

At node a, KCL gives

$$i_{sc} = \frac{10}{5} + 2i_x = 2 + 2(2.5) = 7 \; A$$

Thus,

$$I_N = 7 \; A$$

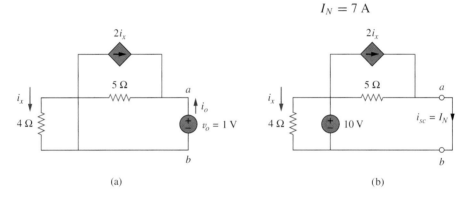

Figure 4.44   For Example 4.12: (a) finding R_N, (b) finding I_N.

PRACTICE PROBLEM 4.12

Figure 4.45   For Practice Prob. 4.12.

Find the Norton equivalent circuit of the circuit in Fig. 4.45.

Answer: $R_N = 1 \; \Omega$, $I_N = 10$ A.

†4.7 DERIVATIONS OF THEVENIN'S AND NORTON'S THEOREMS

In this section, we will prove Thevenin's and Norton's theorems using the superposition principle.

Consider the linear circuit in Fig. 4.46(a). It is assumed that the circuit contains resistors, and dependent and independent sources. We have access to the circuit via terminals a and b, through which current from an external source is applied. Our objective is to ensure that the voltage-current relation at terminals a and b is identical to that of the Thevenin equivalent in Fig. 4.46(b). For the sake of simplicity, suppose the linear circuit in Fig. 4.46(a) contains two independent voltage sources v_{s1} and v_{s2} and two independent current sources i_{s1} and i_{s2}. We may obtain any circuit variable, such as the terminal voltage v, by applying superposition. That is, we consider the contribution due to each independent source including the external source i. By superposition, the terminal voltage v is

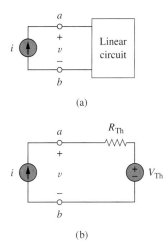

(a)

(b)

Figure 4.46   Derivation of Thevenin equivalent: (a) a current-driven circuit, (b) its Thevenin equivalent.

$$v = A_0 i + A_1 v_{s1} + A_2 v_{s2} + A_3 i_{s1} + A_4 i_{s2} \qquad (4.13)$$

where A_0, A_1, A_2, A_3, and A_4 are constants. Each term on the right-hand side of Eq. (4.13) is the contribution of the related independent source; that is, $A_0 i$ is the contribution to v due to the external current source i, $A_1 v_{s1}$ is the contribution due to the voltage source v_{s1}, and so on. We may collect terms for the internal independent sources together as B_0, so that Eq. (4.13) becomes

$$v = A_0 i + B_0 \qquad (4.14)$$

where $B_0 = A_1 v_{s1} + A_2 v_{s2} + A_3 i_{s1} + A_4 i_{s2}$. We now want to evaluate the values of constants A_0 and B_0. When the terminals a and b are open-circuited, $i = 0$ and $v = B_0$. Thus B_0 is the open-circuit voltage v_{oc}, which is the same as V_{Th}, so

$$B_0 = V_{Th} \qquad (4.15)$$

When all the internal sources are turned off, $B_0 = 0$. The circuit can then be replaced by an equivalent resistance R_{eq}, which is the same as R_{Th}, and Eq. (4.14) becomes

$$v = A_0 i = R_{Th} i \qquad \Longrightarrow \qquad A_0 = R_{Th} \qquad (4.16)$$

Substituting the values of A_0 and B_0 in Eq. (4.14) gives

$$v = R_{Th} i + V_{Th} \qquad (4.17)$$

which expresses the voltage-current relation at terminals a and b of the circuit in Fig. 4.46(b). Thus, the two circuits in Fig. 4.46(a) and 4.46(b) are equivalent.

When the same linear circuit is driven by a voltage source v as shown in Fig. 4.47(a), the current flowing into the circuit can be obtained by superposition as

$$i = C_0 v + D_0 \qquad (4.18)$$

where $C_0 v$ is the contribution to i due to the external voltage source v and D_0 contains the contributions to i due to all internal independent sources. When the terminals a-b are short-circuited, $v = 0$ so that $i = D_0 = -i_{sc}$, where i_{sc} is the short-circuit current flowing out of terminal a, which is the

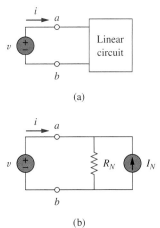

(a)

(b)

Figure 4.47   Derivation of Norton equivalent: (a) a voltage-driven circuit, (b) its Norton equivalent.

same as the Norton current I_N, i.e.,

$$D_0 = -I_N \qquad (4.19)$$

When all the internal independent sources are turned off, $D_0 = 0$ and the circuit can be replaced by an equivalent resistance R_{eq} (or an equivalent conductance $G_{eq} = 1/R_{eq}$), which is the same as R_{Th} or R_N. Thus Eq. (4.19) becomes

$$i = \frac{v}{R_{Th}} - I_N \qquad (4.20)$$

This expresses the voltage-current relation at terminals a-b of the circuit in Fig. 4.47(b), confirming that the two circuits in Fig. 4.47(a) and 4.47(b) are equivalent.

4.8   MAXIMUM POWER TRANSFER

In many practical situations, a circuit is designed to provide power to a load. There are applications in areas such as communications where it is desirable to maximize the power delivered to a load. We now address the problem of delivering the maximum power to a load when given a system with known internal losses. It should be noted that this will result in significant internal losses greater than or equal to the power delivered to the load.

The Thevenin equivalent is useful in finding the maximum power a linear circuit can deliver to a load. We assume that we can adjust the load resistance R_L. If the entire circuit is replaced by its Thevenin equivalent except for the load, as shown in Fig. 4.48, the power delivered to the load is

$$p = i^2 R_L = \left(\frac{V_{Th}}{R_{Th} + R_L} \right)^2 R_L \qquad (4.21)$$

Figure 4.48   The circuit used for maximum power transfer.

For a given circuit, V_{Th} and R_{Th} are fixed. By varying the load resistance R_L, the power delivered to the load varies as sketched in Fig. 4.49. We notice from Fig. 4.49 that the power is small for small or large values of R_L but maximum for some value of R_L between 0 and ∞. We now want to show that this maximum power occurs when R_L is equal to R_{Th}. This is known as the *maximum power theorem*.

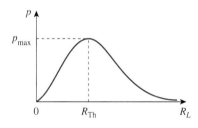

Figure 4.49   Power delivered to the load as a function of R_L.

> Maximum power is transferred to the load when the load resistance equals the Thevenin resistance as seen from the load ($R_L = R_{Th}$).

To prove the maximum power transfer theorem, we differentiate p in Eq. (4.21) with respect to R_L and set the result equal to zero. We obtain

$$\frac{dp}{dR_L} = V_{Th}^2 \left[\frac{(R_{Th} + R_L)^2 - 2R_L(R_{Th} + R_L)}{(R_{Th} + R_L)^4} \right]$$

$$= V_{Th}^2 \left[\frac{(R_{Th} + R_L - 2R_L)}{(R_{Th} + R_L)^3} \right] = 0$$

This implies that

$$0 = (R_{Th} + R_L - 2R_L) = (R_{Th} - R_L) \qquad (4.22)$$

which yields

$$\boxed{R_L = R_{Th}} \qquad (4.23)$$

showing that the maximum power transfer takes place when the load resistance R_L equals the Thevenin resistance R_{Th}. We can readily confirm that Eq. (4.23) gives the maximum power by showing that $d^2p/dR_L^2 < 0$.

The maximum power transferred is obtained by substituting Eq. (4.23) into Eq. (4.21), for

$$\boxed{p_{max} = \frac{V_{Th}^2}{4R_{Th}}} \qquad (4.24)$$

The source and load are said to be *matched* when $R_L = R_{Th}$.

Equation (4.24) applies only when $R_L = R_{Th}$. When $R_L \neq R_{Th}$, we compute the power delivered to the load using Eq. (4.21).

E X A M P L E 4 . 1 3

Find the value of R_L for maximum power transfer in the circuit of Fig. 4.50. Find the maximum power.

Figure 4.50   For Example 4.13.

Solution:

We need to find the Thevenin resistance R_{Th} and the Thevenin voltage V_{Th} across the terminals a-b. To get R_{Th}, we use the circuit in Fig. 4.51(a) and obtain

$$R_{Th} = 2 + 3 + 6 \parallel 12 = 5 + \frac{6 \times 12}{18} = 9 \ \Omega$$

Figure 4.51   For Example 4.13: (a) finding R_{Th}, (b) finding V_{Th}.

To get V_{Th}, we consider the circuit in Fig. 4.51(b). Applying mesh analysis,

$$-12 + 18i_1 - 12i_2 = 0, \qquad i_2 = -2 \text{ A}$$

Solving for i_1, we get $i_1 = -2/3$. Applying KVL around the outer loop to get V_{Th} across terminals a-b, we obtain

$$-12 + 6i_1 + 3i_2 + 2(0) + V_{Th} = 0 \qquad \Longrightarrow \qquad V_{Th} = 22 \text{ V}$$

For maximum power transfer,

$$R_L = R_{Th} = 9 \ \Omega$$

and the maximum power is

$$p_{max} = \frac{V_{Th}^2}{4R_L} = \frac{22^2}{4 \times 9} = 13.44 \text{ W}$$

PRACTICE PROBLEM 4.13

Figure 4.52   For Practice Prob. 4.13.

Determine the value of R_L that will draw the maximum power from the rest of the circuit in Fig. 4.52. Calculate the maximum power.

Answer: 4.22 Ω, 2.901 W.

4.9   VERIFYING CIRCUIT THEOREMS WITH *PSPICE*

In this section, we learn how to use *PSpice* to verify the theorems covered in this chapter. Specifically, we will consider using dc sweep analysis to find the Thevenin or Norton equivalent at any pair of nodes in a circuit and the maximum power transfer to a load. The reader is advised to read Section D.3 of Appendix D in preparation for this section.

To find the Thevenin equivalent of a circuit at a pair of open terminals using *PSpice*, we use the schematic editor to draw the circuit and insert an independent probing current source, say, Ip, at the terminals. The probing current source must have a part name ISRC. We then perform a DC Sweep on Ip, as discussed in Section D.3. Typically, we may let the current through Ip vary from 0 to 1 A in 0.1-A increments. After saving and simulating the circuit, we use Probe to display a plot of the voltage across Ip versus the current through Ip. The zero intercept of the plot gives us the Thevenin equivalent voltage, while the slope of the plot is equal to the Thevenin resistance.

To find the Norton equivalent involves similar steps except that we insert a probing independent voltage source (with a part name VSRC), say, Vp, at the terminals. We perform a DC Sweep on Vp and let Vp vary from 0 to 1 V in 0.1-V increments. A plot of the current through

Vp versus the voltage across Vp is obtained using the Probe menu after simulation. The zero intercept is equal to the Norton current, while the slope of the plot is equal to the Norton conductance.

To find the maximum power transfer to a load using *PSpice* involves performing a dc parametric sweep on the component value of R_L in Fig. 4.48 and plotting the power delivered to the load as a function of R_L. According to Fig. 4.49, the maximum power occurs when $R_L = R_{Th}$. This is best illustrated with an example, and Example 4.15 provides one.

We use VSRC and ISRC as part names for the independent voltage and current sources, respectively.

EXAMPLE 4.14

Consider the circuit in Fig. 4.31 (see Example 4.9). Use *PSpice* to find the Thevenin and Norton equivalent circuits.

Solution:

(a) To find the Thevenin resistance R_{Th} and Thevenin voltage V_{Th} at the terminals *a-b* in the circuit in Fig. 4.31, we first use Schematics to draw the circuit as shown in Fig. 4.53(a). Notice that a probing current source I2 is inserted at the terminals. Under **Analysis/Setput**, we select DC Sweep. In the DC Sweep dialog box, we select Linear for the *Sweep Type* and Current Source for the *Sweep Var. Type*. We enter I2 under the *Name* box, 0 as *Start Value*, 1 as *End Value*, and 0.1 as *Increment*. After simulation, we add trace V(I2:−) from the *PSpice* A/D window and obtain the plot shown in Fig. 4.53(b). From the plot, we obtain

$$V_{Th} = \text{Zero intercept} = 20 \text{ V}, \qquad R_{Th} = \text{Slope} = \frac{26 - 20}{1} = 6 \ \Omega$$

These agree with what we got analytically in Example 4.9.

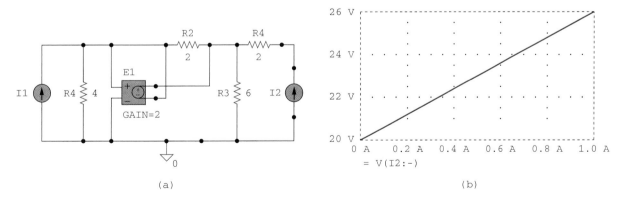

Figure 4.53   For Example 4.14: (a) schematic and (b) plot for finding R_{Th} and V_{Th}.

(b) To find the Norton equivalent, we modify the schematic in Fig. 4.53(a) by replaying the probing current source with a probing voltage source V1. The result is the schematic in Fig. 4.54(a). Again, in the DC Sweep dialog box, we select Linear for the *Sweep Type* and Voltage Source for the *Sweep*

Var. Type. We enter V1 under *Name* box, 0 as *Start Value*, 1 as *End Value*, and 0.1 as *Increment*. Under the *PSpice* A/D Window, we add trace I (V1) and obtain the plot in Fig. 4.54(b). From the plot, we obtain

$$I_N = \text{Zero intercept} = 3.335 \text{ A}$$

$$G_N = \text{Slope} = \frac{3.335 - 3.165}{1} = 0.17 \text{ S}$$

(a)   (b)

Figure 4.54   For Example 4.14: (a) schematic and (b) plot for finding G_N and I_N.

PRACTICE PROBLEM 4.14

Rework Practice Prob. 4.9 using *PSpice*.

Answer: $V_{\text{Th}} = 5.33$ V, $R_{\text{Th}} = 0.44 \ \Omega$.

EXAMPLE 4.15

Figure 4.55   For Example 4.15.

Refer to the circuit in Fig. 4.55. Use *PSpice* to find the maximum power transfer to R_L.

Solution:

We need to perform a dc sweep on R_L to determine when the power across it is maximum. We first draw the circuit using Schematics as shown in Fig. 4.56. Once the circuit is drawn, we take the following three steps to further prepare the circuit for a dc sweep.

The first step involves defining the value of R_L as a parameter, since we want to vary it. To do this:

1. **DCLICKL** the value 1k of R2 (representing R_L) to open up the *Set Attribute Value* dialog box.

2. Replace 1k with {RL} and click **OK** to accept the change.

Note that the curly brackets are necessary.

The second step is to define parameter. To achieve this:

1. Select **Draw/Get New Part/Libraries** · · · **/special.slb**.

2. Type PARAM in the *PartName* box and click **OK**.

3. **DRAG** the box to any position near the circuit.

4. **CLICKL** to end placement mode.

5. **DCLICKL** to open up the *PartName: PARAM* dialog box.

6. **CLICKL** on *NAME1* = and enter RL (with no curly brackets) in the *Value* box, and **CLICKL Save Attr** to accept change.

7. **CLICKL** on *VALUE1* = and enter 2k in the *Value* box, and **CLICKL Save Attr** to accept change.

8. Click **OK**.

The value 2k in item 7 is necessary for a bias point calculation; it cannot be left blank.

The third step is to set up the DC Sweep to sweep the parameter. To do this:

1. Select **Analysis/Setput** to bring up the DC Sweep dialog box.

2. For the *Sweep Type*, select Linear (or Octave for a wide range of R_L).

3. For the *Sweep Var. Type*, select Global Parameter.

4. Under the *Name* box, enter RL.

5. In the *Start Value* box, enter 100.

6. In the *End Value* box, enter 5k.

7. In the *Increment* box, enter 100.

8. Click **OK** and **Close** to accept the parameters.

After taking these steps and saving the circuit, we are ready to simulate. Select **Analysis/Simulate**. If there are no errors, we select **Add Trace** in the *PSpice* A/D window and type $-V(R2:2)*I(R2)$ in the *Trace Command* box. [The negative sign is needed since I(R2) is negative.] This gives the plot of the power delivered to R_L as R_L varies from 100 Ω to 5 kΩ. We can also obtain the power absorbed by R_L by typing V(R2:2)*V(R2:2)/RL in the *Trace Command* box. Either way, we obtain the plot in Fig. 4.57. It is evident from the plot that the maximum power is 250 μW. Notice that the maximum occurs when $R_L = 1$ kΩ, as expected analytically.

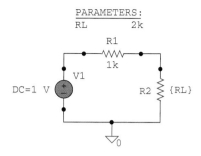

Figure 4.56   Schematic for the circuit in Fig. 4.55.

Figure 4.57   For Example 4.15: the plot of power across R_L.

PRACTICE PROBLEM 4.15

Find the maximum power transferred to R_L if the 1-kΩ resistor in Fig. 4.55 is replaced by a 2-kΩ resistor.

Answer: 125 μW.

†4.10 APPLICATIONS

In this section we will discuss two important practical applications of the concepts covered in this chapter: source modeling and resistance measurement.

4.10.1 Source Modeling

Source modeling provides an example of the usefulness of the Thevenin or the Norton equivalent. An active source such as a battery is often characterized by its Thevenin or Norton equivalent circuit. An ideal voltage source provides a constant voltage irrespective of the current drawn by the load, while an ideal current source supplies a constant current

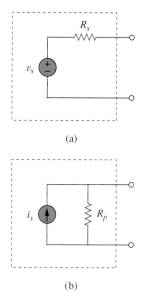

Figure 4.58 (a) Practical voltage source, (b) practical current source.

(a)

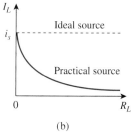

(b)

Figure 4.60 (a) Practical current source connected to a load R_L, (b) load current decreases as R_L increases.

regardless of the load voltage. As Fig. 4.58 shows, practical voltage and current sources are not ideal, due to their *internal resistances* or *source resistances* R_s and R_p. They become ideal as $R_s \to 0$ and $R_p \to \infty$. To show that this is the case, consider the effect of the load on voltage sources, as shown in Fig. 4.59(a). By the voltage division principle, the load voltage is

$$v_L = \frac{R_L}{R_s + R_L} v_s \tag{4.25}$$

As R_L increases, the load voltage approaches a source voltage v_s, as illustrated in Fig. 4.59(b). From Eq. (4.25), we should note that:

1. The load voltage will be constant if the internal resistance R_s of the source is zero or, at least, $R_s \ll R_L$. In other words, the smaller R_s is compared to R_L, the closer the voltage source is to being ideal.

2. When the load is disconnected (i.e., the source is open-circuited so that $R_L \to \infty$), $v_{oc} = v_s$. Thus, v_s may be regarded as the *unloaded source* voltage. The connection of the load causes the terminal voltage to drop in magnitude; this is known as the *loading effect*.

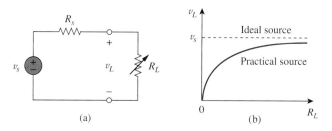

Figure 4.59 (a) Practical voltage source connected to a load R_L, (b) load voltage decreases as R_L decreases.

The same argument can be made for a practical current source when connected to a load as shown in Fig. 4.60(a). By the current division principle,

$$i_L = \frac{R_p}{R_p + R_L} i_s \tag{4.26}$$

Figure 4.60(b) shows the variation in the load current as the load resistance increases. Again, we notice a drop in current due to the load (loading effect), and load current is constant (ideal current source) when the internal resistance is very large (i.e., $R_p \to \infty$ or, at least, $R_p \gg R_L$).

Sometimes, we need to know the unloaded source voltage v_s and the internal resistance R_s of a voltage source. To find v_s and R_s, we follow the procedure illustrated in Fig. 4.61. First, we measure the open-circuit voltage v_{oc} as in Fig. 4.61(a) and set

$$v_s = v_{oc} \tag{4.27}$$

Then, we connect a variable load R_L across the terminals as in Fig. 4.61(b). We adjust the resistance R_L until we measure a load voltage of exactly one-half of the open-circuit voltage, $v_L = v_{oc}/2$, because now $R_L = R_{Th} = R_s$. At that point, we disconnect R_L and measure it. We set

$$R_s = R_L \qquad (4.28)$$

For example, a car battery may have $v_s = 12$ V and $R_s = 0.05$ Ω.

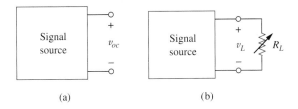

(a)   (b)

Figure 4.61   (a) Measuring v_{oc}, (b) measuring v_L.

EXAMPLE 4.16

The terminal voltage of a voltage source is 12 V when connected to a 2-W load. When the load is disconnected, the terminal voltage rises to 12.4 V. (a) Calculate the source voltage v_s and internal resistance R_s. (b) Determine the voltage when an 8-Ω load is connected to the source.

Solution:

(a) We replace the source by its Thevenin equivalent. The terminal voltage when the load is disconnected is the open-circuit voltage,

$$v_s = v_{oc} = 12.4 \text{ V}$$

When the load is connected, as shown in Fig. 4.62(a), $v_L = 12$ V and $p_L = 2$ W. Hence,

$$p_L = \frac{v_L^2}{R_L} \quad \Longrightarrow \quad R_L = \frac{v_L^2}{p_L} = \frac{12^2}{2} = 72 \text{ Ω}$$

The load current is

$$i_L = \frac{v_L}{R_L} = \frac{12}{72} = \frac{1}{6} \text{ A}$$

The voltage across R_s is the difference between the source voltage v_s and the load voltage v_L, or

$$12.4 - 12 = 0.4 = R_s i_L, \qquad R_s = \frac{0.4}{I_L} = 2.4 \text{ Ω}$$

(b) Now that we have the Thevenin equivalent of the source, we connect the 8-Ω load across the Thevenin equivalent as shown in Fig. 4.62(b). Using voltage division, we obtain

$$v = \frac{8}{8 + 2.4}(12) = 9.231 \text{ V}$$

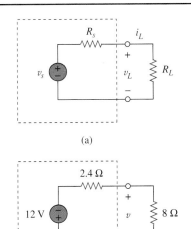

(a)

(b)

Figure 4.62   For Example 4.16.

PRACTICE PROBLEM 4.16

The measured open-circuit voltage across a certain amplifier is 9 V. The voltage drops to 8 V when a 20-Ω loudspeaker is connected to the amplifier. Calculate the voltage when a 10-Ω loudspeaker is used instead.

Answer: 7.2 V.

4.10.2 Resistance Measurement

Although the ohmmeter method provides the simplest way to measure resistance, more accurate measurement may be obtained using the Wheatstone bridge. While ohmmeters are designed to measure resistance in low, mid, or high range, a Wheatstone bridge is used to measure resistance in the mid range, say, between 1 Ω and 1 MΩ. Very low values of resistances are measured with a *milliohmmeter*, while very high values are measured with a *Megger tester.*

Historical note: The bridge was invented by Charles Wheatstone (1802–1875), a British professor who also invented the telegraph, as Samuel Morse did independently in the United States.

The Wheatstone bridge (or resistance bridge) circuit is used in a number of applications. Here we will use it to measure an unknown resistance. The unknown resistance R_x is connected to the bridge as shown in Fig. 4.63. The variable resistance is adjusted until no current flows through the galvanometer, which is essentially a d'Arsonval movement operating as a sensitive current-indicating device like an ammeter in the microamp range. Under this condition $v_1 = v_2$, and the bridge is said to be *balanced*. Since no current flows through the galvanometer, R_1 and R_2 behave as though they were in series; so do R_3 and R_x. The fact that no current flows through the galvanometer also implies that $v_1 = v_2$. Applying the voltage division principle,

$$v_1 = \frac{R_2}{R_1 + R_2} v = v_2 = \frac{R_x}{R_3 + R_x} v \qquad (4.29)$$

Hence, no current flows through the galvanometer when

$$\frac{R_2}{R_1 + R_2} = \frac{R_x}{R_3 + R_x} \qquad \Longrightarrow \qquad R_2 R_3 = R_1 R_x$$

or

$$\boxed{R_x = \frac{R_3}{R_1} R_2} \qquad (4.30)$$

Figure 4.63   The Wheatstone bridge; R_x is the resistance to be measured.

If $R_1 = R_3$, and R_2 is adjusted until no current flows through the galvanometer, then $R_x = R_2$.

How do we find the current through the galvanometer when the Wheatstone bridge is *unbalanced*? We find the Thevenin equivalent (V_{Th} and R_{Th}) with respect to the galvanometer terminals. If R_m is the resistance of the galvanometer, the current through it under the unbalanced condition is

$$I = \frac{V_{Th}}{R_{Th} + R_m} \qquad (4.31)$$

Example 4.18 will illustrate this.

EXAMPLE 4.17

In Fig. 4.63, $R_1 = 500\ \Omega$ and $R_3 = 200\ \Omega$. The bridge is balanced when R_2 is adjusted to be $125\ \Omega$. Determine the unknown resistance R_x.

Solution:

Using Eq. (4.30),

$$R_x = \frac{R_3}{R_1}R_2 = \frac{200}{500}125 = 50\ \Omega$$

PRACTICE PROBLEM 4.17

A Wheatstone bridge has $R_1 = R_3 = 1\ \text{k}\Omega$. R_2 is adjusted until no current flows through the galvanometer. At that point, $R_2 = 3.2\ \text{k}\Omega$. What is the value of the unknown resistance?

Answer: $3.2\ \text{k}\Omega$.

EXAMPLE 4.18

The circuit in Fig. 4.64 represents an unbalanced bridge. If the galvanometer has a resistance of $40\ \Omega$, find the current through the galvanometer.

Figure 4.64   Unbalanced bridge of Example 4.18.

Solution:

We first need to replace the circuit by its Thevenin equivalent at terminals a and b. The Thevenin resistance is found using the circuit in Fig. 4.65(a). Notice that the 3-kΩ and 1-kΩ resistors are in parallel; so are the 400-Ω and 600-Ω resistors. The two parallel combinations form a series combination with respect to terminals a and b. Hence,

$$R_{\text{Th}} = 3000\ \|\ 1000 + 400\ \|\ 600$$
$$= \frac{3000 \times 1000}{3000 + 1000} + \frac{400 \times 600}{400 + 600} = 750 + 240 = 990\ \Omega$$

To find the Thevenin voltage, we consider the circuit in Fig. 4.65(b). Using the voltage division principle,

$$v_1 = \frac{1000}{1000 + 3000}(220) = 55\ \text{V}, \qquad v_2 = \frac{600}{600 + 400}(220) = 132\ \text{V}$$

Applying KVL around loop ab gives

$$-v_1 + V_{\text{Th}} + v_2 = 0 \qquad \text{or} \qquad V_{\text{Th}} = v_1 - v_2 = 55 - 132 = -77\ \text{V}$$

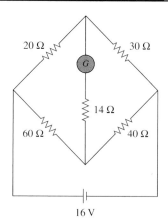

Figure 4.65   For Example 4.18: (a) Finding R_{Th}, (b) finding V_{Th}, (c) determining the current through the galvanometer.

Having determined the Thevenin equivalent, we find the current through the galvanometer using Fig. 4.65(c).

$$I_G = \frac{V_{Th}}{R_{Th} + R_m} = \frac{-77}{990 + 40} = -74.76 \text{ mA}$$

The negative sign indicates that the current flows in the direction opposite to the one assumed, that is, from terminal b to terminal a.

PRACTICE PROBLEM 4.18

Obtain the current through the galvanometer, having a resistance of 14 Ω, in the Wheatstone bridge shown in Fig. 4.66.

Answer: 64 mA.

Figure 4.66   For Practice Prob. 4.18.

4.11 SUMMARY

1. A linear network consists of linear elements, linear dependent sources, and linear independent sources.

2. Network theorems are used to reduce a complex circuit to a simpler one, thereby making circuit analysis much simpler.

3. The superposition principle states that for a circuit having multiple independent sources, the voltage across (or current through) an element is equal to the algebraic sum of all the individual voltages (or currents) due to each independent source acting one at a time.

4. Source transformation is a procedure for transforming a voltage source in series with a resistor to a current source in parallel with a resistor, or vice versa.

5. Thevenin's and Norton's theorems allow us to isolate a portion of a network while the remaining portion of the network is replaced by an equivalent network. The Thevenin equivalent consists of a voltage source V_{Th} in series with a resistor R_{Th}, while the Norton equivalent consists of a current source I_N in parallel with a resistor R_N. The two theorems are related by source transformation.

$$R_N = R_{Th}, \qquad I_N = \frac{V_{Th}}{R_{Th}}$$

6. For a given Thevenin equivalent circuit, maximum power transfer occurs when $R_L = R_{Th}$, that is, when the load resistance is equal to the Thevenin resistance.

7. The maximum power transfer theorem states that the maximum power is delivered by a source to the load R_L when R_L is equal to R_{Th}, the Thevenin resistance at the terminals of the load.

8. *PSpice* can be used to verify the circuit theorems covered in this chapter.

9. Source modeling and resistance measurement using the Wheatstone bridge provide applications for Thevenin's theorem.

REVIEW QUESTIONS

4.1 The current through a branch in a linear network is 2 A when the input source voltage is 10 V. If the voltage is reduced to 1 V and the polarity is reversed, the current through the branch is:

(a) −2   (b) −0.2   (c) 0.2
(d) 2   (e) 20

4.2 For superposition, it is not required that only one independent source be considered at a time; any number of independent sources may be considered simultaneously.

(a) True   (b) False

4.3 The superposition principle applies to power calculation.

(a) True   (b) False

4.4 Refer to Fig. 4.67. The Thevenin resistance at terminals *a* and *b* is:

(a) 25 Ω   (b) 20 Ω
(c) 5 Ω   (d) 4 Ω

Figure 4.67   For Review Questions 4.4 to 4.6.

4.5   The Thevenin voltage across terminals a and b of the circuit in Fig. 4.67 is:

(a) 50 V   (b) 40 V
(c) 20 V   (d) 10 V

4.6   The Norton current at terminals a and b of the circuit in Fig. 4.67 is:

(a) 10 A   (b) 2.5 A
(c) 2 A   (d) 0 A

4.7   The Norton resistance R_N is exactly equal to the Thevenin resistance R_{Th}.

(a) True   (b) False

4.8   Which pair of circuits in Fig. 4.68 are equivalent?

(a) a and b   (b) b and d
(c) a and c   (d) c and d

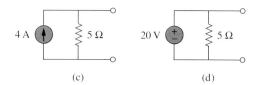

(c)   (d)

Figure 4.68   For Review Question 4.8.

4.9   A load is connected to a network. At the terminals to which the load is connected, $R_{Th} = 10\ \Omega$ and $V_{Th} = 40$ V. The maximum power supplied to the load is:

(a) 160 W   (b) 80 W
(c) 40 W   (d) 1 W

4.10 The source is supplying the maximum power to the load when the load resistance equals the source resistance.

(a) True   (b) False

Answers: 4.1b, 4.2a, 4.3b, 4.4d, 4.5b, 4.6a, 4.7a, 4.8c, 4.9c, 4.10b.

(a)   (b)

PROBLEMS

Section 4.2   Linearity Property

4.1   Calculate the current i_o in the current of Fig. 4.69. What does this current become when the input voltage is raised to 10 V?

Figure 4.69   For Prob. 4.1.

4.2   Find v_o in the circuit of Fig. 4.70. If the source current is reduced to 1 μA, what is v_o?

Figure 4.70   For Prob. 4.2.

4.3   (a) In the circuit in Fig. 4.71, calculate v_o and i_o when $v_s = 1$ V.
         (b) Find v_o and i_o when $v_s = 10$ V.
         (c) What are v_o and i_o when each of the 1-Ω resistors is replaced by a 10-Ω resistor and $v_s = 10$ V?

Figure 4.71   For Prob. 4.3.

4.4   Use linearity to determine i_o in the circuit of Fig. 4.72.

Figure 4.72   For Prob. 4.4.

4.5   For the circuit in Fig. 4.73, assume $v_o = 1$ V, and use linearity to find the actual value of v_o.

Figure 4.73   For Prob. 4.5.

4.6   For the linear circuit in Fig. 4.74, find $k = V_o/V_s$.

Figure 4.74   For Prob. 4.6.

4.7   Consider the network in Fig. 4.75. If $V_s = 12$ V and $I_s = -2$ A, then $I_o = 3$ A, and if $V_s = -6$ V and $I_s = 4$ A, then $I_o = -3$ A. Find I_o when $V_s = 30$ V and $I_s = 6$ A.

Figure 4.75   For Prob. 4.7.

Section 4.3   Superposition

4.8   Apply superposition to find i in the circuit of Fig. 4.76.

Figure 4.76   For Prob. 4.8.

4.9   Given the circuit in Fig. 4.77, calculate i_x and the power dissipated by the 10-Ω resistor using superposition.

Figure 4.77   For Prob. 4.9.

4.10   For the circuit in Fig. 4.78, find the terminal voltage V_{ab} using superposition.

Figure 4.78   For Prob. 4.10.

4.11   Use superposition principle to find i in Fig. 4.79.

Figure 4.79   For Prob. 4.11.

4.12   Determine v_o in the circuit of Fig. 4.80 using the superposition principle.

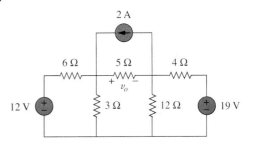

Figure 4.80   For Probs. 4.12 and 4.35.

4.13 Using the superposition principle, find i_o in the circuit shown in Fig. 4.81.

Figure 4.81 For Prob. 4.13.

4.14 Apply the superposition principle to find v_o in the circuit of Fig. 4.82.

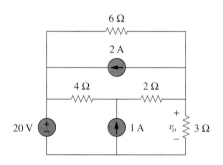

Figure 4.82 For Prob. 4.14.

4.15 For the circuit in Fig. 4.83, use superposition to find i. Calculate the power delivered to the 3-Ω resistor.

Figure 4.83 For Probs. 4.15 and 4.56.

4.16 Given the circuit in Fig. 4.84, use superposition to get i_o.

Figure 4.84 For Probs. 4.16 and 4.28.

4.17 Use superposition to obtain v_x in the circuit of Fig. 4.85. Check your result using *PSpice*.

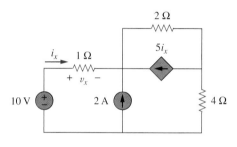

Figure 4.85 For Prob. 4.17.

4.18 Find v_x in Fig. 4.86 by superposition.

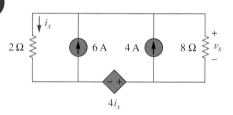

Figure 4.86 For Prob. 4.18.

4.19 Use superposition to solve for v_x in the circuit of Fig. 4.87.

Figure 4.87 For Prob. 4.19.

Section 4.4 Source Transformation

4.20 Find i in Prob. 4.11 using source transformation.

4.21 Apply source transformation to determine v_o and i_o in the circuit in Fig. 4.88.

Figure 4.88 For Prob. 4.21.

4.22 For the circuit in Fig. 4.89, use source transformation to find i.

Figure 4.89 For Prob. 4.22.

4.23 Referring to Fig. 4.90, use source transformation to determine the current and power in the 8-Ω resistor.

Figure 4.90 For Prob. 4.23.

4.24 Use successive source transformation to find V_o in Prob. 4.11.

4.25 Obtain v_o in the circuit of Fig. 4.91 using source transformation. Check your result using *PSpice*.

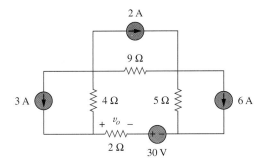

Figure 4.91 For Prob. 4.25.

4.26 Use source transformation to solve Prob. 4.17.

4.27 Apply source transformation to find v_x in the circuit of Fig. 4.92.

Figure 4.92 For Probs. 4.27 and 4.40.

4.28 Given the circuit in Fig. 4.84, use source transformation to find i_o.

4.29 Use source transformation to find v_o in the circuit of Fig. 4.93.

Figure 4.93 For Prob. 4.29.

4.30 Use source transformation on the circuit shown in Fig 4.94 to find i_x.

Figure 4.94 For Prob. 4.30.

4.31 Determine v_x in the circuit of Fig. 4.95 using source transformation.

Figure 4.95 For Prob. 4.31.

4.32 Use source transformation to find i_x in the circuit of Fig. 4.96.

Figure 4.96 For Prob. 4.32.

**Sections 4.5 and 4.6   Thevenin's and Norton's
                                Theorems**

4.33   Determine R_{Th} and V_{Th} at terminals 1-2 of each of
           the circuits in Fig. 4.97.

Figure 4.97   For Probs. 4.33 and 4.46.

4.34   Find the Thevenin equivalent at terminals *a-b* of the
           circuit in Fig. 4.98.

Figure 4.98   For Probs. 4.34 and 4.49.

4.35   Use Thevenin's theorem to find v_o in Prob. 4.12.

4.36   Solve for the current *i* in the circuit of Fig. 4.99 using
           Thevenin's theorem. (*Hint:* Find the Thevenin
           equivalent across the 12-Ω resistor.)

Figure 4.99   For Prob. 4.36.

4.37   Find the Norton equivalent with respect to terminals
           a-b in the circuit shown in Fig. 4.100.

Figure 4.100   For Prob. 4.37.

4.38   Apply Thevenin's theorem to find V_o in the circuit of
           Fig. 4.101.

Figure 4.101   For Prob. 4.38.

4.39   For Prob. 4.10, obtain the Thevenin equivalent at
           terminals *a-b*.

4.40   Given the circuit in Fig. 4.92, obtain the Thevenin
           equivalent at terminals *a-b* and use the result to
           get v_x.

4.41   Find the Thevenin and Norton equivalents at
           terminals *a-b* of the circuit shown in Fig. 4.102.

Figure 4.102   For Prob. 4.41.

*4.42   For the circuit in Fig. 4.103, find the Thevenin equivalent between terminals a and b.

Figure 4.103   For Prob. 4.42.

4.43   Find the Thevenin equivalent looking into terminals a-b of the circuit in Fig. 4.104 and solve for i_x.

Figure 4.104   For Prob. 4.43.

4.44   For the circuit in Fig. 4.105, obtain the Thevenin equivalent as seen from terminals:

   (a) a-b (b) b-c

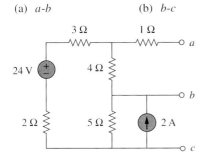

Figure 4.105   For Prob. 4.44.

4.45   Find the Norton equivalent of the circuit in Fig. 4.106.

Figure 4.106   For Prob. 4.45.

4.46   Obtain R_N and I_N at terminals 1 and 2 of each of the circuits in Fig. 4.97.

4.47   Obtain the Thevenin and Norton equivalent circuits of the circuit in Fig. 4.107 with respect to terminals a and b.

Figure 4.107   For Prob. 4.47.

4.48   Determine the Norton equivalent at terminals a-b for the circuit in Fig. 4.108.

Figure 4.108   For Prob. 4.48.

4.49   Find the Norton equivalent looking into terminals a-b of the circuit in Fig. 4.98.

4.50   Obtain the Norton equivalent of the circuit in Fig. 4.109 to the left of terminals a-b. Use the result to find current i.

Figure 4.109   For Prob. 4.50.

4.51   Given the circuit in Fig. 4.110, obtain the Norton equivalent as viewed from terminals:

   (a) a-b (b) c-d

---

*An asterisk indicates a challenging problem.

Figure 4.110   For Prob. 4.51.

4.52   For the transistor model in Fig. 4.111, obtain the Thevenin equivalent at terminals a-b.

Figure 4.111   For Prob. 4.52.

4.53   Find the Norton equivalent at terminals a-b of the circuit in Fig. 4.112.

Figure 4.112   For Prob. 4.53.

4.54   Find the Thevenin equivalent between terminals a-b of the circuit in Fig. 4.113.

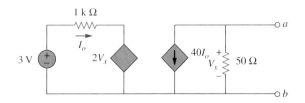

Figure 4.113   For Prob. 4.54.

***4.55**   Obtain the Norton equivalent at terminals a-b of the circuit in Fig. 4.114.

Figure 4.114   For Prob. 4.55.

4.56   Use Norton's theorem to find current i in the circuit of Fig. 4.83.

4.57   Obtain the Thevenin and Norton equivalent circuits at terminals a-b for the circuit in Fig. 4.115.

Figure 4.115   For Probs. 4.57 and 4.79.

4.58   The network in Fig. 4.116 models a bipolar transistor common-emitter amplifier connected to a load. Find the Thevenin resistance seen by the load.

Figure 4.116   For Prob. 4.58.

4.59   Determine the Thevenin and Norton equivalents at terminals a-b of the circuit in Fig. 4.117.

Figure 4.117   For Probs. 4.59 and 4.80.

*4.60 For the circuit in Fig. 4.118, find the Thevenin and Norton equivalent circuits at terminals *a-b*.

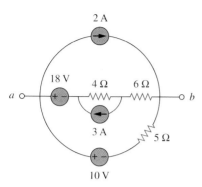

Figure 4.118   For Probs. 4.60 and 4.81.

*4.61 Obtain the Thevenin and Norton equivalent circuits at terminals *a-b* of the circuit in Fig. 4.119.

Figure 4.119   For Prob. 4.61.

*4.62 Find the Thevenin equivalent of the circuit in Fig. 4.120.

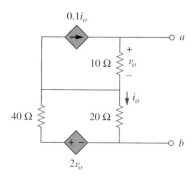

Figure 4.120   For Prob. 4.62.

4.63 Find the Norton equivalent for the circuit in Fig. 4.121.

Figure 4.121   For Prob. 4.63.

4.64 Obtain the Thevenin equivalent seen at terminals *a-b* of the circuit in Fig. 4.122.

Figure 4.122   For Prob. 4.64.

4.65 For the circuit shown in Fig. 4.123, determine the relationship between V_o and I_o.

Figure 4.123   For Prob. 4.65.

Section 4.8   Maximum Power Transfer

4.66 Find the maximum power that can be delivered to the resistor R in the circuit in Fig. 4.124.

Figure 4.124   For Prob. 4.66.

4.67 Refer to Fig. 4.125. For what value of R is the power dissipated in R maximum? Calculate that power.

Figure 4.125 For Prob. 4.67.

*__4.68__ Compute the value of R that results in maximum power transfer to the 10-Ω resistor in Fig. 4.126. Find the maximum power.

Figure 4.126 For Prob. 4.68.

4.69 Find the maximum power transferred to resistor R in the circuit of Fig. 4.127.

Figure 4.127 For Prob. 4.69.

4.70 Determine the maximum power delivered to the variable resistor R shown in the circuit of Fig. 4.128.

Figure 4.128 For Prob. 4.70.

4.71 For the circuit in Fig. 4.129, what resistor connected across terminals a-b will absorb maximum power from the circuit? What is that power?

Figure 4.129 For Prob. 4.71.

4.72 (a) For the circuit in Fig. 4.130, obtain the Thevenin equivalent at terminals a-b.
(b) Calculate the current in $R_L = 8\ \Omega$.
(c) Find R_L for maximum power deliverable to R_L.
(d) Determine that maximum power.

Figure 4.130 For Prob. 4.72.

4.73 Determine the maximum power that can be delivered to the variable resistor R in the circuit of Fig. 4.131.

Figure 4.131 For Prob. 4.73.

4.74 For the bridge circuit shown in Fig. 4.132, find the load R_L for maximum power transfer and the maximum power absorbed by the load.

Figure 4.132 For Prob. 4.74.

4.75 For the circuit in Fig. 4.133, determine the value of R such that the maximum power delivered to the load is 3 mW.

Figure 4.133   For Prob. 4.75.

Section 4.9   Verifying Circuit Theorems with *PSpice*

4.76 Solve Prob. 4.34 using *PSpice*.

4.77 Use *PSpice* to solve Prob. 4.44.

4.78 Use *PSpice* to solve Prob. 4.52.

4.79 Obtain the Thevenin equivalent of the circuit in Fig. 4.115 using *PSpice*.

4.80 Use *PSpice* to find the Thevenin equivalent circuit at terminals *a-b* of the circuit in Fig. 4.117.

4.81 For the circuit in Fig. 4.118, use *PSpice* to find the Thevenin equivalent at terminals *a-b*.

Section 4.10   Applications

4.82 A battery has a short-circuit current of 20 A and an open-circuit voltage of 12 V. If the battery is connected to an electric bulb of resistance 2 Ω, calculate the power dissipated by the bulb.

4.83 The following results were obtained from measurements taken between the two terminals of a resistive network.

Terminal Voltage	12 V	0 V
Terminal Current	0 A	1.5 A

Find the Thevenin equivalent of the network.

4.84 When connected to a 4-Ω resistor, a battery has a terminal voltage of 10.8 V but produces 12 V on an open circuit. Determine the Thevenin equivalent circuit for the battery.

4.85 The Thevenin equivalent at terminals *a-b* of the linear network shown in Fig. 4.134 is to be determined by measurement. When a 10-kΩ resistor is connected to terminals *a-b*, the voltage V_{ab} is measured as 6 V. When a 30-kΩ resistor is connected to the terminals, V_{ab} is measured as 12 V. Determine: (a) the Thevenin equivalent at terminals *a-b*, (b) V_{ab} when a 20-kΩ resistor is connected to terminals *a-b*.

Figure 4.134   For Prob. 4.85.

4.86 A black box with a circuit in it is connected to a variable resistor. An ideal ammeter (with zero resistance) and an ideal voltmeter (with infinite resistance) are used to measure current and voltage as shown in Fig. 4.135. The results are shown in the table below.

Figure 4.135   For Prob. 4.86.

(a) Find i when $R = 4\ \Omega$.

(b) Determine the maximum power from the box.

$R(\Omega)$	$V(V)$	$i(A)$
2	3	1.5
8	8	1.0
14	10.5	0.75

4.87 A transducer is modeled with a current source I_s and a parallel resistance R_s. The current at the terminals of the source is measured to be 9.975 mA when an ammeter with an internal resistance of 20 Ω is used.

(a) If adding a 2-kΩ resistor across the source terminals causes the ammeter reading to fall to 9.876 mA, calculate I_s and R_s.

(b) What will the ammeter reading be if the resistance between the source terminals is changed to 4 kΩ?

4.88 Consider the circuit in Fig. 4.136. An ammeter with internal resistance R_i is inserted between A and B to measure I_o. Determine the reading of the ammeter if: (a) $R_i = 500\ \Omega$, (b) $R_i = 0\ \Omega$. (*Hint*: Find the Thevenin equivalent circuit at terminals A-B.)

Figure 4.136   For Prob. 4.88.

4.89 Consider the circuit in Fig. 4.137. (a) Replace the resistor R_L by a zero resistance ammeter and determine the ammeter reading. (b) To verify the reciprocity theorem, interchange the ammeter and the 12-V source and determine the ammeter reading again.

Figure 4.137   For Prob. 4.89.

4.90 The Wheatstone bridge circuit shown in Fig. 4.138 is used to measure the resistance of a strain gauge. The adjustable resistor has a linear taper with a maximum value of 100 Ω. If the resistance of the strain gauge is found to be 42.6 Ω, what fraction of the full slider travel is the slider when the bridge is balanced?

Figure 4.138   For Prob. 4.90.

4.91 (a) In the Wheatstone bridge circuit of Fig. 4.139, select the values of R_1 and R_3 such that the bridge can measure R_x in the range of 0–10 Ω.

Figure 4.139   For Prob. 4.91.

(b) Repeat for the range of 0–100 Ω.

***4.92** Consider the bridge circuit of Fig. 4.140. Is the bridge balanced? If the 10-kΩ resistor is replaced by an 18-kΩ resistor, what resistor connected between terminals *a-b* absorbs the maximum power? What is this power?

Figure 4.140   For Prob. 4.92.

COMPREHENSIVE PROBLEMS

4.93 The circuit in Fig. 4.141 models a common-emitter transistor amplifier. Find i_x using source transformation.

Figure 4.141   For Prob. 4.93.

4.94   An attenuator is an interface circuit that reduces the voltage level without changing the output resistance.

(a) By specifying R_s and R_p of the interface circuit in Fig. 4.142, design an attenuator that will meet the following requirements:

$$\frac{V_o}{V_g} = 0.125, \qquad R_{eq} = R_{Th} = R_g = 100 \ \Omega$$

(b) Using the interface designed in part (a), calculate the current through a load of $R_L = 50 \ \Omega$ when $V_g = 12$ V.

Figure 4.142   For Prob. 4.94.

4.95   A dc voltmeter with a sensitivity of 20 kΩ/V is used to find the Thevenin equivalent of a linear network. Readings on two scales are as follows:

(a) 0–10 V scale: 4 V   (b) 0–50 V scale: 5 V

Obtain the Thevenin voltage and the Thevenin resistance of the network.

4.96   A resistance array is connected to a load resistor R and a 9-V battery as shown in Fig. 4.143.

(a) Find the value of R such that $V_o = 1.8$ V.

(b) Calculate the value of R that will draw the maximum current. What is the maximum current?

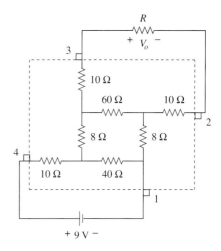

Figure 4.143   For Prob. 4.96.

4.97   A common-emitter amplifier circuit is shown in Fig. 4.144. Obtain the Thevenin equivalent to the left of points B and E.

Figure 4.144   For Prob. 4.97.

4.98   For Practice Prob. 4.20, determine the current through the 40-Ω resistor and the power dissipated by the resistor.

CHAPTER | 5

OPERATIONAL AMPLIFIERS

The purpose of computing is insight, not numbers.

—Richard W. Humming

Enhancing Your Career

Career in Electronic Instrumentation   Engineering involves applying physical principles to design devices for the benefit of humanity. But physical principles cannot be understood without measurement. In fact, physicists often say that physics is the science that measures reality. Just as measurements are a tool for understanding the physical world, instruments are tools for measurement. The operational amplifier introduced in this chapter is a building block of modern electronic instrumentation. Therefore, mastery of operational amplifier fundamentals is paramount to any practical application of electronic circuits.

Electronic instruments are used in all fields of science and engineering. They have proliferated in science and technology to the extent that it would be ridiculous to have a scientific or technical education without exposure to electronic instruments. For example, physicists, physiologists, chemists, and biologists must learn to use electronic instruments. For electrical engineering students in particular, the skill in operating digital and analog electronic instruments is crucial. Such instruments include ammeters, voltmeters, ohmmeters, oscilloscopes, spectrum analyzers, and signal generators.

Beyond developing the skill for operating the instruments, some electrical engineers specialize in designing and constructing electronic instruments. These engineers derive pleasure in building their own instruments. Most

Electronic Instrumentation used in medical research.
Source: Photo Researchers/Geoff Tompkinson/Science Photo Library/.

of them invent and patent their inventions. Specialists in electronic instruments find employment in medical schools, hospitals, research laboratories, aircraft industries, and thousands of other industries where electronic instruments are routinely used.

5.1   INTRODUCTION

Having learned the basic laws and theorems for circuit analysis, we are now ready to study an active circuit element of paramount importance: the *operational amplifier*, or *op amp* for short. The op amp is a versatile circuit building block.

The term *operational amplifier* was introduced in 1947 by John Ragazzini and his colleagues, in their work on analog computers for the National Defense Research Council during World War II. The first op amps used vacuum tubes rather than transistors.

The op amp is an electronic unit that behaves like a voltage-controlled voltage source.

An op amp may also be regarded as a voltage amplifier with very high gain.

It can also be used in making a voltage- or current-controlled current source. An op amp can sum signals, amplify a signal, integrate it, or differentiate it. The ability of the op amp to perform these mathematical operations is the reason it is called an *operational amplifier.* It is also the reason for the widespread use of op amps in analog design. Op amps are popular in practical circuit designs because they are versatile, inexpensive, easy to use, and fun to work with.

We begin by discussing the ideal op amp and later consider the nonideal op amp. Using nodal analysis as a tool, we consider ideal op amp circuits such as the inverter, voltage follower, summer, and difference amplifier. We will also analyze op amp circuits with *PSpice.* Finally, we learn how an op amp is used in digital-to-analog converters and instrumentation amplifiers.

5.2   OPERATIONAL AMPLIFIERS

An operational amplifier is designed so that it performs some mathematical operations when external components, such as resistors and capacitors, are connected to its terminals. Thus,

---

An op amp is an active circuit element designed to perform mathematical operations of addition, subtraction, multiplication, division, differentiation, and integration.

The op amp is an electronic device consisting of a complex arrangement of resistors, transistors, capacitors, and diodes. A full discussion of what is inside the op amp is beyond the scope of this book. It will suffice to treat the op amp as a circuit building block and simply study what takes place at its terminals.

Op amps are commercially available in integrated circuit packages in several forms. Figure 5.1 shows a typical op amp package. A typical one is the eight-pin dual in-line package (or DIP), shown in Fig. 5.2(a). Pin or terminal 8 is unused, and terminals 1 and 5 are of little concern to us. The five important terminals are:

1. The inverting input, pin 2.
2. The noninverting input, pin 3.
3. The output, pin 6.

Figure 5.1   A typical operational amplifier. *(Courtesy of Tech America.)*

The pin diagram in Fig. 5.2(a) corresponds to the 741 general-purpose op amp made by Fairchild Semiconductor.

4. The positive power supply V^+, pin 7.

5. The negative power supply V^-, pin 4.

The circuit symbol for the op amp is the triangle in Fig. 5.2(b); as shown, the op amp has two inputs and one output. The inputs are marked with minus (−) and plus (+) to specify *inverting* and *noninverting* inputs, respectively. An input applied to the noninverting terminal will appear with the same polarity at the output, while an input applied to the inverting terminal will appear inverted at the output.

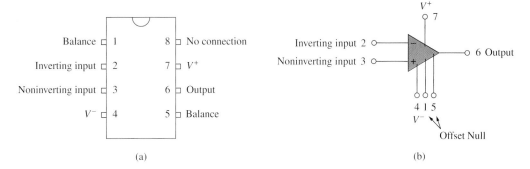

(a)   (b)

Figure 5.2   A typical op amp: (a) pin configuration, (b) circuit symbol.

As an active element, the op amp must be powered by a voltage supply as typically shown in Fig. 5.3. Although the power supplies are often ignored in op amp circuit diagrams for the sake of simplicity, the power supply currents must not be overlooked. By KCL,

$$i_o = i_1 + i_2 + i_+ + i_- \qquad (5.1)$$

The equivalent circuit model of an op amp is shown in Fig. 5.4. The output section consists of a voltage-controlled source in series with the output resistance R_o. It is evident from Fig. 5.4 that the input resistance R_i is the Thevenin equivalent resistance seen at the input terminals, while the output resistance R_o is the Thevenin equivalent resistance seen at the output. The differential input voltage v_d is given by

$$v_d = v_2 - v_1 \qquad (5.2)$$

where v_1 is the voltage between the inverting terminal and ground and v_2 is the voltage between the noninverting terminal and ground. The op amp senses the difference between the two inputs, multiplies it by the gain A, and causes the resulting voltage to appear at the output. Thus, the output v_o is given by

$$v_o = Av_d = A(v_2 - v_1) \qquad (5.3)$$

A is called the *open-loop voltage gain* because it is the gain of the op amp without any external feedback from output to input. Table 5.1 shows typical values of voltage gain A, input resistance R_i, output resistance R_o, and supply voltage V_{CC}.

The concept of feedback is crucial to our understanding of op amp circuits. A negative feedback is achieved when the output is fed back to

Figure 5.3   Powering the op amp.

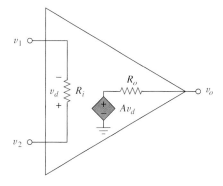

Figure 5.4   The equivalent circuit of the nonideal op amp.

Sometimes, voltage gain is expressed in decibels (dB), as discussed in Chapter 14.

$$A \text{ dB} = 20 \log_{10} A$$

TABLE 5.1   Typical ranges for op amp parameters.

Parameter	Typical range	Ideal values
Open-loop gain, A	10^5 to 10^8	∞
Input resistance, R_i	10^5 to 10^{13} Ω	∞ Ω
Output resistance, R_o	10 to 100 Ω	0 Ω
Supply voltage, V_{cc}	5 to 24 V	

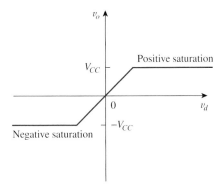

Figure 5.5   Op amp output voltage v_o as a function of the differential input voltage v_d.

the inverting terminal of the op amp. As Example 5.1 shows, when there is a feedback path from output to input, the ratio of the output voltage to the input voltage is called the *closed-loop gain.* As a result of the negative feedback, it can be shown that the closed-loop gain is almost insensitive to the open-loop gain A of the op amp. For this reason, op amps are used in circuits with feedback paths.

A practical limitation of the op amp is that the magnitude of its output voltage cannot exceed $|V_{CC}|$. In other words, the output voltage is dependent on and is limited by the power supply voltage. Figure 5.5 illustrates that the op amp can operate in three modes, depending on the differential input voltage v_d:

1. Positive saturation, $v_o = V_{CC}$.
2. Linear region, $-V_{CC} \leq v_o = A v_d \leq V_{CC}$.
3. Negative saturation, $v_o = -V_{CC}$.

If we attempt to increase v_d beyond the linear range, the op amp becomes saturated and yields $v_o = V_{CC}$ or $v_o = -V_{CC}$. Throughout this book, we will assume that our op amps operate in the linear mode. This means that the output voltage is restricted by

$$-V_{CC} \leq v_o \leq V_{CC} \tag{5.4}$$

Although we shall always operate the op amp in the linear region, the possibility of saturation must be borne in mind when one designs with op amps, to avoid designing op amp circuits that will not work in the laboratory.

Throughout this book, we assume that an op amp operates in the linear range. Keep in mind the voltage constraint on the op amp in this mode.

EXAMPLE 5.1

A 741 op amp has an open-loop voltage gain of 2×10^5, input resistance of 2 MΩ, and output resistance of 50 Ω. The op amp is used in the circuit of Fig. 5.6(a). Find the closed-loop gain v_o/v_s. Determine current i when $v_s = 2$ V.

Solution:

Using the op amp model in Fig. 5.4, we obtain the equivalent circuit of Fig. 5.6(a) as shown in Fig. 5.6(b). We now solve the circuit in Fig. 5.6(b) by using nodal analysis. At node 1, KCL gives

$$\frac{v_s - v_1}{10 \times 10^3} = \frac{v_1}{2000 \times 10^3} + \frac{v_1 - v_o}{20 \times 10^3}$$

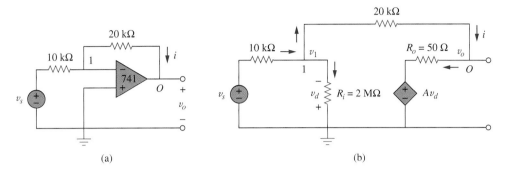

Figure 5.6   For Example 5.1: (a) original circuit, (b) the equivalent circuit.

Multiplying through by 2000×10^3, we obtain

$$200v_s = 301v_1 - 100v_o$$

or

$$2v_s \simeq 3v_1 - v_o \quad \Longrightarrow \quad v_1 = \frac{2v_s + v_o}{3} \qquad (5.1.1)$$

At node O,

$$\frac{v_1 - v_o}{20 \times 10^3} = \frac{v_o - Av_d}{50}$$

But $v_d = -v_1$ and $A = 200{,}000$. Then

$$v_1 - v_o = 400(v_o + 200{,}000v_1) \qquad (5.1.2)$$

Substituting v_1 from Eq. (5.1.1) into Eq. (5.1.2) gives

$$0 \simeq 26{,}667{,}067v_o + 53{,}333{,}333v_s \quad \Longrightarrow \quad \frac{v_o}{v_s} = -1.9999699$$

This is closed-loop gain, because the 20-kΩ feedback resistor closes the loop between the output and input terminals. When $v_s = 2$ V, $v_o = -3.9999398$ V. From Eq. (5.1.1), we obtain $v_1 = 20.066667$ μV. Thus,

$$i = \frac{v_1 - v_o}{20 \times 10^3} = 0.1999 \text{ mA}$$

It is evident that working with a nonideal op amp is tedious, as we are dealing with very large numbers.

PRACTICE PROBLEM 5.1

If the same 741 op amp in Example 5.1 is used in the circuit of Fig. 5.7, calculate the closed-loop gain v_o/v_s. Find i_o when $v_s = 1$ V.

Answer: 9.00041, 0.657 mA.

Figure 5.7   For Practice Prob. 5.1.

5.3   IDEAL OP AMP

To facilitate the understanding of op amp circuits, we will assume ideal op amps. An op amp is ideal if it has the following characteristics:

1. Infinite open-loop gain, $A \simeq \infty$.
2. Infinite input resistance, $R_i \simeq \infty$.
3. Zero output resistance, $R_o \simeq 0$.

> An ideal op amp is an amplifier with infinite open-loop gain, infinite input resistance, and zero output resistance.

Although assuming an ideal op amp provides only an approximate analysis, most modern amplifiers have such large gains and input impedances that the approximate analysis is a good one. Unless stated otherwise, we will assume from now on that every op amp is ideal.

For circuit analysis, the ideal op amp is illustrated in Fig. 5.8, which is derived from the nonideal model in Fig. 5.4. Two important characteristics of the ideal op amp are:

1. The currents into both input terminals are zero:

$$i_1 = 0, \qquad i_2 = 0 \tag{5.5}$$

This is due to infinite input resistance. An infinite resistance between the input terminals implies that an open circuit exists there and current cannot enter the op amp. But the output current is not necessarily zero according to Eq. (5.1).

2. The voltage across the input terminals is negligibly small; i.e.,

$$v_d = v_2 - v_1 \simeq 0 \tag{5.6}$$

or

$$v_1 = v_2 \tag{5.7}$$

Thus, an ideal op amp has zero current into its two input terminals and negligibly small voltage between the two input terminals. Equations (5.5) and (5.7) are extremely important and should be regarded as the key handles to analyzing op amp circuits.

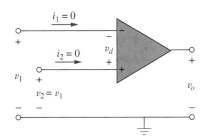

Figure 5.8   Ideal op amp model.

The two characteristics can be exploited by noting that for voltage calculations the input port behaves as a short circuit, while for current calculations the input port behaves as an open circuit.

EXAMPLE 5.2

Rework Practice Prob. 5.1 using the ideal op amp model.

Solution:

We may replace the op amp in Fig. 5.7 by its equivalent model in Fig. 5.9 as we did in Example 5.1. But we do not really need to do this. We just need to keep Eqs. (5.5) and (5.7) in mind as we analyze the circuit in Fig. 5.7. Thus, the Fig. 5.7 circuit is presented as in Fig. 5.9. Notice that

$$v_2 = v_s \tag{5.2.1}$$

Since $i_1 = 0$, the 40-kΩ and 5-kΩ resistors are in series; the same current flows through them. v_1 is the voltage across the 5-kΩ resistor. Hence, using the voltage division principle,

$$v_1 = \frac{5}{5 + 40}v_o = \frac{v_o}{9} \tag{5.2.2}$$

According to Eq. (5.7),

$$v_2 = v_1 \tag{5.2.3}$$

Substituting Eqs. (5.2.1) and (5.2.2) into Eq. (5.2.3) yields the closed-loop gain,

$$v_s = \frac{v_o}{9} \qquad \Longrightarrow \qquad \frac{v_o}{v_s} = 9 \tag{5.2.4}$$

which is very close to the value of 9.00041 obtained with the nonideal model in Practice Prob. 5.1. This shows that negligibly small error results from assuming ideal op amp characteristics.

At node O,

$$i_o = \frac{v_o}{40 + 5} + \frac{v_o}{20} \text{ mA} \tag{5.2.5}$$

From Eq. (5.2.4), when $v_s = 1$ V, $v_o = 9$ V. Substituting for $v_o = 9$ V in Eq. (5.2.5) produces

$$i_o = 0.2 + 0.45 = 0.65 \text{ mA}$$

This, again, is close to the value of 0.657 mA obtained in Practice Prob. 5.1 with the nonideal model.

Figure 5.9   For Example 5.2.

PRACTICE PROBLEM 5.2

Repeat Example 5.1 using the ideal op amp model.

Answer: -2, 0.2 mA.

5.4   INVERTING AMPLIFIER

In this and the following sections, we consider some useful op amp circuits that often serve as modules for designing more complex circuits. The first of such op amp circuits is the inverting amplifier shown in Fig. 5.10. In this circuit, the noninverting input is grounded, v_i is connected to the inverting input through R_1, and the feedback resistor R_f is connected between the inverting input and output. Our goal is to obtain the relationship between the input voltage v_i and the output voltage v_o. Applying KCL at node 1,

$$i_1 = i_2 \qquad \Longrightarrow \qquad \frac{v_i - v_1}{R_1} = \frac{v_1 - v_o}{R_f} \tag{5.8}$$

A key feature of the inverting amplifier is that both the input signal and the feedback are applied at the inverting terminal of the op amp.

But $v_1 = v_2 = 0$ for an ideal op amp, since the noninverting terminal is grounded. Hence,

$$\frac{v_i}{R_1} = -\frac{v_o}{R_f}$$

or

$$v_o = -\frac{R_f}{R_1} v_i \qquad (5.9)$$

Note there are two types of gains: the one here is the closed-loop voltage gain A_v, while the op amp itself has an open-loop voltage gain A.

The voltage gain is $A_v = v_o/v_i = -R_f/R_1$. The designation of the circuit in Fig. 5.10 as an *inverter* arises from the negative sign. Thus,

An inverting amplifier reverses the polarity of the input signal while amplifying it.

Notice that the gain is the feedback resistance divided by the input resistance which means that the gain depends only on the external elements connected to the op amp. In view of Eq. (5.9), an equivalent circuit for the inverting amplifier is shown in Fig. 5.11. The inverting amplifier is used, for example, in a current-to-voltage converter.

Figure 5.10   The inverting amplifier.

Figure 5.11   An equivalent circuit for the inverter in Fig. 5.10.

EXAMPLE 5.3

Figure 5.12   For Example 5.3.

Refer to the op amp in Fig. 5.12. If $v_i = 0.5$ V, calculate: (a) the output voltage v_o, and (b) the current in the 10 kΩ resistor.

Solution:

(a) Using Eq. (5.9),

$$\frac{v_o}{v_i} = -\frac{R_f}{R_1} = -\frac{25}{10} = -2.5$$

$$v_o = -2.5 v_i = -2.5(0.5) = -1.25 \text{ V}$$

(b) The current through the 10-kΩ resistor is

$$i = \frac{v_i - 0}{R_1} = \frac{0.5 - 0}{10 \times 10^3} = 50 \ \mu\text{A}$$

PRACTICE PROBLEM 5.3

Find the output of the op amp circuit shown in Fig. 5.13. Calculate the current through the feedback resistor.

Answer: -120 mV, 8 μA.

Figure 5.13   For Practice Prob. 5.3.

EXAMPLE 5.4

Determine v_o in the op amp circuit shown in Fig. 5.14.

Solution:

Applying KCL at node a,

$$\frac{v_a - v_o}{40 \text{ k}\Omega} = \frac{6 - v_a}{20 \text{ k}\Omega}$$

$$v_a - v_o = 12 - 2v_a \quad \Longrightarrow \quad v_o = 3v_a - 12$$

But $v_a = v_b = 2$ V for an ideal op amp, because of the zero voltage drop across the input terminals of the op amp. Hence,

$$v_o = 6 - 12 = -6 \text{ V}$$

Notice that if $v_b = 0 = v_a$, then $v_o = -12$, as expected from Eq. (5.9).

Figure 5.14   For Example 5.4.

PRACTICE PROBLEM 5.4

Two kinds of current-to-voltage converters (also known as *transresistance amplifiers*) are shown in Fig. 5.15.

(a) Show that for the converter in Fig. 5.15(a),

$$\frac{v_o}{i_s} = -R$$

(b) Show that for the converter in Fig. 5.15(b),

$$\frac{v_o}{i_s} = -R_1\left(1 + \frac{R_3}{R_1} + \frac{R_3}{R_2}\right)$$

Answer: Proof.

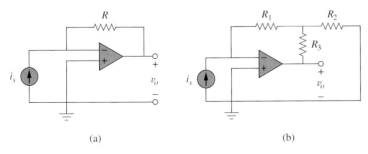

(a)   (b)

Figure 5.15   For Practice Prob. 5.4.

Figure 5.16   The noninverting amplifier.

5.5   NONINVERTING AMPLIFIER

Another important application of the op amp is the noninverting amplifier shown in Fig. 5.16. In this case, the input voltage v_i is applied directly at the noninverting input terminal, and resistor R_1 is connected between the ground and the inverting terminal. We are interested in the output voltage and the voltage gain. Application of KCL at the inverting terminal gives

$$i_1 = i_2 \quad \Longrightarrow \quad \frac{0 - v_1}{R_1} = \frac{v_1 - v_o}{R_f} \quad\quad (5.10)$$

But $v_1 = v_2 = v_i$. Equation (5.10) becomes

$$\frac{-v_i}{R_1} = \frac{v_i - v_o}{R_f}$$

or

$$v_o = \left(1 + \frac{R_f}{R_1} \right) v_i \quad\quad (5.11)$$

The voltage gain is $A_v = v_o/v_i = 1 + R_f/R_1$, which does not have a negative sign. Thus, the output has the same polarity as the input.

A noninverting amplifier is an op amp circuit designed to provide a positive voltage gain.

Again we notice that the gain depends only on the external resistors.

Notice that if feedback resistor $R_f = 0$ (short circuit) or $R_1 = \infty$ (open circuit) or both, the gain becomes 1. Under these conditions ($R_f = 0$ and $R_1 = \infty$), the circuit in Fig. 5.16 becomes that shown in Fig. 5.17, which is called a *voltage follower* (or *unity gain amplifier*) because the output follows the input. Thus, for a voltage follower

$$v_o = v_i \quad\quad (5.12)$$

Such a circuit has a very high input impedance and is therefore useful as an intermediate-stage (or buffer) amplifier to isolate one circuit from another, as portrayed in Fig. 5.18. The voltage follower minimizes interaction between the two stages and eliminates interstage loading.

Figure 5.17   The voltage follower.

Figure 5.18   A voltage follower used to isolate two cascaded stages of a circuit.

EXAMPLE 5.5

For the op amp circuit in Fig. 5.19, calculate the output voltage v_o.

Solution:

We may solve this in two ways: using superposition and using nodal analysis.

METHOD 1 Using superposition, we let

$$v_o = v_{o1} + v_{o2}$$

Figure 5.19   For Example 5.9.

where v_{o1} is due to the 6-V voltage source, and v_{o2} is due to the 4-V input. To get v_{o1}, we set the 4-V source equal to zero. Under this condition, the circuit becomes an inverter. Hence Eq. (5.9) gives

$$v_{o1} = -\frac{10}{4}(6) = -15 \text{ V}$$

To get v_{o2}, we set the 6-V source equal to zero. The circuit becomes a noninverting amplifier so that Eq. (5.11) applies.

$$v_{o2} = \left(1 + \frac{10}{4}\right)4 = 14 \text{ V}$$

Thus,

$$v_o = v_{o1} + v_{o2} = -15 + 14 = -1 \text{ V}$$

METHOD 2 Applying KCL at node a,

$$\frac{6 - v_a}{4} = \frac{v_a - v_o}{10}$$

But $v_a = v_b = 4$, and so

$$\frac{6 - 4}{4} = \frac{4 - v_o}{10} \qquad \Longrightarrow \qquad 5 = 4 - v_o$$

or $v_o = -1$ V, as before.

PRACTICE PROBLEM 5.5

Calculate v_o in the circuit in Fig. 5.20.

Answer: 7 V.

Figure 5.20   For Practice Prob. 5.5.

5.6 SUMMING AMPLIFIER

Besides amplification, the op amp can perform addition and subtraction. The addition is performed by the summing amplifier covered in this section; the subtraction is performed by the difference amplifier covered in the next section.

A summing amplifier is an op amp circuit that combines several inputs and produces an output that is the weighted sum of the inputs.

Figure 5.21   The summing amplifier.

The summing amplifier, shown in Fig. 5.21, is a variation of the inverting amplifier. It takes advantage of the fact that the inverting configuration can handle many inputs at the same time. We keep in mind that the current entering each op amp input is zero. Applying KCL at node a gives

$$i = i_1 + i_2 + i_3 \tag{5.13}$$

But

$$i_1 = \frac{v_1 - v_a}{R_1}, \qquad i_2 = \frac{v_2 - v_a}{R_2}$$

$$i_3 = \frac{v_3 - v_a}{R_3}, \qquad i = \frac{v_a - v_o}{R_f} \tag{5.14}$$

We note that $v_a = 0$ and substitute Eq. (5.14) into Eq. (5.13). We get

$$v_o = -\left(\frac{R_f}{R_1} v_1 + \frac{R_f}{R_2} v_2 + \frac{R_f}{R_3} v_3 \right) \tag{5.15}$$

indicating that the output voltage is a weighted sum of the inputs. For this reason, the circuit in Fig. 5.21 is called a *summer*. Needless to say, the summer can have more than three inputs.

EXAMPLE 5.6

Calculate v_o and i_o in the op amp circuit in Fig. 5.22.

Figure 5.22   For Example 5.6.

Solution:

This is a summer with two inputs. Using Eq. (5.15),

$$v_o = -\left[\frac{10}{5}(2) + \frac{10}{2.5}(1)\right] = -(4 + 4) = -8 \text{ V}$$

The current i_o is the sum of the currents through the 10-kΩ and 2-kΩ resistors. Both of these resistors have voltage $v_o = -8$ V across them, since $v_a = v_b = 0$. Hence,

$$i_o = \frac{v_o - 0}{10} + \frac{v_o - 0}{2} \text{ mA} = -0.8 - 4 = -4.8 \text{ mA}$$

PRACTICE PROBLEM 5.6

Find v_o and i_o in the op amp circuit shown in Fig. 5.23.

Figure 5.23   For Practice Prob. 5.6.

Answer: -3.8 V, -1.425 mA.

5.7 DIFFERENCE AMPLIFIER

Difference (or differential) amplifiers are used in various applications where there is need to amplify the difference between two input signals. They are first cousins of the *instrumentation amplifier*, the most useful and popular amplifier, which we will discuss in Section 5.10.

The difference amplifier is also known as the subtractor, for reasons to be shown later.

A difference amplifier is a device that amplifies the difference between two inputs but rejects any signals common to the two inputs.

Consider the op amp circuit shown in Fig. 5.24. Keep in mind that zero currents enter the op amp terminals. Applying KCL to node a,

$$\frac{v_1 - v_a}{R_1} = \frac{v_a - v_o}{R_2}$$

or

$$v_o = \left(\frac{R_2}{R_1} + 1\right) v_a - \frac{R_2}{R_1} v_1 \tag{5.16}$$

Figure 5.24   Difference amplifier.

Applying KCL to node b,

$$\frac{v_2 - v_b}{R_3} = \frac{v_b - 0}{R_4}$$

or

$$v_b = \frac{R_4}{R_3 + R_4} v_2 \tag{5.17}$$

But $v_a = v_b$. Substituting Eq. (5.17) into Eq. (5.16) yields

$$v_o = \left(\frac{R_2}{R_1} + 1\right) \frac{R_4}{R_3 + R_4} v_2 - \frac{R_2}{R_1} v_1$$

or

$$v_o = \frac{R_2}{R_1} \frac{(1 + R_1/R_2)}{(1 + R_3/R_4)} v_2 - \frac{R_2}{R_1} v_1 \tag{5.18}$$

Since a difference amplifier must reject a signal common to the two inputs, the amplifier must have the property that $v_o = 0$ when $v_1 = v_2$. This property exists when

$$\frac{R_1}{R_2} = \frac{R_3}{R_4} \tag{5.19}$$

Thus, when the op amp circuit is a difference amplifier, Eq. (5.18) becomes

$$v_o = \frac{R_2}{R_1}(v_2 - v_1) \tag{5.20}$$

If $R_2 = R_1$ and $R_3 = R_4$, the difference amplifier becomes a *subtractor*, with the output

$$v_o = v_2 - v_1 \tag{5.21}$$

EXAMPLE 5.7

Design an op amp circuit with inputs v_1 and v_2 such that $v_o = -5v_1 + 3v_2$.

Solution:

The circuit requires that

$$v_o = 3v_2 - 5v_1 \tag{5.7.1}$$

This circuit can be realized in two ways.

DESIGN 1   If we desire to use only one op amp, we can use the op amp circuit of Fig. 5.24. Comparing Eq. (5.7.1) with Eq. (5.18),

$$\frac{R_2}{R_1} = 5 \quad \Longrightarrow \quad R_2 = 5R_1 \qquad (5.7.2)$$

Also,

$$5\frac{(1 + R_1/R_2)}{(1 + R_3/R_4)} = 3 \quad \Longrightarrow \quad \frac{\frac{6}{5}}{1 + R_3/R_4} = \frac{3}{5}$$

or

$$2 = 1 + \frac{R_3}{R_4} \quad \Longrightarrow \quad R_3 = R_4 \qquad (5.7.3)$$

If we choose $R_1 = 10 \text{ k}\Omega$ and $R_3 = 20 \text{ k}\Omega$, then $R_2 = 50 \text{ k}\Omega$ and $R_4 = 20 \text{ k}\Omega$.

DESIGN 2   If we desire to use more than one op amp, we may cascade an inverting amplifier and a two-input inverting summer, as shown in Fig. 5.25. For the summer,

$$v_o = -v_a - 5v_1 \qquad (5.7.4)$$

and for the inverter,

$$v_a = -3v_2 \qquad (5.7.5)$$

Combining Eqs. (5.7.4) and (5.7.5) gives

$$v_o = 3v_2 - 5v_1$$

which is the desired result. In Fig. 5.25, we may select $R_1 = 10 \text{ k}\Omega$ and $R_3 = 20 \text{ k}\Omega$ or $R_1 = R_3 = 10 \text{ k}\Omega$.

Figure 5.25   For Example 5.7.

PRACTICE PROBLEM 5.7

Design a difference amplifier with gain 4.

Answer: Typical: $R_1 = R_3 = 10 \text{ k}\Omega$, $R_2 = R_4 = 40 \text{ k}\Omega$.

EXAMPLE 5.8

An *instrumentation amplifier* shown in Fig. 5.26 is an amplifier of low-level signals used in process control or measurement applications and commercially available in single-package units. Show that

$$v_o = \frac{R_2}{R_1}\left(1 + \frac{2R_3}{R_4}\right)(v_2 - v_1)$$

Solution:

We recognize that the amplifier A_3 in Fig. 5.26 is a difference amplifier. Thus, from Eq. (5.20),

$$v_o = \frac{R_2}{R_1}(v_{o2} - v_{o1}) \qquad (5.8.1)$$

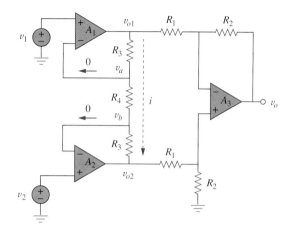

Figure 5.26   Instrumentation amplifier; for Example 5.8.

Since the op amps A_1 and A_2 draw no current, current i flows through the three resistors as though they were in series. Hence,

$$v_{o1} - v_{o2} = i(R_3 + R_4 + R_3) = i(2R_3 + R_4) \qquad (5.8.2)$$

But

$$i = \frac{v_a - v_b}{R_4}$$

and $v_a = v_1$, $v_b = v_2$. Therefore,

$$i = \frac{v_1 - v_2}{R_4} \qquad (5.8.3)$$

Inserting Eqs. (5.8.2) and (5.8.3) into Eq. (5.8.1) gives

$$v_o = \frac{R_2}{R_1}\left(1 + \frac{2R_3}{R_4}\right)(v_2 - v_1)$$

as required. We will discuss the instrumentation amplifier in detail in Section 5.10.

PRACTICE PROBLEM 5.8

Obtain i_o in the instrumentation amplifier circuit of Fig. 5.27.

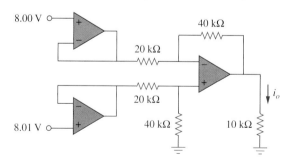

Figure 5.27   Instrumentation amplifier; for Practice Prob. 5.8.

Answer: $2 \ \mu A$.

5.8   CASCADED OP AMP CIRCUITS

As we know, op amp circuits are modules or building blocks for designing complex circuits. It is often necessary in practical applications to connect op amp circuits in cascade (i.e., head to tail) to achieve a large overall gain. In general, two circuits are cascaded when they are connected in tandem, one behind another in a single file.

> A cascade connection is a head-to-tail arrangement of two or more op amp circuits such that the output of one is the input of the next.

When op amp circuits are cascaded, each circuit in the string is called a *stage*; the original input signal is increased by the gain of the individual stage. Op amp circuits have the advantage that they can be cascaded without changing their input-output relationships. This is due to the fact that each (ideal) op amp circuit has infinite input resistance and zero output resistance. Figure 5.28 displays a block diagram representation of three op amp circuits in cascade. Since the output of one stage is the input to the next stage, the overall gain of the cascade connection is the product of the gains of the individual op amp circuits, or

$$A = A_1 A_2 A_3 \qquad (5.22)$$

Although the cascade connection does not affect the op amp input-output relationships, care must be exercised in the design of an actual op amp circuit to ensure that the load due to the next stage in the cascade does not saturate the op amp.

Figure 5.28   A three-stage cascaded connection.

EXAMPLE 5.9

Find v_o and i_o in the circuit in Fig. 5.29.

Solution:

This circuit consists of two noninverting amplifiers cascaded. At the output of the first op amp,

$$v_a = \left(1 + \frac{12}{3}\right)(20) = 100 \text{ mV}$$

At the output of the second op amp,

$$v_o = \left(1 + \frac{10}{4}\right) v_a = (1 + 2.5)100 = 350 \text{ mV}$$

Figure 5.29   For Example 5.9.

The required current i_o is the current through the 10-kΩ resistor.

$$i_o = \frac{v_o - v_b}{10} \text{ mA}$$

But $v_b = v_a = 100$ mV. Hence,

$$i_o = \frac{(350 - 100) \times 10^{-3}}{10 \times 10^3} = 25 \text{ } \mu\text{A}$$

PRACTICE PROBLEM 5.9

Determine v_o and i_o in the op amp circuit in Fig. 5.30.

Answer: 10 V, 1 mA.

Figure 5.30   For Practice Prob. 5.9.

EXAMPLE 5.10

If $v_1 = 1$ V and $v_2 = 2$ V, find v_o in the op amp circuit of Fig. 5.31.

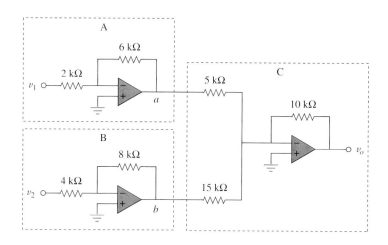

Figure 5.31   For Example 5.10.

Solution:

The circuit consists of two inverters A and B and a summer C as shown in Fig. 5.31. We first find the outputs of the inverters.

$$v_a = -\frac{6}{2}(v_1) = -3(1) = -3 \text{ V}, \qquad v_b = -\frac{8}{4}(v_2) = -2(2) = -4 \text{ V}$$

These become the inputs to the summer so that the output is obtained as

$$v_o = -\left(\frac{10}{5}v_a + \frac{10}{15}v_b\right) = -\left[2(-3) + \frac{2}{3}(-4)\right] = 8.667 \text{ V}$$

PRACTICE PROBLEM 5.10

If $v_1 = 2$ V and $v_2 = 1.5$ V, find v_o in the op amp circuit of Fig. 5.32.

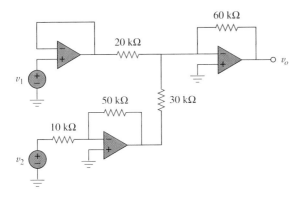

Figure 5.32   For Practice Prob. 5.10.

Answer: 9 V.

5.9   OP AMP CIRCUIT ANALYSIS WITH *PSPICE*

PSpice for Windows does not have a model for an ideal op amp, although one may create one as a subcircuit using the *Create Subcircuit* line in the *Tools* menu. Rather than creating an ideal op amp, we will use one of the four nonideal, commercially available op amps supplied in the *PSpice* library *eval.slb*. The op amp models have the part names LF411, LM111, LM324, and uA741, as shown in Fig. 5.33. Each of them can be obtained from **Draw/Get New Part/libraries** · · · **/eval.lib** or by simply selecting **Draw/Get New Part** and typing the part name in the *PartName* dialog box, as usual. Note that each of them requires dc supplies, without which the op amp will not work. The dc supplies should be connected as shown in Fig. 5.3.

(a) JFET–input op amp subcircuit

(b) Op amp subcircuit

(c) Five–connection op amp subcircuit

(d) Five–connection op amp subcircuit

Figure 5.33   Nonideal op amp model available in *PSpice*.

EXAMPLE 5.11

Use *PSpice* to solve the op amp circuit for Example 5.1.

Solution:

Using Schematics, we draw the circuit in Fig. 5.6(a) as shown in Fig. 5.34. Notice that the positive terminal of the voltage source v_s is connected to the inverting terminal (pin 2) via the 10-kΩ resistor, while the noninverting terminal (pin 3) is grounded as required in Fig. 5.6(a). Also, notice how the op amp is powered; the positive power supply terminal V+ (pin 7) is connected to a 15-V dc voltage source, while the negative power supply terminal V− (pin 4) is connected to −15 V. Pins 1 and 5 are left floating because they are used for offset null adjustment, which does not concern us in this chapter. Besides adding the dc power supplies to the original circuit in Fig. 5.6(a), we have also added pseudocomponents VIEWPOINT and IPROBE to respectively measure the output voltage v_o at pin 6 and the required current i through the 20-kΩ resistor.

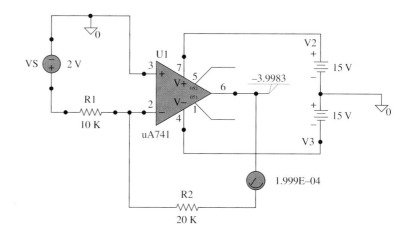

Figure 5.34   Schematic for Example 5.11.

After saving the schematic, we simulate the circuit by selecting **Analysis/Simulate** and have the results displayed on VIEWPOINT and IPROBE. From the results, the closed-loop gain is

$$\frac{v_o}{v_s} = \frac{-3.9983}{2} = -1.99915$$

and $i = 0.1999$ mA, in agreement with the results obtained analytically in Example 5.1.

PRACTICE PROBLEM 5.11

Rework Practice Prob. 5.1 using *PSpice*.

Answer: 9.0027, 0.6502 mA.

†5.10 APPLICATIONS

The op amp is a fundamental building block in modern electronic instrumentation. It is used extensively in many devices, along with resistors and other passive elements. Its numerous practical applications include instrumentation amplifiers, digital-to-analog converters, analog computers, level shifters, filters, calibration circuits, inverters, summers, integrators, differentiators, subtractors, logarithmic amplifiers, comparators, gyrators, oscillators, rectifiers, regulators, voltage-to-current converters, current-to-voltage converters, and clippers. Some of these we have already considered. We will consider two more applications here: the digital-to-analog converter and the instrumentation amplifier.

(a)

(b)

Figure 5.35   Four-bit DAC: (a) block diagram, (b) binary weighted ladder type.

5.10.1 Digital-to-Analog Converter

The digital-to-analog converter (DAC) transforms digital signals into analog form. A typical example of a four-bit DAC is illustrated in Fig. 5.35(a). The four-bit DAC can be realized in many ways. A simple realization is the *binary weighted ladder*, shown in Fig. 5.35(b). The bits are weights according to the magnitude of their place value, by descending value of R_f/R_n so that each lesser bit has half the weight of the next higher. This is obviously an inverting summing amplifier. The output is related to the inputs as shown in Eq. (5.15). Thus,

$$-V_o = \frac{R_f}{R_1}V_1 + \frac{R_f}{R_2}V_2 + \frac{R_f}{R_3}V_3 + \frac{R_f}{R_4}V_4 \qquad (5.23)$$

Input V_1 is called the *most significant bit* (MSB), while input V_4 is the *least significant bit* (LSB). Each of the four binary inputs $V_1, \ldots, V_4$ can assume only two voltage levels: 0 or 1 V. By using the proper input and feedback resistor values, the DAC provides a single output that is proportional to the inputs.

In practice, the voltage levels may be typically 0 and ± 5 V.

EXAMPLE 5.12

In the op amp circuit of Fig. 5.35(b), let $R_f = 10$ kΩ, $R_1 = 10$ kΩ, $R_2 = 20$ kΩ, $R_3 = 40$ kΩ, and $R_4 = 80$ kΩ. Obtain the analog output for binary inputs [0000], [0001], [0010], . . . , [1111].

Solution:

Substituting the given values of the input and feedback resistors in Eq. (5.23) gives

$$-V_o = \frac{R_f}{R_1}V_1 + \frac{R_f}{R_2}V_2 + \frac{R_f}{R_3}V_3 + \frac{R_f}{R_4}V_4$$

$$= V_1 + 0.5V_2 + 0.25V_3 + 0.125V_4$$

Using this equation, a digital input $[V_1 V_2 V_3 V_4] = [0000]$ produces an analog output of $-V_o = 0$ V; $[V_1 V_2 V_3 V_4] = [0001]$ gives $-V_o = 0.125$ V.

Similarly,

$$[V_1 V_2 V_3 V_4] = [0010] \implies -V_o = 0.25 \text{ V}$$
$$[V_1 V_2 V_3 V_4] = [0011] \implies -V_o = 0.25 + 0.125 = 0.375 \text{ V}$$
$$[V_1 V_2 V_3 V_4] = [0100] \implies -V_o = 0.5 \text{ V}$$
$$\vdots$$
$$[V_1 V_2 V_3 V_4] = [1111] \implies -V_o = 1 + 0.5 + 0.25 + 0.125$$
$$= 1.875 \text{ V}$$

Table 5.2 summarizes the result of the digital-to-analog conversion. Note that we have assumed that each bit has a value of 0.125 V. Thus, in this system, we cannot represent a voltage between 1.000 and 1.125, for example. This lack of resolution is a major limitation of digital-to-analog conversions. For greater accuracy, a word representation with a greater number of bits is required. Even then a digital representation of an analog voltage is never exact. In spite of this inexact representation, digital representation has been used to accomplish remarkable things such as audio CDs and digital photography.

TABLE 5.2   Input and output values of the four-bit DAC.

Binary input $[V_1 V_2 V_3 V_4]$	Decimal value	Output $-V_o$
0000	0	0
0001	1	0.125
0010	2	0.25
0011	3	0.375
0100	4	0.5
0101	5	0.625
0110	6	0.75
0111	7	0.875
1000	8	1.0
1001	9	1.125
1010	10	1.25
1011	11	1.375
1100	12	1.5
1101	13	1.625
1110	14	1.75
1111	15	1.875

PRACTICE PROBLEM 5.12

A three-bit DAC is shown in Fig. 5.36.

(a) Determine $|V_o|$ for $[V_1 V_2 V_3] = [010]$.

(b) Find $|V_o|$ if $[V_1 V_2 V_3] = [110]$.

(c) If $|V_o| = 1.25$ V is desired, what should be $[V_1 V_2 V_3]$?

(d) To get $|V_o| = 1.75$ V, what should be $[V_1 V_2 V_3]$?

Answer: 0.5 V, 1.5 V, [101], [111].

Figure 5.36   Three-bit DAC; for Practice Prob. 5.12.

5.10.2 Instrumentation Amplifiers

One of the most useful and versatile op amp circuits for precision measurement and process control is the *instrumentation amplifier* (IA), so called because of its widespread use in measurement systems. Typical applications of IAs include isolation amplifiers, thermocouple amplifiers, and data acquisition systems.

The instrumentation amplifier is an extension of the difference amplifier in that it amplifies the difference between its input signals. As shown in Fig. 5.26 (see Example 5.8), an instrumentation amplifier typically consists of three op amps and seven resistors. For convenience, the amplifier is shown again in Fig. 5.37(a), where the resistors are made equal except for the external gain-setting resistor R_G, connected between the gain set terminals. Figure 5.37(b) shows its schematic symbol. Example 5.8 showed that

$$v_o = A_v(v_2 - v_1) \tag{5.24}$$

where the voltage gain is

$$A_v = 1 + \frac{2R}{R_G} \tag{5.25}$$

As shown in Fig. 5.38, the instrumentation amplifier amplifies small differential signal voltages superimposed on larger common-mode voltages. Since the common-mode voltages are equal, they cancel each other.

(a)

(b)

Figure 5.37   (a) The instrumentation amplifier with an external resistance to adjust the gain, (b) schematic diagram.

Small differential signals riding on larger   Instrumentation amplifier   Amplified differential signal,
common-mode signals   No common-mode signal

Figure 5.38   The IA rejects common voltages but amplifies small signal voltages.
(Source: T. L. Floyd, Electronic Devices, 2nd ed., Englewood Cliffs, NJ: Prentice Hall, 1996, p. 795.)

The IA has three major characteristics:

1. The voltage gain is adjusted by *one* external resistor R_G.
2. The input impedance of both inputs is very high and does not vary as the gain is adjusted.
3. The output v_o depends on the difference between the inputs v_1 and v_2, not on the voltage common to them (common-mode voltage).

Due to the widespread use of IAs, manufacturers have developed these amplifiers on single-package units. A typical example is the LH0036, developed by National Semiconductor. The gain can be varied from 1 to 1,000 by an external resistor whose value may vary from 100 Ω to 10 kΩ.

EXAMPLE 5.13

In Fig. 5.37, let $R = 10$ kΩ, $v_1 = 2.011$ V, and $v_2 = 2.017$ V. If R_G is adjusted to 500 Ω, determine: (a) the voltage gain, (b) the output voltage v_o.

Solution:

(a) The voltage gain is

$$A_v = 1 + \frac{2R}{R_G} = 1 + \frac{2 \times 10,000}{500} = 41$$

(b) The output voltage is

$$v_o = A_v(v_2 - v_1) = 41(2.017 - 2.011) = 41(6) \text{ mV} = 246 \text{ mV}$$

PRACTICE PROBLEM 5.13

Determine the value of the external gain-setting resistor R_G required for the IA in Fig. 5.37 to produce a gain of 142 when $R = 25$ kΩ.

Answer: 354.6 Ω.

5.11 SUMMARY

1. The op amp is a high-gain amplifier that has high input resistance and low output resistance.

2. Table 5.3 summarizes the op amp circuits considered in this chapter. The expression for the gain of each amplifier circuit holds whether the inputs are dc, ac, or time-varying in general.

TABLE 5.3   Summary of basic op amp circuits.

Op amp circuit	Name/output-input relationship
	Inverting amplifier $v_o = -\dfrac{R_2}{R_1} v_i$
	Noninverting amplifier $v_o = \left(1 + \dfrac{R_2}{R_1}\right) v_i$
	Voltage follower $v_o = v_i$
	Summer $v_o = -\left(\dfrac{R_f}{R_1} v_1 + \dfrac{R_f}{R_2} v_2 + \dfrac{R_f}{R_3} v_3\right)$
	Difference amplifier $v_o = \dfrac{R_2}{R_1}(v_2 - v_1)$

3. An ideal op amp has an infinite input resistance, a zero output resistance, and an infinite gain.

4. For an ideal op amp, the current into each of its two input terminals is zero, and the voltage across its input terminals is negligibly small.

5. In an inverting amplifier, the output voltage is a negative multiple of the input.

6. In a noninverting amplifier, the output is a positive multiple of the input.

7. In a voltage follower, the output follows the input.

8. In a summing amplifier, the output is the weighted sum of the inputs.

9. In a difference amplifier, the output is proportional to the difference of the two inputs.

10. Op amp circuits may be cascaded without changing their input-output relationships.

11. *PSpice* can be used to analyze an op amp circuit.

12. Typical applications of the op amp considered in this chapter include the digital-to-analog converter and the instrumentation amplifier.

REVIEW QUESTIONS

5.1 The two input terminals of an op amp are labeled as:

(a) high and low.
(b) positive and negative.
(c) inverting and noninverting.
(d) differential and nondifferential.

5.2 For an ideal op amp, which of the following statements are not true?

(a) The differential voltage across the input terminals is zero.
(b) The current into the input terminals is zero.
(c) The current from the output terminal is zero.
(d) The input resistance is zero.
(e) The output resistance is zero.

5.3 For the circuit in Fig. 5.39, voltage v_o is:

(a) −6 V   (b) −5 V
(c) −1.2 V   (d) −0.2 V

Figure 5.39   For Review Questions 5.3 and 5.4.

5.4 For the circuit in Fig. 5.39, current i_x is:

(a) 0.6 mA   (b) 0.5 mA
(c) 0.2 mA   (d) 1/12 mA

5.5 If $v_s = 0$ in the circuit of Fig. 5.40, current i_o is:

(a) −10 mA   (b) −2.5 mA
(c) 10/12 mA   (d) 10/14 mA

Figure 5.40   For Review Questions 5.5 to 5.7.

5.6 If $v_s = 8$ mV in the circuit of Fig. 5.40, the output voltage is:

(a) −44 mV   (b) −8 mV
(c) 4 mV   (d) 7 mV

5.7 Refer to Fig. 5.40. If $v_s = 8$ mV, voltage v_a is:

(a) −8 mV   (b) 0 mV
(c) 10/3 mV   (d) 8 mV

5.8 The power absorbed by the 4-kΩ resistor in Fig. 5.41 is:

(a) 9 mW   (b) 4 mW
(c) 2 mW   (d) 1 mW

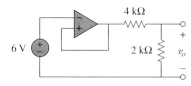

Figure 5.41   For Review Question 5.8.

5.9 Which of these amplifiers is used in a digital-to-analog converter?

(a) noninverter   (b) voltage follower
(c) summer   (d) difference amplifier

5.10   Difference amplifiers are used in:

(a)   instrumentation amplifiers

(b)   voltage followers

(c)   voltage regulators

(d)   buffers

(e)   summing amplifiers

(f)   subtracting amplifiers

Answers: 5.1c, 5.2c,d, 5.3b, 5.4b, 5.5a, 5.6c, 5.7d, 5.8b, 5.9c, 5.10a,f.

PROBLEMS

Section 5.2   Operational Amplifiers

5.1   The equivalent model of a certain op amp is shown in Fig. 5.42. Determine:

(a)   the input resistance

(b)   the output resistance

(c)   the voltage gain in dB.

Figure 5.42   For Prob. 5.1.

5.2   The open-loop gain of an op amp is 100,000. Calculate the output voltage when there are inputs of $+10\ \mu$V on the inverting terminal and $+20\ \mu$V on the noninverting terminal.

5.3   Determine the output voltage when $-20\ \mu$V is applied to the inverting terminal of an op amp and $+30\ \mu$V to its noninverting terminal. Assume that the op amp has an open-loop gain of 200,000.

5.4   The output voltage of an op amp is -4 V when the noninverting input is 1 mV. If the open-loop gain of the op amp is 2×10^6, what is the inverting input?

5.5   For the op amp circuit of Fig. 5.43, the op amp has an open-loop gain of 100,000, an input resistance of 10 kΩ, and an output resistance of 100 Ω. Find the voltage gain v_o/v_i using the nonideal model of the op amp.

Figure 5.43   For Prob. 5.5.

5.6   Using the same parameters for the 741 op amp in Example 5.1, find v_o in the op amp circuit of Fig. 5.44.

Figure 5.44   For Prob. 5.6.

5.7   The op amp in Fig. 5.45 has $R_i = 100$ kΩ, $R_o = 100$ Ω, $A = 100,000$. Find the differential voltage v_d and the output voltage v_o.

Figure 5.45   For Prob. 5.7.

Section 5.3   Ideal Op Amp

5.8   Obtain v_o for each of the op amp circuits in Fig. 5.46.

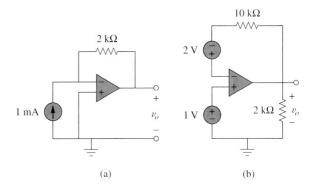

(a)   (b)

Figure 5.46   For Prob. 5.8.

5.9   Determine v_o for each of the op amp circuits in Fig. 5.47.

Figure 5.47 For Prob. 5.9.

5.10 Find the gain v_o/v_s of the circuit in Fig. 5.48.

Figure 5.48 For Prob. 5.10.

5.11 Find v_o and i_o in the circuit in Fig. 5.49.

Figure 5.49 For Prob. 5.11.

5.12 Refer to the op amp circuit in Fig. 5.50. Determine the power supplied by the voltage source.

Figure 5.50 For Prob. 5.12.

5.13 Find v_o and i_o in the circuit of Fig. 5.51.

Figure 5.51 For Prob. 5.13.

5.14 Determine the output voltage v_o in the circuit of Fig. 5.52.

Figure 5.52 For Prob. 5.14.

Section 5.4 Inverting Amplifier

5.15 (a) Determine the ratio v_o/i_s in the op amp circuit of Fig. 5.53.

(b) Evaluate the ratio for $R_1 = 20$ kΩ, $R_2 = 25$ kΩ, $R_3 = 40$ kΩ.

Figure 5.53   For Prob. 5.15.

5.16   Obtain i_x and i_y in the op amp circuit in Fig. 5.54.

Figure 5.54   For Prob. 5.16.

5.17   Calculate the gain v_o/v_i when the switch in Fig. 5.55 is in:

(a) position 1   (b) position 2   (c) position 3

Figure 5.55   For Prob. 5.17.

5.18   Calculate the gain v_o/v_i of the op amp circuit in Fig. 5.56.

Figure 5.56   For Prob. 5.18.

5.19   Determine i_o in the circuit of Fig. 5.57.

Figure 5.57   For Prob. 5.19.

5.20   In the circuit in Fig. 5.58, calculate v_o if $v_s = 0$.

Figure 5.58   For Prob. 5.20.

5.21   Repeat the previous problem if $v_s = 3$ V.

5.22   Design an inverting amplifier with a gain of -15.

5.23   For the op amp circuit in Fig. 5.59, find the voltage gain v_o/v_s.

Figure 5.59   For Prob. 5.23.

5.24 In the circuit shown in Fig. 5.60, find k in the voltage transfer function $v_o = kv_s$.

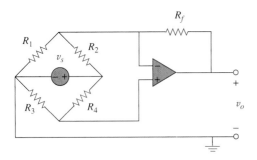

Figure 5.60   For Prob. 5.24.

Section 5.5   Noninverting Amplifier

5.25 Find v_a and v_o in the op amp circuit of Fig. 5.61.

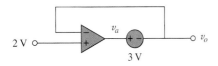

Figure 5.61   For Prob. 5.25.

5.26 Determine i_o in the circuit of Fig. 5.62.

Figure 5.62   For Prob. 5.26.

5.27 Refer to Fig. 5.63.

(a) Determine the overall gain v_o/v_i of the circuit.

(b) What value of v_i will result in $v_o = 15\cos 120\pi t$?

Figure 5.63   For Prob. 5.27.

5.28 Find i_o in the op amp circuit of Fig. 5.64.

Figure 5.64   For Prob. 5.28.

5.29 Determine the voltage gain v_o/v_i of the op amp circuit in Fig. 5.65.

Figure 5.65   For Prob. 5.29.

5.30 In the circuit shown in Fig. 5.66, find i_x and the power absorbed by the 20-kΩ resistor.

Figure 5.66   For Prob. 5.30.

5.31 For the circuit in Fig. 5.67, find i_x.

Figure 5.67   For Prob. 5.31.

5.32   Calculate i_x and v_o in the circuit of Fig. 5.68. Find the power dissipated by the 60-kΩ resistor.

Figure 5.68   For Prob. 5.32.

5.33   Refer to the op amp circuit in Fig. 5.69. Calculate i_x and the power dissipated by the 3-kΩ resistor.

Figure 5.69   For Prob. 5.33.

5.34   Given the op amp circuit shown in Fig. 5.70, express v_o in terms of v_1 and v_2.

Figure 5.70   For Prob. 5.34

5.35   Design a noninverting amplifier with a gain of 10.

5.36   For the circuit shown in Fig. 5.71, find the Thevenin equivalent at terminals a-b. (*Hint*: To find R_{Th}, apply a current source i_o and calculate v_o.)

Figure 5.71   For Prob. 5.36.

Section 5.6   Summing Amplifier

5.37   Determine the output of the summing amplifier in Fig. 5.72.

Figure 5.72   For Prob. 5.37.

5.38   Calculate the output voltage due to the summing amplifier shown in Fig. 5.73.

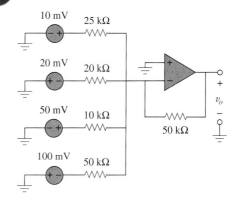

Figure 5.73   For Prob. 5.38.

5.39   For the op amp circuit in Fig. 5.74, determine the value of v_2 in order to make $v_o = -16.5$ V.

Figure 5.74   For Prob. 5.39.

5.40 A noninverting summer is shown in Fig. 5.75. Find v_o in terms of v_1, v_2, and v_3.

Figure 5.75 For Prob. 5.40.

5.41 An *averaging amplifier* is a summer that provides an output equal to the average of the inputs. By using proper input and feedback resistor values, one can get

$$-v_{\text{out}} = \tfrac{1}{4}(v_1 + v_2 + v_3 + v_4)$$

Using a feedback resistor of 10 kΩ, design an averaging amplifier with four inputs.

5.42 A three-input summing amplifier has input resistors with $R_1 = R_2 = R_3 = 30$ kΩ. To produce an averaging amplifier, what value of feedback resistor is needed?

5.43 A four-input summing amplifier has $R_1 = R_2 = R_3 = R_4 = 12$ kΩ. What value of feedback resistor is needed to make it an averaging amplifier?

5.44 Show that the output voltage v_o of the circuit in Fig. 5.76 is

$$v_o = \frac{(R_3 + R_4)}{R_3(R_1 + R_2)}(R_2 v_1 + R_1 v_2)$$

Figure 5.76 For Prob. 5.44.

5.45 Design an op amp circuit to perform the following operation:

$$v_o = 3v_1 - 2v_2$$

All resistances must be ≤100 kΩ.

5.46 Using only two op amps, design a circuit to solve

$$-v_{\text{out}} = \frac{v_1 - v_2}{3} + \frac{v_3}{2}$$

Section 5.7 Difference Amplifier

5.47 Find v_o and i_o in the differential amplifier of Fig. 5.77.

Figure 5.77 For Prob. 5.47.

5.48 The circuit in Fig. 5.78 is a differential amplifier driven by a bridge. Find v_o.

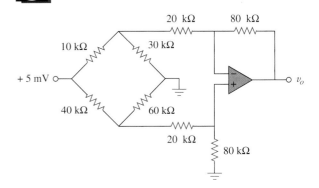

Figure 5.78 For Prob. 5.48.

5.49 Design a difference amplifier to have a gain of 2 and a common-mode input resistance of 10 kΩ at each input.

5.50 Design a circuit to amplify the difference between two inputs by 2.

(a) Use only one op amp.

(b) Use two op amps.

5.51 Using two op amps, design a subtractor.

*5.52   Design an op amp circuit such that

$$v_o = -2v_1 + 4v_2 - 5v_3 - v_4$$

Let all the resistors be in the range of 5 to 100 kΩ.

*5.53   The ordinary difference amplifier for fixed-gain operation is shown in Fig. 5.79(a). It is simple and reliable unless gain is made variable. One way of providing gain adjustment without losing simplicity and accuracy is to use the circuit in Fig. 5.79(b). Another way is to use the circuit in Fig. 5.79(c). Show that:

(a)   for the circuit in Fig. 5.79(a),

$$\frac{v_o}{v_i} = \frac{R_2}{R_1}$$

(b)   for the circuit in Fig. 5.79(b),

$$\frac{v_o}{v_i} = \frac{R_2}{R_1} \frac{1}{1 + \dfrac{R_1}{2R_G}}$$

(c)   for the circuit in Fig. 5.79(c),

$$\frac{v_o}{v_i} = \frac{R_2}{R_1}\left(1 + \frac{R_2}{2R_G}\right)$$

(a)

(b)

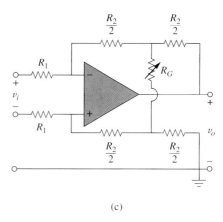

(c)

Figure 5.79   For Prob. 5.53.

Section 5.8   Cascaded Op Amp Circuits

5.54   The individual gains of the stages in a multistage amplifier are shown in Fig. 5.80.

(a)   Calculate the overall voltage gain v_o/v_i.

(b)   Find the voltage gain that would be needed in a fourth stage which would make the overall gain to be 60 dB when added.

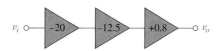

Figure 5.80   For Prob. 5.54.

5.55   In a certain electronic device, a three-stage amplifier is desired, whose overall voltage gain is 42 dB. The individual voltage gains of the first two stages are to be equal, while the gain of the third is to be one-fourth of each of the first two. Calculate the voltage gain of each.

5.56   Refer to the circuit in Fig. 5.81. Calculate i_o if:

(a) $v_s = 12$ mV   (b) $v_s = 10\cos 377t$ mV.

Figure 5.81   For Prob. 5.56.

*An asterisk indicates a challenging problem.

5.57 Given the op amp circuit shown in Fig. 5.82, determine the value of R that will make $v_o = 40$ mV.

Figure 5.82   For Prob. 5.57.

5.58 Calculate i_o in the op amp circuit of Fig. 5.83.

Figure 5.83   For Prob. 5.58.

5.59 Find the voltage gain v_o/v_s of the circuit in Fig. 5.84.

Figure 5.84   For Prob. 5.59.

5.60 Calculate the current gain i_o/i_s of the op amp circuit in Fig. 5.85.

Figure 5.85   For Prob. 5.60.

5.61 Find v_o in terms of v_1 and v_2 in the circuit in Fig. 5.86.

Figure 5.86   For Prob. 5.61.

5.62 Obtain the closed-loop voltage gain v_o/v_i of the circuit in Fig. 5.87.

Figure 5.87   For Prob. 5.62.

5.63 Determine the gain v_o/v_i of the circuit in Fig. 5.88.

Figure 5.88   For Prob. 5.63.

5.64   For the op amp circuit shown in Fig. 5.89, find v_o/v_s.

Figure 5.89   For Prob. 5.64.

5.65   Find v_o in the op amp circuit of Fig. 5.90.

Figure 5.90   For Prob. 5.65.

5.66   For the circuit in Fig. 5.91, find v_o.

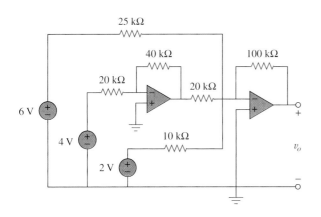

Figure 5.91   For Prob. 5.66.

5.67   Obtain the output v_o in the circuit of Fig. 5.92.

Figure 5.92   For Prob. 5.67.

5.68   Find v_o in the circuit in Fig. 5.93, assuming that $R_f = \infty$ (open circuit).

Figure 5.93   For Probs. 5.68 and 5.69.

5.69   Repeat the previous problem if $R_f = 10$ kΩ.

5.70   Determine v_o in the op amp circuit of Fig. 5.94.

Figure 5.94   For Prob. 5.70.

Figure 5.96   For Prob. 5.72.

5.73   Determine the load voltage v_L in the circuit of Fig. 5.97.

Figure 5.97   For Prob. 5.73.

5.71   Determine v_o in the op amp circuit in Fig. 5.95.

5.74   Find i_o in the op amp circuit of Fig. 5.98.

Figure 5.98   For Prob. 5.74.

Section 5.9   Op Amp Circuit Analysis with PSpice

5.75   Rework Example 5.11 using the nonideal op amp LM324 instead of uA741.

Figure 5.95   For Prob. 5.71.

5.76   Solve Prob. 5.19 using *PSpice* and op amp uA741.

5.72   Find the load voltage v_L in the circuit of Fig. 5.96.

5.77   Solve Prob. 5.48 using *PSpice* and op amp LM324.

5.78   Use *PSpice* to obtain v_o in the circuit of Fig. 5.99.

Figure 5.99   For Prob. 5.78.

5.79   Determine v_o in the op amp circuit of Fig. 5.100, using *PSpice*.

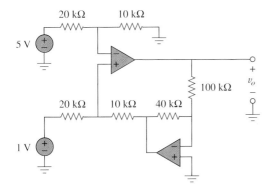

Figure 5.100   For Prob. 5.79.

5.80   Use *PSpice* to solve Prob. 5.70, assuming that the op amps are uA741.

5.81   Use *PSpice* to verify the results in Example 5.9. Assume nonideal op amps LM324.

Section 5.10   Applications

5.82   A five-bit DAC covers a voltage range of 0 to 7.75 V. Calculate how much voltage each bit is worth.

5.83   Design a six-bit digital-to-analog converter.

(a)   If $|V_o| = 1.1875$ V is desired, what should $[V_1 V_2 V_3 V_4 V_5 V_6]$ be?

(b)   Calculate $|V_o|$ if $[V_1 V_2 V_3 V_4 V_5 V_6] = [011011]$.

(c)   What is the maximum value $|V_o|$ can assume?

*****5.84**   A four-bit *R-2R ladder* DAC is presented in Fig. 5.101.

(a)   Show that the output voltage is given by

$$-V_o = R_f \left(\frac{V_1}{2R} + \frac{V_2}{4R} + \frac{V_3}{8R} + \frac{V_4}{16R} \right)$$

(b)   If $R_f = 12$ kΩ and $R = 10$ kΩ, find $|V_o|$ for $[V_1 V_2 V_3 V_4] = [1011]$ and $[V_1 V_2 V_3 V_4] = [0101]$.

Figure 5.101   For Prob. 5.84.

5.85   If $R_G = 100\ \Omega$ and $R = 20$ kΩ, calculate the voltage gain of the IA in Fig. 5.37.

5.86   Assuming a gain of 200 for an IA, find its output voltage for:

(a) $v_1 = 0.402$ V and $v_2 = 0.386$ V

(b) $v_1 = 1.002$ V and $v_2 = 1.011$ V.

5.87   Figure 5.102 displays a two-op-amp instrumentation amplifier. Derive an expression for v_o in terms of v_1 and v_2. How can this amplifier be used as a subtractor?

Figure 5.102   For Prob. 5.87.

*5.88   Figure 5.103 shows an instrumentation amplifier driven by a bridge. Obtain the gain v_o/v_i of the amplifier.

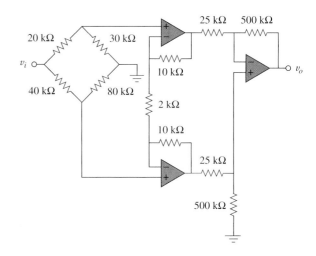

Figure 5.103   For Prob. 5.88.

COMPREHENSIVE PROBLEMS

5.89   A gain of 6 (+ or −, it does not matter) is required in an audio system. Design an op amp circuit to provide the gain with an input resistance of 2 kΩ.

5.90   The op amp circuit in Fig. 5.104 is a *current amplifier.* Find the current gain i_o/i_s of the amplifier.

Figure 5.104   For Prob. 5.90.

5.91   A noninverting current amplifier is portrayed in Fig. 5.105. Calculate the gain i_o/i_s. Take $R_1 = 8$ kΩ and $R_2 = 1$ kΩ.

Figure 5.105   For Prob. 5.91.

5.92   Refer to the *bridge amplifier* shown in Fig. 5.106. Determine the voltage gain v_o/v_i.

Figure 5.106   For Prob. 5.92.

*5.93   A voltage-to-current converter is shown in Fig. 5.107, which means that $i_L = Av_i$ if $R_1 R_2 = R_3 R_4$. Find the constant term A.

Figure 5.107   For Prob. 5.93.

CAPACITORS AND INDUCTORS

Engineering is a great profession. There is the satisfaction of watching a figment of the imagination emerge through the aid of science to a plan on paper. Then it moves to realization in stone or metal or energy. Then it brings jobs and homes to men. Then it elevates the standards of living and adds to the comforts of life. That is the engineer's high privelege.... And the verdict of his fellow professionals is all the accolade he wants.

—Herbert Hoover

Historical Profiles

Michael Faraday (1791–1867) an English chemist and physicist, was probably the greatest experimentalist who ever lived.

Born near London, Faraday realized his boyhood dream by working with the great chemist Sir Humphry Davy at the Royal Institution, where he worked for 54 years. He made several contributions in all areas of physical science and coined such words as electrolysis, anode, and cathode. His discovery of electromagnetic induction in 1831 was a major breakthrough in engineering because it provided a way of generating electricity. The electric motor and generator operate on this principle. The unit of capacitance, the farad, was named in his honor.

Joseph Henry (1797–1878), an American physicist, discovered inductance and constructed an electric motor.

Born in Albany, New York, Henry graduated from Albany Academy and taught philosophy at Princeton University from 1832 to 1846. He was the first secretary of the Smithsonian Institution. He conducted several experiments on electromagnetism and developed powerful electromagnets that could lift objects weighing thousands of pounds. Interestingly, Joseph Henry discovered electromagnetic induction before Faraday but failed to publish his findings. The unit of inductance, the henry, was named after him.

6.1   INTRODUCTION

So far we have limited our study to resistive circuits. In this chapter, we shall introduce two new and important passive linear circuit elements: the capacitor and the inductor. Unlike resistors, which dissipate energy, capacitors and inductors do not dissipate but store energy, which can be retrieved at a later time. For this reason, capacitors and inductors are called *storage* elements.

The application of resistive circuits is quite limited. With the introduction of capacitors and inductors in this chapter, we will be able to analyze more important and practical circuits. Be assured that the circuit analysis techniques covered in Chapters 3 and 4 are equally applicable to circuits with capacitors and inductors.

We begin by introducing capacitors and describing how to combine them in series or in parallel. Later, we do the same for inductors. As typical applications, we explore how capacitors are combined with op amps to form integrators, differentiators, and analog computers.

6.2   CAPACITORS

A capacitor is a passive element designed to store energy in its electric field. Besides resistors, capacitors are the most common electrical components. Capacitors are used extensively in electronics, communications, computers, and power systems. For example, they are used in the tuning circuits of radio receivers and as dynamic memory elements in computer systems.

A capacitor is typically constructed as depicted in Fig. 6.1.

> A capacitor **consists of two conducting plates separated by an insulator (or dielectric).**

In many practical applications, the plates may be aluminum foil while the dielectric may be air, ceramic, paper, or mica.

When a voltage source v is connected to the capacitor, as in Fig. 6.2, the source deposits a positive charge q on one plate and a negative charge $-q$ on the other. The capacitor is said to store the electric charge. The amount of charge stored, represented by q, is directly proportional to the applied voltage v so that

$$q = Cv \qquad (6.1)$$

where C, the constant of proportionality, is known as the *capacitance* of the capacitor. The unit of capacitance is the farad (F), in honor of the English physicist Michael Faraday (1791–1867). From Eq. (6.1), we may derive the following definition.

> Capacitance is the ratio of the charge on one plate of a capacitor to the voltage difference between the two plates, measured in farads (F).

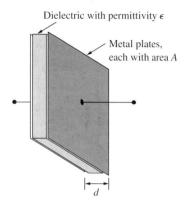

Figure 6.1   A typical capacitor.

Dielectric with permittivity ϵ

Metal plates, each with area A

d

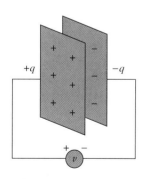

Figure 6.2   A capacitor with applied voltage v.

$+q$ $-q$

v

In contrast to a resistor, which spends or dissipates energy irreversibly, an inductor or capacitor stores or releases energy (i.e., has a memory).

Alternatively, capacitance is the amount of charge stored per plate for a unit voltage difference in a capacitor.

Note from Eq. (6.1) that 1 farad = 1 coulomb/volt.

Although the capacitance C of a capacitor is the ratio of the charge q per plate to the applied voltage v, it does not depend on q or v. It depends on the physical dimensions of the capacitor. For example, for the parallel-plate capacitor shown in Fig. 6.1, the capacitance is given by

$$C = \frac{\epsilon A}{d} \qquad (6.2)$$

where A is the surface area of each plate, d is the distance between the plates, and ϵ is the permittivity of the dielectric material between the plates. Although Eq. (6.2) applies to only parallel-plate capacitors, we may infer from it that, in general, three factors determine the value of the capacitance:

1. The surface area of the plates—the larger the area, the greater the capacitance.

2. The spacing between the plates—the smaller the spacing, the greater the capacitance.

3. The permittivity of the material—the higher the permittivity, the greater the capacitance.

Capacitors are commercially available in different values and types. Typically, capacitors have values in the picofarad (pF) to microfarad (μF) range. They are described by the dielectric material they are made of and by whether they are of fixed or variable type. Figure 6.3 shows the circuit symbols for fixed and variable capacitors. Note that according to the passive sign convention, current is considered to flow into the positive terminal of the capacitor when the capacitor is being charged, and out of the positive terminal when the capacitor is discharging.

Figure 6.4 shows common types of fixed-value capacitors. Polyester capacitors are light in weight, stable, and their change with temperature is predictable. Instead of polyester, other dielectric materials such as mica and polystyrene may be used. Film capacitors are rolled and housed in metal or plastic films. Electrolytic capacitors produce very high capacitance. Figure 6.5 shows the most common types of variable capacitors. The capacitance of a trimmer (or padder) capacitor or a glass piston capacitor is varied by turning the screw. The trimmer capacitor is often placed in parallel with another capacitor so that the equivalent capacitance can be varied slightly. The capacitance of the variable air capacitor (meshed

Capacitor voltage rating and capacitance are typically inversely rated due to the relationships in Eqs. (6.1) and (6.2). Arcing occurs if d is small and V is high.

(a)   (b)

Figure 6.3   Circuit symbols for capacitors: (a) fixed capacitor, (b) variable capacitor.

(a)   (b)   (c)

Figure 6.4   Fixed capacitors: (a) polyester capacitor, (b) ceramic capacitor, (c) electrolytic capacitor. (*Courtesy of Tech America.*)

Figure 6.5   Variable capacitors: (a) trimmer capacitor, (b) filmtrim capacitor. *(Courtesy of Johanson.)*

According to Eq. (6.4), for a capacitor to carry current, its voltage must vary with time. Hence, for constant voltage, $i = 0$.

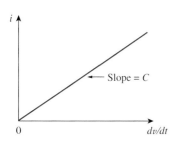

Figure 6.6   Current-voltage relationship of a capacitor.

plates) is varied by turning the shaft. Variable capacitors are used in radio receivers allowing one to tune to various stations. In addition, capacitors are used to block dc, pass ac, shift phase, store energy, start motors, and suppress noise.

To obtain the current-voltage relationship of the capacitor, we take the derivative of both sides of Eq. (6.1). Since

$$i = \frac{dq}{dt} \tag{6.3}$$

differentiating both sides of Eq. (6.1) gives

$$i = C\frac{dv}{dt} \tag{6.4}$$

This is the current-voltage relationship for a capacitor, assuming the passive sign convention. The relationship is illustrated in Fig. 6.6 for a capacitor whose capacitance is independent of voltage. Capacitors that satisfy Eq. (6.4) are said to be *linear*. For a *nonlinear capacitor*, the plot of the current-voltage relationship is not a straight line. Although some capacitors are nonlinear, most are linear. We will assume linear capacitors in this book.

The voltage-current relation of the capacitor can be obtained by integrating both sides of Eq. (6.4). We get

$$v = \frac{1}{C}\int_{-\infty}^{t} i \, dt \tag{6.5}$$

or

$$v = \frac{1}{C}\int_{t_0}^{t} i \, dt + v(t_0) \tag{6.6}$$

where $v(t_0) = q(t_0)/C$ is the voltage across the capacitor at time t_0. Equation (6.6) shows that capacitor voltage depends on the past history of the capacitor current. Hence, the capacitor has memory—a property that is often exploited.

The instantaneous power delivered to the capacitor is

$$p = vi = Cv\frac{dv}{dt} \tag{6.7}$$

The energy stored in the capacitor is therefore

$$w = \int_{-\infty}^{t} p \, dt = C\int_{-\infty}^{t} v\frac{dv}{dt}dt = C\int_{-\infty}^{t} v \, dv = \frac{1}{2}Cv^2\Big|_{t=-\infty}^{t} \tag{6.8}$$

We note that $v(-\infty) = 0$, because the capacitor was uncharged at $t = -\infty$. Thus,

$$w = \frac{1}{2}Cv^2 \tag{6.9}$$

Using Eq. (6.1), we may rewrite Eq. (6.9) as

$$w = \frac{q^2}{2C} \qquad (6.10)$$

Equation (6.9) or (6.10) represents the energy stored in the electric field that exists between the plates of the capacitor. This energy can be retrieved, since an ideal capacitor cannot dissipate energy. In fact, the word *capacitor* is derived from this element's capacity to store energy in an electric field.

We should note the following important properties of a capacitor:

1. Note from Eq. (6.4) that when the voltage across a capacitor is not changing with time (i.e., dc voltage), the current through the capacitor is zero. Thus,

A capacitor is an open circuit to dc.

However, if a battery (dc voltage) is connected across a capacitor, the capacitor charges.

2. The voltage on the capacitor must be continuous.

The voltage on a capacitor cannot change abruptly.

The capacitor resists an abrupt change in the voltage across it. According to Eq. (6.4), a discontinuous change in voltage requires an infinite current, which is physically impossible. For example, the voltage across a capacitor may take the form shown in Fig. 6.7(a), whereas it is not physically possible for the capacitor voltage to take the form shown in Fig. 6.7(b) because of the abrupt changes. Conversely, the current through a capacitor can change instantaneously.

3. The ideal capacitor does not dissipate energy. It takes power from the circuit when storing energy in its field and returns previously stored energy when delivering power to the circuit.

4. A real, nonideal capacitor has a parallel-model leakage resistance, as shown in Fig. 6.8. The leakage resistance may be as high as 100 MΩ and can be neglected for most practical applications. For this reason, we will assume ideal capacitors in this book.

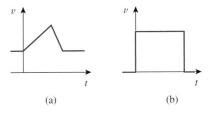

Figure 6.7   Voltage across a capacitor: (a) allowed, (b) not allowable; an abrupt change is not possible.

An alternative way of looking at this is using Eq. (6.9), which indicates that energy is proportional to voltage squared. Since injecting or extracting energy can only be done over some finite time, voltage cannot change instantaneously across a capacitor.

Figure 6.8   Circuit model of a nonideal capacitor.

EXAMPLE 6.1

(a) Calculate the charge stored on a 3-pF capacitor with 20 V across it.
(b) Find the energy stored in the capacitor.

Solution:

(a) Since $q = Cv$,

$$q = 3 \times 10^{-12} \times 20 = 60 \text{ pC}$$

(b) The energy stored is

$$w = \frac{1}{2}Cv^2 = \frac{1}{2} \times 3 \times 10^{-12} \times 400 = 600 \text{ pJ}$$

PRACTICE PROBLEM 6.1

What is the voltage across a 3-μF capacitor if the charge on one plate is 0.12 mC? How much energy is stored?

Answer: 40 V, 2.4 mJ.

EXAMPLE 6.2

The voltage across a 5-μF capacitor is

$$v(t) = 10 \cos 6000t \text{ V}$$

Calculate the current through it.

Solution:

By definition, the current is

$$i(t) = C\frac{dv}{dt} = 5 \times 10^{-6}\frac{d}{dt}(10 \cos 6000t)$$

$$= -5 \times 10^{-6} \times 6000 \times 10 \sin 6000t = -0.3 \sin 6000t \text{ A}$$

PRACTICE PROBLEM 6.2

If a 10-μF capacitor is connected to a voltage source with

$$v(t) = 50 \sin 2000t \text{ V}$$

determine the current through the capacitor.

Answer: $\cos 2000t$ A.

EXAMPLE 6.3

Determine the voltage across a 2-μF capacitor if the current through it is

$$i(t) = 6e^{-3000t} \text{ mA}$$

Assume that the initial capacitor voltage is zero.

Solution:

Since $v = \dfrac{1}{C}\displaystyle\int_0^t i\, dt + v(0)$ and $v(0) = 0$,

$$v = \frac{1}{2 \times 10^{-6}}\int_0^t 6e^{-3000t}\, dt \cdot 10^{-3}$$

$$= \frac{3 \times 10^3}{-3000}e^{-3000t}\Big|_0^t = (1 - e^{-3000t}) \text{ V}$$

PRACTICE PROBLEM 6.3

The current through a 100-μF capacitor is $i(t) = 50 \sin 120\pi t$ mA. Calculate the voltage across it at $t = 1$ ms and $t = 5$ ms. Take $v(0) = 0$.

Answer: 93.137 V, 1.736 V.

EXAMPLE 6.4

Determine the current through a 200-μF capacitor whose voltage is shown in Fig. 6.9.

Solution:

The voltage waveform can be described mathematically as

$$v(t) = \begin{cases} 50t \text{ V} & 0 < t < 1 \\ 100 - 50t \text{ V} & 1 < t < 3 \\ -200 + 50t \text{ V} & 3 < t < 4 \\ 0 & \text{otherwise} \end{cases}$$

Since $i = C \, dv/dt$ and $C = 200 \, \mu$F, we take the derivative of v to obtain

$$i(t) = 200 \times 10^{-6} \times \begin{cases} 50 & 0 < t < 1 \\ -50 & 1 < t < 3 \\ 50 & 3 < t < 4 \\ 0 & \text{otherwise} \end{cases}$$

$$= \begin{cases} 10 \text{ mA} & 0 < t < 1 \\ -10 \text{ mA} & 1 < t < 3 \\ 10 \text{ mA} & 3 < t < 4 \\ 0 & \text{otherwise} \end{cases}$$

Thus the current waveform is as shown in Fig. 6.10.

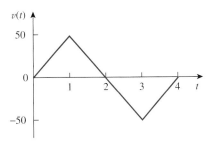

Figure 6.9   For Example 6.4.

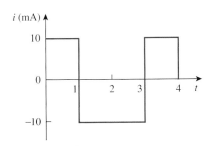

Figure 6.10   For Example 6.4.

PRACTICE PROBLEM 6.4

An initially uncharged 1-mF capacitor has the current shown in Fig. 6.11 across it. Calculate the voltage across it at $t = 2$ ms and $t = 5$ ms.

Answer: 100 mV, 400 mV.

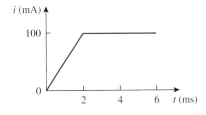

Figure 6.11   For Practice Prob. 6.4.

EXAMPLE 6.5

Obtain the energy stored in each capacitor in Fig. 6.12(a) under dc conditions.

Solution:

Under dc conditions, we replace each capacitor with an open circuit, as shown in Fig. 6.12(b). The current through the series combination

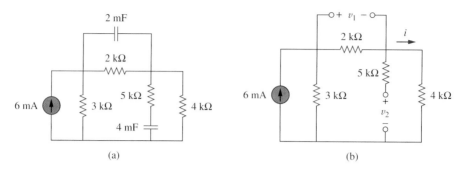

Figure 6.12 For Example 6.5.

of the 2-kΩ and 4-kΩ resistors is obtained by current division as

$$i = \frac{3}{3+2+4}(6 \text{ mA}) = 2 \text{ mA}$$

Hence, the voltages v_1 and v_2 across the capacitors are

$$v_1 = 2000i = 4 \text{ V} \qquad v_2 = 4000i = 8 \text{ V}$$

and the energies stored in them are

$$w_1 = \frac{1}{2}C_1 v_1^2 = \frac{1}{2}(2 \times 10^{-3})(4)^2 = 16 \text{ mJ}$$

$$w_2 = \frac{1}{2}C_2 v_2^2 = \frac{1}{2}(4 \times 10^{-3})(8)^2 = 128 \text{ mJ}$$

PRACTICE PROBLEM 6.5

Figure 6.13 For Practice Prob. 6.5.

Under dc conditions, find the energy stored in the capacitors in Fig. 6.13.

Answer: 405 μJ, 90 μJ.

6.3 SERIES AND PARALLEL CAPACITORS

We know from resistive circuits that series-parallel combination is a powerful tool for reducing circuits. This technique can be extended to series-parallel connections of capacitors, which are sometimes encountered. We desire to replace these capacitors by a single equivalent capacitor C_{eq}.

In order to obtain the equivalent capacitor C_{eq} of N capacitors in parallel, consider the circuit in Fig. 6.14(a). The equivalent circuit is in

Fig. 6.14(b). Note that the capacitors have the same voltage v across them. Applying KCL to Fig. 6.14(a),

$$i = i_1 + i_2 + i_3 + \cdots + i_N \tag{6.11}$$

But $i_k = C_k\, dv/dt$. Hence,

$$
\begin{aligned}
i &= C_1\frac{dv}{dt} + C_2\frac{dv}{dt} + C_3\frac{dv}{dt} + \cdots + C_N\frac{dv}{dt} \\
&= \left(\sum_{k=1}^{N} C_k\right)\frac{dv}{dt} = C_{eq}\frac{dv}{dt}
\end{aligned}
\tag{6.12}
$$

where

$$\boxed{C_{eq} = C_1 + C_2 + C_3 + \cdots + C_N} \tag{6.13}$$

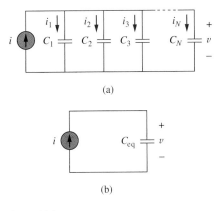

(a)

(b)

Figure 6.14   (a) Parallel-connected N capacitors, (b) equivalent circuit for the parallel capacitors.

The equivalent capacitance of N parallel-connected capacitors is the sum of the individual capacitances.

We observe that capacitors in parallel combine in the same manner as resistors in series.

We now obtain C_{eq} of N capacitors connected in series by comparing the circuit in Fig. 6.15(a) with the equivalent circuit in Fig. 6.15(b). Note that the same current i flows (and consequently the same charge) through the capacitors. Applying KVL to the loop in Fig. 6.15(a),

$$v = v_1 + v_2 + v_3 + \cdots + v_N \tag{6.14}$$

But $v_k = \dfrac{1}{C_k}\displaystyle\int_{t_0}^{t} i(t)\,dt + v_k(t_0)$. Therefore,

$$
\begin{aligned}
v &= \frac{1}{C_1}\int_{t_0}^{t} i(t)\,dt + v_1(t_0) + \frac{1}{C_2}\int_{t_0}^{t} i(t)\,dt + v_2(t_0) \\
&\quad + \cdots + \frac{1}{C_N}\int_{t_0}^{t} i(t)\,dt + v_N(t_0) \\
&= \left(\frac{1}{C_1} + \frac{1}{C_2} + \cdots + \frac{1}{C_N}\right)\int_{t_0}^{t} i(t)\,dt + v_1(t_0) + v_2(t_0) \\
&\qquad\qquad\qquad\qquad\qquad\qquad\qquad\qquad + \cdots + v_N(t_0) \\
&= \frac{1}{C_{eq}}\int_{t_0}^{t} i(t)\,dt + v(t_0)
\end{aligned}
\tag{6.15}
$$

where

$$\boxed{\frac{1}{C_{eq}} = \frac{1}{C_1} + \frac{1}{C_2} + \frac{1}{C_3} + \cdots + \frac{1}{C_N}} \tag{6.16}$$

(a)

(b)

Figure 6.15   (a) Series-connected N capacitors, (b) equivalent circuit for the series capacitor.

The initial voltage $v(t_0)$ across C_{eq} is required by KVL to be the sum of the capacitor voltages at t_0. Or according to Eq. (6.15),

$$v(t_0) = v_1(t_0) + v_2(t_0) + \cdots + v_N(t_0)$$

Thus, according to Eq. (6.16),

> The equivalent capacitance of series-connected capacitors is the reciprocal of the sum of the reciprocals of the individual capacitances.

Note that capacitors in series combine in the same manner as resistors in parallel. For $N = 2$ (i.e., two capacitors in series), Eq. (6.16) becomes

$$\frac{1}{C_{\text{eq}}} = \frac{1}{C_1} + \frac{1}{C_2}$$

or

$$C_{\text{eq}} = \frac{C_1 C_2}{C_1 + C_2} \qquad (6.17)$$

EXAMPLE 6.6

Find the equivalent capacitance seen between terminals a and b of the circuit in Fig. 6.16.

Figure 6.16   For Example 6.6.

Solution:

The 20-μF and 5-μF capacitors are in series; their equivalent capacitance is

$$\frac{20 \times 5}{20 + 5} = 4\ \mu\text{F}$$

This 4-μF capacitor is in parallel with the 6-μF and 20-μF capacitors; their combined capacitance is

$$4 + 6 + 20 = 30\ \mu\text{F}$$

This 30-μF capacitor is in series with the 60-μF capacitor. Hence, the equivalent capacitance for the entire circuit is

$$C_{\text{eq}} = \frac{30 \times 60}{30 + 60} = 20\ \mu\text{F}$$

PRACTICE PROBLEM 6.6

Find the equivalent capacitance seen at the terminals of the circuit in Fig. 6.17.

Answer: $40\ \mu\text{F}$.

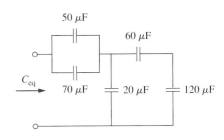

Figure 6.17   For Practice Prob. 6.6.

EXAMPLE 6.7

For the circuit in Fig. 6.18, find the voltage across each capacitor.

Solution:

We first find the equivalent capacitance C_{eq}, shown in Fig. 6.19. The two parallel capacitors in Fig. 6.18 can be combined to get $40 + 20 = 60$ mF. This 60-mF capacitor is in series with the 20-mF and 30-mF capacitors. Thus,

$$C_{eq} = \frac{1}{\frac{1}{60} + \frac{1}{30} + \frac{1}{20}}\ \text{mF} = 10\ \text{mF}$$

The total charge is

$$q = C_{eq}v = 10 \times 10^{-3} \times 30 = 0.3\ \text{C}$$

This is the charge on the 20-mF and 30-mF capacitors, because they are in series with the 30-V source. (A crude way to see this is to imagine that charge acts like current, since $i = dq/dt$.) Therefore,

$$v_1 = \frac{q}{C_1} = \frac{0.3}{20 \times 10^{-3}} = 15\ \text{V} \qquad v_2 = \frac{q}{C_2} = \frac{0.3}{30 \times 10^{-3}} = 10\ \text{V}$$

Having determined v_1 and v_2, we now use KVL to determine v_3 by

$$v_3 = 30 - v_1 - v_2 = 5\ \text{V}$$

Alternatively, since the 40-mF and 20-mF capacitors are in parallel, they have the same voltage v_3 and their combined capacitance is $40 + 20 = 60$ mF. This combined capacitance is in series with the 20-mF and 30-mF capacitors and consequently has the same charge on it. Hence,

$$v_3 = \frac{q}{60\ \text{mF}} = \frac{0.3}{60 \times 10^{-3}} = 5\ \text{V}$$

Figure 6.18   For Example 6.7.

Figure 6.19   Equivalent circuit for Fig. 6.18.

PRACTICE PROBLEM 6.7

Figure 6.20   For Practice Prob. 6.7.

Find the voltage across each of the capacitors in Fig. 6.20.

Answer: $v_1 = 30$ V, $v_2 = 30$ V, $v_3 = 10$ V, $v_4 = 20$ V.

6.4   INDUCTORS

An inductor is a passive element designed to store energy in its magnetic field. Inductors find numerous applications in electronic and power systems. They are used in power supplies, transformers, radios, TVs, radars, and electric motors.

Any conductor of electric current has inductive properties and may be regarded as an inductor. But in order to enhance the inductive effect, a practical inductor is usually formed into a cylindrical coil with many turns of conducting wire, as shown in Fig. 6.21.

An inductor consists of a coil of conducting wire.

If current is allowed to pass through an inductor, it is found that the voltage across the inductor is directly proportional to the time rate of change of the current. Using the passive sign convention,

$$v = L\frac{di}{dt} \qquad (6.18)$$

where L is the constant of proportionality called the *inductance* of the inductor. The unit of inductance is the henry (H), named in honor of the American inventor Joseph Henry (1797–1878). It is clear from Eq. (6.18) that 1 henry equals 1 volt-second per ampere.

Inductance is the property whereby an inductor exhibits opposition to the change of current flowing through it, measured in henrys (H).

The inductance of an inductor depends on its physical dimension and construction. Formulas for calculating the inductance of inductors of different shapes are derived from electromagnetic theory and can be found in standard electrical engineering handbooks. For example, for the inductor (solenoid) shown in Fig. 6.21,

$$L = \frac{N^2 \mu A}{\ell} \qquad (6.19)$$

Figure 6.21   Typical form of an inductor.

In view of Eq. (6.18), for an inductor to have voltage across its terminals, its current must vary with time. Hence, $v = 0$ for constant current through the inductor.

where N is the number of turns, ℓ is the length, A is the cross-sectional area, and μ is the permeability of the core. We can see from Eq. (6.19) that inductance can be increased by increasing the number of turns of coil, using material with higher permeability as the core, increasing the cross-sectional area, or reducing the length of the coil.

Like capacitors, commercially available inductors come in different values and types. Typical practical inductors have inductance values ranging from a few microhenrys (μH), as in communication systems, to tens of henrys (H) as in power systems. Inductors may be fixed or variable. The core may be made of iron, steel, plastic, or air. The terms *coil* and *choke* are also used for inductors. Common inductors are shown in Fig. 6.22. The circuit symbols for inductors are shown in Fig. 6.23, following the passive sign convention.

Equation (6.18) is the voltage-current relationship for an inductor. Figure 6.24 shows this relationship graphically for an inductor whose inductance is independent of current. Such an inductor is known as a *linear inductor*. For a *nonlinear inductor*, the plot of Eq. (6.18) will not be a straight line because its inductance varies with current. We will assume linear inductors in this textbook unless stated otherwise.

The current-voltage relationship is obtained from Eq. (6.18) as

$$di = \frac{1}{L} v \, dt$$

Integrating gives

$$i = \frac{1}{L} \int_{-\infty}^{t} v(t) \, dt \qquad (6.20)$$

or

$$\boxed{i = \frac{1}{L} \int_{t_0}^{t} v(t) \, dt + i(t_0)} \qquad (6.21)$$

where $i(t_0)$ is the total current for $-\infty < t < t_0$ and $i(-\infty) = 0$. The idea of making $i(-\infty) = 0$ is practical and reasonable, because there must be a time in the past when there was no current in the inductor.

The inductor is designed to store energy in its magnetic field. The energy stored can be obtained from Eq. (6.18). The power delivered to the inductor is

$$p = vi = \left(L \frac{di}{dt} \right) i \qquad (6.22)$$

The energy stored is

$$\begin{aligned} w &= \int_{-\infty}^{t} p \, dt = \int_{-\infty}^{t} \left(L \frac{di}{dt} \right) i \, dt \\ &= L \int_{-\infty}^{t} i \, di = \frac{1}{2} L i^2(t) - \frac{1}{2} L i^2(-\infty) \end{aligned} \qquad (6.23)$$

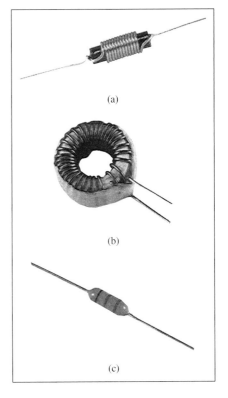

Figure 6.22   Various types of inductors: (a) solenoidal wound inductor, (b) toroidal inductor, (c) chip inductor. *(Courtesy of Tech America.)*

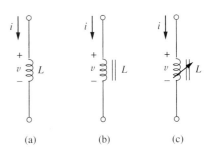

Figure 6.23   Circuit symbols for inductors: (a) air-core, (b) iron-core, (c) variable iron-core.

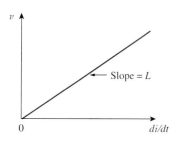

Figure 6.24   Voltage-current relationship of an inductor.

Since $i(-\infty) = 0$,

$$w = \frac{1}{2}Li^2 \qquad (6.24)$$

We should note the following important properties of an inductor.

1. Note from Eq. (6.18) that the voltage across an inductor is zero when the current is constant. Thus,

> An inductor acts like a short circuit to dc.

2. An important property of the inductor is its opposition to the change in current flowing through it.

> The current through an inductor cannot change instantaneously.

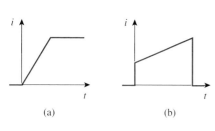

Figure 6.25   Current through an inductor: (a) allowed, (b) not allowable; an abrupt change is not possible.

According to Eq. (6.18), a discontinuous change in the current through an inductor requires an infinite voltage, which is not physically possible. Thus, an inductor opposes an abrupt change in the current through it. For example, the current through an inductor may take the form shown in Fig. 6.25(a), whereas the inductor current cannot take the form shown in Fig. 6.25(b) in real-life situations due to the discontinuities. However, the voltage across an inductor can change abruptly.

3. Like the ideal capacitor, the ideal inductor does not dissipate energy. The energy stored in it can be retrieved at a later time. The inductor takes power from the circuit when storing energy and delivers power to the circuit when returning previously stored energy.

4. A practical, nonideal inductor has a significant resistive component, as shown in Fig. 6.26. This is due to the fact that the inductor is made of a conducting material such as copper, which has some resistance. This resistance is called the *winding resistance* R_w, and it appears in series with the inductance of the inductor. The presence of R_w makes it both an energy storage device and an energy dissipation device. Since R_w is usually very small, it is ignored in most cases. The nonideal inductor also has a *winding capacitance* C_w due to the capacitive coupling between the conducting coils. C_w is very small and can be ignored in most cases, except at high frequencies. We will assume ideal inductors in this book.

Since an inductor is often made of a highly conducting wire, it has a very small resistance.

Figure 6.26   Circuit model for a practical inductor.

EXAMPLE 6.8

The current through a 0.1-H inductor is $i(t) = 10te^{-5t}$ A. Find the voltage across the inductor and the energy stored in it.

Solution:

Since $v = L\, di/dt$ and $L = 0.1$ H,

$$v = 0.1\frac{d}{dt}(10te^{-5t}) = e^{-5t} + t(-5)e^{-5t} = e^{-5t}(1 - 5t) \text{ V}$$

The energy stored is

$$w = \frac{1}{2}Li^2 = \frac{1}{2}(0.1)100t^2e^{-10t} = 5t^2e^{-10t} \text{ J}$$

PRACTICE PROBLEM 6.8

If the current through a 1-mH inductor is $i(t) = 20\cos 100t$ mA, find the terminal voltage and the energy stored.

Answer: $-2\sin 100t$ mV, $0.2\cos^2 100t$ μJ.

EXAMPLE 6.9

Find the current through a 5-H inductor if the voltage across it is

$$v(t) = \begin{cases} 30t^2, & t > 0 \\ 0, & t < 0 \end{cases}$$

Also find the energy stored within $0 < t < 5$ s.

Solution:

Since $i = \dfrac{1}{L}\displaystyle\int_{t_0}^{t} v(t)\, dt + i(t_0)$ and $L = 5$ H,

$$i = \frac{1}{5}\int_{0}^{t} 30t^2\, dt + 0 = 6 \times \frac{t^3}{3} = 2t^3 \text{ A}$$

The power $p = vi = 60t^5$, and the energy stored is then

$$w = \int p\, dt = \int_{0}^{5} 60t^5\, dt = 60\frac{t^6}{6}\bigg|_{0}^{5} = 156.25 \text{ kJ}$$

Alternatively, we can obtain the energy stored using Eq. (6.24), by writing

$$w\bigg|_{0}^{5} = \frac{1}{2}Li^2(5) - \frac{1}{2}Li(0) = \frac{1}{2}(5)(2 \times 5^3)^2 - 0 = 156.25 \text{ kJ}$$

as obtained before.

PRACTICE PROBLEM 6.9

The terminal voltage of a 2-H inductor is $v = 10(1 - t)$ V. Find the current flowing through it at $t = 4$ s and the energy stored in it within $0 < t < 4$ s. Assume $i(0) = 2$ A.

Answer: -18 A, 320 J.

EXAMPLE 6.10

(a)

(b)

Figure 6.27   For Example 6.10.

Consider the circuit in Fig. 6.27(a). Under dc conditions, find: (a) i, v_C, and i_L, (b) the energy stored in the capacitor and inductor.

Solution:

(a) Under dc conditions, we replace the capacitor with an open circuit and the inductor with a short circuit, as in Fig. 6.27(b). It is evident from Fig. 6.27(b) that

$$i = i_L = \frac{12}{1+5} = 2 \text{ A}$$

The voltage v_C is the same as the voltage across the 5-Ω resistor. Hence,

$$v_C = 5i = 10 \text{ V}$$

(b) The energy in the capacitor is

$$w_C = \frac{1}{2}Cv_C^2 = \frac{1}{2}(1)(10^2) = 50 \text{ J}$$

and that in the inductor is

$$w_L = \frac{1}{2}Li_L^2 = \frac{1}{2}(2)(2^2) = 4 \text{ J}$$

PRACTICE PROBLEM 6.10

Figure 6.28   For Practice Prob. 6.10.

Determine v_C, i_L, and the energy stored in the capacitor and inductor in the circuit of Fig. 6.28 under dc conditions.

Answer: 3 V, 3 A, 9 J, 1.125 J.

6.5   SERIES AND PARALLEL INDUCTORS

Now that the inductor has been added to our list of passive elements, it is necessary to extend the powerful tool of series-parallel combination. We need to know how to find the equivalent inductance of a series-connected or parallel-connected set of inductors found in practical circuits.

Consider a series connection of N inductors, as shown in Fig. 6.29(a), with the equivalent circuit shown in Fig. 6.29(b). The inductors have the same current through them. Applying KVL to the loop,

$$v = v_1 + v_2 + v_3 + \cdots + v_N \tag{6.25}$$

Substituting $v_k = L_k \, di/dt$ results in

$$v = L_1 \frac{di}{dt} + L_2 \frac{di}{dt} + L_3 \frac{di}{dt} + \cdots + L_N \frac{di}{dt}$$

$$= (L_1 + L_2 + L_3 + \cdots + L_N) \frac{di}{dt} \tag{6.26}$$

$$= \left(\sum_{k=1}^{N} L_k \right) \frac{di}{dt} = L_{eq} \frac{di}{dt}$$

where

$$\boxed{L_{eq} = L_1 + L_2 + L_3 + \cdots + L_N} \tag{6.27}$$

Thus,

The equivalent inductance of series-connected inductors is the sum of the individual inductances.

Inductors in series are combined in exactly the same way as resistors in series.

We now consider a parallel connection of N inductors, as shown in Fig. 6.30(a), with the equivalent circuit in Fig. 6.30(b). The inductors have the same voltage across them. Using KCL,

$$i = i_1 + i_2 + i_3 + \cdots + i_N \tag{6.28}$$

But $i_k = \dfrac{1}{L_k} \displaystyle\int_{t_0}^{t} v \, dt + i_k(t_0)$; hence,

$$i = \frac{1}{L_1} \int_{t_0}^{t} v \, dt + i_1(t_0) + \frac{1}{L_2} \int_{t_0}^{t} v \, dt + i_2(t_0)$$

$$+ \cdots + \frac{1}{L_N} \int_{t_0}^{t} v \, dt + i_N(t_0)$$

$$= \left(\frac{1}{L_1} + \frac{1}{L_2} + \cdots + \frac{1}{L_N} \right) \int_{t_0}^{t} v \, dt + i_1(t_0) + i_2(t_0)$$

$$+ \cdots + i_N(t_0)$$

$$= \left(\sum_{k=1}^{N} \frac{1}{L_k} \right) \int_{t_0}^{t} v \, dt + \sum_{k=1}^{N} i_k(t_0) = \frac{1}{L_{eq}} \int_{t_0}^{t} v \, dt + i(t_0)$$

$$\tag{6.29}$$

where

$$\boxed{\frac{1}{L_{eq}} = \frac{1}{L_1} + \frac{1}{L_2} + \frac{1}{L_3} + \cdots + \frac{1}{L_N}} \tag{6.30}$$

The initial current $i(t_0)$ through L_{eq} at $t = t_0$ is expected by KCL to be the sum of the inductor currents at t_0. Thus, according to Eq. (6.29),

$$i(t_0) = i_1(t_0) + i_2(t_0) + \cdots + i_N(t_0)$$

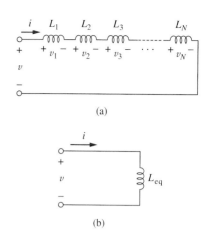

(a)

(b)

Figure 6.29   (a) A series connection of N inductors, (b) equivalent circuit for the series inductors.

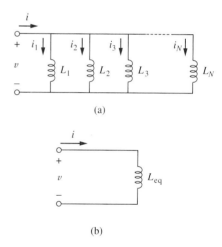

(a)

(b)

Figure 6.30   (a) A parallel connection of N inductors, (b) equivalent circuit for the parallel inductors.

According to Eq. (6.30),

> The equivalent inductance of parallel inductors is the reciprocal of the sum of the reciprocals of the individual inductances.

Note that the inductors in parallel are combined in the same way as resistors in parallel.

For two inductors in parallel ($N = 2$), Eq. (6.30) becomes

$$\frac{1}{L_{eq}} = \frac{1}{L_1} + \frac{1}{L_2} \qquad \text{or} \qquad L_{eq} = \frac{L_1 L_2}{L_1 + L_2} \qquad (6.31)$$

It is appropriate at this point to summarize the most important characteristics of the three basic circuit elements we have studied. The summary is given in Table 6.1.

TABLE 6.1   Important characteristics of the basic elements.[†]

Relation	Resistor (R)	Capacitor (C)	Inductor (L)
v-i:	$v = iR$	$v = \dfrac{1}{C} \displaystyle\int_{t_0}^{t} i\, dt + v(t_0)$	$v = L\dfrac{di}{dt}$
i-v:	$i = v/R$	$i = C\dfrac{dv}{dt}$	$i = \dfrac{1}{L} \displaystyle\int_{t_0}^{t} v\, dt + i(t_0)$
p or w:	$p = i^2 R = \dfrac{v^2}{R}$	$w = \dfrac{1}{2}Cv^2$	$w = \dfrac{1}{2}Li^2$
Series:	$R_{eq} = R_1 + R_2$	$C_{eq} = \dfrac{C_1 C_2}{C_1 + C_2}$	$L_{eq} = L_1 + L_2$
Parallel:	$R_{eq} = \dfrac{R_1 R_2}{R_1 + R_2}$	$C_{eq} = C_1 + C_2$	$L_{eq} = \dfrac{L_1 L_2}{L_1 + L_2}$
At dc:	Same	Open circuit	Short circuit
Circuit variable that cannot change abruptly:	Not applicable	v	i

[†]*Passive sign convention is assumed.*

EXAMPLE 6.11

Figure 6.31   For Example 6.11.

Find the equivalent inductance of the circuit shown in Fig. 6.31.

Solution:

The 10-H, 12-H, and 20-H inductors are in series; thus, combining them gives a 42-H inductance. This 42-H inductor is in parallel with the 7-H inductor so that they are combined, to give

$$\frac{7 \times 42}{7 + 42} = 6\ \text{H}$$

This 6-H inductor is in series with the 4-H and 8-H inductors. Hence,

$$L_{eq} = 4 + 6 + 8 = 18 \text{ H}$$

PRACTICE PROBLEM 6.11

Calculate the equivalent inductance for the inductive ladder network in Fig. 6.32.

Figure 6.32   For Practice Prob. 6.11.

Answer: 25 mH.

EXAMPLE 6.12

For the circuit in Fig. 6.33, $i(t) = 4(2 - e^{-10t})$ mA. If $i_2(0) = -1$ mA, find: (a) $i_1(0)$; (b) $v(t)$, $v_1(t)$, and $v_2(t)$; (c) $i_1(t)$ and $i_2(t)$.

Solution:

(a) From $i(t) = 4(2 - e^{-10t})$ mA, $i(0) = 4(2 - 1) = 4$ mA. Since $i = i_1 + i_2$,

$$i_1(0) = i(0) - i_2(0) = 4 - (-1) = 5 \text{ mA}$$

Figure 6.33   For Example 6.12.

(b) The equivalent inductance is

$$L_{eq} = 2 + 4 \parallel 12 = 2 + 3 = 5 \text{ H}$$

Thus,

$$v(t) = L_{eq}\frac{di}{dt} = 5(4)(-1)(-10)e^{-10t} \text{ mV} = 200e^{-10t} \text{ mV}$$

and

$$v_1(t) = 2\frac{di}{dt} = 2(-4)(-10)e^{-10t} \text{ mV} = 80e^{-10t} \text{ mV}$$

Since $v = v_1 + v_2$,

$$v_2(t) = v(t) - v_1(t) = 120e^{-10t} \text{ mV}$$

(c) The current i_1 is obtained as

$$i_1(t) = \frac{1}{4}\int_0^t v_2 \, dt + i_1(0) = \frac{120}{4}\int_0^t e^{-10t} \, dt + 5 \text{ mA}$$

$$= -3e^{-10t} \Big|_0^t + 5 \text{ mA} = -3e^{-10t} + 3 + 5 = 8 - 3e^{-10t} \text{ mA}$$

Similarly,

$$i_2(t) = \frac{1}{12} \int_0^t v_2 \, dt + i_2(0) = \frac{120}{12} \int_0^t e^{-10t} \, dt - 1 \text{ mA}$$

$$= -e^{-10t} \Big|_0^t - 1 \text{ mA} = -e^{-10t} + 1 - 1 = -e^{-10t} \text{ mA}$$

Note that $i_1(t) + i_2(t) = i(t)$.

PRACTICE PROBLEM 6.12

In the circuit of Fig. 6.34, $i_1(t) = 0.6e^{-2t}$ A. If $i(0) = 1.4$ A, find: (a) $i_2(0)$; (b) $i_2(t)$ and $i(t)$; (c) $v_1(t)$, $v_2(t)$, and $v(t)$.

Answer: (a) 0.8 A, (b) $(-0.4 + 1.2e^{-2t})$ A, $(-0.4 + 1.8e^{-2t})$ A, (c) $-7.2e^{-2t}$ V, $-28.8e^{-2t}$ V, $-36e^{-2t}$ V.

Figure 6.34   For Practice Prob. 6.12.

†6.6 APPLICATIONS

Circuit elements such as resistors and capacitors are commercially available in either discrete form or integrated-circuit (IC) form. Unlike capacitors and resistors, inductors with appreciable inductance are difficult to produce on IC substrates. Therefore, inductors (coils) usually come in discrete form and tend to be more bulky and expensive. For this reason, inductors are not as versatile as capacitors and resistors, and they are more limited in applications. However, there are several applications in which inductors have no practical substitute. They are routinely used in relays, delays, sensing devices, pick-up heads, telephone circuits, radio and TV receivers, power supplies, electric motors, microphones, and loudspeakers, to mention a few.

Capacitors and inductors possess the following three special properties that make them very useful in electric circuits:

1. The capacity to store energy makes them useful as temporary voltage or current sources. Thus, they can be used for generating a large amount of current or voltage for a short period of time.

2. Capacitors oppose any abrupt change in voltage, while inductors oppose any abrupt change in current. This property makes inductors useful for spark or arc suppression and for converting pulsating dc voltage into relatively smooth dc voltage.

3. Capacitors and inductors are frequency sensitive. This property makes them useful for frequency discrimination.

The first two properties are put to use in dc circuits, while the third one is taken advantage of in ac circuits. We will see how useful these properties are in later chapters. For now, consider three applications involving capacitors and op amps: integrator, differentiator, and analog computer.

6.6.1   Integrator

Important op amp circuits that use energy-storage elements include integrators and differentiators. These op amp circuits often involve resistors and capacitors; inductors (coils) tend to be more bulky and expensive.

The op amp integrator is used in numerous applications, especially in analog computers, to be discussed in Section 6.6.3.

> An integrator is an op amp circuit whose output is proportional to the integral of the input signal.

If the feedback resistor R_f in the familiar inverting amplifier of Fig. 6.35(a) is replaced by a capacitor, we obtain an ideal integrator, as shown in Fig. 6.35(b). It is interesting that we can obtain a mathematical representation of integration this way. At node a in Fig. 6.35(b),

$$i_R = i_C \qquad (6.32)$$

But

$$i_R = \frac{v_i}{R}, \qquad i_C = -C\frac{dv_o}{dt}$$

Substituting these in Eq. (6.32), we obtain

$$\frac{v_i}{R} = -C\frac{dv_o}{dt} \qquad (6.33a)$$

$$dv_o = -\frac{1}{RC}v_i \, dt \qquad (6.33b)$$

Integrating both sides gives

$$v_o(t) - v_o(0) = -\frac{1}{RC}\int_0^t v_i(t) \, dt \qquad (6.34)$$

To ensure that $v_o(0) = 0$, it is always necessary to discharge the integrator's capacitor prior to the application of a signal. Assuming $v_o(0) = 0$,

$$\boxed{v_o = -\frac{1}{RC}\int_0^t v_i(t) \, dt} \qquad (6.35)$$

which shows that the circuit in Fig. 6.35(b) provides an output voltage proportional to the integral of the input. In practice, the op amp integrator requires a feedback resistor to reduce dc gain and prevent saturation. Care must be taken that the op amp operates within the linear range so that it does not saturate.

(a)

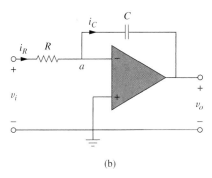

(b)

Figure 6.35   Replacing the feedback resistor in the inverting amplifier in (a) produces an integrator in (b).

EXAMPLE 6.13

Figure 6.36   For Example 6.13.

If $v_1 = 10 \cos 2t$ mV and $v_2 = 0.5t$ mV, find v_o in the op amp circuit in Fig. 6.36. Assume that the voltage across the capacitor is initially zero.

Solution:

This is a summing integrator, and

$$v_o = -\frac{1}{R_1 C}\int v_1 \, dt - \frac{1}{R_2 C}\int v_2 \, dt$$

$$= -\frac{1}{3 \times 10^6 \times 2 \times 10^{-6}}\int_0^t 10 \cos 2t \, dt$$

$$\quad - \frac{1}{100 \times 10^3 \times 2 \times 10^{-6}}\int_0^t 0.5t \, dt$$

$$= -\frac{1}{6}\frac{10}{2}\sin 2t - \frac{1}{0.2}\frac{0.5t^2}{2} = -0.833 \sin 2t - 1.25t^2 \text{ mV}$$

PRACTICE PROBLEM 6.13

The integrator in Fig. 6.35 has $R = 25$ kΩ, $C = 10$ μF. Determine the output voltage when a dc voltage of 10 mV is applied at $t = 0$. Assume that the op amp is initially nulled.

Answer: $-40t$ mV.

6.6.2   Differentiator

> A differentiator is an op amp circuit whose output is proportional to the rate of change of the input signal.

In Fig. 6.35(a), if the input resistor is replaced by a capacitor, the resulting circuit is a differentiator, shown in Fig. 6.37. Applying KCL at node a,

$$i_R = i_C \tag{6.36}$$

But

$$i_R = -\frac{v_o}{R}, \qquad i_C = C\frac{dv_i}{dt}$$

Substituting these in Eq. (6.36) yields

$$v_o = -RC\frac{dv_i}{dt} \tag{6.37}$$

Figure 6.37   An op amp differentiator.

showing that the output is the derivative of the input. Differentiator circuits are electronically unstable because any electrical noise within the circuit is exaggerated by the differentiator. For this reason, the differentiator circuit in Fig. 6.37 is not as useful and popular as the integrator. It is seldom used in practice.

EXAMPLE 6.14

Sketch the output voltage for the circuit in Fig. 6.38(a), given the input voltage in Fig. 6.38(b). Take $v_o = 0$ at $t = 0$.

Solution:

This is a differentiator with

$$RC = 5 \times 10^3 \times 0.2 \times 10^{-6} = 10^{-3} \text{ s}$$

For $0 < t < 4$ ms, we can express the input voltage in Fig. 6.38(b) as

$$v_i = \begin{cases} 2000t & 0 < t < 2 \text{ ms} \\ 8 - 2000t & 2 < t < 4 \text{ ms} \end{cases}$$

This is repeated for $4 < t < 8$ ms. Using Eq. (6.37), the output is obtained as

$$v_o = -RC\frac{dv_i}{dt} = \begin{cases} -2 \text{ V} & 4 < t < 6 \text{ ms} \\ 2 \text{ V} & 6 < t < 8 \text{ ms} \end{cases}$$

Thus, the output is as sketched in Fig. 6.39.

(a)

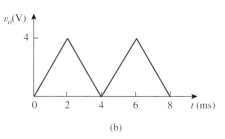

(b)

Figure 6.38   For Example 6.14.

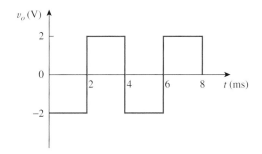

Figure 6.39   Output of the circuit in Fig. 6.38(a).

PRACTICE PROBLEM 6.14

The differentiator in Fig. 6.37 has $R = 10$ kΩ and $C = 2$ μF. Given that $v_i = 3t$ V, determine the output v_o.

Answer: -60 mV.

6.6.3 Analog Computer

Op amps were initially developed for electronic analog computers. Analog computers can be programmed to solve mathematical models of mechanical or electrical systems. These models are usually expressed in terms of differential equations.

To solve simple differential equations using the analog computer requires cascading three types of op amp circuits: integrator circuits, summing amplifiers, and inverting/noninverting amplifiers for negative/

positive scaling. The best way to illustrate how an analog computer solves a differential equation is with an example.

Suppose we desire the solution $x(t)$ of the equation

$$a\frac{d^2x}{dt^2} + b\frac{dx}{dt} + cx = f(t), \qquad t > 0 \tag{6.38}$$

where a, b, and c are constants, and $f(t)$ is an arbitrary forcing function. The solution is obtained by first solving the highest-order derivative term. Solving for d^2x/dt^2 yields

$$\frac{d^2x}{dt^2} = \frac{f(t)}{a} - \frac{b}{a}\frac{dx}{dt} - \frac{c}{a}x \tag{6.39}$$

To obtain dx/dt, the d^2x/dt^2 term is integrated and inverted. Finally, to obtain x, the dx/dt term is integrated and inverted. The forcing function is injected at the proper point. Thus, the analog computer for solving Eq. (6.38) is implemented by connecting the necessary summers, inverters, and integrators. A plotter or oscilloscope may be used to view the output x, or dx/dt, or d^2x/dt^2, depending on where it is connected in the system.

Although the above example is on a second-order differential equation, any differential equation can be simulated by an analog computer comprising integrators, inverters, and inverting summers. But care must be exercised in selecting the values of the resistors and capacitors, to ensure that the op amps do not saturate during the solution time interval.

The analog computers with vacuum tubes were built in the 1950s and 1960s. Recently their use has declined. They have been superseded by modern digital computers. However, we still study analog computers for two reasons. First, the availability of integrated op amps has made it possible to build analog computers easily and cheaply. Second, understanding analog computers helps with the appreciation of the digital computers.

EXAMPLE 6.15

Design an analog computer circuit to solve the differential equation:

$$\frac{d^2v_o}{dt^2} + 2\frac{dv_o}{dt} + v_o = 10\sin 4t \qquad t > 0$$

subject to $v_o(0) = -4$, $v_o'(0) = 1$, where the prime refers to the time derivative.

Solution:

We first solve for the second derivative as

$$\frac{d^2v_o}{dt^2} = 10\sin 4t - 2\frac{dv_o}{dt} - v_o \tag{6.15.1}$$

Solving this requires some mathematical operations, including summing, scaling, and integration. Integrating both sides of Eq. (6.15.1) gives

$$\frac{dv_o}{dt} = -\int_0^t \left(-10\sin 4t + 2\frac{dv_o}{dt} + v_o\right) dt + v_o'(0) \tag{6.15.2}$$

where $v_o'(0) = 1$. We implement Eq. (6.15.2) using the summing integrator shown in Fig. 6.40(a). The values of the resistors and capacitors have been chosen so that $RC = 1$ for the term

$$-\frac{1}{RC} \int_0^t v_o \, dt$$

Other terms in the summing integrator of Eq. (6.15.2) are implemented accordingly. The initial condition $dv_o(0)/dt = 1$ is implemented by connecting a 1-V battery with a switch across the capacitor as shown in Fig. 6.40(a).

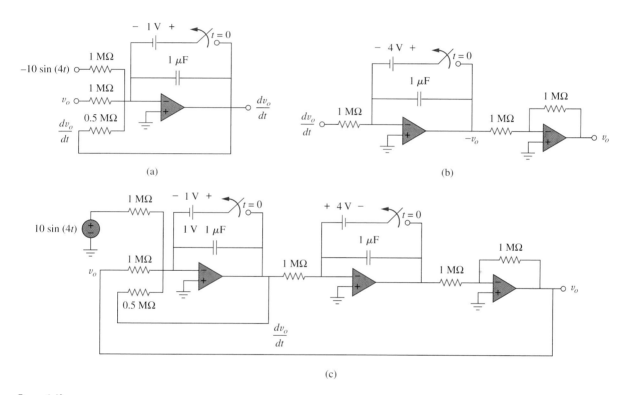

(a)

(b)

(c)

Figure 6.40   For Example 6.15.

The next step is to obtain v_o by integrating dv_o/dt and inverting the result,

$$v_o = -\int_0^t \left(-\frac{dv_o}{dt} \right) dt + v(0) \qquad (6.15.3)$$

This is implemented with the circuit in Fig. 6.40(b) with the battery giving the initial condition of -4 V. We now combine the two circuits in Fig. 6.40 (a) and (b) to obtain the complete circuit shown in Fig. 6.40(c). When the input signal $10 \sin 4t$ is applied, we open the switches at $t = 0$ to obtain the output waveform v_o, which may be viewed on an oscilloscope.

PRACTICE PROBLEM 6.15

Design an analog computer circuit to solve the differential equation:

$$\frac{d^2 v_o}{dt^2} + 3\frac{dv_o}{dt} + 2v_o = 4\cos 10t \qquad t > 0$$

subject to $v_o(0) = 2$, $v_o'(0) = 0$.

Answer: See Fig. 6.41, where $RC = 1$ s.

Figure 6.41   For Practice Prob. 6.15.

6.7   SUMMARY

1. The current through a capacitor is directly proportional to the time rate of change of the voltage across it.

$$i = C\frac{dv}{dt}$$

The current through a capacitor is zero unless the voltage is changing. Thus, a capacitor acts like an open circuit to a dc source.

2. The voltage across a capacitor is directly proportional to the time integral of the current through it.

$$v = \frac{1}{C}\int_{-\infty}^{t} i \, dt = \frac{1}{C}\int_{t_0}^{t} i \, dt + v(t_0)$$

The voltage across a capacitor cannot change instantly.

3. Capacitors in series and in parallel are combined in the same way as conductances.

4. The voltage across an inductor is directly proportional to the time rate of change of the current through it.

$$v = L\frac{di}{dt}$$

The voltage across the inductor is zero unless the current is changing. Thus an inductor acts like a short circuit to a dc source.

5. The current through an inductor is directly proportional to the time integral of the voltage across it.

$$i = \frac{1}{L} \int_{-\infty}^{t} v \, dt = \frac{1}{L} \int_{t_0}^{t} v \, dt + i(t_0)$$

The current through an inductor cannot change instantly.

6. Inductors in series and in parallel are combined in the same way resistors in series and in parallel are combined.

7. At any given time t, the energy stored in a capacitor is $\frac{1}{2}Cv^2$, while the energy stored in an inductor is $\frac{1}{2}Li^2$.

8. Three application circuits, the integrator, the differentiator, and the analog computer, can be realized using resistors, capacitors, and op amps.

REVIEW QUESTIONS

6.1   What charge is on a 5-F capacitor when it is connected across a 120-V source?

(a) 600 C   (b) 300 C
(c) 24 C   (d) 12 C

6.2   Capacitance is measured in:

(a) coulombs   (b) joules
(c) henrys   (d) farads

6.3   When the total charge in a capacitor is doubled, the energy stored:

(a) remains the same   (b) is halved
(c) is doubled   (d) is quadrupled

6.4   Can the voltage waveform in Fig. 6.42 be associated with a capacitor?

(a) Yes   (b) No

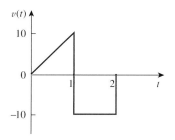

Figure 6.42   For Review Question 6.4.

6.5   The total capacitance of two 40-mF series-connected capacitors in parallel with a 4-mF capacitor is:

(a) 3.8 mF   (b) 5 mF   (c) 24 mF
(d) 44 mF   (e) 84 mF

6.6   In Fig. 6.43, if $i = \cos 4t$ and $v = \sin 4t$, the element is:

(a) a resistor   (b) a capacitor   (c) an inductor

Figure 6.43   For Review Question 6.6.

6.7   A 5-H inductor changes its current by 3 A in 0.2 s. The voltage produced at the terminals of the inductor is:

(a) 75 V   (b) 8.888 V
(c) 3 V   (d) 1.2 V

6.8   If the current through a 10-mH inductor increases from zero to 2 A, how much energy is stored in the inductor?

(a) 40 mJ   (b) 20 mJ
(c) 10 mJ   (d) 5 mJ

6.9 Inductors in parallel can be combined just like resistors in parallel.

    (a) True   (b) False

6.10 For the circuit in Fig. 6.44, the voltage divider formula is:

    (a) $v_1 = \dfrac{L_1 + L_2}{L_1} v_s$ (b) $v_1 = \dfrac{L_1 + L_2}{L_2} v_s$

    (c) $v_1 = \dfrac{L_2}{L_1 + L_2} v_s$ (d) $v_1 = \dfrac{L_1}{L_1 + L_2} v_s$

Figure 6.44   For Review Question 6.10.

Answers: 6.1a, 6.2d, 6.3d, 6.4b, 6.5c, 6.6b, 6.7a, 6.8b, 6.9a, 6.10d.

PROBLEMS

Section 6.2   Capacitors

6.1 If the voltage across a 5-F capacitor is $2te^{-3t}$ V, find the current and the power.

6.2 A 40-μF capacitor is charged to 120 V and is then allowed to discharge to 80 V. How much energy is lost?

6.3 In 5 s, the voltage across a 40-mF capacitor changes from 160 V to 220 V. Calculate the average current through the capacitor.

6.4 A current of 6 sin 4t A flows through a 2-F capacitor. Find the voltage $v(t)$ across the capacitor given that $v(0) = 1$ V.

6.5 If the current waveform in Fig. 6.45 is applied to a 20-μF capacitor, find the voltage $v(t)$ across the capacitor. Assume that $v(0) = 0$.

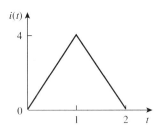

Figure 6.45   For Prob. 6.5.

6.6 The voltage waveform in Fig. 6.46 is applied across a 30-μF capacitor. Draw the current waveform through it.

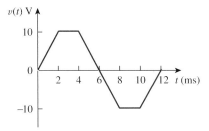

Figure 6.46   For Prob. 6.6.

6.7 At $t = 0$, the voltage across a 50-mF capacitor is 10 V. Calculate the voltage across the capacitor for $t > 0$ when current $4t$ mA flows through it.

6.8 A 4-mF capacitor has the terminal voltage

$$v = \begin{cases} 50 \text{ V}, & t \leq 0 \\ Ae^{-100t} + Be^{-600t} \text{ V}, & t \geq 0 \end{cases}$$

If the capacitor has an initial current of 2 A, find:

    (a) the constants A and B,

    (b) the energy stored in the capacitor at $t = 0$,

    (c) the capacitor current for $t > 0$.

6.9 The current through a 0.5-F capacitor is $6(1 - e^{-t})$ A. Determine the voltage and power at $t = 2$ s. Assume $v(0) = 0$.

6.10 The voltage across a 2-mF capacitor is shown in Fig. 6.47. Determine the current through the capacitor.

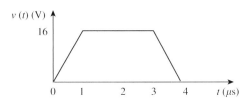

Figure 6.47   For Prob. 6.10.

6.11 The current through an initially uncharged 4-μF capacitor is shown in Fig. 6.48. Find the voltage across the capacitor for $0 < t < 3$.

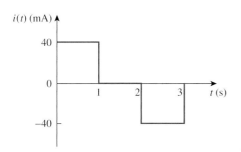

Figure 6.48   For Prob. 6.11.

6.12 A voltage of $60\cos 4\pi t$ V appears across the terminals of a 3-mF capacitor. Calculate the current through the capacitor and the energy stored in it from $t = 0$ to $t = 0.125$ s.

6.13 Find the voltage across the capacitors in the circuit of Fig. 6.49 under dc conditions.

Figure 6.49   For Prob. 6.13.

Section 6.3   Series and Parallel Capacitors

6.14 What is the total capacitance of four 30-mF capacitors connected in:

(a) parallel   (b) series

6.15 Two capacitors (20 μF and 30 μF) are connected to a 100-V source. Find the energy stored in each capacitor if they are connected in:

(a) parallel   (b) series

6.16 The equivalent capacitance at terminals a-b in the circuit in Fig. 6.50 is 30 μF. Calculate the value of C.

Figure 6.50   For Prob. 6.16.

6.17 Determine the equivalent capacitance for each of the circuits in Fig. 6.51.

(a)

(b)

(c)

Figure 6.51   For Prob. 6.17.

6.18 Find C_{eq} for the circuit in Fig. 6.52.

Figure 6.52   For Prob. 6.18.

6.19   Find the equivalent capacitance between terminals a and b in the circuit of Fig. 6.53. All capacitances are in μF.

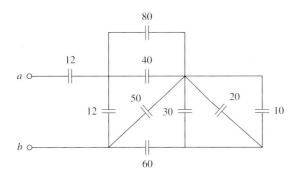

Figure 6.53   For Prob. 6.19.

6.20   Calculate the equivalent capacitance for the circuit in Fig. 6.54. All capacitances are in mF.

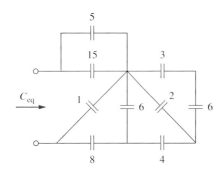

Figure 6.54   For Prob. 6.20.

6.21   Determine the equivalent capacitance at terminals a-b of the circuit in Fig. 6.55.

Figure 6.55   For Prob. 6.21.

6.22   Obtain the equivalent capacitance of the circuit in Fig. 6.56.

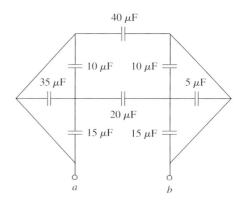

Figure 6.56   For Prob. 6.22.

6.23   For the circuit in Fig. 6.57, determine:

(a)   the voltage across each capacitor,
(b)   the energy stored in each capacitor.

Figure 6.57   For Prob. 6.23.

6.24   Repeat Prob. 6.23 for the circuit in Fig. 6.58.

Figure 6.58   For Prob. 6.24.

6.25   (a)   Show that the voltage-division rule for two capacitors in series as in Fig. 6.59(a) is

$$v_1 = \frac{C_2}{C_1 + C_2} v_s, \qquad v_2 = \frac{C_1}{C_1 + C_2} v_s$$

assuming that the initial conditions are zero.

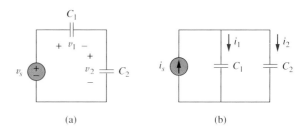

(a)   (b)

Figure 6.59   For Prob. 6.25.

(b) For two capacitors in parallel as in Fig. 6.59(b), show that the current-division rule is

$$i_1 = \frac{C_1}{C_1 + C_2} i_s, \qquad i_2 = \frac{C_2}{C_1 + C_2} i_s$$

assuming that the initial conditions are zero.

6.26 Three capacitors, $C_1 = 5\ \mu F$, $C_2 = 10\ \mu F$, and $C_3 = 20\ \mu F$, are connected in parallel across a 150-V source. Determine:

(a) the total capacitance,

(b) the charge on each capacitor,

(c) the total energy stored in the parallel combination.

6.27 The three capacitors in the previous problem are placed in series with a 200-V source. Compute:

(a) the total capacitance,

(b) the charge on each capacitor,

(c) the total energy stored in the series combination.

***6.28** Obtain the equivalent capacitance of the network shown in Fig. 6.60.

Figure 6.60   For Prob. 6.28.

6.29 Determine C_{eq} for each circuit in Fig. 6.61.

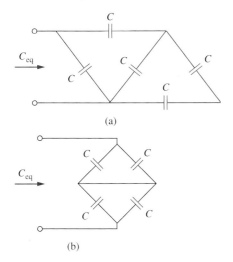

Figure 6.61   For Prob. 6.29.

6.30 Assuming that the capacitors are initially uncharged, find $v_o(t)$ in the circuit in Fig. 6.62.

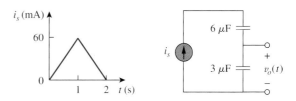

Figure 6.62   For Prob. 6.30.

6.31 If $v(0) = 0$, find $v(t)$, $i_1(t)$, and $i_2(t)$ in the circuit in Fig. 6.63.

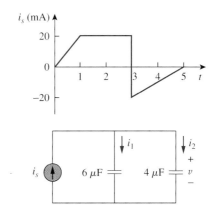

Figure 6.63   For Prob. 6.31.

6.32 In the circuit in Fig. 6.64, let $i_s = 30e^{-2t}$ mA and $v_1(0) = 50$ V, $v_2(0) = 20$ V. Determine: (a) $v_1(t)$ and $v_2(t)$, (b) the energy in each capacitor at $t = 0.5$ s.

Figure 6.64   For Prob. 6.32.

---

*An asterisk indicates a challenging problem.

6.33 Obtain the Thevenin equivalent at the terminals, *a-b*, of the circuit shown in Fig. 6.65. Please note that Thevenin equivalent circuits do not generally exist for circuits involving capacitors and resistors. This is a special case where the Thevenin equivalent circuit does exist.

Figure 6.65   For Prob. 6.33.

Section 6.4   Inductors

6.34 The current through a 10-mH inductor is $6e^{-t/2}$ A. Find the voltage and the power at $t = 3$ s.

6.35 The current in a coil increases uniformly from 0.4 to 1 A in 2 s so that the voltage across the coil is 60 mV. Calculate the inductance of the coil.

6.36 The current through a 0.25-mH inductor is $12 \cos 2t$ A. Determine the terminal voltage and the power.

6.37 The current through a 12-mH inductor is $4 \sin 100t$ A. Find the voltage, across the inductor for $0 < t < \pi/200$ s, and the energy stored at $t = \frac{\pi}{200}$ s.

6.38 The current through a 40-mH inductor is

$$i(t) = \begin{cases} 0, & t < 0 \\ te^{-2t} \text{ A}, & t > 0 \end{cases}$$

Find the voltage $v(t)$.

6.39 The voltage across a 200-mH inductor is given by

$$v(t) = 3t^2 + 2t + 4 \text{ V} \qquad \text{for } t > 0.$$

Determine the current $i(t)$ through the inductor. Assume that $i(0) = 1$ A.

6.40 The current through a 20-mH inductor is shown in Fig. 6.66. Sketch the voltage across the inductor.

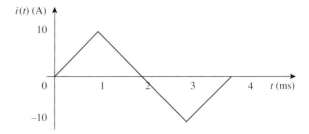

Figure 6.66   For Prob. 6.40.

6.41 The voltage across a 2-H inductor is $20(1 - e^{-2t})$ V. If the initial current through the inductor is 0.3 A, find the current and the energy stored in the inductor at $t = 1$ s.

6.42 If the voltage waveform in Fig. 6.67 is applied across the terminals of a 5-H inductor, calculate the current through the inductor. Assume $i(0) = -1$ A.

Figure 6.67   For Prob. 6.42.

6.43 The current in an 80-mH inductor increases from 0 to 60 mA. How much energy is stored in the inductor?

6.44 A voltage of $(4 + 10 \cos 2t)$ V is applied to a 5-H inductor. Find the current $i(t)$ through the inductor if $i(0) = -1$ A.

6.45 If the voltage waveform in Fig. 6.68 is applied to a 10-mH inductor, find the inductor current $i(t)$. Assume $i(0) = 0$.

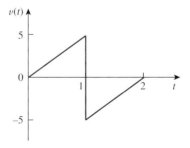

Figure 6.68   For Prob. 6.45.

6.46 Find v_C, i_L, and the energy stored in the capacitor and inductor in the circuit of Fig. 6.69 under dc conditions.

Figure 6.69   For Prob. 6.46.

6.47 For the circuit in Fig. 6.70, calculate the value of R that will make the energy stored in the capacitor the same as that stored in the inductor under dc conditions.

Figure 6.70   For Prob. 6.47.

6.48 Under dc conditions, find the voltage across the capacitors and the current through the inductors in the circuit of Fig. 6.71.

Figure 6.71   For Prob. 6.48.

Section 6.5   Series and Parallel Inductors

6.49 Find the equivalent inductance for each circuit in Fig. 6.72.

(c)

Figure 6.72   For Prob. 6.49.

6.50 Obtain L_{eq} for the inductive circuit of Fig. 6.73. All inductances are in mH.

Figure 6.73   For Prob. 6.50.

6.51 Determine L_{eq} at terminals a-b of the circuit in Fig. 6.74.

Figure 6.74   For Prob. 6.51.

6.52 Find the equivalent inductance at terminals a-b of the circuit in Fig. 6.75.

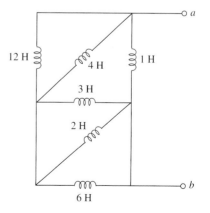

Figure 6.75   For Prob. 6.52.

244   PART I   DC Circuits

6.53 Find L_{eq} at the terminals of the circuit in Fig. 6.76.

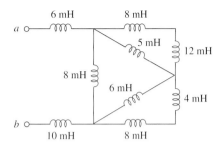

Figure 6.76   For Prob. 6.53.

6.54 Find the equivalent inductance looking into the terminals of the circuit in Fig. 6.77.

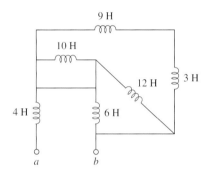

Figure 6.77   For Prob. 6.54.

6.55 Find L_{eq} in each of the circuits of Fig. 6.78.

(a)

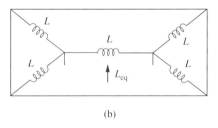

(b)

Figure 6.78   For Prob. 6.55.

6.56 Find L_{eq} in the circuit in Fig. 6.79.

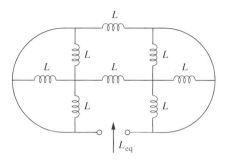

Figure 6.79   For Prob. 6.56.

*__6.57__ Determine L_{eq} that may be used to represent the inductive network of Fig. 6.80 at the terminals.

Figure 6.80   For Prob. 6.57.

6.58 The current waveform in Fig. 6.81 flows through a 3-H inductor. Sketch the voltage across the inductor over the interval $0 < t < 6$ s.

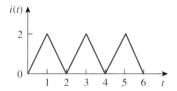

Figure 6.81   For Prob. 6.58.

6.59 (a) For two inductors in series as in Fig. 6.82(a), show that the voltage division principle is

$$v_1 = \frac{L_1}{L_1 + L_2} v_s, \qquad v_2 = \frac{L_2}{L_1 + L_2} v_s,$$

assuming that the initial conditions are zero.

(b) For two inductors in parallel as in Fig. 6.82(b), show that the current-division principle is

$$i_1 = \frac{L_2}{L_1 + L_2} i_s, \qquad i_2 = \frac{L_1}{L_1 + L_2} i_s,$$

assuming that the initial conditions are zero.

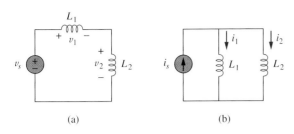

Figure 6.82   For Prob. 6.59.

6.60   In the circuit of Fig. 6.83, $i_o(0) = 2$ A. Determine $i_o(t)$ and $v_o(t)$ for $t > 0$.

Figure 6.83   For Prob. 6.60.

6.61   In the circuit of Fig. 6.84, let $i_s(t) = 6e^{-2t}$ mA, $t \geq 0$ and $i_1(0) = 4$ mA. Find:

(a) $i_2(0)$,

(b) $i_1(t)$ and $i_2(t)$, $t > 0$,

(c) $v_1(t)$ and $v_2(t)$, $t > 0$,

(d)   the energy in each inductor at $t = 0.5$ s.

Figure 6.84   For Prob. 6.61.

6.62   Consider the circuit in Fig. 6.85. Given that $v(t) = 12e^{-3t}$ mV for $t > 0$ and $i_1(0) = -10$ mA, find: (a) $i_2(0)$, (b) $i_1(t)$ and $i_2(t)$.

Figure 6.85   For Prob. 6.62.

6.63   In the circuit in Fig. 6.86, sketch v_o.

Figure 6.86   For Prob. 6.63.

6.64   The switch in Fig. 6.87 has been in position A for a long time. At $t = 0$, the switch moves from position A to B. The switch is a make-before-break type so that there is no interruption in the inductor current. Find: (a) $i(t)$ for $t > 0$, (b) v *just after* the switch has been moved to position B, (c) $v(t)$ long after the switch is in position B.

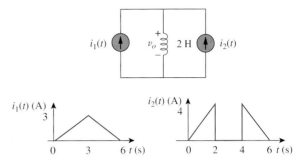

Figure 6.87   For Prob. 6.64.

6.65   The inductors in Fig. 6.88 are initially charged and are connected to the black box at $t = 0$. If $i_1(0) = 4$ A, $i_2(0) = -2$ A, and $v(t) = 50e^{-200t}$ mV, $t \geq 0$, find:

(a)   the energy initially stored in each inductor,

(b)   the total energy delivered to the black box from $t = 0$ to $t = \infty$,

(c) $i_1(t)$ and $i_2(t)$, $t \geq 0$,

(d) $i(t)$, $t \geq 0$.

Figure 6.88   For Prob. 6.65.

6.66 Find i and v in the circuit of Fig. 6.89 assuming that $i(0) = 0 = v(0)$.

Figure 6.89   For Prob. 6.66.

Section 6.6   Applications

6.67 An op amp integrator has $R = 50$ kΩ and $C = 0.04$ μF. If the input voltage is $v_i = 10 \sin 50t$ mV, obtain the output voltage.

6.68 A 10-V dc voltage is applied to an integrator with $R = 50$ kΩ, $C = 100$ μF at $t = 0$. How long will it take for the op amp to saturate if the saturation voltages are $+12$ V and -12 V? Assume that the initial capacitor voltage was zero.

6.69 An op amp integrator with $R = 4$ MΩ and $C = 1$ μF has the input waveform shown in Fig. 6.90. Plot the output waveform.

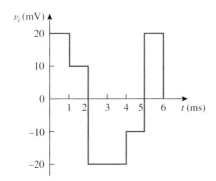

Figure 6.90   For Prob. 6.69.

6.70 Using a single op amp, a capacitor, and resistors of 100 kΩ or less, design a circuit to implement

$$v_o = -50 \int_0^t v_i(t)\, dt$$

Assume $v_o = 0$ at $t = 0$.

6.71 Show how you would use a single op amp to generate

$$v_o = -\int_0^t (v_1 + 4v_2 + 10v_3)\, dt$$

If the integrating capacitor is $C = 2$ μF, obtain other component values.

6.72 At $t = 1.5$ ms, calculate v_o due to the cascaded integrators in Fig. 6.91. Assume that the integrators are reset to 0 V at $t = 0$.

Figure 6.91   For Prob. 6.72.

6.73 Show that the circuit in Fig. 6.92 is a noninverting integrator.

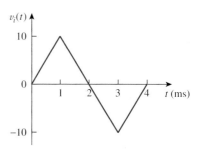

Figure 6.92   For Prob. 6.73.

6.74 The triangular waveform in Fig. 6.93(a) is applied to the input of the op amp differentiator in Fig. 6.93(b). Plot the output.

(a)

(b)

Figure 6.93   For Prob. 6.74.

6.75   An op amp differentiator has $R = 250$ kΩ and $C = 10$ μF. The input voltage is a ramp $r(t) = 12t$ mV. Find the output voltage.

6.76   A voltage waveform has the following characteristics: a positive slope of 20 V/s for 5 ms followed by a negative slope of 10 V/s for 10 ms. If the waveform is applied to a differentiator with $R = 50$ kΩ, $C = 10$ μF, sketch the output voltage waveform.

****6.77**   The output v_o of the op amp circuit of Fig. 6.94(a) is shown in Fig. 6.94(b). Let $R_i = R_f = 1$ MΩ and $C = 1$ μF. Determine the input voltage waveform and sketch it.

(a)

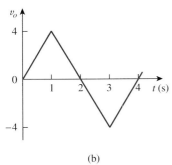

(b)

Figure 6.94   For Prob. 6.77.

6.78   Design an analog computer to simulate

$$\frac{d^2v_o}{dt^2} + 2\frac{dv_o}{dt} + v_o = 10\sin 2t$$

where $v_0(0) = 2$ and $v_0'(0) = 0$.

6.79   Design an analog computer circuit to solve the following ordinary differential equation.

$$\frac{dy(t)}{dt} + 4y(t) = f(t)$$

where $y(0) = 1$ V.

6.80   Figure 6.95 presents an analog computer designed to solve a differential equation. Assuming $f(t)$ is known, set up the equation for $f(t)$.

Figure 6.95   For Prob. 6.80.

6.81   Design an analog computer to simulate the following equation:

$$\frac{d^2v}{dt^2} + 5v = -2f(t)$$

6.82   Design an op amp circuit such that

$$v_o = 10v_s + 2\int v_s\,dt$$

where v_s and v_o are the input voltage and output voltage, respectively.

COMPREHENSIVE PROBLEMS

6.83   Your laboratory has available a large number of 10-μF capacitors rated at 300 V. To design a capacitor bank of 40-μF rated at 600 V, how many 10-μF capacitors are needed and how would you connect them?

6.84   When a capacitor is connected to a dc source, its voltage rises from 20 V to 36 V in 4 μs with an average charging current of 0.6 A. Determine the value of the capacitance.

6.85   A square-wave generator produces the voltage
waveform shown in Fig. 6.96(a). What kind of a
circuit component is needed to convert the voltage
waveform to the triangular current waveform shown
in Fig. 6.96(b)? Calculate the value of the
component, assuming that it is initially uncharged.

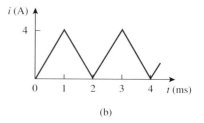

(b)

Figure 6.96   For Prob. 6.85.

6.86   In an electric power plant substation, a capacitor
bank is made of 10 capacitor strings connected in
parallel. Each string consists of eight 1000-μF
capacitors connected in series, with each capacitor
charged to 100 V.

(a)   Calculate the total capacitance of the bank.
(b)   Determine the total energy stored in the bank.

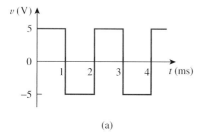

(a)

C H A P T E R   7

FIRST-ORDER CIRCUITS

Use theory to provide insight; use common sense and intuition where it is suitable. A balance cannot be achieved unless one has both *common sense and a facility with theory.*

—David Gries

Enhancing Your Career

Careers in Computer Engineering Electrical engineering education has gone through drastic changes in recent decades. Most departments have come to be known as Department of Electrical and Computer Engineering, emphasizing the rapid changes due to computers. Computers occupy a prominent place in modern society and education. They have become commonplace and are helping to change the face of research, development, production, business, and entertainment. The scientist, engineer, doctor, attorney, teacher, airline pilot, businessperson—almost anyone benefits from a computer's abilities to store large amounts of information and to process that information in very short periods of time. The internet, a computer communication network, is becoming essential in business, education, and library science. Computer usage is growing by leaps and bounds.

Three major disciplines study computer systems: computer science, computer engineering, and information management science. Computer engineering has grown so fast and wide that it is divorcing itself from electrical engineering. But, in many schools of engineering, computer engineering is still an integral part of electrical engineering.

An education in computer engineering should provide breadth in software, hardware design, and basic modeling techniques. It should include courses in data structures, digital systems, computer architecture, microprocessors, interfacing, software engineering, and operating systems.

Computer design of very large scale integrated (VLSI) circuits. Courtesy of Honeywell, Inc.

Electrical engineers who specialize in computer engineering find jobs in computer industries and in numerous fields where computers are being used. Companies that produce software are growing rapidly in number and size and providing employment for those who are skilled in programming. An excellent way to advance one's knowledge of computers is to join the IEEE Computer Society, which sponsors diverse magazines, journals, and conferences.

7.1   INTRODUCTION

Now that we have considered the three passive elements (resistors, capacitors, and capacitors, and inductors) and one active element (the op amp) individually, we are prepared to consider circuits that contain various combinations of two or three of the passive elements. In this chapter, we shall examine two types of simple circuits: a circuit comprising a resistor and capacitor and a circuit comprising a resistor and an inductor. These are called RC and RL circuits, respectively. As simple as these circuits are, they find continual applications in electronics, communications, and control systems, as we shall see.

We carry out the analysis of RC and RL circuits by applying Kirchhoff's laws, as we did for resistive circuits. The only difference is that applying Kirchhoff's laws to purely resistive circuits results in algebraic equations, while applying the laws to RC and RL circuits produces differential equations, which are more difficult to solve than algebraic equations. The differential equations resulting from analyzing RC and RL circuits are of the first order. Hence, the circuits are collectively known as *first-order* circuits.

A first-order circuit is characterized by a first-order differential equation.

In addition to there being two types of first-order circuits (RC and RL), there are two ways to excite the circuits. The first way is by initial conditions of the storage elements in the circuits. In these so-called *source-free circuits*, we assume that energy is initially stored in the capacitive or inductive element. The energy causes current to flow in the circuit and is gradually dissipated in the resistors. Although source-free circuits are by definition free of independent sources, they may have dependent sources. The second way of exciting first-order circuits is by independent sources. In this chapter, the independent sources we will consider are dc sources. (In later chapters, we shall consider sinusoidal and exponential sources.) The two types of first-order circuits and the two ways of exciting them add up to the four possible situations we will study in this chapter.

Finally, we consider four typical applications of RC and RL circuits: delay and relay circuits, a photoflash unit, and an automobile ignition circuit.

7.2   THE SOURCE-FREE RC CIRCUIT

A source-free RC circuit occurs when its dc source is suddenly disconnected. The energy already stored in the capacitor is released to the resistors.

Consider a series combination of a resistor and an initially charged capacitor, as shown in Fig. 7.1. (The resistor and capacitor may be the equivalent resistance and equivalent capacitance of combinations of resistors and capacitors.) Our objective is to determine the circuit response, which, for pedagogic reasons, we assume to be the voltage $v(t)$ across

Figure 7.1   A source-free RC circuit.

A circuit response is the manner in which the circuit reacts to an excitation.

the capacitor. Since the capacitor is initially charged, we can assume that at time $t = 0$, the initial voltage is

$$v(0) = V_0 \tag{7.1}$$

with the corresponding value of the energy stored as

$$w(0) = \frac{1}{2} C V_0^2 \tag{7.2}$$

Applying KCL at the top node of the circuit in Fig. 7.1,

$$i_C + i_R = 0 \tag{7.3}$$

By definition, $i_C = C\, dv/dt$ and $i_R = v/R$. Thus,

$$C\frac{dv}{dt} + \frac{v}{R} = 0 \tag{7.4a}$$

or

$$\frac{dv}{dt} + \frac{v}{RC} = 0 \tag{7.4b}$$

This is a *first-order differential equation*, since only the first derivative of v is involved. To solve it, we rearrange the terms as

$$\frac{dv}{v} = -\frac{1}{RC}\, dt \tag{7.5}$$

Integrating both sides, we get

$$\ln v = -\frac{t}{RC} + \ln A$$

where $\ln A$ is the integration constant. Thus,

$$\ln \frac{v}{A} = -\frac{t}{RC} \tag{7.6}$$

Taking powers of e produces

$$v(t) = Ae^{-t/RC}$$

But from the initial conditions, $v(0) = A = V_0$. Hence,

$$v(t) = V_0 e^{-t/RC} \tag{7.7}$$

This shows that the voltage response of the RC circuit is an exponential decay of the initial voltage. Since the response is due to the initial energy stored and the physical characteristics of the circuit and not due to some external voltage or current source, it is called the *natural response* of the circuit.

> The natural response of a circuit refers to the behavior (in terms of voltages and currents) of the circuit itself, with no external sources of excitation.

The natural response is illustrated graphically in Fig. 7.2. Note that at $t = 0$, we have the correct initial condition as in Eq. (7.1). As t increases, the voltage decreases toward zero. The rapidity with which the voltage decreases is expressed in terms of the *time constant*, denoted by τ, the lower case Greek letter tau.

The natural response depends on the nature of the circuit alone, with no external sources. In fact, the circuit has a response only because of the energy initially stored in the capacitor.

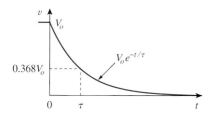

Figure 7.2   The voltage response of the *RC* circuit.

The time constant of a circuit is the time required for the response to decay by a factor of 1/e or 36.8 percent of its initial value.[1]

This implies that at $t = \tau$, Eq. (7.7) becomes

$$V_0 e^{-\tau/RC} = V_0 e^{-1} = 0.368 V_0$$

or

$$\tau = RC \qquad (7.8)$$

In terms of the time constant, Eq. (7.7) can be written as

$$v(t) = V_0 e^{-t/\tau} \qquad (7.9)$$

With a calculator it is easy to show that the value of $v(t)/V_0$ is as shown in Table 7.1. It is evident from Table 7.1 that the voltage $v(t)$ is less than 1 percent of V_0 after 5τ (five time constants). Thus, it is customary to assume that the capacitor is fully discharged (or charged) after five time constants. In other words, it takes 5τ for the circuit to reach its final state or steady state when no changes take place with time. Notice that for every time interval of τ, the voltage is reduced by 36.8 percent of its previous value, $v(t + \tau) = v(t)/e = 0.368 v(t)$, regardless of the value of t.

TABLE 7.1   Values of $v(t)/V_0 = e^{-t/\tau}$.

t	$v(t)/V_0$
τ	0.36788
2τ	0.13534
3τ	0.04979
4τ	0.01832
5τ	0.00674

Observe from Eq. (7.8) that the smaller the time constant, the more rapidly the voltage decreases, that is, the faster the response. This is illustrated in Fig. 7.4. A circuit with a small time constant gives a fast response in that it reaches the steady state (or final state) quickly due to

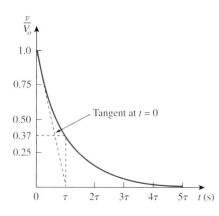

Figure 7.3   Graphical determination of the time constant τ from the response curve.

[1] The time constant may be viewed from another perspective. Evaluating the derivative of $v(t)$ in Eq. (7.7) at $t = 0$, we obtain

$$\frac{d}{dt}\left(\frac{v}{V_0}\right)\bigg|_{t=0} = -\frac{1}{\tau}e^{-t/\tau}\bigg|_{t=0} = -\frac{1}{\tau}$$

Thus the time constant is the initial rate of decay, or the time taken for v/V_0 to decay from unity to zero, assuming a constant rate of decay. This initial slope interpretation of the time constant is often used in the laboratory to find τ graphically from the response curve displayed on an oscilloscope. To find τ from the response curve, draw the tangent to the curve at $t = 0$, as shown in Fig. 7.3. The tangent intercepts with the time axis at $t = \tau$.

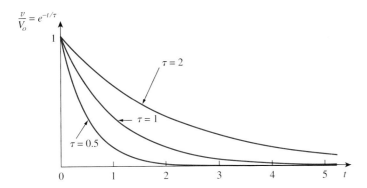

Figure 7.4   Plot of $v/V_0 = e^{-t/\tau}$ for various values of the time constant.

quick dissipation of energy stored, whereas a circuit with a large time constant gives a slow response because it takes longer to reach steady state. At any rate, whether the time constant is small or large, the circuit reaches steady state in five time constants.

With the voltage $v(t)$ in Eq. (7.9), we can find the current $i_R(t)$,

$$i_R(t) = \frac{v(t)}{R} = \frac{V_0}{R}e^{-t/\tau} \tag{7.10}$$

The power dissipated in the resistor is

$$p(t) = vi_R = \frac{V_0^2}{R}e^{-2t/\tau} \tag{7.11}$$

The energy absorbed by the resistor up to time t is

$$w_R(t) = \int_0^t p\, dt = \int_0^t \frac{V_0^2}{R}e^{-2t/\tau}\, dt$$

$$= -\frac{\tau V_0^2}{2R}e^{-2t/\tau}\bigg|_0^t = \frac{1}{2}CV_0^2(1 - e^{-2t/\tau}), \qquad \tau = RC \tag{7.12}$$

Notice that as $t \rightarrow \infty$, $w_R(\infty) \rightarrow \frac{1}{2}CV_0^2$, which is the same as $w_C(0)$, the energy initially stored in the capacitor. The energy that was initially stored in the capacitor is eventually dissipated in the resistor.

In summary:

T h e   K e y   t o   W o r k i n g   w i t h   a   S o u r c e - f r e e   R C   C i r c u i t   I s   F i n d i n g :

1. The initial voltage $v(0) = V_0$ across the capacitor.
2. The time constant τ.

The time constant is the same regardless of what the output is defined to be.

With these two items, we obtain the response as the capacitor voltage $v_C(t) = v(t) = v(0)e^{-t/\tau}$. Once the capacitor voltage is first obtained, other variables (capacitor current i_C, resistor voltage v_R, and resistor current i_R) can be determined. In finding the time constant $\tau = RC$, R is often the Thevenin equivalent resistance at the terminals of the capacitor; that is, we take out the capacitor C and find $R = R_{\text{Th}}$ at its terminals.

When a circuit contains a single capacitor and several resistors and dependent sources, the Thevenin equivalent can be found at the terminals of the capacitor to form a simple *RC* circuit. Also, one can use Thevenin's theorem when several capacitors can be combined to form a single equivalent capacitor.

EXAMPLE 7.1

Figure 7.5   For Example 7.1.

Figure 7.6   Equivalent circuit for the circuit in Fig. 7.5.

In Fig. 7.5, let $v_C(0) = 15$ V. Find v_C, v_x, and i_x for $t > 0$.

Solution:

We first need to make the circuit in Fig. 7.5 conform with the standard *RC* circuit in Fig. 7.1. We find the equivalent resistance or the Thevenin resistance at the capacitor terminals. Our objective is always to first obtain capacitor voltage v_C. From this, we can determine v_x and i_x.

The 8-Ω and 12-Ω resistors in series can be combined to give a 20-Ω resistor. This 20-Ω resistor in parallel with the 5-Ω resistor can be combined so that the equivalent resistance is

$$R_{eq} = \frac{20 \times 5}{20 + 5} = 4 \ \Omega$$

Hence, the equivalent circuit is as shown in Fig. 7.6, which is analogous to Fig. 7.1. The time constant is

$$\tau = R_{eq}C = 4(0.1) = 0.4 \ \text{s}$$

Thus,

$$v = v(0)e^{-t/\tau} = 15e^{-t/0.4} \ \text{V}, \qquad v_C = v = 15e^{-2.5t} \ \text{V}$$

From Fig. 7.5, we can use voltage division to get v_x; so

$$v_x = \frac{12}{12 + 8}v = 0.6(15e^{-2.5t}) = 9e^{-2.5t} \ \text{V}$$

Finally,

$$i_x = \frac{v_x}{12} = 0.75e^{-2.5t} \ \text{A}$$

PRACTICE PROBLEM 7.1

Figure 7.7   For Practice Prob. 7.1.

Refer to the circuit in Fig. 7.7. Let $v_C(0) = 30$ V. Determine v_C, v_x, and i_o for $t \geq 0$.

Answer: $30e^{-0.25t}$ V, $10e^{-0.25t}$ V, $-2.5e^{-0.25t}$ A.

EXAMPLE 7.2

Figure 7.8   For Example 7.2.

The switch in the circuit in Fig. 7.8 has been closed for a long time, and it is opened at $t = 0$. Find $v(t)$ for $t \geq 0$. Calculate the initial energy stored in the capacitor.

Solution:

For $t < 0$, the switch is closed; the capacitor is an open circuit to dc, as represented in Fig. 7.9(a). Using voltage division

$$v_C(t) = \frac{9}{9 + 3}(20) = 15 \ \text{V}, \qquad t < 0$$

Since the voltage across a capacitor cannot change instantaneously, the voltage across the capacitor at $t = 0^-$ is the same at $t = 0$, or

$$v_C(0) = V_0 = 15 \text{ V}$$

For $t > 0$, the switch is opened, and we have the RC circuit shown in Fig. 7.9(b). [Notice that the RC circuit in Fig. 7.9(b) is source free; the independent source in Fig. 7.8 is needed to provide V_0 or the initial energy in the capacitor.] The 1-Ω and 9-Ω resistors in series give

$$R_{\text{eq}} = 1 + 9 = 10 \text{ }\Omega$$

The time constant is

$$\tau = R_{\text{eq}}C = 10 \times 20 \times 10^{-3} = 0.2 \text{ s}$$

Thus, the voltage across the capacitor for $t \geq 0$ is

$$v(t) = v_C(0)e^{-t/\tau} = 15e^{-t/0.2} \text{ V}$$

or

$$v(t) = 15e^{-5t} \text{ V}$$

The initial energy stored in the capacitor is

$$w_C(0) = \frac{1}{2}Cv_C^2(0) = \frac{1}{2} \times 20 \times 10^{-3} \times 15^2 = 2.25 \text{ J}$$

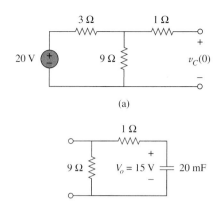

(a)

(b)

Figure 7.9   For Example 7.2: (a) $t < 0$, (b) $t > 0$.

PRACTICE PROBLEM 7.2

If the switch in Fig. 7.10 opens at $t = 0$, find $v(t)$ for $t \geq 0$ and $w_C(0)$.

Answer: $8e^{-2t}$ V, 5.33 J.

Figure 7.10   For Practice Prob. 7.2.

7.3   THE SOURCE-FREE RL CIRCUIT

Consider the series connection of a resistor and an inductor, as shown in Fig. 7.11. Our goal is to determine the circuit response, which we will assume to be the current $i(t)$ through the inductor. We select the inductor current as the response in order to take advantage of the idea that the inductor current cannot change instantaneously. At $t = 0$, we assume that the inductor has an initial current I_0, or

$$i(0) = I_0 \tag{7.13}$$

with the corresponding energy stored in the inductor as

$$w(0) = \frac{1}{2}LI_0^2 \tag{7.14}$$

Figure 7.11   A source-free RL circuit.

Applying KVL around the loop in Fig. 7.11,

$$v_L + v_R = 0 \qquad (7.15)$$

But $v_L = L\,di/dt$ and $v_R = iR$. Thus,

$$L\frac{di}{dt} + Ri = 0$$

or

$$\frac{di}{dt} + \frac{R}{L}i = 0 \qquad (7.16)$$

Rearranging terms and integrating gives

$$\int_{I_0}^{i(t)} \frac{di}{i} = -\int_0^t \frac{R}{L}dt$$

$$\ln i \Big|_{I_0}^{i(t)} = -\frac{Rt}{L}\Big|_0^t \qquad \Longrightarrow \qquad \ln i(t) - \ln I_0 = -\frac{Rt}{L} + 0$$

or

$$\ln\frac{i(t)}{I_0} = -\frac{Rt}{L} \qquad (7.17)$$

Taking the powers of e, we have

$$i(t) = I_0 e^{-Rt/L} \qquad (7.18)$$

This shows that the natural response of the RL circuit is an exponential decay of the initial current. The current response is shown in Fig. 7.12. It is evident from Eq. (7.18) that the time constant for the RL circuit is

$$\boxed{\tau = \frac{L}{R}} \qquad (7.19)$$

with τ again having the unit of seconds. Thus, Eq. (7.18) may be written as

$$\boxed{i(t) = I_0 e^{-t/\tau}} \qquad (7.20)$$

With the current in Eq. (7.20), we can find the voltage across the resistor as

$$v_R(t) = iR = I_0 R e^{-t/\tau} \qquad (7.21)$$

The power dissipated in the resistor is

$$p = v_R i = I_0^2 R e^{-2t/\tau} \qquad (7.22)$$

The energy absorbed by the resistor is

$$w_R(t) = \int_0^t p\,dt = \int_0^t I_0^2 R e^{-2t/\tau}\,dt = -\frac{1}{2}\tau I_0^2 R e^{-2t/\tau}\Big|_0^t, \qquad \tau = \frac{L}{R}$$

or

$$w_R(t) = \frac{1}{2}LI_0^2(1 - e^{-2t/\tau}) \qquad (7.23)$$

Note that as $t \to \infty$, $w_R(\infty) \to \frac{1}{2}LI_0^2$, which is the same as $w_L(0)$, the initial energy stored in the inductor as in Eq. (7.14). Again, the energy initially stored in the inductor is eventually dissipated in the resistor.

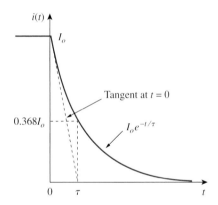

Figure 7.12   The current response of the RL circuit.

The smaller the time constant τ of a circuit, the faster the rate of decay of the response. The larger the time constant, the slower the rate of decay of the response. At any rate, the response decays to less than 1 percent of its initial value (i.e., reaches steady state) after 5τ.

Figure 7.12 shows an initial slope interpretation may be given to τ.

In summary:

> ## The Key to Working with a Source-free RL Circuit is to Find:
> 1. The initial current $i(0) = I_0$ through the inductor.
> 2. The time constant τ of the circuit.

When a circuit has a single inductor and several resistors and dependent sources, the Thevenin equivalent can be found at the terminals of the inductor to form a simple *RL* circuit. Also, one can use Thevenin's theorem when several inductors can be combined to form a single equivalent inductor.

With the two items, we obtain the response as the inductor current $i_L(t) = i(t) = i(0)e^{-t/\tau}$. Once we determine the inductor current i_L, other variables (inductor voltage v_L, resistor voltage v_R, and resistor current i_R) can be obtained. Note that in general, R in Eq. (7.19) is the Thevenin resistance at the terminals of the inductor.

EXAMPLE 7.3

Assuming that $i(0) = 10$ A, calculate $i(t)$ and $i_x(t)$ in the circuit in Fig. 7.13.

Solution:

There are two ways we can solve this problem. One way is to obtain the equivalent resistance at the inductor terminals and then use Eq. (7.20). The other way is to start from scratch by using Kirchhoff's voltage law. Whichever approach is taken, it is always better to first obtain the inductor current.

Figure 7.13   For Example 7.3.

METHOD **1**   The equivalent resistance is the same as the Thevenin resistance at the inductor terminals. Because of the dependent source, we insert a voltage source with $v_o = 1$ V at the inductor terminals *a-b*, as in Fig. 7.14(a). (We could also insert a 1-A current source at the terminals.) Applying KVL to the two loops results in

$$2(i_1 - i_2) + 1 = 0 \quad \Longrightarrow \quad i_1 - i_2 = -\frac{1}{2} \quad (7.3.1)$$

$$6i_2 - 2i_1 - 3i_1 = 0 \quad \Longrightarrow \quad i_2 = \frac{5}{6}i_1 \quad (7.3.2)$$

Substituting Eq. (7.3.2) into Eq. (7.3.1) gives

(a)

(b)

Figure 7.14   Solving the circuit in Fig. 7.13.

$$i_1 = -3 \text{ A}, \qquad i_o = -i_1 = 3 \text{ A}$$

Hence,

$$R_{eq} = R_{Th} = \frac{v_o}{i_o} = \frac{1}{3} \text{ }\Omega$$

The time constant is

$$\tau = \frac{L}{R_{eq}} = \frac{\frac{1}{2}}{\frac{1}{3}} = \frac{3}{2} \text{ s}$$

Thus, the current through the inductor is

$$i(t) = i(0)e^{-t/\tau} = 10e^{-(2/3)t} \text{ A}, \qquad t > 0$$

METHOD 2   We may directly apply KVL to the circuit as in Fig. 7.14(b). For loop 1,

$$\frac{1}{2}\frac{di_1}{dt} + 2(i_1 - i_2) = 0$$

or

$$\frac{di_1}{dt} + 4i_1 - 4i_2 = 0 \tag{7.3.3}$$

For loop 2,

$$6i_2 - 2i_1 - 3i_1 = 0 \qquad \Longrightarrow \qquad i_2 = \frac{5}{6}i_1 \tag{7.3.4}$$

Substituting Eq. (7.3.4) into Eq. (7.3.3) gives

$$\frac{di_1}{dt} + \frac{2}{3}i_1 = 0$$

Rearranging terms,

$$\frac{di_1}{i_1} = -\frac{2}{3}dt$$

Since $i_1 = i$, we may replace i_1 with i and integrate:

$$\ln i \Big|_{i(0)}^{i(t)} = -\frac{2}{3}t \Big|_0^t$$

or

$$\ln \frac{i(t)}{i(0)} = -\frac{2}{3}t$$

Taking the powers of e, we finally obtain

$$i(t) = i(0)e^{-(2/3)t} = 10e^{-(2/3)t} \text{ A}, \qquad t > 0$$

which is the same as by Method 1.

The voltage across the inductor is

$$v = L\frac{di}{dt} = 0.5(10)\left(-\frac{2}{3}\right)e^{-(2/3)t} = -\frac{10}{3}e^{-(2/3)t} \text{ V}$$

Since the inductor and the 2-Ω resistor are in parallel,

$$i_x(t) = \frac{v}{2} = -1.667e^{-(2/3)t} \text{ A}, \qquad t > 0$$

PRACTICE PROBLEM 7.3

Find i and v_x in the circuit in Fig. 7.15. Let $i(0) = 5$ A.

Answer: $5e^{-53t}$ A, $-15e^{-53t}$ V.

Figure 7.15   For Practice Prob. 7.3.

EXAMPLE 7.4

The switch in the circuit of Fig. 7.16 has been closed for a long time. At $t = 0$, the switch is opened. Calculate $i(t)$ for $t > 0$.

Solution:

When $t < 0$, the switch is closed, and the inductor acts as a short circuit to dc. The 16-Ω resistor is short-circuited; the resulting circuit is shown in Fig. 7.17(a). To get i_1 in Fig. 7.17(a), we combine the 4-Ω and 12-Ω resistors in parallel to get

$$\frac{4 \times 12}{4 + 12} = 3 \ \Omega$$

Hence,

$$i_1 = \frac{40}{2 + 3} = 8 \text{ A}$$

We obtain $i(t)$ from i_1 in Fig. 7.17(a) using current division, by writing

$$i(t) = \frac{12}{12 + 4} i_1 = 6 \text{ A}, \qquad t < 0$$

Since the current through an inductor cannot change instantaneously,

$$i(0) = i(0^-) = 6 \text{ A}$$

When $t > 0$, the switch is open and the voltage source is disconnected. We now have the source-free RL circuit in Fig. 7.17(b). Combining the resistors, we have

$$R_{eq} = (12 + 4) \parallel 16 = 8 \ \Omega$$

The time constant is

$$\tau = \frac{L}{R_{eq}} = \frac{2}{8} = \frac{1}{4} \text{ s}$$

Thus,

$$i(t) = i(0)e^{-t/\tau} = 6e^{-4t} \text{ A}$$

Figure 7.16   For Example 7.4.

(a)

(b)

Figure 7.17   Solving the circuit of Fig. 7.16: (a) for $t < 0$, (b) for $t > 0$.

PRACTICE PROBLEM 7.4

Figure 7.18   For Practice Prob. 7.4.

For the circuit in Fig. 7.18, find $i(t)$ for $t > 0$.

Answer: $2e^{-2t}$ A, $t > 0$.

EXAMPLE 7.5

Figure 7.19   For Example 7.5.

In the circuit shown in Fig. 7.19, find i_o, v_o, and i for all time, assuming that the switch was open for a long time.

Solution:

It is better to first find the inductor current i and then obtain other quantities from it.

For $t < 0$, the switch is open. Since the inductor acts like a short circuit to dc, the 6-Ω resistor is short-circuited, so that we have the circuit shown in Fig. 7.20(a). Hence, $i_o = 0$, and

$$i(t) = \frac{10}{2+3} = 2 \text{ A}, \qquad t < 0$$

$$v_o(t) = 3i(t) = 6 \text{ V}, \qquad t < 0$$

Thus, $i(0) = 2$.

For $t > 0$, the switch is closed, so that the voltage source is short-circuited. We now have a source-free RL circuit as shown in Fig. 7.20(b). At the inductor terminals,

$$R_{\text{Th}} = 3 \parallel 6 = 2 \ \Omega$$

so that the time constant is

$$\tau = \frac{L}{R_{\text{Th}}} = 1 \text{ s}$$

Hence,

$$i(t) = i(0)e^{-t/\tau} = 2e^{-t} \text{ A}, \qquad t > 0$$

Since the inductor is in parallel with the 6-Ω and 3-Ω resistors,

$$v_o(t) = -v_L = -L\frac{di}{dt} = -2(-2e^{-t}) = 4e^{-t} \text{ V}, \qquad t > 0$$

and

$$i_o(t) = \frac{v_L}{6} = -\frac{2}{3}e^{-t} \text{ A}, \qquad t > 0$$

(a)

(b)

Figure 7.20   The circuit in Fig. 7.19 for:
(a) $t < 0$, (b) $t > 0$.

Thus, for all time,

$$i_o(t) = \begin{cases} 0 \text{ A}, & t < 0 \\ -\dfrac{2}{3}e^{-t} \text{ A}, & t > 0 \end{cases}, \qquad v_o(t) = \begin{cases} 6 \text{ V}, & t < 0 \\ 4e^{-t} \text{ V}, & t > 0 \end{cases}$$

$$i(t) = \begin{cases} 2 \text{ A}, & t < 0 \\ 2e^{-t} \text{ A}, & t \geq 0 \end{cases}$$

We notice that the inductor current is continuous at $t = 0$, while the current through the 6-Ω resistor drops from 0 to $-2/3$ at $t = 0$, and the voltage across the 3-Ω resistor drops from 6 to 4 at $t = 0$. We also notice that the time constant is the same regardless of what the output is defined to be. Figure 7.21 plots i and i_o.

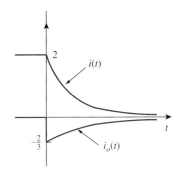

Figure 7.21   A plot of i and i_o.

PRACTICE PROBLEM 7.5

Determine i, i_o, and v_o for all t in the circuit shown in Fig. 7.22. Assume that the switch was closed for a long time.

Answer:
$$i = \begin{cases} 4 \text{ A}, & t < 0 \\ 4e^{-2t} \text{ A}, & t \geq 0 \end{cases}, \quad i_o = \begin{cases} 2 \text{ A}, & t < 0 \\ -(4/3)e^{-2t} \text{ A}, & t > 0 \end{cases},$$

$$v_o = \begin{cases} 8 \text{ V}, & t < 0 \\ -(8/3)e^{-2t} \text{ V}, & t > 0 \end{cases}$$

Figure 7.22   For Practice Prob. 7.5.

7.4 SINGULARITY FUNCTIONS

Before going on with the second half of this chapter, we need to digress and consider some mathematical concepts that will aid our understanding of transient analysis. A basic understanding of singularity functions will help us make sense of the response of first-order circuits to a sudden application of an independent dc voltage or current source.

Singularity functions (also called *switching functions*) are very useful in circuit analysis. They serve as good approximations to the switching signals that arise in circuits with switching operations. They are helpful in the neat, compact description of some circuit phenomena, especially the step response of *RC* or *RL* circuits to be discussed in the next sections. By definition,

> Singularity functions are functions that either are discontinuous or have discontinuous derivatives.

The three most widely used singularity functions in circuit analysis are the *unit step*, the *unit impulse*, and the *unit ramp* functions.

Figure 7.23   The unit step function.

(a)

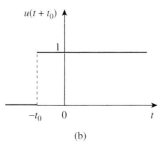

(b)

Figure 7.24   (a) The unit step function delayed by t_0, (b) the unit step advanced by t_0.

Alternatively, we may derive Eqs. (7.25) and (7.26) from Eq. (7.24) by writing $u[f(t)] = 1$, $f(t) > 0$, where $f(t)$ may be $t - t_0$ or $t + t_0$.

> The unit step function $u(t)$ is 0 for negative values of t and 1 for positive values of t.

In mathematical terms,

$$u(t) = \begin{cases} 0, & t < 0 \\ 1, & t > 0 \end{cases} \qquad (7.24)$$

The unit step function is undefined at $t = 0$, where it changes abruptly from 0 to 1. It is dimensionless, like other mathematical functions such as sine and cosine. Figure 7.23 depicts the unit step function. If the abrupt change occurs at $t = t_0$ (where $t_0 > 0$) instead of $t = 0$, the unit step function becomes

$$u(t - t_0) = \begin{cases} 0, & t < t_0 \\ 1, & t > t_0 \end{cases} \qquad (7.25)$$

which is the same as saying that $u(t)$ is delayed by t_0 seconds, as shown in Fig. 7.24(a). To get Eq. (7.25) from Eq. (7.24), we simply replace every t by $t - t_0$. If the change is at $t = -t_0$, the unit step function becomes

$$u(t + t_0) = \begin{cases} 0, & t < -t_0 \\ 1, & t > -t_0 \end{cases} \qquad (7.26)$$

meaning that $u(t)$ is advanced by t_0 seconds, as shown in Fig. 7.24(b).

We use the step function to represent an abrupt change in voltage or current, like the changes that occur in the circuits of control systems and digital computers. For example, the voltage

$$v(t) = \begin{cases} 0, & t < t_0 \\ V_0, & t > t_0 \end{cases} \qquad (7.27)$$

may be expressed in terms of the unit step function as

$$v(t) = V_0 u(t - t_0) \qquad (7.28)$$

If we let $t_0 = 0$, then $v(t)$ is simply the step voltage $V_0 u(t)$. A voltage source of $V_0 u(t)$ is shown in Fig. 7.25(a); its equivalent circuit is shown in Fig. 7.25(b). It is evident in Fig. 7.25(b) that terminals a-b are short-circuited ($v = 0$) for $t < 0$ and that $v = V_0$ appears at the terminals for $t > 0$. Similarly, a current source of $I_0 u(t)$ is shown in Fig. 7.26(a), while its equivalent circuit is in Fig. 7.26(b). Notice that for $t < 0$, there is an open circuit ($i = 0$), and that $i = I_0$ flows for $t > 0$.

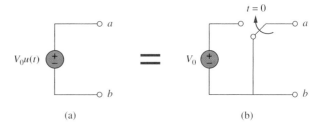

(a)   (b)

Figure 7.25   (a) Voltage source of $V_0 u(t)$, (b) its equivalent circuit.

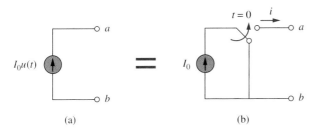

Figure 7.26   (a) Current source of $I_0 u(t)$, (b) its equivalent circuit.

The derivative of the unit step function $u(t)$ is the *unit impulse function* $\delta(t)$, which we write as

$$\delta(t) = \frac{d}{dt}u(t) = \begin{cases} 0, & t < 0 \\ \text{Undefined}, & t = 0 \\ 0, & t > 0 \end{cases} \qquad (7.29)$$

The unit impulse function—also known as the *delta* function—is shown in Fig. 7.27.

> The unit impulse function $\delta(t)$ is zero everywhere except at $t = 0$, where it is undefined.

Impulsive currents and voltages occur in electric circuits as a result of switching operations or impulsive sources. Although the unit impulse function is not physically realizable (just like ideal sources, ideal resistors, etc.), it is a very useful mathematical tool.

The unit impulse may be regarded as an applied or resulting shock. It may be visualized as a very short duration pulse of unit area. This may be expressed mathematically as

$$\int_{0^-}^{0^+} \delta(t)\, dt = 1 \qquad (7.30)$$

where $t = 0^-$ denotes the time just before $t = 0$ and $t = 0^+$ is the time just after $t = 0$. For this reason, it is customary to write 1 (denoting unit area) beside the arrow that is used to symbolize the unit impulse function, as in Fig. 7.27. The unit area is known as the *strength* of the impulse function. When an impulse function has a strength other than unity, the area of the impulse is equal to its strength. For example, an impulse function $10\delta(t)$ has an area of 10. Figure 7.28 shows the impulse functions $5\delta(t + 2)$, $10\delta(t)$, and $-4\delta(t - 3)$.

To illustrate how the impulse function affects other functions, let us evaluate the integral

$$\int_{a}^{b} f(t)\delta(t - t_0)\, dt \qquad (7.31)$$

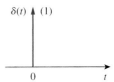

Figure 7.27   The unit impulse function.

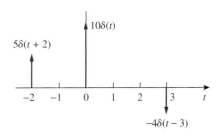

Figure 7.28   Three impulse functions.

where $a < t_0 < b$. Since $\delta(t - t_0) = 0$ except at $t = t_0$, the integrand is zero except at t_0. Thus,

$$\int_a^b f(t)\delta(t - t_0)\, dt = \int_a^b f(t_0)\delta(t - t_0)\, dt$$

$$= f(t_0) \int_a^b \delta(t - t_0)\, dt = f(t_0)$$

or

$$\int_a^b f(t)\delta(t - t_0)\, dt = f(t_0) \tag{7.32}$$

This shows that when a function is integrated with the impulse function, we obtain the value of the function at the point where the impulse occurs. This is a highly useful property of the impulse function known as the *sampling* or *sifting* property. The special case of Eq. (7.31) is for $t_0 = 0$. Then Eq. (7.32) becomes

$$\int_{0^-}^{0^+} f(t)\delta(t)\, dt = f(0) \tag{7.33}$$

Integrating the unit step function $u(t)$ results in the *unit ramp function* $r(t)$; we write

$$r(t) = \int_{-\infty}^t u(t)\, dt = tu(t) \tag{7.34}$$

or

$$r(t) = \begin{cases} 0, & t \le 0 \\ t, & t \ge 0 \end{cases} \tag{7.35}$$

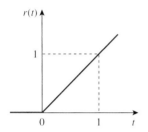

Figure 7.29   The unit ramp function.

The unit ramp function is zero for negative values of t and has a unit slope for positive values of t.

Figure 7.29 shows the unit ramp function. In general, a ramp is a function that changes at a constant rate.

The unit ramp function may be delayed or advanced as shown in Fig. 7.30. For the delayed unit ramp function,

$$r(t - t_0) = \begin{cases} 0, & t \le t_0 \\ t - t_0, & t \ge t_0 \end{cases} \tag{7.36}$$

and for the advanced unit ramp function,

$$r(t + t_0) = \begin{cases} 0, & t \le -t_0 \\ t + t_0, & t \ge -t_0 \end{cases} \tag{7.37}$$

We should keep in mind that the three singularity functions (impulse, step, and ramp) are related by differentiation as

$$\delta(t) = \frac{du(t)}{dt}, \qquad u(t) = \frac{dr(t)}{dt} \tag{7.38}$$

(a)

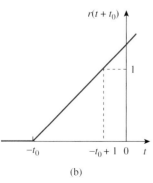

(b)

Figure 7.30   The unit ramp function: (a) delayed by t_0, (b) advanced by t_0.

or by integration as

$$u(t) = \int_{-\infty}^{t} \delta(t)\,dt, \qquad r(t) = \int_{-\infty}^{t} u(t)\,dt \qquad (7.39)$$

Although there are many more singularity functions, we are only interested in these three (the impulse function, the unit step function, and the ramp function) at this point.

EXAMPLE 7.6

Express the voltage pulse in Fig. 7.31 in terms of the unit step. Calculate its derivative and sketch it.

Solution:

The type of pulse in Fig. 7.31 is called the *gate function*. It may be regarded as a step function that switches on at one value of t and switches off at another value of t. The gate function shown in Fig. 7.31 switches on at $t = 2$ s and switches off at $t = 5$ s. It consists of the sum of two unit step functions as shown in Fig. 7.32(a). From the figure, it is evident that

$$v(t) = 10u(t-2) - 10u(t-5) = 10[u(t-2) - u(t-5)]$$

Taking the derivative of this gives

$$\frac{dv}{dt} = 10[\delta(t-2) - \delta(t-5)]$$

which is shown in Fig. 7.32(b). We can obtain Fig. 7.32(b) directly from Fig. 7.31 by simply observing that there is a sudden increase by 10 V at $t = 2$ s leading to $10\delta(t-2)$. At $t = 5$ s, there is a sudden decrease by 10 V leading to -10 V $\delta(t-5)$.

Gate functions are used along with switches to pass or block another signal.

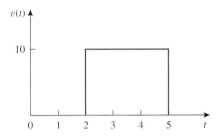

Figure 7.31   For Example 7.6.

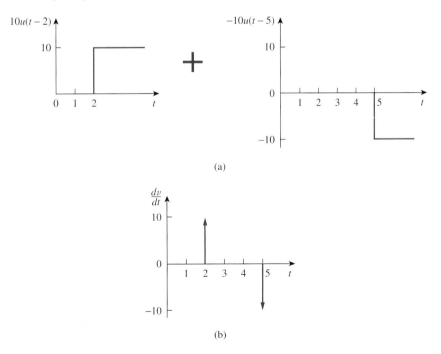

Figure 7.32   (a) Decomposition of the pulse in Fig. 7.31, (b) derivative of the pulse in Fig. 7.31.

PRACTICE PROBLEM 7.6

Express the current pulse in Fig. 7.33 in terms of the unit step. Find its integral and sketch it.

Answer:
$10[u(t) - 2u(t - 2) + u(t - 4)]$, $10[r(t) - 2r(t - 2) + r(t - 4)]$. See Fig. 7.34.

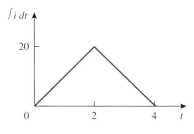

Figure 7.34   Integral of $i(t)$ in Fig. 7.33.

Figure 7.33   For Practice Prob. 7.6.

EXAMPLE 7.7

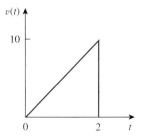

Figure 7.35   For Example 7.7.

Express the *sawtooth* function shown in Fig. 7.35 in terms of singularity functions.

Solution:

There are three ways of solving this problem. The first method is by mere observation of the given function, while the other methods involve some graphical manipulations of the function.

METHOD **I**   By looking at the sketch of $v(t)$ in Fig. 7.35, it is not hard to notice that the given function $v(t)$ is a combination of singularity functions. So we let

$$v(t) = v_1(t) + v_2(t) + \cdots \tag{7.7.1}$$

The function $v_1(t)$ is the ramp function of slope 5, shown in Fig. 7.36(a); that is,

$$v_1(t) = 5r(t) \tag{7.7.2}$$

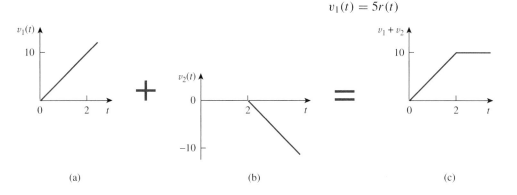

(a)   (b)   (c)

Figure 7.36   Partial decomposition of $v(t)$ in Fig. 7.35.

Since $v_1(t)$ goes to infinity, we need another function at $t = 2$ s in order to get $v(t)$. We let this function be v_2, which is a ramp function of slope -5, as shown in Fig. 7.36(b); that is,

$$v_2(t) = -5r(t - 2) \tag{7.7.3}$$

Adding v_1 and v_2 gives us the signal in Fig. 7.36(c). Obviously, this is not the same as $v(t)$ in Fig. 7.35. But the difference is simply a constant 10 units for $t > 2$ s. By adding a third signal v_3, where

$$v_3 = -10u(t - 2) \tag{7.7.4}$$

we get $v(t)$, as shown in Fig. 7.37. Substituting Eqs. (7.7.2) through (7.7.4) into Eq. (7.7.1) gives

$$v(t) = 5r(t) - 5r(t - 2) - 10u(t - 2)$$

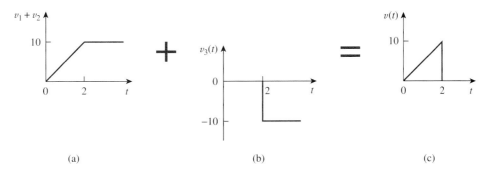

Figure 7.37   Complete decomposition of $v(t)$ in Fig. 7.35.

METHOD **2**   A close observation of Fig. 7.35 reveals that $v(t)$ is a multiplication of two functions: a ramp function and a gate function. Thus,

$$
\begin{aligned}
v(t) &= 5t[u(t) - u(t - 2)] \\
&= 5tu(t) - 5tu(t - 2) \\
&= 5r(t) - 5(t - 2 + 2)u(t - 2) \\
&= 5r(t) - 5(t - 2)u(t - 2) - 10u(t - 2) \\
&= 5r(t) - 5r(t - 2) - 10u(t - 2)
\end{aligned}
$$

the same as before.

METHOD **3**   This method is similar to Method 2. We observe from Fig. 7.35 that $v(t)$ is a multiplication of a ramp function and a unit step function, as shown in Fig. 7.38. Thus,

$$v(t) = 5r(t)u(-t + 2)$$

If we replace $u(-t)$ by $1 - u(t)$, then we can replace $u(-t + 2)$ by $1 - u(t - 2)$. Hence,

$$v(t) = 5r(t)[1 - u(t - 2)]$$

which can be simplified as in Method 2 to get the same result.

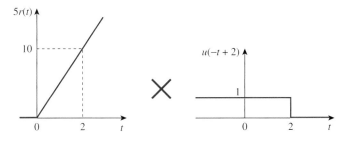

Figure 7.38 Decomposition of $v(t)$ in Fig. 7.35.

PRACTICE PROBLEM 7.7

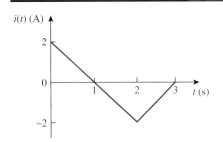

Refer to Fig. 7.39. Express $i(t)$ in terms of singularity functions.

Answer: $2u(t) - 2r(t) + 4r(t-2) - 2r(t-3)$.

Figure 7.39 For Practice Prob. 7.7.

EXAMPLE 7.8

Given the signal

$$g(t) = \begin{cases} 3, & t < 0 \\ -2, & 0 < t < 1 \\ 2t - 4, & t > 1 \end{cases}$$

express $g(t)$ in terms of step and ramp functions.

Solution:

The signal $g(t)$ may be regarded as the sum of three functions specified within the three intervals $t < 0$, $0 < t < 1$, and $t > 1$.

For $t < 0$, $g(t)$ may be regarded as 3 multiplied by $u(-t)$, where $u(-t) = 1$ for $t < 0$ and 0 for $t > 0$. Within the time interval $0 < t < 1$, the function may be considered as -2 multiplied by a gated function $[u(t) - u(t-1)]$. For $t > 1$, the function may be regarded as $2t - 4$ multiplied by the unit step function $u(t-1)$. Thus,

$$\begin{aligned} g(t) &= 3u(-t) - 2[u(t) - u(t-1)] + (2t-4)u(t-1) \\ &= 3u(-t) - 2u(t) + (2t - 4 + 2)u(t-1) \\ &= 3u(-t) - 2u(t) + 2(t-1)u(t-1) \\ &= 3u(-t) - 2u(t) + 2r(t-1) \end{aligned}$$

One may avoid the trouble of using $u(-t)$ by replacing it with $1 - u(t)$. Then

$$g(t) = 3[1 - u(t)] - 2u(t) + 2r(t-1) = 3 - 5u(t) + 2r(t-1)$$

Alternatively, we may plot $g(t)$ and apply Method 1 from Example 7.7.

PRACTICE PROBLEM 7.8

If

$$h(t) = \begin{cases} 0, & t < 0 \\ 4, & 0 < t < 2 \\ 6 - t, & 2 < t < 6 \\ 0, & t > 6 \end{cases}$$

express $h(t)$ in terms of the singularity functions.

Answer: $4u(t) - r(t - 2) + r(t - 6)$.

EXAMPLE 7.9

Evaluate the following integrals involving the impulse function:

$$\int_0^{10} (t^2 + 4t - 2)\delta(t - 2)\, dt$$

$$\int_{-\infty}^{\infty} [\delta(t - 1)e^{-t}\cos t + \delta(t + 1)e^{-t}\sin t]dt$$

Solution:

For the first integral, we apply the sifting property in Eq. (7.32).

$$\int_0^{10} (t^2 + 4t - 2)\delta(t - 2)dt = (t^2 + 4t - 2)|_{t=2} = 4 + 8 - 2 = 10$$

Similarly, for the second integral,

$$\int_{-\infty}^{\infty} [\delta(t - 1)e^{-t}\cos t + \delta(t + 1)e^{-t}\sin t]dt$$
$$= e^{-t}\cos t|_{t=1} + e^{-t}\sin t|_{t=-1}$$
$$= e^{-1}\cos 1 + e^{1}\sin(-1) = 0.1988 - 2.2873 = -2.0885$$

PRACTICE PROBLEM 7.9

Evaluate the following integrals:

$$\int_{-\infty}^{\infty} (t^3 + 5t^2 + 10)\delta(t + 3)\, dt, \qquad \int_0^{10} \delta(t - \pi)\cos 3t\, dt$$

Answer: 28, −1.

7.5   STEP RESPONSE OF AN RC CIRCUIT

When the dc source of an *RC* circuit is suddenly applied, the voltage or current source can be modeled as a step function, and the response is known as a *step response*.

The step response of a circuit is its behavior when the excitation is the step function, which may be a voltage or a current source.

Figure 7.40   An RC circuit with voltage step input.

The step response is the response of the circuit due to a sudden application of a dc voltage or current source.

Consider the RC circuit in Fig. 7.40(a) which can be replaced by the circuit in Fig. 7.40(b), where V_s is a constant, dc voltage source. Again, we select the capacitor voltage as the circuit response to be determined. We assume an initial voltage V_0 on the capacitor, although this is not necessary for the step response. Since the voltage of a capacitor cannot change instantaneously,

$$v(0^-) = v(0^+) = V_0 \tag{7.40}$$

where $v(0^-)$ is the voltage across the capacitor just before switching and $v(0^+)$ is its voltage immediately after switching. Applying KCL, we have

$$C\frac{dv}{dt} + \frac{v - V_s u(t)}{R} = 0$$

or

$$\frac{dv}{dt} + \frac{v}{RC} = \frac{V_s}{RC}u(t) \tag{7.41}$$

where v is the voltage across the capacitor. For $t > 0$, Eq. (7.41) becomes

$$\frac{dv}{dt} + \frac{v}{RC} = \frac{V_s}{RC} \tag{7.42}$$

Rearranging terms gives

$$\frac{dv}{dt} = -\frac{v - V_s}{RC}$$

or

$$\frac{dv}{v - V_s} = -\frac{dt}{RC} \tag{7.43}$$

Integrating both sides and introducing the initial conditions,

$$\ln(v - V_s)\Big|_{V_0}^{v(t)} = -\frac{t}{RC}\Big|_0^t$$

$$\ln(v(t) - V_s) - \ln(V_0 - V_s) = -\frac{t}{RC} + 0$$

or

$$\ln\frac{v - V_s}{V_0 - V_s} = -\frac{t}{RC} \tag{7.44}$$

Taking the exponential of both sides

$$\frac{v - V_s}{V_0 - V_s} = e^{-t/\tau}, \qquad \tau = RC$$

$$v - V_s = (V_0 - V_s)e^{-t/\tau}$$

or

$$v(t) = V_s + (V_0 - V_s)e^{-t/\tau}, \qquad t > 0 \tag{7.45}$$

Thus,

$$v(t) = \begin{cases} V_0, & t < 0 \\ V_s + (V_0 - V_s)e^{-t/\tau}, & t > 0 \end{cases} \tag{7.46}$$

This is known as the *complete response* (or total response) of the *RC* circuit to a sudden application of a dc voltage source, assuming the capacitor is initially charged. The reason for the term "complete" will become evident a little later. Assuming that $V_s > V_0$, a plot of $v(t)$ is shown in Fig. 7.41.

If we assume that the capacitor is uncharged initially, we set $V_0 = 0$ in Eq. (7.46) so that

$$v(t) = \begin{cases} 0, & t < 0 \\ V_s(1 - e^{-t/\tau}), & t > 0 \end{cases} \tag{7.47}$$

which can be written alternatively as

$$v(t) = V_s(1 - e^{-t/\tau})u(t) \tag{7.48}$$

This is the complete step response of the *RC* circuit when the capacitor is initially uncharged. The current through the capacitor is obtained from Eq. (7.47) using $i(t) = C \, dv/dt$. We get

$$i(t) = C\frac{dv}{dt} = \frac{C}{\tau}V_s e^{-t/\tau}, \qquad \tau = RC, \quad t > 0$$

or

$$i(t) = \frac{V_s}{R}e^{-t/\tau}u(t) \tag{7.49}$$

Figure 7.42 shows the plots of capacitor voltage $v(t)$ and capacitor current $i(t)$.

Rather than going through the derivations above, there is a systematic approach—or rather, a short-cut method—for finding the step response of an *RC* or *RL* circuit. Let us reexamine Eq. (7.45), which is more general than Eq. (7.48). It is evident that $v(t)$ has two components.

Classically there are two ways of decomposing this into two components. The first is to break it into a "natural response and a forced response" and the second is to break it into a "transient response and a steady-state response." Starting with the natural response and forced response, we write the total or complete response as

> Complete Response = Natural response + Forced Response
> stored energy   independent source

or

$$v = v_n + v_f \tag{7.50}$$

where

$$v_n = V_o e^{-t/\tau}$$

and

$$v_f = V_s(1 - e^{-t/\tau})$$

We are familiar with the natural response v_n of the circuit, as discussed in Section 7.2. v_f is known as the *forced* response because it is produced by the circuit when an external "force" (a voltage source in this case) is applied. It represents what the circuit is forced to do by the input excitation. The natural response eventually dies out along with the transient component of the forced response, leaving only the steady-state component of the forced response.

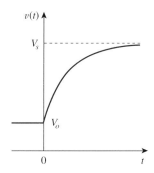

Figure 7.41   Response of an *RC* circuit with initially charged capacitor.

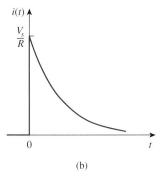

Figure 7.42   Step response of an *RC* circuit with initially uncharged capacitor: (a) voltage response, (b) current response.

Another way of looking at the complete response is to break into two components—one temporary and the other permanent, i.e.

Complete Response = Transient Response + Steady-state Response
temporary part   permanent part

or

$$v = v_t + v_{ss} \tag{7.51}$$

where

$$v_t = (V_o - V_s)e^{-t/\tau} \tag{7.52a}$$

and

$$v_{ss} = V_s \tag{7.52b}$$

The *transient response* v_t is temporary; it is the portion of the complete response that decays to zero as time approaches infinity. Thus,

The transient response is the circuit's temporary response that will die out with time.

The *steady-state response* v_{ss} is the portion of the complete response that remains after the transient reponse has died out. Thus,

The steady-state response is the behavior of the circuit a long time after an external excitation is applied.

The first decomposition of the complete response is in terms of the source of the responses, while the second decomposition is in term of the permanency of the responses. Under certain conditions, the natural response and transient response are the same. The same can be said about the forced response and steady-state response.

Whichever way we look at it, the complete response in Eq. (7.45) may be written as

$$v(t) = v(\infty) + [v(0) - v(\infty)]e^{-t/\tau} \tag{7.53}$$

where $v(0)$ is the initial voltage at $t = 0^+$ and $v(\infty)$ is the final or steady-state value. Thus, to find the step response of an RC circuit requires three things:

1. The initial capacitor voltage $v(0)$.
2. The final capacitor voltage $v(\infty)$.
3. The time constant τ.

We obtain item 1 from the given circuit for $t < 0$ and items 2 and 3 from the circuit for $t > 0$. Once these items are determined, we obtain the

This is the same as saying that the complete response is the sum of the transient response and the steady-state response.

Once we know $x(0)$, $x(\infty)$, and τ, almost all the circuit problems in this chapter can be solved using the formula

$$x(t) = x(\infty) + [x(0) - x(\infty)]e^{-t/\tau}$$

response using Eq. (7.53). This technique equally applies to RL circuits, as we shall see in the next section.

Note that if the switch changes position at time $t = t_0$ instead of at $t = 0$, there is a time delay in the response so that Eq. (7.53) becomes

$$v(t) = v(\infty) + [v(t_0) - v(\infty)]e^{-(t-t_0)/\tau} \qquad (7.54)$$

where $v(t_0)$ is the initial value at $t = t_0^+$. Keep in mind that Eq. (7.53) or (7.54) applies only to step responses, that is, when the input excitation is constant.

EXAMPLE 7.10

The switch in Fig. 7.43 has been in position A for a long time. At $t = 0$, the switch moves to B. Determine $v(t)$ for $t > 0$ and calculate its value at $t = 1$ s and 4 s.

Figure 7.43   For Example 7.10.

Solution:

For $t < 0$, the switch is at position A. The capacitor acts like an open circuit to dc, but v is the same as the voltage across the 5-kΩ resistor. Hence, the voltage across the capacitor just before $t = 0$ is obtained by voltage division as

$$v(0^-) = \frac{5}{5+3}(24) = 15 \text{ V}$$

Using the fact that the capacitor voltage cannot change instantaneously,

$$v(0) = v(0^-) = v(0^+) = 15 \text{ V}$$

For $t > 0$, the switch is in position B. The Thevenin resistance connected to the capacitor is $R_{\text{Th}} = 4$ kΩ, and the time constant is

$$\tau = R_{\text{Th}}C = 4 \times 10^3 \times 0.5 \times 10^{-3} = 2 \text{ s}$$

Since the capacitor acts like an open circuit to dc at steady state, $v(\infty) = 30$ V. Thus,

$$v(t) = v(\infty) + [v(0) - v(\infty)]e^{-t/\tau}$$
$$= 30 + (15 - 30)e^{-t/2} = (30 - 15e^{-0.5t}) \text{ V}$$

At $t = 1$,

$$v(1) = 30 - 15e^{-0.5} = 20.902 \text{ V}$$

At $t = 4$,

$$v(4) = 30 - 15e^{-2} = 27.97 \text{ V}$$

PRACTICE PROBLEM 7.10

Figure 7.44   For Practice Prob. 7.10.

Find $v(t)$ for $t > 0$ in the circuit in Fig. 7.44. Assume the switch has been open for a long time and is closed at $t = 0$. Calculate $v(t)$ at $t = 0.5$.

Answer: $-5 + 15e^{-2t}$ V, 0.5182 V.

EXAMPLE 7.11

In Fig. 7.45, the switch has been closed for a long time and is opened at $t = 0$. Find i and v for all time.

Figure 7.45   For Example 7.11.

Solution:

The resistor current i can be discontinuous at $t = 0$, while the capacitor voltage v cannot. Hence, it is always better to find v and then obtain i from v.

By definition of the unit step function,

$$30u(t) = \begin{cases} 0, & t < 0 \\ 30, & t > 0 \end{cases}$$

For $t < 0$, the switch is closed and $30u(t) = 0$, so that the $30u(t)$ voltage source is replaced by a short circuit and should be regarded as contributing nothing to v. Since the switch has been closed for a long time, the capacitor voltage has reached steady state and the capacitor acts like an open circuit. Hence, the circuit becomes that shown in Fig. 7.46(a) for $t < 0$. From this circuit we obtain

$$v = 10 \text{ V}, \qquad i = -\frac{v}{10} = -1 \text{ A}$$

Since the capacitor voltage cannot change instantaneously,

$$v(0) = v(0^-) = 10 \text{ V}$$

For $t > 0$, the switch is opened and the 10-V voltage source is disconnected from the circuit. The $30u(t)$ voltage source is now operative, so the circuit becomes that shown in Fig. 7.46(b). After a long time, the circuit reaches steady state and the capacitor acts like an open circuit

(a)

(b)

Figure 7.46   Solution of Example 7.11: (a) for $t < 0$, (b) for $t > 0$.

again. We obtain $v(\infty)$ by using voltage division, writing

$$v(\infty) = \frac{20}{20 + 10}(30) = 20 \text{ V}$$

The Thevenin resistance at the capacitor terminals is

$$R_{\text{Th}} = 10 \parallel 20 = \frac{10 \times 20}{30} = \frac{20}{3}\,\Omega$$

and the time constant is

$$\tau = R_{\text{Th}}C = \frac{20}{3} \cdot \frac{1}{4} = \frac{5}{3}\,\text{s}$$

Thus,

$$v(t) = v(\infty) + [v(0) - v(\infty)]e^{-t/\tau}$$
$$= 20 + (10 - 20)e^{-(3/5)t} = (20 - 10e^{-0.6t})\,\text{V}$$

To obtain i, we notice from Fig. 7.46(b) that i is the sum of the currents through the 20-Ω resistor and the capacitor; that is,

$$i = \frac{v}{20} + C\frac{dv}{dt}$$
$$= 1 - 0.5e^{-0.6t} + 0.25(-0.6)(-10)e^{-0.6t} = (1 + e^{-0.6t})\,\text{A}$$

Notice from Fig. 7.46(b) that $v + 10i = 30$ is satisfied, as expected. Hence,

$$v = \begin{cases} 10 \text{ V}, & t < 0 \\ (20 - 10e^{-0.6t})\,\text{V}, & t \geq 0 \end{cases}$$

$$i = \begin{cases} -1 \text{ A}, & t < 0 \\ (1 + e^{-0.6t})\,\text{A}, & t > 0 \end{cases}$$

Notice that the capacitor voltage is continuous while the resistor current is not.

PRACTICE PROBLEM 7.11

The switch in Fig. 7.47 is closed at $t = 0$. Find $i(t)$ and $v(t)$ for all time. Note that $u(-t) = 1$ for $t < 0$ and 0 for $t > 0$. Also, $u(-t) = 1 - u(t)$.

Figure 7.47   For Practice Prob. 7.11.

Answer: $i(t) = \begin{cases} 0, & t < 0 \\ -2(1 + e^{-1.5t})\,\text{A}, & t > 0 \end{cases}$,

$v = \begin{cases} 20 \text{ V}, & t < 0 \\ 10(1 + e^{-1.5t})\,\text{V}, & t > 0 \end{cases}$

Figure 7.48   An RL circuit with a step input voltage.

7.6   STEP RESPONSE OF AN RL CIRCUIT

Consider the RL circuit in Fig. 7.48(a), which may be replaced by the circuit in Fig. 7.48(b). Again, our goal is to find the inductor current i as the circuit response. Rather than apply Kirchhoff's laws, we will use the simple technique in Eqs. (7.50) through (7.53). Let the response be the sum of the natural current and the forced current,

$$i = i_n + i_f \qquad (7.55)$$

We know that the natural response is always a decaying exponential, that is,

$$i_n = Ae^{-t/\tau}, \qquad \tau = \frac{L}{R} \qquad (7.56)$$

where A is a constant to be determined.

The forced response is the value of the current a long time after the switch in Fig. 7.48(a) is closed. We know that the natural response essentially dies out after five time constants. At that time, the inductor becomes a short circuit, and the voltage across it is zero. The entire source voltage V_s appears across R. Thus, the forced response is

$$i_f = \frac{V_s}{R} \qquad (7.57)$$

Substituting Eqs. (7.56) and (7.57) into Eq. (7.55) gives

$$i = Ae^{-t/\tau} + \frac{V_s}{R} \qquad (7.58)$$

We now determine the constant A from the initial value of i. Let I_0 be the initial current through the inductor, which may come from a source other than V_s. Since the current through the inductor cannot change instantaneously,

$$i(0^+) = i(0^-) = I_0 \qquad (7.59)$$

Thus at $t = 0$, Eq. (7.58) becomes

$$I_0 = A + \frac{V_s}{R}$$

From this, we obtain A as

$$A = I_0 - \frac{V_s}{R}$$

Substituting for A in Eq. (7.58), we get

$$i(t) = \frac{V_s}{R} + \left(I_0 - \frac{V_s}{R}\right)e^{-t/\tau} \qquad (7.60)$$

This is the complete response of the RL circuit. It is illustrated in Fig. 7.49. The response in Eq. (7.60) may be written as

$$\boxed{i(t) = i(\infty) + [i(0) - i(\infty)]e^{-t/\tau}} \qquad (7.61)$$

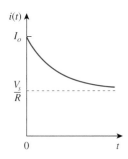

Figure 7.49   Total response of the RL circuit with initial inductor current I_0.

where $i(0)$ and $i(\infty)$ are the initial and final values of i. Thus, to find the step response of an RL circuit requires three things:

1. The initial inductor current $i(0)$ at $t = 0^+$.
2. The final inductor current $i(\infty)$.
3. The time constant τ.

We obtain item 1 from the given circuit for $t < 0$ and items 2 and 3 from the circuit for $t > 0$. Once these items are determined, we obtain the response using Eq. (7.61). Keep in mind that this technique applies only for step responses.

Again, if the switching takes place at time $t = t_0$ instead of $t = 0$, Eq. (7.61) becomes

$$i(t) = i(\infty) + [i(t_0) - i(\infty)]e^{-(t-t_0)/\tau} \qquad (7.62)$$

If $I_0 = 0$, then

$$i(t) = \begin{cases} 0, & t < 0 \\ \dfrac{V_s}{R}(1 - e^{-t/\tau}), & t > 0 \end{cases} \qquad (7.63a)$$

or

$$i(t) = \frac{V_s}{R}(1 - e^{-t/\tau})u(t) \qquad (7.63b)$$

This is the step response of the RL circuit with no initial inductor current. The voltage across the inductor is obtained from Eq. (7.63) using $v = L\,di/dt$. We get

$$v(t) = L\frac{di}{dt} = V_s\frac{L}{\tau R}e^{-t/\tau}, \qquad \tau = \frac{L}{R}, \quad t > 0$$

or

$$v(t) = V_s e^{-t/\tau}u(t) \qquad (7.64)$$

Figure 7.50 shows the step responses in Eqs. (7.63) and (7.64).

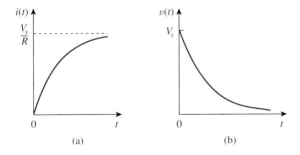

Figure 7.50   Step responses of an RL circuit with no initial inductor current: (a) current response, (b) voltage response.

EXAMPLE 7.12

Find $i(t)$ in the circuit in Fig. 7.51 for $t > 0$. Assume that the switch has been closed for a long time.

Figure 7.51　For Example 7.12.

Solution:

When $t < 0$, the 3-Ω resistor is short-circuited, and the inductor acts like a short circuit. The current through the inductor at $t = 0^-$ (i.e., just before $t = 0$) is

$$i(0^-) = \frac{10}{2} = 5 \text{ A}$$

Since the inductor current cannot change instantaneously,

$$i(0) = i(0^+) = i(0^-) = 5 \text{ A}$$

When $t > 0$, the switch is open. The 2-Ω and 3-Ω resistors are in series, so that

$$i(\infty) = \frac{10}{2+3} = 2 \text{ A}$$

The Thevenin resistance across the inductor terminals is

$$R_{\text{Th}} = 2 + 3 = 5 \ \Omega$$

For the time constant,

$$\tau = \frac{L}{R_{\text{Th}}} = \frac{\frac{1}{3}}{5} = \frac{1}{15} \text{ s}$$

Thus,

$$i(t) = i(\infty) + [i(0) - i(\infty)]e^{-t/\tau}$$
$$= 2 + (5 - 2)e^{-15t} = 2 + 3e^{-15t} \text{ A}, \qquad t > 0$$

Check: In Fig. 7.51, for $t > 0$, KVL must be satisfied; that is,

$$10 = 5i + L\frac{di}{dt}$$

$$5i + L\frac{di}{dt} = [10 + 15e^{-15t}] + \left[\frac{1}{3}(3)(-15)e^{-15t}\right] = 10$$

This confirms the result.

PRACTICE PROBLEM 7.12

Figure 7.52　For Practice Prob. 7.12.

The switch in Fig. 7.52 has been closed for a long time. It opens at $t = 0$. Find $i(t)$ for $t > 0$.

Answer: $(2 + e^{-10t})$ A, $t > 0$.

EXAMPLE 7.13

At $t = 0$, switch 1 in Fig. 7.53 is closed, and switch 2 is closed 4 s later. Find $i(t)$ for $t > 0$. Calculate i for $t = 2$ s and $t = 5$ s.

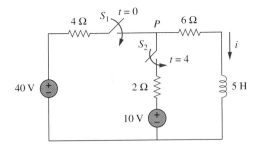

Figure 7.53   For Example 7.13.

Solution:

We need to consider the three time intervals $t \leq 0$, $0 \leq t \leq 4$, and $t \geq 4$ separately. For $t < 0$, switches S_1 and S_2 are open so that $i = 0$. Since the inductor current cannot change instantly,

$$i(0^-) = i(0) = i(0^+) = 0$$

For $0 \leq t \leq 4$, S_1 is closed so that the 4-Ω and 6-Ω resistors are in series. (Remember, at this time, S_2 is still open.) Hence, assuming for now that S_1 is closed forever,

$$i(\infty) = \frac{40}{4+6} = 4 \text{ A}, \qquad R_{\text{Th}} = 4 + 6 = 10 \text{ }\Omega$$

$$\tau = \frac{L}{R_{\text{Th}}} = \frac{5}{10} = \frac{1}{2} \text{ s}$$

Thus,

$$i(t) = i(\infty) + [i(0) - i(\infty)]e^{-t/\tau}$$
$$= 4 + (0 - 4)e^{-2t} = 4(1 - e^{-2t}) \text{ A}, \qquad 0 \leq t \leq 4$$

For $t \geq 4$, S_2 is closed; the 10-V voltage source is connected, and the circuit changes. This sudden change does not affect the inductor current because the current cannot change abruptly. Thus, the initial current is

$$i(4) = i(4^-) = 4(1 - e^{-8}) \simeq 4 \text{ A}$$

To find $i(\infty)$, let v be the voltage at node P in Fig. 7.53. Using KCL,

$$\frac{40 - v}{4} + \frac{10 - v}{2} = \frac{v}{6} \qquad \Longrightarrow \qquad v = \frac{180}{11} \text{ V}$$

$$i(\infty) = \frac{v}{6} = \frac{30}{11} = 2.727 \text{ A}$$

The Thevenin resistance at the inductor terminals is

$$R_{\text{Th}} = 4 \parallel 2 + 6 = \frac{4 \times 2}{6} + 6 = \frac{22}{3} \text{ }\Omega$$

and

$$\tau = \frac{L}{R_{\text{Th}}} = \frac{5}{\frac{22}{3}} = \frac{15}{22} \text{ s}$$

Hence,

$$i(t) = i(\infty) + [i(4) - i(\infty)]e^{-(t-4)/\tau}, \qquad t \geq 4$$

We need $(t - 4)$ in the exponential because of the time delay. Thus,

$$i(t) = 2.727 + (4 - 2.727)e^{-(t-4)/\tau}, \qquad \tau = \frac{15}{22}$$

$$= 2.727 + 1.273e^{-1.4667(t-4)}, \qquad t \geq 4$$

Putting all this together,

$$i(t) = \begin{cases} 0, & t \leq 0 \\ 4(1 - e^{-2t}), & 0 \leq t \leq 4 \\ 2.727 + 1.273e^{-1.4667(t-4)}, & t \geq 4 \end{cases}$$

At $t = 2$,

$$i(2) = 4(1 - e^{-4}) = 3.93 \text{ A}$$

At $t = 5$,

$$i(5) = 2.727 + 1.273e^{-1.4667} = 3.02 \text{ A}$$

PRACTICE PROBLEM 7.13

Switch S_1 in Fig. 7.54 is closed at $t = 0$, and switch S_2 is closed at $t = 2$ s. Calculate $i(t)$ for all t. Find $i(1)$ and $i(3)$.

Answer:

$$i(t) = \begin{cases} 0, & t < 0 \\ 2(1 - e^{-9t}), & 0 < t < 2 \\ 3.6 - 1.6e^{-5(t-2)}, & t > 2 \end{cases}$$

$i(1) = 1.9997$ A, $i(3) = 3.589$ A.

Figure 7.54   For Practice Prob. 7.13.

†7.7 FIRST-ORDER OP AMP CIRCUITS

An op amp circuit containing a storage element will exhibit first-order behavior. Differentiators and integrators treated in Section 6.6 are examples of first-order op amp circuits. Again, for practical reasons, inductors are hardly ever used in op amp circuits; therefore, the op amp circuits we consider here are of the RC type.

As usual, we analyze op amp circuits using nodal analysis. Sometimes, the Thevenin equivalent circuit is used to reduce the op amp circuit to one that we can easily handle. The following three examples illustrate the concepts. The first one deals with a source-free op amp circuit, while the other two involve step responses. The three examples have been carefully selected to cover all possible RC types of op amp circuits, depending on the location of the capacitor with respect to the op amp; that is, the capacitor can be located in the input, the output, or the feedback loop.

EXAMPLE 7.14

For the op amp circuit in Fig. 7.55(a) , find v_o for $t > 0$, given that $v(0) = 3$ V. Let $R_f = 80$ kΩ, $R_1 = 20$ kΩ, and $C = 5$ μF.

Figure 7.55   For Example 7.14.

Solution:

This problem can be solved in two ways:

METHOD **1**   Consider the circuit in Fig. 7.55(a). Let us derive the appropriate differential equation using nodal analysis. If v_1 is the voltage at node 1, at that node, KCL gives

$$\frac{0 - v_1}{R_1} = C\frac{dv}{dt} \qquad (7.14.1)$$

Since nodes 2 and 3 must be at the same potential, the potential at node 2 is zero. Thus, $v_1 - 0 = v$ or $v_1 = v$ and Eq. (7.14.1) becomes

$$\frac{dv}{dt} + \frac{v}{CR_1} = 0 \qquad (7.14.2)$$

This is similar to Eq. (7.4b) so that the solution is obtained the same way as in Section 7.2, i.e.,

$$v(t) = V_0 e^{-t/\tau}, \qquad \tau = R_1 C \qquad (7.14.3)$$

where V_0 is the initial voltage across the capacitor. But $v(0) = 3 = V_0$ and $\tau = 20 \times 10^3 \times 5 \times 10^{-6} = 0.1$. Hence,

$$v(t) = 3e^{-10t} \qquad (7.14.4)$$

Applying KCL at node 2 gives

$$C\frac{dv}{dt} = \frac{0 - v_o}{R_f}$$

or

$$v_o = -R_f C\frac{dv}{dt} \qquad (7.14.5)$$

Now we can find v_0 as

$$v_o = -80 \times 10^3 \times 5 \times 10^{-6}(-30e^{-10t}) = 12e^{-10t} \text{ V}, \qquad t > 0$$

$\boxed{\text{METHOD } 2}$ Let us apply the short-cut method from Eq. (7.53). We need to find $v_o(0^+)$, $v_o(\infty)$, and τ. Since $v(0^+) = v(0^-) = 3$ V, we apply KCL at node 2 in the circuit of Fig. 7.55(b) to obtain

$$\frac{3}{20,000} + \frac{0 - v_o(0^+)}{80,000} = 0$$

or $v_o(0^+) = 12$ V. Since the circuit is source free, $v(\infty) = 0$ V. To find τ, we need the equivalent resistance R_{eq} across the capacitor terminals. If we remove the capacitor and replace it by a 1-A current source, we have the circuit shown in Fig. 7.55(c). Applying KVL to the input loop yields

$$20,000(1) - v = 0 \qquad \Longrightarrow \qquad v = 20 \text{ kV}$$

Then

$$R_{eq} = \frac{v}{1} = 20 \text{ k}\Omega$$

and $\tau = R_{eq}C = 0.1$. Thus,

$$v_o(t) = v_o(\infty) + [v_o(0) - v_o(\infty)]e^{-t/\tau}$$
$$= 0 + (12 - 0)e^{-10t} = 12e^{-10t} \text{ V}, \qquad t > 0$$

as before.

PRACTICE PROBLEM 7.14

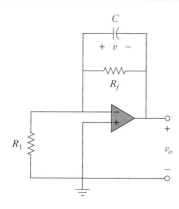

Figure 7.56   For Practice Prob. 7.14.

For the op amp circuit in Fig. 7.56, find v_o for $t > 0$ if $v(0) = 4$ V. Assume that $R_f = 50$ kΩ, $R_1 = 10$ kΩ, and $C = 10$ μF.

Answer: $-4e^{-2t}$ V, $t > 0$.

EXAMPLE 7.15

Determine $v(t)$ and $v_o(t)$ in the circuit of Fig. 7.57.

Solution:

This problem can be solved in two ways, just like the previous example. However, we will apply only the second method. Since what we are looking for is the step response, we can apply Eq. (7.53) and write

$$v(t) = v(\infty) + [v(0) - v(\infty)]e^{-t/\tau}, \qquad t > 0 \qquad (7.15.1)$$

where we need only find the time constant τ, the initial value $v(0)$, and the final value $v(\infty)$. Notice that this applies strictly to the capacitor voltage

due a step input. Since no current enters the input terminals of the op
amp, the elements on the feedback loop of the op amp constitute an *RC*
circuit, with

$$\tau = RC = 50 \times 10^3 \times 10^{-6} = 0.05 \qquad (7.15.2)$$

For $t < 0$, the switch is open and there is no voltage across the capacitor.
Hence, $v(0) = 0$. For $t > 0$, we obtain the voltage at node 1 by voltage
division as

$$v_1 = \frac{20}{20 + 10}3 = 2 \text{ V} \qquad (7.15.3)$$

Since there is no storage element in the input loop, v_1 remains constant
for all t. At steady state, the capacitor acts like an open circuit so that the
op amp circuit is a noninverting amplifier. Thus,

$$v_o(\infty) = \left(1 + \frac{50}{20}\right)v_1 = 3.5 \times 2 = 7 \text{ V} \qquad (7.15.4)$$

But

$$v_1 - v_o = v \qquad (7.15.5)$$

so that

$$v(\infty) = 2 - 7 = -5 \text{ V}$$

Substituting τ, $v(0)$, and $v(\infty)$ into Eq. (7.15.1) gives

$$v(t) = -5 + [0 - (-5)]e^{-20t} = 5(e^{-20t} - 1) \text{ V}, \qquad t > 0 \qquad (7.15.6)$$

From Eqs. (7.15.3), (7.15.5), and (7.15.6), we obtain

$$v_o(t) = v_1(t) - v(t) = 7 - 5e^{-20t} \text{ V}, \qquad t > 0 \qquad (7.15.7)$$

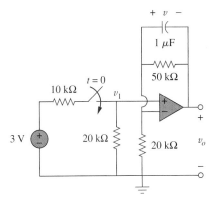

Figure 7.57   For Example 7.15.

PRACTICE PROBLEM 7.15

Find $v(t)$ and $v_o(t)$ in the op amp circuit of Fig. 7.58.

Answer: $40(1 - e^{-10t})$ mV, $40(e^{-10t} - 1)$ mV.

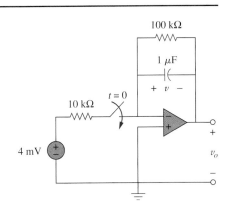

Figure 7.58   For Practice Prob. 7.15.

EXAMPLE 7.16

Find the step response $v_o(t)$ for $t > 0$ in the op amp circuit of Fig. 7.59.
Let $v_i = 2u(t)$ V, $R_1 = 20$ kΩ, $R_f = 50$ kΩ, $R_2 = R_3 = 10$ kΩ,
$C = 2$ μF.

Figure 7.59 For Example 7.16.

Solution:

Notice that the capacitor in Example 7.14 is located in the input loop, while the capacitor in Example 7.15 is located in the feedback loop. In this example, the capacitor is located in the output of the op amp. Again, we can solve this problem directly using nodal analysis. However, using the Thevenin equivalent circuit may simplify the problem.

We temporarily remove the capacitor and find the Thevenin equivalent at its terminals. To obtain V_{Th}, consider the circuit in Fig. 7.60(a). Since the circuit is an inverting amplifier,

$$V_{ab} = -\frac{R_f}{R_1} v_i$$

By voltage division,

$$V_{Th} = \frac{R_3}{R_2 + R_3} V_{ab} = -\frac{R_3}{R_2 + R_3} \frac{R_f}{R_1} v_i$$

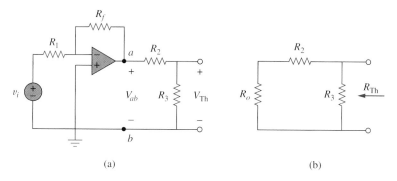

(a)

(b)

Figure 7.60 Obtaining V_{Th} and R_{Th} across the capacitor in Fig. 7.59.

To obtain R_{Th}, consider the circuit in Fig. 7.60(b), where R_o is the output resistance of the op amp. Since we are assuming an ideal op amp, $R_o = 0$, and

$$R_{Th} = R_2 \parallel R_3 = \frac{R_2 R_3}{R_2 + R_3}$$

Substituting the given numerical values,

$$V_{Th} = -\frac{R_3}{R_2 + R_3} \frac{R_f}{R_1} v_i = -\frac{10}{20} \frac{50}{20} 2u(t) = -2.5u(t)$$

$$R_{Th} = \frac{R_2 R_3}{R_2 + R_3} = 5 \text{ k}\Omega$$

The Thevenin equivalent circuit is shown in Fig. 7.61, which is similar to Fig. 7.40. Hence, the solution is similar to that in Eq. (7.48); that is,

$$v_o(t) = -2.5(1 - e^{-t/\tau}) u(t)$$

where $\tau = R_{Th}C = 5 \times 10^3 \times 2 \times 10^{-6} = 0.01$. Thus, the step response for $t > 0$ is

$$v_o(t) = 2.5(e^{-100t} - 1) u(t) \text{ V}$$

Figure 7.61 Thevenin equivalent circuit of the circuit in Fig. 7.59.

PRACTICE PROBLEM 7.16

Obtain the step response $v_o(t)$ for the circuit of Fig. 7.62. Let $v_i = 2u(t)$ V, $R_1 = 20$ kΩ, $R_f = 40$ kΩ, $R_2 = R_3 = 10$ kΩ, $C = 2$ μF.

Answer: $6(1 - e^{-50t})u(t)$ V.

Figure 7.62   For Practice Prob. 7.16.

7.8   TRANSIENT ANALYSIS WITH PSPICE

As we discussed in Section 7.5, the transient response is the temporary response of the circuit that soon disappears. *PSpice* can be used to obtain the transient response of a circuit with storage elements. Section D.4 in Appendix D provides a review of transient analysis using *PSpice for Windows*. It is recommended that you read Section D.4 before continuing with this section.

If necessary, dc *PSpice* analysis is first carried out to determine the initial conditions. Then the initial conditions are used in the transient *PSpice* analysis to obtain the transient responses. It is recommended but not necessary that during this dc analysis, all capacitors should be open-circuited while all inductors should be short-circuited.

> *PSpice uses "transient" to mean "function of time." Therefore, the transient response in PSpice may not actually die out as expected.*

EXAMPLE 7.17

Use *PSpice* to find the response $i(t)$ for $t > 0$ in the circuit of Fig. 7.63.

Solution:

Solving this problem by hand gives $i(0) = 0$, $i(\infty) = 2$ A, $R_{Th} = 6$, $\tau = 3/6 = 0.5$ s, so that

$$i(t) = i(\infty) + [i(0) - i(\infty)]e^{-t/\tau} = 2(1 - e^{-2t}), \qquad t > 0$$

To use *PSpice*, we first draw the schematic as shown in Fig. 7.64. We recall from Appendix D that the part name for a close switch is Sw_tclose. We do not need to specify the initial condition of the inductor because *PSpice* will determine that from the circuit. By selecting **Analysis/Setup/Transient**, we set *Print Step* to 25 ms and *Final Step* to $5\tau = 2.5$ s. After saving the circuit, we simulate by selecting **Analysis/Simulate**. In the *PSpice* A/D window, we select **Trace/Add** and display $-I(L1)$ as the current through the inductor. Figure 7.65 shows the plot of $i(t)$, which agrees with that obtained by hand calculation.

Note that the negative sign on I(L1) is needed because the current enters through the upper terminal of the inductor, which happens to be

Figure 7.63   For Example 7.17.

Figure 7.64   The schematic of the circuit in
Fig. 7.63.

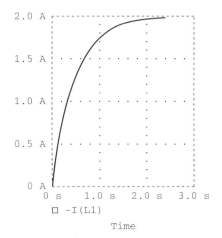

Figure 7.65   For Example 7.17; the response
of the circuit in Fig. 7.63.

the negative terminal after one counterclockwise rotation. A way to avoid
the negative sign is to ensure that current enters pin 1 of the inductor. To
obtain this desired direction of positive current flow, the initially horizontal inductor symbol should be rotated counterclockwise 270° and placed
in the desired location.

PRACTICE PROBLEM 7.17

Figure 7.66   For Practice Prob. 7.17.

For the circuit in Fig. 7.66, use *PSpice* to find $v(t)$ for $t > 0$.

Answer: $v(t) = 8(1 - e^{-t})$ V, $t > 0$. The response is similar in shape
to that in Fig. 7.65.

EXAMPLE 7.18

In the circuit in Fig. 7.67, determine the response $v(t)$.

Figure 7.67   For Example 7.18.

Solution:

There are two ways of solving this problem using *PSpice*.

METHOD **1** One way is to first do the dc *PSpice* analysis to determine the initial capacitor voltage. The schematic of the revelant circuit is in Fig. 7.68(a). Two pseudocomponent VIEWPOINTs are inserted to measure the voltages at nodes 1 and 2. When the circuit is simulated, we obtain the displayed values in Fig. 7.68(a) as $V_1 = 0$ V and $V_2 = 8$ V. Thus the initial capacitor voltage is $v(0) = V_1 - V_2 = -8$ V. The *PSpice* transient analysis uses this value along with the schematic in Fig. 7.68(b). Once the circuit in Fig. 7.68(b) is drawn, we insert the capacitor initial voltage as IC $= -8$. We select **Analysis/Setup/Transient** and set *Print Step* to 0.1 s and *Final Step* to $4\tau = 4$ s. After saving the circuit, we select **Analysis/Simulate** to simulate the circuit. In the *PSpice* A/D window, we select **Trace/Add** and display V(R2:2) $-$ V(R3:2) or V(C1:1) $-$ V(C1:2) as the capacitor voltage $v(t)$. The plot of $v(t)$ is shown in Fig. 7.69. This agrees with the result obtained by hand calculation, $v(t) = 10 - 18e^{-t}$.

(a)

(b)

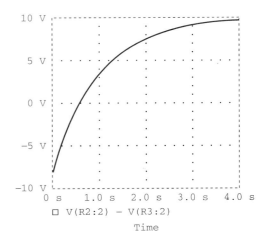

Figure 7.69   Response $v(t)$ for the circuit in Fig. 7.67.

Figure 7.68   (a) Schematic for dc analysis to get $v(0)$, (b) schematic for transient analysis used in getting the response $v(t)$.

METHOD **2** We can simulate the circuit in Fig. 7.67 directly, since *PSpice* can handle the open and close switches and determine the initial conditions automatically. Using this approach, the schematic is drawn as shown in Fig. 7.70. After drawing the circuit, we select **Analysis/Setup/Transient** and set *Print Step* to 0.1 s and *Final Step* to $4\tau = 4$ s. We save the circuit, then select **Analysis/Simulate** to simulate the circuit. In the *PSpice* A/D window, we select **Trace/Add** and display V(R2:2)−V(R3:2) as the capacitor voltage $v(t)$. The plot of $v(t)$ is the same as that shown in Fig. 7.69.

Figure 7.70   For Example 7.18.

Figure 7.71   For Practice Prob. 7.18.

The switch in Fig. 7.71 was open for a long time but closed at $t = 0$. If $i(0) = 10$ A, find $i(t)$ for $t > 0$ by hand and also by *PSpice*.

Answer: $i(t) = 6 + 4e^{-5t}$ A. The plot of $i(t)$ obtained by *PSpice* analysis is shown in Fig. 7.72.

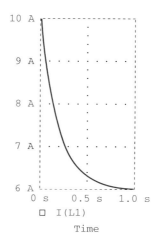

Figure 7.72   For Practice Prob. 7.18.

†7.9   APPLICATIONS

The various devices in which RC and RL circuits find applications include filtering in dc power supplies, smoothing circuits in digital communications, differentiators, integrators, delay circuits, and relay circuits. Some of these applications take advantage of the short or long time constants of the RC or RL circuits. We will consider four simple applications here. The first two are RC circuits, the last two are RL circuits.

Figure 7.73   An *RC* delay circuit.

7.9.1   Delay Circuits

An *RC* circuit can be used to provide various time delays. Figure 7.73 shows such a circuit. It basically consists of an *RC* circuit with the capacitor connected in parallel with a neon lamp. The voltage source can provide enough voltage to fire the lamp. When the switch is closed, the capacitor voltage increases gradually toward 110 V at a rate determined by the circuit's time constant, $(R_1 + R_2)C$. The lamp will act as an open circuit and not emit light until the voltage across it exceeds a particular level, say 70 V. When the voltage level is reached, the lamp fires (goes on), and the capacitor discharges through it. Due to the low resistance of the lamp when on, the capacitor voltage drops fast and the lamp turns off. The lamp acts again as an open circuit and the capacitor recharges. By adjusting R_2, we can introduce either short or long time delays into the circuit and make the lamp fire, recharge, and fire repeatedly every time constant $\tau = (R_1 + R_2)C$, because it takes a time period τ to get the capacitor voltage high enough to fire or low enough to turn off.

The warning blinkers commonly found on road construction sites are one example of the usefulness of such an *RC* delay circuit.

E X A M P·L E   7 . 1 9

Consider the circuit in Fig. 7.73, and assume that $R_1 = 1.5$ MΩ, $0 < R_2 < 2.5$ MΩ. (a) Calculate the extreme limits of the time constant of the circuit. (b) How long does it take for the lamp to glow for the first time after the switch is closed? Let R_2 assume its largest value.

Solution:

(a) The smallest value for R_2 is 0 Ω, and the corresponding time constant for the circuit is

$$\tau = (R_1 + R_2)C = (1.5 \times 10^6 + 0) \times 0.1 \times 10^{-6} = 0.15 \text{ s}$$

The largest value for R_2 is 2.5 MΩ, and the corresponding time constant for the circuit is

$$\tau = (R_1 + R_2)C = (1.5 + 2.5) \times 10^6 \times 0.1 \times 10^{-6} = 0.4 \text{ s}$$

Thus, by proper circuit design, the time constant can be adjusted to introduce a proper time delay in the circuit.

(b) Assuming that the capacitor is initially uncharged, $v_C(0) = 0$, while $v_C(\infty) = 110$. But

$$v_C(t) = v_C(\infty) + [v_C(0) - v_C(\infty)]e^{-t/\tau} = 110[1 - e^{-t/\tau}]$$

where $\tau = 0.4$ s, as calculated in part (a). The lamp glows when $v_C = 70$ V. If $v_C(t) = 70$ V at $t = t_0$, then

$$70 = 110[1 - e^{-t_0/\tau}] \implies \frac{7}{11} = 1 - e^{-t_0/\tau}$$

or

$$e^{-t_0/\tau} = \frac{4}{11} \implies e^{t_0/\tau} = \frac{11}{4}$$

Taking the natural logarithm of both sides gives

$$t_0 = \tau \ln \frac{11}{4} = 0.4 \ln 2.75 = 0.4046 \text{ s}$$

A more general formula for finding t_0 is

$$t_0 = \tau \ln \frac{v(0) - v(\infty)}{v(t_0) - v(\infty)}$$

The lamp will fire repeatedly every τ seconds if and only if $t_0 < \tau$. In this example, that condition is not satisfied.

PRACTICE PROBLEM 7.19

Figure 7.74   For Practice Prob. 7.19.

The RC circuit in Fig. 7.74 is designed to operate an alarm which activates when the current through it exceeds 120 μA. If $0 \leq R \leq 6$ kΩ, find the range of the time delay that the circuit can cause.

Answer: Between 47.23 ms and 124 ms.

7.9.2   Photoflash Unit

Figure 7.75   Circuit for a flash unit providing slow charge in position 1 and fast discharge in position 2.

An electronic flash unit provides a common example of an RC circuit. This application exploits the ability of the capacitor to oppose any abrupt change in voltage. Figure 7.75 shows a simplified circuit. It consists essentially of a high-voltage dc supply, a current-limiting large resistor R_1, and a capacitor C in parallel with the flashlamp of low resistance R_2. When the switch is in position 1, the capacitor charges slowly due to the large time constant ($\tau_1 = R_1 C$). As shown in Fig. 7.76, the capacitor voltage rises gradually from zero to V_s, while its current decreases gradually from $I_1 = V_s/R_1$ to zero. The charging time is approximately five times the time constant,

$$t_{\text{charge}} = 5 R_1 C \qquad (7.65)$$

With the switch in position 2, the capacitor voltage is discharged. The low resistance R_2 of the photolamp permits a high discharge current with peak $I_2 = V_s/R_2$ in a short duration, as depicted in Fig. 7.76(b). Discharging takes place in approximately five times the time constant,

$$t_{\text{discharge}} = 5 R_2 C \qquad (7.66)$$

Thus, the simple RC circuit of Fig. 7.75 provides a short-duration, high-current pulse. Such a circuit also finds applications in electric spot welding and the radar transmitter tube.

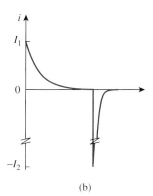

(a)   (b)

Figure 7.76   (a) Capacitor voltage showing slow charge and fast discharge,
(b) capacitor current showing low charging current $I_1 = V_s/R_1$ and high discharge
current $I_2 = V_s/R_2$.

EXAMPLE 7.20

An electronic flashgun has a current-limiting 6-kΩ resistor and 2000-μF
electrolytic capacitor charged to 240 V. If the lamp resistance is 12 Ω,
find: (a) the peak charging current, (b) the time required for the capacitor
to fully charge, (c) the peak discharging current, (d) the total energy stored
in the capacitor, and (e) the average power dissipated by the lamp.

Solution:

(a) The peak charging current is

$$I_1 = \frac{V_s}{R_1} = \frac{240}{6 \times 10^3} = 40 \text{ mA}$$

(b) From Eq. (7.65),

$$t_{\text{charge}} = 5R_1C = 5 \times 6 \times 10^3 \times 2000 \times 10^{-6} = 60 \text{ s} = 1 \text{ minute}$$

(c) The peak discharging current is

$$I_2 = \frac{V_s}{R_2} = \frac{240}{12} = 20 \text{ A}$$

(d) The energy stored is

$$W = \frac{1}{2}CV_s^2 = \frac{1}{2} \times 2000 \times 10^{-6} \times 240^2 = 57.6 \text{ J}$$

(e) The energy stored in the capacitor is dissipated across the lamp during
the discharging period. From Eq. (7.66),

$$t_{\text{discharge}} = 5R_2C = 5 \times 12 \times 2000 \times 10^{-6} = 0.12 \text{ s}$$

Thus, the average power dissipated is

$$p = \frac{W}{t_{\text{discharge}}} = \frac{57.6}{0.12} = 480 \text{ W}$$

PRACTICE PROBLEM 7.20

The flash unit of a camera has a 2-mF capacitor charged to 80 V.

(a) How much charge is on the capacitor?

(b) What is the energy stored in the capacitor?

(c) If the flash fires in 0.8 ms, what is the average current through the flashtube?

(d) How much power is delivered to the flashtube?

(e) After a picture has been taken, the capacitor needs to be recharged by a power unit which supplies a maximum of 5 mA. How much time does it take to charge the capacitor?

Answer: (a) 0.16 C, (b) 6.4 J, (c) 200 A, (d) 8 kW, (e) 32 s.

7.9.3   Relay Circuits

A magnetically controlled switch is called a *relay*. A relay is essentially an electromagnetic device used to open or close a switch that controls another circuit. Figure 7.77(a) shows a typical relay circuit. The coil circuit is an RL circuit like that in Fig. 7.77(b), where R and L are the resistance and inductance of the coil. When switch S_1 in Fig. 7.77(a) is closed, the coil circuit is energized. The coil current gradually increases and produces a magnetic field. Eventually the magnetic field is sufficiently strong to pull the movable contact in the other circuit and close switch S_2. At this point, the relay is said to be *pulled in*. The time interval t_d between the closure of switches S_1 and S_2 is called the *relay delay time*.

Relays were used in the earliest digital circuits and are still used for switching high-power circuits.

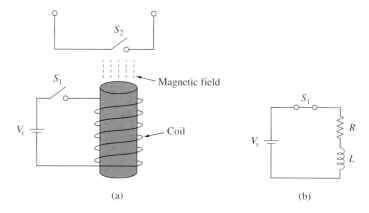

(a)

(b)

Figure 7.77   A relay circuit.

EXAMPLE 7.21

The coil of a certain relay is operated by a 12-V battery. If the coil has a resistance of 150 Ω and an inductance of 30 mH and the current needed to pull in is 50 mA, calculate the relay delay time.

Solution:

The current through the coil is given by

$$i(t) = i(\infty) + [i(0) - i(\infty)]e^{-t/\tau}$$

where

$$i(0) = 0, \qquad i(\infty) = \frac{12}{150} = 80 \text{ mA}$$

$$\tau = \frac{L}{R} = \frac{30 \times 10^{-3}}{150} = 0.2 \text{ ms}$$

Thus,

$$i(t) = 80[1 - e^{-t/\tau}] \text{ mA}$$

If $i(t_d) = 50$ mA, then

$$50 = 80[1 - e^{-t_d/\tau}] \implies \frac{5}{8} = 1 - e^{-t_d/\tau}$$

or

$$e^{-t_d/\tau} = \frac{3}{8} \implies e^{t_d/\tau} = \frac{8}{3}$$

By taking the natural logarithm of both sides, we get

$$t_d = \tau \ln\frac{8}{3} = 0.2 \ln\frac{8}{3} \text{ ms} = 0.1962 \text{ ms}$$

Alternatively, we may find t_d using

$$t_d = \tau \ln\frac{i(0) - i(\infty)}{i(t_d) - i(\infty)}$$

PRACTICE PROBLEM 7.21

A relay has a resistance of 200 Ω and an inductance of 500 mH. The relay contacts close when the current through the coil reaches 350 mA. What time elapses between the application of 110 V to the coil and contact closure?

Answer: 2.529 ms.

7.9.4 Automobile Ignition Circuit
The ability of inductors to oppose rapid change in current makes them useful for arc or spark generation. An automobile ignition system takes advantage of this feature.

The gasoline engine of an automobile requires that the fuel-air mixture in each cylinder be ignited at proper times. This is achieved by means of a spark plug (Fig. 7.78), which essentially consists of a pair of electrodes separated by an air gap. By creating a large voltage (thousands of volts) between the electrodes, a spark is formed across the air gap, thereby igniting the fuel. But how can such a large voltage be obtained from the car battery, which supplies only 12 V? This is achieved by means of an inductor (the spark coil) L. Since the voltage across the inductor is $v = L \, di/dt$, we can make di/dt large by creating a large change

Figure 7.78   Circuit for an automobile ignition system.

in current in a very short time. When the ignition switch in Fig. 7.78 is closed, the current through the inductor increases gradually and reaches the final value of $i = V_s/R$, where $V_s = 12$ V. Again, the time taken for the inductor to charge is five times the *time constant* of the circuit $(\tau = L/R)$,

$$t_{\text{charge}} = 5\frac{L}{R} \tag{7.67}$$

Since at steady state, i is constant, $di/dt = 0$ and the inductor voltage $v = 0$. When the switch suddenly opens, a large voltage is developed across the inductor (due to the rapidly collapsing field) causing a spark or arc in the air gap. The spark continues until the energy stored in the inductor is dissipated in the spark discharge. In laboratories, when one is working with inductive circuits, this same effect causes a very nasty shock, and one must exercise caution.

| EXAMPLE 7.22 |

A solenoid with resistance 4 Ω and inductance 6 mH is used in an automobile ignition circuit similar to that in Fig. 7.78. If the battery supplies 12 V, determine: the final current through the solenoid when the switch is closed, the energy stored in the coil, and the voltage across the air gap, assuming that the switch takes 1 μs to open.

Solution:

The final current through the coil is

$$I = \frac{V_s}{R} = \frac{12}{4} = 3 \text{ A}$$

The energy stored in the coil is

$$W = \frac{1}{2}LI^2 = \frac{1}{2} \times 6 \times 10^{-3} \times 3^2 = 27 \text{ mJ}$$

The voltage across the gap is

$$V = L\frac{\Delta I}{\Delta t} = 6 \times 10^{-3} \times \frac{3}{1 \times 10^{-6}} = 18 \text{ kV}$$

| PRACTICE PROBLEM 7.22 |

The spark coil of an automobile ignition system has a 20-mH inductance and a 5-Ω resistance. With a supply voltage of 12 V, calculate: the time needed for the coil to fully charge, the energy stored in the coil, and the voltage developed at the spark gap if the switch opens in 2 μs.

Answer:　20 ms, 57.6 mJ, and 24 kV.

7.10　SUMMARY

1. The analysis in this chapter is applicable to any circuit that can be reduced to an equivalent circuit comprising a resistor and a single energy-storage element (inductor or capacitor). Such a circuit is first-order because its behavior is described by a first-order differential equation. When analyzing RC and RL circuits, one must

always keep in mind that the capacitor is an open circuit to steady-state dc conditions while the inductor is a short circuit to steady-state dc conditions.

2. The natural response is obtained when no independent source is present. It has the general form

$$x(t) = x(0)e^{-t/\tau}$$

where x represents current through (or voltage across) a resistor, a capacitor, or an inductor, and $x(0)$ is the initial value of x. Because most practical always have losses, the natural response is a transient response, i.e. it dies out with time.

3. The time constant τ is the time required for a response to decay to $1/e$ of its initial value. For RC circuits, $\tau = RC$ and for RL circuits, $\tau = L/R$.

4. The singularity functions include the unit step, the unit ramp function, and the unit impulse functions. The unit step function $u(t)$ is

$$u(t) = \begin{cases} 0, & t < 0 \\ 1, & t > 0 \end{cases}$$

The unit impulse function is

$$\delta(t) = \begin{cases} 0, & t < 0 \\ \text{Undefined}, & t = 0 \\ 0, & t > 0 \end{cases}$$

The unit ramp function is

$$r(t) = \begin{cases} 0, & t \leq 0 \\ t, & t \geq 0 \end{cases}$$

5. The steady-state response is the behavior of the circuit after an independent source has been applied for a long time. The transient response is the component of the complete response that dies out with time.

6. The total or complete response consists of the steady-state response and the transient response.

7. The step response is the response of the circuit to a sudden application of a dc current or voltage. Finding the step response of a first-order circuit requires the initial value $x(0^+)$, the final value $x(\infty)$, and the time constant τ. With these three items, we obtain the step response as

$$x(t) = x(\infty) + [x(0^+) - x(\infty)]e^{-t/\tau}$$

A more general form of this equation is

$$x(t) = x(\infty) + [x(t_0^+) - x(\infty)]e^{-(t-t_0)/\tau}$$

Or we may write it as

$$\text{Instantaneous value} = \text{Final} + [\text{Initial} - \text{Final}]e^{-(t-t_0)/\tau}$$

8. *PSpice* is very useful for obtaining the transient response of a circuit.

9. Four practical applications of RC and RL circuits are: a delay circuit, a photoflash unit, a relay circuit, and an automobile ignition circuit.

REVIEW QUESTIONS

7.1 An RC circuit has $R = 2\ \Omega$ and $C = 4$ F. The time constant is:

(a) 0.5 s   (b) 2 s   (c) 4 s
(d) 8 s   (e) 15 s

7.2 The time constant for an RL circuit with $R = 2\ \Omega$ and $L = 4$ H is:

(a) 0.5 s   (b) 2 s   (c) 4 s
(d) 8 s   (e) 15 s

7.3 A capacitor in an RC circuit with $R = 2\ \Omega$ and $C = 4$ F is being charged. The time required for the capacitor voltage to reach 63.2 percent of its steady-state value is:

(a) 2 s   (b) 4 s   (c) 8 s
(d) 16 s   (e) none of the above

7.4 An RL circuit has $R = 2\ \Omega$ and $L = 4$ H. The time needed for the inductor current to reach 40 percent of its steady-state value is:

(a) 0.5 s   (b) 1 s   (c) 2 s
(d) 4 s   (e) none of the above

7.5 In the circuit of Fig. 7.79, the capacitor voltage just before $t = 0$ is:

(a) 10 V   (b) 7 V   (c) 6 V
(d) 4 V   (e) 0 V

7.6 In the circuit of Fig. 7.79, $v(\infty)$ is:

(a) 10 V   (b) 7 V   (c) 6 V
(d) 4 V   (e) 0 V

7.7 For the circuit of Fig. 7.80, the inductor current just before $t = 0$ is:

(a) 8 A   (b) 6 A   (c) 4 A
(d) 2 A   (e) 0 A

Figure 7.80 For Review Questions 7.7 and 7.8.

7.8 In the circuit of Fig. 7.80, $i(\infty)$ is:

(a) 10 A   (b) 6 A   (c) 4 A
(d) 2 A   (e) 0 A

7.9 If v_s changes from 2 V to 4 V at $t = 0$, we may express v_s as:

(a) $\delta(t)$ V   (b) $2u(t)$ V
(c) $2u(-t) + 4u(t)$ V   (d) $2 + 2u(t)$ V
(e) $4u(t) - 2$ V

7.10 The pulse in Fig. 7.114(a) can be expressed in terms of singularity functions as:

(a) $2u(t) + 2u(t-1)$ V   (b) $2u(t) - 2u(t-1)$ V
(c) $2u(t) - 4u(t-1)$ V   (d) $2u(t) + 4u(t-1)$ V

Answers: 7.1d, 7.2b, 7.3c, 7.4b, 7.5d, 7.6a, 7.7c, 7.8e, 7.9c,d, 7.10b.

Figure 7.79 For Review Questions 7.5 and 7.6.

PROBLEMS

Section 7.2   The Source-Free *RC* Circuit

7.1   Show that Eq. (7.9) can be obtained by working with the current *i* in the *RC* circuit rather than working with the voltage *v*.

7.2   Find the time constant for the *RC* circuit in Fig. 7.81.

Figure 7.81   For Prob. 7.2.

7.3   Find the time constant of each of the circuits in Fig. 7.82.

(a)

(b)

Figure 7.82   For Prob. 7.3.

7.4   Obtain the time constant of the circuit in Fig. 7.83.

Figure 7.83   For Prob. 7.4.

7.5   The switch in Fig. 7.84 has been in position *a* for a long time, until $t = 4$ s when it is moved to position *b* and left there. Determine $v(t)$ at $t = 10$ s.

Figure 7.84   For Prob. 7.5.

7.6   The switch in Fig. 7.85 has been closed for a long time, and it opens at $t = 0$. Find $v(t)$ for $t \geq 0$.

Figure 7.85   For Prob. 7.6.

7.7   If $v(0) = 20$ V in the circuit in Fig. 7.86, obtain $v(t)$ for $t > 0$.

Figure 7.86   For Prob. 7.7.

7.8   For the circuit in Fig. 7.87, if

$$v = 10e^{-4t} \text{ V} \qquad \text{and} \qquad i = 0.2e^{-4t} \text{ A}, \qquad t > 0$$

(a) Find *R* and *C*.
(b) Determine the time constant.
(c) Calculate the initial energy in the capacitor.
(d) Obtain the time it takes to dissipate 50 percent of the initial energy.

Figure 7.87   For Prob. 7.8.

7.9   In the circuit of Fig. 7.88, $v(0) = 20$ V. Find $v(t)$ for $t > 0$.

Figure 7.88   For Prob. 7.9.

7.10   Given that $i(0) = 3$ A, find $i(t)$ for $t > 0$ in the circuit in Fig. 7.89.

Figure 7.89   For Prob. 7.10.

Section 7.3   The Source-Free *RL* Circuit

7.11   Derive Eq. (7.20) by working with voltage v across the inductor of the *RL* circuit instead of working with the current i.

7.12   The switch in the circuit in Fig. 7.90 has been closed for a long time. At $t = 0$, the switch is opened. Calculate $i(t)$ for $t > 0$.

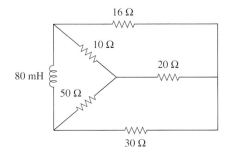

Figure 7.90   For Prob. 7.12.

7.13   For the circuit shown in Fig. 7.91, calculate the time constant.

Figure 7.91   For Prob. 7.13.

7.14   Obtain the time constant for the circuit in Fig. 7.92.

Figure 7.92   For Prob. 7.14.

7.15   Find the time constant for each of the circuits in Fig. 7.93.

(a)

(b)

Figure 7.93   For Prob. 7.15.

7.16   Determine the time constant for each of the circuits in Fig. 7.94.

(a)

(b)

Figure 7.94   For Prob. 7.16.

7.17   Consider the circuit of Fig. 7.95. Find $v_o(t)$ if $i(0) = 2$ A and $v(t) = 0$.

Figure 7.95   For Prob. 7.17.

7.18   For the circuit in Fig. 7.96, determine $v_o(t)$ when $i(0) = 1$ A and $v(t) = 0$.

Figure 7.96   For Prob. 7.18.

7.19   In the circuit of Fig. 7.97, find $i(t)$ for $t > 0$ if $i(0) = 2$ A.

Figure 7.97   For Prob. 7.19.

7.20   For the circuit in Fig. 7.98,

$$v = 120e^{-50t} \text{ V}$$

and

$$i = 30e^{-50t} \text{ A}, \qquad t > 0$$

(a) Find L and R.
(b) Determine the time constant.
(c) Calculate the initial energy in the inductor.
(d) What fraction of the initial energy is dissipated in 10 ms?

Figure 7.98   For Prob. 7.20.

7.21   In the circuit in Fig. 7.99, find the value of R for which energy stored in the inductor will be 1 J.

Figure 7.99   For Prob. 7.21.

7.22   Find $i(t)$ and $v(t)$ for $t > 0$ in the circuit of Fig. 7.100 if $i(0) = 10$ A.

Figure 7.100   For Prob. 7.22.

7.23   Consider the circuit in Fig. 7.101. Given that $v_o(0) = 2$ V, find v_o and v_x for $t > 0$.

Figure 7.101   For Prob. 7.23.

Section 7.4   Singularity Functions

7.24   Express the following signals in terms of singularity functions.

(a) $v(t) = \begin{cases} 0, & t < 0 \\ -5, & t > 0 \end{cases}$

(b) $i(t) = \begin{cases} 0, & t < 1 \\ -10, & 1 < t < 3 \\ 10, & 3 < t < 5 \\ 0, & t > 5 \end{cases}$

(c) $x(t) = \begin{cases} t - 1, & 1 < t < 2 \\ 1, & 2 < t < 3 \\ 4 - t, & 3 < t < 4 \\ 0, & \text{Otherwise} \end{cases}$

(d) $y(t) = \begin{cases} 2, & t < 0 \\ -5, & 0 < t < 1 \\ 0, & t > 1 \end{cases}$

7.25 Express the signal shown in Fig. 7.102 in terms of the unit step and the unit ramp functions.

Figure 7.102   For Prob. 7.25.

7.26 Express the signals in Fig. 7.103 in terms of singularity functions.

(a)

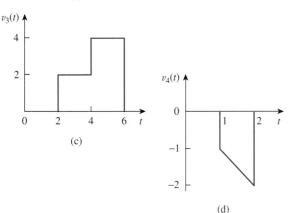

(b)

(c)

(d)

Figure 7.103   For Prob. 7.26.

7.27 Sketch the waveform that is represented by

$$v(t) = u(t) + u(t - 1) - 3u(t - 2) + 2u(t - 3)$$

7.28 Sketch the waveform represented by

$$i(t) = r(t) - r(t - 1) - u(t - 2) - r(t - 2)$$
$$+ r(t - 3) + u(t - 4)$$

7.29 Sketch the following functions:

(a) $x(t) = 10e^{-t}u(t - 1)$

(b) $y(t) = 10e^{-(t-1)}u(t)$

(c) $z(t) = \cos 4t\delta(t - 1)$

7.30 Evaluate the following integrals involving the impulse functions:

(a) $\displaystyle\int_{-\infty}^{\infty} 4t^2\delta(t - 1)\,dt$

(b) $\displaystyle\int_{-\infty}^{\infty} 4t^2 \cos 2\pi t\delta(t - 0.5)\,dt$

7.31 Evaluate the following integrals:

(a) $\displaystyle\int_{-\infty}^{\infty} e^{-4t^2}\delta(t - 2)\,dt$

(b) $\displaystyle\int_{-\infty}^{\infty} [5\delta(t) + e^{-t}\delta(t) + \cos 2\pi t\delta(t)]dt$

7.32 Evaluate the following integrals:

(a) $\int_1^t u(\lambda)\,d\lambda$

(b) $\int_0^4 r(t - 1)\,dt$

(c) $\int_1^5 (t - 6)^2\,\delta(t - 2)\,dt$

7.33 The voltage across a 10-mH inductor is $20\delta(t - 2)$ mV. Find the inductor current, assuming that the inductor is initially uncharged.

7.34 Evaluate the following derivatives:

(a) $\dfrac{d}{dt}[u(t - 1)u(t + 1)]$

(b) $\dfrac{d}{dt}[r(t - 6)u(t - 2)]$

(c) $\dfrac{d}{dt}[\sin 4tu(t - 3)]$

7.35 Find the solution of the following first-order differential equations subject to the specified initial conditions.

(a) $5\,dv/dt + 3v = 0$, $\qquad v(0) = -2$

(b) $4\,dv/dt - 6v = 0$, $\qquad v(0) = 5$

7.36 Solve for v in the following differential equations, subject to the stated initial condition.

(a) $dv/dt + v = u(t)$, $\qquad v(0) = 0$

(b) $2\,dv/dt - v = 3u(t)$, $\qquad v(0) = -6$

7.37 A circuit is described by

$$4\frac{dv}{dt} + v = 10$$

(a) What is the time constant of the circuit?

(b) What is $v(\infty)$, the final value of v?

(c) If $v(0) = 2$, find $v(t)$ for $t \geq 0$.

7.38 A circuit is described by

$$\frac{di}{dt} + 3i = 2u(t)$$

Find $i(t)$ for $t > 0$ given that $i(0) = 0$.

Section 7.5   Step Response of an *RC* Circuit

7.39 Calculate the capacitor voltage for $t < 0$ and $t > 0$ for each of the circuits in Fig. 7.104.

(a)

(b)

Figure 7.104   For Prob. 7.39.

7.40 Find the capacitor voltage for $t < 0$ and $t > 0$ for each of the circuits in Fig. 7.105.

(a)

(b)

Figure 7.105   For Prob. 7.40.

7.41 For the circuit in Fig. 7.106, find $v(t)$ for $t > 0$.

Figure 7.106   For Prob. 7.41.

7.42 (a) If the switch in Fig. 7.107 has been open for a long time and is closed at $t = 0$, find $v_o(t)$.

(b) Suppose that the switch has been closed for a long time and is opened at $t = 0$. Find $v_o(t)$.

Figure 7.107   For Prob. 7.42.

7.43 Consider the circuit in Fig. 7.108. Find $i(t)$ for $t < 0$ and $t > 0$.

Figure 7.108   For Prob. 7.43.

7.44 The switch in Fig. 7.109 has been in position a for a long time. At $t = 0$, it moves to position b. Calculate $i(t)$ for all $t > 0$.

Figure 7.109   For Prob. 7.44.

7.45 Find the step responses $v(t)$ and $i(t)$ to $v_s = 5u(t)$ V in the circuit of Fig. 7.110.

Figure 7.110   For Prob. 7.45.

7.46 For the circuit in Fig. 7.111, $i_s(t) = 5u(t)$. Find $v(t)$.

Figure 7.111   For Prob. 7.46.

7.47 Determine $v(t)$ for $t > 0$ in the circuit in Fig. 7.112 if $v(0) = 0$.

Figure 7.112   For Prob. 7.47.

7.48 Find $v(t)$ and $i(t)$ in the circuit of Fig. 7.113.

Figure 7.113   For Prob. 7.48.

7.49 If the waveform in Fig. 7.114(a) is applied to the circuit of Fig. 7.114(b), find $v(t)$. Assume $v(0) = 0$.

(a)

(b)

Figure 7.114   For Prob. 7.49 and Review Question 7.10.

*__7.50__ In the circuit in Fig. 7.115, find i_x for $t > 0$. Let $R_1 = R_2 = 1$ kΩ, $R_3 = 2$ kΩ, and $C = 0.25$ mF.

Figure 7.115   For Prob. 7.50.

Section 7.6   Step Response of an *RL* Circuit

7.51 Rather than applying the short-cut technique used in Section 7.6, use KVL to obtain Eq. (7.60).

---

*An asterisk indicates a challenging problem.

7.52   For the circuit in Fig. 7.116, find $i(t)$ for $t > 0$.

Figure 7.116   For Prob. 7.52.

7.53   Determine the inductor current $i(t)$ for both $t < 0$ and $t > 0$ for each of the circuits in Fig. 7.117.

(a)

(b)

Figure 7.117   For Prob. 7.53.

7.54   Obtain the inductor current for both $t < 0$ and $t > 0$ in each of the circuits in Fig. 7.118.

(a)

(b)

Figure 7.118   For Prob. 7.54.

7.55   Find $v(t)$ for $t < 0$ and $t > 0$ in the circuit in Fig. 7.119.

Figure 7.119   For Prob. 7.55.

7.56   For the network shown in Fig. 7.120, find $v(t)$ for $t > 0$.

Figure 7.120   For Prob. 7.56.

*7.57   Find $i_1(t)$ and $i_2(t)$ for $t > 0$ in the circuit of Fig. 7.121.

Figure 7.121   For Prob. 7.57.

7.58   Rework Prob. 7.17 if $i(0) = 10$ A and $v(t) = 20u(t)$ V.

7.59   Determine the step response $v_o(t)$ to $v_s = 18u(t)$ in the circuit of Fig. 7.122.

Figure 7.122   For Prob. 7.59.

7.60   Find $v(t)$ for $t > 0$ in the circuit of Fig. 7.123 if the initial current in the inductor is zero.

Figure 7.123   For Prob. 7.60.

7.61   In the circuit in Fig. 7.124, i_s changes from 5 A to 10 A at $t = 0$; that is, $i_s = 5u(-t) + 10u(t)$. Find v and i.

Figure 7.124   For Prob. 7.61.

7.62   For the circuit in Fig. 7.125, calculate $i(t)$ if $i(0) = 0$.

Figure 7.125   For Prob. 7.62.

7.63   Obtain $v(t)$ and $i(t)$ in the circuit of Fig. 7.126.

Figure 7.126   For Prob. 7.63.

7.64   Find $v_o(t)$ for $t > 0$ in the circuit of Fig. 7.127.

Figure 7.127   For Prob. 7.64.

7.65   If the input pulse in Fig. 7.128(a) is applied to the circuit in Fig. 7.128(b), determine the response $i(t)$.

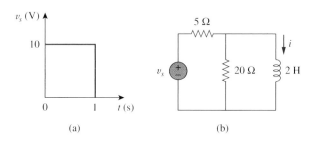

Figure 7.128   For Prob. 7.65.

Section 7.7   First-order Op Amp Circuits

7.66   Find the output current i_o for $t > 0$ in the op amp circuit of Fig. 7.129. Let $v(0) = -4$ V.

Figure 7.129   For Prob. 7.66.

7.67   If $v(0) = 5$ V, find $v_o(t)$ for $t > 0$ in the op amp circuit in Fig. 7.130. Let $R = 10$ kΩ and $C = 1$ μF.

Figure 7.130   For Prob. 7.67.

7.68   Obtain v_o for $t > 0$ in the circuit of Fig. 7.131.

Figure 7.131   For Prob. 7.68.

7.69   For the op amp circuit in Fig. 7.132, find $v_o(t)$ for $t > 0$.

Figure 7.132   For Prob. 7.69.

7.70   Determine v_o for $t > 0$ when $v_s = 20$ mV in the op amp circuit of Fig. 7.133.

Figure 7.133   For Prob. 7.70.

7.71   For the op amp circuit in Fig. 7.134, find i_o for $t > 2$.

Figure 7.134   For Prob. 7.71.

7.72   Find i_o in the op amp circuit in Fig. 7.135. Assume that $v(0) = -2$ V, $R = 10$ kΩ, and $C = 10$ μF.

Figure 7.135   For Prob. 7.72.

7.73   For the op amp circuit of Fig. 7.136, let $R_1 = 10$ kΩ, $R_f = 20$ kΩ, $C = 20$ μF, and $v(0) = 1$ V. Find v_o.

Figure 7.136   For Prob. 7.73.

7.74   Determine $v_o(t)$ for $t > 0$ in the circuit of Fig. 7.137. Let $i_s = 10u(t)$ μA and assume that the capacitor is initially uncharged.

Figure 7.137   For Prob. 7.74.

7.75   In the circuit of Fig. 7.138, find v_o and i_o, given that $v_s = 4u(t)$ V and $v(0) = 1$ V.

Figure 7.138   For Prob. 7.75.

Section 7.8   Transient Analysis with *PSpice*

7.76   Repeat Prob. 7.49 using *PSpice*.

7.77   The switch in Fig. 7.139 opens at $t = 0$. Use *PSpice* to determine $v(t)$ for $t > 0$.

Figure 7.139   For Prob. 7.77.

7.78   The switch in Fig. 7.140 moves from position a to b at $t = 0$. Use *PSpice* to find $i(t)$ for $t > 0$.

Figure 7.140   For Prob. 7.78.

7.79   In the circuit in Fig. 7.141, the switch has been in position a for a long time but moves instantaneously to position b at $t = 0$. Determine $i_o(t)$.

Figure 7.141   For Prob. 7.79.

7.80   In the circuit of Fig. 7.142, assume that the switch has been in position a for a long time, find:

  (a) $i_1(0)$, $i_2(0)$, and $v_o(0)$

  (b) $i_L(t)$

  (c) $i_1(\infty)$, $i_2(\infty)$, and $v_o(\infty)$.

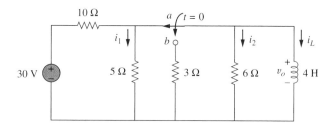

Figure 7.142   For Prob. 7.80.

7.81   Repeat Prob. 7.65 using *PSpice*.

Section 7.9   Applications

7.82   In designing a signal-switching circuit, it was found that a 100-μF capacitor was needed for a time constant of 3 ms. What value resistor is necessary for the circuit?

7.83   An *RC* circuit consists of a series connection of a 120-V source, a switch, a 34-MΩ resistor, and a 15-μF capacitor. The circuit is used in estimating the speed of a horse running a 4-km racetrack. The switch closes when the horse begins and opens when the horse crosses the finish line. Assuming that the capacitor charges to 85.6 V, calculate the speed of the horse.

7.84   The resistance of a 160-mH coil is 8 Ω. Find the time required for the current to build up to 60 percent of its final value when voltage is applied to the coil.

7.85   A simple relaxation oscillator circuit is shown in Fig. 7.143. The neon lamp fires when its voltage reaches 75 V and turns off when its voltage drops to 30 V. Its resistance is 120 Ω when on and infinitely high when off.

   (a)   For how long is the lamp on each time the capacitor discharges?

   (b)   What is the time interval between light flashes?

Figure 7.143   For Prob. 7.85.

7.86   Figure 7.144 shows a circuit for setting the length of time voltage is applied to the electrodes of a welding machine. The time is taken as how long it takes the capacitor to charge from 0 to 8 V. What is the time range covered by the variable resistor?

Figure 7.144   For Prob. 7.86.

7.87   A 120-V dc generator energizes a motor whose coil has an inductance of 50 H and a resistance of 100 Ω. A field discharge resistor of 400 Ω is connected in parallel with the motor to avoid damage to the motor, as shown in Fig. 7.145. The system is at steady state. Find the current through the discharge resistor 100 ms after the breaker is tripped.

Figure 7.145   For Prob. 7.87.

COMPREHENSIVE PROBLEMS

7.88   The circuit in Fig. 7.146(a) can be designed as an approximate differentiator or an integrator, depending on whether the output is taken across the resistor or the capacitor, and also on the time constant $\tau = RC$ of the circuit and the width T of the input pulse in Fig. 7.146(b). The circuit is a differentiator if $\tau \ll T$, say $\tau < 0.1T$, or an integrator if $\tau \gg T$, say $\tau > 10T$.

   (a)   What is the minimum pulse width that will allow a differentiator output to appear across the capacitor?

   (b)   If the output is to be an integrated form of the input, what is the maximum value the pulse width can assume?

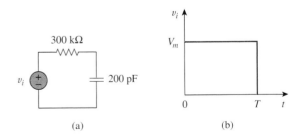

Figure 7.146   For Prob. 7.88.

7.89   An *RL* circuit may be used as a differentiator if the
output is taken across the inductor and $\tau \ll T$ (say
$\tau < 0.1T$), where T is the width of the input pulse. If
R is fixed at 200 kΩ, determine the maximum value
of L required to differentiate a pulse with $T = 10\ \mu$s.

7.90   An attenuator probe employed with oscilloscopes
was designed to reduce the magnitude of the input
voltage v_i by a factor of 10. As shown in Fig. 7.147,
the oscilloscope has internal resistance R_s and
capacitance C_s, while the probe has an internal
resistance R_p. If R_p is fixed at 6 MΩ, find R_s and C_s
for the circuit to have a time constant of 15 μs.

Figure 7.147   For Prob. 7.90.

7.91   The circuit in Fig. 7.148 is used by a biology student
to study "frog kick." She noticed that the frog kicked
a little when the switch was closed but kicked
violently for 5 s when the switch was opened. Model
the frog as a resistor and calculate its resistance.
Assume that it takes 10 mA for the frog to kick
violently.

Figure 7.148   For Prob. 7.91.

7.92   To move a spot of a cathode-ray tube across the
screen requires a linear increase in the voltage across
the deflection plates, as shown in Fig. 7.149. Given
that the capacitance of the plates is 4 nF, sketch the
current flowing through the plates.

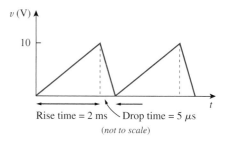

Figure 7.149   For Prob. 7.92.

CHAPTER | 8

SECOND-ORDER CIRCUITS

Engineering is the art of modelling materials we do not wholly understand, into shapes we cannot precisely analyse so as to withstand forces we cannot properly assess, in such a way that the public has no reason to suspect the extent of our ignorance.

—A. Dykes

Enhancing Your Career

To increase your engineering career opportunities after graduation, develop a strong fundamental understanding in a broad set of engineering areas. When possible, this might best be accomplished by working toward a graduate degree immediately upon receiving your undergraduate degree.

Each degree in engineering represents certain skills the students acquire. At the Bachelor degree level, you learn the language of engineering and the fundamentals of engineering and design. At the Master's level, you acquire the ability to do advanced engineering projects and to communicate your work effectively both orally and in writing. The Ph.D. represents a thorough understanding of the fundamentals of electrical engineering and a mastery of the skills necessary both for working at the frontiers of an engineering area and for communicating one's effort to others.

If you have no idea what career you should pursue after graduation, a graduate degree program will enhance your ability to explore career options. Since your undergraduate degree will only provide you with the fundamentals of engineering, a Master's degree in engineering supplemented by business courses benefits more engineering students than does getting a Master's of Business Administration (MBA). The best time to get your MBA is after you have been a practicing engineer for some years and decide your career path would be enhanced by strengthening your business skills.

Engineers should constantly educate themselves, formally and informally, taking advantage of all means of education. Perhaps there is no better way to enhance your career than to join a professional society such as IEEE and be an active member.

Enhancing your career involves understanding your goals, adapting to changes, anticipating opportunities, and planning your own niche.(Courtesy of Institute of Electrical and Electronics Engineers (IEEE).)

8.1   INTRODUCTION

In the previous chapter we considered circuits with a single storage element (a capacitor or an inductor). Such circuits are first-order because the differential equations describing them are first-order. In this chapter we will consider circuits containing two storage elements. These are known as *second-order* circuits because their responses are described by differential equations that contain second derivatives.

Typical examples of second-order circuits are RLC circuits, in which the three kinds of passive elements are present. Examples of such circuits are shown in Fig. 8.1(a) and (b). Other examples are RC and RL circuits, as shown in Fig. 8.1(c) and (d). It is apparent from Fig. 8.1 that a second-order circuit may have two storage elements of different type or the same type (provided elements of the same type cannot be represented by an equivalent single element). An op amp circuit with two storage elements may also be a second-order circuit. As with first-order circuits, a second-order circuit may contain several resistors and dependent and independent sources.

(a)

(b)

(c)

(d)

Figure 8.1   Typical examples of second-order circuits: (a) series RLC circuit, (b) parallel RLC circuit, (c) RL circuit, (d) RC circuit.

> A second-order circuit is characterized by a second-order differential equation. It consists of resistors and the equivalent of two energy storage elements.

Our analysis of second-order circuits will be similar to that used for first-order. We will first consider circuits that are excited by the initial conditions of the storage elements. Although these circuits may contain dependent sources, they are free of independent sources. These source-free circuits will give natural responses as expected. Later we will consider circuits that are excited by independent sources. These circuits will give both the transient response and the steady-state response. We consider only dc independent sources in this chapter. The case of sinusoidal and exponential sources is deferred to later chapters.

We begin by learning how to obtain the initial conditions for the circuit variables and their derivatives, as this is crucial to analyzing second-order circuits. Then we consider series and parallel RLC circuits such as shown in Fig. 8.1 for the two cases of excitation: by initial conditions of the energy storage elements and by step inputs. Later we examine other types of second-order circuits, including op amp circuits. We will consider *PSpice* analysis of second-order circuits. Finally, we consider the automobile ignition system and smoothing circuits as typical applications of the circuits treated in this chapter. Other applications such as resonant circuits and filters will be covered in Chapter 14.

8.2   FINDING INITIAL AND FINAL VALUES

Perhaps the major problem students face in handling second-order circuits is finding the initial and final conditions on circuit variables. Students are usually comfortable getting the initial and final values of v and i

but often have difficulty finding the initial values of their derivatives: dv/dt and di/dt. For this reason, this section is explicitly devoted to the subtleties of getting $v(0), i(0), dv(0)/dt, di(0)/dt, i(\infty)$, and $v(\infty)$. Unless otherwise stated in this chapter, v denotes capacitor voltage, while i is the inductor current.

There are two key points to keep in mind in determining the initial conditions.

First—as always in circuit analysis—we must carefully handle the polarity of voltage $v(t)$ across the capacitor and the direction of the current $i(t)$ through the inductor. Keep in mind that v and i are defined strictly according to the passive sign convention (see Figs. 6.3 and 6.23). One should carefully observe how these are defined and apply them accordingly.

Second, keep in mind that the capacitor voltage is always continuous so that

$$v(0^+) = v(0^-) \qquad (8.1a)$$

and the inductor current is always continuous so that

$$i(0^+) = i(0^-) \qquad (8.1b)$$

where $t = 0^-$ denotes the time just before a switching event and $t = 0^+$ is the time just after the switching event, assuming that the switching event takes place at $t = 0$.

Thus, in finding initial conditions, we first focus on those variables that cannot change abruptly, capacitor voltage and inductor current, by applying Eq. (8.1). The following examples illustrate these ideas.

EXAMPLE 8.1

The switch in Fig. 8.2 has been closed for a long time. It is open at $t = 0$. Find: (a) $i(0^+), v(0^+)$, (b) $di(0^+)/dt, dv(0^+)/dt$, (c) $i(\infty), v(\infty)$.

Solution:

(a) If the switch is closed a long time before $t = 0$, it means that the circuit has reached dc steady state at $t = 0$. At dc steady state, the inductor acts like a short circuit, while the capacitor acts like an open circuit, so we

Figure 8.2   For Example 8.1.

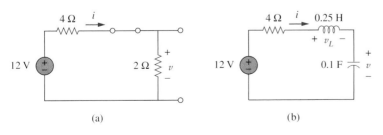

Figure 8.3   Equivalent circuit of that in Fig. 8.2 for: (a) $t = 0^-$, (b) $t = 0^+$, (c) $t \to \infty$.

have the circuit in Fig. 8.3(a) at $t = 0^-$. Thus,

$$i(0^-) = \frac{12}{4 + 2} = 2 \text{ A}, \qquad v(0^-) = 2i(0^-) = 4 \text{ V}$$

As the inductor current and the capacitor voltage cannot change abruptly,

$$i(0^+) = i(0^-) = 2 \text{ A}, \qquad v(0^+) = v(0^-) = 4 \text{ V}$$

(b) At $t = 0^+$, the switch is open; the equivalent circuit is as shown in Fig. 8.3(b). The same current flows through both the inductor and capacitor. Hence,

$$i_C(0^+) = i(0^+) = 2 \text{ A}$$

Since $C \, dv/dt = i_C, \, dv/dt = i_C/C$, and

$$\frac{dv(0^+)}{dt} = \frac{i_C(0^+)}{C} = \frac{2}{0.1} = 20 \text{ V/s}$$

Similarly, since $L \, di/dt = v_L, \, di/dt = v_L/L$. We now obtain v_L by applying KVL to the loop in Fig. 8.3(b). The result is

$$-12 + 4i(0^+) + v_L(0^+) + v(0^+) = 0$$

or

$$v_L(0^+) = 12 - 8 - 4 = 0$$

Thus,

$$\frac{di(0^+)}{dt} = \frac{v_L(0^+)}{L} = \frac{0}{0.25} = 0 \text{ A/s}$$

(c) For $t > 0$, the circuit undergoes transience. But as $t \to \infty$, the circuit reaches steady state again. The inductor acts like a short circuit and the capacitor like an open circuit, so that the circuit in Fig. 8.3(b) becomes that shown in Fig. 8.3(c), from which we have

$$i(\infty) = 0 \text{ A}, \qquad v(\infty) = 12 \text{ V}$$

PRACTICE PROBLEM 8.1

The switch in Fig. 8.4 was open for a long time but closed at $t = 0$. Determine: (a) $i(0^+), v(0^+)$, (b) $di(0^+)/dt, dv(0^+)/dt$, (c) $i(\infty), v(\infty)$.

Figure 8.4   For Practice Prob. 8.1.

Answer: (a) 2 A, 4 V, (b) 50 A/s, 0 V/s, (c) 12 A, 24 V.

EXAMPLE 8.2

In the circuit of Fig. 8.5, calculate: (a) $i_L(0^+)$, $v_C(0^+)$, $v_R(0^+)$, (b) $di_L(0^+)/dt$, $dv_C(0^+)/dt$, $dv_R(0^+)/dt$, (c) $i_L(\infty)$, $v_C(\infty)$, $v_R(\infty)$.

Figure 8.5   For Example 8.2.

Solution:

(a) For $t < 0$, $3u(t) = 0$. At $t = 0^-$, since the circuit has reached steady state, the inductor can be replaced by a short circuit, while the capacitor is replaced by an open circuit as shown in Fig. 8.6(a). From this figure we obtain

$$i_L(0^-) = 0, \qquad v_R(0^-) = 0, \qquad v_C(0^-) = -20 \text{ V} \qquad (8.2.1)$$

Although the derivatives of these quantities at $t = 0^-$ are not required, it is evident that they are all zero, since the circuit has reached steady state and nothing changes.

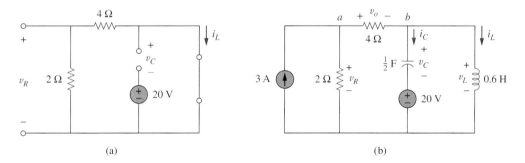

(a)   (b)

Figure 8.6   The circuit in Fig. 8.5 for: (a) $t = 0^-$, (b) $t = 0^+$.

For $t > 0$, $3u(t) = 3$, so that the circuit is now equivalent to that in Fig. 8.6(b). Since the inductor current and capacitor voltage cannot change abruptly,

$$i_L(0^+) = i_L(0^-) = 0, \qquad v_C(0^+) = v_C(0^-) = -20 \text{ V} \qquad (8.2.2)$$

Although the voltage across the 4-Ω resistor is not required, we will use it to apply KVL and KCL; let it be called v_o. Applying KCL at node a in Fig. 8.6(b) gives

$$3 = \frac{v_R(0^+)}{2} + \frac{v_o(0^+)}{4} \qquad (8.2.3)$$

Applying KVL to the middle mesh in Fig. 8.6(b) yields

$$-v_R(0^+) + v_o(0^+) + v_C(0^+) + 20 = 0 \qquad (8.2.4)$$

Since $v_C(0+) = -20$ V from Eq. (8.2.2), Eq. (8.2.4) implies that

$$v_R(0^+) = v_o(0^+) \qquad (8.2.5)$$

From Eqs. (8.2.3) and (8.2.5), we obtain

$$v_R(0^+) = v_o(0^+) = 4 \text{ V} \qquad (8.2.6)$$

(b) Since $L \, di_L/dt = v_L$,

$$\frac{di_L(0^+)}{dt} = \frac{v_L(0^+)}{L}$$

But applying KVL to the right mesh in Fig. 8.6(b) gives

$$v_L(0^+) = v_C(0^+) + 20 = 0$$

Hence,

$$\frac{di_L(0^+)}{dt} = 0 \qquad (8.2.7)$$

Similarly, since $C \, dv_C/dt = i_C$, then $dv_C/dt = i_C/C$. We apply KCL at node b in Fig. 8.6(b) to get i_C:

$$\frac{v_o(0^+)}{4} = i_C(0^+) + i_L(0^+) \qquad (8.2.8)$$

Since $v_o(0^+) = 4$ and $i_L(0^+) = 0$, $i_C(0^+) = 4/4 = 1$ A. Then

$$\frac{dv_C(0^+)}{dt} = \frac{i_C(0^+)}{C} = \frac{1}{0.5} = 2 \text{ V/s} \qquad (8.2.9)$$

To get $dv_R(0^+)/dt$, we apply KCL to node a and obtain

$$3 = \frac{v_R}{2} + \frac{v_o}{4}$$

Taking the derivative of each term and setting $t = 0^+$ gives

$$0 = 2\frac{dv_R(0^+)}{dt} + \frac{dv_o(0^+)}{dt} \qquad (8.2.10)$$

We also apply KVL to the middle mesh in Fig. 8.6(b) and obtain

$$-v_R + v_C + 20 + v_o = 0$$

Again, taking the derivative of each term and setting $t = 0^+$ yields

$$-\frac{dv_R(0^+)}{dt} + \frac{dv_C(0^+)}{dt} + \frac{dv_o(0^+)}{dt} = 0$$

Substituting for $dv_C(0^+)/dt = 2$ gives

$$\frac{dv_R(0^+)}{dt} = 2 + \frac{dv_o(0^+)}{dt} \qquad (8.2.11)$$

From Eqs. (8.2.10) and (8.2.11), we get

$$\frac{dv_R(0^+)}{dt} = \frac{2}{3} \text{ V/s}$$

We can find $di_R(0^+)/dt$ although it is not required. Since $v_R = 5i_R$,

$$\frac{di_R(0^+)}{dt} = \frac{1}{5}\frac{dv_R(0^+)}{dt} = \frac{1}{5}\frac{2}{3} = \frac{2}{15} \text{ A/s}$$

(c) As $t \to \infty$, the circuit reaches steady state. We have the equivalent circuit in Fig. 8.6(a) except that the 3-A current source is now operative. By current division principle,

$$i_L(\infty) = \frac{2}{2+4}3 \text{ A} = 1 \text{ A}$$

$$v_R(\infty) = \frac{4}{2+4}3 \text{ A} \times 2 = 4 \text{ V}, \qquad v_C(\infty) = -20 \text{ V}$$

$$(8.2.12)$$

PRACTICE PROBLEM 8.2

For the circuit in Fig. 8.7, find: (a) $i_L(0^+)$, $v_C(0^+)$, $v_R(0^+)$, (b) $di_L(0^+)/dt$, $dv_C(0^+)/dt$, $dv_R(0^+)/dt$, (c) $i_L(\infty)$, $v_C(\infty)$, $v_R(\infty)$.

Figure 8.7   For Practice Prob. 8.2.

Answer: (a) -3 A, 0, 0, (b) 0, 10 V/s, 0, (c) -1 A, 10 V, 10 V.

8.3   THE SOURCE-FREE SERIES *RLC* CIRCUIT

An understanding of the natural response of the series *RLC* circuit is a necessary background for future studies in filter design and communications networks.

Consider the series *RLC* circuit shown in Fig. 8.8. The circuit is being excited by the energy initially stored in the capacitor and inductor. The energy is represented by the initial capacitor voltage V_0 and initial inductor current I_0. Thus, at $t = 0$,

$$v(0) = \frac{1}{C}\int_{-\infty}^{0} i \, dt = V_0 \qquad (8.2a)$$

$$i(0) = I_0 \qquad (8.2b)$$

Applying KVL around the loop in Fig. 8.8,

$$Ri + L\frac{di}{dt} + \frac{1}{C}\int_{-\infty}^{t} i \, dt = 0 \qquad (8.3)$$

Figure 8.8   A source-free series *RLC* circuit.

To eliminate the integral, we differentiate with respect to t and rearrange terms. We get

$$\frac{d^2i}{dt^2} + \frac{R}{L}\frac{di}{dt} + \frac{i}{LC} = 0 \tag{8.4}$$

This is a *second-order differential equation* and is the reason for calling the RLC circuits in this chapter second-order circuits. Our goal is to solve Eq. (8.4). To solve such a second-order differential equation requires that we have two initial conditions, such as the initial value of i and its first derivative or initial values of some i and v. The initial value of i is given in Eq. (8.2b). We get the initial value of the derivative of i from Eqs. (8.2a) and (8.3); that is,

$$Ri(0) + L\frac{di(0)}{dt} + V_0 = 0$$

or

$$\frac{di(0)}{dt} = -\frac{1}{L}(RI_0 + V_0) \tag{8.5}$$

With the two initial conditions in Eqs. (8.2b) and (8.5), we can now solve Eq. (8.4). Our experience in the preceding chapter on first-order circuits suggests that the solution is of exponential form. So we let

$$i = Ae^{st} \tag{8.6}$$

where A and s are constants to be determined. Substituting Eq. (8.6) into Eq. (8.4) and carrying out the necessary differentiations, we obtain

$$As^2e^{st} + \frac{AR}{L}se^{st} + \frac{A}{LC}e^{st} = 0$$

or

$$Ae^{st}\left(s^2 + \frac{R}{L}s + \frac{1}{LC}\right) = 0 \tag{8.7}$$

Since $i = Ae^{st}$ is the assumed solution we are trying to find, only the expression in parentheses can be zero:

$$s^2 + \frac{R}{L}s + \frac{1}{LC} = 0 \tag{8.8}$$

This quadratic equation is known as the *characteristic equation* of the differential Eq. (8.4), since the roots of the equation dictate the character of i. The two roots of Eq. (8.8) are

See Appendix C.1 for the formula to find the roots of a quadratic equation.

$$s_1 = -\frac{R}{2L} + \sqrt{\left(\frac{R}{2L}\right)^2 - \frac{1}{LC}} \tag{8.9a}$$

$$s_2 = -\frac{R}{2L} - \sqrt{\left(\frac{R}{2L}\right)^2 - \frac{1}{LC}} \tag{8.9b}$$

A more compact way of expressing the roots is

$$s_1 = -\alpha + \sqrt{\alpha^2 - \omega_0^2}, \qquad s_2 = -\alpha - \sqrt{\alpha^2 - \omega_0^2} \tag{8.10}$$

where

$$\alpha = \frac{R}{2L}, \qquad \omega_0 = \frac{1}{\sqrt{LC}} \tag{8.11}$$

The roots s_1 and s_2 are called *natural frequencies*, measured in nepers per second (Np/s), because they are associated with the natural response of the circuit; ω_0 is known as the *resonant frequency* or strictly as the *undamped natural frequency*, expressed in radians per second (rad/s); and α is the *neper frequency* or the *damping factor*, expressed in nepers per second. In terms of α and ω_0, Eq. (8.8) can be written as

$$s^2 + 2\alpha s + \omega_0^2 = 0 \qquad (8.8a)$$

The variables s and ω_0 are important quantities we will be discussing throughout the rest of the text.

The two values of s in Eq. (8.10) indicate that there are two possible solutions for i, each of which is of the form of the assumed solution in Eq. (8.6); that is,

$$i_1 = A_1 e^{s_1 t}, \qquad i_2 = A_2 e^{s_2 t} \qquad (8.12)$$

Since Eq. (8.4) is a linear equation, any linear combination of the two distinct solutions i_1 and i_2 is also a solution of Eq. (8.4). A complete or total solution of Eq. (8.4) would therefore require a linear combination of i_1 and i_2. Thus, the natural response of the series RLC circuit is

$$i(t) = A_1 e^{s_1 t} + A_2 e^{s_2 t} \qquad (8.13)$$

where the constants A_1 and A_2 are determined from the initial values $i(0)$ and $di(0)/dt$ in Eqs. (8.2b) and (8.5).

From Eq. (8.10), we can infer that there are three types of solutions:

1. If $\alpha > \omega_0$, we have the *overdamped* case.
2. If $\alpha = \omega_0$, we have the *critically damped* case.
3. If $\alpha < \omega_0$, we have the *underdamped* case.

We will consider each of these cases separately.

Overdamped Case($\alpha > \omega_0$)

From Eqs. (8.9) and (8.10), $\alpha > \omega_0$ implies $C > 4L/R^2$. When this happens, both roots s_1 and s_2 are negative and real. The response is

$$\boxed{i(t) = A_1 e^{s_1 t} + A_2 e^{s_2 t}} \qquad (8.14)$$

which decays and approaches zero as t increases. Figure 8.9(a) illustrates a typical overdamped response.

Critically Damped Case($\alpha = \omega_0$)

When $\alpha = \omega_0$, $C = 4L/R^2$ and

$$s_1 = s_2 = -\alpha = -\frac{R}{2L} \qquad (8.15)$$

For this case, Eq. (8.13) yields

$$i(t) = A_1 e^{-\alpha t} + A_2 e^{-\alpha t} = A_3 e^{-\alpha t}$$

where $A_3 = A_1 + A_2$. This cannot be the solution, because the two initial conditions cannot be satisfied with the single constant A_3. What then could be wrong? Our assumption of an exponential solution is incorrect

The *neper* (Np) is a dimensionless unit named after John Napier (1550–1617), a Scottish mathematician.

The ratio α/ω_0 is known as the *damping ratio* ζ.

The response is *overdamped* when the roots of the circuit's characteristic equation are unequal and real, *critically damped* when the roots are equal and real, and *underdamped* when the roots are complex.

(a)

(b)

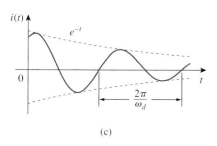

(c)

Figure 8.9   (a) Overdamped response, (b) critically damped response, (c) underdamped response.

for the special case of critical damping. Let us go back to Eq. (8.4). When $\alpha = \omega_0 = R/2L$, Eq. (8.4) becomes

$$\frac{d^2i}{dt^2} + 2\alpha\frac{di}{dt} + \alpha^2 i = 0$$

or

$$\frac{d}{dt}\left(\frac{di}{dt} + \alpha i\right) + \alpha\left(\frac{di}{dt} + \alpha i\right) = 0 \tag{8.16}$$

If we let

$$f = \frac{di}{dt} + \alpha i \tag{8.17}$$

then Eq. (8.16) becomes

$$\frac{df}{dt} + \alpha f = 0$$

which is a first-order differential equation with solution $f = A_1 e^{-\alpha t}$, where A_1 is a constant. Equation (8.17) then becomes

$$\frac{di}{dt} + \alpha i = A_1 e^{-\alpha t}$$

or

$$e^{\alpha t}\frac{di}{dt} + e^{\alpha t}\alpha i = A_1 \tag{8.18}$$

This can be written as

$$\frac{d}{dt}(e^{\alpha t}i) = A_1 \tag{8.19}$$

Integrating both sides yields

$$e^{\alpha t}i = A_1 t + A_2$$

or

$$i = (A_1 t + A_2)e^{-\alpha t} \tag{8.20}$$

where A_2 is another constant. Hence, the natural response of the critically damped circuit is a sum of two terms: a negative exponential and a negative exponential multiplied by a linear term, or

$$\boxed{i(t) = (A_2 + A_1 t)e^{-\alpha t}} \tag{8.21}$$

A typical critically damped response is shown in Fig. 8.9(b). In fact, Fig. 8.9(b) is a sketch of $i(t) = te^{-\alpha t}$, which reaches a maximum value of e^{-1}/α at $t = 1/\alpha$, one time constant, and then decays all the way to zero.

Underdamped Case ($\alpha < \omega_0$)

For $\alpha < \omega_0$, $C < 4L/R^2$. The roots may be written as

$$s_1 = -\alpha + \sqrt{-(\omega_0^2 - \alpha^2)} = -\alpha + j\omega_d \tag{8.22a}$$

$$s_2 = -\alpha - \sqrt{-(\omega_0^2 - \alpha^2)} = -\alpha - j\omega_d \tag{8.22b}$$

where $j = \sqrt{-1}$ and $\omega_d = \sqrt{\omega_0^2 - \alpha^2}$, which is called the *damping frequency*. Both ω_0 and ω_d are natural frequencies because they help determine the natural response; while ω_0 is often called the *undamped natural frequency*, ω_d is called the *damped natural frequency*. The natural response is

$$
\begin{aligned}
i(t) &= A_1 e^{-(\alpha - j\omega_d)t} + A_2 e^{-(\alpha + j\omega_d)t} \\
&= e^{-\alpha t}(A_1 e^{j\omega_d t} + A_2 e^{-j\omega_d t})
\end{aligned}
\tag{8.23}
$$

Using Euler's identities,

$$
e^{j\theta} = \cos\theta + j\sin\theta, \qquad e^{-j\theta} = \cos\theta - j\sin\theta \tag{8.24}
$$

we get

$$
\begin{aligned}
i(t) &= e^{-\alpha t}\,[A_1(\cos\omega_d t + j\sin\omega_d t) + A_2(\cos\omega_d t - j\sin\omega_d t)] \\
&= e^{-\alpha t}\,[(A_1 + A_2)\cos\omega_d t + j(A_1 - A_2)\sin\omega_d t]
\end{aligned}
\tag{8.25}
$$

Replacing constants $(A_1 + A_2)$ and $j(A_1 - A_2)$ with constants B_1 and B_2, we write

$$
\boxed{i(t) = e^{-\alpha t}(B_1 \cos\omega_d t + B_2 \sin\omega_d t)} \tag{8.26}
$$

With the presence of sine and cosine functions, it is clear that the natural response for this case is exponentially damped and oscillatory in nature. The response has a time constant of $1/\alpha$ and a period of $T = 2\pi/\omega_d$. Figure 8.9(c) depicts a typical underdamped response. [Figure 8.9 assumes for each case that $i(0) = 0$.]

Once the inductor current $i(t)$ is found for the RLC series circuit as shown above, other circuit quantities such as individual element voltages can easily be found. For example, the resistor voltage is $v_R = Ri$, and the inductor voltage is $v_L = L\,di/dt$. The inductor current $i(t)$ is selected as the key variable to be determined first in order to take advantage of Eq. (8.1b).

We conclude this section by noting the following interesting, peculiar properties of an RLC network:

1. The behavior of such a network is captured by the idea of *damping*, which is the gradual loss of the initial stored energy, as evidenced by the continuous decrease in the amplitude of the response. The damping effect is due to the presence of resistance R. The damping factor α determines the rate at which the response is damped. If $R = 0$, then $\alpha = 0$, and we have an LC circuit with $1/\sqrt{LC}$ as the undamped natural frequency. Since $\alpha < \omega_0$ in this case, the response is not only undamped but also oscillatory. The circuit is said to be *lossless*, because the dissipating or damping element (R) is absent. By adjusting the value of R, the response may be made undamped, overdamped, critically damped, or underdamped.

2. Oscillatory response is possible due to the presence of the two types of storage elements. Having both L and C allows the flow of energy back and forth between the two. The damped oscillation exhibited by the underdamped response is known as *ringing*. It stems from the ability of the storage elements L and C to transfer energy back and forth between them.

$R = 0$ produces a perfectly sinusoidal response. This response cannot be practically accomplished with L and C because of the inherent losses in them. See Figs 6.8 and 6.26. An electronic device called an *oscillator* can produce a perfectly sinusoidal response.

Examples 8.5 and 8.7 demonstrate the effect of varying R.

The response of a second-order circuit with two storage elements of the same type, as in Fig. 8.1(c) and (d), cannot be oscillatory.

3. Observe from Fig. 8.9 that the waveforms of the responses differ. In general, it is difficult to tell from the waveforms the difference between the overdamped and critically damped responses. The critically damped case is the borderline between the underdamped and overdamped cases and it decays the fastest. With the same initial conditions, the overdamped case has the longest settling time, because it takes the longest time to dissipate the initial stored energy. If we desire the fastest response without oscillation or ringing, the critically damped circuit is the right choice.

What this means in most practical circuits is that we seek an overdamped circuit that is as close as possible to a critically damped circuit.

EXAMPLE 8.3

In Fig. 8.8, $R = 40\ \Omega$, $L = 4$ H, and $C = 1/4$ F. Calculate the characteristic roots of the circuit. Is the natural response overdamped, underdamped, or critically damped?

Solution:

We first calculate

$$\alpha = \frac{R}{2L} = \frac{40}{2(4)} = 5, \qquad \omega_0 = \frac{1}{\sqrt{LC}} = \frac{1}{\sqrt{4 \times \frac{1}{4}}} = 1$$

The roots are

$$s_{1,2} = -\alpha \pm \sqrt{\alpha^2 - \omega_0^2} = -5 \pm \sqrt{25 - 1}$$

or

$$s_1 = -0.101, \qquad s_2 = -9.899$$

Since $\alpha > \omega_0$, we conclude that the response is overdamped. This is also evident from the fact that the roots are real and negative.

PRACTICE PROBLEM 8.3

If $R = 10\ \Omega$, $L = 5$ H, and $C = 2$ mF in Fig. 8.8, find α, ω_0, s_1, and s_2. What type of natural response will the circuit have?

Answer: 1, 10, $-1 \pm j9.95$, underdamped.

EXAMPLE 8.4

Find $i(t)$ in the circuit in Fig. 8.10. Assume that the circuit has reached steady state at $t = 0^-$.

Figure 8.10   For Example 8.4.

Solution:

For $t < 0$, the switch is closed. The capacitor acts like an open circuit while the inductor acts like a shunted circuit. The equivalent circuit is shown in Fig. 8.11(a). Thus, at $t = 0$,

$$i(0) = \frac{10}{4 + 6} = 1 \text{ A}, \qquad v(0) = 6i(0) = 6 \text{ V}$$

where $i(0)$ is the initial current through the inductor and $v(0)$ is the initial voltage across the capacitor.

Figure 8.11   The circuit in Fig. 8.10: (a) for $t < 0$, (b) for $t > 0$.

For $t > 0$, the switch is opened and the voltage source is disconnected. The equivalent circuit is shown in Fig. 8.11(b), which is a source-free series RLC circuit. Notice that the 3-Ω and 6-Ω resistors, which are in series in Fig. 8.10 when the switch is opened, have been combined to give $R = 9\ \Omega$ in Fig. 8.11(b). The roots are calculated as follows:

$$\alpha = \frac{R}{2L} = \frac{9}{2\left(\frac{1}{2}\right)} = 9, \qquad \omega_0 = \frac{1}{\sqrt{LC}} = \frac{1}{\sqrt{\frac{1}{2} \times \frac{1}{50}}} = 10$$

$$s_{1,2} = -\alpha \pm \sqrt{\alpha^2 - \omega_0^2} = -9 \pm \sqrt{81 - 100}$$

or

$$s_{1,2} = -9 \pm j4.359$$

Hence, the response is underdamped ($\alpha < \omega$); that is,

$$i(t) = e^{-9t}(A_1 \cos 4.359t + A_2 \sin 4.359t) \qquad (8.4.1)$$

We now obtain A_1 and A_2 using the initial conditions. At $t = 0$,

$$i(0) = 1 = A_1 \qquad (8.4.2)$$

From Eq. (8.5),

$$\left.\frac{di}{dt}\right|_{t=0} = -\frac{1}{L}[Ri(0) + v(0)] = -2[9(1) - 6] = -6\ \text{A/s} \qquad (8.4.3)$$

Note that $v(0) = V_0 = -6$ V is used, because the polarity of v in Fig. 8.11(b) is opposite that in Fig. 8.8. Taking the derivative of $i(t)$ in Eq. (8.4.1),

$$\frac{di}{dt} = -9e^{-9t}(A_1 \cos 4.359t + A_2 \sin 4.359t)$$

$$+ e^{-9t}(4.359)(-A_1 \sin 4.359t + A_2 \cos 4.359t)$$

Imposing the condition in Eq. (8.4.3) at $t = 0$ gives

$$-6 = -9(A_1 + 0) + 4.359(-0 + A_2)$$

But $A_1 = 1$ from Eq. (8.4.2). Then

$$-6 = -9 + 4.359A_2 \qquad \Longrightarrow \qquad A_2 = 0.6882$$

Substituting the values of A_1 and A_2 in Eq. (8.4.1) yields the complete solution as

$$i(t) = e^{-9t}(\cos 4.359t + 0.6882 \sin 4.359t)\ \text{A}$$

PRACTICE PROBLEM 8.4

The circuit in Fig. 8.12 has reached steady state at $t = 0^-$. If the make-before-break switch moves to position b at $t = 0$, calculate $i(t)$ for $t > 0$.

Answer: $e^{-2.5t}(5\cos 1.6583t - 7.5378\sin 1.6583t)$ A.

Figure 8.12   For Practice Prob. 8.4.

8.4   THE SOURCE-FREE PARALLEL RLC CIRCUIT

Parallel RLC circuits find many practical applications, notably in communications networks and filter designs.

Consider the parallel RLC circuit shown in Fig. 8.13. Assume initial inductor current I_0 and initial capacitor voltage V_0,

$$i(0) = I_0 = \frac{1}{L}\int_\infty^0 v(t)\,dt \tag{8.27a}$$

$$v(0) = V_0 \tag{8.27b}$$

Figure 8.13   A source-free parallel RLC circuit.

Since the three elements are in parallel, they have the same voltage v across them. According to passive sign convention, the current is entering each element; that is, the current through each element is leaving the top node. Thus, applying KCL at the top node gives

$$\frac{v}{R} + \frac{1}{L}\int_{-\infty}^t v\,dt + C\frac{dv}{dt} = 0 \tag{8.28}$$

Taking the derivative with respect to t and dividing by C results in

$$\frac{d^2v}{dt^2} + \frac{1}{RC}\frac{dv}{dt} + \frac{1}{LC}v = 0 \tag{8.29}$$

We obtain the characteristic equation by replacing the first derivative by s and the second derivative by s^2. By following the same reasoning used in establishing Eqs. (8.4) through (8.8), the characteristic equation is obtained as

$$s^2 + \frac{1}{RC}s + \frac{1}{LC} = 0 \tag{8.30}$$

The roots of the characteristic equation are

$$s_{1,2} = -\frac{1}{2RC} \pm \sqrt{\left(\frac{1}{2RC}\right)^2 - \frac{1}{LC}}$$

or

$$\boxed{s_{1,2} = -\alpha \pm \sqrt{\alpha^2 - \omega_0^2}} \tag{8.31}$$

where

$$\alpha = \frac{1}{2RC}, \qquad \omega_0 = \frac{1}{\sqrt{LC}} \tag{8.32}$$

The names of these terms remain the same as in the preceding section, as they play the same role in the solution. Again, there are three possible solutions, depending on whether $\alpha > \omega_0$, $\alpha = \omega_0$, or $\alpha < \omega_0$. Let us consider these cases separately.

Overdamped Case ($\alpha > \omega_0$)

From Eq. (8.32), $\alpha > \omega_0$ when $L > 4R^2C$. The roots of the characteristic equation are real and negative. The response is

$$v(t) = A_1 e^{s_1 t} + A_2 e^{s_2 t} \tag{8.33}$$

Critically Damped Case ($\alpha = \omega_0$)

For $\alpha = \omega$, $L = 4R^2C$. The roots are real and equal so that the response is

$$v(t) = (A_1 + A_2 t)e^{-\alpha t} \tag{8.34}$$

Underdamped Case ($\alpha < \omega_0$)

When $\alpha < \omega_0$, $L < 4R^2C$. In this case the roots are complex and may be expressed as

$$s_{1,2} = -\alpha \pm j\omega_d \tag{8.35}$$

where

$$\omega_d = \sqrt{\omega_0^2 - \alpha^2} \tag{8.36}$$

The response is

$$v(t) = e^{-\alpha t}(A_1 \cos \omega_d t + A_2 \sin \omega_d t) \tag{8.37}$$

The constants A_1 and A_2 in each case can be determined from the initial conditions. We need $v(0)$ and $dv(0)/dt$. The first term is known from Eq. (8.27b). We find the second term by combining Eqs. (8.27) and (8.28), as

$$\frac{V_0}{R} + I_0 + C\frac{dv(0)}{dt} = 0$$

or

$$\frac{dv(0)}{dt} = -\frac{(V_0 + RI_0)}{RC} \tag{8.38}$$

The voltage waveforms are similar to those shown in Fig. 8.9 and will depend on whether the circuit is overdamped, underdamped, or critically damped.

Having found the capacitor voltage $v(t)$ for the parallel RLC circuit as shown above, we can readily obtain other circuit quantities such as individual element currents. For example, the resistor current is $i_R = v/R$ and the capacitor voltage is $v_C = C\, dv/dt$. We have selected the capacitor voltage $v(t)$ as the key variable to be determined first in order to take advantage of Eq. (8.1a). Notice that we first found the inductor current $i(t)$ for the RLC series circuit, whereas we first found the capacitor voltage $v(t)$ for the parallel RLC circuit.

EXAMPLE 8.5

In the parallel circuit of Fig. 8.13, find $v(t)$ for $t > 0$, assuming $v(0) = 5$ V, $i(0) = 0$, $L = 1$ H, and $C = 10$ mF. Consider these cases: $R = 1.923\ \Omega$, $R = 5\ \Omega$, and $R = 6.25\ \Omega$.

Solution:

CASE 1 If $R = 1.923\ \Omega$,

$$\alpha = \frac{1}{2RC} = \frac{1}{2 \times 1.923 \times 10 \times 10^{-3}} = 26$$

$$\omega_0 = \frac{1}{\sqrt{LC}} = \frac{1}{\sqrt{1 \times 10 \times 10^{-3}}} = 10$$

Since $\alpha > \omega_0$ in this case, the response is overdamped. The roots of the characteristic equation are

$$s_{1,2} = -\alpha \pm \sqrt{\alpha^2 - \omega_0^2} = -2, -50$$

and the corresponding response is

$$v(t) = A_1 e^{-2t} + A_2 e^{-50t} \qquad (8.5.1)$$

We now apply the initial conditions to get A_1 and A_2.

$$v(0) = 5 = A_1 + A_2 \qquad (8.5.2)$$

$$\frac{dv(0)}{dt} = -\frac{v(0) + Ri(0)}{RC} = -\frac{5 + 0}{1.923 \times 10 \times 10^{-3}} = -260$$

But differentiating Eq. (8.5.1),

$$\frac{dv}{dt} = -2A_1 e^{-2t} - 50A_2 e^{-50t}$$

At $t = 0$,

$$-260 = -2A_1 - 50A_2 \qquad (8.5.3)$$

From Eqs. (8.5.2) and (8.5.3), we obtain $A_1 = -0.2083$ and $A_2 = 5.208$. Substituting A_1 and A_2 in Eq. (8.5.1) yields

$$v(t) = -0.2083 e^{-2t} + 5.208 e^{-50t} \qquad (8.5.4)$$

CASE 2 When $R = 5\ \Omega$,

$$\alpha = \frac{1}{2RC} = \frac{1}{2 \times 5 \times 10 \times 10^{-3}} = 10$$

while $\omega_0 = 10$ remains the same. Since $\alpha = \omega_0 = 10$, the response is critically damped. Hence, $s_1 = s_2 = -10$, and

$$v(t) = (A_1 + A_2 t)e^{-10t} \tag{8.5.5}$$

To get A_1 and A_2, we apply the initial conditions

$$v(0) = 5 = A_1 \tag{8.5.6}$$

$$\frac{dv(0)}{dt} = -\frac{v(0) + Ri(0)}{RC} = -\frac{5 + 0}{5 \times 10 \times 10^{-3}} = -100$$

But differentiating Eq. (8.5.5),

$$\frac{dv}{dt} = (-10A_1 - 10A_2 t + A_2)e^{-10t}$$

At $t = 0$,

$$-100 = -10A_1 + A_2 \tag{8.5.7}$$

From Eqs. (8.5.6) and (8.5.7), $A_1 = 5$ and $A_2 = -50$. Thus,

$$v(t) = (5 - 50t)e^{-10t} \text{ V} \tag{8.5.8}$$

$\boxed{\text{CASE } \mathbf{3}}$ When $R = 6.25 \; \Omega$,

$$\alpha = \frac{1}{2RC} = \frac{1}{2 \times 6.25 \times 10 \times 10^{-3}} = 8$$

while $\omega_0 = 10$ remains the same. As $\alpha < \omega_0$ in this case, the response is underdamped. The roots of the characteristic equation are

$$s_{1,2} = -\alpha \pm \sqrt{\alpha^2 - \omega_0^2} = -8 \pm j6$$

Hence,

$$v(t) = (A_1 \cos 6t + A_2 \sin 6t)e^{-8t} \tag{8.5.9}$$

We now obtain A_1 and A_2, as

$$v(0) = 5 = A_1 \tag{8.5.10}$$

$$\frac{dv(0)}{dt} = -\frac{v(0) + Ri(0)}{RC} = -\frac{5 + 0}{6.25 \times 10 \times 10^{-3}} = -80$$

But differentiating Eq. (8.5.9),

$$\frac{dv}{dt} = (-8A_1 \cos 6t - 8A_2 \sin 6t - 6A_1 \sin 6t + 6A_2 \cos 6t)e^{-8t}$$

At $t = 0$,

$$-80 = -8A_1 + 6A_2 \tag{8.5.11}$$

From Eqs. (8.5.10) and (8.5.11), $A_1 = 5$ and $A_2 = -6.667$. Thus,

$$v(t) = (5 \cos 6t - 6.667 \sin 6t)e^{-8t} \tag{8.5.12}$$

Notice that by increasing the value of R, the degree of damping decreases and the responses differ. Figure 8.14 plots the three cases.

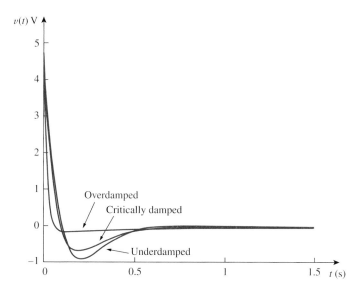

Figure 8.14   For Example 8.5: responses for three degrees of damping.

8.5

In Fig. 8.13, let $R = 2\ \Omega$, $L = 0.4$ H, $C = 25$ mF, $v(0) = 0$, $i(0) = 3$ A. Find $v(t)$ for $t > 0$.

Answer: $-120te^{-10t}$ V.

EXAMPLE 8.6

Find $v(t)$ for $t > 0$ in the *RLC* circuit of Fig. 8.15.

Figure 8.15   For Example 8.6.

Solution:

When $t < 0$, the switch is open; the inductor acts like a short circuit while the capacitor behaves like an open circuit. The initial voltage across the capacitor is the same as the voltage across the 50-Ω resistor; that is,

$$v(0) = \frac{50}{30 + 50}(40) = \frac{5}{8} \times 40 = 25 \text{ V} \qquad (8.6.1)$$

The initial current through the inductor is

$$i(0) = -\frac{40}{30 + 50} = -0.5 \text{ A}$$

The direction of i is as indicated in Fig. 8.15 to conform with the direction of I_0 in Fig. 8.13, which is in agreement with the convention that current flows into the positive terminal of an inductor (see Fig. 6.23). We need to express this in terms of dv/dt, since we are looking for v.

$$\frac{dv(0)}{dt} = -\frac{v(0) + Ri(0)}{RC} = -\frac{25 - 50 \times 0.5}{50 \times 20 \times 10^{-6}} = 0 \qquad (8.6.2)$$

When $t > 0$, the switch is closed. The voltage source along with the 30-Ω resistor is separated from the rest of the circuit. The parallel RLC circuit acts independently of the voltage source, as illustrated in Fig. 8.16. Next, we determine that the roots of the characteristic equation are

$$\alpha = \frac{1}{2RC} = \frac{1}{2 \times 50 \times 20 \times 10^{-6}} = 500$$

$$\omega_0 = \frac{1}{\sqrt{LC}} = \frac{1}{\sqrt{0.4 \times 20 \times 10^{-6}}} = 354$$

$$s_{1,2} = -\alpha \pm \sqrt{\alpha^2 - \omega_0^2}$$

$$= -500 \pm \sqrt{250,000 - 124,997.6} = -500 \pm 354$$

or

$$s_1 = -854, \qquad s_2 = -146$$

Since $\alpha > \omega_0$, we have the overdamped response

$$v(t) = A_1 e^{-854t} + A_2 e^{-146t} \qquad (8.6.3)$$

At $t = 0$, we impose the condition in Eq. (8.6.1),

$$v(0) = 25 = A_1 + A_2 \qquad \Longrightarrow \qquad A_2 = 25 - A_1 \qquad (8.6.4)$$

Taking the derivative of $v(t)$ in Eq. (8.6.3),

$$\frac{dv}{dt} = -854A_1 e^{-854t} - 146A_2 e^{-146t}$$

Imposing the condition in Eq. (8.6.2),

$$\frac{dv(0)}{dt} = 0 = -854A_1 - 146A_2$$

Figure 8.16   The circuit in Fig. 8.15 when $t > 0$. The parallel RLC circuit on the left-hand side acts independently of the circuit on the right-hand side of the junction.

or

$$0 = 854A_1 + 146A_2 \qquad (8.6.5)$$

Solving Eqs. (8.6.4) and (8.6.5) gives

$$A_1 = -5.156, \qquad A_2 = 30.16$$

Thus, the complete solution in Eq. (8.6.3) becomes

$$v(t) = -5.156e^{-854t} + 30.16e^{-146t} \text{ V}$$

PRACTICE PROBLEM 8.6

Refer to the circuit in Fig. 8.17. Find $v(t)$ for $t > 0$.

Answer: $66.67(e^{-10t} - e^{-2.5t})$ V.

Figure 8.17   For Practice Prob. 8.6.

8.5   STEP RESPONSE OF A SERIES *RLC* CIRCUIT

Figure 8.18   Step voltage applied to a series *RLC* circuit.

As we learned in the preceding chapter, the step response is obtained by the sudden application of a dc source. Consider the series *RLC* circuit shown in Fig. 8.18. Applying KVL around the loop for $t > 0$,

$$L\frac{di}{dt} + Ri + v = V_s \qquad (8.39)$$

But

$$i = C\frac{dv}{dt}$$

Substituting for i in Eq. (8.39) and rearranging terms,

$$\frac{d^2v}{dt^2} + \frac{R}{L}\frac{dv}{dt} + \frac{v}{LC} = \frac{V_s}{LC} \qquad (8.40)$$

which has the same form as Eq. (8.4). More specifically, the coefficients are the same (and that is important in determining the frequency parameters) but the variable is different. (Likewise, see Eq. (8.47).) Hence, the characteristic equation for the series *RLC* circuit is not affected by the presence of the dc source.

The solution to Eq. (8.40) has two components: the transient response $v_t(t)$ and the steady-state response $v_{ss}(t)$; that is,

$$v(t) = v_t(t) + v_{ss}(t) \qquad (8.41)$$

The transient response $v_t(t)$ is the component of the total response that dies out with time. The form of the transient response is the same as the form of the solution obtained in Section 8.3 for the source-free circuit, given by Eq. (8.14), (8.21), and (8.26). Therefore, the transient repsonse $v_t(t)$ for the overdamped, underdamped, and critically damped cases are:

$$v_t(t) = A_1 e^{s_1 t} + A_2 e^{s_2 t} \quad \text{(Overdamped)} \tag{8.42a}$$

$$v_t(t) = (A_1 + A_2 t)e^{-\alpha t} \quad \text{(Critically damped)} \tag{8.42b}$$

$$v_t(t) = (A_1 \cos \omega_d t + A_2 \sin \omega_d t)e^{-\alpha t} \quad \text{(Underdamped)} \tag{8.42c}$$

The steady-state response is the final value of $v(t)$. In the circuit in Fig. 8.18, the final value of the capacitor voltage is the same as the source voltage V_s. Hence,

$$v_{ss}(t) = v(\infty) = V_s \tag{8.43}$$

Thus, the complete solutions for the overdamped, underdamped, and critically damped cases are:

$$v(t) = V_s + A_1 e^{s_1 t} + A_2 e^{s_2 t} \quad \text{(Overdamped)} \tag{8.44a}$$

$$v(t) = V_s + (A_1 + A_2 t)e^{-\alpha t} \quad \text{(Critically damped)} \tag{8.44b}$$

$$v(t) = V_s + (A_1 \cos \omega_d t + A_2 \sin \omega_d t)e^{-\alpha t} \quad \text{(Underdamped)} \tag{8.44c}$$

The values of the constants A_1 and A_2 are obtained from the initial conditions: $v(0)$ and $dv(0)/dt$. Keep in mind that v and i are, respectively, the voltage across the capacitor and the current through the inductor. Therefore, Eq. (8.44) only applies for finding v. But once the capacitor voltage $v_C = v$ is known, we can determine $i = C\, dv/dt$, which is the same current through the capacitor, inductor, and resistor. Hence, the voltage across the resistor is $v_R = iR$, while the inductor voltage is $v_L = L\, di/dt$.

   Alternatively, the complete response for any variable $x(t)$ can be found directly, because it has the general form

$$x(t) = x_{ss}(t) + x_t(t) \tag{8.45}$$

where the $x_{ss} = x(\infty)$ is the final value and $x_t(t)$ is the transient response. The final value is found as in Section 8.2. The transient response has the same form as in Eq. (8.42), and the associated constants are determined from Eq. (8.44) based on the values of $x(0)$ and $dx(0)/dt$.

EXAMPLE 8.7

For the circuit in Fig. 8.19, find $v(t)$ and $i(t)$ for $t > 0$. Consider these cases: $R = 5\,\Omega$, $R = 4\,\Omega$, and $R = 1\,\Omega$.

Solution:

CASE 1 When $R = 5\,\Omega$. For $t < 0$, the switch is closed for a long time. The capacitor behaves like an open circuit while the inductor acts like a short circuit. The initial current through the inductor is

$$i(0) = \frac{24}{5+1} = 4 \text{ A}$$

Figure 8.19   For Example 8.7.

and the initial voltage across the capacitor is the same as the voltage across the 1-Ω resistor; that is,

$$v(0) = 1i(0) = 4 \text{ V}$$

For $t > 0$, the switch is opened, so that we have the 1-Ω resistor disconnected. What remains is the series RLC circuit with the voltage source. The characteristic roots are determined as follows.

$$\alpha = \frac{R}{2L} = \frac{5}{2 \times 1} = 2.5, \qquad \omega_0 = \frac{1}{\sqrt{LC}} = \frac{1}{\sqrt{1 \times 0.25}} = 2$$

$$s_{1,2} = -\alpha \pm \sqrt{\alpha^2 - \omega_0^2} = -1, -4$$

Since $\alpha > \omega_0$, we have the overdamped natural response. The total response is therefore

$$v(t) = v_{ss} + (A_1 e^{-t} + A_2 e^{-4t})$$

where v_{ss} is the steady-state response. It is the final value of the capacitor voltage. In Fig. 8.19, $v_f = 24$ V. Thus,

$$v(t) = 24 + (A_1 e^{-t} + A_2 e^{-4t}) \tag{8.7.1}$$

We now need to find A_1 and A_2 using the initial conditions.

$$v(0) = 4 = 24 + A_1 + A_2$$

or

$$-20 = A_1 + A_2 \tag{8.7.2}$$

The current through the inductor cannot change abruptly and is the same current through the capacitor at $t = 0^+$ because the inductor and capacitor are now in series. Hence,

$$i(0) = C\frac{dv(0)}{dt} = 4 \qquad \Longrightarrow \qquad \frac{dv(0)}{dt} = \frac{4}{C} = \frac{4}{0.25} = 16$$

Before we use this condition, we need to take the derivative of v in Eq. (8.7.1).

$$\frac{dv}{dt} = -A_1 e^{-t} - 4A_2 e^{-4t} \tag{8.7.3}$$

At $t = 0$,

$$\frac{dv(0)}{dt} = 16 = -A_1 - 4A_2 \tag{8.7.4}$$

From Eqs. (8.7.2) and (8.7.4), $A_1 = -64/3$ and $A_2 = 4/3$. Substituting A_1 and A_2 in Eq. (8.7.1), we get

$$v(t) = 24 + \frac{4}{3}(-16e^{-t} + e^{-4t}) \text{ V} \tag{8.7.5}$$

Since the inductor and capacitor are in series for $t > 0$, the inductor current is the same as the capacitor current. Hence,

$$i(t) = C\frac{dv}{dt}$$

Multiplying Eq. (8.7.3) by $C = 0.25$ and substituting the values of A_1 and A_2 gives

$$i(t) = \frac{4}{3}(4e^{-t} - e^{-4t}) \text{ A} \tag{8.7.6}$$

Note that $i(0) = 4$ A, as expected.

CASE **2** When $R = 4$ Ω. Again, the initial current through the inductor is

$$i(0) = \frac{24}{4 + 1} = 4.8 \text{ A}$$

and the initial capacitor voltage is

$$v(0) = 1i(0) = 4.8 \text{ V}$$

For the characteristic roots,

$$\alpha = \frac{R}{2L} = \frac{4}{2 \times 1} = 2$$

while $\omega_0 = 2$ remains the same. In this case, $s_1 = s_2 = -\alpha = -2$, and we have the critically damped natural response. The total response is therefore

$$v(t) = v_{ss} + (A_1 + A_2 t)e^{-2t}$$

and, as before $v_{ss} = 24$ V,

$$v(t) = 24 + (A_1 + A_2 t)e^{-2t} \tag{8.7.7}$$

To find A_1 and A_2, we use the initial conditions. We write

$$v(0) = 4.8 = 24 + A_1 \qquad \Longrightarrow \qquad A_1 = -19.2 \tag{8.7.8}$$

Since $i(0) = C \, dv(0)/dt = 4.8$ or

$$\frac{dv(0)}{dt} = \frac{4.8}{C} = 19.2$$

From Eq. (8.7.7),

$$\frac{dv}{dt} = (-2A_1 - 2tA_2 + A_2)e^{-2t} \tag{8.7.9}$$

At $t = 0$,

$$\frac{dv(0)}{dt} = 19.2 = -2A_1 + A_2 \tag{8.7.10}$$

From Eqs. (8.7.8) and (8.7.10), $A_1 = -19.2$ and $A_2 = -19.2$. Thus, Eq. (8.7.7) becomes

$$v(t) = 24 - 19.2(1 + t)e^{-2t} \text{ V} \tag{8.7.11}$$

The inductor current is the same as the capacitor current, that is,

$$i(t) = C\frac{dv}{dt}$$

Multiplying Eq. (8.7.9) by $C = 0.25$ and substituting the values of A_1 and A_2 gives

$$i(t) = (4.8 + 9.6t)e^{-2t} \text{ A} \tag{8.7.12}$$

Note that $i(0) = 4.8$ A, as expected.

$\boxed{\text{CASE } \boxed{3}}$ When $R = 1 \ \Omega$. The initial inductor current is

$$i(0) = \frac{24}{1+1} = 12 \text{ A}$$

and the initial voltage across the capacitor is the same as the voltage across the 1-Ω resistor,

$$v(0) = 1i(0) = 12 \text{ V}$$

$$\alpha = \frac{R}{2L} = \frac{1}{2 \times 1} = 0.5$$

Since $\alpha = 0.5 < \omega_0 = 2$, we have the underdamped response

$$s_{1,2} = -\alpha \pm \sqrt{\alpha^2 - \omega_0^2} = -0.5 \pm j1.936$$

The total response is therefore

$$v(t) = 24 + (A_1 \cos 1.936t + A_2 \sin 1.936t)e^{-0.5t} \qquad (8.7.13)$$

We now determine A_1 and A_2. We write

$$v(0) = 12 = 24 + A_1 \qquad \Longrightarrow \qquad A_1 = -12 \qquad (8.7.14)$$

Since $i(0) = C \, dv(0)/dt = 12$,

$$\frac{dv(0)}{dt} = \frac{12}{C} = 48 \qquad (8.7.15)$$

But

$$\frac{dv}{dt} = e^{-0.5t}(-1.936A_1 \sin 1.936t + 1.936A_2 \cos 1.936t)$$
$$- 0.5e^{-0.5t}(A_1 \cos 1.936t + A_2 \sin 1.936t) \qquad (8.7.16)$$

At $t = 0$,

$$\frac{dv(0)}{dt} = 48 = (-0 + 1.936A_2) - 0.5(A_1 + 0)$$

Substituting $A_1 = -12$ gives $A_2 = 21.694$, and Eq. (8.7.13) becomes

$$v(t) = 24 + (21.694 \sin 1.936t - 12 \cos 1.936t)e^{-0.5t} \text{ V} \qquad (8.7.17)$$

The inductor current is

$$i(t) = C\frac{dv}{dt}$$

Multiplying Eq. (8.7.16) by $C = 0.25$ and substituting the values of A_1 and A_2 gives

$$i(t) = (3.1 \sin 1.936t + 12 \cos 1.936t)e^{-0.5t} \text{ A} \qquad (8.7.18)$$

Note that $i(0) = 12$ A, as expected.

Figure 8.20 plots the responses for the three cases. From this figure, we observe that the critically damped response approaches the step input of 24 V the fastest.

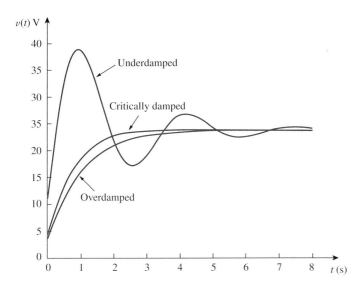

Figure 8.20   For Example 8.7: response for three degrees of damping.

Having been in position a for a long time, the switch in Fig. 8.21 is moved to position b at $t = 0$. Find $v(t)$ and $v_R(t)$ for $t > 0$.

Figure 8.21   For Practice Prob. 8.7.

Answer: $10 - (1.1547 \sin 3.464t + 2 \cos 3.464t)e^{-2t}$ V, $2.31e^{-2t} \sin 3.464t$ V.

8.6   STEP RESPONSE OF A PARALLEL RLC CIRCUIT

Consider the parallel RLC circuit shown in Fig. 8.22. We want to find i due to a sudden application of a dc current. Applying KCL at the top node for $t > 0$,

$$\frac{v}{R} + i + C\frac{dv}{dt} = I_s \tag{8.46}$$

But

$$v = L\frac{di}{dt}$$

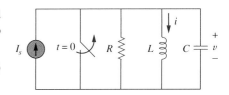

Figure 8.22   Parallel RLC circuit with an applied current.

Substituting for v in Eq. (8.46) and dividing by LC, we get

$$\frac{d^2i}{dt^2} + \frac{1}{RC}\frac{di}{dt} + \frac{i}{LC} = \frac{I_s}{LC} \qquad (8.47)$$

which has the same characteristic equation as Eq. (8.29).

The complete solution to Eq. (8.47) consists of the transient response $i_t(t)$ and the steady-state response i_{ss}; that is,

$$i(t) = i_t(t) + i_{ss}(t) \qquad (8.48)$$

The transient response is the same as what we had in Section 8.4. The steady-state response is the final value of i. In the circuit in Fig. 8.22, the final value of the current through the inductor is the same as the source current I_s. Thus,

$$
\begin{aligned}
i(t) &= I_s + A_1 e^{s_1 t} + A_2 e^{s_2 t} \quad \text{(Overdamped)} \\
i(t) &= I_s + (A_1 + A_2 t)e^{-\alpha t} \quad \text{(Critically damped)} \\
i(t) &= I_s + (A_1 \cos \omega_d t + A_2 \sin \omega_d t)e^{-\alpha t} \quad \text{(Underdamped)}
\end{aligned}
\qquad (8.49)
$$

The constants A_1 and A_2 in each case can be determined from the initial conditions for i and di/dt. Again, we should keep in mind that Eq. (8.49) only applies for finding the inductor current i. But once the inductor current $i_L = i$ is known, we can find $v = L\, di/dt$, which is the same voltage across inductor, capacitor, and resistor. Hence, the current through the resistor is $i_R = v/R$, while the capacitor current is $i_C = C\, dv/dt$. Alternatively, the complete response for any variable $x(t)$ may be found directly, using

$$x(t) = x_{ss}(t) + x_t(t) \qquad (8.50)$$

where x_{ss} and x_t are its final value and transient response, respectively.

EXAMPLE 8.8

In the circuit in Fig. 8.23, find $i(t)$ and $i_R(t)$ for $t > 0$.

Figure 8.23 For Example 8.8.

Solution:

For $t < 0$, the switch is open, and the circuit is partitioned into two independent subcircuits. The 4-A current flows through the inductor, so that

$$i(0) = 4 \text{ A}$$

Since $30u(-t) = 30$ when $t < 0$ and 0 when $t > 0$, the voltage source is operative for $t < 0$ under consideration. The capacitor acts like an open circuit and the voltage across it is the same as the voltage across the 20-Ω resistor connected in parallel with it. By voltage division, the initial capacitor voltage is

$$v(0) = \frac{20}{20 + 20}(30) = 15 \text{ V}$$

For $t > 0$, the switch is closed, and we have a parallel RLC circuit with a current source. The voltage source is off or short-circuited. The two 20-Ω resistors are now in parallel. They are combined to give $R = 20 \parallel 20 = 10 \ \Omega$. The characteristic roots are determined as follows:

$$\alpha = \frac{1}{2RC} = \frac{1}{2 \times 10 \times 8 \times 10^{-3}} = 6.25$$

$$\omega_0 = \frac{1}{\sqrt{LC}} = \frac{1}{\sqrt{20 \times 8 \times 10^{-3}}} = 2.5$$

$$s_{1,2} = -\alpha \pm \sqrt{\alpha^2 - \omega_0^2} = -6.25 \pm \sqrt{39.0625 - 6.25}$$
$$= -6.25 \pm 5.7282$$

or

$$s_1 = -11.978, \qquad s_2 = -0.5218$$

Since $\alpha > \omega_0$, we have the overdamped case. Hence,

$$i(t) = I_s + A_1 e^{-11.978t} + A_2 e^{-0.5218t} \tag{8.8.1}$$

where $I_s = 4$ is the final value of $i(t)$. We now use the initial conditions to determine A_1 and A_2. At $t = 0$,

$$i(0) = 4 = 4 + A_1 + A_2 \qquad \Longrightarrow \qquad A_2 = -A_1 \tag{8.8.2}$$

Taking the derivative of $i(t)$ in Eq. (8.8.1),

$$\frac{di}{dt} = -11.978 A_1 e^{-11.978t} - 0.5218 A_2 e^{-0.5218t}$$

so that at $t = 0$,

$$\frac{di(0)}{dt} = -11.978 A_1 - 0.5218 A_2 \tag{8.8.3}$$

But

$$L\frac{di(0)}{dt} = v(0) = 15 \qquad \Longrightarrow \qquad \frac{di(0)}{dt} = \frac{15}{L} = \frac{15}{20} = 0.75$$

Substituting this into Eq. (8.8.3) and incorporating Eq. (8.8.2), we get

$$0.75 = (11.978 - 0.5218)A_2 \qquad \Longrightarrow \qquad A_2 = 0.0655$$

Thus, $A_1 = -0.0655$ and $A_2 = 0.0655$. Inserting A_1 and A_2 in Eq. (8.8.1) gives the complete solution as

$$i(t) = 4 + 0.0655(e^{-0.5218t} - e^{-11.978t}) \text{ A}$$

From $i(t)$, we obtain $v(t) = L\,di/dt$ and

$$i_R(t) = \frac{v(t)}{20} = \frac{L}{20}\frac{di}{dt} = 0.785e^{-11.978t} - 0.0342e^{-0.5218t}\text{ A}$$

PRACTICE PROBLEM 8.8

$20u(t)$ A $v \;\genfrac{}{}{0pt}{}{+}{-}\; 0.2$ F   5 H $\downarrow i$

Find $i(t)$ and $v(t)$ for $t > 0$ in the circuit in Fig. 8.24.

Answer: $20(1 - \cos t)$ A, $100 \sin t$ V.

Figure 8.24   For Practice Prob. 8.8.

8.7   GENERAL SECOND-ORDER CIRCUITS

Now that we have mastered series and parallel RLC circuits, we are prepared to apply the ideas to any second-order circuit having one or more independent sources with constant values. Although the series and parallel RLC circuits are the second-order circuits of greatest interest, other second-order circuits including op amps are also useful. Given a second-order circuit, we determine its step response $x(t)$ (which may be voltage or current) by taking the following four steps:

1. We first determine the initial conditions $x(0)$ and $dx(0)/dt$ and the final value $x(\infty)$, as discussed in Section 8.2.

2. We find the transient response $x_t(t)$ by applying KCL and KVL. Once a second-order differential equation is obtained, we determine its characteristic roots. Depending on whether the response is overdamped, critically damped, or underdamped, we obtain $x_t(t)$ with two unknown constants as we did in the previous sections.

3. We obtain the forced response as

$$x_f(t) = x(\infty) \qquad (8.51)$$

where $x(\infty)$ is the final value of x, obtained in step 1.

4. The total response is now found as the sum of the transient response and steady-state response

$$x(t) = x_t(t) + x_{ss}(t) \qquad (8.52)$$

We finally determine the constants associated with the transient response by imposing the initial conditions $x(0)$ and $dx(0)/dt$, determined in step 1.

We can apply this general procedure to find the step response of any second-order circuit, including those with op amps. The following examples illustrate the four steps.

A circuit may look complicated at first. But once the sources are turned off in an attempt to find the natural response, it may be reducible to a first-order circuit, when the storage elements can be combined, or to a parallel/series RLC circuit. If it is reducible to a first-order circuit, the solution becomes simply what we had in Chapter 7. If it is reducible to a parallel or series RLC circuit, we apply the techniques of previous sections in this chapter.

EXAMPLE 8.9

Find the complete response v and then i for $t > 0$ in the circuit of Fig. 8.25.

Solution:

We first find the initial and final values. At $t = 0^-$, the circuit is at steady state. The switch is open, the equivalent circuit is shown in Fig. 8.26(a). It is evident from the figure that

$$v(0^-) = 12 \text{ V}, \qquad i(0^-) = 0$$

Figure 8.25   For Example 8.9.

At $t = 0^+$, the switch is closed; the equivalent circuit is in Fig. 8.26(b). By the continuity of capacitor voltage and inductor current, we know that

$$v(0^+) = v(0^-) = 12 \text{ V}, \qquad i(0^+) = i(0^-) = 0 \qquad (8.9.1)$$

To get $dv(0^+)/dt$, we use $C \, dv/dt = i_C$ or $dv/dt = i_C/C$. Applying KCL at node a in Fig. 8.26(b),

$$i(0^+) = i_C(0^+) + \frac{v(0^+)}{2}$$

$$0 = i_C(0^+) + \frac{12}{2} \qquad \Longrightarrow \qquad i_C(0^+) = -6 \text{ A}$$

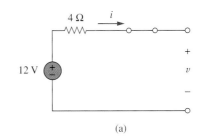

(a)

Hence,

$$\frac{dv(0^+)}{dt} = \frac{-6}{0.5} = -12 \text{ V/s} \qquad (8.9.2)$$

The final values are obtained when the inductor is replaced by a short circuit and the capacitor by an open circuit in Fig. 8.26(b), giving

$$i(\infty) = \frac{12}{4 + 2} = 2 \text{ A}, \qquad v(\infty) = 2i(\infty) = 4 \text{ V} \qquad (8.9.3)$$

(b)

Figure 8.26   Equivalent circuit of the circuit in Fig. 8.25 for: (a) $t = 0$, (b) $t > 0$.

Next, we obtain the natural response for $t > 0$. By turning off the 12-V voltage source, we have the circuit in Fig. 8.27. Applying KCL at node a in Fig. 8.27 gives

$$i = \frac{v}{2} + \frac{1}{2}\frac{dv}{dt} \qquad (8.9.4)$$

Applying KVL to the left mesh results in

$$4i + 1\frac{di}{dt} + v = 0 \qquad (8.9.5)$$

Since we are interested in v for the moment, we substitute i from Eq. (8.9.4) into Eq. (8.9.5). We obtain

$$2v + 2\frac{dv}{dt} + \frac{1}{2}\frac{dv}{dt} + \frac{1}{2}\frac{d^2v}{dt^2} + v = 0$$

or

$$\frac{d^2v}{dt^2} + 5\frac{dv}{dt} + 6v = 0$$

From this, we obtain the characteristic equation as

$$s^2 + 5s + 6 = 0$$

Figure 8.27   Obtaining the natural response for Example 8.9.

with roots $s = -2$ and $s = -3$. Thus, the natural response is

$$v_n(t) = Ae^{-2t} + Be^{-3t} \qquad (8.9.6)$$

where A and B are unknown constants to be determined later. The forced response is

$$v_f(t) = v(\infty) = 4 \qquad (8.9.7)$$

The complete response is

$$v(t) = v_n + v_f = 4 + Ae^{-2t} + Be^{-3t} \qquad (8.9.8)$$

We now determine A and B using the initial values. From Eq. (8.9.1), $v(0) = 12$. Substituting this into Eq. (8.9.8) at $t = 0$ gives

$$12 = 4 + A + B \qquad \Longrightarrow \qquad A + B = 8 \qquad (8.9.9)$$

Taking the derivative of v in Eq. (8.9.8),

$$\frac{dv}{dt} = -2Ae^{-2t} - 3Be^{-3t} \qquad (8.9.10)$$

Substituting Eq. (8.9.2) into Eq. (8.9.10) at $t = 0$ gives

$$-12 = -2A - 3B \qquad \Longrightarrow \qquad 2A + 3B = 12 \qquad (8.9.11)$$

From Eqs. (8.9.9) and (8.9.11), we obtain

$$A = 12, \qquad B = -4$$

so that Eq. (8.9.8) becomes

$$v(t) = 4 + 12e^{-2t} - 4e^{-3t} \text{ V}, \qquad t > 0 \qquad (8.9.12)$$

From v, we can obtain other quantities of interest by referring to Fig. 8.26(b). To obtain i, for example,

$$i = \frac{v}{2} + \frac{1}{2}\frac{dv}{dt} = 2 + 6e^{-2t} - 2e^{-3t} - 12e^{-2t} + 6e^{-3t}$$
$$= 2 - 6e^{-2t} + 4e^{-3t} \text{ A}, \qquad t > 0 \qquad (8.9.13)$$

Notice that $i(0) = 0$, in agreement with Eq. (8.9.1).

PRACTICE PROBLEM 8.9

Figure 8.28   For Practice Prob. 8.9.

Determine v and i for $t > 0$ in the circuit of Fig. 8.28.

Answer: $8(1 - e^{-5t})$ V, $2(1 - e^{-5t})$ A.

EXAMPLE 8.10

Find $v_o(t)$ for $t > 0$ in the circuit of Fig. 8.29.

Solution:

This is an example of a second-order circuit with two inductors. We first obtain the mesh currents i_1 and i_2, which happen to be the currents through the inductors. We need to obtain the initial and final values of these currents.

Figure 8.29   For Example 8.10.

For $t < 0$, $7u(t) = 0$, so that $i_1(0^-) = 0 = i_2(0^-)$. For $t > 0$, $7u(t) = 7$, so that the equivalent circuit is as shown in Fig. 8.30(a). Due to the continuity of inductor current,

$$i_1(0^+) = i_1(0^-) = 0, \qquad i_2(0^+) = i_2(0^-) = 0 \qquad (8.10.1)$$

$$v_{L_2}(0^+) = v_o(0^+) = 1[(i_1(0^+) - i_2(0^+)] = 0 \qquad (8.10.2)$$

Applying KVL to the left loop in Fig. 8.30(a) at $t = 0^+$,

$$7 = 3i_1(0^+) + v_{L_1}(0+) + v_o(0^+)$$

or

$$v_{L_1}(0^+) = 7 \text{ V}$$

Since $L_1 \, di_1/dt = v_{L_1}$,

$$\frac{di_1(0^+)}{dt} = \frac{v_{L_1}}{L_1} = \frac{7}{\frac{1}{2}} = 14 \text{ V/s} \qquad (8.10.3)$$

Similarly, since $L_2 \, di_2/dt = v_{L_2}$,

$$\frac{di_2(0^+)}{dt} = \frac{v_{L_2}}{L_2} = 0 \qquad (8.10.4)$$

As $t \to \infty$, the circuit reaches steady state, and the inductors can be replaced by short circuits, as shown in Fig. 8.30(b). From this figure,

$$i_1(\infty) = i_2(\infty) = \frac{7}{3} \text{ A} \qquad (8.10.5)$$

(a)   (b)

Figure 8.30   Equivalent circuit of that in Fig. 8.29 for: (a) $t > 0$, (b) $t \to \infty$.

Next, we obtain the natural responses by removing the voltage source, as shown in Fig. 8.31. Applying KVL to the two meshes yields

$$4i_1 - i_2 + \frac{1}{2}\frac{di_1}{dt} = 0 \qquad (8.10.6)$$

Figure 8.31 Obtaining the natural response for Example 8.10.

and

$$i_2 + \frac{1}{5}\frac{di_2}{dt} - i_1 = 0 \qquad (8.10.7)$$

From Eq. (8.10.6),

$$i_2 = 4i_1 + \frac{1}{2}\frac{di_1}{dt} \qquad (8.10.8)$$

Substituting Eq. (12.10.8) into Eq. (8.10.7) gives

$$4i_1 + \frac{1}{2}\frac{di_1}{dt} + \frac{4}{5}\frac{di_1}{dt} + \frac{1}{10}\frac{d^2i_1}{dt^2} - i_1 = 0$$

$$\frac{d^2i_1}{dt^2} + 13\frac{di_1}{dt} + 30i_1 = 0$$

From this we obtain the characteristic equation as

$$s^2 + 13s + 30 = 0$$

which has roots $s = -3$ and $s = -10$. Hence, the natural response is

$$i_{1n} = Ae^{-3t} + Be^{-10t} \qquad (8.10.9)$$

where A and B are constants. The forced response is

$$i_{1f} = i_1(\infty) = \frac{7}{3} \text{ A} \qquad (8.10.10)$$

From Eqs. (8.10.9) and (8.10.10), we obtain the complete response as

$$i_1(t) = \frac{7}{3} + Ae^{-3t} + Be^{-10t} \qquad (8.10.11)$$

We finally obtain A and B from the initial values. From Eqs. (8.10.1) and (8.10.11),

$$0 = \frac{7}{3} + A + B \qquad (8.10.12)$$

Taking the derivative of Eq. (8.10.11), setting $t = 0$ in the derivative, and enforcing Eq. (8.10.3), we obtain

$$14 = -3A - 10B \qquad (8.10.13)$$

From Eqs. (8.10.12) and (8.10.13), $A = -4/3$ and $B = -1$. Thus,

$$i_1(t) = \frac{7}{3} - \frac{4}{3}e^{-3t} - e^{-10t} \qquad (8.10.14)$$

We now obtain i_2 from i_1. Applying KVL to the left loop in Fig. 8.30(a) gives

$$7 = 4i_1 - i_2 + \frac{1}{2}\frac{di_1}{dt} \qquad \Longrightarrow \qquad i_2 = -7 + 4i_1 + \frac{1}{2}\frac{di_1}{dt}$$

Substituting for i_1 in Eq. (8.10.14) gives

$$i_2(t) = -7 + \frac{28}{3} - \frac{16}{3}e^{-3t} - 4e^{-10t} + 2e^{-3t} + 5e^{-10t}$$

$$\qquad (8.10.15)$$

$$= \frac{7}{3} - \frac{10}{3}e^{-3t} + e^{-10t}$$

From Fig. 8.29,

$$v_o(t) = 1[i_1(t) - i_2(t)] \qquad (8.10.16)$$

Substituting Eqs. (8.10.14) and (8.10.15) into Eq. (8.10.16) yields

$$v_o(t) = 2(e^{-3t} - e^{-10t}) \qquad (8.10.17)$$

Note that $v_o(0) = 0$, as expected from Eq. (8.10.2).

PRACTICE PROBLEM 8.10

For $t > 0$, obtain $v_o(t)$ in the circuit of Fig. 8.32.
(*Hint:* First find v_1 and v_2.)

Answer: $2(e^{-t} - e^{-6t})$ V, $t > 0$.

Figure 8.32   For Practice Prob. 8.10.

8.8   SECOND-ORDER OP AMP CIRCUITS

An op amp circuit with two storage elements that cannot be combined into a single equivalent element is second-order. Because inductors are bulky and heavy, they are rarely used in practical op amp circuits. For this reason, we will only consider RC second-order op amp circuits here. Such circuits find a wide range of applications in devices such as filters and oscillators.

> The use of op amps in second-order circuits avoids the use of inductors, which are somewhat undesirable in some applications.

The analysis of a second-order op amp circuit follows the same four steps given and demonstrated in the previous section.

EXAMPLE 8.11

In the op amp circuit of Fig. 8.33, find $v_o(t)$ for $t > 0$ when $v_s = 10u(t)$ mV. Let $R_1 = R_2 = 10$ kΩ, $C_1 = 20$ μF, and $C_2 = 100$ μF.

Solution:

Although we could follow the same four steps given in the previous section to solve this problem, we will solve it a little differently. Due to

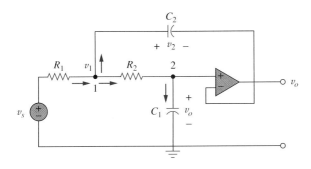

Figure 8.33   For Example 8.11.

the voltage follower configuration, the voltage across C_1 is v_o. Applying KCL at node 1,

$$\frac{v_s - v_1}{R_1} = C_2 \frac{dv_2}{dt} + \frac{v_1 - v_o}{R_2} \tag{8.11.1}$$

At node 2, KCL gives

$$\frac{v_1 - v_o}{R_2} = C_1 \frac{dv_o}{dt} \tag{8.11.2}$$

But

$$v_2 = v_1 - v_o \tag{8.11.3}$$

We now try to eliminate v_1 and v_2 in Eqs. (8.11.1) to (8.11.3). Substituting Eqs. (8.11.2) and (8.11.3) into Eq. (8.11.1) yields

$$\frac{v_s - v_1}{R_1} = C_2 \frac{dv_1}{dt} - C_2 \frac{dv_o}{dt} + C_1 \frac{dv_o}{dt} \tag{8.11.4}$$

From Eq. (8.11.2),

$$v_1 = v_o + R_2 C_1 \frac{dv_o}{dt} \tag{8.11.5}$$

Substituting Eq. (8.11.5) into Eq. (8.11.4), we obtain

$$\frac{v_s}{R_1} = \frac{v_o}{R_1} + \frac{R_2 C_1}{R_1} \frac{dv_o}{dt} + C_2 \frac{dv_o}{dt} + R_2 C_1 C_2 \frac{d^2 v_o}{dt^2} - C_2 \frac{dv_o}{dt} + C_1 \frac{dv_o}{dt}$$

or

$$\frac{d^2 v_o}{dt^2} + \left(\frac{1}{R_1 C_2} + \frac{1}{R_2 C_2} \right) \frac{dv_o}{dt} + \frac{v_o}{R_1 R_2 C_1 C_2} = \frac{v_s}{R_1 R_2 C_1 C_2} \tag{8.11.6}$$

With the given values of R_1, R_2, C_1, and C_2, Eq. (8.11.6) becomes

$$\frac{d^2 v_o}{dt^2} + 2 \frac{dv_o}{dt} + 5 v_o = 5 v_s \tag{8.11.7}$$

To obtain the natural response, set $v_s = 0$ in Eq. (8.11.7), which is the same as turning off the source. The characteristic equation is

$$s^2 + 2s + 5 = 0$$

which has complex roots $s_{1,2} = -1 \pm j2$. Hence, the natural response is

$$v_{on} = e^{-t}(A \cos 2t + B \sin 2t) \tag{8.11.8}$$

where A and B are unknown constants to be determined.

As $t \rightarrow \infty$, the circuit reaches the steady-state condition, and the capacitors can be replaced by open circuits. Since no current flows through C_1 and C_2 under steady-state conditions and no current can enter the input terminals of the ideal op amp, current does not flow through R_1 and R_2.

Thus,

$$v_o(\infty) = v_1(\infty) = v_s$$

The forced response is then

$$v_{of} = v_o(\infty) = v_s = 10 \text{ mV}, \qquad t > 0 \qquad (8.11.9)$$

The complete response is

$$v_o(t) = v_{on} + v_{of} = 10 + e^{-t}(A \cos 2t + B \sin 2t) \text{ mV} \qquad (8.11.10)$$

To determine A and B, we need the initial conditions. For $t < 0$, $v_s = 0$, so that

$$v_o(0^-) = v_2(0^-) = 0$$

For $t > 0$, the source is operative. However, due to capacitor voltage continuity,

$$v_o(0^+) = v_2(0^+) = 0 \qquad (8.11.11)$$

From Eq. (8.11.3),

$$v_1(0^+) = v_2(0^+) + v_o(0^+) = 0$$

and hence, from Eq. (8.11.2),

$$\frac{dv_o(0^+)}{dt} = \frac{v_1 - v_o}{R_2 C_1} = 0 \qquad (8.11.12)$$

We now impose Eq. (8.11.11) on the complete response in Eq. (8.11.10) at $t = 0$, for

$$0 = 10 + A \qquad \Longrightarrow \qquad A = -10 \qquad (8.11.13)$$

Taking the derivative of Eq. (8.11.10),

$$\frac{dv_o}{dt} = e^{-t}(-A \cos 2t - B \sin 2t - 2A \sin 2t + 2B \cos 2t)$$

Setting $t = 0$ and incorporating Eq. (8.11.12), we obtain

$$0 = -A + 2B \qquad (8.11.14)$$

From Eqs. (8.11.13) and (8.11.14), $A = -10$ and $B = -5$. Thus the step response becomes

$$v_o(t) = 10 - e^{-t}(10 \cos 2t + 5 \sin 2t) \text{ mV}, \qquad t > 0$$

PRACTICE PROBLEM 8.11

In the op amp circuit shown in Fig. 8.34, $v_s = 4u(t)$ V, find $v_o(t)$ for $t > 0$. Assume that $R_1 = R_2 = 10 \text{ k}\Omega$, $C_1 = 20 \text{ }\mu\text{F}$, and $C_2 = 100 \text{ }\mu\text{F}$.

Answer: $4 - 5e^{-t} + e^{-5t}$ V, $t > 0$.

Figure 8.34   For Practice Prob. 8.11.

8.9   PSPICE ANALYSIS OF RLC CIRCUITS

RLC circuits can be analyzed with great ease using *PSpice*, just like the *RC* or *RL* circuits of Chapter 7. The following two examples will illustrate this. The reader may review Section D.4 in Appendix D on *PSpice* for transient analysis.

EXAMPLE 8.12

(a)

(b)

Figure 8.35   For Example 8.12.

The input voltage in Fig. 8.35(a) is applied to the circuit in Fig. 8.35(b). Use *PSpice* to plot $v(t)$ for $0 < t < 4$s.

Solution:

The given circuit is drawn using Schematics as in Fig. 8.36. The pulse is specified using VPWL voltage source, but VPULSE could be used instead. Using the piecewise linear function, we set the attributes of VPWL as T1 = 0, V1 = 0, T2 = 0.001, V2 = 12, and so forth, as shown in Fig. 8.36. Two voltage markers are inserted to plot the input and output voltages. Once the circuit is drawn and the attributes are set, we select **Analysis/Setup/Transient** to open up the *Transient Analysis* dialog box. As a parallel RLC circuit, the roots of the characteristic equation are −1 and −9. Thus, we may set *Final Time* as 4 s (four times the magnitude of the lower root). When the schematic is saved, we select **Analysis/Simulate** and obtain the plots for the input and output voltages under the *PSpice* A/D window as shown in Fig. 8.37.

Figure 8.36   Schematic for the circuit in Fig. 8.35(b).

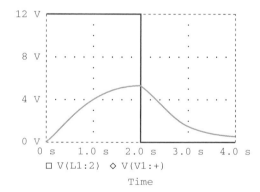

Figure 8.37   For Example 8.12: the input and output voltages.

PRACTICE PROBLEM 8.12

Find $i(t)$ using *PSpice* for $0 < t < 4$ s if the pulse voltage in Fig. 8.35(a) is applied to the circuit in Fig. 8.38.

Answer: See Fig. 8.39.

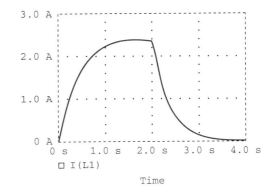

Figure 8.38   For Practice Prob. 8.12.

Figure 8.39   Plot of $i(t)$ for Practice Prob. 8.12.

EXAMPLE 8.13

For the circuit in Fig. 8.40, use *PSpice* to obtain $i(t)$ for $0 < t < 3$ s.

Figure 8.40   For Example 8.13.

Solution:

When the switch is in position a, the 6-Ω resistor is redundant. The schematic for this case is shown in Fig. 8.41(a). To ensure that current $i(t)$ enters pin 1, the inductor is rotated three times before it is placed in the circuit. The same applies for the capacitor. We insert pseudocomponents

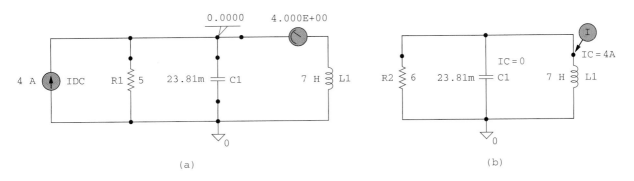

Figure 8.41   For Example 8.13: (a) for dc analysis, (b) for transient analysis.

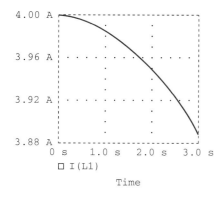

Figure 8.42   Plot of $i(t)$ for Example 8.13.

VIEWPOINT and IPROBE to determine the initial capacitor voltage and initial inductor current. We carry out a dc *PSpice* analysis by selecting **Analysis/Simulate**. As shown in Fig. 8.41(a), we obtain the initial capacitor voltage as 0 V and the initial inductor current $i(0)$ as 4 A from the dc analysis. These initial values will be used in the transient analysis.

When the switch is moved to position b, the circuit becomes a source-free parallel RLC circuit with the schematic in Fig. 8.41(b). We set the initial condition IC = 0 for the capacitor and IC = 4 A for the inductor. A current marker is inserted at pin 1 of the inductor. We select **Analysis/Setup/Transient** to open up the *Transient Analysis* dialog box and set *Final Time* to 3 s. After saving the schematic, we select **Analysis/Transient**. Figure 8.42 shows the plot of $i(t)$. The plot agrees with $i(t) = 4.8e^{-t} - 0.8e^{-6t}$ A, which is the solution by hand calculation.

PRACTICE PROBLEM 8.13

Refer to the circuit in Fig. 8.21 (see Practice Prob. 8.7). Use *PSpice* to obtain $v(t)$ for $0 < t < 2$.

Answer: See Fig. 8.43.

Figure 8.43   Plot of $v(t)$ for Practice Prob. 8.13.

†8.10 DUALITY

The concept of duality is a time-saving, effort-effective measure of solving circuit problems. Consider the similarity between Eq. (8.4) and Eq. (8.29). The two equations are the same, except that we must interchange the following quantities: (1) voltage and current, (2) resistance and conductance, (3) capacitance and inductance. Thus, it sometimes occurs in circuit analysis that two different circuits have the same equations and solutions, except that the roles of certain complementary elements are interchanged. This interchangeability is known as the principle of *duality*.

The duality principle asserts a parallelism between pairs of characterizing equations and theorems of electric circuits.

Dual pairs are shown in Table 8.1. Note that power does not appear in Table 8.1, because power has no dual. The reason for this is the principle of linearity; since power is not linear, duality does not apply. Also notice from Table 8.1 that the principle of duality extends to circuit elements, configurations, and theorems.

Two circuits that are described by equations of the same form, but in which the variables are interchanged, are said to be dual to each other.

Two circuits are said to be duals of one another if they are described by the same characterizing equations with dual quantities interchanged.

TABLE 8.1	Dual pairs.
Resistance R	Conductance G
Inductance L	Capacitance C
Voltage v	Current i
Voltage source	Current source
Node	Mesh
Series path	Parallel path
Open circuit	Short circuit
KVL	KCL
Thevenin	Norton

Even when the principle of linearity applies, a circuit element or variable may not have a dual. For example, mutual inductance (to be covered in Chapter 13) has no dual.

The usefulness of the duality principle is self-evident. Once we know the solution to one circuit, we automatically have the solution for the dual circuit. It is obvious that the circuits in Figs. 8.8 and 8.13 are dual. Consequently, the result in Eq. (8.32) is the dual of that in Eq. (8.11). We must keep in mind that the principle of duality is limited to planar circuits. Nonplanar circuits have no duals, as they cannot be described by a system of mesh equations.

To find the dual of a given circuit, we do not need to write down the mesh or node equations. We can use a graphical technique. Given a planar circuit, we construct the dual circuit by taking the following three steps:

1. Place a node at the center of each mesh of the given circuit. Place the reference node (the ground) of the dual circuit outside the given circuit.

2. Draw lines between the nodes such that each line crosses an element. Replace that element by its dual (see Table 8.1).

3. To determine the polarity of voltage sources and direction of current sources, follow this rule: A voltage source that produces a positive (clockwise) mesh current has as its dual a current source whose reference direction is from the ground to the nonreference node.

In case of doubt, one may verify the dual circuit by writing the nodal or mesh equations. The mesh (or nodal) equations of the original circuit are similar to the nodal (or mesh) equations of the dual circuit. The duality principle is illustrated with the following two examples.

EXAMPLE 8.14

Construct the dual of the circuit in Fig. 8.44.

Figure 8.44   For Example 8.14.

Solution:

As shown in Fig. 8.45(a), we first locate nodes 1 and 2 in the two meshes and also the ground node 0 for the dual circuit. We draw a line between one node and another crossing an element. We replace the line joining the nodes by the duals of the elements which it crosses. For example, a line between nodes 1 and 2 crosses a 2-H inductor, and we place a 2-F capacitor (an inductor's dual) on the line. A line between nodes 1 and 0 crossing the 6-V voltage source will contain a 6-A current source. By drawing lines crossing all the elements, we construct the dual circuit on the given circuit as in Fig. 8.45(a). The dual circuit is redrawn in Fig. 8.45(b) for clarity.

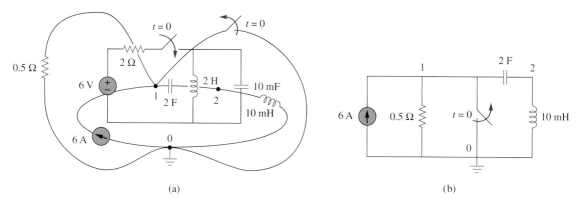

(a)   (b)

Figure 8.45   (a) Construction of the dual circuit of Fig. 8.44, (b) dual circuit redrawn.

PRACTICE PROBLEM 8.14

Draw the dual circuit of the one in Fig. 8.46.

Answer: See Fig. 8.47.

Figure 8.46   For Practice Prob. 8.14.

Figure 8.47   Dual of the circuit in Fig. 8.46.

EXAMPLE 8.15

Obtain the dual of the circuit in Fig. 8.48.

Solution:

The dual circuit is constructed on the original circuit as in Fig. 8.49(a). We first locate nodes 1 to 3 and the reference node 0. Joining nodes 1 and 2, we cross the 2-F capacitor, which is replaced by a 2-H inductor.

Figure 8.48   For Example 8.15.

Joining nodes 2 and 3, we cross the 20-Ω resistor, which is replaced by a 1/20-Ω resistor. We keep doing this until all the elements are crossed. The result is in Fig. 8.49(a). The dual circuit is redrawn in Fig. 8.49(b).

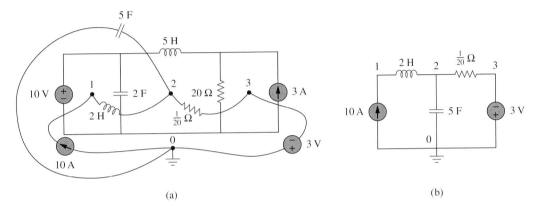

Figure 8.49   For Example 8.15: (a) construction of the dual circuit of Fig. 8.48, (b) dual circuit redrawn.

To verify the polarity of the voltage source and the direction of the current source, we may apply mesh currents i_1, i_2, and i_3 (all in the clockwise direction) in the original circuit in Fig. 8.48. The 10-V voltage source produces positive mesh current i_1, so that its dual is a 10-A current source directed from 0 to 1. Also, $i_3 = -3$ A in Fig. 8.48 has as its dual $v_3 = -3$ V in Fig. 8.49(b).

PRACTICE PROBLEM 8.15

For the circuit in Fig. 8.50, obtain the dual circuit.

Answer: See Fig. 8.51.

Figure 8.50   For Practice Prob. 8.15.

Figure 8.51   Dual of the circuit in Fig. 8.50.

†8.11 APPLICATIONS

Practical applications of RLC circuits are found in control and communications circuits such as ringing circuits, peaking circuits, resonant circuits, smoothing circuits, and filters. Most of these circuits cannot be covered until we treat ac sources. For now, we will limit ourselves to two simple applications: automobile ignition and smoothing circuits.

8.11.1 Automobile Ignition System

In Section 7.9.4, we considered the automobile ignition system as a charging system. That was only a part of the system. Here, we consider another part—the voltage generating system. The system is modeled by the circuit shown in Fig. 8.52. The 12-V source is due to the battery and alternator. The 4-Ω resistor represents the resistance of the wiring. The ignition coil is modeled by the 8-mH inductor. The 1-μF capacitor (known as the *condenser* to automechanics) is in parallel with the switch (known as the *breaking points* or *electronic ignition*). In the following example, we determine how the RLC circuit in Fig. 8.52 is used in generating high voltage.

Figure 8.52   Automobile ignition circuit.

EXAMPLE 8.16

Assuming that the switch in Fig. 8.52 is closed prior to $t = 0^-$, find the inductor voltage v_L for $t > 0$.

Solution:

If the switch is closed prior to $t = 0^-$ and the circuit is in steady state, then

$$i(0^-) = \frac{12}{4} = 3 \text{ A}, \qquad v_C(0^-) = 0$$

At $t = 0^+$, the switch is opened. The continuity conditions require that

$$i(0^+) = 3 \text{ A}, \qquad v_C(0^+) = 0 \qquad\qquad (8.16.1)$$

We obtain $di(0^+)/dt$ from $v_L(0^+)$. Applying KVL to the mesh at $t = 0^+$ yields

$$-12 + 4i(0^+) + v_L(0^+) + v_C(0^+) = 0$$
$$-12 + 4 \times 3 + v_L(0^+) + 0 = 0 \qquad \Longrightarrow \qquad v_L(0^+) = 0$$

Hence,

$$\frac{di(0^+)}{dt} = \frac{v_L(0^+)}{L} = 0 \qquad (8.16.2)$$

As $t \to \infty$, the system reaches steady state, so that the capacitor acts like an open circuit. Then

$$i(\infty) = 0 \qquad (8.16.3)$$

If we apply KVL to the mesh for $t > 0$, we obtain

$$12 = Ri + L\frac{di}{dt} + \frac{1}{C}\int_0^t i\,dt + v_C(0)$$

Taking the derivative of each term yields

$$\frac{d^2i}{dt^2} + \frac{R}{L}\frac{di}{dt} + \frac{i}{LC} = 0 \qquad (8.16.4)$$

We obtain the natural response by following the procedure in Section 8.3. Substituting $R = 4\ \Omega$, $L = 8$ mH, and $C = 1\ \mu$F, we get

$$\alpha = \frac{R}{2L} = 250, \qquad \omega_0 = \frac{1}{\sqrt{LC}} = 1.118 \times 10^4$$

Since $\alpha < \omega_0$, the response is underdamped. The damped natural frequency is

$$\omega_d = \sqrt{\omega_0^2 - \alpha^2} \simeq \omega_0 = 1.118 \times 10^4$$

The natural response is

$$i_n(t) = e^{-\alpha}(A\cos\omega_d t + B\sin\omega_d t) \qquad (8.16.5)$$

where A and B are constants. The forced response is

$$i_f(t) = i(\infty) = 0 \qquad (8.16.6)$$

so that the complete response is

$$i(t) = i_n(t) + i_f(t) = e^{-250t}(A\cos 11,180t + B\sin 11,180t) \qquad (8.16.7)$$

We now determine A and B.

$$i(0) = 3 = A + 0 \qquad \Longrightarrow \qquad A = 3$$

Taking the derivative of Eq. (8.16.7),

$$\frac{di}{dt} = -250e^{-250t}(A\cos 11,180t + B\sin 11,180t)$$

$$+ e^{-250t}(-11,180A\sin 11,180t + 11,180B\cos 11,180t)$$

Setting $t = 0$ and incorporating Eq. (8.16.2),

$$0 = -250A + 11,180B \qquad \Longrightarrow \qquad B = 0.0671$$

Thus

$$i(t) = e^{-250t}(3\cos 11,180t + 0.0671\sin 11,180t) \qquad (8.16.8)$$

The voltage across the inductor is then

$$v_L(t) = L\frac{di}{dt} = -268e^{-250t}\sin 11,180t \qquad (8.16.9)$$

This has a maximum value when sine is unity, that is, at $11,180t_0 = \pi/2$ or $t_0 = 140.5\ \mu s$. At time $= t_0$, the inductor voltage reaches its peak, which is

$$v_L(t_0) = -268e^{-250t_0} = -259\ V \qquad (8.16.10)$$

Although this is far less than the voltage range of 6000 to 10,000 V required to fire the spark plug in a typical automobile, a device known as a *transformer* (to be discussed in Chapter 13) is used to step up the inductor voltage to the required level.

PRACTICE PROBLEM 8.16

In Fig. 8.52, find the capacitor voltage v_C for $t > 0$.

Answer: $12 - 12e^{-250t}\cos 11,180t + 267.7e^{-250t}\sin 11,180t$ V.

8.11.2 Smoothing Circuits

In a typical digital communication system, the signal to be transmitted is first sampled. Sampling refers to the procedure of selecting samples of a signal for processing, as opposed to processing the entire signal. Each sample is converted into a binary number represented by a series of pulses. The pulses are transmitted by a transmission line such as a coaxial cable, twisted pair, or optical fiber. At the receiving end, the signal is applied to a digital-to-analog (D/A) converter whose output is a "staircase" function, that is, constant at each time interval. In order to recover the transmitted analog signal, the output is smoothed by letting it pass through a "smoothing" circuit, as illustrated in Fig. 8.53. An RLC circuit may be used as the smoothing circuit.

Figure 8.53   A series of pulses is applied to the digital-to-analog (D/A) converter, whose output is applied to the smoothing circuit.

EXAMPLE 8.17

The output of a D/A converter is shown in Fig. 8.54(a). If the RLC circuit in Fig. 8.54(b) is used as the smoothing circuit, determine the output voltage $v_o(t)$.

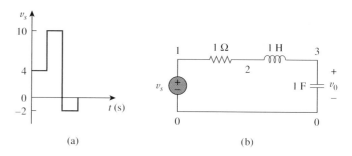

(a)   (b)

Figure 8.54   For Example 8.17: (a) output of a D/A converter, (b) an RLC smoothing circuit.

Solution:

This problem is best solved using *PSpice*. The schematic is shown in Fig. 8.55(a). The pulse in Fig. 8.54(a) is specified using the piecewise linear function. The attributes of V1 are set as T1 = 0, V1 = 0, T2 = 0.001, V2 = 4, T3 = 1, V3 = 4, and so on. To be able to plot both input and output voltages, we insert two voltage markers as shown. We select **Analysis/Setup/Transient** to open up the *Transient Analysis* dialog box and set *Final Time* as 6 s. Once the schematic is saved, we select **Analysis/Simulate** to run and obtain the plots shown in Fig. 8.55(b).

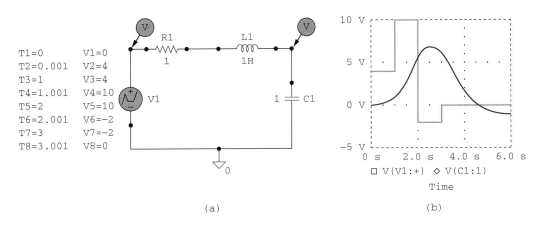

(a)   (b)

Figure 8.55   For Example 8.17: (a) schematic, (b) input and output voltages.

PRACTICE PROBLEM 8.17

Rework Example 8.17 if the output of the D/A converter is as shown in Fig. 8.56.

Answer: See Fig. 8.57.

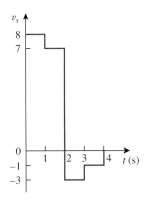

Figure 8.56   For Practice Prob. 8.17.

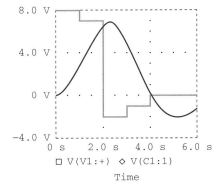

Figure 8.57   Result of Practice Prob. 8.17.

8.12 SUMMARY

1. The determination of the initial values $x(0)$ and $dx(0)/dt$ and final value $x(\infty)$ is crucial to analyzing second-order circuits.

2. The RLC circuit is second-order because it is described by a second-order differential equation. Its characteristic equation is $s^2 + 2\alpha s + \omega_0^2 = 0$, where α is the damping factor and ω_0 is the undamped natural frequency. For a series circuit, $\alpha = R/2L$, for a parallel circuit $\alpha = 1/2RC$, and for both cases $\omega_0 = 1/\sqrt{LC}$.

3. If there are no independent sources in the circuit after switching (or sudden change), we regard the circuit as source-free. The complete solution is the natural response.

4. The natural response of an RLC circuit is overdamped, under-damped, or critically damped, depending on the roots of the characteristic equation. The response is critically damped when the roots are equal ($s_1 = s_2$ or $\alpha = \omega_0$), overdamped when the roots are real and unequal ($s_1 \neq s_2$ or $\alpha > \omega_0$), or underdamped when the roots are complex conjugate ($s_1 = s_2^*$ or $\alpha < \omega_0$).

5. If independent sources are present in the circuit after switching, the complete response is the sum of the transient response and the steady-state response.

6. *PSpice* is used to analyze RLC circuits in the same way as for RC or RL circuits.

7. Two circuits are dual if the mesh equations that describe one circuit have the same form as the nodal equations that describe the other. The analysis of one circuit gives the analysis of its dual circuit.

8. The automobile ignition circuit and the smoothing circuit are typical applications of the material covered in this chapter.

REVIEW QUESTIONS

8.1 For the circuit in Fig. 8.58, the capacitor voltage at $t = 0^-$ (just before the switch is closed) is:

(a) 0 V   (b) 4 V   (c) 8 V   (d) 12 V

Figure 8.58   For Review Questions 8.1 and 8.2.

8.2 For the circuit in Fig. 8.58, the initial inductor current (at $t = 0$) is:

(a) 0 A   (b) 2 A   (c) 6 A   (d) 12 A

8.3 When a step input is applied to a second-order circuit, the final values of the circuit variables are found by:

(a) Replacing capacitors with closed circuits and inductors with open circuits.

(b) Replacing capacitors with open circuits and inductors with closed circuits.

(c) Doing neither of the above.

8.4 If the roots of the characteristic equation of an RLC circuit are -2 and -3, the response is:

(a) $(A \cos 2t + B \sin 2t)e^{-3t}$

(b) $(A + 2Bt)e^{-3t}$

(c) $Ae^{-2t} + Bte^{-3t}$

(d) $Ae^{-2t} + Be^{-3t}$

where A and B are constants.

8.5 In a series RLC circuit, setting $R = 0$ will produce:

(a) an overdamped response
(b) a critically damped response
(c) an underdamped response
(d) an undamped response
(e) none of the above

8.6 A parallel RLC circuit has $L = 2$ H and $C = 0.25$ F. The value of R that will produce unity damping factor is:

(a) 0.5 Ω   (b) 1 Ω   (c) 2 Ω   (d) 4 Ω

8.7 Refer to the series RLC circuit in Fig. 8.59. What kind of response will it produce?

(a) overdamped
(b) underdamped
(c) critically damped
(d) none of the above

Figure 8.59   For Review Question 8.7.

8.8 Consider the parallel RLC circuit in Fig. 8.60. What type of response will it produce?

(a) overdamped
(b) underdamped
(c) critically damped
(d) none of the above

Figure 8.60   For Review Question 8.8.

8.9 Match the circuits in Fig. 8.61 with the following items:

(i) first-order circuit
(ii) second-order series circuit
(iii) second-order parallel circuit
(iv) none of the above

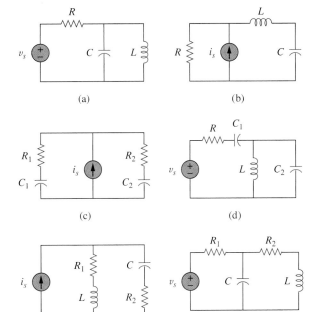

Figure 8.61   For Review Question 8.9.

8.10 In an electric circuit, the dual of resistance is:

(a) conductance   (b) inductance
(c) capacitance   (d) open circuit
(e) short circuit

Answers: 8.1a, 8.2c, 8.3b, 8.4d, 8.5d, 8.6c, 8.7b, 8.8b, 8.9 (i)-c, (ii)-b, e, (iii)-a, (iv)-d, f, 8.10a.

PROBLEMS

Section 8.2   Finding Initial and Final Values

8.1 For the circuit in Fig. 8.62, find:

(a) $i(0^+)$ and $v(0^+)$,
(b) $di(0^+)/dt$ and $dv(0^+)/dt$,
(c) $i(\infty)$ and $v(\infty)$.

Figure 8.62   For Prob. 8.1.

8.2   In the circuit of Fig. 8.63, determine:

(a) $i_R(0^+)$, $i_L(0^+)$, and $i_C(0^+)$,

(b) $di_R(0^+)/dt$, $di_L(0^+)/dt$, and $di_C(0^+)/dt$,

(c) $i_R(\infty)$, $i_L(\infty)$, and $i_C(\infty)$.

Figure 8.63   For Prob. 8.2.

8.3   Refer to the circuit shown in Fig. 8.64. Calculate:

(a) $i_L(0^+)$, $v_C(0^+)$, and $v_R(0^+)$,

(b) $di_L(0^+)/dt$, $dv_C(0^+)/dt$, and $dv_R(0^+)/dt$,

(c) $i_L(\infty)$, $v_C(\infty)$, and $v_R(\infty)$.

Figure 8.64   For Prob. 8.3.

8.4   In the circuit of Fig. 8.65, find:

(a) $v(0^+)$ and $i(0^+)$,

(b) $dv(0^+)/dt$ and $di(0^+)/dt$,

(c) $v(\infty)$ and $i(\infty)$.

Figure 8.65   For Prob. 8.4.

8.5   Refer to the circuit in Fig. 8.66. Determine:

(a) $i(0^+)$ and $v(0^+)$,

(b) $di(0^+)/dt$ and $dv(0^+)/dt$,

(c) $i(\infty)$ and $v(\infty)$.

Figure 8.66   For Prob. 8.5.

8.6   In the circuit of Fig. 8.67, find:

(a) $v_R(0^+)$ and $v_L(0^+)$,

(b) $dv_R(0^+)/dt$ and $dv_L(0^+)/dt$,

(c) $v_R(\infty)$ and $v_L(\infty)$.

Figure 8.67   For Prob. 8.6.

Section 8.3   Source-Free Series *RLC* Circuit

8.7   The voltage in an *RLC* network is described by the differential equation

$$\frac{d^2v}{dt^2} + 4\frac{dv}{dt} + 4v = 0$$

subject to the initial conditions $v(0) = 1$ and $dv(0)/dt = -1$. Determine the characteristic equation. Find $v(t)$ for $t > 0$.

8.8   The branch current in an *RLC* circuit is described by the differential equation

$$\frac{d^2i}{dt^2} + 6\frac{di}{dt} + 9i = 0$$

and the initial conditions are $i(0) = 0$, $di(0)/dt = 4$. Obtain the characteristic equation and determine $i(t)$ for $t > 0$.

8.9   The current in an *RLC* circuit is described by

$$\frac{d^2i}{dt^2} + 10\frac{di}{dt} + 25i = 0$$

If $i(0) = 10$ and $di(0)/dt = 0$, find $i(t)$ for $t > 0$.

8.10   The differential equation that describes the voltage in an *RLC* network is

$$\frac{d^2v}{dt^2} + 5\frac{dv}{dt} + 4v = 0$$

Given that $v(0) = 0$, $dv(0)/dt = 10$, obtain $v(t)$.

8.11   The natural response of an RLC circuit is described by the differential equation

$$\frac{d^2v}{dt^2} + 2\frac{dv}{dt} + v = 0$$

for which the initial conditions are $v(0) = 10$ and $dv(0)/dt = 0$. Solve for $v(t)$.

8.12   If $R = 20\ \Omega$, $L = 0.6$ H, what value of C will make an RLC series circuit:

(a) overdamped,   (b) critically damped,
(c) underdamped?

8.13   For the circuit in Fig. 8.68, calculate the value of R needed to have a critically damped response.

60 Ω

R 0.01 F   4 H

Figure 8.68   For Prob. 8.13.

8.14   Find $v(t)$ for $t > 0$ if $v(0) = 6$ V and $i(0) = 2$ A in the circuit shown in Fig. 8.69.

$i(t)$ 0.02 F

60 Ω   30 Ω   2 H $v(t)$

Figure 8.69   For Prob. 8.14.

8.15   The responses of a series RLC circuit are

$$v_C(t) = 30 - 10e^{-20t} + 30e^{-10t}\ \text{V}$$
$$i_L(t) = 40e^{-20t} - 60e^{-10t}\ \text{mA}$$

where v_C and i_L are the capacitor voltage and inductor current, respectively. Determine the values of R, L, and C.

8.16   Find $i(t)$ for $t > 0$ in the circuit of Fig. 8.70.

Figure 8.70   For Prob. 8.16.

8.17   In the circuit of Fig. 8.71, the switch instantaneously moves from position A to B at $t = 0$. Find $v(t)$ for all $t \geq 0$.

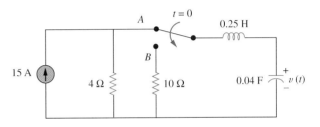

Figure 8.71   For Prob. 8.17.

8.18   Find the voltage across the capacitor as a function of time for $t > 0$ for the circuit in Fig. 8.72. Assume steady-state conditions exist at $t = 0^-$.

Figure 8.72   For Prob. 8.18.

8.19   Obtain $v(t)$ for $t > 0$ in the circuit of Fig. 8.73.

Figure 8.73   For Prob. 8.19.

8.20 The switch in the circuit of Fig. 8.74 has been closed for a long time but is opened at $t = 0$. Determine $i(t)$ for $t > 0$.

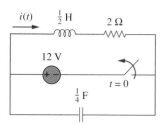

Figure 8.74 For Prob. 8.20.

*__8.21__ Calculate $v(t)$ for $t > 0$ in the circuit of Fig. 8.75.

Figure 8.75 For Prob. 8.21.

Section 8.4 Source-Free Parallel *RLC* Circuit

8.22 For a parallel RLC circuit, the responses are

$$v_L(t) = 4e^{-20t} \cos 50t - 10e^{-20t} \sin 50t \text{ V}$$

$$i_C(t) = -6.5e^{-20t} \cos 50t \text{ mA}$$

where i_C and v_L are the capacitor current and inductor voltage, respectively. Determine the values of R, L, and C.

8.23 For the network in Fig. 8.76, what value of C is needed to make the response underdamped with unity damping factor ($\alpha = 1$)?

Figure 8.76 For Prob. 8.23.

8.24 Find $v(t)$ for $t > 0$ in the circuit in Fig. 8.77.

Figure 8.77 For Prob. 8.24.

8.25 In the circuit in Fig. 8.78, calculate $i_o(t)$ and $v_o(t)$ for $t > 0$.

Figure 8.78 For Prob. 8.25.

Section 8.5 Step Response of a Series *RLC* Circuit

8.26 The step response of an RLC circuit is given by

$$\frac{d^2i}{dt^2} + 2\frac{di}{dt} + 5i = 10$$

Given that $i(0) = 2$ and $di(0)/dt = 4$, solve for $i(t)$.

8.27 A branch voltage in an RLC circuit is described by

$$\frac{d^2v}{dt^2} + 4\frac{dv}{dt} + 8v = 24$$

If the initial conditions are $v(0) = 0 = dv(0)/dt$, find $v(t)$.

8.28 The current in a second-order circuit is governed by the differential equation

$$\frac{d^2i}{dt^2} + 6\frac{di}{dt} + 8i = 12$$

subject to $i(0) = 0$, $di(0)/dt = 2$ A/s. Determine $i(t)$.

8.29 Solve the following differential equations subject to the specified initial conditions

(a) $d^2v/dt^2 + 4v = 12$, $v(0) = 0$, $dv(0)/dt = 2$

(b) $d^2i/dt^2 + 5\,di/dt + 4i = 8$, $i(0) = -1$, $di(0)/dt = 0$

(c) $d^2v/dt^2 + 2\,dv/dt + v = 3$, $v(0) = 5$, $dv(0)/dt = 1$

(d) $d^2i/dt^2 + 2\,di/dt + 5i = 10$, $i(0) = 4$, $di(0)/dt = -2$

---

*An asterisk indicates a challenging problem.

8.30   The natural response of a series *RLC* circuit is

$$i(t) = 10e^{-500t} + 12e^{-800t} \quad \text{mA}, \qquad t \geq 0.$$

If $R = 200 \, \Omega$, find L and C.

8.31   Consider the circuit in Fig. 8.79. Find $v_L(0)$ and $v_C(0)$.

Figure 8.79   For Prob. 8.31.

8.32   For the circuit in Fig. 8.80, find $v(t)$ for $t > 0$.

Figure 8.80   For Prob. 8.32.

8.33   Find $v(t)$ for $t > 0$ in the circuit in Fig. 8.81.

Figure 8.81   For Prob. 8.33.

8.34   Calculate $i(t)$ for $t > 0$ in the circuit in Fig. 8.82.

Figure 8.82   For Prob. 8.34.

8.35   Determine $v(t)$ for $t > 0$ in the circuit in Fig. 8.83.

Figure 8.83   For Prob. 8.35.

8.36   Obtain $v(t)$ and $i(t)$ for $t > 0$ in the circuit in Fig. 8.84.

Figure 8.84   For Prob. 8.36.

*8.37   For the network in Fig. 8.85, solve for $i(t)$ for $t > 0$.

Figure 8.85   For Prob. 8.37.

8.38   Refer to the circuit in Fig. 8.86. Calculate $i(t)$ for $t > 0$.

Figure 8.86   For Prob. 8.38.

8.39   Determine $v(t)$ for $t > 0$ in the circuit in Fig. 8.87.

Figure 8.87   For Prob. 8.39.

8.40   The switch in the circuit of Fig. 8.88 is moved from position a to b at $t = 0$. Determine $i(t)$ for $t > 0$.

Figure 8.88   For Prob. 8.40.

*8.41   For the network in Fig. 8.89, find $i(t)$ for $t > 0$.

Figure 8.89   For Prob. 8.41.

*8.42   Given the network in Fig. 8.90, find $v(t)$ for $t > 0$.

Figure 8.90   For Prob. 8.42.

8.43   The switch in Fig. 8.91 is opened at $t = 0$ after the circuit has reached steady state. Choose R and C such that $\alpha = 8$ Np/s and $\omega_d = 30$ rad/s.

Figure 8.91   For Prob. 8.43.

8.44   A series RLC circuit has the following parameters: $R = 1$ kΩ, $L = 1$ H, and $C = 10$ nF. What type of damping does this circuit exhibit?

Section 8.6   Step Response of a Parallel RLC Circuit

8.45   In the circuit of Fig. 8.92, find $v(t)$ and $i(t)$ for $t > 0$. Assume $v(0) = 0$ V and $i(0) = 1$ A.

Figure 8.92   For Prob. 8.45.

8.46   Find $i(t)$ for $t > 0$ in the circuit in Fig. 8.93.

Figure 8.93   For Prob. 8.46.

8.47   Find the output voltage $v_o(t)$ in the circuit of Fig. 8.94.

Figure 8.94   For Prob. 8.47.

8.48 Given the circuit in Fig. 8.95, find $i(t)$ and $v(t)$ for $t > 0$.

Figure 8.95   For Prob. 8.48.

8.49 Determine $i(t)$ for $t > 0$ in the circuit of Fig. 8.96.

Figure 8.96   For Prob. 8.49.

8.50 For the circuit in Fig. 8.97, find $i(t)$ for $t > 0$.

Figure 8.97   For Prob. 8.50.

8.51 Find $v(t)$ for $t > 0$ in the circuit in Fig. 8.98.

Figure 8.98   For Prob. 8.51.

8.52 The step response of a parallel RLC circuit is

$$v = 10 + 20e^{-300t}(\cos 400t - 2 \sin 400t) \text{ V}, \quad t \geq 0$$

when the inductor is 50 mH. Find R and C.

Section 8.7   General Second-Order Circuits

8.53 Derive the second-order differential equation for v_o in the circuit of Fig. 8.99.

Figure 8.99   For Prob. 8.53.

8.54 For the circuit of Fig. 8.100, let $v(0) = 2$ V and $dv(0)/dt = 0$. Find $v(t)$ for $t \geq 0$.

Figure 8.100   For Prob. 8.54.

8.55 For the circuit in Fig. 8.101, find $v(t)$ for $t > 0$. Assume that $v(0^+) = 4$ V and $i(0^+) = 2$ A.

Figure 8.101   For Prob. 8.55.

8.56 In the circuit of Fig. 8.102, find $i(t)$ for $t > 0$.

Figure 8.102   For Prob. 8.56.

8.57 If the switch in Fig. 8.103 has been closed for a long time before $t = 0$ but is opened at $t = 0$, determine:

(a) the characteristic equation of the circuit,

(b) i_x and v_R for $t > 0$.

Figure 8.103   For Prob. 8.57.

8.58 In the circuit of Fig. 8.104, the switch has been in position 1 for a long time but moved to position 2 at $t = 0$. Find:

(a) $v(0^+)$, $dv(0^+)/dt$

(b) $v(t)$ for $t \geq 0$.

Figure 8.104   For Prob. 8.58.

8.59 The switch in Fig. 8.105 has been in position 1 for $t < 0$. At $t = 0$, it is moved instantaneously to position 2. Determine $v(t)$.

Figure 8.105   For Prob. 8.59.

8.60 Obtain i_1 and i_2 for $t > 0$ in the circuit of Fig. 8.106.

Figure 8.106   For Prob. 8.60.

8.61 For the circuit in Prob. 8.5, find i and v for $t > 0$.

8.62 Find the response $v_R(t)$ for $t > 0$ in the circuit in Fig. 8.107. Let $R = 3\ \Omega$, $L = 2$ H, and $C = 1/18$ F.

Figure 8.107   For Prob. 8.62.

Section 8.8   Second-Order Op Amp Circuits

8.63 Derive the differential equation relating v_o to v_s in the second-order op amp circuit of Fig. 8.108.

Figure 8.108   For Prob. 8.63.

8.64 Obtain the differential equation for $v_o(t)$ in the network of Fig. 8.109.

Figure 8.109   For Prob. 8.64.

8.65 Determine the differential equation for the op amp circuit in Fig. 8.110. If $v_1(0^+) = 2$ V and $v_2(0^+) = 0$ V, find v_o for $t > 0$. Let $R = 100$ kΩ and $C = 1$ μF.

Figure 8.110   For Prob. 8.65.

8.66 Given that $v_s = 2u(t)$ V in the op amp circuit of Fig. 8.111, find $v_o(t)$ for $t > 0$. Let $R_1 = R_2 = 10$ kΩ, $R_3 = 20$ kΩ, $R_4 = 40$ kΩ, $C_1 = C_2 = 100$ μF.

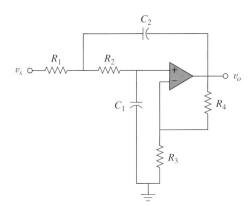

Figure 8.111   For Prob. 8.66.

*8.67 In the op amp circuit of Fig. 8.112, determine $v_o(t)$ for $t > 0$. Let $v_{in} = u(t)$ V, $R_1 = R_2 = 10$ kΩ, $C_1 = C_2 = 100$ μF.

Figure 8.112   For Prob. 8.67.

Section 8.9   *PSpice* Analysis of *RLC* Circuit

8.68 For the step function $v_s = u(t)$, use *PSpice* to find the response $v(t)$ for $0 < t < 6$ s in the circuit of Fig. 8.113.

Figure 8.113   For Prob. 8.68.

8.69 Given the source-free circuit in Fig. 8.114, use *PSpice* to get $i(t)$ for $0 < t < 20$ s. Take $v(0) = 30$ V and $i(0) = 2$ A.

Figure 8.114   For Prob. 8.69.

8.70 For the circuit of Fig. 8.115, use *PSpice* to obtain $v(t)$ for $0 < t < 4$ s. Assume that the capacitor voltage and inductor current at $t = 0$ are both zero.

Figure 8.115   For Prob. 8.70.

8.71 Obtain $v(t)$ for $0 < t < 4$ s in the circuit of Fig. 8.116 using *PSpice*.

Figure 8.116   For Prob. 8.71.

8.72 The switch in Fig. 8.117 has been in position 1 for a long time. At $t = 0$, it is switched to position 2. Use *PSpice* to find $i(t)$ for $0 < t < 0.2$ s.

Figure 8.117   For Prob. 8.72.

8.73 Rework Prob. 8.25 using *PSpice*. Plot $v_o(t)$ for $0 < t < 4$ s.

Section 8.10   Duality

8.74 Determine the dual of the circuit in Fig. 8.118.

Figure 8.118   For Prob. 8.74.

8.75 Obtain the dual of the circuit in Fig. 8.119.

Figure 8.119   For Prob. 8.75.

8.76 Find the dual of the circuit in Fig. 8.120.

Figure 8.120   For Prob. 8.76.

8.77 Draw the dual of the circuit in Fig. 8.121.

Figure 8.121   For Prob. 8.77.

Section 8.11   Applications

8.78 An automobile airbag igniter is modeled by the circuit in Fig. 8.122. Determine the time it takes the voltage across the igniter to reach its first peak after switching from A to B. Let $R = 3$ Ω, $C = 1/30$ F, and $L = 60$ mH.

Figure 8.122   For Prob. 8.78.

8.79 A load is modeled as a 250-mH inductor in parallel with a 12-Ω resistor. A capacitor is needed to be connected to the load so that the network is critically damped at 60 Hz. Calculate the size of the capacitor.

COMPREHENSIVE PROBLEMS

8.80 A mechanical system is modeled by a series RLC circuit. It is desired to produce an overdamped response with time constants 0.1 ms and 0.5 ms. If a series 50-kΩ resistor is used, find the values of L and C.

8.81 An oscillogram can be adequately modeled by a second-order system in the form of a parallel RLC circuit. It is desired to give an underdamped voltage across a 200-Ω resistor. If the damping frequency is 4 kHz and the time constant of the envelope is 0.25 s, find the necessary values of L and C.

8.82 The circuit in Fig. 8.123 is the electrical analog of body functions used in medical schools to study convulsions. The analog is as follows:

C_1 = Volume of fluid in a drug

C_2 = Volume of blood stream in a specified region

R_1 = Resistance in the passage of the drug from the input to the blood stream

R_2 = Resistance of the excretion mechanism, such as kidney, etc.

v_0 = Initial concentration of the drug dosage

$v(t)$ = Percentage of the drug in the blood stream

Find $v(t)$ for $t > 0$ given that $C_1 = 0.5\ \mu F$, $C_2 = 5\ \mu F$, $R_1 = 5\ M\Omega$, $R_2 = 2.5\ M\Omega$, and $v_0 = 60u(t)$ V.

Figure 8.123   For Prob. 8.82.

8.83 Figure 8.124 shows a typical tunnel-diode oscillator circuit. The diode is modeled as a nonlinear resistor with $i_D = f(v_D)$, i.e., the diode current is a nonlinear function of the voltage across the diode. Derive the differential equation for the circuit in terms of v and i_D.

Figure 8.124   For Prob. 8.83.

AC CIRCUITS

Chapter **9** *Sinusoids and Phasors*

Chapter **10** *Sinusoidal Steady-State Analysis*

Chapter **11** *AC Power Analysis*

Chapter **12** *Three-Phase Circuits*

Chapter **13** *Magnetically Coupled Circuits*

Chapter **14** *Frequency Response*

C H A P T E R 9

SINUSOIDS AND PHASORS

Engineers create reality out of dreams, and engineers are the world's greatest dreamers.

—Charles K. Alexander

Historical Profiles

Heinrich Rudorf Hertz (1857–1894), a German experimental physicist, demonstrated that electromagnetic waves obey the same fundamental laws as light. His work confirmed James Clerk Maxwell's celebrated 1864 theory and prediction that such waves existed.

Hertz was born into a prosperous family in Hamburg, Germany. He attended the University of Berlin and did his doctorate under the prominent physicist Hermann von Helmholtz. He became a professor at Karlsruhe, where he began his quest for electromagnetic waves. Hertz successfully generated and detected electromagnetic waves; he was the first to show that light is electromagnetic energy. In 1887, Hertz noted for the first time the photoelectric effect of electrons in a molecular structure. Although Hertz only lived to the age of 37, his discovery of electromagnetic waves paved the way for the practical use of such waves in radio, television, and other communication systems. The unit of frequency, the hertz, bears his name.

Charles Proteus Steinmetz (1865–1923), a German-Austrian mathematician and engineer, introduced the phasor method (covered in this chapter) in ac circuit analysis. He is also noted for his work on the theory of hysteresis.

Steinmetz was born in Breslau, Germany, and lost his mother at the age of one. As a youth, he was forced to leave Germany because of his political activities just as he was about to complete his doctoral dissertation in mathematics at the University of Breslau. He migrated to Switzerland and later to the United States, where he was employed by General Electric in 1893. That same year, he published a paper in which complex numbers were used to analyze ac circuits for the first time. This led to one of his many textbooks, *Theory and Calculation of ac Phenomena*, published by McGraw-Hill in 1897. In 1901, he became the president of the American Institute of Electrical Engineers, which later became the IEEE.

9.1 INTRODUCTION

Thus far our analysis has been limited for the most part to dc circuits: those circuits excited by constant or time-invariant sources. We have restricted the forcing function to dc sources for the sake of simplicity, for pedagogic reasons, and also for historic reasons. Historically, dc sources were the main means of providing electric power up until the late 1800s. At the end of that century, the battle of direct current versus alternating current began. Both had their advocates among the electrical engineers of the time. Because ac is more efficient and economical to transmit over long distances, ac systems ended up the winner. Thus, it is in keeping with the historical sequence of events that we considered dc sources first.

We now begin the analysis of circuits in which the source voltage or current is time-varying. In this chapter, we are particularly interested in sinusoidally time-varying excitation, or simply, excitation by a *sinusoid*.

A sinusoid is a signal that has the form of the sine or cosine function.

A sinusoidal current is usually referred to as *alternating current* (*ac*). Such a current reverses at regular time intervals and has alternately positive and negative values. Circuits driven by sinusoidal current or voltage sources are called *ac circuits.*

We are interested in sinusoids for a number of reasons. First, nature itself is characteristically sinusoidal. We experience sinusoidal variation in the motion of a pendulum, the vibration of a string, the ripples on the ocean surface, and the natural response of underdamped second-order systems, to mention but a few. Second, a sinusoidal signal is easy to generate and transmit. It is the form of voltage generated throughout the world and supplied to homes, factories, laboratories, and so on. It is the dominant form of signal in the communications and electric power industries. Third, through Fourier analysis, any practical periodic signal can be represented by a sum of sinusoids. Sinusoids, therefore, play an important role in the analysis of periodic signals. Lastly, a sinusoid is easy to handle mathematically. The derivative and integral of a sinusoid are themselves sinusoids. For these and other reasons, the sinusoid is an extremely important function in circuit analysis.

A sinusoidal forcing function produces both a transient response and a steady-state response, much like the step function, which we studied in Chapters 7 and 8. The transient response dies out with time so that only the steady-state response remains. When the transient response has become negligibly small compared with the steady-state response, we say that the circuit is operating at sinusoidal steady state. It is this *sinusoidal steady-state response* that is of main interest to us in this chapter.

We begin with a basic discussion of sinusoids and phasors. We then introduce the concepts of impedance and admittance. The basic circuit laws, Kirchhoff's and Ohm's, introduced for dc circuits, will be applied to ac circuits. Finally, we consider applications of ac circuits in phase-shifters and bridges.

9.2   SINUSOIDS

Consider the sinusoidal voltage

$$v(t) = V_m \sin \omega t \qquad (9.1)$$

where

V_m = the *amplitude* of the sinusoid

ω = the *angular frequency* in radians/s

ωt = the *argument* of the sinusoid

The sinusoid is shown in Fig. 9.1(a) as a function of its argument and in Fig. 9.1(b) as a function of time. It is evident that the sinusoid repeats itself every T seconds; thus, T is called the *period* of the sinusoid. From the two plots in Fig. 9.1, we observe that $\omega T = 2\pi$,

$$\boxed{T = \frac{2\pi}{\omega}} \qquad (9.2)$$

The fact that $v(t)$ repeats itself every T seconds is shown by replacing t by $t + T$ in Eq. (9.1). We get

$$v(t+T) = V_m \sin \omega (t+T) = V_m \sin \omega \left(t + \frac{2\pi}{\omega} \right) \qquad (9.3)$$

$$= V_m \sin(\omega t + 2\pi) = V_m \sin \omega t = v(t)$$

Hence,

$$\boxed{v(t+T) = v(t)} \qquad (9.4)$$

that is, v has the same value at $t + T$ as it does at t and $v(t)$ is said to be *periodic*. In general,

A periodic function is one that satisfies $f(t) = f(t + nT)$, for all t and for all integers n.

As mentioned, the *period T* of the periodic function is the time of one complete cycle or the number of seconds per cycle. The reciprocal of

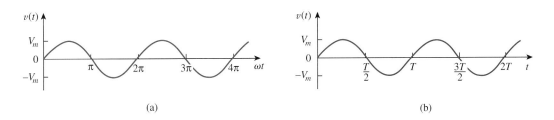

(a)   (b)

Figure 9.1   A sketch of $V_m \sin \omega t$: (a) as a function of ωt, (b) as a function of t.

this quantity is the number of cycles per second, known as the *cyclic frequency f* of the sinusoid. Thus,

$$f = \frac{1}{T} \tag{9.5}$$

From Eqs. (9.2) and (9.5), it is clear that

$$\omega = 2\pi f \tag{9.6}$$

The unit of f is named after the German physicist Heinrich R. Hertz (1857–1894).

While ω is in radians per second (rad/s), f is in hertz (Hz).

Let us now consider a more general expression for the sinusoid,

$$v(t) = V_m \sin(\omega t + \phi) \tag{9.7}$$

where $(\omega t + \phi)$ is the argument and ϕ is the *phase*. Both argument and phase can be in radians or degrees.

Let us examine the two sinusoids

$$v_1(t) = V_m \sin \omega t \qquad \text{and} \qquad v_2(t) = V_m \sin(\omega t + \phi) \tag{9.8}$$

shown in Fig. 9.2. The starting point of v_2 in Fig. 9.2 occurs first in time. Therefore, we say that v_2 *leads* v_1 by ϕ or that v_1 *lags* v_2 by ϕ. If $\phi \neq 0$, we also say that v_1 and v_2 are *out of phase*. If $\phi = 0$, then v_1 and v_2 are said to be *in phase*; they reach their minima and maxima at exactly the same time. We can compare v_1 and v_2 in this manner because they operate at the same frequency; they do not need to have the same amplitude.

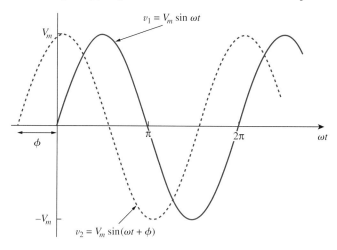

Figure 9.2   Two sinusoids with different phases.

A sinusoid can be expressed in either sine or cosine form. When comparing two sinusoids, it is expedient to express both as either sine or cosine with positive amplitudes. This is achieved by using the following trigonometric identities:

$$\sin(A \pm B) = \sin A \cos B \pm \cos A \sin B$$
$$\cos(A \pm B) = \cos A \cos B \mp \sin A \sin B \tag{9.9}$$

With these identities, it is easy to show that

$$\sin(\omega t \pm 180°) = -\sin \omega t$$
$$\cos(\omega t \pm 180°) = -\cos \omega t$$
$$\sin(\omega t \pm 90°) = \pm \cos \omega t$$
$$\cos(\omega t \pm 90°) = \mp \sin \omega t$$

(9.10)

Using these relationships, we can transform a sinusoid from sine form to cosine form or vice versa.

A graphical approach may be used to relate or compare sinusoids as an alternative to using the trigonometric identities in Eqs. (9.9) and (9.10). Consider the set of axes shown in Fig. 9.3(a). The horizontal axis represents the magnitude of cosine, while the vertical axis (pointing down) denotes the magnitude of sine. Angles are measured positively counterclockwise from the horizontal, as usual in polar coordinates. This graphical technique can be used to relate two sinusoids. For example, we see in Fig. 9.3(a) that subtracting 90° from the argument of $\cos \omega t$ gives $\sin \omega t$, or $\cos(\omega t - 90°) = \sin \omega t$. Similarly, adding 180° to the argument of $\sin \omega t$ gives $-\sin \omega t$, or $\sin(\omega t - 180°) = -\sin \omega t$, as shown in Fig. 9.3(b).

The graphical technique can also be used to add two sinusoids of the same frequency when one is in sine form and the other is in cosine form. To add $A \cos \omega t$ and $B \sin \omega t$, we note that A is the magnitude of $\cos \omega t$ while B is the magnitude of $\sin \omega t$, as shown in Fig. 9.4(a). The magnitude and argument of the resultant sinusoid in cosine form is readily obtained from the triangle. Thus,

$$A \cos \omega t + B \sin \omega t = C \cos(\omega t - \theta)$$

(9.11)

where

$$C = \sqrt{A^2 + B^2}, \qquad \theta = \tan^{-1} \frac{B}{A}$$

(9.12)

For example, we may add $3 \cos \omega t$ and $-4 \sin \omega t$ as shown in Fig. 9.4(b) and obtain

$$3 \cos \omega t - 4 \sin \omega t = 5 \cos(\omega t + 53.1°)$$

(9.13)

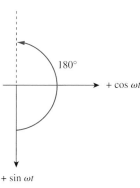

Figure 9.3   A graphical means of relating cosine and sine: (a) $\cos(\omega t - 90°) = \sin \omega t$, (b) $\sin(\omega t + 180°) = -\sin \omega t$.

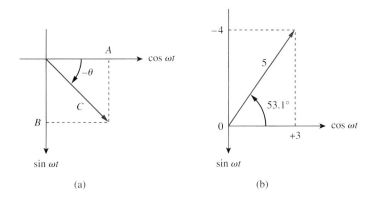

(a)   (b)

Figure 9.4   (a) Adding $A \cos \omega t$ and $B \sin \omega t$, (b) adding $3 \cos \omega t$ and $-4 \sin \omega t$.

Compared with the trigonometric identities in Eqs. (9.9) and (9.10), the graphical approach eliminates memorization. However, we must not confuse the sine and cosine axes with the axes for complex numbers to be discussed in the next section. Something else to note in Figs. 9.3 and 9.4 is that although the natural tendency is to have the vertical axis point up, the positive direction of the sine function is down in the present case.

EXAMPLE 9.1

Find the amplitude, phase, period, and frequency of the sinusoid

$$v(t) = 12\cos(50t + 10°)$$

Solution:

The amplitude is $V_m = 12$ V.

The phase is $\phi = 10°$.

The angular frequency is $\omega = 50$ rad/s.

The period $T = \dfrac{2\pi}{\omega} = \dfrac{2\pi}{50} = 0.1257$ s.

The frequency is $f = \dfrac{1}{T} = 7.958$ Hz.

PRACTICE PROBLEM 9.1

Given the sinusoid $5\sin(4\pi t - 60°)$, calculate its amplitude, phase, angular frequency, period, and frequency.

Answer: 5, $-60°$, 12.57 rad/s, 0.5 s, 2 Hz.

EXAMPLE 9.2

Calculate the phase angle between $v_1 = -10\cos(\omega t + 50°)$ and $v_2 = 12\sin(\omega t - 10°)$. State which sinusoid is leading.

Solution:

Let us calculate the phase in three ways. The first two methods use trigonometric identities, while the third method uses the graphical approach.

METHOD 1   In order to compare v_1 and v_2, we must express them in the same form. If we express them in cosine form with positive amplitudes,

$$v_1 = -10\cos(\omega t + 50°) = 10\cos(\omega t + 50° - 180°)$$

$$v_1 = 10\cos(\omega t - 130°) \qquad \text{or} \qquad v_1 = 10\cos(\omega t + 230°) \qquad (9.2.1)$$

and

$$v_2 = 12\sin(\omega t - 10°) = 12\cos(\omega t - 10° - 90°)$$

$$v_2 = 12\cos(\omega t - 100°) \qquad (9.2.2)$$

It can be deduced from Eqs. (9.2.1) and (9.2.2) that the phase difference between v_1 and v_2 is $30°$. We can write v_2 as

$$v_2 = 12\cos(\omega t - 130° + 30°) \quad \text{or} \quad v_2 = 12\cos(\omega t + 260°) \quad (9.2.3)$$

Comparing Eqs. (9.2.1) and (9.2.3) shows clearly that v_2 leads v_1 by $30°$.

METHOD **2**   Alternatively, we may express v_1 in sine form:

$$v_1 = -10\cos(\omega t + 50°) = 10\sin(\omega t + 50° - 90°)$$
$$= 10\sin(\omega t - 40°) = 10\sin(\omega t - 10° - 30°)$$

But $v_2 = 12\sin(\omega t - 10°)$. Comparing the two shows that v_1 lags v_2 by $30°$. This is the same as saying that v_2 leads v_1 by $30°$.

METHOD **3**   We may regard v_1 as simply $-10\cos\omega t$ with a phase shift of $+50°$. Hence, v_1 is as shown in Fig. 9.5. Similarly, v_2 is $12\sin\omega t$ with a phase shift of $-10°$, as shown in Fig. 9.5. It is easy to see from Fig. 9.5 that v_2 leads v_1 by $30°$, that is, $90° - 50° - 10°$.

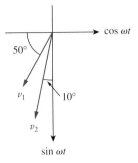

Figure 9.5   For Example 9.2.

PRACTICE PROBLEM 9.2

Find the phase angle between

$$i_1 = -4\sin(377t + 25°) \quad \text{and} \quad i_2 = 5\cos(377t - 40°)$$

Does i_1 lead or lag i_2?

Answer: $155°$, i_1 leads i_2.

9.3 PHASORS

Sinusoids are easily expressed in terms of phasors, which are more convenient to work with than sine and cosine functions.

◇ A phasor is a complex number that represents the amplitude and phase of a sinusoid.

Phasors provide a simple means of analyzing linear circuits excited by sinusoidal sources; solutions of such circuits would be intractable otherwise. The notion of solving ac circuits using phasors was first introduced by Charles Steinmetz in 1893. Before we completely define phasors and apply them to circuit analysis, we need to be thoroughly familiar with complex numbers.

A complex number z can be written in rectangular form as

$$z = x + jy \tag{9.14a}$$

where $j = \sqrt{-1}$; x is the real part of z; y is the imaginary part of z. In this context, the variables x and y do not represent a location as in two-dimensional vector analysis but rather the real and imaginary parts of z in the complex plane. Nevertheless, we note that there are some

Charles Proteus Steinmetz (1865–1923) was a German-Austrian mathematician and electrical engineer.

Appendix B presents a short tutorial on complex numbers.

resemblances between manipulating complex numbers and manipulating two-dimensional vectors.

The complex number z can also be written in polar or exponential form as

$$z = r \underline{/\phi} = re^{j\phi} \tag{9.14b}$$

where r is the magnitude of z, and ϕ is the phase of z. We notice that z can be represented in three ways:

$$
\begin{aligned}
z &= x + jy & \text{Rectangular form} \\
z &= r \underline{/\phi} & \text{Polar form} \\
z &= re^{j\phi} & \text{Exponential form}
\end{aligned}
\tag{9.15}
$$

The relationship between the rectangular form and the polar form is shown in Fig. 9.6, where the x axis represents the real part and the y axis represents the imaginary part of a complex number. Given x and y, we can get r and ϕ as

$$r = \sqrt{x^2 + y^2}, \qquad \phi = \tan^{-1} \frac{y}{x} \tag{9.16a}$$

On the other hand, if we know r and ϕ, we can obtain x and y as

$$x = r \cos \phi, \qquad y = r \sin \phi \tag{9.16b}$$

Thus, z may be written as

$$\boxed{z = x + jy = r \underline{/\phi} = r(\cos \phi + j \sin \phi)} \tag{9.17}$$

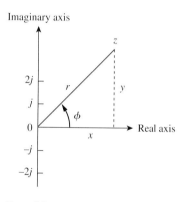

Imaginary axis

Figure 9.6   Representation of a complex number $z = x + jy = r \underline{/\phi}$.

Addition and subtraction of complex numbers are better performed in rectangular form; multiplication and division are better done in polar form. Given the complex numbers

$$z = x + jy = r \underline{/\phi}, \qquad z_1 = x_1 + jy_1 = r_1 \underline{/\phi_1}$$
$$z_2 = x_2 + jy_2 = r_2 \underline{/\phi_2}$$

the following operations are important.

Addition:

$$z_1 + z_2 = (x_1 + x_2) + j(y_1 + y_2) \tag{9.18a}$$

Subtraction:

$$z_1 - z_2 = (x_1 - x_2) + j(y_1 - y_2) \tag{9.18b}$$

Multiplication:

$$z_1 z_2 = r_1 r_2 \underline{/\phi_1 + \phi_2} \tag{9.18c}$$

Division:

$$\frac{z_1}{z_2} = \frac{r_1}{r_2} \underline{/\phi_1 - \phi_2} \tag{9.18d}$$

Reciprocal:

$$\frac{1}{z} = \frac{1}{r} \underline{/-\phi} \tag{9.18e}$$

Square Root:

$$\sqrt{z} = \sqrt{r} \underline{/\phi/2} \tag{9.18f}$$

Complex Conjugate:

$$z^* = x - jy = r\,\underline{/-\phi} = re^{-j\phi} \qquad (9.18g)$$

Note that from Eq. (9.18e),

$$\frac{1}{j} = -j \qquad (9.18h)$$

These are the basic properties of complex numbers we need. Other properties of complex numbers can be found in Appendix B.

The idea of phasor representation is based on Euler's identity. In general,

$$\boxed{e^{\pm j\phi} = \cos\phi \pm j\sin\phi} \qquad (9.19)$$

which shows that we may regard $\cos\phi$ and $\sin\phi$ as the real and imaginary parts of $e^{j\phi}$; we may write

$$\cos\phi = \mathrm{Re}(e^{j\phi}) \qquad (9.20a)$$

$$\sin\phi = \mathrm{Im}(e^{j\phi}) \qquad (9.20b)$$

where Re and Im stand for the *real part of* and the *imaginary part of*. Given a sinusoid $v(t) = V_m\cos(\omega t + \phi)$, we use Eq. (9.20a) to express $v(t)$ as

$$v(t) = V_m\cos(\omega t + \phi) = \mathrm{Re}(V_m e^{j(\omega t + \phi)}) \qquad (9.21)$$

or

$$v(t) = \mathrm{Re}(V_m e^{j\phi} e^{j\omega t}) \qquad (9.22)$$

Thus,

$$\boxed{v(t) = \mathrm{Re}(\mathbf{V}e^{j\omega t})} \qquad (9.23)$$

where

$$\mathbf{V} = V_m e^{j\phi} = V_m\,\underline{/\phi} \qquad (9.24)$$

$\mathbf{V}$ is thus the *phasor representation* of the sinusoid $v(t)$, as we said earlier. In other words, a phasor is a complex representation of the magnitude and phase of a sinusoid. Either Eq. (9.20a) or Eq. (9.20b) can be used to develop the phasor, but the standard convention is to use Eq. (9.20a).

One way of looking at Eqs. (9.23) and (9.24) is to consider the plot of the *sinor* $\mathbf{V}e^{j\omega t} = V_m e^{j(\omega t + \phi)}$ on the complex plane. As time increases, the sinor rotates on a circle of radius V_m at an angular velocity ω in the counterclockwise direction, as shown in Fig. 9.7(a). We may regard $v(t)$ as the projection of the sinor $\mathbf{V}e^{j\omega t}$ on the real axis, as shown in Fig. 9.7(b). The value of the sinor at time $t = 0$ is the phasor $\mathbf{V}$ of the sinusoid $v(t)$. The sinor may be regarded as a rotating phasor. Thus, whenever a sinusoid is expressed as a phasor, the term $e^{j\omega t}$ is implicitly present. It is therefore important, when dealing with phasors, to keep in mind the frequency ω of the phasor; otherwise we can make serious mistakes.

A phasor may be regarded as a mathematical equivalent of a sinusoid with the time dependence dropped.

If we use sine for the phasor instead of cosine, then $v(t) = V_m\sin(\omega t + \phi) = \mathrm{Im}(V_m e^{j(\omega t + \phi)})$ and the corresponding phasor is the same as that in Eq. (9.24).

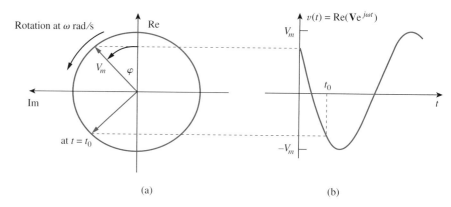

Figure 9.7   Representation of $\mathbf{V}e^{j\omega t}$: (a) sinor rotating counterclockwise, (b) its projection on the real axis, as a function of time.

We use lightface italic letters such as z to represent complex numbers but boldface letters such as $\mathbf{V}$ to represent phasors, because phasors are vectorlike quantities.

Equation (9.23) states that to obtain the sinusoid corresponding to a given phasor $\mathbf{V}$, multiply the phasor by the time factor $e^{j\omega t}$ and take the real part. As a complex quantity, a phasor may be expressed in rectangular form, polar form, or exponential form. Since a phasor has magnitude and phase ("direction"), it behaves as a vector and is printed in boldface. For example, phasors $\mathbf{V} = V_m \underline{/\phi}$ and $\mathbf{I} = I_m \underline{/-\theta}$ are graphically represented in Fig. 9.8. Such a graphical representation of phasors is known as a *phasor diagram*.

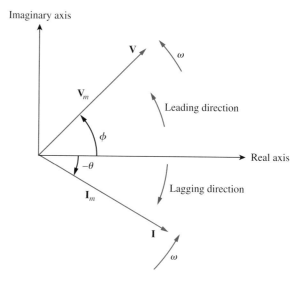

Figure 9.8   A phasor diagram showing $\mathbf{V} = V_m \underline{/\phi}$ and $\mathbf{I} = I_m \underline{/-\theta}$.

Equations (9.21) through (9.23) reveal that to get the phasor corresponding to a sinusoid, we first express the sinusoid in the cosine form so that the sinusoid can be written as the real part of a complex number. Then we take out the time factor $e^{j\omega t}$, and whatever is left is the phasor corresponding to the sinusoid. By suppressing the time factor, we transform the sinusoid from the time domain to the phasor domain. This transformation is summarized as follows:

$$v(t) = V_m \cos(\omega t + \phi) \quad \Longleftrightarrow \quad \mathbf{V} = V_m \underline{/\phi} \qquad (9.25)$$
(Time-domain representation)   (Phasor-domain representation)

Given a sinusoid $v(t) = V_m \cos(\omega t + \phi)$, we obtain the corresponding phasor as $\mathbf{V} = V_m \underline{/\phi}$. Equation (9.25) is also demonstrated in Table 9.1, where the sine function is considered in addition to the cosine function. From Eq. (9.25), we see that to get the phasor representation of a sinusoid, we express it in cosine form and take the magnitude and phase. Given a phasor, we obtain the time-domain representation as the cosine function with the same magnitude as the phasor and the argument as ωt plus the phase of the phasor. The idea of expressing information in alternate domains is fundamental to all areas of engineering.

TABLE 9.1   Sinusoid-phasor transformation.

Time-domain representation	Phasor-domain representation
$V_m \cos(\omega t + \phi)$	$V_m \underline{/\phi}$
$V_m \sin(\omega t + \phi)$	$V_m \underline{/\phi - 90°}$
$I_m \cos(\omega t + \theta)$	$I_m \underline{/\theta}$
$I_m \sin(\omega t + \theta)$	$I_m \underline{/\theta - 90°}$

Note that in Eq. (9.25) the frequency (or time) factor $e^{j\omega t}$ is suppressed, and the frequency is not explicitly shown in the phasor-domain representation because ω is constant. However, the response depends on ω. For this reason, the phasor domain is also known as the *frequency domain*.

From Eqs. (9.23) and (9.24), $v(t) = \text{Re}(\mathbf{V}e^{j\omega t}) = V_m \cos(\omega t + \phi)$, so that

$$\frac{dv}{dt} = -\omega V_m \sin(\omega t + \phi) = \omega V_m \cos(\omega t + \phi + 90°) \qquad (9.26)$$
$$= \text{Re}(\omega V_m e^{j\omega t} e^{j\phi} e^{j90°}) = \text{Re}(j\omega \mathbf{V} e^{j\omega t})$$

This shows that the derivative $v(t)$ is transformed to the phasor domain as $j\omega \mathbf{V}$

$$\frac{dv}{dt} \quad \Longleftrightarrow \quad j\omega \mathbf{V} \qquad (9.27)$$
(Time domain)   (Phasor domain)

Differentiating a sinusoid is equivalent to multiplying its corresponding phasor by $j\omega$.

Similarly, the integral of $v(t)$ is transformed to the phasor domain as $\mathbf{V}/j\omega$

$$\int v \, dt \quad \Longleftrightarrow \quad \frac{\mathbf{V}}{j\omega} \qquad (9.28)$$
(Time domain)   (Phasor domain)

Integrating a sinusoid is equivalent to dividing its corresponding phasor by $j\omega$.

Equation (9.27) allows the replacement of a derivative with respect to time with multiplication of $j\omega$ in the phasor domain, whereas Eq. (9.28) allows the replacement of an integral with respect to time with division by $j\omega$ in the phasor domain. Equations (9.27) and (9.28) are useful in finding the steady-state solution, which does not require knowing the initial values of the variable involved. This is one of the important applications of phasors.

Besides time differentiation and integration, another important use of phasors is found in summing sinusoids of the same frequency. This is best illustrated with an example, and Example 9.6 provides one.

The differences between $v(t)$ and $\mathbf{V}$ should be emphasized:

1. $v(t)$ is the *instantaneous or time-domain* representation, while $\mathbf{V}$ is the *frequency or phasor-domain* representation.

2. $v(t)$ is time dependent, while $\mathbf{V}$ is not. (This fact is often forgotten by students.)

3. $v(t)$ is always real with no complex term, while $\mathbf{V}$ is generally complex.

Finally, we should bear in mind that phasor analysis applies only when frequency is constant; it applies in manipulating two or more sinusoidal signals only if they are of the same frequency.

Adding sinusoids of the same frequency is equivalent to adding their corresponding phasors.

EXAMPLE 9.3

Evaluate these complex numbers:

(a) $(40\underline{/50^\circ} + 20\underline{/-30^\circ})^{1/2}$

(b) $\dfrac{10\underline{/-30^\circ} + (3 - j4)}{(2 + j4)(3 - j5)^*}$

Solution:

(a) Using polar to rectangular transformation,

$$40\underline{/50^\circ} = 40(\cos 50^\circ + j\sin 50^\circ) = 25.71 + j30.64$$

$$20\underline{/-30^\circ} = 20[\cos(-30^\circ) + j\sin(-30^\circ)] = 17.32 - j10$$

Adding them up gives

$$40\underline{/50^\circ} + 20\underline{/-30^\circ} = 43.03 + j20.64 = 47.72\underline{/25.63^\circ}$$

Taking the square root of this,

$$(40\underline{/50^\circ} + 20\underline{/-30^\circ})^{1/2} = 6.91\underline{/12.81^\circ}$$

(b) Using polar-rectangular transformation, addition, multiplication, and division,

$$\frac{10\underline{/-30^\circ} + (3 - j4)}{(2 + j4)(3 - j5)^*} = \frac{8.66 - j5 + (3 - j4)}{(2 + j4)(3 + j5)}$$

$$= \frac{11.66 - j9}{-14 + j22} = \frac{14.73\underline{/-37.66^\circ}}{26.08\underline{/122.47^\circ}}$$

$$= 0.565\underline{/-160.13^\circ}$$

PRACTICE PROBLEM 9.3

Evaluate the following complex numbers:

(a) $[(5 + j2)(-1 + j4) - 5\underline{/60°}]^*$

(b) $\dfrac{10 + j5 + 3\underline{/40°}}{-3 + j4} + 10\underline{/30°}$

Answer: (a) $-15.5 - j13.67$, (b) $8.293 + j2.2$.

EXAMPLE 9.4

Transform these sinusoids to phasors:

(a) $i = 6\cos(50t - 40°)$ A

(b) $v = -4\sin(30t + 50°)$ V

Solution:

(a) $i = 6\cos(50t - 40°)$ has the phasor

$$\mathbf{I} = 6\underline{/-40°} \text{ A}$$

(b) Since $-\sin A = \cos(A + 90°)$,

$$v = -4\sin(30t + 50°) = 4\cos(30t + 50° + 90°)$$
$$= 4\cos(30t + 140°) \text{ V}$$

The phasor form of v is

$$\mathbf{V} = 4\underline{/140°} \text{ V}$$

PRACTICE PROBLEM 9.4

Express these sinusoids as phasors:

(a) $v = -7\cos(2t + 40°)$ V

(b) $i = 4\sin(10t + 10°)$ A

Answer: (a) $\mathbf{V} = 7\underline{/220°}$ V, (b) $\mathbf{I} = 4\underline{/-80°}$ A.

EXAMPLE 9.5

Find the sinusoids represented by these phasors:

(a) $\mathbf{I} = -3 + j4$ A

(b) $\mathbf{V} = j8e^{-j20°}$ V

Solution:

(a) $\mathbf{I} = -3 + j4 = 5\underline{/126.87°}$. Transforming this to the time domain gives

$$i(t) = 5\cos(\omega t + 126.87°) \text{ A}$$

(b) Since $j = 1\underline{/90°}$,

$$\mathbf{V} = j8\underline{/-20°} = (1\underline{/90°})(8\underline{/-20°})$$
$$= 8\underline{/90° - 20°} = 8\underline{/70°} \text{ V}$$

Converting this to the time domain gives

$$v(t) = 8\cos(\omega t + 70°) \text{ V}$$

PRACTICE PROBLEM 9.5

Find the sinusoids corresponding to these phasors:

(a) $\mathbf{V} = -10\underline{/30°}$ V

(b) $\mathbf{I} = j(5 - j12)$ A

Answer: (a) $v(t) = 10\cos(\omega t + 210°)$ V, (b)
$i(t) = 13\cos(\omega t + 22.62°)$ A.

EXAMPLE 9.6

Given $i_1(t) = 4\cos(\omega t + 30°)$ A and $i_2(t) = 5\sin(\omega t - 20°)$ A, find
their sum.

Solution:

Here is an important use of phasors—for summing sinusoids of the same
frequency. Current $i_1(t)$ is in the standard form. Its phasor is

$$\mathbf{I}_1 = 4\underline{/30°}$$

We need to express $i_2(t)$ in cosine form. The rule for converting sine to
cosine is to subtract 90°. Hence,

$$i_2 = 5\cos(\omega t - 20° - 90°) = 5\cos(\omega t - 110°)$$

and its phasor is

$$\mathbf{I_2} = 5\underline{/-110°}$$

If we let $i = i_1 + i_2$, then

$$\mathbf{I} = \mathbf{I}_1 + \mathbf{I}_2 = 4\underline{/30°} + 5\underline{/-110°}$$
$$= 3.464 + j2 - 1.71 - j4.698 = 1.754 - j2.698$$
$$= 3.218\underline{/-56.97°} \text{ A}$$

Transforming this to the time domain, we get

$$i(t) = 3.218\cos(\omega t - 56.97°) \text{ A}$$

Of course, we can find $i_1 + i_2$ using Eq. (9.9), but that is the hard way.

PRACTICE PROBLEM 9.6

If $v_1 = -10\sin(\omega t + 30°)$ V and $v_2 = 20\cos(\omega t - 45°)$ V, find $v = v_1 + v_2$.

Answer: $v(t) = 10.66\cos(\omega t - 30.95°)$ V.

EXAMPLE 9.7

Using the phasor approach, determine the current $i(t)$ in a circuit
described by the integrodifferential equation

$$4i + 8\int i\,dt - 3\frac{di}{dt} = 50\cos(2t + 75°)$$

Solution:

We transform each term in the equation from time domain to phasor domain. Keeping Eqs. (9.27) and (9.28) in mind, we obtain the phasor form of the given equation as

$$4\mathbf{I} + \frac{8\mathbf{I}}{j\omega} - 3j\omega\mathbf{I} = 50\underline{/75°}$$

But $\omega = 2$, so

$$\mathbf{I}(4 - j4 - j6) = 50\underline{/75°}$$

$$\mathbf{I} = \frac{50\underline{/75°}}{4 - j10} = \frac{50\underline{/75°}}{10.77\underline{/-68.2°}} = 4.642\underline{/143.2°}\ \text{A}$$

Converting this to the time domain,

$$i(t) = 4.642\cos(2t + 143.2°)\ \text{A}$$

Keep in mind that this is only the steady-state solution, and it does not require knowing the initial values.

PRACTICE PROBLEM 9.7

Find the voltage $v(t)$ in a circuit described by the integrodifferential equation

$$2\frac{dv}{dt} + 5v + 10\int v\,dt = 20\cos(5t - 30°)$$

using the phasor approach.

Answer: $v(t) = 2.12\cos(5t - 88°)\ \text{V}.$

9.4 PHASOR RELATIONSHIPS FOR CIRCUIT ELEMENTS

Now that we know how to represent a voltage or current in the phasor or frequency domain, one may legitimately ask how we apply this to circuits involving the passive elements R, L, and C. What we need to do is to transform the voltage-current relationship from the time domain to the frequency domain for each element. Again, we will assume the passive sign convention.

We begin with the resistor. If the current through a resistor R is $i = I_m \cos(\omega t + \phi)$, the voltage across it is given by Ohm's law as

$$v = iR = RI_m \cos(\omega t + \phi) \tag{9.29}$$

The phasor form of this voltage is

$$\mathbf{V} = RI_m\underline{/\phi} \tag{9.30}$$

But the phasor representation of the current is $\mathbf{I} = I_m\underline{/\phi}$. Hence,

$$\mathbf{V} = R\mathbf{I} \tag{9.31}$$

Figure 9.9   Voltage-current relations for a resistor in the: (a) time domain, (b) frequency domain.

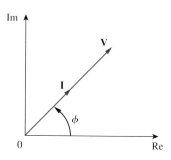

Figure 9.10   Phasor diagram for the resistor.

Although it is equally correct to say that the inductor voltage leads the current by 90°, convention gives the current phase relative to the voltage.

Figure 9.11   Voltage-current relations for an inductor in the: (a) time domain, (b) frequency domain.

showing that the voltage-current relation for the resistor in the phasor domain continues to be Ohm's law, as in the time domain. Figure 9.9 illustrates the voltage-current relations of a resistor. We should note from Eq. (9.31) that voltage and current are in phase, as illustrated in the phasor diagram in Fig. 9.10.

For the inductor L, assume the current through it is $i = I_m \cos(\omega t + \phi)$. The voltage across the inductor is

$$v = L\frac{di}{dt} = -\omega L I_m \sin(\omega t + \phi) \tag{9.32}$$

Recall from Eq. (9.10) that $-\sin A = \cos(A + 90°)$. We can write the voltage as

$$v = \omega L I_m \cos(\omega t + \phi + 90°) \tag{9.33}$$

which transforms to the phasor

$$\mathbf{V} = \omega L I_m e^{j(\phi + 90°)} = \omega L I_m e^{j\phi} e^{j90°} = \omega L I_m \underline{/\phi + 90°} e^{j90°} \tag{9.34}$$

But $I_m \underline{/\phi} = \mathbf{I}$, and from Eq. (9.19), $e^{j90°} = j$. Thus,

$$\mathbf{V} = j\omega L \mathbf{I} \tag{9.35}$$

showing that the voltage has a magnitude of $\omega L I_m$ and a phase of $\phi + 90°$. The voltage and current are 90° out of phase. Specifically, the current lags the voltage by 90°. Figure 9.11 shows the voltage-current relations for the inductor. Figure 9.12 shows the phasor diagram.

For the capacitor C, assume the voltage across it is $v = V_m \cos(\omega t + \phi)$. The current through the capacitor is

$$i = C\frac{dv}{dt} \tag{9.36}$$

By following the same steps as we took for the inductor or by applying Eq. (9.27) on Eq. (9.36), we obtain

$$\mathbf{I} = j\omega C \mathbf{V} \quad \Longrightarrow \quad \mathbf{V} = \frac{\mathbf{I}}{j\omega C} \tag{9.37}$$

showing that the current and voltage are 90° out of phase. To be specific, the current leads the voltage by 90°. Figure 9.13 shows the voltage-current

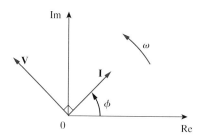

Figure 9.12   Phasor diagram for the inductor; $\mathbf{I}$ lags $\mathbf{V}$.

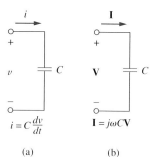

Figure 9.13   Voltage-current relations for a capacitor in the: (a) time domain, (b) frequency domain.

relations for the capacitor; Fig. 9.14 gives the phasor diagram. Table 9.2 summarizes the time-domain and phasor-domain representations of the circuit elements.

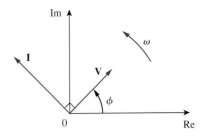

Figure 9.14   Phasor diagram for the capacitor; **I** leads **V**.

TABLE 9.2   Summary of voltage-current relationships.

Element	Time domain	Frequency domain
R	$v = Ri$	$\mathbf{V} = R\mathbf{I}$
L	$v = L\dfrac{di}{dt}$	$\mathbf{V} = j\omega L\mathbf{I}$
C	$i = C\dfrac{dv}{dt}$	$\mathbf{V} = \dfrac{\mathbf{I}}{j\omega C}$

EXAMPLE 9.8

The voltage $v = 12\cos(60t + 45°)$ is applied to a 0.1-H inductor. Find the steady-state current through the inductor.

Solution:

For the inductor, $\mathbf{V} = j\omega L\mathbf{I}$, where $\omega = 60$ rad/s and $\mathbf{V} = 12\underline{/45°}$ V. Hence

$$\mathbf{I} = \frac{\mathbf{V}}{j\omega L} = \frac{12\underline{/45°}}{j60 \times 0.1} = \frac{12\underline{/45°}}{6\underline{/90°}} = 2\underline{/-45°}\,\text{A}$$

Converting this to the time domain,

$$i(t) = 2\cos(60t - 45°)\ \text{A}$$

PRACTICE PROBLEM 9.8

If voltage $v = 6\cos(100t - 30°)$ is applied to a 50 μF capacitor, calculate the current through the capacitor.

Answer: $30\cos(100t + 60°)$ mA.

9.5   IMPEDANCE AND ADMITTANCE

In the preceding section, we obtained the voltage-current relations for the three passive elements as

$$\mathbf{V} = R\mathbf{I}, \qquad \mathbf{V} = j\omega L\mathbf{I}, \qquad \mathbf{V} = \frac{\mathbf{I}}{j\omega C} \qquad (9.38)$$

These equations may be written in terms of the ratio of the phasor voltage to the phasor current as

$$\frac{\mathbf{V}}{\mathbf{I}} = R, \qquad \frac{\mathbf{V}}{\mathbf{I}} = j\omega L, \qquad \frac{\mathbf{V}}{\mathbf{I}} = \frac{1}{j\omega C} \qquad (9.39)$$

From these three expressions, we obtain Ohm's law in phasor form for any type of element as

$$\mathbf{Z} = \frac{\mathbf{V}}{\mathbf{I}} \qquad \text{or} \qquad \mathbf{V} = \mathbf{ZI} \qquad (9.40)$$

where $\mathbf{Z}$ is a frequency-dependent quantity known as *impedance*, measured in ohms.

> The impedance $\mathbf{Z}$ of a circuit is the ratio of the phasor voltage $\mathbf{V}$ to the phasor current $\mathbf{I}$, measured in ohms (Ω).

The impedance represents the opposition which the circuit exhibits to the flow of sinusoidal current. Although the impedance is the ratio of two phasors, it is not a phasor, because it does not correspond to a sinusoidally varying quantity.

The impedances of resistors, inductors, and capacitors can be readily obtained from Eq. (9.39). Table 9.3 summarizes their impedances. From the table we notice that $\mathbf{Z}_L = j\omega L$ and $\mathbf{Z}_C = -j/\omega C$. Consider two extreme cases of angular frequency. When $\omega = 0$ (i.e., for dc sources), $\mathbf{Z}_L = 0$ and $\mathbf{Z}_C \rightarrow \infty$, confirming what we already know—that the inductor acts like a short circuit, while the capacitor acts like an open circuit. When $\omega \rightarrow \infty$ (i.e., for high frequencies), $\mathbf{Z}_L \rightarrow \infty$ and $\mathbf{Z}_C = 0$, indicating that the inductor is an open circuit to high frequencies, while the capacitor is a short circuit. Figure 9.15 illustrates this.

As a complex quantity, the impedance may be expressed in rectangular form as

$$\mathbf{Z} = R + jX \qquad (9.41)$$

where $R = \text{Re}\,\mathbf{Z}$ is the *resistance* and $X = \text{Im}\,\mathbf{Z}$ is the *reactance*. The reactance X may be positive or negative. We say that the impedance is inductive when X is positive or capacitive when X is negative. Thus, impedance $\mathbf{Z} = R + jX$ is said to be *inductive* or lagging since current lags voltage, while impedance $\mathbf{Z} = R - jX$ is capacitive or leading because current leads voltage. The impedance, resistance, and reactance are all measured in ohms. The impedance may also be expressed in polar form as

$$\mathbf{Z} = |\mathbf{Z}| \underline{/\theta} \qquad (9.42)$$

Comparing Eqs. (9.41) and (9.42), we infer that

$$\mathbf{Z} = R + jX = |\mathbf{Z}| \underline{/\theta} \qquad (9.43)$$

where

$$|\mathbf{Z}| = \sqrt{R^2 + X^2}, \qquad \theta = \tan^{-1}\frac{X}{R} \qquad (9.44)$$

and

$$R = |\mathbf{Z}| \cos\theta, \qquad X = |\mathbf{Z}| \sin\theta \qquad (9.45)$$

TABLE 9.3   Impedances and admittances of passive elements.

Element	Impedance	Admittance
R	$\mathbf{Z} = R$	$\mathbf{Y} = \dfrac{1}{R}$
L	$\mathbf{Z} = j\omega L$	$\mathbf{Y} = \dfrac{1}{j\omega L}$
C	$\mathbf{Z} = \dfrac{1}{j\omega C}$	$\mathbf{Y} = j\omega C$

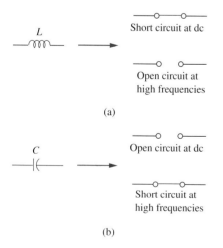

Figure 9.15   Equivalent circuits at dc and high frequencies: (a) inductor, (b) capacitor.

It is sometimes convenient to work with the reciprocal of impedance, known as *admittance*.

The admittance **Y** is the reciprocal of impedance, measured in siemens (S).

The admittance **Y** of an element (or a circuit) is the ratio of the phasor current through it to the phasor voltage across it, or

$$\mathbf{Y} = \frac{1}{\mathbf{Z}} = \frac{\mathbf{I}}{\mathbf{V}}$$

(9.46)

The admittances of resistors, inductors, and capacitors can be obtained from Eq. (9.39). They are also summarized in Table 9.3.

As a complex quantity, we may write **Y** as

$$\mathbf{Y} = G + jB$$

(9.47)

where $G = \text{Re }\mathbf{Y}$ is called the *conductance* and $B = \text{Im }\mathbf{Y}$ is called the *susceptance*. Admittance, conductance, and susceptance are all expressed in the unit of siemens (or mhos). From Eqs. (9.41) and (9.47),

$$G + jB = \frac{1}{R + jX}$$

(9.48)

By rationalization,

$$G + jB = \frac{1}{R + jX} \cdot \frac{R - jX}{R - jX} = \frac{R - jX}{R^2 + X^2}$$

(9.49)

Equating the real and imaginary parts gives

$$G = \frac{R}{R^2 + X^2}, \qquad B = -\frac{X}{R^2 + X^2}$$

(9.50)

showing that $G \neq 1/R$ as it is in resistive circuits. Of course, if $X = 0$, then $G = 1/R$.

E X A M P L E   9 . 9

Find $v(t)$ and $i(t)$ in the circuit shown in Fig. 9.16.

Solution:

From the voltage source $10\cos 4t$, $\omega = 4$,

$$\mathbf{V}_s = 10\underline{/0^\circ}\text{ V}$$

The impedance is

$$\mathbf{Z} = 5 + \frac{1}{j\omega C} = 5 + \frac{1}{j4 \times 0.1} = 5 - j2.5\ \Omega$$

Hence the current

$$\mathbf{I} = \frac{\mathbf{V}_s}{\mathbf{Z}} = \frac{10\underline{/0^\circ}}{5 - j2.5} = \frac{10(5 + j2.5)}{5^2 + 2.5^2}$$

(9.9.1)

$$= 1.6 + j0.8 = 1.789\underline{/26.57^\circ}\text{ A}$$

Figure 9.16   For Example 9.9.

The voltage across the capacitor is

$$\mathbf{V} = \mathbf{I}Z_C = \frac{\mathbf{I}}{j\omega C} = \frac{1.789\underline{/26.57^\circ}}{j4 \times 0.1}$$

$$= \frac{1.789\underline{/26.57^\circ}}{0.4\underline{/90^\circ}} = 4.47\underline{/-63.43^\circ}\ \text{V}$$

(9.9.2)

Converting $\mathbf{I}$ and $\mathbf{V}$ in Eqs. (9.9.1) and (9.9.2) to the time domain, we get

$$i(t) = 1.789\cos(4t + 26.57^\circ)\ \text{A}$$

$$v(t) = 4.47\cos(4t - 63.43^\circ)\ \text{V}$$

Notice that $i(t)$ leads $v(t)$ by 90° as expected.

PRACTICE PROBLEM 9.9

$v_s = 5\sin 10t$

Refer to Fig. 9.17. Determine $v(t)$ and $i(t)$.

Answer: $2.236\sin(10t + 63.43^\circ)$ V, $1.118\sin(10t - 26.57^\circ)$ A.

Figure 9.17   For Practice Prob. 9.9.

†9.6 KIRCHHOFF'S LAWS IN THE FREQUENCY DOMAIN

We cannot do circuit analysis in the frequency domain without Kirchhoff's current and voltage laws. Therefore, we need to express them in the frequency domain.

For KVL, let $v_1, v_2, \ldots, v_n$ be the voltages around a closed loop. Then

$$v_1 + v_2 + \cdots + v_n = 0 \tag{9.51}$$

In the sinusoidal steady state, each voltage may be written in cosine form, so that Eq. (9.51) becomes

$$V_{m1}\cos(\omega t + \theta_1) + V_{m2}\cos(\omega t + \theta_2)$$
$$+ \cdots + V_{mn}\cos(\omega t + \theta_n) = 0 \tag{9.52}$$

This can be written as

$$\text{Re}(V_{m1}e^{j\theta_1}e^{j\omega t}) + \text{Re}(V_{m2}e^{j\theta_2}e^{j\omega t}) + \cdots + \text{Re}(V_{mn}e^{j\theta_n}e^{j\omega t}) = 0$$

or

$$\text{Re}[(V_{m1}e^{j\theta_1} + V_{m2}e^{j\theta_2} + \cdots + V_{mn}e^{j\theta_n})e^{j\omega t}] = 0 \tag{9.53}$$

If we let $\mathbf{V}_k = V_{mk}e^{j\theta_k}$, then

$$\text{Re}[(\mathbf{V}_1 + \mathbf{V}_2 + \cdots + \mathbf{V}_n)e^{j\omega t}] = 0 \tag{9.54}$$

Since $e^{j\omega t} \neq 0$,

$$\mathbf{V}_1 + \mathbf{V}_2 + \cdots + \mathbf{V}_n = 0 \tag{9.55}$$

indicating that Kirchhoff's voltage law holds for phasors.

By following a similar procedure, we can show that Kirchhoff's current law holds for phasors. If we let $i_1, i_2, \ldots, i_n$ be the current leaving or entering a closed surface in a network at time t, then

$$i_1 + i_2 + \cdots + i_n = 0 \qquad (9.56)$$

If $\mathbf{I}_1, \mathbf{I}_2, \ldots, \mathbf{I}_n$ are the phasor forms of the sinusoids $i_1, i_2, \ldots, i_n$, then

$$\mathbf{I}_1 + \mathbf{I}_2 + \cdots + \mathbf{I}_n = 0 \qquad (9.57)$$

which is Kirchhoff's current law in the frequency domain.

Once we have shown that both KVL and KCL hold in the frequency domain, it is easy to do many things, such as impedance combination, nodal and mesh analyses, superposition, and source transformation.

9.7 IMPEDANCE COMBINATIONS

Consider the N series-connected impedances shown in Fig. 9.18. The same current $\mathbf{I}$ flows through the impedances. Applying KVL around the loop gives

$$\mathbf{V} = \mathbf{V}_1 + \mathbf{V}_2 + \cdots + \mathbf{V}_N = \mathbf{I}(\mathbf{Z}_1 + \mathbf{Z}_2 + \cdots + \mathbf{Z}_N) \qquad (9.58)$$

The equivalent impedance at the input terminals is

$$\mathbf{Z}_{eq} = \frac{\mathbf{V}}{\mathbf{I}} = \mathbf{Z}_1 + \mathbf{Z}_2 + \cdots + \mathbf{Z}_N$$

or

$$\boxed{\mathbf{Z}_{eq} = \mathbf{Z}_1 + \mathbf{Z}_2 + \cdots + \mathbf{Z}_N} \qquad (9.59)$$

showing that the total or equivalent impedance of series-connected impedances is the sum of the individual impedances. This is similar to the series connection of resistances.

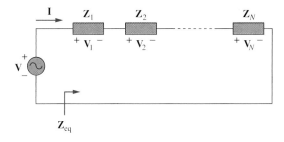

Figure 9.18 N impedances in series.

If $N = 2$, as shown in Fig. 9.19, the current through the impedances is

$$\mathbf{I} = \frac{\mathbf{V}}{\mathbf{Z}_1 + \mathbf{Z}_2} \qquad (9.60)$$

Since $\mathbf{V}_1 = \mathbf{Z}_1\mathbf{I}$ and $\mathbf{V}_2 = \mathbf{Z}_2\mathbf{I}$, then

$$\boxed{\mathbf{V}_1 = \frac{\mathbf{Z}_1}{\mathbf{Z}_1 + \mathbf{Z}_2}\mathbf{V}, \qquad \mathbf{V}_2 = \frac{\mathbf{Z}_2}{\mathbf{Z}_1 + \mathbf{Z}_2}\mathbf{V}} \qquad (9.61)$$

which is the *voltage-division* relationship.

Figure 9.19   Voltage division.

In the same manner, we can obtain the equivalent impedance or admittance of the N parallel-connected impedances shown in Fig. 9.20. The voltage across each impedance is the same. Applying KCL at the top node,

$$\mathbf{I} = \mathbf{I}_1 + \mathbf{I}_2 + \cdots + \mathbf{I}_N = \mathbf{V}\left(\frac{1}{\mathbf{Z}_1} + \frac{1}{\mathbf{Z}_2} + \cdots + \frac{1}{\mathbf{Z}_N}\right) \qquad (9.62)$$

The equivalent impedance is

$$\frac{1}{\mathbf{Z}_{\text{eq}}} = \frac{\mathbf{I}}{\mathbf{V}} = \frac{1}{\mathbf{Z}_1} + \frac{1}{\mathbf{Z}_2} + \cdots + \frac{1}{\mathbf{Z}_N} \qquad (9.63)$$

and the equivalent admittance is

$$\boxed{\mathbf{Y}_{\text{eq}} = \mathbf{Y}_1 + \mathbf{Y}_2 + \cdots + \mathbf{Y}_N} \qquad (9.64)$$

This indicates that the equivalent admittance of a parallel connection of admittances is the sum of the individual admittances.

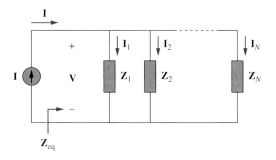

Figure 9.20 N impedances in parallel.

When $N = 2$, as shown in Fig. 9.21, the equivalent impedance becomes

$$\mathbf{Z}_{\text{eq}} = \frac{1}{\mathbf{Y}_{\text{eq}}} = \frac{1}{\mathbf{Y}_1 + \mathbf{Y}_2} = \frac{1}{1/\mathbf{Z}_1 + 1/\mathbf{Z}_2} = \frac{\mathbf{Z}_1\mathbf{Z}_2}{\mathbf{Z}_1 + \mathbf{Z}_2} \qquad (9.65)$$

Also, since

$$\mathbf{V} = \mathbf{I}\mathbf{Z}_{\text{eq}} = \mathbf{I}_1\mathbf{Z}_1 = \mathbf{I}_2\mathbf{Z}_2$$

the currents in the impedances are

$$\boxed{\mathbf{I}_1 = \frac{\mathbf{Z}_2}{\mathbf{Z}_1 + \mathbf{Z}_2}\mathbf{I}, \qquad \mathbf{I}_2 = \frac{\mathbf{Z}_1}{\mathbf{Z}_1 + \mathbf{Z}_2}\mathbf{I}} \qquad (9.66)$$

Figure 9.21   Current division.

which is the *current-division* principle.

The delta-to-wye and wye-to-delta transformations that we applied to resistive circuits are also valid for impedances. With reference to Fig. 9.22, the conversion formulas are as follows.

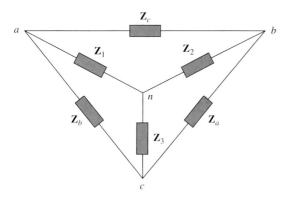

Figure 9.22   Superimposed Y and Δ networks.

Y-Δ Conversion:

$$\mathbf{Z}_a = \frac{\mathbf{Z}_1 \mathbf{Z}_2 + \mathbf{Z}_2 \mathbf{Z}_3 + \mathbf{Z}_3 \mathbf{Z}_1}{\mathbf{Z}_1}$$

$$\mathbf{Z}_b = \frac{\mathbf{Z}_1 \mathbf{Z}_2 + \mathbf{Z}_2 \mathbf{Z}_3 + \mathbf{Z}_3 \mathbf{Z}_1}{\mathbf{Z}_2} \qquad (9.67)$$

$$\mathbf{Z}_c = \frac{\mathbf{Z}_1 \mathbf{Z}_2 + \mathbf{Z}_2 \mathbf{Z}_3 + \mathbf{Z}_3 \mathbf{Z}_1}{\mathbf{Z}_3}$$

Δ-Y Conversion:

$$\mathbf{Z}_1 = \frac{\mathbf{Z}_b \mathbf{Z}_c}{\mathbf{Z}_a + \mathbf{Z}_b + \mathbf{Z}_c}$$

$$\mathbf{Z}_2 = \frac{\mathbf{Z}_c \mathbf{Z}_a}{\mathbf{Z}_a + \mathbf{Z}_b + \mathbf{Z}_c} \qquad (9.68)$$

$$\mathbf{Z}_3 = \frac{\mathbf{Z}_a \mathbf{Z}_b}{\mathbf{Z}_a + \mathbf{Z}_b + \mathbf{Z}_c}$$

A delta or wye circuit is said to be balanced if it has equal impedances in all three branches.

When a Δ-Y circuit is balanced, Eqs. (9.67) and (9.68) become

$$\mathbf{Z}_\Delta = 3\mathbf{Z}_Y \qquad \text{or} \qquad \mathbf{Z}_Y = \frac{1}{3}\mathbf{Z}_\Delta \qquad (9.69)$$

where $\mathbf{Z}_Y = \mathbf{Z}_1 = \mathbf{Z}_2 = \mathbf{Z}_3$ and $\mathbf{Z}_\Delta = \mathbf{Z}_a = \mathbf{Z}_b = \mathbf{Z}_c$.

As you see in this section, the principles of voltage division, current division, circuit reduction, impedance equivalence, and Y-Δ transformation all apply to ac circuits. Chapter 10 will show that other circuit techniques—such as superposition, nodal analysis, mesh analysis, source transformation, the Thevenin theorem, and the Norton theorem—are all applied to ac circuits in a manner similar to their application in dc circuits.

EXAMPLE 9.10

Figure 9.23   For Example 9.10.

Find the input impedance of the circuit in Fig. 9.23. Assume that the circuit operates at $\omega = 50$ rad/s.

Solution:

Let

$\mathbf{Z}_1$ = Impedance of the 2-mF capacitor

$\mathbf{Z}_2$ = Impedance of the 3-Ω resistor in series with the 10-mF capacitor

$\mathbf{Z}_3$ = Impedance of the 0.2-H inductor in series with the 8-Ω resistor

Then

$$\mathbf{Z}_1 = \frac{1}{j\omega C} = \frac{1}{j50 \times 2 \times 10^{-3}} = -j10 \ \Omega$$

$$\mathbf{Z}_2 = 3 + \frac{1}{j\omega C} = 3 + \frac{1}{j50 \times 10 \times 10^{-3}} = (3 - j2) \ \Omega$$

$$\mathbf{Z}_3 = 8 + j\omega L = 8 + j50 \times 0.2 = (8 + j10) \ \Omega$$

The input impedance is

$$\mathbf{Z}_{in} = \mathbf{Z}_1 + \mathbf{Z}_2 \parallel \mathbf{Z}_3 = -j10 + \frac{(3 - j2)(8 + j10)}{11 + j8}$$

$$= -j10 + \frac{(44 + j14)(11 - j8)}{11^2 + 8^2} = -j10 + 3.22 - j1.07 \ \Omega$$

Thus,

$$\mathbf{Z}_{in} = 3.22 - j11.07 \ \Omega$$

PRACTICE PROBLEM 9.10

Figure 9.24   For Practice Prob. 9.10.

Determine the input impedance of the circuit in Fig. 9.24 at $\omega = 10$ rad/s.

Answer: $32.38 - j73.76 \ \Omega$.

EXAMPLE 9.11

Determine $v_o(t)$ in the circuit in Fig. 9.25.

Figure 9.25   For Example 9.11.

Solution:

To do the analysis in the frequency domain, we must first transform the time-domain circuit in Fig. 9.25 to the phasor-domain equivalent in Fig. 9.26. The transformation produces

$$v_s = 20\cos(4t - 15°) \implies \mathbf{V}_s = 20\underline{/-15°}\,\text{V}, \qquad \omega = 4$$

$$10\text{ mF} \implies \frac{1}{j\omega C} = \frac{1}{j4 \times 10 \times 10^{-3}}$$

$$= -j25\ \Omega$$

$$5\text{ H} \implies j\omega L = j4 \times 5 = j20\ \Omega$$

Figure 9.26   The frequency-domain equivalent of the circuit in Fig. 9.25.

Let

$\mathbf{Z}_1$ = Impedance of the 60-Ω resistor

$\mathbf{Z}_2$ = Impedance of the parallel combination of the 10-mF capacitor and the 5-H inductor

Then $\mathbf{Z}_1 = 60\ \Omega$ and

$$\mathbf{Z}_2 = -j25 \parallel j20 = \frac{-j25 \times j20}{-j25 + j20} = j100\ \Omega$$

By the voltage-division principle,

$$\mathbf{V}_o = \frac{\mathbf{Z}_2}{\mathbf{Z}_1 + \mathbf{Z}_2}\mathbf{V}_s = \frac{j100}{60 + j100}(20\underline{/-15°})$$

$$= (0.8575\underline{/30.96°})(20\underline{/-15°}) = 17.15\underline{/15.96°}\ \text{V}.$$

We convert this to the time domain and obtain

$$v_o(t) = 17.15\cos(4t + 15.96°)\text{V}$$

PRACTICE PROBLEM 9.11

Calculate v_o in the circuit in Fig. 9.27.

Answer: $v_o(t) = 7.071\cos(10t - 60°)$ V.

Figure 9.27   For Practice Prob. 9.11.

EXAMPLE 9.12

Find current **I** in the circuit in Fig. 9.28.

Figure 9.28   For Example 9.12.

Solution:

The delta network connected to nodes a, b, and c can be converted to the Y network of Fig. 9.29. We obtain the Y impedances as follows using Eq. (9.68):

$$\mathbf{Z}_{an} = \frac{j4(2 - j4)}{j4 + 2 - j4 + 8} = \frac{4(4 + j2)}{10} = (1.6 + j0.8)\ \Omega$$

$$\mathbf{Z}_{bn} = \frac{j4(8)}{10} = j3.2\ \Omega, \qquad \mathbf{Z}_{cn} = \frac{8(2 - j4)}{10} = (1.6 - j3.2)\ \Omega$$

The total impedance at the source terminals is

$$\mathbf{Z} = 12 + \mathbf{Z}_{an} + (\mathbf{Z}_{bn} - j3)\ \|\ (\mathbf{Z}_{cn} + j6 + 8)$$

$$= 12 + 1.6 + j0.8 + (j0.2)\ \|\ (9.6 + j2.8)$$

$$= 13.6 + j0.8 + \frac{j0.2(9.6 + j2.8)}{9.6 + j3}$$

$$= 13.6 + j1 = 13.64\underline{/4.204°}\ \Omega$$

The desired current is

$$\mathbf{I} = \frac{\mathbf{V}}{\mathbf{Z}} = \frac{50\underline{/0°}}{13.64\underline{/4.204°}} = 3.666\underline{/-4.204°}\ \text{A}$$

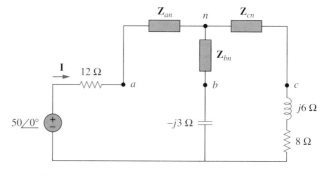

Figure 9.29   The circuit in Fig. 9.28 after delta-to-wye transformation.

Find **I** in the circuit in Fig. 9.30.

Answer: $6.364\underline{/3.802°}$ A.

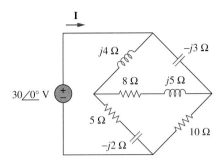

Figure 9.30   For Practice Prob. 9.12.

†9.8 APPLICATIONS

In Chapters 7 and 8, we saw certain uses of RC, RL, and RLC circuits in dc applications. These circuits also have ac applications; among them are coupling circuits, phase-shifting circuits, filters, resonant circuits, ac bridge circuits, and transformers. This list of applications is inexhaustive. We will consider some of them later. It will suffice here to observe two simple ones: RC phase-shifting circuits, and ac bridge circuits.

9.8.1 Phase-Shifters

A phase-shifting circuit is often employed to correct an undesirable phase shift already present in a circuit or to produce special desired effects. An RC circuit is suitable for this purpose because its capacitor causes the circuit current to lead the applied voltage. Two commonly used RC circuits are shown in Fig. 9.31. (RL circuits or any reactive circuits could also serve the same purpose.)

In Fig. 9.31(a), the circuit current **I** leads the applied voltage $\mathbf{V}_i$ by some phase angle θ, where $0 < \theta < 90°$, depending on the values of R and C. If $X_C = -1/\omega C$, then the total impedance is $\mathbf{Z} = R + jX_C$, and the phase shift is given by

$$\theta = \tan^{-1}\frac{X_C}{R} \tag{9.70}$$

This shows that the amount of phase shift depends on the values of R, C, and the operating frequency. Since the output voltage $\mathbf{V}_o$ across the resistor is in phase with the current, $\mathbf{V}_o$ leads (positive phase shift) $\mathbf{V}_i$ as shown in Fig. 9.32(a).

In Fig. 9.31(b), the output is taken across the capacitor. The current **I** leads the input voltage $\mathbf{V}_i$ by θ, but the output voltage $v_o(t)$ across the capacitor lags (negative phase shift) the input voltage $v_i(t)$ as illustrated in Fig. 9.32(b).

We should keep in mind that the simple RC circuits in Fig. 9.31 also act as voltage dividers. Therefore, as the phase shift θ approaches 90°, the output voltage $\mathbf{V}_o$ approaches zero. For this reason, these simple RC circuits are used only when small amounts of phase shift are required.

Figure 9.31   Series RC shift circuits: (a) leading output, (b) lagging output.

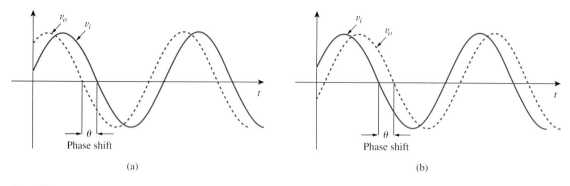

Figure 9.32　Phase shift in RC circuits: (a) leading output, (b) lagging output.

If it is desired to have phase shifts greater than $60°$, simple RC networks are cascaded, thereby providing a total phase shift equal to the sum of the individual phase shifts. In practice, the phase shifts due to the stages are not equal, because the succeeding stages load down the earlier stages unless op amps are used to separate the stages.

EXAMPLE 9.13

Design an RC circuit to provide a phase of $90°$ leading.

Solution:

If we select circuit components of equal ohmic value, say $R = |X_C| = 20 \Omega$, at a particular frequency, according to Eq. (9.70), the phase shift is exactly $45°$. By cascading two similar RC circuits in Fig. 9.31(a), we obtain the circuit in Fig. 9.33, providing a positive or leading phase shift of $90°$, as we shall soon show. Using the series-parallel combination technique, $\mathbf{Z}$ in Fig. 9.33 is obtained as

$$\mathbf{Z} = 20 \parallel (20 - j20) = \frac{20(20 - j20)}{40 - j20} = 12 - j4 \ \Omega \qquad (9.13.1)$$

Using voltage division,

$$\mathbf{V}_1 = \frac{\mathbf{Z}}{\mathbf{Z} - j20}\mathbf{V}_i = \frac{12 - j4}{12 - j24}\mathbf{V}_i = \frac{\sqrt{2}}{3}\underline{/45°}\,\mathbf{V}_i \qquad (9.13.2)$$

and

$$\mathbf{V}_o = \frac{20}{20 - j20}\mathbf{V}_1 = \frac{\sqrt{2}}{2}\underline{/45°}\,\mathbf{V}_1 \qquad (9.13.3)$$

Substituting Eq. (9.13.2) into Eq. (9.13.3) yields

$$\mathbf{V}_o = \left(\frac{\sqrt{2}}{2}\underline{/45°}\right)\left(\frac{\sqrt{2}}{3}\underline{/45°}\,\mathbf{V}_i\right) = \frac{1}{3}\underline{/90°}\,\mathbf{V}_i$$

Thus, the output leads the input by $90°$ but its magnitude is only about 33 percent of the input.

Figure 9.33　An RC phase shift circuit with $90°$ leading phase shift; for Example 9.13.

PRACTICE PROBLEM 9.13

Design an *RC* circuit to provide a 90° lagging phase shift. If a voltage of 10 V is applied, what is the output voltage?

Answer: Figure 9.34 shows a typical design; 3.33 V.

Figure 9.34   For Practice Prob. 9.13.

EXAMPLE 9.14

For the *RL* circuit shown in Fig. 9.35(a), calculate the amount of phase shift produced at 2 kHz.

Solution:

At 2 kHz, we transform the 10-mH and 5-mH inductances to the corresponding impedances.

$$10 \text{ mH} \implies X_L = \omega L = 2\pi \times 2 \times 10^3 \times 10 \times 10^{-3}$$
$$= 40\pi = 125.7 \ \Omega$$

$$5 \text{ mH} \implies X_L = \omega L = 2\pi \times 2 \times 10^3 \times 5 \times 10^{-3}$$
$$= 20\pi = 62.83 \ \Omega$$

Figure 9.35   For Example 9.14.

Consider the circuit in Fig. 9.35(b). The impedance **Z** is the parallel combination of $j125.7 \ \Omega$ and $100 + j62.83 \ \Omega$. Hence,

$$\mathbf{Z} = j125.7 \parallel (100 + j62.83)$$
$$= \frac{j125.7(100 + j62.83)}{100 + j188.5} = 69.56 \underline{/60.1°} \ \Omega \tag{9.14.1}$$

Using voltage division,

$$\mathbf{V}_1 = \frac{\mathbf{Z}}{\mathbf{Z} + 150} \mathbf{V}_i = \frac{69.56 \underline{/60.1°}}{184.7 + j60.3} \mathbf{V}_i \tag{9.14.2}$$
$$= 0.3582 \underline{/42.02°} \ \mathbf{V}_i$$

and

$$\mathbf{V}_o = \frac{j62.832}{100 + j62.832} \mathbf{V}_1 = 0.532 \underline{/57.86°} \ \mathbf{V}_1 \tag{9.14.3}$$

Combining Eqs. (9.14.2) and (9.14.3),

$$\mathbf{V}_o = (0.532 \underline{/57.86°})(0.3582 \underline{/42.02°}) \ \mathbf{V}_i = 0.1906 \underline{/100°} \ \mathbf{V}_i$$

showing that the output is about 19 percent of the input in magnitude but leading the input by 100°. If the circuit is terminated by a load, the load will affect the phase shift.

PRACTICE PROBLEM 9.14

Figure 9.36 For Practice Prob. 9.14.

Refer to the *RL* circuit in Fig. 9.36. If 1 V is applied, find the magnitude and the phase shift produced at 5 kHz. Specify whether the phase shift is leading or lagging.

Answer: 0.172, 120.4°, lagging.

9.8.2 AC Bridges

An ac bridge circuit is used in measuring the inductance L of an inductor or the capacitance C of a capacitor. It is similar in form to the Wheatstone bridge for measuring an unknown resistance (discussed in Section 4.10) and follows the same principle. To measure L and C, however, an ac source is needed as well as an ac meter instead of the galvanometer. The ac meter may be a sensitive ac ammeter or voltmeter.

Consider the general ac bridge circuit displayed in Fig. 9.37. The bridge is *balanced* when no current flows through the meter. This means that $\mathbf{V}_1 = \mathbf{V}_2$. Applying the voltage division principle,

$$\mathbf{V}_1 = \frac{\mathbf{Z}_2}{\mathbf{Z}_1 + \mathbf{Z}_2}\mathbf{V}_s = \mathbf{V}_2 = \frac{\mathbf{Z}_x}{\mathbf{Z}_3 + \mathbf{Z}_x}\mathbf{V}_s \qquad (9.71)$$

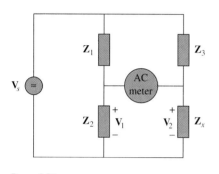

Figure 9.37 A general ac bridge.

Thus,

$$\frac{\mathbf{Z}_2}{\mathbf{Z}_1 + \mathbf{Z}_2} = \frac{\mathbf{Z}_x}{\mathbf{Z}_3 + \mathbf{Z}_x} \qquad \Longrightarrow \qquad \mathbf{Z}_2\mathbf{Z}_3 = \mathbf{Z}_1\mathbf{Z}_x \qquad (9.72)$$

or

$$\boxed{\mathbf{Z}_x = \frac{\mathbf{Z}_3}{\mathbf{Z}_1}\mathbf{Z}_2} \qquad (9.73)$$

This is the balanced equation for the ac bridge and is similar to Eq. (4.30) for the resistance bridge except that the R's are replaced by $\mathbf{Z}$'s.

Specific ac bridges for measuring L and C are shown in Fig. 9.38, where L_x and C_x are the unknown inductance and capacitance to be measured while L_s and C_s are a standard inductance and capacitance (the values of which are known to great precision). In each case, two resistors, R_1 and R_2, are varied until the ac meter reads zero. Then the bridge is balanced. From Eq. (9.73), we obtain

$$L_x = \frac{R_2}{R_1}L_s \qquad (9.74)$$

and

$$C_x = \frac{R_1}{R_2}C_s \qquad (9.75)$$

Notice that the balancing of the ac bridges in Fig. 9.38 does not depend on the frequency f of the ac source, since f does not appear in the relationships in Eqs. (9.74) and (9.75).

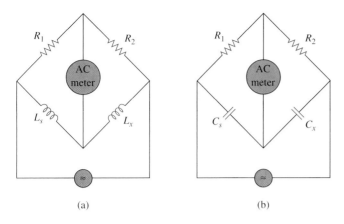

Figure 9.38   Specific ac bridges: (a) for measuring L, (b) for measuring C.

EXAMPLE 9.15

The ac bridge circuit of Fig. 9.37 balances when $\mathbf{Z}_1$ is a 1-kΩ resistor, $\mathbf{Z}_2$ is a 4.2-kΩ resistor, $\mathbf{Z}_3$ is a parallel combination of a 1.5-MΩ resistor and a 12-pF capacitor, and $f = 2$ kHz. Find: (a) the series components that make up $\mathbf{Z}_x$, and (b) the parallel components that make up $\mathbf{Z}_x$.

Solution:

From Eq. (9.73),

$$\mathbf{Z}_x = \frac{\mathbf{Z}_3}{\mathbf{Z}_1}\mathbf{Z}_2 \tag{9.15.1}$$

where $\mathbf{Z}_x = R_x + jX_x$,

$$\mathbf{Z}_1 = 1000\ \Omega, \qquad \mathbf{Z}_2 = 4200\ \Omega \tag{9.15.2}$$

and

$$\mathbf{Z}_3 = R_3 \parallel \frac{1}{j\omega C_3} = \frac{\dfrac{R_3}{j\omega C_3}}{R_3 + 1/j\omega C_3} = \frac{R_3}{1 + j\omega R_3 C_3}$$

Since $R_3 = 1.5$ MΩ and $C_3 = 12$ pF,

$$\mathbf{Z}_3 = \frac{1.5 \times 10^6}{1 + j2\pi \times 2 \times 10^3 \times 1.5 \times 10^6 \times 12 \times 10^{-12}} = \frac{1.5 \times 10^6}{1 + j0.2262}$$

or

$$\mathbf{Z}_3 = 1.427 - j0.3228\ \text{M}\Omega \tag{9.15.3}$$

(a) Assuming that $\mathbf{Z}_x$ is made up of series components, we substitute Eqs. (9.15.2) and (9.15.3) in Eq. (9.15.1) and obtain

$$R_x + jX_x = \frac{4200}{1000}(1.427 - j0.3228) \times 10^6$$

$$= (5.993 - j1.356)\ \text{M}\Omega$$

Equating the real and imaginary parts yields $R_x = 5.993$ MΩ and a capacitive reactance

$$X_x = \frac{1}{\omega C} = 1.356 \times 10^6$$

or

$$C = \frac{1}{\omega X_x} = \frac{1}{2\pi \times 2 \times 10^3 \times 1.356 \times 10^6} = 58.69 \text{ pF}$$

(b) If $\mathbf{Z}_x$ is made up of parallel components, we notice that $\mathbf{Z}_3$ is also a parallel combination. Hence, Eq. (9.15.1) becomes

$$\mathbf{Z}_x = \frac{4200}{1000} R_3 \left\| \frac{1}{j\omega C_3} = 4.2 R_3 \right\| \frac{1}{j\omega C_3} = 4.2\mathbf{Z}_3 \qquad (9.15.4)$$

This simply means that unknown impedance $\mathbf{Z}_x$ is 4.2 times $\mathbf{Z}_3$. Thus

$$\mathbf{Z}_x = R_x + jX_x = 4.3\mathbf{Z}_3 = 4.3 \left(R_3 \left\| \frac{1}{j\omega C_3} \right) = 4.3 \frac{\dfrac{R_3}{j\omega C_3}}{R_3 + \dfrac{1}{j\omega C_3}} \right.$$

$$= \frac{4.3 R_3}{1 + j\omega R_3 C_3}$$

$$R_x + jX_x = \frac{4.3 \times 1.5 \times 10^6}{1 + j2\pi \times 2 \times 10^3 \times 1.5 \times 10^6 \times 12 \times 10^{-12}}$$

$$= \frac{6.45 \times 10^6}{1 + j0.2262} = (6.137 - j1.387) \times 10^6$$

Equating real and imaginary parts leads to

$$R_x = 6.137 \text{ M}\Omega$$

$$X_x = \frac{1}{\omega C_x} = 1.387 \times 10^6 \Rightarrow C_x = \frac{1}{2\pi \times 2 \times 10^3 \times 1.387 \times 10^6}$$

$$= 57.4 \text{ pF}$$

PRACTICE PROBLEM 9.15

In the ac bridge circuit of Fig. 9.37, suppose that balance is achieved when $\mathbf{Z}_1$ is a 4.8-kΩ resistor, $\mathbf{Z}_2$ is a 10-Ω resistor in series with a 0.25-μH inductor, $\mathbf{Z}_3$ is a 12-kΩ resistor, and $f = 6$ MHz. Determine the series components that make up $\mathbf{Z}_x$.

Answer: A 25-Ω resistor in series with a 0.625-μH inductor.

9.9   SUMMARY

1. A sinusoid is a signal in the form of the sine or cosine function. It has the general form

$$v(t) = V_m \cos(\omega t + \phi)$$

where V_m is the amplitude, $\omega = 2\pi f$ is the angular frequency, $(\omega t + \phi)$ is the argument, and ϕ is the phase.

2. A phasor is a complex quantity that represents both the magnitude and the phase of a sinusoid. Given the sinusoid $v(t) = V_m \cos(\omega t + \phi)$, its phasor $\mathbf{V}$ is

$$\mathbf{V} = V_m \underline{/\phi}$$

3. In ac circuits, voltage and current phasors always have a fixed relation to one another at any moment of time. If $v(t) = V_m \cos(\omega t + \phi_v)$ represents the voltage through an element and $i(t) = I_m \cos(\omega t + \phi_i)$ represents the current through the element, then $\phi_i = \phi_v$ if the element is a resistor, ϕ_i leads ϕ_v by 90° if the element is a capacitor, and ϕ_i lags ϕ_v by 90° if the element is an inductor.

4. The impedance $\mathbf{Z}$ of a circuit is the ratio of the phasor voltage across it to the phasor current through it:

$$\mathbf{Z} = \frac{\mathbf{V}}{\mathbf{I}} = R(\omega) + jX(\omega)$$

The admittance $\mathbf{Y}$ is the reciprocal of impedance:

$$\mathbf{Y} = \frac{1}{\mathbf{Z}} = G(\omega) + jB(\omega)$$

Impedances are combined in series or in parallel the same way as resistances in series or parallel; that is, impedances in series add while admittances in parallel add.

5. For a resistor $\mathbf{Z} = R$, for an inductor $\mathbf{Z} = jX = j\omega L$, and for a capacitor $\mathbf{Z} = -jX = 1/j\omega C$.

6. Basic circuit laws (Ohm's and Kirchhoff's) apply to ac circuits in the same manner as they do for dc circuits; that is,

$$\mathbf{V} = \mathbf{ZI}$$
$$\sum \mathbf{I}_k = 0 \quad \text{(KCL)}$$
$$\sum \mathbf{V}_k = 0 \quad \text{(KVL)}$$

7. The techniques of voltage/current division, series/parallel combination of impedance/admittance, circuit reduction, and Y-Δ transformation all apply to ac circuit analysis.

8. AC circuits are applied in phase-shifters and bridges.

REVIEW QUESTIONS

9.1 Which of the following is *not* a right way to express the sinusoid $A \cos \omega t$?

   (a) $A \cos 2\pi ft$ (b) $A \cos(2\pi t/T)$
   (c) $A \cos \omega(t - T)$ (d) $A \sin(\omega t - 90°)$

9.2 A function that repeats itself after fixed intervals is said to be:

   (a) a phasor   (b) harmonic
   (c) periodic   (d) reactive

9.3 Which of these frequencies has the shorter period?

   (a) 1 krad/s   (b) 1 kHz

9.4 If $v_1 = 30 \sin(\omega t + 10°)$ and $v_2 = 20 \sin(\omega t + 50°)$, which of these statements are true?

   (a) v_1 leads v_2 (b) v_2 leads v_1
   (c) v_2 lags v_1 (d) v_1 lags v_2
   (e) v_1 and v_2 are in phase

9.5 The voltage across an inductor leads the current through it by 90°.

   (a) True   (b) False

9.6 The imaginary part of impedance is called:

   (a) resistance   (b) admittance
   (c) susceptance   (d) conductance
   (e) reactance

9.7 The impedance of a capacitor increases with increasing frequency.

(a) True   (b) False

9.8 At what frequency will the output voltage $v_o(t)$ in Fig. 9.39 be equal to the input voltage $v(t)$?

(a) 0 rad/s   (b) 1 rad/s   (c) 4 rad/s
(d) ∞ rad/s   (e) none of the above

Figure 9.39   For Review Question 9.8.

9.9 A series RC circuit has $V_R = 12$ V and $V_C = 5$ V. The supply voltage is:

(a) -7 V   (b) 7 V   (c) 13 V   (d) 17 V

9.10 A series RCL circuit has $R = 30$ Ω, $X_C = -50$ Ω, and $X_L = 90$ Ω. The impedance of the circuit is:

(a) $30 + j140$ Ω   (b) $30 + j40$ Ω
(c) $30 - j40$ Ω   (d) $-30 - j40$ Ω
(e) $-30 + j40$ Ω

Answers: 9.1d, 9.2c, 9.3b, 9.4b,d, 9.5a, 9.6e, 9.7b, 9.8d, 9.9c, 9.10b.

PROBLEMS

Section 9.2   Sinusoids

9.1 In a linear circuit, the voltage source is

$$v_s = 12 \sin(10^3 t + 24°) \text{ V}$$

(a) What is the angular frequency of the voltage?
(b) What is the frequency of the source?
(c) Find the period of the voltage.
(d) Express v_s in cosine form.
(e) Determine v_s at $t = 2.5$ ms.

9.2 A current source in a linear circuit has

$$i_s = 8 \cos(500\pi t - 25°) \text{ A}$$

(a) What is the amplitude of the current?
(b) What is the angular frequency?
(c) Find the frequency of the current.
(d) Calculate i_s at $t = 2$ ms.

9.3 Express the following functions in cosine form:

(a) $4 \sin(\omega t - 30°)$ (b) $-2 \sin 6t$
(c) $-10 \sin(\omega t + 20°)$

9.4 (a) Express $v = 8 \cos(7t + 15°)$ in sine form.
(b) Convert $i = -10 \sin(3t - 85°)$ to cosine form.

9.5 Given $v_1 = 20 \sin(\omega t + 60°)$ and $v_2 = 60 \cos(\omega t - 10°)$, determine the phase angle between the two sinusoids and which one lags the other.

9.6 For the following pairs of sinusoids, determine which one leads and by how much.

(a) $v(t) = 10 \cos(4t - 60°)$ and
$i(t) = 4 \sin(4t + 50°)$
(b) $v_1(t) = 4 \cos(377t + 10°)$ and
$v_2(t) = -20 \cos 377t$
(c) $x(t) = 13 \cos 2t + 5 \sin 2t$ and
$y(t) = 15 \cos(2t - 11.8°)$

Section 9.3   Phasors

9.7 If $f(\phi) = \cos\phi + j \sin\phi$, show that $f(\phi) = e^{j\phi}$.

9.8 Calculate these complex numbers and express your results in rectangular form:

(a) $\dfrac{15/45°}{3 - j4} + j2$

(b) $\dfrac{8/-20°}{(2 + j)(3 - j4)} + \dfrac{10}{-5 + j12}$

(c) $10 + (8/50°)(5 - j12)$

9.9 Evaluate the following complex numbers and express your results in rectangular form:

(a) $2 + \dfrac{3 + j4}{5 - j8}$ (b) $4/-10° + \dfrac{1 - j2}{3/6°}$

(c) $\dfrac{8/10° + 6/-20°}{9/80° - 4/50°}$

9.10   Given that $z_1 = 6 - j8$, $z_2 = 10\underline{/-30°}$, and $z_3 = 8e^{-j120°}$, find:

(a) $z_1 + z_2 + z_3$

(b) $\dfrac{z_1 z_2}{z_3}$

9.11   Given the complex numbers $z_1 = -3 + j4$ and $z_2 = 12 + j5$, find:

(a) $z_1 z_2$ (b) $\dfrac{z_1}{z_2^*}$ (c) $\dfrac{z_1 + z_2}{z_1 - z_2}$

9.12   Let $\mathbf{X} = 8\underline{/40°}$ and $\mathbf{Y} = 10\underline{/-30°}$. Evaluate the following quantities and express your results in polar form.

(a) $(\mathbf{X} + \mathbf{Y})\mathbf{X}^*$ (b) $(\mathbf{X} - \mathbf{Y})^*$ (c) $(\mathbf{X} + \mathbf{Y})/\mathbf{X}$

9.13   Evaluate the following complex numbers:

(a) $\dfrac{2 + j3}{1 - j6} + \dfrac{7 - j8}{-5 + j11}$

(b) $\dfrac{(5\underline{/10°})(10\underline{/-40°})}{(4\underline{/-80°})(-6\underline{/50°})}$

(c) $\begin{vmatrix} 2 + j3 & -j2 \\ -j2 & 8 - j5 \end{vmatrix}$

9.14   Simplify the following expressions:

(a) $\dfrac{(5 - j6) - (2 + j8)}{(-3 + j4)(5 - j) + (4 - j6)}$

(b) $\dfrac{(240\underline{/75°} + 160\underline{/-30°})(60 - j80)}{(67 + j84)(20\underline{/32°})}$

(c) $\left(\dfrac{10 + j20}{3 + j4}\right)^2 \sqrt{(10 + j5)(16 - j20)}$

9.15   Evaluate these determinants:

(a) $\begin{vmatrix} 10 + j6 & 2 - j3 \\ -5 & -1 + j \end{vmatrix}$

(b) $\begin{vmatrix} 20\underline{/-30°} & -4\underline{/-10°} \\ 16\underline{/0°} & 3\underline{/45°} \end{vmatrix}$

(c) $\begin{vmatrix} 1 - j & -j & 0 \\ j & 1 & -j \\ 1 & j & 1 + j \end{vmatrix}$

9.16   Transform the following sinusoids to phasors:

(a) $-10\cos(4t + 75°)$ (b) $5\sin(20t - 10°)$
(c) $4\cos 2t + 3\sin 2t$

9.17   Express the sum of the following sinusoidal signals in the form of $A\cos(\omega t + \theta)$ with $A > 0$ and $0 < \theta < 360°$.

(a) $8\cos(5t - 30°) + 6\cos 5t$

(b) $20\cos(120\pi t + 45°) - 30\sin(120\pi t + 20°)$

(c) $4\sin 8t + 3\sin(8t - 10°)$

9.18   Obtain the sinusoids corresponding to each of the following phasors:

(a) $\mathbf{V}_1 = 60\underline{/15°}$ V, $\omega = 1$

(b) $\mathbf{V}_2 = 6 + j8$ V, $\omega = 40$

(c) $\mathbf{I}_1 = 2.8e^{-j\pi/3}$ A, $\omega = 377$

(d) $\mathbf{I}_2 = -0.5 - j1.2$ A, $\omega = 10^3$

9.19   Using phasors, find:

(a) $3\cos(20t + 10°) - 5\cos(20t - 30°)$

(b) $40\sin 50t + 30\cos(50t - 45°)$

(c) $20\sin 400t + 10\cos(400t + 60°)$
        $- 5\sin(400t - 20°)$

9.20   Use phasors to simplify the following:

(a) $v = 4\sin(377t - 60°) - 5\cos(377t + 40°)$ V

(b) $i = 10\cos 5t + 8\dfrac{d}{dt}\sin(5t + 20°)$ A

9.21   Simplify the following:

(a) $f(t) = 5\cos(2t + 15°) - 4\sin(2t - 30°)$

(b) $g(t) = 8\sin t + 4\cos(t + 50°)$

(c) $h(t) = \displaystyle\int_0^t (10\cos 40t + 50\sin 40t)\,dt$

9.22   An alternating voltage is given by $v(t) = 20\cos(5t - 30°)$ V. Use phasors to find

$$10v(t) + 4\frac{dv}{dt} - 2\int_{-\infty}^t v(t)\,dt$$

Assume that the value of the integral is zero at $t = -\infty$.

9.23   Find a single sinusoid corresponding to each of these phasors:

(a) $\mathbf{V} = 40\underline{/-60°}$ V

(b) $\mathbf{V} = -30\underline{/10°} + 50\underline{/60°}$ V

(c) $\mathbf{I} = j6e^{-j10°}$ A   (d) $\mathbf{I} = \dfrac{2}{j} + 10\underline{/-45°}$ A

9.24   Find $v(t)$ in the following integrodifferential equations using the phasor approach:

(a) $v(t) + \displaystyle\int v\,dt = 10\cos t$

(b) $\dfrac{dv}{dt} + 5v(t) + 4\displaystyle\int v\,dt = 20\sin(4t + 10°)$

9.25 Using phasors, determine $i(t)$ in the following equations:

(a) $2\dfrac{di}{dt} + 3i(t) = 4\cos(2t - 45°)$

(b) $10\displaystyle\int i\,dt + \dfrac{di}{dt} + 6i(t) = 5\cos(5t + 22°)$

9.26 The loop equation for a series RLC circuit gives

$$\frac{di}{dt} + 2i + \int_{-\infty}^{t} i\,dt = \cos 2t$$

Assuming that the value of the integral at $t = -\infty$ is zero, find $i(t)$ using the phasor method.

9.27 A parallel RLC circuit has the node equation

$$\frac{dv}{dt} + 50v + 100\int v\,dt = 110\cos(377t - 10°)$$

Determine $v(t)$ using the phasor method. You may assume that the value of the integral at $t = -\infty$ is zero.

Section 9.4   Phasor Relationships for Circuit Elements

9.28 Determine the current that flows through an 8-Ω resistor connected to a voltage source $v_s = 110\cos 377t$ V.

9.29 What is the instantaneous voltage across a 2-μF capacitor when the current through it is $i = 4\sin(10^6 t + 25°)$ A?

9.30 The voltage across a 4-mH inductor is $v = 60\cos(500t - 65°)$ V. Find the instantaneous current through it.

9.31 A current source of $i(t) = 10\sin(377t + 30°)$ A is applied to a single-element load. The resulting voltage across the element is $v(t) = -65\cos(377t + 120°)$ V. What type of element is this? Calculate its value.

9.32 Two elements are connected in series as shown in Fig. 9.40. If $i = 12\cos(2t - 30°)$ A, find the element values.

180 cos(2t + 10°) V

Figure 9.40   For Prob. 9.32.

9.33 A series RL circuit is connected to a 110-V ac source. If the voltage across the resistor is 85 V, find the voltage across the inductor.

9.34 What value of ω will cause the forced response v_o in Fig. 9.41 to be zero?

50 cos ωt V

Figure 9.41   For Prob. 9.34.

Section 9.5   Impedance and Admittance

9.35 If $v_s = 5\cos 2t$ V in the circuit of Fig. 9.42, find v_o.

Figure 9.42   For Prob. 9.35.

9.36 In the circuit of Fig. 9.43, determine i. Let $v_s = 60\cos(200t - 10°)$ V.

Figure 9.43   For Prob. 9.36.

9.37 Find i_x when $i_s = 2\sin 5t$ A is supplied to the circuit in Fig. 9.44.

Figure 9.44   For Prob. 9.37.

9.38 Find $i(t)$ and $v(t)$ in each of the circuits of Fig. 9.45.

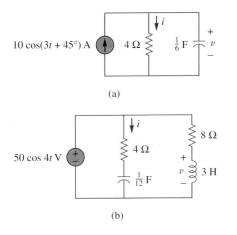

(a)

(b)

Figure 9.45   For Prob. 9.38.

9.39 Calculate $i_1(t)$ and $i_2(t)$ in the circuit of Fig. 9.46 if the source frequency is 60 Hz.

Figure 9.46   For Prob. 9.39.

9.40 In the circuit of Fig. 9.47, find i_o when:

(a) $\omega = 1$ rad/s   (b) $\omega = 5$ rad/s
(c) $\omega = 10$ rad/s

Figure 9.47   For Prob. 9.40.

9.41 Find $v(t)$ in the RLC circuit of Fig. 9.48.

Figure 9.48   For Prob. 9.41.

9.42 Calculate $v_o(t)$ in the circuit in Fig. 9.49.

Figure 9.49   For Prob. 9.42.

9.43 Determine $i_o(t)$ in the RLC circuit of Fig. 9.50.

Figure 9.50   For Prob. 9.43.

9.44 Calculate $i(t)$ in the circuit of Fig. 9.51.

Figure 9.51   For Prob. 9.44.

9.45 Find current $\mathbf{I}_o$ in the network of Fig. 9.52.

Figure 9.52   For Prob. 9.45.

9.46 If $i_s = 5\cos(10t + 40°)$ A in the circuit in Fig. 9.53, find i_o.

Figure 9.53   For Prob. 9.46.

9.47 In the circuit of Fig. 9.54, determine the value of $i_s(t)$.

Figure 9.54 For Prob. 9.47.

9.48 Given that $v_s(t) = 20\sin(100t - 40°)$ in Fig. 9.55, determine $i_x(t)$.

Figure 9.55 For Prob. 9.48.

9.49 Find $v_s(t)$ in the circuit of Fig. 9.56 if the current i_x through the 1-Ω resistor is $0.5\sin 200t$ A.

Figure 9.56 For Prob. 9.49.

9.50 Determine v_x in the circuit of Fig. 9.57. Let $i_s(t) = 5\cos(100t + 40°)$ A.

Figure 9.57 For Prob. 9.50.

9.51 If the voltage v_o across the 2-Ω resistor in the circuit of Fig. 9.58 is $10\cos 2t$ V, obtain i_s.

Figure 9.58 For Prob. 9.51.

9.52 If $V_o = 8\underline{/30°}$ V in the circuit of Fig. 9.59, find I_s.

Figure 9.59 For Prob. 9.52.

9.53 Find I_o in the circuit of Fig. 9.60.

Figure 9.60 For Prob. 9.53.

9.54 In the circuit of Fig. 9.61, find V_s if $I_o = 2\underline{/0°}$ A.

Figure 9.61 For Prob. 9.54.

9.55 Find Z in the network of Fig. 9.62, given that $V_o = 4\underline{/0°}$ V.

Figure 9.62 For Prob. 9.55.

Section 9.7   Impedance Combinations

9.56   Find the input impedance for the circuit of Fig. 9.63
given that $\omega = 10$ rad/s.

Figure 9.63   For Prob. 9.56.

9.57   At $\omega = 1$ rad/s, obtain the input admittance in the
circuit of Fig. 9.64.

Figure 9.64   For Prob. 9.57.

9.58   At $\omega = 50$ rad/s, determine $\mathbf{Z}_{in}$ for each of the
circuits in Fig. 9.65.

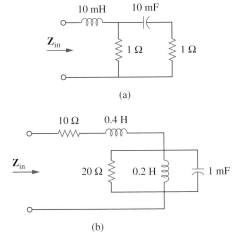

(a)

(b)

Figure 9.65   For Prob. 9.58.

9.59   Calculate $\mathbf{Z}_{eq}$ for the circuit in Fig. 9.66.

Figure 9.66   For Prob. 9.59.

9.60   Obtain $\mathbf{Z}_{in}$ for the circuit in Fig. 9.67.

Figure 9.67   For Prob. 9.60.

9.61   Find $\mathbf{Z}_{eq}$ in the circuit of Fig. 9.68.

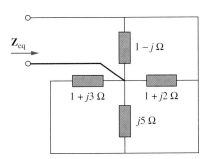

Figure 9.68   For Prob. 9.61.

9.62   For the circuit in Fig. 9.69, find the input impedance
$\mathbf{Z}_{in}$ at 10 krad/s.

Figure 9.69   For Prob. 9.62.

9.63   For the circuit in Fig. 9.70, find the value of $\mathbf{Z}_T$.

Figure 9.70   For Prob. 9.63.

9.64   Find $\mathbf{Z}_T$ and $\mathbf{I}$ in the circuit of Fig. 9.71.

Figure 9.71   For Prob. 9.64.

9.65   Determine $\mathbf{I}$ and $\mathbf{Z}_T$ for the circuit in Fig. 9.72.

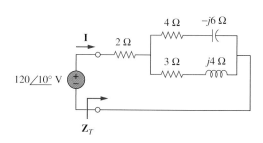

Figure 9.72   For Prob. 9.65.

9.66   For the circuit in Fig. 9.73, calculate $\mathbf{Z}_T$ and $\mathbf{V}_{ab}$.

Figure 9.73   For Prob. 9.66.

9.67   At $\omega = 10^3$ rad/s, find the input admittance of each of the circuits in Fig. 9.74.

(a)

(b)

Figure 9.74   For Prob. 9.67.

9.68   Determine $\mathbf{Y}_{eq}$ for the circuit in Fig. 9.75.

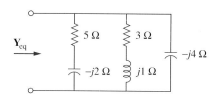

Figure 9.75   For Prob. 9.68.

9.69   Find the equivalent admittance $\mathbf{Y}_{eq}$ of the circuit in Fig. 9.76.

Figure 9.76   For Prob. 9.69.

9.70   Find the equivalent impedance of the circuit in Fig. 9.77.

Figure 9.77   For Prob. 9.70.

9.71 Obtain the equivalent impedance of the circuit in Fig. 9.78.

Figure 9.78   For Prob. 9.71.

9.72 Calculate the value of $\mathbf{Z}_{ab}$ in the network of Fig. 9.79.

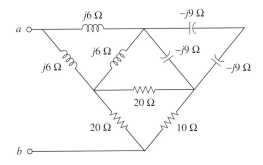

Figure 9.79   For Prob. 9.72.

9.73 Determine the equivalent impedance of the circuit in Fig. 9.80.

Figure 9.80   For Prob. 9.73.

Section 9.8   Applications

9.74 Design an RL circuit to provide a 90° leading phase shift.

9.75 Design a circuit that will transform a sinusoidal input to a cosinusoidal output.

9.76 A capacitor in series with a 66-Ω resistor is connected to a 120-V, 60-Hz source. If the impedance of the circuit is 116 Ω, determine the size of the capacitor.

9.77 Refer to the RC circuit in Fig. 9.81.

(a) Calculate the phase shift at 2 MHz.
(b) Find the frequency where the phase shift is 45°.

Figure 9.81   For Prob. 9.77.

9.78 A coil with impedance $8 + j6\ \Omega$ is connected in series with a capacitive reactance X. The series combination is connected in parallel with a resistor R. Given that the equivalent impedance of the resulting circuit is $5\underline{/0°}\ \Omega$, find the value of R and X.

9.79 (a) Calculate the phase shift of the circuit in Fig. 9.82.
(b) State whether the phase shift is leading or lagging (output with respect to input).
(c) Determine the magnitude of the output when the input is 120 V.

Figure 9.82   For Prob. 9.79.

9.80 Consider the phase-shifting circuit in Fig. 9.83. Let $\mathbf{V}_i = 120$ V operating at 60 Hz. Find:

(a) $\mathbf{V}_o$ when R is maximum
(b) $\mathbf{V}_o$ when R is minimum
(c) the value of R that will produce a phase shift of 45°

Figure 9.83   For Prob. 9.80.

9.81 The ac bridge in Fig. 9.37 is balanced when $R_1 = 400 \, \Omega$, $R_2 = 600 \, \Omega$, $R_3 = 1.2 \, k\Omega$, and $C_2 = 0.3 \, \mu F$. Find R_x and C_x.

9.82 A capacitance bridge balances when $R_1 = 100 \, \Omega$, $R_2 = 2 \, k\Omega$, and $C_s = 40 \, \mu F$. What is C_x, the capacitance of the capacitor under test?

9.83 An inductive bridge balances when $R_1 = 1.2 \, k\Omega$, $R_2 = 500 \, \Omega$, and $L_s = 250 \, mH$. What is the value of L_x, the inductance of the inductor under test?

9.84 The ac bridge shown in Fig. 9.84 is known as a *Maxwell bridge* and is used for accurate measurement of inductance and resistance of a coil in terms of a standard capacitance C_s. Show that when the bridge is balanced,

$$L_x = R_2 R_3 C_s \quad \text{and} \quad R_x = \frac{R_2}{R_1} R_3$$

Find L_x and R_x for $R_1 = 40 \, k\Omega$, $R_2 = 1.6 \, k\Omega$, $R_3 = 4 \, k\Omega$, and $C_s = 0.45 \, \mu F$.

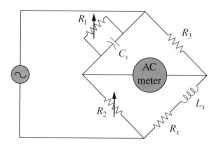

Figure 9.84 Maxwell bridge; for Prob. 9.84.

9.85 The ac bridge circuit of Fig. 9.85 is called a *Wien bridge*. It is used for measuring the frequency of a source. Show that when the bridge is balanced,

$$f = \frac{1}{2\pi \sqrt{R_2 R_4 C_2 C_4}}$$

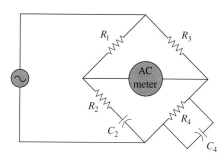

Figure 9.85 Wein bridge; for Prob. 9.85.

COMPREHENSIVE PROBLEMS

9.86 The circuit shown in Fig. 9.86 is used in a television receiver. What is the total impedance of this circuit?

Figure 9.86 For Prob. 9.86.

9.87 The network in Fig. 9.87 is part of the schematic describing an industrial electronic sensing device. What is the total impedance of the circuit at 2 kHz?

Figure 9.87 For Prob. 9.87.

9.88 A series audio circuit is shown in Fig. 9.88.

(a) What is the impedance of the circuit?

(b) If the frequency were halved, what would be the impedance of the circuit?

Figure 9.88 For Prob. 9.88.

9.89 An industrial load is modeled as a series combination of a capacitance and a resistance as shown in Fig. 9.89. Calculate the value of an inductance L across the series combination so that the net impedance is resistive at a frequency of 5 MHz.

Figure 9.89   For Prob. 9.89.

Figure 9.91   For Prob. 9.91.

9.90 An industrial coil is modeled as a series combination of an inductance L and resistance R, as shown in Fig. 9.90. Since an ac voltmeter measures only the magnitude of a sinusoid, the following measurements are taken at 60 Hz when the circuit operates in the steady state:

$$|\mathbf{V}_s| = 145 \text{ V}, \qquad |\mathbf{V}_1| = 50 \text{ V}, \qquad |\mathbf{V}_o| = 110 \text{ V}$$

Use these measurements to determine the values of L and R.

Figure 9.90   For Prob. 9.90.

9.91 Figure 9.91 shows a parallel combination of an inductance and a resistance. If it is desired to connect a capacitor in series with the parallel combination such that the net impedance is resistive at 10 MHz, what is the required value of C?

9.92 A transmission line has a series impedance of $\mathbf{Z} = 100\underline{/75°}\ \Omega$ and a shunt admittance of $\mathbf{Y} = 450\underline{/48°}\ \mu$S. Find: (a) the characteristic impedance $\mathbf{Z}_o = \sqrt{\mathbf{Z}/\mathbf{Y}}$, (b) the propagation constant $\gamma = \sqrt{\mathbf{ZY}}$.

9.93 A power transmission system is modeled as shown in Fig. 9.92. Given the following;
Source voltage $\mathbf{V}_s = 115\underline{/0°}$ V,
Source impedance $\mathbf{Z}_s = 1 + j0.5\ \Omega$,
Line impedance $\mathbf{Z}_\ell = 0.4 + j0.3\ \Omega$,
Load impedance $\mathbf{Z}_L = 23.2 + j18.9\ \Omega$,
find the load current $\mathbf{I}_L$.

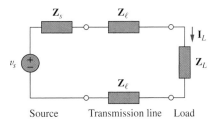

Figure 9.92   For Prob. 9.93.

CHAPTER 10

SINUSOIDAL STEADY-STATE ANALYSIS

One humiliating thing about science is that it is gradually filling our homes with appliances smarter than we are.

—Anonymous

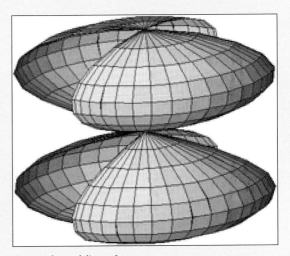

10.1 INTRODUCTION

In Chapter 9, we learned that the forced or steady-state response of circuits to sinusoidal inputs can be obtained by using phasors. We also know that Ohm's and Kirchhoff's laws are applicable to ac circuits. In this chapter, we want to see how nodal analysis, mesh analysis, Thevenin's theorem, Norton's theorem, superposition, and source transformations are applied in analyzing ac circuits. Since these techniques were already introduced for dc circuits, our major effort here will be to illustrate with examples.

Analyzing ac circuits usually requires three steps.

Steps to Analyze ac Circuits:

1. Transform the circuit to the phasor or frequency domain.
2. Solve the problem using circuit techniques (nodal analysis, mesh analysis, superposition, etc.).
3. Transform the resulting phasor to the time domain.

Step 1 is not necessary if the problem is specified in the frequency domain. In step 2, the analysis is performed in the same manner as dc circuit analysis except that complex numbers are involved. Having read Chapter 9, we are adept at handling step 3.

Toward the end of the chapter, we learn how to apply *PSpice* in solving ac circuit problems. We finally apply ac circuit analysis to two practical ac circuits: oscillators and ac transistor circuits.

> Frequency-domain analysis of an ac circuit via phasors is much easier than analysis of the circuit in the time domain.

10.2 NODAL ANALYSIS

The basis of nodal analysis is Kirchhoff's current law. Since KCL is valid for phasors, as demonstrated in Section 9.6, we can analyze ac circuits by nodal analysis. The following examples illustrate this.

EXAMPLE 10.1

Find i_x in the circuit of Fig. 10.1 using nodal analysis.

Figure 10.1 For Example 10.1.

Solution:

We first convert the circuit to the frequency domain:

$$20\cos 4t \quad \Longrightarrow \quad 20\underline{/0°}, \qquad \omega = 4 \text{ rad/s}$$

$$1\text{ H} \quad \Longrightarrow \quad j\omega L = j4$$

$$0.5\text{ H} \quad \Longrightarrow \quad j\omega L = j2$$

$$0.1\text{ F} \quad \Longrightarrow \quad \frac{1}{j\omega C} = -j2.5$$

Thus, the frequency-domain equivalent circuit is as shown in Fig. 10.2.

Figure 10.2   Frequency-domain equivalent of the circuit in Fig. 10.1.

Applying KCL at node 1,

$$\frac{20 - \mathbf{V}_1}{10} = \frac{\mathbf{V}_1}{-j2.5} + \frac{\mathbf{V}_1 - \mathbf{V}_2}{j4}$$

or

$$(1 + j1.5)\mathbf{V}_1 + j2.5\mathbf{V}_2 = 20 \qquad (10.1.1)$$

At node 2,

$$2\mathbf{I}_x + \frac{\mathbf{V}_1 - \mathbf{V}_2}{j4} = \frac{\mathbf{V}_2}{j2}$$

But $\mathbf{I}_x = \mathbf{V}_1/-j2.5$. Substituting this gives

$$\frac{2\mathbf{V}_1}{-j2.5} + \frac{\mathbf{V}_1 - \mathbf{V}_2}{j4} = \frac{\mathbf{V}_2}{j2}$$

By simplifying, we get

$$11\mathbf{V}_1 + 15\mathbf{V}_2 = 0 \qquad (10.1.2)$$

Equations (10.1.1) and (10.1.2) can be put in matrix form as

$$\begin{bmatrix} 1 + j1.5 & j2.5 \\ 11 & 15 \end{bmatrix} \begin{bmatrix} \mathbf{V}_1 \\ \mathbf{V}_2 \end{bmatrix} = \begin{bmatrix} 20 \\ 0 \end{bmatrix}$$

We obtain the determinants as

$$\Delta = \begin{vmatrix} 1 + j1.5 & j2.5 \\ 11 & 15 \end{vmatrix} = 15 - j5$$

$$\Delta_1 = \begin{vmatrix} 20 & j2.5 \\ 0 & 15 \end{vmatrix} = 300, \qquad \Delta_2 = \begin{vmatrix} 1 + j1.5 & 20 \\ 11 & 0 \end{vmatrix} = -220$$

$$\mathbf{V}_1 = \frac{\Delta_1}{\Delta} = \frac{300}{15 - j5} = 18.97\underline{/18.43°} \text{ V}$$

$$\mathbf{V}_2 = \frac{\Delta_2}{\Delta} = \frac{-220}{15 - j5} = 13.91\underline{/198.3°} \text{ V}$$

The current $\mathbf{I}_x$ is given by

$$\mathbf{I}_x = \frac{\mathbf{V}_1}{-j2.5} = \frac{18.97\underline{/18.43°}}{2.5\underline{/-90°}} = 7.59\underline{/108.4°} \text{ A}$$

Transforming this to the time domain,

$$i_x = 7.59\cos(4t + 108.4°) \text{ A}$$

PRACTICE PROBLEM 10.1

Using nodal analysis, find v_1 and v_2 in the circuit of Fig. 10.3.

Figure 10.3   For Practice Prob. 10.1.

Answer: $v_1(t) = 11.32\sin(2t + 60.01°)$ V,
$v_2(t) = 33.02\sin(2t + 57.12°)$ V.

EXAMPLE 10.2

Compute $\mathbf{V}_1$ and $\mathbf{V}_2$ in the circuit of Fig. 10.4.

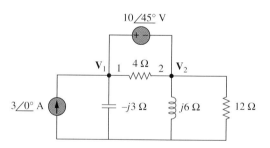

Figure 10.4   For Example 10.2.

Solution:

Nodes 1 and 2 form a supernode as shown in Fig. 10.5. Applying KCL at the supernode gives

$$3 = \frac{\mathbf{V}_1}{-j3} + \frac{\mathbf{V}_2}{j6} + \frac{\mathbf{V}_2}{12}$$

or

$$36 = j4\mathbf{V}_1 + (1 - j2)\mathbf{V}_2 \qquad (10.2.1)$$

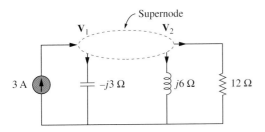

Figure 10.5   A supernode in the circuit of Fig. 10.4.

But a voltage source is connected between nodes 1 and 2, so that

$$\mathbf{V}_1 = \mathbf{V}_2 + 10\underline{/45°} \qquad (10.2.2)$$

Substituting Eq. (10.2.2) in Eq. (10.2.1) results in

$$36 - 40\underline{/135°} = (1 + j2)\mathbf{V}_2 \quad \Longrightarrow \quad \mathbf{V}_2 = 31.41\underline{/-87.18°}\ \text{V}$$

From Eq. (10.2.2),

$$\mathbf{V}_1 = \mathbf{V}_2 + 10\underline{/45°} = 25.78\underline{/-70.48°}\ \text{V}$$

PRACTICE PROBLEM 10.2

Calculate $\mathbf{V}_1$ and $\mathbf{V}_2$ in the circuit shown in Fig. 10.6.

Figure 10.6   For Practice Prob. 10.2.

Answer: $\mathbf{V}_1 = 19.36\underline{/69.67°}\ \text{V}, \mathbf{V}_2 = 3.376\underline{/165.7°}\ \text{V}.$

10.3   MESH ANALYSIS

Kirchhoff's voltage law (KVL) forms the basis of mesh analysis. The validity of KVL for ac circuits was shown in Section 9.6 and is illustrated in the following examples.

EXAMPLE 10.3

Determine current $\mathbf{I}_o$ in the circuit of Fig. 10.7 using mesh analysis.

Solution:

Applying KVL to mesh 1, we obtain

$$(8 + j10 - j2)\mathbf{I}_1 - (-j2)\mathbf{I}_2 - j10\mathbf{I}_3 = 0 \qquad (10.3.1)$$

Figure 10.7   For Example 10.3.

For mesh 2,

$$(4 - j2 - j2)\mathbf{I}_2 - (-j2)\mathbf{I}_1 - (-j2)\mathbf{I}_3 + 20\underline{/90°} = 0 \qquad (10.3.2)$$

For mesh 3, $\mathbf{I}_3 = 5$. Substituting this in Eqs. (10.3.1) and (10.3.2), we get

$$(8 + j8)\mathbf{I}_1 + j2\mathbf{I}_2 = j50 \qquad (10.3.3)$$

$$j2\mathbf{I}_1 + (4 - j4)\mathbf{I}_2 = -j20 - j10 \qquad (10.3.4)$$

Equations (10.3.3) and (10.3.4) can be put in matrix form as

$$\begin{bmatrix} 8 + j8 & j2 \\ j2 & 4 - j4 \end{bmatrix} \begin{bmatrix} \mathbf{I}_1 \\ \mathbf{I}_2 \end{bmatrix} = \begin{bmatrix} j50 \\ -j30 \end{bmatrix}$$

from which we obtain the determinants

$$\Delta = \begin{vmatrix} 8 + j8 & j2 \\ j2 & 4 - j4 \end{vmatrix} = 32(1 + j)(1 - j) + 4 = 68$$

$$\Delta_2 = \begin{vmatrix} 8 + j8 & j50 \\ j2 & -j30 \end{vmatrix} = 340 - j240 = 416.17\underline{/-35.22°}$$

$$\mathbf{I}_2 = \frac{\Delta_2}{\Delta} = \frac{416.17\underline{/-35.22°}}{68} = 6.12\underline{/-35.22°} \text{ A}$$

The desired current is

$$\mathbf{I}_o = -\mathbf{I}_2 = 6.12\underline{/144.78°} \text{ A}$$

PRACTICE PROBLEM 10.3

Figure 10.8   For Practice Prob. 10.3.

Find $\mathbf{I}_o$ in Fig. 10.8 using mesh analysis.

Answer: $1.194\underline{/65.45°}$ A.

EXAMPLE 10.4

Solve for $\mathbf{V}_o$ in the circuit in Fig. 10.9 using mesh analysis.

Figure 10.9   For Example 10.4.

Solution:

As shown in Fig. 10.10, meshes 3 and 4 form a supermesh due to the current source between the meshes. For mesh 1, KVL gives

$$-10 + (8 - j2)\mathbf{I}_1 - (-j2)\mathbf{I}_2 - 8\mathbf{I}_3 = 0$$

or

$$(8 - j2)\mathbf{I}_1 + j2\mathbf{I}_2 - 8\mathbf{I}_3 = 10 \qquad (10.4.1)$$

For mesh 2,

$$\mathbf{I}_2 = -3 \qquad (10.4.2)$$

For the supermesh,

$$(8 - j4)\mathbf{I}_3 - 8\mathbf{I}_1 + (6 + j5)\mathbf{I}_4 - j5\mathbf{I}_2 = 0 \qquad (10.4.3)$$

Due to the current source between meshes 3 and 4, at node A,

$$\mathbf{I}_4 = \mathbf{I}_3 + 4 \qquad (10.4.4)$$

METHOD **1**   Rather than solving the above four equations, we reduce them to two by elimination.

Combining Eqs. (10.4.1) and (10.4.2),

$$(8 - j2)\mathbf{I}_1 - 8\mathbf{I}_3 = 10 + j6 \qquad (10.4.5)$$

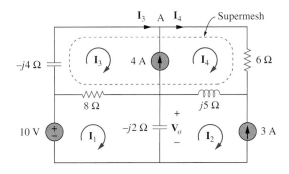

Figure 10.10   Analysis of the circuit in Fig. 10.9.

Combining Eqs. (10.4.2) to (10.4.4),

$$-8\mathbf{I}_1 + (14 + j)\mathbf{I}_3 = -24 - j35 \qquad (10.4.6)$$

From Eqs. (10.4.5) and (10.4.6), we obtain the matrix equation

$$\begin{bmatrix} 8 - j2 & -8 \\ -8 & 14 + j \end{bmatrix} \begin{bmatrix} \mathbf{I}_1 \\ \mathbf{I}_3 \end{bmatrix} = \begin{bmatrix} 10 + j6 \\ -24 - j35 \end{bmatrix}$$

We obtain the following determinants

$$\Delta = \begin{vmatrix} 8 - j2 & -8 \\ -8 & 14 + j \end{vmatrix} = 112 + j8 - j28 + 2 - 64 = 50 - j20$$

$$\Delta_1 = \begin{vmatrix} 10 + j6 & -8 \\ -24 - j35 & 14 + j \end{vmatrix} = 140 + j10 + j84 - 6 - 192 - j280$$

$$= -58 - j186$$

Current $\mathbf{I}_1$ is obtained as

$$\mathbf{I}_1 = \frac{\Delta_1}{\Delta} = \frac{-58 - j186}{50 - j20} = 3.618\underline{/274.5°} \text{ A}$$

The required voltage $\mathbf{V}_o$ is

$$\mathbf{V}_o = -j2(\mathbf{I}_1 - \mathbf{I}_2) = -j2(3.618\underline{/274.5°} + 3)$$

$$= -7.2134 - j6.568 = 9.756\underline{/222.32°} \text{ V}$$

$\boxed{\text{METHOD } \mathbf{2}}$ We can use *MATLAB* to solve Eqs. (10.4.1) to (10.4.4). We first cast the equations as

$$\begin{bmatrix} 8 - j2 & j2 & -8 & 0 \\ 0 & 1 & 0 & 0 \\ -8 & -j5 & 8 - j4 & 6 + j5 \\ 0 & 0 & -1 & 1 \end{bmatrix} \begin{bmatrix} \mathbf{I}_1 \\ \mathbf{I}_2 \\ \mathbf{I}_3 \\ \mathbf{I}_4 \end{bmatrix} = \begin{bmatrix} 10 \\ -3 \\ 0 \\ 4 \end{bmatrix} \qquad (10.4.7\text{a})$$

or

$$\mathbf{AI} = \mathbf{B}$$

By inverting $\mathbf{A}$, we can obtain $\mathbf{I}$ as

$$\mathbf{I} = \mathbf{A}^{-1}\mathbf{B} \qquad (10.4.7\text{b})$$

We now apply *MATLAB* as follows:

```
>> A = [(8-j*2)  j*2    -8        0;
         0       1      0         0;
        -8      -j*5   (8-j*4)  (6+j*5);
         0       0      -1        1];
>> B = [10 -3 0 4]';
>> I = inv(A)*B

I =
  0.2828 - 3.6069i
 -3.0000
 -1.8690 - 4.4276i
  2.1310 - 4.4276i
```

```
>> Vo = -2*j*(I(1) - I(2))

Vo =
  -7.2138 - 6.5655i
```

as obtained previously.

PRACTICE PROBLEM 10.4

Calculate current $\mathbf{I}_o$ in the circuit of Fig. 10.11.

Answer: $5.075\underline{/5.943°}$ A.

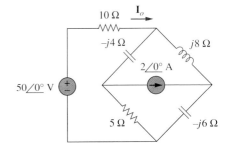

Figure 10.11   For Practice Prob. 10.4.

10.4 SUPERPOSITION THEOREM

Since ac circuits are linear, the superposition theorem applies to ac circuits the same way it applies to dc circuits. The theorem becomes important if the circuit has sources operating at *different* frequencies. In this case, since the impedances depend on frequency, we must have a different frequency-domain circuit for each frequency. The total response must be obtained by adding the individual responses in the *time* domain. It is incorrect to try to add the responses in the phasor or frequency domain. Why? Because the exponential factor $e^{j\omega t}$ is implicit in sinusoidal analysis, and that factor would change for every angular frequency ω. It would therefore not make sense to add responses at different frequencies in the phasor domain. Thus, when a circuit has sources operating at different frequencies, one must add the responses due to the individual frequencies in the time domain.

EXAMPLE 10.5

Use the superposition theorem to find $\mathbf{I}_o$ in the circuit in Fig. 10.7.

Solution:

Let

$$\mathbf{I}_o = \mathbf{I}_o' + \mathbf{I}_o'' \tag{10.5.1}$$

where $\mathbf{I}_o'$ and $\mathbf{I}_o''$ are due to the voltage and current sources, respectively. To find $\mathbf{I}_o'$, consider the circuit in Fig. 10.12(a). If we let $\mathbf{Z}$ be the parallel combination of $-j2$ and $8 + j10$, then

$$\mathbf{Z} = \frac{-j2(8 + j10)}{-2j + 8 + j10} = 0.25 - j2.25$$

Figure 10.12   Solution of Example 10.5.

and current $\mathbf{I}'_o$ is

$$\mathbf{I}'_o = \frac{j20}{4 - j2 + \mathbf{Z}} = \frac{j20}{4.25 - j4.25}$$

or

$$\mathbf{I}'_o = -2.353 + j2.353 \tag{10.5.2}$$

To get $\mathbf{I}''_o$, consider the circuit in Fig. 10.12(b). For mesh 1,

$$(8 + j8)\mathbf{I}_1 - j10\mathbf{I}_3 + j2\mathbf{I}_2 = 0 \tag{10.5.3}$$

For mesh 2,

$$(4 - j4)\mathbf{I}_2 + j2\mathbf{I}_1 + j2\mathbf{I}_3 = 0 \tag{10.5.4}$$

For mesh 3,

$$\mathbf{I}_3 = 5 \tag{10.5.5}$$

From Eqs. (10.5.4) and (10.5.5),

$$(4 - j4)\mathbf{I}_2 + j2\mathbf{I}_1 + j10 = 0$$

Expressing $\mathbf{I}_1$ in terms of $\mathbf{I}_2$ gives

$$\mathbf{I}_1 = (2 + j2)\mathbf{I}_2 - 5 \tag{10.5.6}$$

Substituting Eqs. (10.5.5) and (10.5.6) into Eq. (10.5.3), we get

$$(8 + j8)[(2 + j2)\mathbf{I}_2 - 5] - j50 + j2\mathbf{I}_2 = 0$$

or

$$\mathbf{I}_2 = \frac{90 - j40}{34} = 2.647 - j1.176$$

Current $\mathbf{I}''_o$ is obtained as

$$\mathbf{I}''_o = -\mathbf{I}_2 = -2.647 + j1.176 \tag{10.5.7}$$

From Eqs. (10.5.2) and (10.5.7), we write

$$\mathbf{I}_o = \mathbf{I}'_o + \mathbf{I}''_o = -5 + j3.529 = 6.12\underline{/144.78°}\ \text{A}$$

which agrees with what we got in Example 10.3. It should be noted that applying the superposition theorem is not the best way to solve this problem. It seems that we have made the problem twice as hard as the original one by using superposition. However, in Example 10.6, superposition is clearly the easiest approach.

PRACTICE PROBLEM 10.5

Find current $\mathbf{I}_o$ in the circuit of Fig. 10.8 using the superposition theorem.

Answer: $1.194\underline{/65.45°}$ A.

E X A M P L E 1 0 . 6

Find v_o in the circuit in Fig. 10.13 using the superposition theorem.

Figure 10.13   For Example 10.6.

Solution:

Since the circuit operates at three different frequencies ($\omega = 0$ for the dc voltage source), one way to obtain a solution is to use superposition, which breaks the problem into single-frequency problems. So we let

$$v_o = v_1 + v_2 + v_3 \qquad (10.6.1)$$

where v_1 is due to the 5-V dc voltage source, v_2 is due to the $10 \cos 2t$ V voltage source, and v_3 is due to the $2 \sin 5t$ A current source.

To find v_1, we set to zero all sources except the 5-V dc source. We recall that at steady state, a capacitor is an open circuit to dc while an inductor is a short circuit to dc. There is an alternative way of looking at this. Since $\omega = 0$, $j\omega L = 0$, $1/j\omega C = \infty$. Either way, the equivalent circuit is as shown in Fig. 10.14(a). By voltage division,

$$-v_1 = \frac{1}{1+4}(5) = 1 \text{ V} \qquad (10.6.2)$$

To find v_2, we set to zero both the 5-V source and the $2 \sin 5t$ current source and transform the circuit to the frequency domain.

$$10 \cos 2t \quad \Longrightarrow \quad 10\underline{/0^\circ}, \qquad \omega = 2 \text{ rad/s}$$

$$2 \text{ H} \quad \Longrightarrow \quad j\omega L = j4 \ \Omega$$

$$0.1 \text{ F} \quad \Longrightarrow \quad \frac{1}{j\omega C} = -j5 \ \Omega$$

The equivalent circuit is now as shown in Fig. 10.14(b). Let

$$\mathbf{Z} = -j5 \parallel 4 = \frac{-j5 \times 4}{4 - j5} = 2.439 - j1.951$$

(a)   (b)   (c)

Figure 10.14   Solution of Example 10.6: (a) setting all sources to zero except the 5-V dc source, (b) setting all sources to zero except the ac voltage source, (c) setting all sources to zero except the ac current source.

By voltage division,

$$\mathbf{V}_2 = \frac{1}{1 + j4 + \mathbf{Z}}(10\underline{/0°}) = \frac{10}{3.439 + j2.049} = 2.498\underline{/-30.79°}$$

In the time domain,

$$v_2 = 2.498\cos(2t - 30.79°) \tag{10.6.3}$$

To obtain v_3, we set the voltage sources to zero and transform what is left to the frequency domain.

$$2\sin 5t \quad\Longrightarrow\quad 2\underline{/-90°}, \qquad \omega = 5 \text{ rad/s}$$

$$2\text{ H} \quad\Longrightarrow\quad j\omega L = j10\ \Omega$$

$$0.1\text{ F} \quad\Longrightarrow\quad \frac{1}{j\omega C} = -j2\ \Omega$$

The equivalent circuit is in Fig. 10.14(c). Let

$$\mathbf{Z}_1 = -j2 \parallel 4 = \frac{-j2 \times 4}{4 - j2} = 0.8 - j1.6\ \Omega$$

By current division,

$$\mathbf{I}_1 = \frac{j10}{j10 + 1 + \mathbf{Z}_1}(2\underline{/-90°})\text{ A}$$

$$\mathbf{V}_3 = \mathbf{I}_1 \times 1 = \frac{j10}{1.8 + j8.4}(-j2) = 2.328\underline{/-80°}\text{ V}$$

In the time domain,

$$v_3 = 2.33\cos(5t - 80°) = 2.33\sin(5t + 10°)\text{ V} \tag{10.6.4}$$

Substituting Eqs. (10.6.2) to (10.6.4) into Eq. (10.6.1), we have

$$v_o(t) = -1 + 2.498\cos(2t - 30.79°) + 2.33\sin(5t + 10°)\text{ V}$$

PRACTICE PROBLEM 10.6

Calculate v_o in the circuit of Fig. 10.15 using the superposition theorem.

Figure 10.15   For Practice Prob. 10.6.

Answer: $4.631\sin(5t - 81.12°) + 1.051\cos(10t - 86.24°)$ V.

10.5 SOURCE TRANSFORMATION

As Fig. 10.16 shows, source transformation in the frequency domain involves transforming a voltage source in series with an impedance to a current source in parallel with an impedance, or vice versa. As we go from one source type to another, we must keep the following relationship in mind:

$$\mathbf{V}_s = \mathbf{Z}_s\mathbf{I}_s \qquad \Longleftrightarrow \qquad \mathbf{I}_s = \frac{\mathbf{V}_s}{\mathbf{Z}_s} \tag{10.1}$$

Figure 10.16   Source transformation.

EXAMPLE 10.7

Calculate $\mathbf{V}_x$ in the circuit of Fig. 10.17 using the method of source transformation.

Figure 10.17   For Example 10.7.

Solution:

We transform the voltage source to a current source and obtain the circuit in Fig. 10.18(a), where

$$\mathbf{I}_s = \frac{20\angle{-90°}}{5} = 4\angle{-90°} = -j4 \text{ A}$$

The parallel combination of 5-Ω resistance and $(3 + j4)$ impedance gives

$$\mathbf{Z}_1 = \frac{5(3 + j4)}{8 + j4} = 2.5 + j1.25 \ \Omega$$

Converting the current source to a voltage source yields the circuit in Fig. 10.18(b), where

$$\mathbf{V}_s = \mathbf{I}_s\mathbf{Z}_1 = -j4(2.5 + j1.25) = 5 - j10 \text{ V}$$

(a)   (b)

Figure 10.18   Solution of the circuit in Fig. 10.17.

By voltage division,

$$\mathbf{V}_x = \frac{10}{10 + 2.5 + j1.25 + 4 - j13}(5 - j10) = 5.519\underline{/-28°}\text{ V}$$

PRACTICE PROBLEM 10.7

Find $\mathbf{I}_o$ in the circuit of Fig. 10.19 using the concept of source transformation.

Figure 10.19   For Practice Prob. 10.7.

Answer: $3.288\underline{/99.46°}$ A.

10.6   THEVENIN AND NORTON EQUIVALENT CIRCUITS

Figure 10.20   Thevenin equivalent.

Thevenin's and Norton's theorems are applied to ac circuits in the same way as they are to dc circuits. The only additional effort arises from the need to manipulate complex numbers. The frequency-domain version of a Thevenin equivalent circuit is depicted in Fig. 10.20, where a linear circuit is replaced by a voltage source in series with an impedance. The Norton equivalent circuit is illustrated in Fig. 10.21, where a linear circuit is replaced by a current source in parallel with an impedance. Keep in mind that the two equivalent circuits are related as

$$\mathbf{V}_{Th} = \mathbf{Z}_N \mathbf{I}_N, \qquad \mathbf{Z}_{Th} = \mathbf{Z}_N \tag{10.2}$$

just as in source transformation. $\mathbf{V}_{Th}$ is the open-circuit voltage while $\mathbf{I}_N$ is the short-circuit current.

If the circuit has sources operating at different frequencies (see Example 10.6, for example), the Thevenin or Norton equivalent circuit must be determined at each frequency. This leads to entirely different equivalent circuits, one for each frequency, not one equivalent circuit with equivalent sources and equivalent impedances.

Figure 10.21   Norton equivalent.

EXAMPLE 10.8

Obtain the Thevenin equivalent at terminals a-b of the circuit in Fig. 10.22.

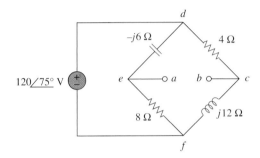

Figure 10.22   For Example 10.8.

Solution:

We find $\mathbf{Z}_{\text{Th}}$ by setting the voltage source to zero. As shown in Fig. 10.23(a), the 8-Ω resistance is now in parallel with the $-j6$ reactance, so that their combination gives

$$\mathbf{Z}_1 = -j6 \parallel 8 = \frac{-j6 \times 8}{8 - j6} = 2.88 - j3.84 \ \Omega$$

Similarly, the 4-Ω resistance is in parallel with the $j12$ reactance, and their combination gives

$$\mathbf{Z}_2 = 4 \parallel j12 = \frac{j12 \times 4}{4 + j12} = 3.6 + j1.2 \ \Omega$$

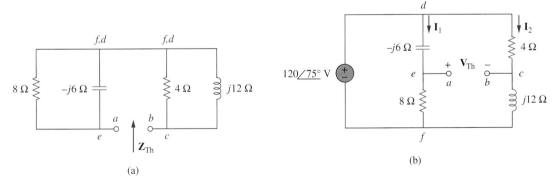

Figure 10.23   Solution of the circuit in Fig. 10.22: (a) finding $\mathbf{Z}_{\text{Th}}$, (b) finding $\mathbf{V}_{\text{Th}}$.

The Thevenin impedance is the series combination of $\mathbf{Z}_1$ and $\mathbf{Z}_2$; that is,

$$\mathbf{Z}_{\text{Th}} = \mathbf{Z}_1 + \mathbf{Z}_2 = 6.48 - j2.64 \ \Omega$$

To find $\mathbf{V}_{\text{Th}}$, consider the circuit in Fig. 10.23(b). Currents $\mathbf{I}_1$ and $\mathbf{I}_2$ are obtained as

$$\mathbf{I}_1 = \frac{120\underline{/75°}}{8 - j6} \text{ A}, \qquad \mathbf{I}_2 = \frac{120\underline{/75°}}{4 + j12} \text{ A}$$

Applying KVL around loop $bcdeab$ in Fig. 10.23(b) gives

$$\mathbf{V}_{\text{Th}} - 4\mathbf{I}_2 + (-j6)\mathbf{I}_1 = 0$$

or

$$\begin{aligned}
\mathbf{V}_{\text{Th}} = 4\mathbf{I}_2 + j6\mathbf{I}_1 &= \frac{480\underline{/75°}}{4 + j12} + \frac{720\underline{/75° + 90°}}{8 - j6} \\
&= 37.95\underline{/3.43°} + 72\underline{/201.87°} \\
&= -28.936 - j24.55 = 37.95\underline{/220.31°} \text{ V}
\end{aligned}$$

PRACTICE PROBLEM 10.8

Find the Thevenin equivalent at terminals a-b of the circuit in Fig. 10.24.

Figure 10.24   For Practice Prob. 10.8.

Answer: $\mathbf{Z}_{\text{Th}} = 12.4 - j3.2 \ \Omega$, $\mathbf{V}_{\text{Th}} = 18.97\underline{/-51.57°}$ V.

EXAMPLE 10.9

Find the Thevenin equivalent of the circuit in Fig. 10.25 as seen from terminals a-b.

Figure 10.25   For Example 10.9.

Solution:

To find $\mathbf{V}_{\text{Th}}$, we apply KCL at node 1 in Fig. 10.26(a).

$$15 = \mathbf{I}_o + 0.5\mathbf{I}_o \qquad \Longrightarrow \qquad \mathbf{I}_o = 10 \text{ A}$$

Applying KVL to the loop on the right-hand side in Fig. 10.26(a), we obtain

$$-\mathbf{I}_o(2 - j4) + 0.5\mathbf{I}_o(4 + j3) + \mathbf{V}_{Th} = 0$$

or

$$\mathbf{V}_{Th} = 10(2 - j4) - 5(4 + j3) = -j55$$

Thus, the Thevenin voltage is

$$\mathbf{V}_{Th} = 55\underline{/-90°} \text{ V}$$

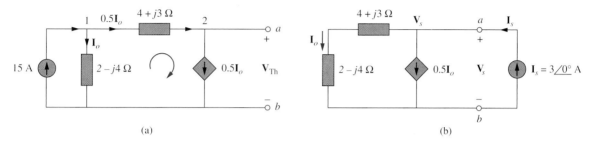

Figure 10.26   Solution of the problem in Fig. 10.25: (a) finding $\mathbf{V}_{Th}$, (b) finding $\mathbf{Z}_{Th}$.

To obtain $\mathbf{Z}_{Th}$, we remove the independent source. Due to the presence of the dependent current source, we connect a 3-A current source (3 is an arbitrary value chosen for convenience here, a number divisible by the sum of currents leaving the node) to terminals a-b as shown in Fig. 10.26(b). At the node, KCL gives

$$3 = \mathbf{I}_o + 0.5\mathbf{I}_o \qquad \Longrightarrow \qquad \mathbf{I}_o = 2 \text{ A}$$

Applying KVL to the outer loop in Fig. 10.26(b) gives

$$\mathbf{V}_s = \mathbf{I}_o(4 + j3 + 2 - j4) = 2(6 - j)$$

The Thevenin impedance is

$$\mathbf{Z}_{Th} = \frac{\mathbf{V}_s}{\mathbf{I}_s} = \frac{2(6 - j)}{3} = 4 - j0.6667 \ \Omega$$

PRACTICE PROBLEM 10.9

Determine the Thevenin equivalent of the circuit in Fig. 10.27 as seen from the terminals a-b.

Answer: $\mathbf{Z}_{Th} = 4.473\underline{/-7.64°} \ \Omega$, $\mathbf{V}_{Th} = 7.35\underline{/72.9°}$ V.

Figure 10.27   For Practice Prob. 10.9.

EXAMPLE 10.10

Obtain current $\mathbf{I}_o$ in Fig. 10.28 using Norton's theorem.

Figure 10.28   For Example 10.10.

Solution:

Our first objective is to find the Norton equivalent at terminals a-b. $\mathbf{Z}_N$ is found in the same way as $\mathbf{Z}_{\text{Th}}$. We set the sources to zero as shown in Fig. 10.29(a). As evident from the figure, the $(8 - j2)$ and $(10 + j4)$ impedances are short-circuited, so that

$$\mathbf{Z}_N = 5 \; \Omega$$

To get $\mathbf{I}_N$, we short-circuit terminals a-b as in Fig. 10.29(b) and apply mesh analysis. Notice that meshes 2 and 3 form a supermesh because of the current source linking them. For mesh 1,

$$-j40 + (18 + j2)\mathbf{I}_1 - (8 - j2)\mathbf{I}_2 - (10 + j4)\mathbf{I}_3 = 0 \qquad (10.10.1)$$

For the supermesh,

$$(13 - j2)\mathbf{I}_2 + (10 + j4)\mathbf{I}_3 - (18 + j2)\mathbf{I}_1 = 0 \qquad (10.10.2)$$

At node a, due to the current source between meshes 2 and 3,

$$\mathbf{I}_3 = \mathbf{I}_2 + 3 \qquad (10.10.3)$$

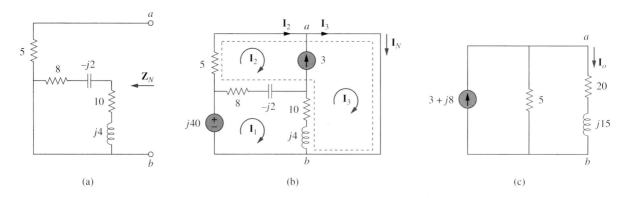

    (a)   (b)   (c)

Figure 10.29   Solution of the circuit in Fig. 10.28: (a) finding $\mathbf{Z}_N$, (b) finding $\mathbf{V}_N$, (c) calculating $\mathbf{I}_o$.

Adding Eqs. (10.10.1) and (10.10.2) gives

$$-j40 + 5\mathbf{I}_2 = 0 \qquad \Longrightarrow \qquad \mathbf{I}_2 = j8$$

From Eq. (10.10.3),

$$\mathbf{I}_3 = \mathbf{I}_2 + 3 = 3 + j8$$

The Norton current is

$$\mathbf{I}_N = \mathbf{I}_3 = (3 + j8) \text{ A}$$

Figure 10.29(c) shows the Norton equivalent circuit along with the impedance at terminals a-b. By current division,

$$\mathbf{I}_o = \frac{5}{5 + 20 + j15}\mathbf{I}_N = \frac{3 + j8}{5 + j3} = 1.465\underline{/38.48°} \text{ A}$$

PRACTICE PROBLEM 10.10

Determine the Norton equivalent of the circuit in Fig. 10.30 as seen from terminals a-b. Use the equivalent to find $\mathbf{I}_o$.

Figure 10.30   For Practice Prob. 10.10.

Answer: $\mathbf{Z}_N = 3.176 + j0.706 \ \Omega$, $\mathbf{I}_N = 8.396\underline{/-32.68°}$ A,
$\mathbf{I}_o = 1.971\underline{/-2.101°}$ A.

10.7 OP AMP AC CIRCUITS

The three steps stated in Section 10.1 also apply to op amp circuits, as long as the op amp is operating in the linear region. As usual, we will assume ideal op amps. (See Section 5.2.) As discussed in Chapter 5, the key to analyzing op amp circuits is to keep two important properties of an ideal op amp in mind:

1. No current enters either of its input terminals.
2. The voltage across its input terminals is zero.

The following examples will illustrate these ideas.

EXAMPLE 10.11

Determine $v_o(t)$ for the op amp circuit in Fig. 10.31(a) if $v_s = 3\cos 1000t$ V.

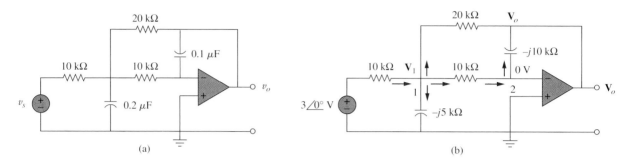

Figure 10.31   For Example 10.11: (a) the original circuit in the time domain, (b) its frequency-domain equivalent.

Solution:

We first transform the circuit to the frequency domain, as shown in Fig. 10.31(b), where $\mathbf{V}_s = 3\underline{/0°}$, $\omega = 1000$ rad/s. Applying KCL at node 1, we obtain

$$\frac{3\underline{/0°} - \mathbf{V}_1}{10} = \frac{\mathbf{V}_1}{-j5} + \frac{\mathbf{V}_1 - 0}{10} + \frac{\mathbf{V}_1 - \mathbf{V}_o}{20}$$

or

$$6 = (5 + j4)\mathbf{V}_1 - \mathbf{V}_o \qquad (10.11.1)$$

At node 2, KCL gives

$$\frac{\mathbf{V}_1 - 0}{10} = \frac{0 - \mathbf{V}_o}{-j10}$$

which leads to

$$\mathbf{V}_1 = -j\mathbf{V}_o \qquad (10.11.2)$$

Substituting Eq. (10.11.2) into Eq. (10.11.1) yields

$$6 = -j(5 + j4)\mathbf{V}_o - \mathbf{V}_o = (3 - j5)\mathbf{V}_o$$
$$\mathbf{V}_o = \frac{6}{3 - j5} = 1.029\underline{/59.04°}$$

Hence,

$$v_o(t) = 1.029\cos(1000t + 59.04°) \text{ V}$$

PRACTICE PROBLEM 10.11

Find v_o and i_o in the op amp circuit of Fig. 10.32. Let $v_s = 2 \cos 5000t$ V.

Figure 10.32   For Practice Prob. 10.11.

Answer: $0.667 \sin 5000t$ V, $66.67 \sin 5000t$ μA.

EXAMPLE 10.12

Compute the closed-loop gain and phase shift for the circuit in Fig. 10.33. Assume that $R_1 = R_2 = 10$ kΩ, $C_1 = 2$ μF, $C_2 = 1$ μF, and $\omega = 200$ rad/s.

Solution:

The feedback and input impedances are calculated as

$$\mathbf{Z}_f = R_2 \left\| \frac{1}{j\omega C_2} = \frac{R_2}{1 + j\omega R_2 C_2} \right.$$

$$\mathbf{Z}_i = R_1 + \frac{1}{j\omega C_1} = \frac{1 + j\omega R_1 C_1}{j\omega C_1}$$

Figure 10.33   For Example 10.12.

Since the circuit in Fig. 10.33 is an inverting amplifier, the closed-loop gain is given by

$$\mathbf{G} = \frac{\mathbf{V}_o}{\mathbf{V}_s} = -\frac{\mathbf{Z}_f}{\mathbf{Z}_i} = \frac{-j\omega C_1 R_2}{(1 + j\omega R_1 C_1)(1 + j\omega R_2 C_2)}$$

Substituting the given values of R_1, R_2, C_1, C_2, and ω, we obtain

$$\mathbf{G} = \frac{-j4}{(1 + j4)(1 + j2)} = 0.434 \underline{/130.6^\circ}$$

Thus the closed-loop gain is 0.434 and the phase shift is 130.6°.

PRACTICE PROBLEM 10.12

Obtain the closed-loop gain and phase shift for the circuit in Fig. 10.34. Let $R = 10$ kΩ, $C = 1$ μF, and $\omega = 1000$ rad/s.

Answer: 1.015, −5.599°.

Figure 10.34   For Practice Prob. 10.12.

10.8 AC ANALYSIS USING *PSPICE*

PSpice affords a big relief from the tedious task of manipulating complex numbers in ac circuit analysis. The procedure for using *PSpice* for ac analysis is quite similar to that required for dc analysis. The reader should read Section D.5 in Appendix D for a review of *PSpice* concepts for ac analysis. AC circuit analysis is done in the phasor or frequency domain, and all sources must have the same frequency. Although AC analysis with *PSpice* involves using AC Sweep, our analysis in this chapter requires a single frequency $f = \omega/2\pi$. The output file of *PSpice* contains voltage and current phasors. If necessary, the impedances can be calculated using the voltages and currents in the output file.

EXAMPLE 10.13

Obtain v_o and i_o in the circuit of Fig. 10.35 using *PSpice*.

Figure 10.35   For Example 10.13.

Solution:

We first convert the sine function to cosine.

$$8\sin(1000t + 50°) = 8\cos(1000t + 50° - 90°) = 8\cos(1000t - 40°)$$

The frequency f is obtained from ω as

$$f = \frac{\omega}{2\pi} = \frac{1000}{2\pi} = 159.155 \text{ Hz}$$

The schematic for the circuit is shown in Fig. 10.36. Notice that the current-controlled current source F1 is connected such that its current flows from node 0 to node 3 in conformity with the original circuit in Fig. 10.35. Since we only want the magnitude and phase of v_o and i_o, we set the attributes of IPRINT and VPRINT1 each to $AC = yes$, $MAG = yes$, $PHASE = yes$. As a single-frequency analysis, we select **Analysis/Setup/AC Sweep** and enter *Total Pts* = 1, *Start Freq* = 159.155, and *Final Freq* = 159.155. After saving the schematic, we simulate it by selecting **Analysis/Simulate**. The output file includes the source frequency in addition to the attributes checked for the pseudocomponents IPRINT and VPRINT1,

```
FREQ         IM(V_PRINT3)   IP(V_PRINT3)
1.592E+02    3.264E-03      -3.743E+01


FREQ         VM(3)          VP(3)
1.592E+02    1.550E+00      -9.518E+01
```

Figure 10.36   The schematic of the circuit in Fig. 10.35.

From this output file, we obtain

$$\mathbf{V}_o = 1.55 \underline{/-95.18°} \text{ V}, \qquad \mathbf{I}_o = 3.264 \underline{/-37.43°} \text{ mA}$$

which are the phasors for

$$v_o = 1.55 \cos(1000t - 95.18°) = 1.55 \sin(1000t - 5.18°) \text{ V}$$

and

$$i_o = 3.264 \cos(1000t - 37.43°) \text{ mA}$$

PRACTICE PROBLEM 10.13

Use *PSpice* to obtain v_o and i_o in the circuit of Fig. 10.37.

Figure 10.37   For Practice Prob. 10.13.

Answer: $0.2682 \cos(3000t - 154.6°)$ V, $0.544 \cos(3000t - 55.12°)$ mA.

EXAMPLE 10.14

Find $\mathbf{V}_1$ and $\mathbf{V}_2$ in the circuit of Fig. 10.38.

Solution:

The circuit in Fig. 10.35 is in the time domain, whereas the one in Fig. 10.38 is in the frequency domain. Since we are not given a particular frequency and *PSpice* requires one, we select any frequency consistent

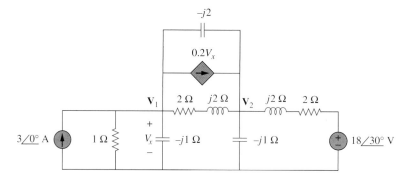

Figure 10.38   For Example 10.14.

with the given impedances. For example, if we select $\omega = 1$ rad/s, the corresponding frequency is $f = \omega/2\pi = 0.159155$ Hz. We obtain the values of the capacitance ($C = 1/\omega X_C$) and inductances ($L = X_L/\omega$). Making these changes results in the schematic in Fig. 10.39. To ease wiring, we have exchanged the positions of the voltage-controlled current source G1 and the $2 + j2$ Ω impedance. Notice that the current of G1 flows from node 1 to node 3, while the controlling voltage is across the capacitor C2, as required in Fig. 10.38. The attributes of pseudocomponents VPRINT1 are set as shown. As a single-frequency analysis, we select **Analysis/Setup/AC Sweep** and enter *Total Pts* = 1, *Start Freq* = 0.159155, and *Final Freq* = 0.159155. After saving the schematic, we select **Analysis/Simulate** to simulate the circuit. When this is done, the output file includes

```
FREQ          VM(1)        VP(1)
1.592E−01     2.708E+00    −5.673E+01


FREQ          VM(3)        VP(3)
1.592E−01     4.468E+00    −1.026E+02
```

Figure 10.39   Schematic for the circuit in Fig. 10.38.

from which we obtain

$$\mathbf{V}_1 = 2.708\underline{/-56.73°}\text{ V}, \qquad \mathbf{V}_2 = 4.468\underline{/-102.6°}\text{ V}$$

PRACTICE PROBLEM 10.14

Obtain $\mathbf{V}_x$ and $\mathbf{I}_x$ in the circuit depicted in Fig. 10.40.

Figure 10.40   For Practice Prob. 10.14.

Answer: $9.842\underline{/44.78°}$ V, $2.584\underline{/158°}$ A.

†10.9 APPLICATIONS

The concepts learned in this chapter will be applied in later chapters to calculate electric power and determine frequency response. The concepts are also used in analyzing coupled circuits, three-phase circuits, ac transistor circuits, filters, oscillators, and other ac circuits. In this section, we apply the concepts to develop two practical ac circuits: the capacitance multiplier and the sine wave oscillators.

10.9.1   Capacitance Multiplier

The op amp circuit in Fig. 10.41 is known as a *capacitance multiplier*, for reasons that will become obvious. Such a circuit is used in integrated-circuit technology to produce a multiple of a small physical capacitance C when a large capacitance is needed. The circuit in Fig. 10.41 can be used to multiply capacitance values by a factor up to 1000. For example, a 10-pF capacitor can be made to behave like a 100-nF capacitor.

In Fig. 10.41, the first op amp operates as a voltage follower, while the second one is an inverting amplifier. The voltage follower isolates the capacitance formed by the circuit from the loading imposed by the inverting amplifier. Since no current enters the input terminals of the op amp, the input current $\mathbf{I}_i$ flows through the feedback capacitor. Hence, at node 1,

$$\mathbf{I}_i = \frac{\mathbf{V}_i - \mathbf{V}_o}{1/j\omega C} = j\omega C(\mathbf{V}_i - \mathbf{V}_o) \tag{10.3}$$

Figure 10.41   Capacitance multiplier.

Applying KCL at node 2 gives

$$\frac{\mathbf{V}_i - 0}{R_1} = \frac{0 - \mathbf{V}_o}{R_2}$$

or

$$\mathbf{V}_o = -\frac{R_2}{R_1}\mathbf{V}_i \tag{10.4}$$

Substituting Eq. (10.4) into (10.3) gives

$$\mathbf{I}_i = j\omega C\left(1 + \frac{R_2}{R_1}\right)\mathbf{V}_i$$

or

$$\frac{\mathbf{I}_i}{\mathbf{V}_i} = j\omega\left(1 + \frac{R_2}{R_1}\right)C \tag{10.5}$$

The input impedance is

$$\mathbf{Z}_i = \frac{\mathbf{V}_i}{\mathbf{I}_i} = \frac{1}{j\omega C_{eq}} \tag{10.6}$$

where

$$C_{eq} = \left(1 + \frac{R_2}{R_1}\right)C \tag{10.7}$$

Thus, by a proper selection of the values of R_1 and R_2, the op amp circuit in Fig. 10.41 can be made to produce an effective capacitance between the input terminal and ground, which is a multiple of the physical capacitance C. The size of the effective capacitance is practically limited by the inverted output voltage limitation. Thus, the larger the capacitance multiplication, the smaller is the allowable input voltage to prevent the op amps from reaching saturation.

A similar op amp circuit can be designed to simulate inductance. (See Prob. 10.89.) There is also an op amp circuit configuration to create a resistance multiplier.

E X A M P L E   1 0 . 1 5

Calculate C_{eq} in Fig. 10.41 when $R_1 = 10\,\text{k}\Omega$, $R_2 = 1\,\text{M}\Omega$, and $C = 1\,\text{nF}$.

Solution:

From Eq. (10.7)

$$C_{eq} = \left(1 + \frac{R_2}{R_1}\right)C = \left(1 + \frac{1 \times 10^6}{10 \times 10^3}\right)1\text{ nF} = 101\text{ nF}$$

PRACTICE PROBLEM 10.15

Determine the equivalent capacitance of the op amp circuit in Fig. 10.41 if $R_1 = 10\text{ k}\Omega$, $R_2 = 10\text{ M}\Omega$, and $C = 10\text{ nF}$.

Answer: $10\ \mu\text{F}$.

10.9.2 Oscillators

We know that dc is produced by batteries. But how do we produce ac? One way is using *oscillators*, which are circuits that convert dc to ac.

> An oscillator is a circuit that produces an ac waveform as output when powered by a dc input.

The only external source an oscillator needs is the dc power supply. Ironically, the dc power supply is usually obtained by converting the ac supplied by the electric utility company to dc. Having gone through the trouble of conversion, one may wonder why we need to use the oscillator to convert the dc to ac again. The problem is that the ac supplied by the utility company operates at a preset frequency of 60 Hz in the United States (50 Hz in some other nations), whereas many applications such as electronic circuits, communication systems, and microwave devices require internally generated frequencies that range from 0 to 10 GHz or higher. Oscillators are used for generating these frequencies.

In order for sine wave oscillators to sustain oscillations, they must meet the *Barkhausen criteria:*

1. The overall gain of the oscillator must be unity or greater. Therefore, losses must be compensated for by an amplifying device.

2. The overall phase shift (from input to output and back to the input) must be zero.

Three common types of sine wave oscillators are phase-shift, twin T, and Wien-bridge oscillators. Here we consider only the Wien-bridge oscillator.

The *Wien-bridge oscillator* is widely used for generating sinusoids in the frequency range below 1 MHz. It is an RC op amp circuit with only a few components, easily tunable and easy to design. As shown in Fig. 10.42, the oscillator essentially consists of a noninverting amplifier with two feedback paths: the positive feedback path to the noninverting input creates oscillations, while the negative feedback path to the inverting

This corresponds to $\omega = 2\pi f = 377$ rad/s.

Figure 10.42   Wien-bridge oscillator.

input controls the gain. If we define the impedances of the RC series and parallel combinations as $\mathbf{Z}_s$ and $\mathbf{Z}_p$, then

$$\mathbf{Z}_s = R_1 + \frac{1}{j\omega C_1} = R_1 - \frac{j}{\omega C_1} \tag{10.8}$$

$$\mathbf{Z}_p = R_2 \parallel \frac{1}{j\omega C_2} = \frac{R_2}{1 + j\omega R_2 C_2} \tag{10.9}$$

The feedback ratio is

$$\frac{\mathbf{V}_2}{\mathbf{V}_o} = \frac{\mathbf{Z}_p}{\mathbf{Z}_s + \mathbf{Z}_p} \tag{10.10}$$

Substituting Eqs. (10.8) and (10.9) into Eq. (10.10) gives

$$\frac{\mathbf{V}_2}{\mathbf{V}_o} = \frac{R_2}{R_2 + \left(R_1 - \dfrac{j}{\omega C_1} \right)(1 + j\omega R_2 C_2)}$$

$$= \frac{\omega R_2 C_1}{\omega(R_2 C_1 + R_1 C_1 + R_2 C_2) + j(\omega^2 R_1 C_1 R_2 C_2 - 1)} \tag{10.11}$$

To satisfy the second Barkhausen criterion, $\mathbf{V}_2$ must be in phase with $\mathbf{V}_o$, which implies that the ratio in Eq. (10.11) must be purely real. Hence, the imaginary part must be zero. Setting the imaginary part equal to zero gives the oscillation frequency ω_o as

$$\omega_o^2 R_1 C_1 R_2 C_2 - 1 = 0$$

or

$$\omega_o = \frac{1}{\sqrt{R_1 R_2 C_1 C_2}} \tag{10.12}$$

In most practical applications, $R_1 = R_2 = R$ and $C_1 = C_2 = C$, so that

$$\omega_o = \frac{1}{RC} = 2\pi f_o \tag{10.13}$$

or

$$\boxed{f_o = \frac{1}{2\pi RC}} \tag{10.14}$$

Substituting Eq. (10.13) and $R_1 = R_2 = R$, $C_1 = C_2 = C$ into Eq. (10.11) yields

$$\frac{\mathbf{V}_2}{\mathbf{V}_o} = \frac{1}{3} \tag{10.15}$$

Thus in order to satisfy the first Barkhausen criterion, the op amp must compensate by providing a gain of 3 or greater so that the overall gain is at least 1 or unity. We recall that for a noninverting amplifier,

$$\frac{\mathbf{V}_o}{\mathbf{V}_2} = 1 + \frac{R_f}{R_g} = 3 \tag{10.16}$$

or

$$R_f = 2R_g \tag{10.17}$$

Due to the inherent delay caused by the op amp, Wien-bridge oscillators are limited to operating in the frequency range of 1 MHz or less.

EXAMPLE 10.16

Design a Wien-bridge circuit to oscillate at 100 kHz.

Solution:

Using Eq. (10.14), we obtain the time constant of the circuit as

$$RC = \frac{1}{2\pi f_o} = \frac{1}{2\pi \times 100 \times 10^3} = 1.59 \times 10^{-6} \qquad (10.16.1)$$

If we select $R = 10$ kΩ, then we can select $C = 159$ pF to satisfy Eq. (10.16.1). Since the gain must be 3, $R_f/R_g = 2$. We could select $R_f = 20$ kΩ while $R_g = 10$ kΩ.

PRACTICE PROBLEM 10.16

In the Wien-bridge oscillator circuit in Fig. 10.42, let $R_1 = R_2 = 2.5$ kΩ, $C_1 = C_2 = 1$ nF. Determine the frequency f_o of the oscillator.

Answer: 63.66 kHz.

10.10 SUMMARY

1. We apply nodal and mesh analysis to ac circuits by applying KCL and KVL to the phasor form of the circuits.

2. In solving for the steady-state response of a circuit that has independent sources with different frequencies, each independent source *must* be considered separately. The most natural approach to analyzing such circuits is to apply the superposition theorem. A separate phasor circuit for each frequency *must* be solved independently, and the corresponding response should be obtained in the time domain. The overall response is the sum of the time-domain responses of all the individual phasor circuits.

3. The concept of source transformation is also applicable in the frequency domain.

4. The Thevenin equivalent of an ac circuit consists of a voltage source $\mathbf{V}_{Th}$ in series with the Thevenin impedance $\mathbf{Z}_{Th}$.

5. The Norton equivalent of an ac circuit consists of a current source $\mathbf{I}_N$ in parallel with the Norton impedance $\mathbf{Z}_N$ ($=\mathbf{Z}_{Th}$).

6. *PSpice* is a simple and powerful tool for solving ac circuit problems. It relieves us of the tedious task of working with the complex numbers involved in steady-state analysis.

7. The capacitance multiplier and the ac oscillator provide two typical applications for the concepts presented in this chapter. A capacitance multiplier is an op amp circuit used in producing a multiple of a physical capacitance. An oscillator is a device that uses a dc input to generate an ac output.

REVIEW QUESTIONS

10.1 The voltage $\mathbf{V}_o$ across the capacitor in Fig. 10.43 is:

   (a) $5\underline{/0°}$ V   (b) $7.071\underline{/45°}$ V
   (c) $7.071\underline{/-45°}$ V   (d) $5\underline{/-45°}$ V

Figure 10.43   For Review Question 10.1.

10.2 The value of the current $\mathbf{I}_o$ in the circuit in Fig. 10.44 is:

   (a) $4\underline{/0°}$ A   (b) $2.4\underline{/-90°}$ A
   (c) $0.6\underline{/0°}$ A   (d) -1 A

Figure 10.44   For Review Question 10.2.

10.3 Using nodal analysis, the value of $\mathbf{V}_o$ in the circuit of Fig. 10.45 is:

   (a) -24 V   (b) -8 V
   (c) 8 V   (d) 24 V

Figure 10.45   For Review Question 10.3.

10.4 In the circuit of Fig. 10.46, current $i(t)$ is:

   (a) $10\cos t$ A   (b) $10\sin t$ A   (c) $5\cos t$ A
   (d) $5\sin t$ A   (e) $4.472\cos(t - 63.43°)$ A

Figure 10.46   For Review Question 10.4.

10.5 Refer to the circuit in Fig. 10.47 and observe that the two sources do not have the same frequency. The current $i_x(t)$ can be obtained by:

   (a) source transformation
   (b) the superposition theorem
   (c) *PSpice*

Figure 10.47   For Review Question 10.5.

10.6 For the circuit in Fig. 10.48, the Thevenin impedance at terminals a-b is:

   (a) $1\ \Omega$ (b) $0.5 - j0.5\ \Omega$
   (c) $0.5 + j0.5\ \Omega$ (d) $1 + j2\ \Omega$
   (e) $1 - j2\ \Omega$

Figure 10.48   For Review Questions 10.6 and 10.7.

10.7 In the circuit of Fig. 10.48, the Thevenin voltage at terminals a-b is:

   (a) $3.535\underline{/-45°}$ V   (b) $3.535\underline{/45°}$ V
   (c) $7.071\underline{/-45°}$ V   (d) $7.071\underline{/45°}$ V

10.8 Refer to the circuit in Fig. 10.49. The Norton equivalent impedance at terminals a-b is:

   (a) $-j4\ \Omega$ (b) $-j2\ \Omega$
   (c) $j2\ \Omega$ (d) $j4\ \Omega$

Figure 10.49   For Review Questions 10.8 and 10.9.

10.9   The Norton current at terminals *a-b* in the circuit of Fig. 10.49 is:

(a) $1\underline{/0°}$ A   (b) $1.5\underline{/-90°}$ A

(c) $1.5\underline{/90°}$ A   (d) $3\underline{/90°}$ A

10.10   *PSpice* can handle a circuit with two independent sources of different frequencies.

(a) True   (b) False

Answers: 10.1c, 10.2a, 10.3d, 10.4a, 10.5b, 10.6c, 10.7a, 10.8a, 10.9d, 10.10b.

PROBLEMS

Section 10.2   Nodal Analysis

10.1   Find v_o in the circuit in Fig. 10.50.

Figure 10.50   For Prob. 10.1.

10.2   For the circuit depicted in Fig. 10.51 below, determine i_o.

10.3   Determine v_o in the circuit of Fig. 10.52.

Figure 10.52   For Prob. 10.3.

10.4   Compute $v_o(t)$ in the circuit of Fig. 10.53.

Figure 10.53   For Prob. 10.4.

10.5   Compute the value of $\mathbf{I}_x$ in Fig. 10.54.

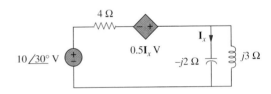

Figure 10.54   For Prob. 10.5.

10.6   Determine $\mathbf{V}_x$ in Fig. 10.55.

Figure 10.55   For Prob. 10.6.

Figure 10.51   For Prob. 10.2.

10.7 Use nodal analysis to find **V** in the circuit of Fig. 10.56.

Figure 10.56　For Prob. 10.7.

10.8 Use nodal analysis to find current i_o in the circuit of Fig. 10.57. Let $i_o = 6\cos(200t + 15°)$ A.

Figure 10.57　For Prob. 10.8.

10.9 Use nodal analysis to find v_o in the circuit of Fig. 10.58.

Figure 10.58　For Prob. 10.9.

10.10 Use nodal analysis to find v_o in the circuit of Fig. 10.59. Let $\omega = 2$ krad/s.

Figure 10.59　For Prob. 10.10.

10.11 Using nodal analysis, find $i_o(t)$ in the circuit in Fig. 10.60.

Figure 10.60　For Prob. 10.11.

10.12 By nodal analysis, find i_o in the circuit in Fig. 10.61.

Figure 10.61　For Prob. 10.12.

10.13 Determine $\mathbf{V}_x$ in the circuit of Fig. 10.62 using any method of your choice.

Figure 10.62　For Prob. 10.13.

10.14 Calculate the voltage at nodes 1 and 2 in the circuit of Fig. 10.63 using nodal analysis.

Figure 10.63　For Prob. 10.14.

10.15 Solve for the current **I** in the circuit of Fig. 10.64 using nodal analysis.

Figure 10.64   For Prob. 10.15.

10.16 Using nodal analysis, find $\mathbf{V}_1$ and $\mathbf{V}_2$ in the circuit of Fig. 10.65.

Figure 10.65   For Prob. 10.16.

10.17 By nodal analysis, obtain current $\mathbf{I}_o$ in the circuit in Fig. 10.66.

Figure 10.66   For Prob. 10.17.

10.18 Use nodal analysis to obtain $\mathbf{V}_o$ in the circuit of Fig. 10.67 below.

10.19 Obtain $\mathbf{V}_o$ in Fig. 10.68 using nodal analysis.

Figure 10.68   For Prob. 10.19.

10.20 Refer to Fig. 10.69. If $v_s(t) = V_m \sin \omega t$ and $v_o(t) = A \sin(\omega t + \phi)$, derive the expressions for A and ϕ.

Figure 10.69   For Prob. 10.20.

10.21 For each of the circuits in Fig. 10.70, find $\mathbf{V}_o/\mathbf{V}_i$ for $\omega = 0$, $\omega \rightarrow \infty$, and $\omega^2 = 1/LC$.

(a)   (b)

Figure 10.70   For Prob. 10.21.

Figure 10.67   For Prob. 10.18.

10.22   For the circuit in Fig. 10.71, determine $\mathbf{V}_o/\mathbf{V}_s$.

Figure 10.71   For Prob. 10.22.

10.23   Using nodal analysis obtain $\mathbf{V}$ in the circuit of Fig. 10.72.

Figure 10.72   For Prob. 10.23.

Section 10.3   Mesh Analysis

10.24   Obtain the mesh currents $\mathbf{I}_1$ and $\mathbf{I}_2$ in the circuit of Fig. 10.73.

Figure 10.73   For Prob. 10.24.

10.25   Solve for i_o in Fig. 10.74 using mesh analysis.

Figure 10.74   For Prob. 10.25.

10.26   Rework Prob. 10.9 using mesh analysis.

10.27   Using mesh analysis, find $\mathbf{I}_1$ and $\mathbf{I}_2$ in the circuit of Fig. 10.75.

Figure 10.75   For Prob. 10.27.

10.28   In the circuit of Fig. 10.76, determine the mesh currents i_1 and i_2. Let $v_1 = 10\cos 4t$ V and $v_2 = 20\cos(4t - 30°)$ V.

Figure 10.76   For Prob. 10.28.

10.29   By using mesh analysis, find $\mathbf{I}_1$ and $\mathbf{I}_2$ in the circuit depicted in Fig. 10.77.

Figure 10.77   For Prob. 10.29.

10.30   Repeat Prob. 10.17 using mesh analysis.

10.31   Use mesh analysis to determine current $\mathbf{I}_o$ in the circuit of Fig. 10.78 on the bottom of the next page.

10.32   Determine $\mathbf{V}_o$ and $\mathbf{I}_o$ in the circuit of Fig. 10.79 using mesh analysis.

Figure 10.79   For Prob. 10.32.

10.33 Compute **I** in Prob. 10.15 using mesh analysis.

10.34 Use mesh analysis to find $\mathbf{I}_o$ in Fig. 10.28 (for Example 10.10).

10.35 Calculate $\mathbf{I}_o$ in Fig. 10.30 (for Practice Prob. 10.10) using mesh analysis.

10.36 Compute $\mathbf{V}_o$ in the circuit of Fig. 10.80 using mesh analysis.

Figure 10.80   For Prob. 10.36.

10.37 Use mesh analysis to find currents $\mathbf{I}_1$, $\mathbf{I}_2$, and $\mathbf{I}_3$ in the circuit of Fig. 10.81.

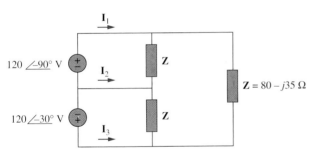

Figure 10.81   For Prob. 10.37.

10.38 Using mesh analysis, obtain $\mathbf{I}_o$ in the circuit shown in Fig. 10.82.

Figure 10.82   For Prob. 10.38.

10.39 Find $\mathbf{I}_1$, $\mathbf{I}_2$, $\mathbf{I}_3$, and $\mathbf{I}_x$ in the circuit of Fig. 10.83.

Figure 10.83   For Prob. 10.39.

Section 10.4   Superposition Theorem

10.40 Find i_o in the circuit shown in Fig. 10.84 using superposition.

Figure 10.84   For Prob. 10.40.

Figure 10.78   For Prob. 10.31.

10.41 Use superposition to calculate v_x in the circuit of Fig. 10.85.

Figure 10.85 For Prob. 10.41.

10.42 In the circuit of Fig. 10.86, calculate $i_x(t)$ using superposition. Let $v_s = 12\cos(4t - 30°)$ V and $i_s = 6\sin(2t)$ A.

Figure 10.86 For Prob. 10.42.

10.43 Using the superposition principle, find i_x in the circuit of Fig. 10.87.

Figure 10.87 For Prob. 10.43.

10.44 Use the superposition principle to obtain v_x in the circuit of Fig. 10.88. Let $v_s = 50\sin 2t$ V and $i_s = 12\cos(6t + 10°)$ A.

Figure 10.88 For Prob. 10.44.

10.45 Rework Prob. 10.2 using the superposition theorem.

10.46 Solve for $v_o(t)$ in the circuit of Fig. 10.89 using the superposition principle.

Figure 10.89 For Prob. 10.46.

10.47 Determine i_o in the circuit of Fig. 10.90.

Figure 10.90 For Prob. 10.47.

10.48 Find i_o in the circuit in Fig. 10.91 using superposition.

Figure 10.91 For Prob. 10.48.

Section 10.5 Source Transformation

10.49 Using source transformation, find i in the circuit of Fig. 10.92.

Figure 10.92 For Prob. 10.49.

10.50 Use source transformation to find v_o in the circuit of Fig. 10.93.

Figure 10.93   For Prob. 10.50.

10.51 Solve Prob. 10.27 using source transformation.

10.52 Use the method of source transformation to find $\mathbf{I}_x$ in the circuit of Fig. 10.94.

Figure 10.94   For Prob. 10.52.

10.53 Use the concept of source transformation to find $\mathbf{V}_o$ in the circuit of Fig. 10.95.

Figure 10.95   For Prob. 10.53.

10.54 Rework Prob. 10.7 using source transformation.

Section 10.6   Thevenin and Norton Equivalent Circuits

10.55 Find the Thevenin and Norton equivalent circuits at terminals a-b for each of the circuits in Fig. 10.96.

(a)

(b)

Figure 10.96   For Prob. 10.55.

10.56 For each of the circuits in Fig. 10.97, obtain Thevenin and Norton equivalent circuits at terminals a-b.

(a)

(b)

Figure 10.97   For Prob. 10.56.

10.57 Find the Thevenin and Norton equivalent circuits for the circuit shown in Fig. 10.98.

Figure 10.98   For Prob. 10.57.

10.58 For the circuit depicted in Fig. 10.99, find the Thevenin equivalent circuit at terminals *a-b*.

Figure 10.99 For Prob. 10.58.

10.59 Repeat Prob. 10.1 using Thevenin's theorem.

10.60 Find the Thevenin equivalent of the circuit in Fig. 10.100 as seen from:

    (a) terminals *a-b*   (b) terminals *c-d*

Figure 10.100 For Prob. 10.60.

10.61 Solve Prob. 10.3 using Thevenin's theorem.

10.62 Using Thevenin's theorem, find v_o in the circuit in Fig. 10.101.

Figure 10.101 For Prob. 10.62.

10.63 Obtain the Norton equivalent of the circuit depicted in Fig. 10.102 at terminals *a-b*.

Figure 10.102 For Prob. 10.63.

10.64 For the circuit shown in Fig. 10.103, find the Norton equivalent circuit at terminals *a-b*.

Figure 10.103 For Prob. 10.64.

10.65 Compute i_o in Fig. 10.104 using Norton's theorem.

Figure 10.104 For Prob. 10.65.

10.66 At terminals *a-b*, obtain Thevenin and Norton equivalent circuits for the network depicted in Fig. 10.105. Take $\omega = 10$ rad/s.

Figure 10.105 For Prob. 10.66.

10.67 Find the Thevenin and Norton equivalent circuits at terminals *a-b* in the circuit of Fig. 10.106.

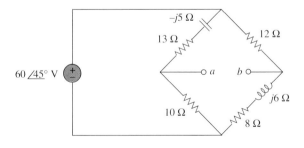

Figure 10.106 For Prob. 10.67.

10.68 Find the Thevenin equivalent at terminals *a-b* in the circuit of Fig. 10.107.

Figure 10.107   For Prob. 10.68.

Section 10.7   Op Amp AC Circuits

10.69 For the differentiator shown in Fig. 10.108, obtain $\mathbf{V}_o/\mathbf{V}_s$. Find $v_o(t)$ when $v_s(t) = V_m \sin \omega t$ and $\omega = 1/RC$.

Figure 10.108   For Prob. 10.69.

10.70 The circuit in Fig. 10.109 is an integrator with a feedback resistor. Calculate $v_o(t)$ if $v_s = 2 \cos 4 \times 10^4 t$ V.

Figure 10.109   For Prob. 10.70.

10.71 Find v_o in the op amp circuit of Fig. 10.110.

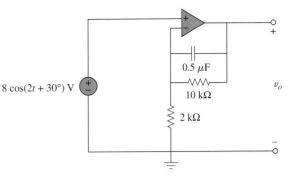

Figure 10.110   For Prob. 10.71.

10.72 Compute $i_o(t)$ in the op amp circuit in Fig. 10.111 if $v_s = 4 \cos 10^4 t$ V.

Figure 10.111   For Prob. 10.72.

10.73 If the input impedance is defined as $\mathbf{Z}_{\text{in}} = \mathbf{V}_s/\mathbf{I}_s$, find the input impedance of the op amp circuit in Fig. 10.112 when $R_1 = 10$ kΩ, $R_2 = 20$ kΩ, $C_1 = 10$ nF, $C_2 = 20$ nF, and $\omega = 5000$ rad/s.

Figure 10.112   For Prob. 10.73.

10.74 Evaluate the voltage gain $\mathbf{A}_v = \mathbf{V}_o/\mathbf{V}_s$ in the op amp circuit of Fig. 10.113. Find $\mathbf{A}_v$ at $\omega = 0$, $\omega \to \infty$, $\omega = 1/R_1C_1$, and $\omega = 1/R_2C_2$.

Figure 10.113   For Prob. 10.74.

10.75 In the op amp circuit of Fig. 10.114, find the closed-loop gain and phase shift if $C_1 = C_2 = 1$ nF, $R_1 = R_2 = 100$ kΩ, $R_3 = 20$ kΩ, $R_4 = 40$ kΩ, and $\omega = 2000$ rad/s.

Figure 10.114   For Prob. 10.75.

10.76 Determine $\mathbf{V}_o$ and $\mathbf{I}_o$ in the op amp circuit of Fig. 10.115.

10.77 Compute the closed-loop gain $\mathbf{V}_o/\mathbf{V}_s$ for the op amp circuit of Fig. 10.116.

Figure 10.116   For Prob. 10.77.

10.78 Determine $v_o(t)$ in the op amp circuit in Fig. 10.117 below.

10.79 For the op amp circuit in Fig. 10.118, obtain $v_o(t)$.

Figure 10.115   For Prob. 10.76.

Figure 10.118   For Prob. 10.79.

Figure 10.117   For Prob. 10.78.

10.80   Obtain $v_o(t)$ for the op amp circuit in Fig. 10.119 if $v_s = 4 \cos(1000t - 60°)$ V.

Figure 10.119   For Prob. 10.80.

Section 10.8   AC Analysis Using *PSpice*

10.81   Use *PSpice* to solve Example 10.10.

10.82   Solve Prob. 10.19 using *PSpice*.

10.83   Use *PSpice* to find $v_o(t)$ in the circuit of Fig. 10.120. Let $i_s = 2 \cos(10^3 t)$ A.

Figure 10.120   For Prob. 10.83.

10.84   Obtain $\mathbf{V}_o$ in the circuit of Fig. 10.121 using *PSpice*.

Figure 10.121   For Prob. 10.84.

10.85   Use *PSpice* to find $\mathbf{V}_o$ in the circuit of Fig. 10.122.

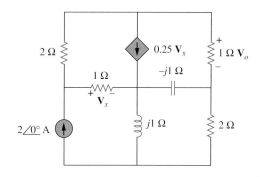

Figure 10.122   For Prob. 10.85.

10.86   Use *PSpice* to find $\mathbf{V}_1$, $\mathbf{V}_2$, and $\mathbf{V}_3$ in the network of Fig. 10.123.

Figure 10.123   For Prob. 10.86.

10.87   Determine $\mathbf{V}_1$, $\mathbf{V}_2$, and $\mathbf{V}_3$ in the circuit of Fig. 10.124 using *PSpice*.

Figure 10.124   For Prob. 10.87.

10.88   Use *PSpice* to find v_o and i_o in the circuit of Fig. 10.125 on the bottom of the next page.

Section 10.9   Applications

10.89   The op amp circuit in Fig. 10.126 is called an *inductance simulator*. Show that the input impedance is given by

$$\mathbf{Z}_{in} = \frac{\mathbf{V}_{in}}{\mathbf{I}_{in}} = j\omega L_{eq}$$

where

$$L_{eq} = \frac{R_1 R_3 R_4}{R_2} C$$

Figure 10.126   For Prob. 10.89.

10.90   Figure 10.127 shows a Wien-bridge network. Show that the frequency at which the phase shift between the input and output signals is zero is $f = \frac{1}{2}\pi RC$, and that the necessary gain is $\mathbf{A}_v = \mathbf{V}_o/\mathbf{V}_i = 3$ at that frequency.

Figure 10.127   For Prob. 10.90.

10.91   Consider the oscillator in Fig. 10.128.

(a)   Determine the oscillation frequency.

(b)   Obtain the minimum value of R for which oscillation takes place.

Figure 10.128   For Prob. 10.91.

10.92   The oscillator circuit in Fig. 10.129 uses an ideal op amp.

(a)   Calculate the minimum value of R_o that will cause oscillation to occur.

(b)   Find the frequency of oscillation.

Figure 10.129   For Prob. 10.92.

10.93   Figure 10.130 shows a *Colpitts oscillator*. Show that the oscillation frequency is

$$f_o = \frac{1}{2\pi \sqrt{LC_T}}$$

where $C_T = C_1 C_2/(C_1 + C_2)$. Assume $R_i \gg X_{C_2}$.

Figure 10.130   A Colpitts oscillator; for Prob. 10.93.

(*Hint:* Set the imaginary part of the impedance in the feedback circuit equal to zero.)

10.94   Design a Colpitts oscillator that will operate at 50 kHz.

Figure 10.125   For Prob. 10.88.

10.95 Figure 10.131 shows a *Hartley oscillator*. Show that the frequency of oscillation is

$$f_o = \frac{1}{2\pi \sqrt{C(L_1 + L_2)}}$$

Figure 10.131   A Hartley oscillator; for Prob. 10.95.

10.96 Refer to the oscillator in Fig. 10.132.

(a) Show that

$$\frac{\mathbf{V}_2}{\mathbf{V}_o} = \frac{1}{3 + j(\omega L/R - R/\omega L)}$$

(b) Determine the oscillation frequency f_o.

(c) Obtain the relationship between R_1 and R_2 in order for oscillation to occur.

Figure 10.132   For Prob. 10.96.

C H A P T E R 11

AC POWER ANALYSIS

Engineers are not superhuman. They make mistakes in their assumptions, in their calculations, in their conclusions. That they make mistakes is forgivable; that they catch them is imperative. Thus it is the essence of modern engineering not only to be able to check one's own work but also to have one's work checked and to be able to check the work of others.

—Henry Petroski

Enhancing Your Career

Career in Power Systems   The discovery of the principle of an ac generator by Michael Faraday in 1831 was a major breakthrough in engineering; it provided a convenient way of generating the electric power that is needed in every electronic, electrical, or electromechanical device we use now.

Electric power is obtained by converting energy from sources such as fossil fuels (gas, oil, and coal), nuclear fuel (uranium), hydro energy (water falling through a head), geothermal energy (hot water, steam), wind energy, tidal energy, and biomass energy (wastes). These various ways of generating electric power are studied in detail in the field of power engineering, which has become an indispensable subdiscipline of electrical engineering. An electrical engineer should be familiar with the analysis, generation, transmission, distribution, and cost of electric power.

The electric power industry is a very large employer of electrical engineers. The industry includes thousands of electric utility systems ranging from large, interconnected systems serving large regional areas to small power companies serving individual communities or factories. Due to the complexity of the power industry, there are numerous electrical engineering jobs in different areas of the industry: power plant (generation), transmission and distribution, maintenance, research, data acquisition and flow control, and management. Since electric power is used everywhere, electric utility companies are everywhere, offering exciting

A pole-type transformer with a low-voltage, three-wire distribution system. Source: W. N. Alerich, Electricity, 3rd ed. Albany, NY: Delmar Publishers, 1981, p. 152. (Courtesy of General Electric.)

training and steady employment for men and women in thousands of communities throughout the world.

11.1   INTRODUCTION

Our effort in ac circuit analysis so far has been focused mainly on calculating voltage and current. Our major concern in this chapter is power analysis.

Power analysis is of paramount importance. Power is the most important quantity in electric utilities, electronic, and communication systems, because such systems involve transmission of power from one point to another. Also, every industrial and household electrical device—every fan, motor, lamp, pressing iron, TV, personal computer—has a power rating that indicates how much power the equipment requires; exceeding the power rating can do permanent damage to an appliance. The most common form of electric power is 50- or 60-Hz ac power. The choice of ac over dc allowed high-voltage power transmission from the power generating plant to the consumer.

We will begin by defining and deriving *instantaneous power* and *average power*. We will then introduce other power concepts. As practical applications of these concepts, we will discuss how power is measured and reconsider how electric utility companies charge their customers.

11.2   INSTANTANEOUS AND AVERAGE POWER

As mentioned in Chapter 2, the *instantaneous power* $p(t)$ absorbed by an element is the product of the instantaneous voltage $v(t)$ across the element and the instantaneous current $i(t)$ through it. Assuming the passive sign convention,

$$p(t) = v(t)i(t) \qquad (11.1)$$

The instantaneous power (in watts) is the power at any instant of time.

It is the rate at which an element absorbs energy.

Consider the general case of instantaneous power absorbed by an arbitrary combination of circuit elements under sinusoidal excitation, as shown in Fig. 11.1. Let the voltage and current at the terminals of the circuit be

$$v(t) = V_m \cos(\omega t + \theta_v) \qquad (11.2a)$$

$$i(t) = I_m \cos(\omega t + \theta_i) \qquad (11.2b)$$

where V_m and I_m are the amplitudes (or peak values), and θ_v and θ_i are the phase angles of the voltage and current, respectively. The instantaneous power absorbed by the circuit is

$$p(t) = v(t)i(t) = V_m I_m \cos(\omega t + \theta_v) \cos(\omega t + \theta_i) \qquad (11.3)$$

We apply the trigonometric identity

$$\cos A \cos B = \frac{1}{2}[\cos(A - B) + \cos(A + B)] \qquad (11.4)$$

We can also think of the instantaneous power as the power absorbed by the element at a specific instant of time. Instantaneous quantities are denoted by lowercase letters.

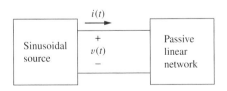

Figure 11.1   Sinusoidal source and passive linear circuit.

and express Eq. (11.3) as

$$p(t) = \frac{1}{2}V_m I_m \cos(\theta_v - \theta_i) + \frac{1}{2}V_m I_m \cos(2\omega t + \theta_v + \theta_i) \qquad (11.5)$$

This shows us that the instantaneous power has two parts. The first part is constant or time independent. Its value depends on the phase difference between the voltage and the current. The second part is a sinusoidal function whose frequency is 2ω, which is twice the angular frequency of the voltage or current.

A sketch of $p(t)$ in Eq. (11.5) is shown in Fig. 11.2, where $T = 2\pi/\omega$ is the period of voltage or current. We observe that $p(t)$ is periodic, $p(t) = p(t + T_0)$, and has a period of $T_0 = T/2$, since its frequency is twice that of voltage or current. We also observe that $p(t)$ is positive for some part of each cycle and negative for the rest of the cycle. When $p(t)$ is positive, power is absorbed by the circuit. When $p(t)$ is negative, power is absorbed by the source; that is, power is transferred from the circuit to the source. This is possible because of the storage elements (capacitors and inductors) in the circuit.

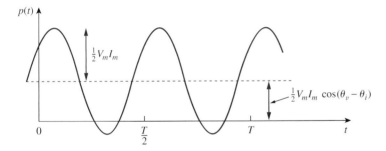

Figure 11.2   The instantaneous power $p(t)$ entering a circuit.

The instantaneous power changes with time and is therefore difficult to measure. The *average* power is more convenient to measure. In fact, the wattmeter, the instrument for measuring power, responds to average power.

> The average power, in watts, is the average of the instantaneous power over one period.

Thus, the average power is given by

$$P = \frac{1}{T}\int_0^T p(t)\,dt \qquad (11.6)$$

Although Eq. (11.6) shows the averaging done over T, we would get the same result if we performed the integration over the actual period of $p(t)$ which is $T_0 = T/2$.

Substituting $p(t)$ in Eq. (11.5) into Eq. (11.6) gives

$$
\begin{aligned}
P &= \frac{1}{T} \int_0^T \frac{1}{2} V_m I_m \cos(\theta_v - \theta_i)\, dt \\
&\quad + \frac{1}{T} \int_0^T \frac{1}{2} V_m I_m \cos(2\omega t + \theta_v + \theta_i)\, dt \\
&= \frac{1}{2} V_m I_m \cos(\theta_v - \theta_i) \frac{1}{T} \int_0^T dt \\
&\quad + \frac{1}{2} V_m I_m \frac{1}{T} \int_0^T \cos(2\omega t + \theta_v + \theta_i)\, dt
\end{aligned}
\tag{11.7}
$$

The first integrand is constant, and the average of a constant is the same constant. The second integrand is a sinusoid. We know that the average of a sinusoid over its period is zero because the area under the sinusoid during a positive half-cycle is canceled by the area under it during the following negative half-cycle. Thus, the second term in Eq. (11.7) vanishes and the average power becomes

$$
P = \frac{1}{2} V_m I_m \cos(\theta_v - \theta_i)
\tag{11.8}
$$

Since $\cos(\theta_v - \theta_i) = \cos(\theta_i - \theta_v)$, what is important is the difference in the phases of the voltage and current.

Note that $p(t)$ is time-varying while P does not depend on time. To find the instantaneous power, we must necessarily have $v(t)$ and $i(t)$ in the time domain. But we can find the average power when voltage and current are expressed in the time domain, as in Eq. (11.8), or when they are expressed in the frequency domain. The phasor forms of $v(t)$ and $i(t)$ in Eq. (11.2) are $\mathbf{V} = V_m \underline{/\theta_v}$ and $\mathbf{I} = I_m \underline{/\theta_i}$, respectively. P is calculated using Eq. (11.8) or using phasors $\mathbf{V}$ and $\mathbf{I}$. To use phasors, we notice that

$$
\begin{aligned}
\frac{1}{2} \mathbf{V} \mathbf{I}^* &= \frac{1}{2} V_m I_m \underline{/\theta_v - \theta_i} \\
&= \frac{1}{2} V_m I_m \left[\cos(\theta_v - \theta_i) + j \sin(\theta_v - \theta_i)\right]
\end{aligned}
\tag{11.9}
$$

We recognize the real part of this expression as the average power P according to Eq. (11.8). Thus,

$$
\boxed{P = \frac{1}{2} \operatorname{Re}\left[\mathbf{V}\mathbf{I}^*\right] = \frac{1}{2} V_m I_m \cos(\theta_v - \theta_i)}
\tag{11.10}
$$

Consider two special cases of Eq. (11.10). When $\theta_v = \theta_i$, the voltage and current are in phase. This implies a purely resistive circuit or resistive load R, and

$$
P = \frac{1}{2} V_m I_m = \frac{1}{2} I_m^2 R = \frac{1}{2} |\mathbf{I}|^2 R
\tag{11.11}
$$

where $|\mathbf{I}|^2 = \mathbf{I} \times \mathbf{I}^*$. Equation (11.11) shows that a purely resistive circuit absorbs power at all times. When $\theta_v - \theta_i = \pm 90°$, we have a purely reactive circuit, and

$$P = \frac{1}{2} V_m I_m \cos 90° = 0 \tag{11.12}$$

showing that a purely reactive circuit absorbs no average power. In summary,

---
A resistive load (R) absorbs power at all times, while a reactive load (L or C) absorbs zero average power.

EXAMPLE 11.1

Given that

$$v(t) = 120 \cos(377t + 45°) \text{ V} \qquad \text{and} \qquad i(t) = 10 \cos(377t - 10°) \text{ A}$$

find the instantaneous power and the average power absorbed by the passive linear network of Fig. 11.1.

Solution:

The instantaneous power is given by

$$p = vi = 1200 \cos(377t + 45°) \cos(377t - 10°)$$

Applying the trigonometric identity

$$\cos A \cos B = \frac{1}{2}[\cos(A + B) + \cos(A - B)]$$

gives

$$p = 600[\cos(754t + 35°) + \cos 55°]$$

or

$$p(t) = 344.2 + 600 \cos(754t + 35°) \text{ W}$$

The average power is

$$P = \frac{1}{2} V_m I_m \cos(\theta_v - \theta_i) = \frac{1}{2} 120(10) \cos[45° - (-10°)]$$

$$= 600 \cos 55° = 344.2 \text{ W}$$

which is the constant part of $p(t)$ above.

PRACTICE PROBLEM 11.1

Calculate the instantaneous power and average power absorbed by the passive linear network of Fig. 11.1 if

$$v(t) = 80 \cos(10t + 20°) \text{ V} \qquad \text{and} \qquad i(t) = 15 \sin(10t + 60°) \text{ A}$$

Answer: $385.7 + 600 \cos(20t - 10°)$ W, 385.7 W.

EXAMPLE 11.2

Calculate the average power absorbed by an impedance $\mathbf{Z} = 30 - j70\ \Omega$ when a voltage $\mathbf{V} = 120\underline{/0°}$ is applied across it.

Solution:

The current through the impedance is

$$\mathbf{I} = \frac{\mathbf{V}}{\mathbf{Z}} = \frac{120\underline{/0°}}{30 - j70} = \frac{120\underline{/0°}}{76.16\underline{/-66.8°}} = 1.576\underline{/66.8°}\ \text{A}$$

The average power is

$$P = \frac{1}{2}V_m I_m \cos(\theta_v - \theta_i) = \frac{1}{2}(120)(1.576)\cos(0 - 66.8°) = 37.24\ \text{W}$$

PRACTICE PROBLEM 11.2

A current $\mathbf{I} = 10\underline{/30°}$ flows through an impedance $\mathbf{Z} = 20\underline{/-22°}\ \Omega$. Find the average power delivered to the impedance.

Answer: 927.2 W.

EXAMPLE 11.3

Figure 11.3   For Example 11.3.

For the circuit shown in Fig. 11.3, find the average power supplied by the source and the average power absorbed by the resistor.

Solution:

The current $\mathbf{I}$ is given by

$$\mathbf{I} = \frac{5\underline{/30°}}{4 - j2} = \frac{5\underline{/30°}}{4.472\underline{/-26.57°}} = 1.118\underline{/56.57°}\ \text{A}$$

The average power supplied by the voltage source is

$$P = \frac{1}{2}(5)(1.118)\cos(30° - 56.57°) = 2.5\ \text{W}$$

The current through the resistor is

$$\mathbf{I}_R = \mathbf{I} = 1.118\underline{/56.57°}\ \text{A}$$

and the voltage across it is

$$\mathbf{V}_R = 4\mathbf{I}_R = 4.472\underline{/56.57°}\ \text{V}$$

The average power absorbed by the resistor is

$$P = \frac{1}{2}(4.472)(1.118) = 2.5\ \text{W}$$

which is the same as the average power supplied. Zero average power is absorbed by the capacitor.

PRACTICE PROBLEM 11.3

In the circuit of Fig. 11.4, calculate the average power absorbed by the resistor and inductor. Find the average power supplied by the voltage source.

Answer: 9.6 W, 0 W, 9.6 W.

Figure 11.4   For Practice Prob. 11.3.

EXAMPLE 11.4

Determine the power generated by each source and the average power absorbed by each passive element in the circuit of Fig. 11.5(a).

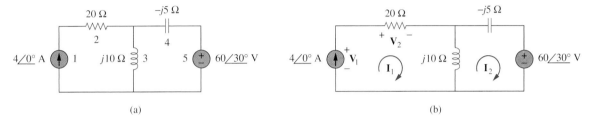

(a)   (b)

Figure 11.5   For Example 11.4.

Solution:

We apply mesh analysis as shown in Fig. 11.5(b). For mesh 1,

$$\mathbf{I}_1 = 4 \text{ A}$$

For mesh 2,

$$(j10 - j5)\mathbf{I}_2 - j10\mathbf{I}_1 + 60\underline{/30^\circ} = 0, \qquad \mathbf{I}_1 = 4 \text{ A}$$

or

$$j5\mathbf{I}_2 = -60\underline{/30^\circ} + j40 \qquad \Longrightarrow \qquad \mathbf{I}_2 = -12\underline{/-60^\circ} + 8$$
$$= 10.58\underline{/79.1^\circ} \text{ A}$$

For the voltage source, the current flowing from it is $\mathbf{I}_2 = 10.58\underline{/79.1^\circ}$ A and the voltage across it is $60\underline{/30^\circ}$ V, so that the average power is

$$P_5 = \frac{1}{2}(60)(10.58)\cos(30^\circ - 79.1^\circ) = 207.8 \text{ W}$$

Following the passive sign convention (see Fig. 1.8), this average power is absorbed by the source, in view of the direction of $\mathbf{I}_2$ and the polarity of the voltage source. That is, the circuit is delivering average power to the voltage source.

For the current source, the current through it is $\mathbf{I}_1 = 4\underline{/0^\circ}$ and the voltage across it is

$$\mathbf{V}_1 = 20\mathbf{I}_1 + j10(\mathbf{I}_1 - \mathbf{I}_2) = 80 + j10(4 - 2 - j10.39)$$
$$= 183.9 + j20 = 184.984\underline{/6.21^\circ} \text{ V}$$

The average power supplied by the current source is

$$P_1 = -\frac{1}{2}(184.984)(4)\cos(6.21° - 0) = -367.8 \text{ W}$$

It is negative according to the passive sign convention, meaning that the current source is supplying power to the circuit.

For the resistor, the current through it is $\mathbf{I}_1 = 4\underline{/0°}$ and the voltage across it is $20\mathbf{I}_1 = 80\underline{/0°}$, so that the power absorbed by the resistor is

$$P_2 = \frac{1}{2}(80)(4) = 160 \text{ W}$$

For the capacitor, the current through it is $\mathbf{I}_2 = 10.58\underline{/79.1°}$ and the voltage across it is $-j5\mathbf{I}_2 = (5\underline{/-90°})(10.58\underline{/79.1°}) = 52.9\underline{/79.1° - 90°}$. The average power absorbed by the capacitor is

$$P_4 = \frac{1}{2}(52.9)(10.58)\cos(-90°) = 0$$

For the inductor, the current through it is $\mathbf{I}_1 - \mathbf{I}_2 = 2 - j10.39 = 10.58\underline{/-79.1°}$. The voltage across it is $j10(\mathbf{I}_1 - \mathbf{I}_2) = 105.8\underline{/-79.1° + 90°}$. Hence, the average power absorbed by the inductor is

$$P_3 = \frac{1}{2}(105.8)(10.58)\cos 90° = 0$$

Notice that the inductor and the capacitor absorb zero average power and that the total power supplied by the current source equals the power absorbed by the resistor and the voltage source, or

$$P_1 + P_2 + P_3 + P_4 + P_5 = -367.8 + 160 + 0 + 0 + 207.8 = 0$$

indicating that power is conserved.

PRACTICE PROBLEM 11.4

Calculate the average power absorbed by each of the five elements in the circuit of Fig. 11.6.

Figure 11.6   For Practice Prob. 11.4.

Answer: 40-V Voltage source: -60 W; $j20$-V Voltage source: -40 W; resistor: 100 W; others: 0 W.

11.3 MAXIMUM AVERAGE POWER TRANSFER

In Section 4.8 we solved the problem of maximizing the power delivered by a power-supplying resistive network to a load R_L. Representing the circuit by its Thevenin equivalent, we proved that the maximum power would be delivered to the load if the load resistance is equal to the Thevenin resistance $R_L = R_{Th}$. We now extend that result to ac circuits.

Consider the circuit in Fig. 11.7, where an ac circuit is connected to a load $\mathbf{Z}_L$ and is represented by its Thevenin equivalent. The load is usually represented by an impedance, which may model an electric motor, an antenna, a TV, and so forth. In rectangular form, the Thevenin impedance $\mathbf{Z}_{Th}$ and the load impedance $\mathbf{Z}_L$ are

$$\mathbf{Z}_{Th} = R_{Th} + jX_{Th} \tag{11.13a}$$

$$\mathbf{Z}_L = R_L + jX_L \tag{11.13b}$$

The current through the load is

$$\mathbf{I} = \frac{\mathbf{V}_{Th}}{\mathbf{Z}_{Th} + \mathbf{Z}_L} = \frac{\mathbf{V}_{Th}}{(R_{Th} + jX_{Th}) + (R_L + jX_L)} \tag{11.14}$$

From Eq. (11.11), the average power delivered to the load is

$$P = \frac{1}{2}|\mathbf{I}|^2 R_L = \frac{|\mathbf{V}_{Th}|^2 R_L / 2}{(R_{Th} + R_L)^2 + (X_{Th} + X_L)^2} \tag{11.15}$$

Our objective is to adjust the load parameters R_L and X_L so that P is maximum. To do this we set $\partial P / \partial R_L$ and $\partial P / \partial X_L$ equal to zero. From Eq. (11.15), we obtain

$$\frac{\partial P}{\partial X_L} = -\frac{|\mathbf{V}_{Th}|^2 R_L (X_{Th} + X_L)}{[(R_{Th} + R_L)^2 + (X_{Th} + X_L)^2]^2} \tag{11.16a}$$

$$\frac{\partial P}{\partial R_L} = \frac{|\mathbf{V}_{Th}|^2 [(R_{Th} + R_L)^2 + (X_{Th} + X_L)^2 - 2R_L(R_{Th} + R_L)]}{2[(R_{Th} + R_L)^2 + (X_{Th} + X_L)^2]^2} \tag{11.16b}$$

Setting $\partial P / \partial X_L$ to zero gives

$$X_L = -X_{Th} \tag{11.17}$$

and setting $\partial P / \partial R_L$ to zero results in

$$R_L = \sqrt{R_{Th}^2 + (X_{Th} + X_L)^2} \tag{11.18}$$

Combining Eqs. (11.17) and (11.18) leads to the conclusion that for maximum average power transfer, $\mathbf{Z}_L$ must be selected so that $X_L = -X_{Th}$ and $R_L = R_{Th}$, i.e.,

$$\boxed{\mathbf{Z}_L = R_L + jX_L = R_{Th} - jX_{Th} = \mathbf{Z}_{Th}^*} \tag{11.19}$$

For maximum average power transfer, the load impedance $\mathbf{Z}_L$ must be equal to the complex conjugate of the Thevenin impedance $\mathbf{Z}_{Th}$.

This result is known as the *maximum average power transfer theorem* for the sinusoidal steady state. Setting $R_L = R_{Th}$ and $X_L = -X_{Th}$ in

(a)

(b)

Figure 11.7   Finding the maximum average power transfer: (a) circuit with a load, (b) the Thevenin equivalent.

When $\mathbf{Z}_L = \mathbf{Z}_{Th}^*$, we say that the load is matched to the source.

Eq. (11.15) gives us the maximum average power as

$$P_{\max} = \frac{|\mathbf{V}_{Th}|^2}{8R_{Th}}$$

(11.20)

In a situation in which the load is purely real, the condition for maximum power transfer is obtained from Eq. (11.18) by setting $X_L = 0$; that is,

$$R_L = \sqrt{R_{Th}^2 + X_{Th}^2} = |\mathbf{Z}_{Th}|$$

(11.21)

This means that for maximum average power transfer to a purely resistive load, the load impedance (or resistance) is equal to the magnitude of the Thevenin impedance.

EXAMPLE 11.5

Figure 11.8　For Example 11.5.

Determine the load impedance $\mathbf{Z}_L$ that maximizes the average power drawn from the circuit of Fig. 11.8. What is the maximum average power?

Solution:

First we obtain the Thevenin equivalent at the load terminals. To get $\mathbf{Z}_{Th}$, consider the circuit shown in Fig. 11.9(a). We find

$$\mathbf{Z}_{Th} = j5 + 4 \parallel (8 - j6) = j5 + \frac{4(8 - j6)}{4 + 8 - j6} = 2.933 + j4.467 \ \Omega$$

To find $\mathbf{V}_{Th}$, consider the circuit in Fig. 11.8(b). By voltage division,

$$\mathbf{V}_{Th} = \frac{8 - j6}{4 + 8 - j6}(10) = 7.454\underline{/-10.3^\circ} \ \text{V}$$

The load impedance draws the maximum power from the circuit when

$$\mathbf{Z}_L = \mathbf{Z}_{Th}^* = 2.933 - j4.467 \ \Omega$$

According to Eq. (11.20), the maximum average power is

$$P_{\max} = \frac{|\mathbf{V}_{Th}|^2}{8R_{Th}} = \frac{(7.454)^2}{8(2.933)} = 2.368 \ \text{W}$$

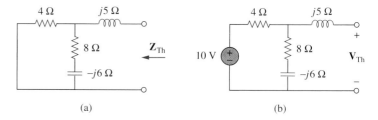

(a)　　　　　　　　　　(b)

Figure 11.9　Finding the Thevenin equivalent of the circuit in Fig. 11.8.

PRACTICE PROBLEM 11.5

For the circuit shown in Fig. 11.10, find the load impedance $\mathbf{Z}_L$ that absorbs the maximum average power. Calculate that maximum average power.

Answer: $3.415 - j0.7317\ \Omega$, 1.429 W.

Figure 11.10   For Practice Prob. 11.5.

EXAMPLE 11.6

In the circuit in Fig. 11.11, find the value of R_L that will absorb the maximum average power. Calculate that power.

Solution:

We first find the Thevenin equivalent at the terminals of R_L.

$$\mathbf{Z}_{\text{Th}} = (40 - j30) \parallel j20 = \frac{j20(40 - j30)}{j20 + 40 - j30} = 9.412 + j22.35\ \Omega$$

Figure 11.11   For Example 11.6.

By voltage division,

$$\mathbf{V}_{\text{Th}} = \frac{j20}{j20 + 40 - j30}(150\underline{/30^\circ}) = 72.76\underline{/134^\circ}\ \text{V}$$

The value of R_L that will absorb the maximum average power is

$$R_L = |\mathbf{Z}_{\text{Th}}| = \sqrt{9.412^2 + 22.35^2} = 24.25\ \Omega$$

The current through the load is

$$\mathbf{I} = \frac{\mathbf{V}_{\text{Th}}}{\mathbf{Z}_{\text{Th}} + R_L} = \frac{72.76\underline{/134^\circ}}{33.66 + j22.35} = 1.8\underline{/100.42^\circ}\ \text{A}$$

The maximum average power absorbed by R_L is

$$P_{\text{max}} = \frac{1}{2}|\mathbf{I}|^2 R_L = \frac{1}{2}(1.8)^2(24.25) = 39.29\ \text{W}$$

PRACTICE PROBLEM 11.6

In Fig. 11.12, the resistor R_L is adjusted until it absorbs the maximum average power. Calculate R_L and the maximum average power absorbed by it.

Figure 11.12   For Practice Prob. 11.6.

Answer: $30\ \Omega$, 6.863 W.

11.4 EFFECTIVE OR RMS VALUE

The idea of *effective value* arises from the need to measure the effectiveness of a voltage or current source in delivering power to a resistive load.

The effective value of a periodic current is the dc current that delivers the same average power to a resistor as the periodic current.

In Fig. 11.13, the circuit in (a) is ac while that of (b) is dc. Our objective is to find I_{eff} that will transfer the same power to resistor R as the sinusoid i. The average power absorbed by the resistor in the ac circuit is

$$P = \frac{1}{T}\int_0^T i^2 R \, dt = \frac{R}{T}\int_0^T i^2 \, dt \qquad (11.22)$$

while the power absorbed by the resistor in the dc circuit is

$$P = I_{\text{eff}}^2 R \qquad (11.23)$$

Equating the expressions in Eqs. (11.22) and (11.23) and solving for I_{eff}, we obtain

$$I_{\text{eff}} = \sqrt{\frac{1}{T}\int_0^T i^2 \, dt} \qquad (11.24)$$

The effective value of the voltage is found in the same way as current; that is,

$$V_{\text{eff}} = \sqrt{\frac{1}{T}\int_0^T v^2 \, dt} \qquad (11.25)$$

This indicates that the effective value is the (square) *root* of the *mean* (or average) of the *square* of the periodic signal. Thus, the effective value is often known as the *root-mean-square* value, or *rms* value for short; and we write

$$I_{\text{eff}} = I_{\text{rms}}, \qquad V_{\text{eff}} = V_{\text{rms}} \qquad (11.26)$$

For any periodic function $x(t)$ in general, the rms value is given by

$$X_{\text{rms}} = \sqrt{\frac{1}{T}\int_0^T x^2 \, dt} \qquad (11.27)$$

(a)

(b)

Figure 11.13   Finding the effective current: (a) ac circuit, (b) dc circuit.

The effective value of a periodic signal is its root mean square (rms) value.

Equation 11.27 states that to find the rms value of $x(t)$, we first find its *square* x^2 and then find the *mean* of that, or

$$\frac{1}{T}\int_0^T x^2 \, dt$$

and then the square *root* ($\sqrt{}$) of that mean. The rms value of a constant is the constant itself. For the sinusoid $i(t) = I_m \cos \omega t$, the effective or rms value is

$$I_{\text{rms}} = \sqrt{\frac{1}{T} \int_0^T I_m^2 \cos^2 \omega t \, dt}$$

$$= \sqrt{\frac{I_m^2}{T} \int_0^T \frac{1}{2}(1 + \cos 2\omega t) \, dt} = \frac{I_m}{\sqrt{2}} \qquad (11.28)$$

Similarly, for $v(t) = V_m \cos \omega t$,

$$V_{\text{rms}} = \frac{V_m}{\sqrt{2}} \qquad (11.29)$$

Keep in mind that Eqs. (11.28) and (11.29) are only valid for sinusoidal signals.

The average power in Eq. (11.8) can be written in terms of the rms values.

$$P = \frac{1}{2} V_m I_m \cos(\theta_v - \theta_i) = \frac{V_m}{\sqrt{2}} \frac{I_m}{\sqrt{2}} \cos(\theta_v - \theta_i)$$

$$= V_{\text{rms}} I_{\text{rms}} \cos(\theta_v - \theta_i) \qquad (11.30)$$

Similarly, the average power absorbed by a resistor R in Eq. (11.11) can be written as

$$P = I_{\text{rms}}^2 R = \frac{V_{\text{rms}}^2}{R} \qquad (11.31)$$

When a sinusoidal voltage or current is specified, it is often in terms of its maximum (or peak) value or its rms value, since its average value is zero. The power industries specify phasor magnitudes in terms of their rms values rather than peak values. For instance, the 110 V available at every household is the rms value of the voltage from the power company. It is convenient in power analysis to express voltage and current in their rms values. Also, analog voltmeters and ammeters are designed to read directly the rms value of voltage and current, respectively.

EXAMPLE 11.7

Determine the rms value of the current waveform in Fig. 11.14. If the current is passed through a 2-Ω resistor, find the average power absorbed by the resistor.

Solution:

The period of the waveform is $T = 4$. Over a period, we can write the current waveform as

$$i(t) = \begin{cases} 5t, & 0 < t < 2 \\ -10, & 2 < t < 4 \end{cases}$$

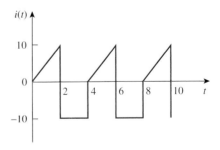

Figure 11.14   For Example 11.7.

The rms value is

$$I_{\text{rms}} = \sqrt{\frac{1}{T} \int_0^T i^2 \, dt} = \sqrt{\frac{1}{4} \left[\int_0^2 (5t)^2 \, dt + \int_2^4 (-10)^2 \, dt \right]}$$

$$= \sqrt{\frac{1}{4} \left[25 \frac{t^3}{3} \Big|_0^2 + 100t \Big|_2^4 \right]} = \sqrt{\frac{1}{4} \left(\frac{200}{3} + 200 \right)} = 8.165 \text{ A}$$

The power absorbed by a 2-Ω resistor is

$$P = I_{\text{rms}}^2 R = (8.165)^2(2) = 133.3 \text{ W}$$

PRACTICE PROBLEM 11.7

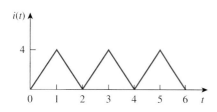

Figure 11.15   For Practice Prob. 11.7.

Find the rms value of the current waveform of Fig. 11.15. If the current flows through a 9-Ω resistor, calculate the average power absorbed by the resistor.

Answer: 2.309 A, 48 W.

EXAMPLE 11.8

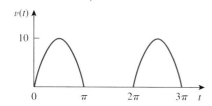

Figure 11.16   For Example 11.8.

The waveform shown in Fig. 11.16 is a half-wave rectified sine wave. Find the rms value and the amount of average power dissipated in a 10-Ω resistor.

Solution:

The period of the voltage waveform is $T = 2\pi$, and

$$v(t) = \begin{cases} 10 \sin t, & 0 < t < \pi \\ 0, & \pi < t < 2\pi \end{cases}$$

The rms value is obtained as

$$V_{\text{rms}}^2 = \frac{1}{T} \int_0^T v^2(t)\, dt = \frac{1}{2\pi}\left[\int_0^\pi (10 \sin t)^2\, dt + \int_\pi^{2\pi} 0^2\, dt \right]$$

But $\sin^2 t = \frac{1}{2}(1 - \cos 2t)$. Hence

$$V_{\text{rms}}^2 = \frac{1}{2\pi}\int_0^\pi \frac{100}{2}(1 - \cos 2t)\, dt = \frac{50}{2\pi}\left(t - \frac{\sin 2t}{2} \right)\Bigg|_0^\pi$$

$$= \frac{50}{2\pi}\left(\pi - \frac{1}{2}\sin 2\pi - 0 \right) = 25, \qquad V_{\text{rms}} = 5 \text{ V}$$

The average power absorbed is

$$P = \frac{V_{\text{rms}}^2}{R} = \frac{5^2}{10} = 2.5 \text{ W}$$

PRACTICE PROBLEM 11.8

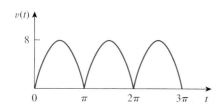

Figure 11.17   For Practice Prob. 11.8.

Find the rms value of the full-wave rectified sine wave in Fig. 11.17. Calculate the average power dissipated in a 6-Ω resistor.

Answer: 5.657 V, 5.334 W.

11.5 APPARENT POWER AND POWER FACTOR

In Section 11.2 we saw that if the voltage and current at the terminals of a circuit are

$$v(t) = V_m \cos(\omega t + \theta_v) \qquad \text{and} \qquad i(t) = I_m \cos(\omega t + \theta_i) \quad (11.32)$$

or, in phasor form, $\mathbf{V} = V_m \underline{/\theta_v}$ and $\mathbf{I} = I_m \underline{/\theta_i}$, the average power is

$$P = \frac{1}{2} V_m I_m \cos(\theta_v - \theta_i) \qquad (11.33)$$

In Section 11.4, we saw that

$$P = V_{\text{rms}} I_{\text{rms}} \cos(\theta_v - \theta_i) = S \cos(\theta_v - \theta_i) \qquad (11.34)$$

We have added a new term to the equation:

$$\boxed{S = V_{\text{rms}} I_{\text{rms}}} \qquad (11.35)$$

The average power is a product of two terms. The product $V_{\text{rms}} I_{\text{rms}}$ is known as the *apparent power* S. The factor $\cos(\theta_v - \theta_i)$ is called the *power factor* (pf).

◇ **The apparent power (in VA) is the product of the rms values of voltage and current.**

The apparent power is so called because it seems apparent that the power should be the voltage-current product, by analogy with dc resistive circuits. It is measured in volt-amperes or VA to distinguish it from the average or real power, which is measured in watts. The power factor is dimensionless, since it is the ratio of the average power to the apparent power,

$$\boxed{\text{pf} = \frac{P}{S} = \cos(\theta_v - \theta_i)} \qquad (11.36)$$

The angle $\theta_v - \theta_i$ is called the *power factor angle*, since it is the angle whose cosine is the power factor. The power factor angle is equal to the angle of the load impedance if $\mathbf{V}$ is the voltage across the load and $\mathbf{I}$ is the current through it. This is evident from the fact that

$$\mathbf{Z} = \frac{\mathbf{V}}{\mathbf{I}} = \frac{V_m \underline{/\theta_v}}{I_m \underline{/\theta_i}} = \frac{V_m}{I_m} \underline{/\theta_v - \theta_i} \qquad (11.37)$$

Alternatively, since

$$\mathbf{V}_{\text{rms}} = \frac{\mathbf{V}}{\sqrt{2}} = V_{\text{rms}} \underline{/\theta_v} \qquad (11.38\text{a})$$

and

$$\mathbf{I}_{\text{rms}} = \frac{\mathbf{I}}{\sqrt{2}} = I_{\text{rms}} \underline{/\theta_i} \qquad (11.38\text{b})$$

the impedance is

$$\mathbf{Z} = \frac{\mathbf{V}}{\mathbf{I}} = \frac{\mathbf{V}_{\text{rms}}}{\mathbf{I}_{\text{rms}}} = \frac{V_{\text{rms}}}{I_{\text{rms}}} \underline{/\theta_v - \theta_i} \qquad (11.39)$$

The power factor is the cosine of the phase difference between voltage and current. It is also the cosine of the angle of the load impedance.

From Eq. (11.36), the power factor may also be regarded as the ratio of the real power dissipated in the load to the apparent power of the load.

From Eq. (11.36), the power factor may be seen as that factor by which the apparent power must be multiplied to obtain the real or average power. The value of pf ranges between zero and unity. For a purely resistive load, the voltage and current are in phase, so that $\theta_v - \theta_i = 0$ and pf = 1. This implies that the apparent power is equal to the average power. For a purely reactive load, $\theta_v - \theta_i = \pm 90°$ and pf = 0. In this case the average power is zero. In between these two extreme cases, pf is said to be *leading* or *lagging*. Leading power factor means that current leads voltage, which implies a capacitive load. Lagging power factor means that current lags voltage, implying an inductive load. Power factor affects the electric bills consumers pay the electric utility companies, as we will see in Section 11.9.2.

EXAMPLE 11.9

A series-connected load draws a current $i(t) = 4\cos(100\pi t + 10°)$ A when the applied voltage is $v(t) = 120\cos(100\pi t - 20°)$ V. Find the apparent power and the power factor of the load. Determine the element values that form the series-connected load.

Solution:

The apparent power is

$$S = V_{\text{rms}}I_{\text{rms}} = \frac{120}{\sqrt{2}}\frac{4}{\sqrt{2}} = 240 \text{ VA}$$

The power factor is

$$\text{pf} = \cos(\theta_v - \theta_i) = \cos(-20° - 10°) = 0.866 \qquad \text{(leading)}$$

The pf is leading because the current leads the voltage. The pf may also be obtained from the load impedance.

$$\mathbf{Z} = \frac{\mathbf{V}}{\mathbf{I}} = \frac{120\underline{/-20°}}{4\underline{/10°}} = 30\underline{/-30°} = 25.98 - j15 \text{ } \Omega$$

$$\text{pf} = \cos(-30°) = 0.866 \qquad \text{(leading)}$$

The load impedance $\mathbf{Z}$ can be modeled by a 25.98-Ω resistor in series with a capacitor with

$$X_C = -15 = -\frac{1}{\omega C}$$

or

$$C = \frac{1}{15\omega} = \frac{1}{15 \times 100\pi} = 212.2 \text{ } \mu\text{F}$$

PRACTICE PROBLEM 11.9

Obtain the power factor and the apparent power of a load whose impedance is $\mathbf{Z} = 60 + j40\ \Omega$ when the applied voltage is $v(t) = 150\cos(377t + 10°)$ V.

Answer: 0.832 lagging, 156 VA.

EXAMPLE 11.10

Determine the power factor of the entire circuit of Fig. 11.18 as seen by the source. Calculate the average power delivered by the source.

Solution:

The total impedance is

$$\mathbf{Z} = 6 + 4 \parallel (-j2) = 6 + \frac{-j2 \times 4}{4 - j2} = 6.8 - j1.6 = 7\underline{/-13.24}\ \Omega$$

Figure 11.18   For Example 11.10.

The power factor is

$$pf = \cos(-13.24) = 0.9734 \qquad (\text{leading})$$

since the impedance is capacitive. The rms value of the current is

$$\mathbf{I}_{\text{rms}} = \frac{\mathbf{V}_{\text{rms}}}{\mathbf{Z}} = \frac{30\underline{/0°}}{7\underline{/-13.24°}} = 4.286\underline{/13.24°}\ \text{A}$$

The average power supplied by the source is

$$P = V_{\text{rms}}I_{\text{rms}}\, pf = (30)(4.286)0.9734 = 125\ \text{W}$$

or

$$P = I_{\text{rms}}^2 R = (4.286)^2(6.8) = 125\ \text{W}$$

where R is the resistive part of $\mathbf{Z}$.

PRACTICE PROBLEM 11.10

Calculate the power factor of the entire circuit of Fig. 11.19 as seen by the source. What is the average power supplied by the source?

Answer: 0.936 lagging, 118 W.

Figure 11.19   For Practice Prob. 11.10.

11.6 COMPLEX POWER

Considerable effort has been expended over the years to express power relations as simply as possible. Power engineers have coined the term *complex power*, which they use to find the total effect of parallel loads. Complex power is important in power analysis because it contains *all* the information pertaining to the power absorbed by a given load.

Figure 11.20 The voltage and current phasors associated with a load.

When working with the rms values of currents or voltages, we may drop the subscript rms if no confusion will be caused by doing so.

Consider the ac load in Fig. 11.20. Given the phasor form $\mathbf{V} = V_m \underline{/\theta_v}$ and $\mathbf{I} = I_m \underline{/\theta_i}$ of voltage $v(t)$ and current $i(t)$, the *complex power* $\mathbf{S}$ absorbed by the ac load is the product of the voltage and the complex conjugate of the current, or

$$\mathbf{S} = \frac{1}{2}\mathbf{VI}^* \tag{11.40}$$

assuming the passive sign convention (see Fig. 11.20). In terms of the rms values,

$$\mathbf{S} = \mathbf{V}_{\text{rms}}\mathbf{I}_{\text{rms}}^* \tag{11.41}$$

where

$$\mathbf{V}_{\text{rms}} = \frac{\mathbf{V}}{\sqrt{2}} = V_{\text{rms}}\underline{/\theta_v} \tag{11.42}$$

and

$$\mathbf{I}_{\text{rms}} = \frac{\mathbf{I}}{\sqrt{2}} = I_{\text{rms}}\underline{/\theta_i} \tag{11.43}$$

Thus we may write Eq. (11.41) as

$$\begin{aligned}
\mathbf{S} &= V_{\text{rms}}I_{\text{rms}}\underline{/\theta_v - \theta_i} \\
&= V_{\text{rms}}I_{\text{rms}}\cos(\theta_v - \theta_i) + jV_{\text{rms}}I_{\text{rms}}\sin(\theta_v - \theta_i)
\end{aligned} \tag{11.44}$$

This equation can also be obtained from Eq. (11.9). We notice from Eq. (11.44) that the magnitude of the complex power is the apparent power; hence, the complex power is measured in volt-amperes (VA). Also, we notice that the angle of the complex power is the power factor angle.

The complex power may be expressed in terms of the load impedance $\mathbf{Z}$. From Eq. (11.37), the load impedance $\mathbf{Z}$ may be written as

$$\mathbf{Z} = \frac{\mathbf{V}}{\mathbf{I}} = \frac{\mathbf{V}_{\text{rms}}}{\mathbf{I}_{\text{rms}}} = \frac{V_{\text{rms}}}{I_{\text{rms}}}\underline{/\theta_v - \theta_i} \tag{11.45}$$

Thus, $\mathbf{V}_{\text{rms}} = \mathbf{Z}\mathbf{I}_{\text{rms}}$. Substituting this into Eq. (11.41) gives

$$\mathbf{S} = I_{\text{rms}}^2\mathbf{Z} = \frac{V_{\text{rms}}^2}{\mathbf{Z}^*} = \mathbf{V}_{\text{rms}}\mathbf{I}_{\text{rms}}^* \tag{11.46}$$

Since $\mathbf{Z} = R + jX$, Eq. (11.46) becomes

$$\mathbf{S} = I_{\text{rms}}^2(R + jX) = P + jQ \tag{11.47}$$

where P and Q are the real and imaginary parts of the complex power; that is,

$$P = \text{Re}(\mathbf{S}) = I_{\text{rms}}^2 R \tag{11.48}$$

$$Q = \text{Im}(\mathbf{S}) = I_{\text{rms}}^2 X \tag{11.49}$$

P is the average or real power and it depends on the load's resistance R. Q depends on the load's reactance X and is called the *reactive* (or quadrature) power.

Comparing Eq. (11.44) with Eq. (11.47), we notice that

$$P = V_{\text{rms}}I_{\text{rms}}\cos(\theta_v - \theta_i), \qquad Q = V_{\text{rms}}I_{\text{rms}}\sin(\theta_v - \theta_i) \tag{11.50}$$

The real power P is the average power in watts delivered to a load; it is the only useful power. It is the actual power dissipated by the load. The reactive power Q is a measure of the energy exchange between the source and the reactive part of the load. The unit of Q is the *volt-ampere reactive* (VAR) to distinguish it from the real power, whose unit is the watt. We know from Chapter 6 that energy storage elements neither dissipate nor supply power, but exchange power back and forth with the rest of the network. In the same way, the reactive power is being transferred back and forth between the load and the source. It represents a lossless interchange between the load and the source. Notice that:

1. $Q = 0$ for resistive loads (unity pf).

2. $Q < 0$ for capacitive loads (leading pf).

3. $Q > 0$ for inductive loads (lagging pf).

Thus,

> Complex power (in VA) is the product of the rms voltage phasor and the complex conjugate of the rms current phasor. As a complex quantity, its real part is real power P and its imaginary part is reactive power Q.

Introducing the complex power enables us to obtain the real and reactive powers directly from voltage and current phasors.

$$
\begin{aligned}
\text{Complex Power} = \mathbf{S} = P + jQ &= \frac{1}{2}\mathbf{V}\mathbf{I}^* \\
&= V_{\text{rms}} I_{\text{rms}} \underline{/\theta_v - \theta_i} \\
\text{Apparent Power} = S = |\mathbf{S}| &= V_{\text{rms}} I_{\text{rms}} = \sqrt{P^2 + Q^2} \\
\text{Real Power} = P = \text{Re}(\mathbf{S}) &= S\cos(\theta_v - \theta_i) \\
\text{Reactive Power} = Q = \text{Im}(\mathbf{S}) &= S\sin(\theta_v - \theta_i) \\
\text{Power Factor} = \frac{P}{S} &= \cos(\theta_v - \theta_i)
\end{aligned}
\tag{11.51}
$$

This shows how the complex power contains *all* the relevant power information in a given load.

It is a standard practice to represent $\mathbf{S}$, P, and Q in the form of a triangle, known as the *power triangle*, shown in Fig. 11.21(a). This is similar to the impedance triangle showing the relationship between $\mathbf{Z}$, R, and X, illustrated in Fig. 11.21(b). The power triangle has four items—the apparent/complex power, real power, reactive power, and the power factor angle. Given two of these items, the other two can easily be obtained from the triangle. As shown in Fig. 11.22, when $\mathbf{S}$ lies in the first quadrant, we have an inductive load and a lagging pf. When $\mathbf{S}$ lies in the fourth quadrant, the load is capacitive and the pf is leading. It is also possible for the complex power to lie in the second or third quadrant. This requires that the load impedance have a negative resistance, which is possible with active circuits.

$\mathbf{S}$ contains *all* power information of a load. The real part of $\mathbf{S}$ is the real power P; its imaginary part is the reactive power Q; its magnitude is the apparent power S; and the cosine of its phase angle is the power factor pf.

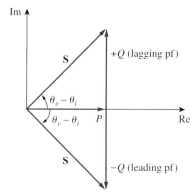

Figure 11.21   (a) Power triangle,
(b) impedance triangle.

Figure 11.22   Power triangle.

EXAMPLE 11.11

The voltage across a load is $v(t) = 60\cos(\omega t - 10°)$ V and the current through the element in the direction of the voltage drop is $i(t) = 1.5\cos(\omega t + 50°)$ A. Find: (a) the complex and apparent powers, (b) the real and reactive powers, and (c) the power factor and the load impedance.

Solution:

(a) For the rms values of the voltage and current, we write

$$\mathbf{V}_{\text{rms}} = \frac{60}{\sqrt{2}}\underline{/-10°}, \qquad \mathbf{I}_{\text{rms}} = \frac{1.5}{\sqrt{2}}\underline{/+50°}$$

The complex power is

$$\mathbf{S} = \mathbf{V}_{\text{rms}}\mathbf{I}^*_{\text{rms}} = \left(\frac{60}{\sqrt{2}}\underline{/-10°}\right)\left(\frac{1.5}{\sqrt{2}}\underline{/-50°}\right) = 45\underline{/-60°} \text{ VA}$$

The apparent power is

$$S = |\mathbf{S}| = 45 \text{ VA}$$

(b) We can express the complex power in rectangular form as

$$\mathbf{S} = 45\underline{/-60°} = 45[\cos(-60°) + j\sin(-60°)] = 22.5 - j38.97$$

Since $\mathbf{S} = P + jQ$, the real power is

$$P = 22.5 \text{ W}$$

while the reactive power is

$$Q = -38.97 \text{ VAR}$$

(c) The power factor is

$$\text{pf} = \cos(-60°) = 0.5 \text{ (leading)}$$

It is leading, because the reactive power is negative. The load impedance is

$$\mathbf{Z} = \frac{\mathbf{V}}{\mathbf{I}} = \frac{60\underline{/-10°}}{1.5\underline{/+50°}} = 40\underline{/-60°} \text{ } \Omega$$

which is a capacitive impedance.

PRACTICE PROBLEM 11.11

For a load, $\mathbf{V}_{rms} = 110\underline{/85°}$ V, $\mathbf{I}_{rms} = 0.4\underline{/15°}$ A. Determine: (a) the complex and apparent powers, (b) the real and reactive powers, and (c) the power factor and the load impedance.

Answer: (a) $44\underline{/70°}$ VA, 44 VA, (b) 15.05 W, 41.35 VAR, (c) 0.342 lagging, $94.06 + j258.4\ \Omega$.

EXAMPLE 11.12

A load $\mathbf{Z}$ draws 12 kVA at a power factor of 0.856 lagging from a 120-V rms sinusoidal source. Calculate: (a) the average and reactive powers delivered to the load, (b) the peak current, and (c) the load impedance.

Solution:

(a) Given that pf $= \cos\theta = 0.856$, we obtain the power angle as $\theta = \cos^{-1} 0.856 = 31.13°$. If the apparent power is $S = 12,000$ VA, then the average or real power is

$$P = S\cos\theta = 12,000 \times 0.856 = 10.272\ \text{kW}$$

while the reactive power is

$$Q = S\sin\theta = 12,000 \times 0.517 = 6.204\ \text{kVA}$$

(b) Since the pf is lagging, the complex power is

$$\mathbf{S} = P + jQ = 10.272 + j6.204\ \text{kVA}$$

From $\mathbf{S} = \mathbf{V}_{rms}\mathbf{I}_{rms}^*$, we obtain

$$\mathbf{I}_{rms}^* = \frac{\mathbf{S}}{\mathbf{V}_{rms}} = \frac{10,272 + j6204}{120\underline{/0°}} = 85.6 + j51.7\ \text{A} = 100\underline{/31.13°}\ \text{A}$$

Thus $\mathbf{I}_{rms} = 100\underline{/-31.13°}$ and the peak current is

$$I_m = \sqrt{2}I_{rms} = \sqrt{2}(100) = 141.4\ \text{A}$$

(c) The load impedance

$$\mathbf{Z} = \frac{\mathbf{V}_{rms}}{\mathbf{I}_{rms}} = \frac{120\underline{/0°}}{100\underline{/-31.13°}} = 1.2\underline{/31.13°}\ \Omega$$

which is an inductive impedance.

PRACTICE PROBLEM 11.12

A sinusoidal source supplies 10 kVAR reactive power to load $\mathbf{Z} = 250\underline{/-75°}\ \Omega$. Determine: (a) the power factor, (b) the apparent power delivered to the load, and (c) the peak voltage.

Answer: (a) 0.2588 leading, (b) +10.35 kVA, (c) 2.275 kV.

†11.7 CONSERVATION OF AC POWER

In fact, we already saw in Examples 11.3 and 11.4 that average power is conserved in ac circuits.

The principle of conservation of power applies to ac circuits as well as to dc circuits (see Section 1.5).

To see this, consider the circuit in Fig. 11.23(a), where two load impedances $\mathbf{Z}_1$ and $\mathbf{Z}_2$ are connected in parallel across an ac source $\mathbf{V}$. KCL gives

$$\mathbf{I} = \mathbf{I}_1 + \mathbf{I}_2 \tag{11.52}$$

The complex power supplied by the source is

$$\mathbf{S} = \frac{1}{2}\mathbf{V}\mathbf{I}^* = \frac{1}{2}\mathbf{V}(\mathbf{I}_1^* + \mathbf{I}_2^*) = \frac{1}{2}\mathbf{V}\mathbf{I}_1^* + \frac{1}{2}\mathbf{V}\mathbf{I}_2^* = \mathbf{S}_1 + \mathbf{S}_2 \tag{11.53}$$

where $\mathbf{S}_1$ and $\mathbf{S}_2$ denote the complex powers delivered to loads $\mathbf{Z}_1$ and $\mathbf{Z}_2$, respectively.

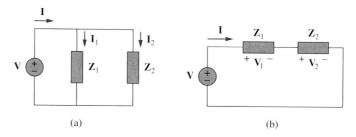

(a)   (b)

Figure 11.23   An ac voltage source supplied loads connected in: (a) parallel, (b) series.

If the loads are connected in series with the voltage source, as shown in Fig. 11.23(b), KVL yields

$$\mathbf{V} = \mathbf{V}_1 + \mathbf{V}_2 \tag{11.54}$$

The complex power supplied by the source is

$$\mathbf{S} = \frac{1}{2}\mathbf{V}\mathbf{I}^* = \frac{1}{2}(\mathbf{V}_1 + \mathbf{V}_2)\mathbf{I}^* = \frac{1}{2}\mathbf{V}_1\mathbf{I}^* + \frac{1}{2}\mathbf{V}_2\mathbf{I}^* = \mathbf{S}_1 + \mathbf{S}_2 \tag{11.55}$$

where $\mathbf{S}_1$ and $\mathbf{S}_2$ denote the complex powers delivered to loads $\mathbf{Z}_1$ and $\mathbf{Z}_2$, respectively.

We conclude from Eqs. (11.53) and (11.55) that whether the loads are connected in series or in parallel (or in general), the total power *supplied* by the source equals the total power *delivered* to the load. Thus, in general, for a source connected to N loads,

$$\boxed{\mathbf{S} = \mathbf{S}_1 + \mathbf{S}_1 + \cdots + \mathbf{S}_N} \tag{11.56}$$

In fact, all forms of ac power are conserved: instantaneous, real, reactive, and complex.

This means that the total complex power in a network is the sum of the complex powers of the individual components. (This is also true of real power and reactive power, but not true of apparent power.) This expresses the principle of conservation of ac power:

The complex, real, and reactive powers of the sources equal the respective sums of the complex, real, and reactive powers of the individual loads.

From this we imply that the real (or reactive) power flow from sources in a network equals the real (or reactive) power flow into the other elements in the network.

EXAMPLE 11.13

Figure 11.24 shows a load being fed by a voltage source through a transmission line. The impedance of the line is represented by the $(4 + j2)$ Ω impedance and a return path. Find the real power and reactive power absorbed by: (a) the source, (b) the line, and (c) the load.

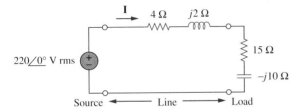

Figure 11.24   For Example 11.13.

Solution:

The total impedance is

$$\mathbf{Z} = (4 + j2) + (15 - j10) = 19 - j8 = 20.62\underline{/-22.83°}\ \Omega$$

The current through the circuit is

$$\mathbf{I} = \frac{\mathbf{V}_s}{\mathbf{Z}} = \frac{220\underline{/0°}}{20.62\underline{/-22.83°}} = 10.67\underline{/22.83°}\ \text{A rms}$$

(a) For the source, the complex power is

$$\mathbf{S}_s = \mathbf{V}_s\mathbf{I}^* = (220\underline{/0°})(10.67\underline{/-22.83°})$$

$$= 2347.4\underline{/-22.83°} = (2163.5 - j910.8)\ \text{VA}$$

From this, we obtain the real power as 2163.5 W and the reactive power as 910.8 VAR (leading).

(b) For the line, the voltage is

$$\mathbf{V}_{\text{line}} = (4 + j2)\mathbf{I} = (4.472\underline{/26.57°})(10.67\underline{/22.83°})$$

$$= 47.72\underline{/49.4°}\ \text{V rms}$$

The complex power absorbed by the line is

$$\mathbf{S}_{\text{line}} = \mathbf{V}_{\text{line}}\mathbf{I}^* = (47.72\underline{/49.4°})(10.67\underline{/-22.83°})$$

$$= 509.2\underline{/26.57°} = 455.4 + j227.7\ \text{VA}$$

or

$$\mathbf{S}_{\text{line}} = |\mathbf{I}|^2\mathbf{Z}_{\text{line}} = (10.67)^2(4 + j2) = 455.4 + j227.7\ \text{VA}$$

That is, the real power is 455.4 W and the reactive power is 227.76 VAR (lagging).

(c) For the load, the voltage is

$$\mathbf{V}_L = (15 - j10)\mathbf{I} = (18.03\underline{/-33.7^\circ})(10.67\underline{/22.83^\circ})$$

$$= 192.38\underline{/-10.87^\circ} \text{ V rms}$$

The complex power absorbed by the load is

$$\mathbf{S}_L = \mathbf{V}_L\mathbf{I}^* = (192.38\underline{/-10.87^\circ})(10.67\underline{/-22.83^\circ})$$

$$= 2053\underline{/-33.7^\circ} = (1708 - j1139) \text{ VA}$$

The real power is 1708 W and the reactive power is 1139 VAR (leading). Note that $\mathbf{S}_s = \mathbf{S}_{\text{line}} + \mathbf{S}_L$, as expected. We have used the rms values of voltages and currents.

PRACTICE PROBLEM 11.13

Figure 11.25   For Practice Prob. 11.13.

In the circuit in Fig. 11.25, the 60-Ω resistor absorbs an average power of 240 W. Find **V** and the complex power of each branch of the circuit. What is the overall complex power of the circuit? (Assume the current through the 60Ω resistor has no phase shift.)

Answer: $240.67\underline{/21.45^\circ}$ V (rms); the 20-Ω resistor: 656 VA; the $(30 - j10)\ \Omega$ impedance: $480 - j160$ VA; the $(60 + j20)\ \Omega$ impedance: $240 + j80$ VA; overall: $1376 - j80$ VA.

EXAMPLE 11.14

Figure 11.26   For Example 11.14.

In the circuit of Fig. 11.26, $\mathbf{Z}_1 = 60\underline{/-30^\circ}\ \Omega$ and $\mathbf{Z}_2 = 40\underline{/45^\circ}\ \Omega$. Calculate the total: (a) apparent power, (b) real power, (c) reactive power, and (d) pf.

Solution:

The current through $\mathbf{Z}_1$ is

$$\mathbf{I}_1 = \frac{\mathbf{V}}{\mathbf{Z}_1} = \frac{120\underline{/10^\circ}}{60\underline{/-30^\circ}} = 2\underline{/40^\circ} \text{ A rms}$$

while the current through $\mathbf{Z}_2$ is

$$\mathbf{I}_2 = \frac{\mathbf{V}}{\mathbf{Z}_2} = \frac{120\underline{/10^\circ}}{40\underline{/45^\circ}} = 3\underline{/-35^\circ} \text{ A rms}$$

The complex powers absorbed by the impedances are

$$\mathbf{S}_1 = \frac{V_{\text{rms}}^2}{\mathbf{Z}_1^*} = \frac{(120)^2}{60\underline{/30^\circ}} = 240\underline{/-30^\circ} = 207.85 - j120 \text{ VA}$$

$$\mathbf{S}_2 = \frac{V_{\text{rms}}^2}{\mathbf{Z}_2^*} = \frac{(120)^2}{40\underline{/-45^\circ}} = 360\underline{/45^\circ} = 254.6 + j254.6 \text{ VA}$$

The total complex power is

$$\mathbf{S}_t = \mathbf{S}_1 + \mathbf{S}_2 = 462.4 + j134.6 \text{ VA}$$

(a) The total apparent power is

$|\mathbf{S}_t| = \sqrt{462.4^2 + 134.6^2} = 481.6$ VA.

(b) The total real power is

$P_t = \text{Re}(\mathbf{S}_t) = 462.4$ W or $P_t = P_1 + P_2$.

(c) The total reactive power is

$Q_t = \text{Im}(\mathbf{S}_t) = 134.6$ VAR or $Q_t = Q_1 + Q_2$.

(d) The pf $= P_t/|\mathbf{S}_t| = 462.4/481.6 = 0.96$ (lagging).

We may cross check the result by finding the complex power $\mathbf{S}_s$ supplied by the source.

$$\mathbf{I}_t = \mathbf{I}_1 + \mathbf{I}_2 = (1.532 + j1.286) + (2.457 - j1.721)$$

$$= 4 - j0.435 = 4.024\underline{/-6.21°} \text{ A rms}$$

$$\mathbf{S}_s = \mathbf{VI}_t^* = (120\underline{/10°})(4.024\underline{/6.21°})$$

$$= 482.88\underline{/16.21°} = 463 + j135 \text{ VA}$$

which is the same as before.

PRACTICE PROBLEM 11.14

Two loads connected in parallel are respectively 2 kW at a pf of 0.75 leading and 4 kW at a pf of 0.95 lagging. Calculate the pf of the two loads. Find the complex power supplied by the source.

Answer: 0.9972 (leading), $6 - j0.4495$ kVA.

11.8 POWER FACTOR CORRECTION

Most domestic loads (such as washing machines, air conditioners, and refrigerators) and industrial loads (such as induction motors) are inductive and operate at a low lagging power factor. Although the inductive nature of the load cannot be changed, we can increase its power factor.

> The process of increasing the power factor without altering the voltage or current to the original load is known as power factor correction.

Alternatively, power factor correction may be viewed as the addition of a reactive element (usually a capacitor) in parallel with the load in order to make the power factor closer to unity.

An inductive load is modeled as a series combination of an inductor and a resistor.

Since most loads are inductive, as shown in Fig. 11.27(a), a load's power factor is improved or corrected by deliberately installing a capacitor in parallel with the load, as shown in Fig. 11.27(b). The effect of adding the capacitor can be illustrated using either the power triangle or the phasor diagram of the currents involved. Figure 11.28 shows the latter, where it is assumed that the circuit in Fig. 11.27(a) has a power factor of $\cos\theta_1$, while the one in Fig. 11.27(b) has a power factor of $\cos\theta_2$. It is evident from Fig. 11.28 that adding the capacitor has caused the phase angle between the supplied voltage and current to reduce from θ_1 to θ_2, thereby increasing the power factor. We also notice from the magnitudes of the vectors in Fig. 11.28 that with the same supplied voltage, the circuit in Fig. 11.27(a) draws larger current I_L than the current I drawn by the

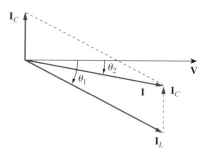

Figure 11.27   Power factor correction: (a) original inductive load, (b) inductive load with improved power factor.

Figure 11.28   Phasor diagram showing the effect of adding a capacitor in parallel with the inductive load.

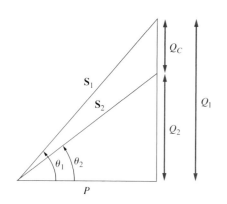

Figure 11.29   Power triangle illustrating power factor correction.

circuit in Fig. 11.27(b). Power companies charge more for larger currents, because they result in increased power losses (by a squared factor, since $P = I_L^2 R$). Therefore, it is beneficial to both the power company and the consumer that every effort is made to minimize current level or keep the power factor as close to unity as possible. By choosing a suitable size for the capacitor, the current can be made to be completely in phase with the voltage, implying unity power factor.

We can look at the power factor correction from another perspective. Consider the power triangle in Fig. 11.29. If the original inductive load has apparent power S_1, then

$$P = S_1 \cos \theta_1, \qquad Q_1 = S_1 \sin \theta_1 = P \tan \theta_1 \qquad (11.57)$$

If we desire to increase the power factor from $\cos \theta_1$ to $\cos \theta_2$ without altering the real power (i.e., $P = S_2 \cos \theta_2$), then the new reactive power is

$$Q_2 = P \tan \theta_2 \qquad (11.58)$$

The reduction in the reactive power is caused by the shunt capacitor, that is,

$$Q_C = Q_1 - Q_2 = P(\tan \theta_1 - \tan \theta_2) \qquad (11.59)$$

But from Eq. (11.46), $Q_C = V_{rms}^2 / X_C = \omega C V_{rms}^2$. The value of the required shunt capacitance C is determined as

$$C = \frac{Q_C}{\omega V_{rms}^2} = \frac{P(\tan \theta_1 - \tan \theta_2)}{\omega V_{rms}^2} \qquad (11.60)$$

Note that the real power P dissipated by the load is not affected by the power factor correction because the average power due to the capacitance is zero.

Although the most common situation in practice is that of an inductive load, it is also possible that the load is capacitive, that is, the load is operating at a leading power factor. In this case, an inductor should be connected across the load for power factor correction. The required shunt inductance L can be calculated from

$$Q_L = \frac{V_{rms}^2}{X_L} = \frac{V_{rms}^2}{\omega L} \qquad \Longrightarrow \qquad L = \frac{V_{rms}^2}{\omega Q_L} \qquad (11.61)$$

where $Q_L = Q_1 - Q_2$, the difference between the new and old reactive powers.

EXAMPLE 11.15

When connected to a 120-V (rms), 60-Hz power line, a load absorbs 4 kW at a lagging power factor of 0.8. Find the value of capacitance necessary to raise the pf to 0.95.

Solution:

If the pf = 0.8, then

$$\cos \theta_1 = 0.8 \qquad \Longrightarrow \qquad \theta_1 = 36.87°$$

where θ_1 is the phase difference between voltage and current. We obtain the apparent power from the real power and the pf as

$$S_1 = \frac{P}{\cos \theta_1} = \frac{4000}{0.8} = 5000 \text{ VA}$$

The reactive power is

$$Q_1 = S_1 \sin \theta = 5000 \sin 36.87 = 3000 \text{ VAR}$$

When the pf is raised to 0.95,

$$\cos \theta_2 = 0.95 \qquad \Longrightarrow \qquad \theta_2 = 18.19°$$

The real power P has not changed. But the apparent power has changed; its new value is

$$S_2 = \frac{P}{\cos \theta_2} = \frac{4000}{0.95} = 4210.5 \text{ VA}$$

The new reactive power is

$$Q_2 = S_2 \sin \theta_2 = 1314.4 \text{ VAR}$$

The difference between the new and old reactive powers is due to the parallel addition of the capacitor to the load. The reactive power due to the capacitor is

$$Q_C = Q_1 - Q_2 = 3000 - 1314.4 = 1685.6 \text{ VAR}$$

and

$$C = \frac{Q_C}{\omega V_{rms}^2} = \frac{1685.6}{2\pi \times 60 \times 120^2} = 310.5 \ \mu\text{F}$$

PRACTICE PROBLEM 11.15

Find the value of parallel capacitance needed to correct a load of 140 kVAR at 0.85 lagging pf to unity pf. Assume that the load is supplied by a 110-V (rms), 60-Hz line.

Answer: 30.69 mF.

†11.9 APPLICATIONS

In this section, we consider two important application areas: how power is measured and how electric utility companies determine the cost of electricity consumption.

11.9.1 Power Measurement

The average power absorbed by a load is measured by an instrument called the *wattmeter*.

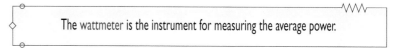

> The wattmeter is the instrument for measuring the average power.

Figure 11.30 shows a wattmeter that consists essentially of two coils: the current coil and the voltage coil. A current coil with very low impedance (ideally zero) is connected in series with the load (Fig. 11.31) and responds to the load current. The voltage coil with very high impedance (ideally infinite) is connected in parallel with the load as shown in Fig. 11.31 and responds to the load voltage. The current coil acts like a short circuit because of its low impedance; the voltage coil behaves like an open circuit because of its high impedance. As a result, the presence of the wattmeter does not disturb the circuit or have an effect on the power measurement.

Figure 11.31   The wattmeter connected to the load.

When the two coils are energized, the mechanical inertia of the moving system produces a deflection angle that is proportional to the average value of the product $v(t)i(t)$. If the current and voltage of the load are $v(t) = V_m \cos(\omega t + \theta_v)$ and $i(t) = I_m \cos(\omega t + \theta_i)$, their corresponding rms phasors are

$$\mathbf{V}_{\text{rms}} = \frac{V_m}{\sqrt{2}} \underline{/\theta_v} \qquad \text{and} \qquad \mathbf{I}_{\text{rms}} = \frac{I_m}{\sqrt{2}} \underline{/\theta_i} \qquad (11.62)$$

and the wattmeter measures the average power given by

$$P = |\mathbf{V}_{\text{rms}}||\mathbf{I}_{\text{rms}}| \cos(\theta_v - \theta_i) = \frac{1}{2} V_m I_m \cos(\theta_v - \theta_i) \qquad (11.63)$$

As shown in Fig. 11.31, each wattmeter coil has two terminals with one marked ±. To ensure upscale deflection, the ± terminal of the current coil is toward the source, while the ± terminal of the voltage coil is connected to the same line as the current coil. Reversing both coil connections still results in upscale deflection. However, reversing one

Reactive power is measured by an instrument called the *varmeter*. The varmeter is often connected to the load in the same way as the wattmeter.

Some wattmeters do not have coils; the wattmeter considered here is the electromagnetic type.

Figure 11.30   A wattmeter.

coil and not the other results in downscale deflection and no wattmeter reading.

EXAMPLE 11.16

Find the wattmeter reading of the circuit in Fig. 11.32.

Figure 11.32   For Example 11.16.

Solution:

In Fig. 11.32, the wattmeter reads the average power absorbed by the $(8 - j6)\ \Omega$ impedance because the current coil is in series with the impedance while the voltage coil is in parallel with it. The current through the circuit is

$$\mathbf{I}_{rms} = \frac{150\angle 0^\circ}{(12 + j10) + (8 - j6)} = \frac{150}{20 + j4}\ \text{A}$$

The voltage across the $(8 - j6)\ \Omega$ impedance is

$$\mathbf{V}_{rms} = \mathbf{I}_{rms}(8 - j6) = \frac{150(8 - j6)}{20 + j4}\ \text{V}$$

The complex power is

$$\mathbf{S} = \mathbf{V}_{rms}\mathbf{I}_{rms}^* = \frac{150(8 - j6)}{20 + j4} \cdot \frac{150}{20 - j4} = \frac{150^2(8 - j6)}{20^2 + 4^2}$$

$$= 423.7 - j324.6\ \text{VA}$$

The wattmeter reads

$$P = \text{Re}(\mathbf{S}) = 432.7\ \text{W}$$

PRACTICE PROBLEM 11.16

For the circuit in Fig. 11.33, find the wattmeter reading.

Figure 11.33   For Practice Prob. 11.16.

Answer: 1437 W.

11.9.2 Electricity Consumption Cost

In Section 1.7, we considered a simplified model of the way the cost of electricity consumption is determined. But the concept of power factor was not included in the calculations. Now we consider the importance of power factor in electricity consumption cost.

Loads with low power factors are costly to serve because they require large currents, as explained in Section 11.8. The ideal situation would be to draw minimum current from a supply so that $S = P$, $Q = 0$, and pf $= 1$. A load with nonzero Q means that energy flows forth and back between the load and the source, giving rise to additional power losses. In view of this, power companies often encourage their customers to have power factors as close to unity as possible and penalize some customers who do not improve their load power factors.

Utility companies divide their customers into categories: as residential (domestic), commercial, and industrial, or as small power, medium power, and large power. They have different rate structures for each category. The amount of energy consumed in units of kilowatt-hours (kWh) is measured using a kilowatt-hour meter installed at the customer's premises.

Although utility companies use different methods for charging customers, the tariff or charge to a consumer is often two-part. The first part is fixed and corresponds to the cost of generation, transmission, and distribution of electricity to meet the load requirements of the consumers. This part of the tariff is generally expressed as a certain price per kW of maximum demand. Or it may be based on kVA of maximum demand, to account for the power factor (pf) of the consumer. A pf penalty charge may be imposed on the consumer whereby a certain percentage of kW or kVA maximum demand is charged for every 0.01 fall in pf below a prescribed value, say 0.85 or 0.9. On the other hand, a pf credit may be given for every 0.01 that the pf exceeds the prescribed value.

The second part is proportional to the energy consumed in kWh; it may be in graded form, for example, the first 100 kWh at 16 cents/kWh, the next 200 kWh at 10 cents/kWh and so forth. Thus, the bill is determined based on the following equation:

$$\text{Total Cost} = \text{Fixed Cost} + \text{Cost of Energy} \qquad (11.64)$$

EXAMPLE 11.17

A manufacturing industry consumes 200 MWh in one month. If the maximum demand is 1600 kW, calculate the electricity bill based on the following two-part rate:

Demand charge: $5.00 per month per kW of billing demand.

Energy charge: 8 cents per kWh for the first 50,000 kWh, 5 cents per kWh for the remaining energy.

Solution:

The demand charge is

$$\$5.00 \times 1600 = \$8000 \qquad (11.17.1)$$

The energy charge for the first 50,000 kWh is

$$\$0.08 \times 50,000 = \$4000 \qquad (11.17.2)$$

The remaining energy is 200,000 kWh $-$ 50,000 kWh $=$ 150,000 kWh, and the corresponding energy charge is

$$\$0.05 \times 150,000 = \$7500 \qquad (11.17.3)$$

Adding Eqs. (11.17.1) to (11.17.3) gives

Total bill for the month $= \$8000 + \$4000 + \$7500 = \$19,500$

It may appear that the cost of electricity is too high. But this is often a small fraction of the overall cost of production of the goods manufactured or the selling price of the finished product.

PRACTICE PROBLEM 11.17

The monthly reading of a paper mill's meter is as follows:

Maximum demand: 32,000 kW

Energy consumed: 500 MWh

Using the two-part rate in Example 11.17, calculate the monthly bill for the paper mill.

Answer: $186,500.

EXAMPLE 11.18

A 300-kW load supplied at 13 kV (rms) operates 520 hours a month at 80 percent power factor. Calculate the average cost per month based on this simplified tariff:

Energy charge: 6 cents per kWh

Power-factor penalty: 0.1 percent of energy charge for every 0.01 that pf falls below 0.85.

Power-factor credit: 0.1 percent of energy charge for every 0.01 that pf exceeds 0.85.

Solution:

The energy consumed is

$$W = 300 \text{ kW} \times 520 \text{ h} = 156,000 \text{ kWh}$$

The operating power factor pf $= 80\% = 0.8$ is 5×0.01 below the prescribed power factor of 0.85. Since there is 0.1 percent energy charge for every 0.01, there is a power-factor penalty charge of 0.5 percent. This amounts to an energy charge of

$$\Delta W = 156,000 \times \frac{5 \times 0.1}{100} = 780 \text{ kWh}$$

The total energy is

$$W_t = W + \Delta W = 156,000 + 780 = 156,780 \text{ kWh}$$

The cost per month is given by

$$\text{Cost} = 6 \text{ cents} \times W_t = \$0.06 \times 156,780 = \$9406.80$$

An 800-kW induction furnace at 0.88 power factor operates 20 hours per day for 26 days in a month. Determine the electricity bill per month based on the tariff in Example 11.16.

Answer: $24,885.12.

11.10 SUMMARY

1. The instantaneous power absorbed by an element is the product of the element's terminal voltage and the current through the element: $p = vi$.

2. Average or real power P (in watts) is the average of instantaneous power p:

$$P = \frac{1}{T} \int_0^T p\, dt$$

If $v(t) = V_m \cos(\omega t + \theta_v)$ and $i(t) = I_m \cos(\omega t + \theta_i)$, then $V_{rms} = V_m/\sqrt{2}$, $I_{rms} = I_m/\sqrt{2}$, and

$$P = \frac{1}{2} V_m I_m \cos(\theta_v - \theta_i) = V_{rms} I_{rms} \cos(\theta_v - \theta_i)$$

Inductors and capacitors absorb no average power, while the average power absorbed by a resistor is $1/2\, I_m^2 R = I_{rms}^2 R$.

3. Maximum average power is transferred to a load when the load impedance is the complex conjugate of the Thevenin impedance as seen from the load terminals, $\mathbf{Z}_L = \mathbf{Z}_{Th}^*$.

4. The effective value of a periodic signal $x(t)$ is its root-mean-square (rms) value.

$$X_{eff} = X_{rms} = \sqrt{\frac{1}{T} \int_0^T x^2\, dt}$$

For a sinusoid, the effective or rms value is its amplitude divided by $\sqrt{2}$.

5. The power factor is the cosine of the phase difference between voltage and current:

$$\text{pf} = \cos(\theta_v - \theta_i)$$

It is also the cosine of the angle of the load impedance or the ratio of real power to apparent power. The pf is lagging if the current lags voltage (inductive load) and is leading when the current leads voltage (capacitive load).

6. Apparent power S (in VA) is the product of the rms values of voltage and current:

$$S = V_{rms} I_{rms}$$

It is also given by $S = |\mathbf{S}| = \sqrt{P^2 + Q^2}$, where Q is reactive power.

7. Reactive power (in VAR) is:

$$Q = \frac{1}{2} V_m I_m \sin(\theta_v - \theta_i) = V_{rms} I_{rms} \sin(\theta_v - \theta_i)$$

8. Complex power $\mathbf{S}$ (in VA) is the product of the rms voltage phasor and the complex conjugate of the rms current phasor. It is also the complex sum of real power P and reactive power Q.

$$\mathbf{S} = \mathbf{V}_{rms}\mathbf{I}_{rms}^* = V_{rms}I_{rms}\underline{/\theta_v - \theta_i} = P + jQ$$

Also,

$$\mathbf{S} = I_{rms}^2\mathbf{Z} = \frac{V_{rms}^2}{\mathbf{Z}^*}$$

9. The total complex power in a network is the sum of the complex powers of the individual components. Total real power and reactive power are also, respectively, the sums of the individual real powers and the reactive powers, but the total apparent power is not calculated by the process.

10. Power factor correction is necessary for economic reasons; it is the process of improving the power factor of a load by reducing the overall reactive power.

11. The wattmeter is the instrument for measuring the average power. Energy consumed is measured with a kilowatt-hour meter.

REVIEW QUESTIONS

11.1 The average power absorbed by an inductor is zero.

(a) True   (b) False

11.2 The Thevenin impedance of a network seen from the load terminals is $80 + j55\ \Omega$. For maximum power transfer, the load impedance must be:

(a) $-80 + j55\ \Omega$ (b) $-80 - j55\ \Omega$
(c) $80 - j55\ \Omega$ (d) $80 + j55\ \Omega$

11.3 The amplitude of the voltage available in the 60-Hz, 120-V power outlet in your home is:

(a) 110 V   (b) 120 V
(c) 170 V   (d) 210 V

11.4 If the load impedance is $20 - j20$, the power factor is

(a) $\underline{/-45°}$ (b) 0   (c) 1
(d) 0.7071   (e) none of these

11.5 A quantity that contains all the power information in a given load is the

(a) power factor   (b) apparent power
(c) average power   (d) reactive power
(e) complex power

11.6 Reactive power is measured in:

(a) watts   (b) VA
(c) VAR   (d) none of these

11.7 In the power triangle shown in Fig. 11.34(a), the reactive power is:

(a) 1000 VAR leading   (b) 1000 VAR lagging
(c) 866 VAR leading   (d) 866 VAR lagging

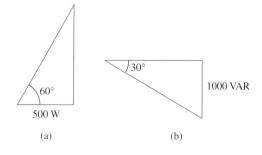

Figure 11.34   For Review Questions 11.7 and 11.8.

11.8 For the power triangle in Fig. 11.34(b), the apparent power is:

(a) 2000 VA   (b) 1000 VAR
(c) 866 VAR   (d) 500 VAR

11.9   A source is connected to three loads $\mathbf{Z}_1$, $\mathbf{Z}_2$, and $\mathbf{Z}_3$
in parallel. Which of these is not true?

(a) $P = P_1 + P_2 + P_3$ (b) $Q = Q_1 + Q_2 + Q_3$
(c) $S = S_1 + S_2 + S_3$ (d) $\mathbf{S} = \mathbf{S}_1 + \mathbf{S}_2 + \mathbf{S}_3$

11.10   The instrument for measuring average power is the:

(a) voltmeter   (b) ammeter
(c) wattmeter   (d) varmeter
(e) kilowatt-hour meter

----

*Answers: 11.1a, 11.2c, 11.3c, 11.4d, 11.5e, 11.6c, 11.7d,
11.8a, 11.9c, 11.10c.*

PROBLEMS

Section 11.2   **Instantaneous and Average Power**

11.1   If $v(t) = 160 \cos 50t \, \text{V}$ and $i(t) =
-20 \sin(50t - 30°) \, \text{A}$, calculate the instantaneous
power and the average power.

11.2   At $t = 2$ s, find the instantaneous power on each of
the elements in the circuit of Fig. 11.35.

Figure 11.35   For Prob. 11.2.

11.3   Refer to the circuit depicted in Fig. 11.36. Find the
average power absorbed by each element.

Figure 11.36   For Prob. 11.3.

11.4   Given the circuit in Fig. 11.37, find the average
power absorbed by each of the elements.

Figure 11.37   For Prob. 11.4.

11.5   Assuming that $v_s = 8 \cos(2t - 40°) \, \text{V}$ in the circuit
of Fig. 11.38, find the average power delivered to
each of the passive elements.

Figure 11.38   For Prob. 11.5.

11.6   Compute the average power absorbed by the 4-Ω
resistor in the circuit of Fig. 11.39.

Figure 11.39   For Prob. 11.6.

11.7   Given the circuit of Fig. 11.40, find the average
power absorbed by the 10-Ω resistor.

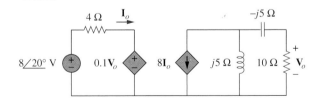

Figure 11.40   For Prob. 11.7.

11.8   In the circuit of Fig. 11.41, determine the average power absorbed by the 40-Ω resistor.

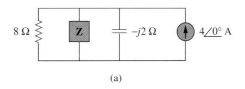

Figure 11.41   For Prob. 11.8.

11.9   Calculate the average power absorbed by each resistor in the op amp circuit of Fig. 11.42 if the rms value of v_s is 2 V.

Figure 11.42   For Prob. 11.9.

11.10   In the op amp circuit in Fig. 11.43, find the total average power absorbed by the resistors.

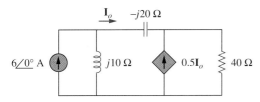

Figure 11.43   For Prob. 11.10.

11.11   For the network in Fig. 11.44, assume that the port impedance is

$$\mathbf{Z}_{ab} = \frac{R}{\sqrt{1 + \omega^2 R^2 C^2}} \angle{-\tan^{-1} \omega RC}$$

Find the average power consumed by the network when $R = 10$ kΩ, $C = 200$ nF, and $i = 2\sin(377t + 22°)$ mA.

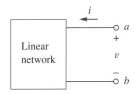

Figure 11.44   For Prob. 11.11.

Section 11.3   Maximum Average Power Transfer

11.12   For each of the circuits in Fig. 11.45, determine the value of load **Z** for maximum power transfer and the maximum average power transferred.

(a)

(b)

Figure 11.45   For Prob. 11.12.

11.13   For the circuit in Fig. 11.46, find:

(a) the value of the load impedance that absorbs the maximum average power

(b) the value of the maximum average power absorbed

Figure 11.46   For Prob. 11.13.

11.14   In the circuit of Fig. 11.47, find the value of **Z** that will result in the maximum power being delivered to **Z**. Calculate the maximum power delivered to **Z**.

Figure 11.47   For Prob. 11.14.

11.15 In the circuit of Fig. 11.48, find the value of $\mathbf{Z}_L$ that will absorb the maximum power and the value of the maximum power.

Figure 11.48   For Prob. 11.15.

11.16 For the circuit of Fig. 11.49, find the maximum power delivered to the load $\mathbf{Z}_L$.

Figure 11.49   For Prob. 11.16.

11.17 Calculate the value of $\mathbf{Z}_L$ in the circuit of Fig. 11.50 in order for $\mathbf{Z}_L$ to receive maximum average power. What is the maximum average power received by $\mathbf{Z}$?

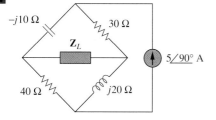

Figure 11.50   For Prob. 11.17.

11.18 Find the value of $\mathbf{Z}_L$ in the circuit of Fig. 11.51 for maximum power transfer.

Figure 11.51   For Prob. 11.18.

11.19 The variable resistor R in the circuit of Fig. 11.52 is adjusted until it absorbs the maximum average power. Find R and the maximum average power absorbed.

Figure 11.52   For Prob. 11.19.

11.20 The load resistance R_L in Fig. 11.53 is adjusted until it absorbs the maximum average power. Calculate the value of R_L and the maximum average power.

Figure 11.53   For Prob. 11.20.

11.21 Assuming that the load impedance is to be purely resistive, what load should be connected to terminals *a-b* of the circuits in Fig. 11.54 so that the maximum power is transferred to the load?

Figure 11.54   For Prob. 11.21.

Section 11.4   Effective or RMS Value

11.22 Find the rms value of the rectified sine wave shown in Fig. 11.55.

Figure 11.55   For Prob. 11.22.

11.23 Find the rms value of the periodic signal in Fig. 11.56.

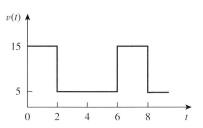

Figure 11.56   For Prob. 11.23.

11.24 Determine the rms value of the waveform in Fig. 11.57.

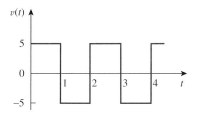

Figure 11.57   For Prob. 11.24.

11.25 Find the rms value of the signal shown in Fig. 11.58.

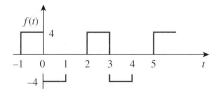

Figure 11.58   For Prob. 11.25.

11.26 Find the effective value of the voltage waveform in Fig. 11.59.

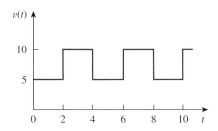

Figure 11.59   For Prob. 11.26.

11.27 Calculate the rms value of the current waveform of Fig. 11.60.

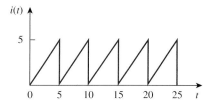

Figure 11.60   For Prob. 11.27.

11.28 Find the rms value of the voltage waveform of Fig. 11.61 as well as the average power absorbed by a 2-Ω resistor when the voltage is applied across the resistor.

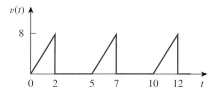

Figure 11.61   For Prob. 11.28.

11.29 Calculate the effective value of the current waveform in Fig. 11.62 and the average power delivered to a 12-Ω resistor when the current runs through the resistor.

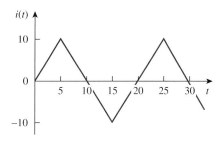

Figure 11.62   For Prob. 11.29.

11.30 Compute the rms value of the waveform depicted in Fig. 11.63.

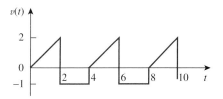

Figure 11.63   For Prob. 11.30.

11.31 Find the rms value of the signal shown in Fig. 11.64.

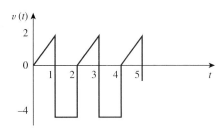

Figure 11.64   For Prob. 11.31.

11.32 Obtain the rms value of the current waveform shown in Fig. 11.65.

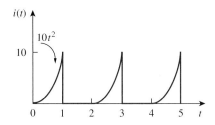

Figure 11.65   For Prob. 11.32.

11.33 Determine the effective value of the periodic waveform in Fig. 11.66.

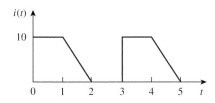

Figure 11.66   For Prob. 11.33.

11.34 Find the effective value of $f(t)$ defined in Fig. 11.67.

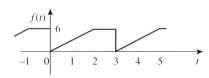

Figure 11.67   For Prob. 11.34.

11.35 One cycle of a periodic voltage waveform is depicted in Fig. 11.68. Find the effective value of the voltage.

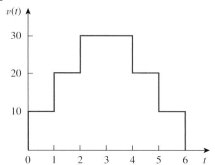

Figure 11.68   For Prob. 11.35.

11.36 Calculate the rms value for each of the following functions:

(a) $i(t) = 10$ A   (b) $v(t) = 4 + 3\cos 5t$ V
(c) $i(t) = 8 - 6\sin 2t$ A (d) $v(t) = 5\sin t + 4\cos t$ V

11.37 Calculate the rms value of the sum of these three currents:

$$i_1 = 8, \qquad i_2 = 4\sin(t + 10°), \qquad i_3 = 6\cos(2t + 30°) \text{ A}$$

Section 11.5   Apparent Power and Power Factor

11.38 A relay coil is connected to a 210-V, 50-Hz supply. If it has a resistance of 30 Ω and an inductance of 0.5 H, calculate the apparent power and the power factor.

11.39 A certain load comprises $12 - j8$ Ω in parallel with $j4$ Ω. Determine the overall power factor.

11.40 For the circuit of Fig. 11.69, find:

(a) the real power dissipated by each element
(b) the total apparent power supplied by the circuit
(c) the power factor of the circuit

Figure 11.69   For Prob. 11.40.

11.41 Obtain the power factor for each of the circuits in Fig. 11.70. Specify each power factor as leading or lagging.

(a)

(b)

Figure 11.70   For Prob. 11.41.

Section 11.6   Complex Power

11.42 A load draws 5 kVAR at a power factor of 0.86 (leading) from a 220-V rms source. Calculate the peak current and the apparent power supplied to the load.

11.43 The voltage applied to a 10-Ω resistor is

$$v(t) = 5 + 3\cos(t + 10°) + \cos(2t + 30°) \text{ V}$$

(a) Calculate the rms value of the voltage.
(b) Determine the average power dissipated in the resistor.

11.44 A source delivers 50 kVA to a load with a power factor of 65 percent lagging. Find the load's average and reactive powers.

11.45 The voltage across a load and the current through it are given by

$$v(t) = 20 + 60\cos 100t \text{ V}$$
$$i(t) = 1 - 0.5\sin 100t \text{ A}$$

Find:

(a) the rms values of the voltage and of the current
(b) the average power dissipated in the load

11.46 For the following voltage and current phasors, calculate the complex power, apparent power, real power, and reactive power. Specify whether the pf is leading or lagging.

(a) $\mathbf{V} = 220\underline{/30°}$ V rms, $\mathbf{I} = 0.5\underline{/60°}$ A rms
(b) $\mathbf{V} = 250\underline{/-10°}$ V rms, $\mathbf{I} = 6.2\underline{/-25°}$ A rms

(c) $\mathbf{V} = 120\underline{/0°}$ V rms, $\mathbf{I} = 2.4\underline{/-15°}$ A rms
(d) $\mathbf{V} = 160\underline{/45°}$ V rms, $\mathbf{I} = 8.5\underline{/90°}$ A rms

11.47 For each of the following cases, find the complex power, the average power, and the reactive power:

(a) $v(t) = 112\cos(\omega t + 10°)$ V,
    $i(t) = 4\cos(\omega t - 50°)$ A
(b) $v(t) = 160\cos 377t$ V,
    $i(t) = 4\cos(377t + 45°)$ A
(c) $\mathbf{V} = 80\underline{/60°}$ V rms, $\mathbf{Z} = 50\underline{/30°}$ Ω
(d) $\mathbf{I} = 10\underline{/60°}$ A rms, $\mathbf{Z} = 100\underline{/45°}$ Ω

11.48 Determine the complex power for the following cases:

(a) $P = 269$ W, $Q = 150$ VAR (capacitive)
(b) $Q = 2000$ VAR, pf = 0.9 (leading)
(c) $S = 600$ VA, $Q = 450$ VAR (inductive)
(d) $V_{rms} = 220$ V, $P = 1$ kW,
    $|\mathbf{Z}| = 40$ Ω (inductive)

11.49 Find the complex power for the following cases:

(a) $P = 4$ kW, pf = 0.86 (lagging)
(b) $S = 2$ kVA, $P = 1.6$ kW (capacitive)
(c) $\mathbf{V}_{rms} = 208\underline{/20°}$ V, $\mathbf{I}_{rms} = 6.5\underline{/-50°}$ A
(d) $\mathbf{V}_{rms} = 120\underline{/30°}$ V, $\mathbf{Z} = 40 + j60$ Ω

11.50 Obtain the overall impedance for the following cases:

(a) $P = 1000$ W, pf = 0.8 (leading),
    $V_{rms} = 220$ V
(b) $P = 1500$ W, $Q = 2000$ VAR (inductive),
    $I_{rms} = 12$ A
(c) $\mathbf{S} = 4500\underline{/60°}$ VA, $\mathbf{V} = 120\underline{/45°}$ V

11.51 For the entire circuit in Fig. 11.71, calculate:

(a) the power factor
(b) the average power delivered by the source
(c) the reactive power
(d) the apparent power
(e) the complex power

Figure 11.71   For Prob. 11.51.

11.52 In the circuit of Fig. 11.72, device A receives 2 kW at 0.8 pf lagging, device B receives 3 kVA at 0.4 pf leading, while device C is inductive and consumes 1 kW and receives 500 VARs.

(a) Determine the power factor of the entire system.
(b) Find $\mathbf{I}$ given that $\mathbf{V}_s = 120\underline{/45°}$ V rms.

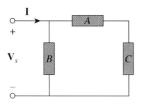

Figure 11.72   For Prob. 11.52.

11.53 In the circuit of Fig. 11.73, load A receives 4 kVA at 0.8 pf leading. Load B receives 2.4 kVA at 0.6 pf lagging. Box C is an inductive load that consumes 1 kW and receives 500 VARs.

(a) Determine $\mathbf{I}$.
(b) Calculate the power factor of the combination.

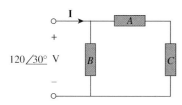

Figure 11.73   For Prob. 11.53.

Section 11.7   Conservation of AC Power

11.54 For the network in Fig. 11.74, find the complex power absorbed by each element.

Figure 11.74   For Prob. 11.54.

11.55 Find the complex power absorbed by each of the five elements in the circuit of Fig. 11.75.

Figure 11.75   For Prob. 11.55.

11.56 Obtain the complex power delivered by the source in the circuit of Fig. 11.76.

Figure 11.76   For Prob. 11.56.

11.57 For the circuit in Fig. 11.77, find the average, reactive, and complex power delivered by the dependent current source.

Figure 11.77   For Prob. 11.57.

11.58 Obtain the complex power delivered to the 10-kΩ resistor in Fig. 11.78 below.

Figure 11.78   For Prob. 11.58.

11.59 Calculate the reactive power in the inductor and capacitor in the circuit of Fig. 11.79.

Figure 11.79   For Prob. 11.59.

11.60 For the circuit in Fig. 11.80, find $\mathbf{V}_o$ and the input power factor.

Figure 11.80   For Prob. 11.60.

11.61 Given the circuit in Fig. 11.81, find $\mathbf{I}_o$ and the overall complex power supplied.

Figure 11.81   For Prob. 11.61.

11.62 For the circuit in Fig. 11.82, find $\mathbf{V}_s$.

Figure 11.82   For Prob. 11.62.

11.63 Find $\mathbf{I}_o$ in the circuit of Fig. 11.83.

11.64 Determine $\mathbf{I}_s$ in the circuit of Fig. 11.84, if the voltage source supplies 2.5 kW and 0.4 kVAR (leading).

Figure 11.84   For Prob. 11.64.

11.65 In the op amp circuit of Fig. 11.85, $v_s = 4\cos 10^4 t$ V. Find the average power delivered to the 50-kΩ resistor.

Figure 11.85   For Prob. 11.65.

11.66 Obtain the average power absorbed by the 6-kΩ resistor in the op amp circuit in Fig. 11.86.

Figure 11.86   For Prob. 11.66.

Figure 11.83   For Prob. 11.63.

11.67   For the op amp circuit in Fig. 11.87, calculate:

(a) the complex power delivered by the voltage source

(b) the average power in the 12-Ω resistor

Figure 11.87   For Prob. 11.67.

11.68   Compute the complex power supplied by the current source in the series *RLC* circuit in Fig. 11.88.

Figure 11.88   For Prob. 11.68.

Section 11.8   Power Factor Correction

11.69   Refer to the circuit shown in Fig. 11.89.

(a) What is the power factor?

(b) What is the average power dissipated?

(c) What is the value of the capacitance that will give a unity power factor when connected to the load?

Figure 11.89   For Prob. 11.69.

11.70   An 880-VA, 220-V, 50-Hz load has a power factor of 0.8 lagging. What value of parallel capacitance will correct the load power factor to unity?

11.71   Two loads are placed in parallel across a 120-V rms 60-Hz line. The first load draws 150 VA at a lagging power factor of 0.707, while the second load draws 50 VAR at a leading power factor of 0.8. A third load is purely capacitive and is placed in parallel across the 120-V line in order to make the pf of the system equal unity. Calculate the value of the capacitance.

11.72   A 40-kW induction motor, with a lagging power factor of 0.76, is supplied by a 120-V 60-Hz sinusoidal voltage source. Find the capacitance needed in parallel with the motor to raise the power factor to:

(a) 0.9 lagging   (b) 1.0.

11.73   A 240-V rms 60-Hz supply serves a load that is 10 kW (resistive), 15 kVAR (capacitive), and 22 kVAR (inductive). Find:

(a) the apparent power

(b) the current drawn from the supply

(c) the kVAR rating and capacitance required to improve the power factor to 0.96 lagging

(d) the current drawn from the supply under the new power-factor conditions

11.74   A 120-V rms 60-Hz source supplies two loads connected in parallel, as shown in Fig. 11.90.

(a) Find the power factor of the parallel combination.

(b) Calculate the value of the capacitance connected in parallel that will raise the power factor to unity.

Figure 11.90   For Prob. 11.74.

11.75   Consider the power system shown in Fig. 11.91. Calculate:

(a) the total complex power

(b) the power factor

(c) the capacitance necessary to establish a unity power factor

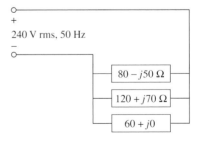

Figure 11.91   For Prob. 11.75.

Section 11.9   Applications

11.76   Obtain the wattmeter reading of the circuit in Fig. 11.92 below.

11.77   What is the reading of the wattmeter in the network of Fig. 11.93?

Figure 11.93   For Prob. 11.77.

11.78   Find the wattmeter reading of the circuit shown in Fig. 11.94 below.

11.79   Determine the wattmeter reading of the circuit in Fig. 11.95.

Figure 11.95   For Prob. 11.79.

11.80   The circuit of Fig. 11.96 portrays a wattmeter connected into an ac network.

(a)   Find the load current.

(b)   Calculate the wattmeter reading.

Figure 11.96   For Prob. 11.80.

11.81   The kilowatthour-meter of a home is read once a month. For a particular month, the previous and present readings are as follows:

Previous reading: 3246 kWh

Present reading: 4017 kWh

Calculate the electricity bill for that month based on the following residential rate schedule:

Minimum monthly charge—$12.00

First 100 kWh per month at 16 cents/kWh

Next 200 kWh per month at 10 cents/kWh

Over 300 kWh per month at 6 cents/kWh

11.82   A 240-V rms 60-Hz source supplies a parallel combination of a 5-kW heater and a 30-kVA induction motor whose power factor is 0.82. Determine:

(a)   the system apparent power

(b)   the system reactive power

(c)   the kVA rating of a capacitor required to adjust the system power factor to 0.9 lagging

(d)   the value of the capacitor required

Figure 11.92   For Prob. 11.76.

Figure 11.94   For Prob. 11.78.

11.83 Oscilloscope measurements indicate that the voltage across a load and the current through it are, respectively, $210\underline{/60°}$ V and $8\underline{/25°}$ A. Determine:

(a) the real power
(b) the apparent power
(c) the reactive power
(d) the power factor

11.84 A consumer has an annual consumption of 1200 MWh with a maximum demand of 2.4 MVA. The maximum demand charge is $30 per kVA per annum, and the energy charge per kWh is 4 cents.

(a) Determine the annual cost of energy.
(b) Calculate the charge per kWh with a flat-rate tariff if the revenue to the utility company is to remain the same as for the two-part tariff.

11.85 A regular household system of a single-phase three-wire circuit allows the operation of both 120-V and 240-V, 60-Hz appliances. The household circuit is modeled as shown in Fig. 11.97. Calculate:

(a) the currents $\mathbf{I}_1$, $\mathbf{I}_2$, and $\mathbf{I}_n$
(b) the total complex power supplied
(c) the overall power factor of the circuit

Figure 11.97   For Prob. 11.85.

COMPREHENSIVE PROBLEMS

11.86 A transmitter delivers maximum power to an antenna when the antenna is adjusted to represent a load of 75-Ω resistance in series with an inductance of 4 μH. If the transmitter operates at 4.12 MHz, find its internal impedance.

11.87 In a TV transmitter, a series circuit has an impedance of 3 kΩ and a total current of 50 mA. If the voltage across the resistor is 80 V, what is the power factor of the circuit?

11.88 A certain electronic circuit is connected to a 110-V ac line. The root-mean-square value of the current drawn is 2 A, with a phase angle of 55°.

(a) Find the true power drawn by the circuit.
(b) Calculate the apparent power.

11.89 An industrial heater has a nameplate which reads:
210 V   60 Hz   12 kVA   0.78 pf lagging
Determine:

(a) the apparent and the complex power
(b) the impedance of the heater

*__11.90__ A 2000-kW turbine-generator of 0.85 power factor operates at the rated load. An additional load of 300 kW at 0.8 power factor is added. What kVAR of capacitors is required to operate the turbine-generator but keep it from being overloaded?

11.91 The nameplate of an electric motor has the following information:

      Line voltage: 220 V rms
      Line current: 15 A rms
      Line frequency: 60 Hz
      Power: 2700 W

Determine the power factor (lagging) of the motor. Find the value of the capacitance C that must be connected across the motor to raise the pf to unity.

11.92 As shown in Fig. 11.98, a 550-V feeder line supplies an industrial plant consisting of a motor drawing 60 kW at 0.75 pf (inductive), a capacitor with a rating of 20 kVAR, and lighting drawing 20 kW.

(a) Calculate the total reactive power and apparent power absorbed by the plant.
(b) Determine the overall pf.
(c) Find the current in the feeder line.

Figure 11.98   For Prob. 11.92.

11.93 A factory has the following four major loads:
- A motor rated at 5 hp, 0.8 pf lagging (1 hp = 0.7457 kW).
- A heater rated at 1.2 kW, 1.0 pf.
- Ten 120-W lightbulbs.
- A synchronous motor rated at 1.6 kVAR, 0.6 pf leading.

(a) Calculate the total real and reactive power.

(b) Find the overall power factor.

11.94 A 1-MVA substation operates at full load at 0.7 power factor. It is desired to improve the power factor to 0.95 by installing capacitors. Assume that new substation and distribution facilities cost $120 per kVA installed, and capacitors cost $30 per kVA installed.

(a) Calculate the cost of capacitors needed.

(b) Find the savings in substation capacity released.

(c) Are capacitors economical for releasing the amount of substation capacity?

11.95 A coupling capacitor is used to block dc current from an amplifier as shown in Fig. 11.99(a). The amplifier and the capacitor act as the source, while the speaker is the load as in Fig. 11.99(b).

(a) At what frequency is maximum power transferred to the speaker?

(b) If $V_s = 4.6$ V rms, how much power is delivered to the speaker at that frequency?

(a)

(b)

Figure 11.99   For Prob. 11.95.

11.96 A power amplifier has an output impedance of $40 + j8\ \Omega$. It produces a no-load output voltage of 146 V at 300 Hz.

(a) Determine the impedance of the load that achieves maximum power transfer.

(b) Calculate the load power under this matching condition.

11.97 A power transmission system is modeled as shown in Fig. 11.100. If $\mathbf{V}_s = 240\underline{/0°}$ rms, find the average power absorbed by the load.

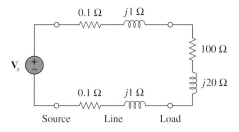

Figure 11.100   For Prob. 11.97.

THREE-PHASE CIRCUITS

I know this world is ruled by Intelligence. It required Infinite Intelligence to create it and it requires Infinite Intelligence to keep it on its course. Everything that surrounds us—everything that exists—proves that there are Infinite Laws behind it. There can be no denying this fact. It is mathematical in its precision.

—Thomas Alva Edison

Historical Profiles

Thomas Alva Edison (1847–1931) was perhaps the greatest American inventor. He patented 1093 inventions, including such history-making inventions as the incandescent electric bulb, the phonograph, and the first commercial motion pictures.

Born in Milan, Ohio, the youngest of seven children, Edison received only three months of formal education because he hated school. He was home-schooled by his mother and quickly began to read on his own. In 1868, Edison read one of Faraday's books and found his calling. He moved to Menlo Park, New Jersey, in 1876, where he managed a well-staffed research laboratory. Most of his inventions came out of this laboratory. His laboratory served as a model for modern research organizations. Because of his diverse interests and the overwhelming number of his inventions and patents, Edison began to establish manufacturing companies for making the devices he invented. He designed the first electric power station to supply electric light. Formal electrical engineering education began in the mid-1880s with Edison as a role model and leader.

Nikola Tesla (1856–1943) was a Croatian-American engineer whose inventions— among them the induction motor and the first polyphase ac power system—greatly influenced the settlement of the ac versus dc debate in favor of ac. He was also responsible for the adoption of 60 Hz as the standard for ac power systems in the United States.

Born in Austria-Hungary (now Croatia), to a clergyman, Tesla had an incredible memory and a keen affinity for mathematics. He moved to the United States in 1884 and first worked for Thomas Edison. At that time, the country was in the "battle of the currents" with George Westinghouse (1846–1914) promoting ac and Thomas Edison rigidly leading the dc forces. Tesla left Edison and joined Westinghouse because of his interest in ac. Through Westinghouse, Tesla gained the reputation and acceptance of his polyphase ac generation, transmission, and distribution system. He held 700 patents in his lifetime. His other inventions include high-voltage apparatus (the tesla coil) and a wireless transmission system. The unit of magnetic flux density, the tesla, was named in honor of him.

12.1 INTRODUCTION

So far in this text, we have dealt with single-phase circuits. A single-phase ac power system consists of a generator connected through a pair of wires (a transmission line) to a load. Figure 12.1(a) depicts a single-phase two-wire system, where V_p is the magnitude of the source voltage and ϕ is the phase. What is more common in practice is a single-phase three-wire system, shown in Fig. 12.1(b). It contains two identical sources (equal magnitude and the same phase) which are connected to two loads by two outer wires and the neutral. For example, the normal household system is a single-phase three-wire system because the terminal voltages have the same magnitude and the same phase. Such a system allows the connection of both 120-V and 240-V appliances.

Historical note: Thomas Edison invented a *three-wire system*, using three wires instead of four.

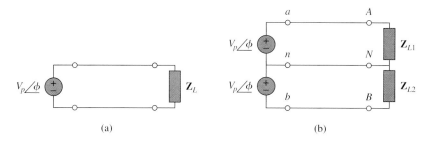

Figure 12.1   Single-phase systems: (a) two-wire type, (b) three-wire type.

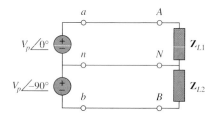

Figure 12.2   Two-phase three-wire system.

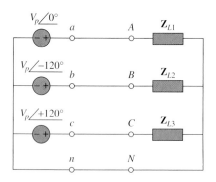

Figure 12.3   Three-phase four-wire system.

Circuits or systems in which the ac sources operate at the same frequency but different phases are known as *polyphase*. Figure 12.2 shows a two-phase three-wire system, and Fig. 12.3 shows a three-phase four-wire system. As distinct from a single-phase system, a two-phase system is produced by a generator consisting of two coils placed perpendicular to each other so that the voltage generated by one lags the other by 90°. By the same token, a three-phase system is produced by a generator consisting of three sources having the same amplitude and frequency but out of phase with each other by 120°. Since the three-phase system is by far the most prevalent and most economical polyphase system, discussion in this chapter is mainly on three-phase systems.

Three-phase systems are important for at least three reasons. First, nearly all electric power is generated and distributed in three-phase, at the operating frequency of 60 Hz (or $\omega = 377$ rad/s) in the United States or 50 Hz (or $\omega = 314$ rad/s) in some other parts of the world. When one-phase or two-phase inputs are required, they are taken from the three-phase system rather than generated independently. Even when more than three phases are needed—such as in the aluminum industry, where 48 phases are required for melting purposes—they can be provided by manipulating the three phases supplied. Second, the instantaneous power in a three-phase system can be constant (not pulsating), as we will see in Section 12.7. This results in uniform power transmission and less vibration of three-phase machines. Third, for the same amount of power, the three-phase system is more economical than the single-phase. The amount of wire required for a three-phase system is less than that required for an equivalent single-phase system.

We begin with a discussion of balanced three-phase voltages. Then we analyze each of the four possible configurations of balanced three-phase systems. We also discuss the analysis of unbalanced three-phase systems. We learn how to use *PSpice for Windows* to analyze a balanced or unbalanced three-phase system. Finally, we apply the concepts developed in this chapter to three-phase power measurement and residential electrical wiring.

12.2 BALANCED THREE-PHASE VOLTAGES

Three-phase voltages are often produced with a three-phase ac generator (or alternator) whose cross-sectional view is shown in Fig. 12.4. The generator basically consists of a rotating magnet (called the *rotor*) surrounded by a stationary winding (called the *stator*). Three separate windings or coils with terminals a-a', b-b', and c-c' are physically placed 120° apart around the stator. Terminals a and a', for example, stand for one of the ends of coils going into and the other end coming out of the page. As the rotor rotates, its magnetic field "cuts" the flux from the three coils and induces voltages in the coils. Because the coils are placed 120° apart, the induced voltages in the coils are equal in magnitude but out of phase by 120° (Fig. 12.5). Since each coil can be regarded as a single-phase generator by itself, the three-phase generator can supply power to both single-phase and three-phase loads.

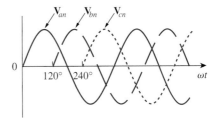

Figure 12.5   The generated voltages are 120° apart from each other.

Figure 12.4   A three-phase generator.

A typical three-phase system consists of three voltage sources connected to loads by three or four wires (or transmission lines). (Three-phase current sources are very scarce.) A three-phase system is equivalent to three single-phase circuits. The voltage sources can be either wye-connected as shown in Fig. 12.6(a) or delta-connected as in Fig. 12.6(b).

Let us consider the wye-connected voltages in Fig. 12.6(a) for now. The voltages $\mathbf{V}_{an}$, $\mathbf{V}_{bn}$, and $\mathbf{V}_{cn}$ are respectively between lines a, b, and c,

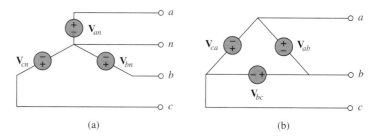

(a)   (b)

Figure 12.6   Three-phase voltage sources: (a) Y-connected source, (b) Δ-connected source.

(a)

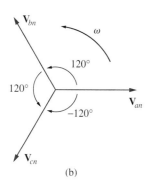

(b)

Figure 12.7   Phase sequences:
(a) *abc* or positive sequence,
(b) *acb* or negative sequence.

As a common tradition in power systems, voltage and current in this chapter are in rms values unless otherwise stated.

and the neutral line *n*. These voltages are called *phase voltages*. If the voltage sources have the same amplitude and frequency ω and are out of phase with each other by 120°, the voltages are said to be *balanced*. This implies that

$$\mathbf{V}_{an} + \mathbf{V}_{bn} + \mathbf{V}_{cn} = 0 \qquad (12.1)$$

$$|\mathbf{V}_{an}| = |\mathbf{V}_{bn}| = |\mathbf{V}_{cn}| \qquad (12.2)$$

Thus,

> Balanced phase voltages are equal in magnitude and are out of phase with each other by 120°.

Since the three-phase voltages are 120° out of phase with each other, there are two possible combinations. One possibility is shown in Fig. 12.7(a) and expressed mathematically as

$$\mathbf{V}_{an} = V_p \underline{/0°}$$
$$\mathbf{V}_{bn} = V_p \underline{/-120°} \qquad (12.3)$$
$$\mathbf{V}_{cn} = V_p \underline{/-240°} = V_p \underline{/+120°}$$

where V_p is the effective or rms value of the phase voltages. This is known as the *abc sequence* or *positive sequence*. In this phase sequence, $\mathbf{V}_{an}$ leads $\mathbf{V}_{bn}$, which in turn leads $\mathbf{V}_{cn}$. This sequence is produced when the rotor in Fig. 12.4 rotates counterclockwise. The other possibility is shown in Fig. 12.7(b) and is given by

$$\mathbf{V}_{an} = V_p \underline{/0°}$$
$$\mathbf{V}_{cn} = V_p \underline{/-120°} \qquad (12.4)$$
$$\mathbf{V}_{bn} = V_p \underline{/-240°} = V_p \underline{/+120°}$$

This is called the *acb sequence* or *negative sequence*. For this phase sequence, $\mathbf{V}_{an}$ leads $\mathbf{V}_{cn}$, which in turn leads $\mathbf{V}_{bn}$. The *acb* sequence is produced when the rotor in Fig. 12.4 rotates in the clockwise direction. It is easy to show that the voltages in Eqs. (12.3) or (12.4) satisfy Eqs. (12.1) and (12.2). For example, from Eq. (12.3),

$$\mathbf{V}_{an} + \mathbf{V}_{bn} + \mathbf{V}_{cn} = V_p\angle 0° + V_p\angle{-120°} + V_p\angle{+120°}$$

$$= V_p(1.0 - 0.5 - j0.866 - 0.5 + j0.866) \quad (12.5)$$

$$= 0$$

The phase sequence is the time order in which the voltages pass through their respective maximum values.

The phase sequence may also be regarded as the order in which the phase voltages reach their peak (or maximum) values with respect to time.

The phase sequence is determined by the order in which the phasors pass through a fixed point in the phase diagram.

In Fig. 12.7(a), as the phasors rotate in the counterclockwise direction with frequency ω, they pass through the horizontal axis in a sequence *abcabca* .... Thus, the sequence is *abc* or *bca* or *cab*. Similarly, for the phasors in Fig. 12.7(b), as they rotate in the counterclockwise direction, they pass the horizontal axis in a sequence *acbacba* .... This describes the *acb* sequence. The phase sequence is important in three-phase power distribution. It determines the direction of the rotation of a motor connected to the power source, for example.

Reminder: As time increases, each phasor (or sinor) rotates at an angular velocity ω.

Like the generator connections, a three-phase load can be either wye-connected or delta-connected, depending on the end application. Figure 12.8(a) shows a wye-connected load, and Fig. 12.8(b) shows a delta-connected load. The neutral line in Fig. 12.8(a) may or may not be there, depending on whether the system is four- or three-wire. (And, of course, a neutral connection is topologically impossible for a delta connection.) A wye- or delta-connected load is said to be *unbalanced* if the phase impedances are not equal in magnitude or phase.

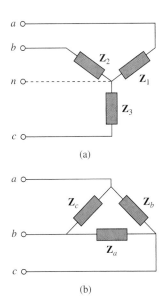

A balanced load is one in which the phase impedances are equal in magnitude and in phase.

Figure 12.8   Two possible three-phase load configurations: (a) a Y-connected load, (b) a Δ-connected load

For a *balanced* wye-connected load,

$$\mathbf{Z}_1 = \mathbf{Z}_2 = \mathbf{Z}_3 = \mathbf{Z}_Y \quad (12.6)$$

where $\mathbf{Z}_Y$ is the load impedance per phase. For a *balanced* delta-connected load,

$$\mathbf{Z}_a = \mathbf{Z}_b = \mathbf{Z}_c = \mathbf{Z}_\Delta \quad (12.7)$$

where $\mathbf{Z}_\Delta$ is the load impedance per phase in this case. We recall from Eq. (9.69) that

$$\mathbf{Z}_\Delta = 3\mathbf{Z}_Y \quad \text{or} \quad \mathbf{Z}_Y = \frac{1}{3}\mathbf{Z}_\Delta \quad (12.8)$$

so we know that a wye-connected load can be transformed into a delta-connected load, or vice versa, using Eq. (12.8).

Reminder: A Y-connected load consists of three impedances connected to a neutral node, while a Δ-connected load consists of three impedances connected around a loop. The load is balanced when the three impedances are equal in either case.

Since both the three-phase source and the three-phase load can be either wye- or delta-connected, we have four possible connections:

- Y-Y connection (i.e., Y-connected source with a Y-connected load).
- Y-Δ connection.
- Δ-Δ connection.
- Δ-Y connection.

In subsequent sections, we will consider each of these possible configurations.

It is appropriate to mention here that a balanced delta-connected load is more common than a balanced wye-connected load. This is due to the ease with which loads may be added or removed from each phase of a delta-connected load. This is very difficult with a wye-connected load because the neutral may not be accessible. On the other hand, delta-connected sources are not common in practice because of the circulating current that will result in the delta-mesh if the three-phase voltages are slightly unbalanced.

EXAMPLE 12.1

Determine the phase sequence of the set of voltages

$$v_{an} = 200\cos(\omega t + 10°)$$
$$v_{bn} = 200\cos(\omega t - 230°), \qquad v_{cn} = 200\cos(\omega t - 110°)$$

Solution:

The voltages can be expressed in phasor form as

$$\mathbf{V}_{an} = 200\underline{/10°}, \qquad \mathbf{V}_{bn} = 200\underline{/-230°}, \qquad \mathbf{V}_{cn} = 200\underline{/-110°}$$

We notice that $\mathbf{V}_{an}$ leads $\mathbf{V}_{cn}$ by 120° and $\mathbf{V}_{cn}$ in turn leads $\mathbf{V}_{bn}$ by 120°. Hence, we have an *acb* sequence.

PRACTICE PROBLEM 12.1

Given that $\mathbf{V}_{bn} = 110\underline{/30°}$, find $\mathbf{V}_{an}$ and $\mathbf{V}_{cn}$, assuming a positive (*abc*) sequence.

Answer: $110\underline{/150°}$, $110\underline{/-90°}$.

12.3   BALANCED WYE-WYE CONNECTION

We begin with the Y-Y system, because any balanced three-phase system can be reduced to an equivalent Y-Y system. Therefore, analysis of this system should be regarded as the key to solving all balanced three-phase systems.

> A balanced Y-Y system is a three-phase system with a balanced Y-connected source and a balanced Y-connected load.

Consider the balanced four-wire Y-Y system of Fig. 12.9, where a Y-connected load is connected to a Y-connected source. We assume a balanced load so that load impedances are equal. Although the impedance $\mathbf{Z}_Y$ is the total load impedance per phase, it may also be regarded as the sum of the source impedance $\mathbf{Z}_s$, line impedance $\mathbf{Z}_\ell$, and load impedance $\mathbf{Z}_L$ for each phase, since these impedances are in series. As illustrated in Fig. 12.9, $\mathbf{Z}_s$ denotes the internal impedance of the phase winding of the generator; $\mathbf{Z}_\ell$ is the impedance of the line joining a phase of the source with a phase of the load; $\mathbf{Z}_L$ is the impedance of each phase of the load; and $\mathbf{Z}_n$ is the impedance of the neutral line. Thus, in general

$$\mathbf{Z}_Y = \mathbf{Z}_s + \mathbf{Z}_\ell + \mathbf{Z}_L \qquad (12.9)$$

$\mathbf{Z}_s$ and $\mathbf{Z}_\ell$ are often very small compared with $\mathbf{Z}_L$, so one can assume that $\mathbf{Z}_Y = \mathbf{Z}_L$ if no source or line impedance is given. In any event, by lumping the impedances together, the Y-Y system in Fig. 12.9 can be simplified to that shown in Fig. 12.10.

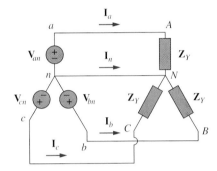

Figure 12.10   Balanced Y-Y connection.

Figure 12.9   A balanced Y-Y system, showing the source, line, and load impedances.

Assuming the positive sequence, the *phase* voltages (or line-to-neutral voltages) are

$$\mathbf{V}_{an} = V_p\underline{/0°}$$
$$\mathbf{V}_{bn} = V_p\underline{/-120°}, \qquad \mathbf{V}_{cn} = V_p\underline{/+120°} \qquad (12.10)$$

The *line-to-line* voltages or simply *line* voltages $\mathbf{V}_{ab}$, $\mathbf{V}_{bc}$, and $\mathbf{V}_{ca}$ are related to the phase voltages. For example,

$$\mathbf{V}_{ab} = \mathbf{V}_{an} + \mathbf{V}_{nb} = \mathbf{V}_{an} - \mathbf{V}_{bn} = V_p\underline{/0°} - V_p\underline{/-120°}$$
$$= V_p\left(1 + \frac{1}{2} + j\frac{\sqrt{3}}{2}\right) = \sqrt{3}V_p\underline{/30°} \qquad (12.11a)$$

Similarly, we can obtain

$$\mathbf{V}_{bc} = \mathbf{V}_{bn} - \mathbf{V}_{cn} = \sqrt{3}V_p\underline{/-90°} \qquad (12.11b)$$

$$\mathbf{V}_{ca} = \mathbf{V}_{cn} - \mathbf{V}_{an} = \sqrt{3}V_p\underline{/-210°} \qquad (12.11c)$$

Thus, the magnitude of the line voltages V_L is $\sqrt{3}$ times the magnitude of the phase voltages V_p, or

$$\boxed{V_L = \sqrt{3}V_p} \qquad (12.12)$$

where

$$V_p = |\mathbf{V}_{an}| = |\mathbf{V}_{bn}| = |\mathbf{V}_{cn}| \qquad (12.13)$$

and

$$V_L = |\mathbf{V}_{ab}| = |\mathbf{V}_{bc}| = |\mathbf{V}_{ca}| \qquad (12.14)$$

Also the line voltages lead their corresponding phase voltages by $30°$. Figure 12.11(a) illustrates this. Figure 12.11(a) also shows how to determine $\mathbf{V}_{ab}$ from the phase voltages, while Fig. 12.11(b) shows the same for the three line voltages. Notice that $\mathbf{V}_{ab}$ leads $\mathbf{V}_{bc}$ by $120°$, and $\mathbf{V}_{bc}$ leads $\mathbf{V}_{ca}$ by $120°$, so that the line voltages sum up to zero as do the phase voltages.

Applying KVL to each phase in Fig. 12.10, we obtain the line currents as

$$\mathbf{I}_a = \frac{\mathbf{V}_{an}}{\mathbf{Z}_Y}, \qquad \mathbf{I}_b = \frac{\mathbf{V}_{bn}}{\mathbf{Z}_Y} = \frac{\mathbf{V}_{an}\underline{/-120°}}{\mathbf{Z}_Y} = \mathbf{I}_a\underline{/-120°}$$

$$\mathbf{I}_c = \frac{\mathbf{V}_{cn}}{\mathbf{Z}_Y} = \frac{\mathbf{V}_{an}\underline{/-240°}}{\mathbf{Z}_Y} = \mathbf{I}_a\underline{/-240°} \qquad (12.15)$$

We can readily infer that the line currents add up to zero,

$$\mathbf{I}_a + \mathbf{I}_b + \mathbf{I}_c = 0 \qquad (12.16)$$

so that

$$\mathbf{I}_n = -(\mathbf{I}_a + \mathbf{I}_b + \mathbf{I}_c) = 0 \qquad (12.17a)$$

or

$$\mathbf{V}_{nN} = \mathbf{Z}_n\mathbf{I}_n = 0 \qquad (12.17b)$$

that is, the voltage across the neutral wire is zero. The neutral line can thus be removed without affecting the system. In fact, in long distance power transmission, conductors in multiples of three are used with the earth itself acting as the neutral conductor. Power systems designed in this way are well grounded at all critical points to ensure safety.

While the *line* current is the current in each line, the *phase* current is the current in each phase of the source or load. In the Y-Y system, the line current is the same as the phase current. We will use single subscripts for line currents because it is natural and conventional to assume that line currents flow from the source to the load.

An alternative way of analyzing a balanced Y-Y system is to do so on a "per phase" basis. We look at one phase, say phase a, and analyze the single-phase equivalent circuit in Fig. 12.12. The single-phase analysis yields the line current $\mathbf{I}_a$ as

$$\boxed{\mathbf{I}_a = \frac{\mathbf{V}_{an}}{\mathbf{Z}_Y}} \qquad (12.18)$$

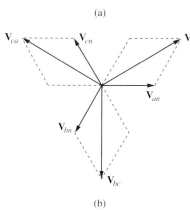

Figure 12.11   Phasor diagrams illustrating the relationship between line voltages and phase voltages.

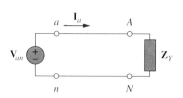

Figure 12.12   A single-phase equivalent circuit.

From $\mathbf{I}_a$, we use the phase sequence to obtain other line currents. Thus, as long as the system is balanced, we need only analyze one phase. We may do this even if the neutral line is absent, as in the three-wire system.

EXAMPLE 12.2

Calculate the line currents in the three-wire Y-Y system of Fig. 12.13.

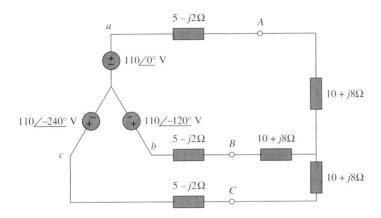

Figure 12.13   Three-wire Y-Y system; for Example 12.2.

Solution:

The three-phase circuit in Fig. 12.13 is balanced; we may replace it with its single-phase equivalent circuit such as in Fig. 12.12. We obtain $\mathbf{I}_a$ from the single-phase analysis as

$$\mathbf{I}_a = \frac{\mathbf{V}_{an}}{\mathbf{Z}_Y}$$

where $\mathbf{Z}_Y = (5 - j2) + (10 + j8) = 15 + j6 = 16.155\underline{/21.8°}$. Hence,

$$\mathbf{I}_a = \frac{110\underline{/0°}}{16.155\underline{/21.8°}} = 6.81\underline{/-21.8°} \text{ A}$$

Since the source voltages in Fig. 12.13 are in positive sequence and the line currents are also in positive sequence,

$$\mathbf{I}_b = \mathbf{I}_a\underline{/-120°} = 6.81\underline{/-141.8°} \text{ A}$$

$$\mathbf{I}_c = \mathbf{I}_a\underline{/-240°} = 6.81\underline{/-261.8°} \text{ A} = 6.81\underline{/98.2°} \text{ A}$$

PRACTICE PROBLEM 12.2

A Y-connected balanced three-phase generator with an impedance of $0.4 + j0.3$ Ω per phase is connected to a Y-connected balanced load with an impedance of $24 + j19$ Ω per phase. The line joining the generator and the load has an impedance of $0.6 + j0.7$ Ω per phase. Assuming a positive sequence for the source voltages and that $\mathbf{V}_{an} = 120\underline{/30°}$ V, find: (a) the line voltages, (b) the line currents.

Answer: (a) $207.85\underline{/60°}$ V, $207.85\underline{/-60°}$ V, $207.85\underline{/-180°}$ V, (b) $3.75\underline{/-8.66°}$ A, $3.75\underline{/-128.66°}$ A, $3.75\underline{/-248.66°}$ A.

12.4 BALANCED WYE-DELTA CONNECTION

A balanced Y-$\triangle$ system consists of a balanced Y-connected source feeding a balanced $\triangle$-connected load.

This is perhaps the most practical three-phase system, as the three-phase sources are usually Y-connected while the three-phase loads are usually $\triangle$-connected.

The balanced Y-delta system is shown in Fig. 12.14, where the source is wye-connected and the load is $\triangle$-connected. There is, of course, no neutral connection from source to load for this case. Assuming the positive sequence, the phase voltages are again

$$\mathbf{V}_{an} = V_p\underline{/0°}$$
$$\mathbf{V}_{bn} = V_p\underline{/-120°}, \qquad \mathbf{V}_{cn} = V_p\underline{/+120°} \tag{12.19}$$

As shown in Section 12.3, the line voltages are

$$\mathbf{V}_{ab} = \sqrt{3}V_p\underline{/30°} = \mathbf{V}_{AB}, \qquad \mathbf{V}_{bc} = \sqrt{3}V_p\underline{/-90°} = \mathbf{V}_{BC}$$
$$\mathbf{V}_{ca} = \sqrt{3}V_p\underline{/-210°} = \mathbf{V}_{CA} \tag{12.20}$$

showing that the line voltages are equal to the voltages across the load impedances for this system configuration. From these voltages, we can obtain the phase currents as

$$\mathbf{I}_{AB} = \frac{\mathbf{V}_{AB}}{\mathbf{Z}_\triangle}, \qquad \mathbf{I}_{BC} = \frac{\mathbf{V}_{BC}}{\mathbf{Z}_\triangle}, \qquad \mathbf{I}_{CA} = \frac{\mathbf{V}_{CA}}{\mathbf{Z}_\triangle} \tag{12.21}$$

These currents have the same magnitude but are out of phase with each other by 120°.

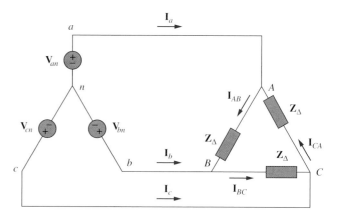

Figure 12.14   Balanced Y-$\triangle$ connection.

Another way to get these phase currents is to apply KVL. For example, applying KVL around loop $aABbna$ gives

$$-\mathbf{V}_{an} + \mathbf{Z}_\Delta \mathbf{I}_{AB} + \mathbf{V}_{bn} = 0$$

or

$$\mathbf{I}_{AB} = \frac{\mathbf{V}_{an} - \mathbf{V}_{bn}}{\mathbf{Z}_\Delta} = \frac{\mathbf{V}_{ab}}{\mathbf{Z}_\Delta} = \frac{\mathbf{V}_{AB}}{\mathbf{Z}_\Delta} \qquad (12.22)$$

which is the same as Eq. (12.21). This is the more general way of finding the phase currents.

The line currents are obtained from the phase currents by applying KCL at nodes A, B, and C. Thus,

$$\mathbf{I}_a = \mathbf{I}_{AB} - \mathbf{I}_{CA}, \qquad \mathbf{I}_b = \mathbf{I}_{BC} - \mathbf{I}_{AB}, \qquad \mathbf{I}_c = \mathbf{I}_{CA} - \mathbf{I}_{BC} \qquad (12.23)$$

Since $\mathbf{I}_{CA} = \mathbf{I}_{AB}\underline{/-240^\circ}$,

$$\mathbf{I}_a = \mathbf{I}_{AB} - \mathbf{I}_{CA} = \mathbf{I}_{AB}(1 - 1\underline{/-240^\circ})$$
$$= \mathbf{I}_{AB}(1 + 0.5 - j0.866) = \mathbf{I}_{AB}\sqrt{3}\underline{/-30^\circ} \qquad (12.24)$$

showing that the magnitude I_L of the line current is $\sqrt{3}$ times the magnitude I_p of the phase current, or

$$\boxed{I_L = \sqrt{3}I_p} \qquad (12.25)$$

where

$$I_L = |\mathbf{I}_a| = |\mathbf{I}_b| = |\mathbf{I}_c| \qquad (12.26)$$

and

$$I_p = |\mathbf{I}_{AB}| = |\mathbf{I}_{BC}| = |\mathbf{I}_{CA}| \qquad (12.27)$$

Also, the line currents lag the corresponding phase currents by 30°, assuming the positive sequence. Figure 12.15 is a phasor diagram illustrating the relationship between the phase and line currents.

An alternative way of analyzing the Y-Δ circuit is to transform the Δ-connected load to an equivalent Y-connected load. Using the Δ-Y transformation formula in Eq. (9.69),

$$\boxed{\mathbf{Z}_Y = \frac{\mathbf{Z}_\Delta}{3}} \qquad (12.28)$$

After this transformation, we now have a Y-Y system as in Fig. 12.10. The three-phase Y-Δ system in Fig. 12.14 can be replaced by the single-phase equivalent circuit in Fig. 12.16. This allows us to calculate only the line currents. The phase currents are obtained using Eq. (12.25) and utilizing the fact that each of the phase currents leads the corresponding line current by 30°.

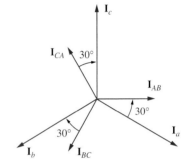

Figure 12.15   Phasor diagram illustrating the relationship between phase and line currents.

Figure 12.16   A single-phase equivalent circuit of a balanced Y-Δ circuit.

EXAMPLE 12.3

A balanced abc-sequence Y-connected source with $\mathbf{V}_{an} = 100\underline{/10^\circ}$ V is connected to a Δ-connected balanced load $(8 + j4)$ Ω per phase. Calculate the phase and line currents.

Solution:

This can be solved in two ways.

METHOD **1** The load impedance is

$$\mathbf{Z}_\Delta = 8 + j4 = 8.944\underline{/26.57°}\ \Omega$$

If the phase voltage $\mathbf{V}_{an} = 100\underline{/10°}$, then the line voltage is

$$\mathbf{V}_{ab} = \mathbf{V}_{an}\sqrt{3}\underline{/30°} = 100\sqrt{3}\underline{/10° + 30°} = \mathbf{V}_{AB}$$

or

$$\mathbf{V}_{AB} = 173.2\underline{/40°}\ \text{V}$$

The phase currents are

$$\mathbf{I}_{AB} = \frac{\mathbf{V}_{AB}}{\mathbf{Z}_\Delta} = \frac{173.2\underline{/40°}}{8.944\underline{/26.57°}} = 19.36\underline{/13.43°}\ \text{A}$$

$$\mathbf{I}_{BC} = \mathbf{I}_{AB}\underline{/-120°} = 19.36\underline{/-106.57°}\ \text{A}$$

$$\mathbf{I}_{CA} = \mathbf{I}_{AB}\underline{/+120°} = 19.36\underline{/133.43°}\ \text{A}$$

The line currents are

$$\mathbf{I}_a = \mathbf{I}_{AB}\sqrt{3}\underline{/-30°} = \sqrt{3}(19.36)\underline{/13.43° - 30°}$$

$$= 33.53\underline{/-16.57°}\ \text{A}$$

$$\mathbf{I}_b = \mathbf{I}_a\underline{/-120°} = 33.53\underline{/-136.57°}\ \text{A}$$

$$\mathbf{I}_c = \mathbf{I}_a\underline{/+120°} = 33.53\underline{/103.43°}\ \text{A}$$

METHOD **2** Alternatively, using single-phase analysis,

$$\mathbf{I}_a = \frac{\mathbf{V}_{an}}{\mathbf{Z}_\Delta/3} = \frac{100\underline{/10°}}{2.981\underline{/26.57°}} = 33.54\underline{/-16.57°}\ \text{A}$$

as above. Other line currents are obtained using the *abc* phase sequence.

PRACTICE PROBLEM 12.3

One line voltage of a balanced Y-connected source is $\mathbf{V}_{AB} = 180\underline{/-20°}$ V. If the source is connected to a Δ-connected load of $20\underline{/40°}\ \Omega$, find the phase and line currents. Assume the *abc* sequence.

Answer:
$9\underline{/-60°}$, $9\underline{/-180°}$, $9\underline{/60°}$, $15.59\underline{/-90°}$, $15.59\underline{/-210°}$, $15.59\underline{/30°}$ A.

12.5 BALANCED DELTA-DELTA CONNECTION

A balanced $\triangle$-$\triangle$ system is one in which both the balanced source and balanced load are $\triangle$-connected.

The source as well as the load may be delta-connected as shown in Fig. 12.17. Our goal is to obtain the phase and line currents as usual. Assuming a positive sequence, the phase voltages for a delta-connected source are

$$\mathbf{V}_{ab} = V_p\underline{/0^\circ}$$
$$\mathbf{V}_{bc} = V_p\underline{/-120^\circ}, \qquad \mathbf{V}_{ca} = V_p\underline{/+120^\circ} \tag{12.29}$$

The line voltages are the same as the phase voltages. From Fig. 12.17, assuming there is no line impedances, the phase voltages of the delta-connected source are equal to the voltages across the impedances; that is,

$$\mathbf{V}_{ab} = \mathbf{V}_{AB}, \qquad \mathbf{V}_{bc} = \mathbf{V}_{BC}, \qquad \mathbf{V}_{ca} = \mathbf{V}_{CA} \tag{12.30}$$

Hence, the phase currents are

$$\mathbf{I}_{AB} = \frac{\mathbf{V}_{AB}}{\mathbf{Z}_\Delta} = \frac{\mathbf{V}_{ab}}{\mathbf{Z}_\Delta}, \qquad \mathbf{I}_{BC} = \frac{\mathbf{V}_{BC}}{\mathbf{Z}_\Delta} = \frac{\mathbf{V}_{bc}}{\mathbf{Z}_\Delta}$$
$$\mathbf{I}_{CA} = \frac{\mathbf{V}_{CA}}{\mathbf{Z}_\Delta} = \frac{\mathbf{V}_{ca}}{\mathbf{Z}_\Delta} \tag{12.31}$$

Since the load is delta-connected just as in the previous section, some of the formulas derived there apply here. The line currents are obtained from the phase currents by applying KCL at nodes A, B, and C, as we did in the previous section:

$$\mathbf{I}_a = \mathbf{I}_{AB} - \mathbf{I}_{CA}, \qquad \mathbf{I}_b = \mathbf{I}_{BC} - \mathbf{I}_{AB}, \qquad \mathbf{I}_c = \mathbf{I}_{CA} - \mathbf{I}_{BC} \tag{12.32}$$

Also, as shown in the last section, each line current lags the corresponding phase current by 30°; the magnitude I_L of the line current is $\sqrt{3}$ times the magnitude I_p of the phase current,

$$I_L = \sqrt{3}I_p \tag{12.33}$$

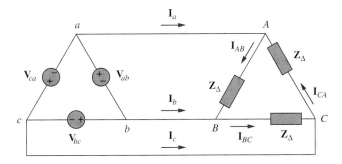

Figure 12.17   A balanced Δ-Δ connection.

An alternative way of analyzing the Δ-Δ circuit is to convert both the source and the load to their Y equivalents. We already know that $\mathbf{Z}_Y = \mathbf{Z}_\Delta/3$. To convert a Δ-connected source to a Y-connected source, see the next section.

EXAMPLE 12.4

A balanced $\triangle$-connected load having an impedance $20 - j15 \ \Omega$ is connected to a $\triangle$-connected, positive-sequence generator having $\mathbf{V}_{ab} = 330\underline{/0°}$ V. Calculate the phase currents of the load and the line currents.

Solution:

The load impedance per phase is

$$\mathbf{Z}_\triangle = 20 - j15 = 25\underline{/-36.87°} \ \Omega$$

Since $\mathbf{V}_{AB} = \mathbf{V}_{ab}$, the phase currents are

$$\mathbf{I}_{AB} = \frac{\mathbf{V}_{AB}}{\mathbf{Z}_\triangle} = \frac{330\underline{/0°}}{25\underline{/-36.87}} = 13.2\underline{/36.87°} \ \text{A}$$

$$\mathbf{I}_{BC} = \mathbf{I}_{AB}\underline{/-120°} = 13.2\underline{/-83.13°} \ \text{A}$$

$$\mathbf{I}_{CA} = \mathbf{I}_{AB}\underline{/+120°} = 13.2\underline{/156.87°} \ \text{A}$$

For a delta load, the line current always lags the corresponding phase current by 30° and has a magnitude $\sqrt{3}$ times that of the phase current. Hence, the line currents are

$$\mathbf{I}_a = \mathbf{I}_{AB}\sqrt{3}\underline{/-30°} = (13.2\underline{/36.87°})(\sqrt{3}\underline{/-30°})$$

$$= 22.86\underline{/6.87°} \ \text{A}$$

$$\mathbf{I}_b = \mathbf{I}_a\underline{/-120°} = 22.86\underline{/-113.13°} \ \text{A}$$

$$\mathbf{I}_c = \mathbf{I}_a\underline{/+120°} = 22.86\underline{/126.87°} \ \text{A}$$

PRACTICE PROBLEM 12.4

A positive-sequence, balanced $\triangle$-connected source supplies a balanced $\triangle$-connected load. If the impedance per phase of the load is $18 + j12 \ \Omega$ and $\mathbf{I}_a = 22.5\underline{/35°}$ A, find $\mathbf{I}_{AB}$ and $\mathbf{V}_{AB}$.

Answer: $13\underline{/65°}$ A, $281.2\underline{/98.69°}$ V.

12.6   BALANCED DELTA-WYE CONNECTION

A balanced $\triangle$-Y system consists of a balanced $\triangle$-connected source feeding a balanced Y-connected load.

Consider the $\triangle$-Y circuit in Fig. 12.18. Again, assuming the abc sequence, the phase voltages of a delta-connected source are

$$\mathbf{V}_{ab} = V_p\underline{/0°}, \qquad \mathbf{V}_{bc} = V_p\underline{/-120°}$$

$$\mathbf{V}_{ca} = V_p\underline{/+120°} \tag{12.34}$$

These are also the line voltages as well as the phase voltages.

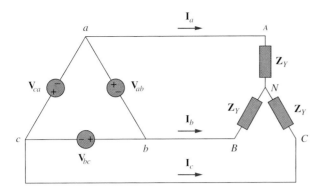

Figure 12.18   A balanced Δ-Y connection.

We can obtain the line currents in many ways. One way is to apply KVL to loop $aANBba$ in Fig. 12.18, writing

$$-\mathbf{V}_{ab} + \mathbf{Z}_Y \mathbf{I}_a - \mathbf{Z}_Y \mathbf{I}_b = 0$$

or

$$\mathbf{Z}_Y(\mathbf{I}_a - \mathbf{I}_b) = \mathbf{V}_{ab} = V_p \underline{/0°}$$

Thus,

$$\mathbf{I}_a - \mathbf{I}_b = \frac{V_p \underline{/0°}}{\mathbf{Z}_Y} \qquad (12.35)$$

But $\mathbf{I}_b$ lags $\mathbf{I}_a$ by 120°, since we assumed the *abc* sequence; that is, $\mathbf{I}_b = \mathbf{I}_a \underline{/-120°}$. Hence,

$$\mathbf{I}_a - \mathbf{I}_b = \mathbf{I}_a(1 - 1\underline{/-120°})$$
$$= \mathbf{I}_a\left(1 + \frac{1}{2} + j\frac{\sqrt{3}}{2}\right) = \mathbf{I}_a\sqrt{3}\underline{/30°} \qquad (12.36)$$

Substituting Eq. (12.36) into Eq. (12.35) gives

$$\mathbf{I}_a = \frac{V_p/\sqrt{3}\underline{/-30°}}{\mathbf{Z}_Y} \qquad (12.37)$$

From this, we obtain the other line currents $\mathbf{I}_b$ and $\mathbf{I}_c$ using the positive phase sequence, i.e., $\mathbf{I}_b = \mathbf{I}_a\underline{/-120°}$, $\mathbf{I}_c = \mathbf{I}_a\underline{/+120°}$. The phase currents are equal to the line currents.

Another way to obtain the line currents is to replace the delta-connected source with its equivalent wye-connected source, as shown in Fig. 12.19. In Section 12.3, we found that the line-to-line voltages of a wye-connected source lead their corresponding phase voltages by 30°. Therefore, we obtain each phase voltage of the equivalent wye-connected source by dividing the corresponding line voltage of the delta-connected source by $\sqrt{3}$ and shifting its phase by $-30°$. Thus, the equivalent wye-connected source has the phase voltages

$$\mathbf{V}_{an} = \frac{V_p}{\sqrt{3}}\underline{/-30°}$$

$$\mathbf{V}_{bn} = \frac{V_p}{\sqrt{3}}\underline{/-150°}, \qquad \mathbf{V}_{cn} = \frac{V_p}{\sqrt{3}}\underline{/+90°} \qquad (12.38)$$

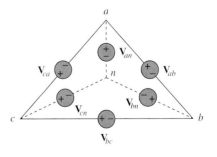

Figure 12.19   Transforming a Δ-connected source to an equivalent Y-connected source.

If the delta-connected source has source impedance $\mathbf{Z}_s$ per phase, the equivalent wye-connected source will have a source impedance of $\mathbf{Z}_s/3$ per phase, according to Eq. (9.69).

Once the source is transformed to wye, the circuit becomes a wye-wye system. Therefore, we can use the equivalent single-phase circuit shown in Fig. 12.20, from which the line current for phase a is

$$\mathbf{I}_a = \frac{V_p/\sqrt{3}\underline{/-30^\circ}}{\mathbf{Z}_Y} \tag{12.39}$$

which is the same as Eq. (12.37).

Alternatively, we may transform the wye-connected load to an equivalent delta-connected load. This results in a delta-delta system, which can be analyzed as in Section 12.5. Note that

$$\mathbf{V}_{AN} = \mathbf{I}_a\mathbf{Z}_Y = \frac{V_p}{\sqrt{3}}\underline{/-30^\circ} \tag{12.40}$$

$$\mathbf{V}_{BN} = \mathbf{V}_{AN}\underline{/-120^\circ}, \qquad \mathbf{V}_{CN} = \mathbf{V}_{AN}\underline{/+120^\circ}$$

As stated earlier, the delta-connected load is more desirable than the wye-connected load. It is easier to alter the loads in any one phase of the delta-connected loads, as the individual loads are connected directly across the lines. However, the delta-connected source is hardly used in practice, because any slight imbalance in the phase voltages will result in unwanted circulating currents.

Table 12.1 presents a summary of the formulas for phase currents and voltages and line currents and voltages for the four connections. Students are advised not to memorize the formulas but to understand

Figure 12.20　The single-phase equivalent circuit.

TABLE 12.1　Summary of phase and line voltages/currents for balanced three-phase systems[1].

Connection	Phase voltages/currents	Line voltages/currents
Y-Y	$\mathbf{V}_{an} = V_p\underline{/0^\circ}$	$\mathbf{V}_{ab} = \sqrt{3}V_p\underline{/30^\circ}$
	$\mathbf{V}_{bn} = V_p\underline{/-120^\circ}$	$\mathbf{V}_{bc} = \mathbf{V}_{ab}\underline{/-120^\circ}$
	$\mathbf{V}_{cn} = V_p\underline{/+120^\circ}$	$\mathbf{V}_{ca} = \mathbf{V}_{ab}\underline{/+120^\circ}$
	Same as line currents	$\mathbf{I}_a = \mathbf{V}_{an}/\mathbf{Z}_Y$
		$\mathbf{I}_b = \mathbf{I}_a\underline{/-120^\circ}$
		$\mathbf{I}_c = \mathbf{I}_a\underline{/+120^\circ}$
Y-Δ	$\mathbf{V}_{an} = V_p\underline{/0^\circ}$	$\mathbf{V}_{ab} = \mathbf{V}_{AB} = \sqrt{3}V_p\underline{/30^\circ}$
	$\mathbf{V}_{bn} = V_p\underline{/-120^\circ}$	$\mathbf{V}_{bc} = \mathbf{V}_{BC} = \mathbf{V}_{ab}\underline{/-120^\circ}$
	$\mathbf{V}_{cn} = V_p\underline{/+120^\circ}$	$\mathbf{V}_{ca} = \mathbf{V}_{CA} = \mathbf{V}_{ab}\underline{/+120^\circ}$
	$\mathbf{I}_{AB} = \mathbf{V}_{AB}/\mathbf{Z}_\Delta$	$\mathbf{I}_a = \mathbf{I}_{AB}\sqrt{3}\underline{/-30^\circ}$
	$\mathbf{I}_{BC} = \mathbf{V}_{BC}/\mathbf{Z}_\Delta$	$\mathbf{I}_b = \mathbf{I}_a\underline{/-120^\circ}$
	$\mathbf{I}_{CA} = \mathbf{V}_{CA}/\mathbf{Z}_\Delta$	$\mathbf{I}_c = \mathbf{I}_a\underline{/+120^\circ}$

[1] *Positive or abc sequence is assumed.*

TABLE 12.1   (*continued*)

Connection	Phase voltages/currents	Line voltages/currents
Δ-Δ	$\mathbf{V}_{ab} = V_p\underline{/0°}$	Same as phase voltages
	$\mathbf{V}_{bc} = V_p\underline{/-120°}$	
	$\mathbf{V}_{ca} = V_p\underline{/+120°}$	
	$\mathbf{I}_{AB} = \mathbf{V}_{ab}/\mathbf{Z}_\Delta$	$\mathbf{I}_a = \mathbf{I}_{AB}\sqrt{3}\underline{/-30°}$
	$\mathbf{I}_{BC} = \mathbf{V}_{bc}/\mathbf{Z}_\Delta$	$\mathbf{I}_b = \mathbf{I}_a\underline{/-120°}$
	$\mathbf{I}_{CA} = \mathbf{V}_{ca}/\mathbf{Z}_\Delta$	$\mathbf{I}_c = \mathbf{I}_a\underline{/+120°}$
Δ-Y	$\mathbf{V}_{ab} = V_p\underline{/0°}$	Same as phase voltages
	$\mathbf{V}_{bc} = V_p\underline{/-120°}$	
	$\mathbf{V}_{ca} = V_p\underline{/+120°}$	
	Same as line currents	$\mathbf{I}_a = \dfrac{V_p\underline{/-30°}}{\sqrt{3}\mathbf{Z}_Y}$
		$\mathbf{I}_b = \mathbf{I}_a\underline{/-120°}$
		$\mathbf{I}_c = \mathbf{I}_a\underline{/+120°}$

how they are derived. The formulas can always be obtained by directly applying KCL and KVL to the appropriate three-phase circuits.

EXAMPLE 12.5

A balanced Y-connected load with a phase impedance of $40 + j25\ \Omega$ is supplied by a balanced, positive sequence Δ-connected source with a line voltage of 210 V. Calculate the phase currents. Use $\mathbf{V}_{ab}$ as reference.

Solution:

The load impedance is

$$\mathbf{Z}_Y = 40 + j25 = 47.17\underline{/32°}\ \Omega$$

and the source voltage is

$$\mathbf{V}_{ab} = 210\underline{/0°}\ \text{V}$$

When the Δ-connected source is transformed to a Y-connected source,

$$\mathbf{V}_{an} = \frac{\mathbf{V}_{ab}}{\sqrt{3}}\underline{/-30°} = 121.2\underline{/-30°}\ \text{V}$$

The line currents are

$$\mathbf{I}_a = \frac{\mathbf{V}_{an}}{\mathbf{Z}_Y} = \frac{121.2\underline{/-30°}}{47.12\underline{/32°}} = 2.57\underline{/-62°}\ \text{A}$$

$$\mathbf{I}_b = \mathbf{I}_a\underline{/-120°} = 2.57\underline{/-182°}\ \text{A}$$

$$\mathbf{I}_c = \mathbf{I}_a\underline{/120°} = 2.57\underline{/58°}\ \text{A}$$

which are the same as the phase currents.

PRACTICE PROBLEM 12.5

In a balanced Δ-Y circuit, $\mathbf{V}_{ab} = 240\underline{/15°}$ and $\mathbf{Z}_Y = (12 + j15) \, \Omega$. Calculate the line currents.

Answer: $7.21\underline{/-66.34°}, 7.21\underline{/-186.34°}, 7.21\underline{/53.66°}$ A.

12.7 POWER IN A BALANCED SYSTEM

Let us now consider the power in a balanced three-phase system. We begin by examining the instantaneous power absorbed by the load. This requires that the analysis be done in the time domain. For a Y-connected load, the phase voltages are

$$v_{AN} = \sqrt{2}V_p \cos \omega t, \qquad v_{BN} = \sqrt{2}V_p \cos(\omega t - 120°)$$
$$v_{CN} = \sqrt{2}V_p \cos(\omega t + 120°)$$

(12.41)

where the factor $\sqrt{2}$ is necessary because V_p has been defined as the rms value of the phase voltage. If $\mathbf{Z}_Y = Z\underline{/\theta}$, the phase currents lag behind their corresponding phase voltages by θ. Thus,

$$i_a = \sqrt{2}I_p \cos(\omega t - \theta), \qquad i_b = \sqrt{2}I_p \cos(\omega t - \theta - 120°)$$
$$i_c = \sqrt{2}I_p \cos(\omega t - \theta + 120°)$$

(12.42)

where I_p is the rms value of the phase current. The total instantaneous power in the load is the sum of the instantaneous powers in the three phases; that is,

$$\begin{aligned}
p &= p_a + p_b + p_c = v_{AN}i_a + v_{BN}i_b + v_{CN}i_c \\
&= 2V_p I_p[\cos \omega t \cos(\omega t - \theta) \\
&\qquad + \cos(\omega t - 120°) \cos(\omega t - \theta - 120°) \\
&\qquad + \cos(\omega t + 120°) \cos(\omega t - \theta + 120°)]
\end{aligned}$$

(12.43)

Applying the trigonometric identity

$$\cos A \cos B = \frac{1}{2} [\cos(A + B) + \cos(A - B)]$$

(12.44)

gives

$$\begin{aligned}
p &= V_p I_p[3 \cos \theta + \cos(2\omega t - \theta) + \cos(2\omega t - \theta - 240°) \\
&\qquad + \cos(2\omega t - \theta + 240°)] \\
&= V_p I_p[3 \cos \theta + \cos \alpha + \cos \alpha \cos 240° + \sin \alpha \sin 240° \\
&\qquad + \cos \alpha \cos 240° - \sin \alpha \sin 240°] \\
&\qquad \text{where } \alpha = 2\omega t - \theta \\
&= V_p I_p \left[3 \cos \theta + \cos \alpha + 2 \left(-\frac{1}{2} \right) \cos \alpha \right] = 3V_p I_p \cos \theta
\end{aligned}$$

(12.45)

Thus the total instantaneous power in a balanced three-phase system is constant—it does not change with time as the instantaneous power of each phase does. This result is true whether the load is Y- or Δ-connected. This is one important reason for using a three-phase system to generate and distribute power. We will look into another reason a little later.

Since the total instantaneous power is independent of time, the average power per phase P_p for either the Δ-connected load or the Y-connected load is $p/3$, or

$$P_p = V_p I_p \cos \theta \qquad (12.46)$$

and the reactive power per phase is

$$Q_p = V_p I_p \sin \theta \qquad (12.47)$$

The apparent power per phase is

$$S_p = V_p I_p \qquad (12.48)$$

The complex power per phase is

$$\mathbf{S}_p = P_p + j Q_p = \mathbf{V}_p \mathbf{I}_p^* \qquad (12.49)$$

where $\mathbf{V}_p$ and $\mathbf{I}_p$ are the phase voltage and phase current with magnitudes V_p and I_p, respectively. The total average power is the sum of the average powers in the phases:

$$P = P_a + P_b + P_c = 3P_p = 3V_p I_p \cos \theta = \sqrt{3} V_L I_L \cos \theta \qquad (12.50)$$

For a Y-connected load, $I_L = I_p$ but $V_L = \sqrt{3} V_p$, whereas for a Δ-connected load, $I_L = \sqrt{3} I_p$ but $V_L = V_p$. Thus, Eq. (12.50) applies for both Y-connected and Δ-connected loads. Similarly, the total reactive power is

$$Q = 3V_p I_p \sin \theta = 3Q_p = \sqrt{3} V_L I_L \sin \theta \qquad (12.51)$$

and the total complex power is

$$\boxed{\mathbf{S} = 3\mathbf{S}_p = 3\mathbf{V}_p \mathbf{I}_p^* = 3I_p^2 \mathbf{Z}_p = \frac{3V_p^2}{\mathbf{Z}_p^*}} \qquad (12.52)$$

where $\mathbf{Z}_p = Z_p \underline{/\theta}$ is the load impedance per phase. ($\mathbf{Z}_p$ could be $\mathbf{Z}_Y$ or $\mathbf{Z}_\Delta$.) Alternatively, we may write Eq. (12.52) as

$$\boxed{\mathbf{S} = P + jQ = \sqrt{3} V_L I_L \underline{/\theta}} \qquad (12.53)$$

Remember that V_p, I_p, V_L, and I_L are all rms values and that θ is the angle of the load impedance or the angle between the phase voltage and the phase current.

A second major advantage of three-phase systems for power distribution is that the three-phase system uses a lesser amount of wire than the single-phase system for the same line voltage V_L and the same absorbed power P_L. We will compare these cases and assume in both that the wires are of the same material (e.g., copper with resistivity ρ), of the same length ℓ, and that the loads are resistive (i.e., unity power factor). For the two-wire single-phase system in Fig. 12.21(a), $I_L = P_L/V_L$, so the power loss in the two wires is

$$P_{\text{loss}} = 2I_L^2 R = 2R \frac{P_L^2}{V_L^2} \qquad (12.54)$$

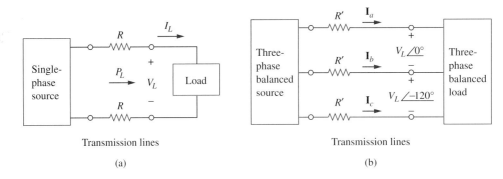

Figure 12.21   Comparing the power loss in (a) a single-phase system, and (b) a three-phase system.

For the three-wire three-phase system in Fig. 12.21(b), $I'_L = |\mathbf{I}_a| = |\mathbf{I}_b| = |\mathbf{I}_c| = P_L/\sqrt{3}V_L$ from Eq. (12.50). The power loss in the three wires is

$$P'_{\text{loss}} = 3(I'_L)^2 R' = 3R'\frac{P_L^2}{3V_L^2} = R'\frac{P_L^2}{V_L^2} \tag{12.55}$$

Equations (12.54) and (12.55) show that for the same total power delivered P_L and same line voltage V_L,

$$\frac{P_{\text{loss}}}{P'_{\text{loss}}} = \frac{2R}{R'} \tag{12.56}$$

But from Chapter 2, $R = \rho\ell/\pi r^2$ and $R' = \rho\ell/\pi r'^2$, where r and r' are the radii of the wires. Thus,

$$\frac{P_{\text{loss}}}{P'_{\text{loss}}} = \frac{2r'^2}{r^2} \tag{12.57}$$

If the same power loss is tolerated in both systems, then $r^2 = 2r'^2$. The ratio of material required is determined by the number of wires and their volumes, so

$$\frac{\text{Material for single-phase}}{\text{Material for three-phase}} = \frac{2(\pi r^2 \ell)}{3(\pi r'^2 \ell)} = \frac{2r^2}{3r'^2}$$

$$= \frac{2}{3}(2) = 1.333 \tag{12.58}$$

since $r^2 = 2r'^2$. Equation (12.58) shows that the single-phase system uses 33 percent more material than the three-phase system or that the three-phase system uses only 75 percent of the material used in the equivalent single-phase system. In other words, considerably less material is needed to deliver the same power with a three-phase system than is required for a single-phase system.

EXAMPLE 12.6

Refer to the circuit in Fig. 12.13 (in Example 12.2). Determine the total average power, reactive power, and complex power at the source and at the load.

Solution:

It is sufficient to consider one phase, as the system is balanced. For phase a,

$$\mathbf{V}_p = 110\underline{/0°} \text{ V} \qquad \text{and} \qquad \mathbf{I}_p = 6.81\underline{/-21.8°} \text{ A}$$

Thus, at the source, the complex power supplied is

$$\mathbf{S}_s = -3\mathbf{V}_p\mathbf{I}_p^* = -3(110\underline{/0°})(6.81\underline{/21.8°})$$

$$= -2247\underline{/21.8°} = -(2087 + j834.6) \text{ VA}$$

The real or average power supplied is -2087 W and the reactive power is -834.6 VAR.

At the load, the complex power absorbed is

$$\mathbf{S}_L = 3|\mathbf{I}_p|^2\mathbf{Z}_p$$

where $\mathbf{Z}_p = 10 + j8 = 12.81\underline{/38.66°}$ and $\mathbf{I}_p = \mathbf{I}_a = 6.81\underline{/-21.8°}$. Hence

$$\mathbf{S}_L = 3(6.81)^2 12.81\underline{/38.66°} = 1782\underline{/38.66}$$

$$= (1392 + j1113) \text{ VA}$$

The real power absorbed is 1391.7 W and the reactive power absorbed is 1113.3 VAR. The difference between the two complex powers is absorbed by the line impedance $(5 - j2)$ Ω. To show that this is the case, we find the complex power absorbed by the line as

$$\mathbf{S}_\ell = 3|\mathbf{I}_p|^2\mathbf{Z}_\ell = 3(6.81)^2(5 - j2) = 695.6 - j278.3 \text{ VA}$$

which is the difference between $\mathbf{S}_s$ and $\mathbf{S}_L$, that is, $\mathbf{S}_s + \mathbf{S}_\ell + \mathbf{S}_L = 0$, as expected.

PRACTICE PROBLEM 12.6

For the Y-Y circuit in Practice Prob. 12.2, calculate the complex power at the source and at the load.

Answer: $(1054 + j843.3)$ VA, $(1012 + j801.6)$ VA.

EXAMPLE 12.7

A three-phase motor can be regarded as a balanced Y-load. A three-phase motor draws 5.6 kW when the line voltage is 220 V and the line current is 18.2 A. Determine the power factor of the motor.

Solution:

The apparent power is

$$S = \sqrt{3}V_L I_L = \sqrt{3}(220)(18.2) = 6935.13 \text{ VA}$$

Since the real power is

$$P = S\cos\theta = 5600 \text{ W}$$

the power factor is

$$\text{pf} = \cos\theta = \frac{P}{S} = \frac{5600}{6935.13} = 0.8075$$

PRACTICE PROBLEM 12.7

Calculate the line current required for a 30-kW three-phase motor having a power factor of 0.85 lagging if it is connected to a balanced source with a line voltage of 440 V.

Answer: 46.31 A.

EXAMPLE 12.8

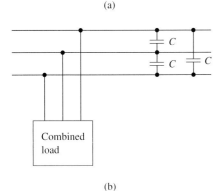

(a)

(b)

Figure 12.22   For Example 12.8: (a) The original balanced loads, (b) the combined load with improved power factor.

Two balanced loads are connected to a 240-kV rms 60-Hz line, as shown in Fig. 12.22(a). Load 1 draws 30 kW at a power factor of 0.6 lagging, while load 2 draws 45 kVAR at a power factor of 0.8 lagging. Assuming the *abc* sequence, determine: (a) the complex, real, and reactive powers absorbed by the combined load, (b) the line currents, and (c) the kVAR rating of the three capacitors Δ-connected in parallel with the load that will raise the power factor to 0.9 lagging and the capacitance of each capacitor.

Solution:

(a) For load 1, given that $P_1 = 30$ kW and $\cos\theta_1 = 0.6$, then $\sin\theta_1 = 0.8$. Hence,

$$S_1 = \frac{P_1}{\cos\theta_1} = \frac{30 \text{ kW}}{0.6} = 50 \text{ kVA}$$

and $Q_1 = S_1 \sin\theta_1 = 50(0.8) = 40$ kVAR. Thus, the complex power due to load 1 is

$$\mathbf{S}_1 = P_1 + jQ_1 = 30 + j40 \text{ kVA} \qquad (12.8.1)$$

For load 2, if $Q_2 = 45$ kVAR and $\cos\theta_2 = 0.8$, then $\sin\theta_2 = 0.6$. We find

$$S_2 = \frac{Q_2}{\sin\theta_2} = \frac{45 \text{ kVA}}{0.6} = 75 \text{ kVA}$$

and $P_2 = S_2 \cos\theta_2 = 75(0.8) = 60$ kW. Therefore the complex power due to load 2 is

$$\mathbf{S}_2 = P_2 + jQ_2 = 60 + j45 \text{ kVA} \qquad (12.8.2)$$

From Eqs. (12.8.1) and (12.8.2), the total complex power absorbed by the load is

$$\mathbf{S} = \mathbf{S}_1 + \mathbf{S}_2 = 90 + j85 \text{ kVA} = 123.8\underline{/43.36°} \text{ kVA} \qquad (12.8.3)$$

which has a power factor of $\cos 43.36° = 0.727$ lagging. The real power is then 90 kW, while the reactive power is 85 kVAR.

(b) Since $S = \sqrt{3} V_L I_L$, the line current is

$$I_L = \frac{S}{\sqrt{3} V_L} \qquad (12.8.4)$$

We apply this to each load, keeping in mind that for both loads, $V_L = 240$ kV. For load 1,

$$I_{L1} = \frac{50,000}{\sqrt{3}\,240,000} = 120.28 \text{ mA}$$

Since the power factor is lagging, the line current lags the line voltage by $\theta_1 = \cos^{-1} 0.6 = 53.13°$. Thus,

$$\mathbf{I}_{a1} = 120.28\underline{/-53.13°}$$

For load 2,

$$I_{L2} = \frac{75,000}{\sqrt{3}\,240,000} = 180.42 \text{ mA}$$

and the line current lags the line voltage by $\theta_2 = \cos^{-1} 0.8 = 36.87°$. Hence,

$$\mathbf{I}_{a2} = 180.42\underline{/-36.87°}$$

The total line current is

$$\mathbf{I}_a = \mathbf{I}_{a1} + \mathbf{I}_{a2} = 120.28\underline{/-53.13°} + 180.42\underline{/-36.87°}$$
$$= (72.168 - j96.224) + (144.336 - j108.252)$$
$$= 216.5 - j204.472 = 297.8\underline{/-43.36°} \text{ mA}$$

Alternatively, we could obtain the current from the total complex power using Eq. (12.8.4) as

$$I_L = \frac{123,800}{\sqrt{3}\,240,000} = 297.82 \text{ mA}$$

and

$$\mathbf{I}_a = 297.82\underline{/-43.36°} \text{ mA}$$

which is the same as before. The other line currents, $\mathbf{I}_{b2}$ and $\mathbf{I}_{ca}$, can be obtained according to the *abc* sequence (i.e., $\mathbf{I}_b = 297.82\underline{/-163.36°}$ mA and $\mathbf{I}_c = 297.82\underline{/76.64°}$ mA).

(c) We can find the reactive power needed to bring the power factor to 0.9 lagging using Eq. (11.59),

$$Q_C = P(\tan\theta_{\text{old}} - \tan\theta_{\text{new}})$$

where $P = 90$ kW, $\theta_{\text{old}} = 43.36°$, and $\theta_{\text{new}} = \cos^{-1} 0.9 = 25.84°$. Hence,

$$Q_C = 90,000(\tan 43.36° - \tan 25.84°) = 41.4 \text{ kVAR}$$

This reactive power is for the three capacitors. For each capacitor, the rating $Q'_C = 13.8$ kVAR. From Eq. (11.60), the required capacitance is

$$C = \frac{Q'_C}{\omega V_{\text{rms}}^2}$$

Since the capacitors are Δ-connected as shown in Fig. 12.22(b), V_{rms} in the above formula is the line-to-line or line voltage, which is 240 kV. Thus,

$$C = \frac{13,800}{(2\pi 60)(240,000)^2} = 635.5 \text{ pF}$$

PRACTICE PROBLEM 12.8

Assume that the two balanced loads in Fig. 12.22(a) are supplied by an 840-V rms 60-Hz line. Load 1 is Y-connected with $30 + j40\ \Omega$ per phase, while load 2 is a balanced three-phase motor drawing 48 kW at a power factor of 0.8 lagging. Assuming the *abc* sequence, calculate: (a) the complex power absorbed by the combined load, (b) the kVAR rating of each of the three capacitors Δ-connected in parallel with the load to raise the power factor to unity, and (c) the current drawn from the supply at unity power factor condition.

Answer: (a) $56.47 + j47.29$ kVA, (b) 15.7 kVAR, (c) 38.813 A.

†12.8 UNBALANCED THREE-PHASE SYSTEMS

This chapter would be incomplete without mentioning unbalanced three-phase systems. An unbalanced system is caused by two possible situations: (1) the source voltages are not equal in magnitude and/or differ in phase by angles that are unequal, or (2) load impedances are unequal. Thus,

> An unbalanced system is due to unbalanced voltage sources or an unbalanced load.

To simplify analysis, we will assume balanced source voltages, but an unbalanced load.

Unbalanced three-phase systems are solved by direct application of mesh and nodal analysis. Figure 12.23 shows an example of an unbalanced three-phase system that consists of balanced source voltages (not shown in the figure) and an unbalanced Y-connected load (shown in the figure). Since the load is unbalanced, $\mathbf{Z}_A$, $\mathbf{Z}_B$, and $\mathbf{Z}_C$ are not equal. The line currents are determined by Ohm's law as

$$\mathbf{I}_a = \frac{\mathbf{V}_{AN}}{\mathbf{Z}_A}, \qquad \mathbf{I}_b = \frac{\mathbf{V}_{BN}}{\mathbf{Z}_B}, \qquad \mathbf{I}_c = \frac{\mathbf{V}_{CN}}{\mathbf{Z}_C} \qquad (12.59)$$

This set of unbalanced line currents produces current in the neutral line, which is not zero as in a balanced system. Applying KCL at node N gives the neutral line current as

$$\mathbf{I}_n = -(\mathbf{I}_a + \mathbf{I}_b + \mathbf{I}_c) \qquad (12.60)$$

In a three-wire system where the neutral line is absent, we can still find the line currents $\mathbf{I}_a$, $\mathbf{I}_b$, and $\mathbf{I}_c$ using mesh analysis. At node N, KCL must be satisfied so that $\mathbf{I}_a + \mathbf{I}_b + \mathbf{I}_c = 0$ in this case. The same could be done for a Δ-Y, Y-Δ, or Δ-Δ three-wire system. As mentioned earlier, in long distance power transmission, conductors in multiples of three

A special technique for handling unbalanced three-phase systems is the method of *symmetrical components*, which is beyond the scope of this text.

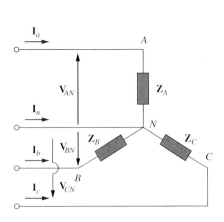

Figure 12.23   Unbalanced three-phase Y-connected load.

(multiple three-wire systems) are used, with the earth itself acting as the neutral conductor.

To calculate power in an unbalanced three-phase system requires that we find the power in each phase using Eqs. (12.46) to (12.49). The total power is not simply three times the power in one phase but the sum of the powers in the three phases.

EXAMPLE 12.9

The unbalanced Y-load of Fig. 12.23 has balanced voltages of 100 V and the *acb* sequence. Calculate the line currents and the neutral current. Take $\mathbf{Z}_A = 15\ \Omega$, $\mathbf{Z}_B = 10 + j5\ \Omega$, $\mathbf{Z}_C = 6 - j8\ \Omega$.

Solution:

Using Eq. (12.59), the line currents are

$$\mathbf{I}_a = \frac{100\underline{/0°}}{15} = 6.67\underline{/0°}\ \text{A}$$

$$\mathbf{I}_b = \frac{100\underline{/120°}}{10 + j5} = \frac{100\underline{/120°}}{11.18\underline{/26.56°}} = 8.94\underline{/93.44°}\ \text{A}$$

$$\mathbf{I}_c = \frac{100\underline{/-120°}}{6 - j8} = \frac{100\underline{/-120°}}{10\underline{/-53.13°}} = 10\underline{/-66.87°}\ \text{A}$$

Using Eq. (12.60), the current in the neutral line is

$$\mathbf{I}_n = -(\mathbf{I}_a + \mathbf{I}_b + \mathbf{I}_c) = -(6.67 - 0.54 + j8.92 + 3.93 - j9.2)$$
$$= -10.06 + j0.28 = 10.06\underline{/178.4°}\ \text{A}$$

PRACTICE PROBLEM 12.9

The unbalanced Δ-load of Fig. 12.24 is supplied by balanced voltages of 200 V in the positive sequence. Find the line currents. Take $\mathbf{V}_{ab}$ as reference.

Answer: $18.05\underline{/-41.06°}$, $29.15\underline{/220.2°}$, $31.87\underline{/74.27°}$ A.

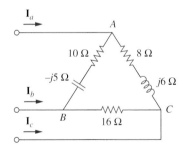

Figure 12.24   Unbalanced Δ-load; for Practice Prob. 12.9.

EXAMPLE 12.10

For the unbalanced circuit in Fig. 12.25, find: (a) the line currents, (b) the total complex power absorbed by the load, and (c) the total complex power supplied by the source.

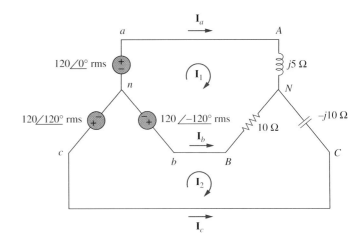

Figure 12.25   For Example 12.10.

Solution:

(a) We use mesh analysis to find the required currents. For mesh 1,

$$120\underline{/-120^\circ} - 120\underline{/0^\circ} + (10 + j5)\mathbf{I}_1 - 10\mathbf{I}_2 = 0$$

or

$$(10 + j5)\mathbf{I}_1 - 10\mathbf{I}_2 = 120\sqrt{3}\underline{/30^\circ} \qquad (12.10.1)$$

For mesh 2,

$$120\underline{/120^\circ} - 120\underline{/-120^\circ} + (10 - j10)\mathbf{I}_2 - 10\mathbf{I}_1 = 0$$

or

$$-10\mathbf{I}_1 + (10 - j10)\mathbf{I}_2 = 120\sqrt{3}\underline{/-90^\circ} \qquad (12.10.2)$$

Equations (12.10.1) and (12.10.2) form a matrix equation:

$$\begin{bmatrix} 10 + j5 & -10 \\ -10 & 10 - j10 \end{bmatrix} \begin{bmatrix} \mathbf{I}_1 \\ \mathbf{I}_2 \end{bmatrix} = \begin{bmatrix} 120\sqrt{3}\underline{/30^\circ} \\ 120\sqrt{3}\underline{/-90^\circ} \end{bmatrix}$$

The determinants are

$$\Delta = \begin{vmatrix} 10 + j5 & -10 \\ -10 & 10 - j10 \end{vmatrix} = 50 - j50 = 70.71\underline{/-45^\circ}$$

$$\Delta_1 = \begin{vmatrix} 120\sqrt{3}\underline{/30^\circ} & -10 \\ 120\sqrt{3}\underline{/-90^\circ} & 10 - j10 \end{vmatrix} = 207.85(13.66 - j13.66)$$

$$= 4015\underline{/-45^\circ}$$

$$\Delta_2 = \begin{vmatrix} 10 + j5 & 120\sqrt{3}\underline{/30^\circ} \\ -10 & 120\sqrt{3}\underline{/-90^\circ} \end{vmatrix} = 207.85(13.66 - j5)$$

$$= 3023\underline{/-20.1^\circ}$$

The mesh currents are

$$\mathbf{I}_1 = \frac{\Delta_1}{\Delta} = \frac{4015.23\,\underline{/-45°}}{70.71\,\underline{/-45°}} = 56.78 \text{ A}$$

$$\mathbf{I}_2 = \frac{\Delta_2}{\Delta} = \frac{3023.4\,\underline{/-20.1°}}{70.71\,\underline{/-45°}} = 42.75\,\underline{/24.9°} \text{ A}$$

The line currents are

$$\mathbf{I}_a = \mathbf{I}_1 = 56.78 \text{ A}, \qquad \mathbf{I}_c = -\mathbf{I}_2 = 42.75\,\underline{/-155.1°} \text{ A}$$

$$\mathbf{I}_b = \mathbf{I}_2 - \mathbf{I}_1 = 38.78 + j18 - 56.78 = 25.46\,\underline{/135°} \text{ A}$$

(b) We can now calculate the complex power absorbed by the load. For phase A,

$$\mathbf{S}_A = |\mathbf{I}_a|^2\mathbf{Z}_A = (56.78)^2(j5) = j16,120 \text{ VA}$$

For phase B,

$$\mathbf{S}_B = |\mathbf{I}_b|^2\mathbf{Z}_B = (25.46)^2(10) = 6480 \text{ VA}$$

For phase C,

$$\mathbf{S}_C = |\mathbf{I}_c|^2\mathbf{Z}_C = (42.75)^2(-j10) = -j18,276 \text{ VA}$$

The total complex power absorbed by the load is

$$\mathbf{S}_L = \mathbf{S}_A + \mathbf{S}_B + \mathbf{S}_C = 6480 - j2156 \text{ VA}$$

(c) We check the result above by finding the power supplied by the source. For the voltage source in phase a,

$$\mathbf{S}_a = -\mathbf{V}_{an}\mathbf{I}_a^* = -(120\,\underline{/0°})(56.78) = -6813.6 \text{ VA}$$

For the source in phase b,

$$\mathbf{S}_b = -\mathbf{V}_{bn}\mathbf{I}_b^* = -(120\,\underline{/-120°})(25.46\,\underline{/-135°})$$

$$= -3055.2\,\underline{/105°} = 790 - j2951.1 \text{ VA}$$

For the source in phase c,

$$\mathbf{S}_c = -\mathbf{V}_{bn}\mathbf{I}_c^* = -(120\,\underline{/120°})(42.75\,\underline{/155.1°})$$

$$= -5130\,\underline{/275.1°} = -456.03 + j5109.7 \text{ VA}$$

The total complex power supplied by the three-phase source is

$$\mathbf{S}_s = \mathbf{S}_a + \mathbf{S}_b + \mathbf{S}_c = -6480 + j2156 \text{ VA}$$

showing that $\mathbf{S}_s + \mathbf{S}_L = 0$ and confirming the conservation principle of ac power.

PRACTICE PROBLEM 12.10

Find the line currents in the unbalanced three-phase circuit of Fig. 12.26 and the real power absorbed by the load.

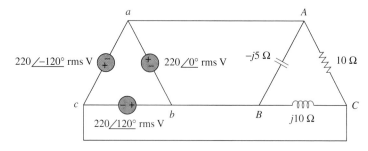

Figure 12.26   For Practice Prob. 12.10.

Answer: $64\underline{/80.1°}$, $38.1\underline{/-60°}$, $42.5\underline{/225°}$ A, 4.84 kW.

12.9 PSPICE FOR THREE-PHASE CIRCUITS

PSpice can be used to analyze three-phase balanced or unbalanced circuits in the same way it is used to analyze single-phase ac circuits. However, a delta-connected source presents two major problems to *PSpice*. First, a delta-connected source is a loop of voltage sources—which *PSpice* does not like. To avoid this problem, we insert a resistor of negligible resistance (say, 1 $\mu\Omega$ per phase) into each phase of the delta-connected source. Second, the delta-connected source does not provide a convenient node for the ground node, which is necessary to run *PSpice*. This problem can be eliminated by inserting balanced wye-connected large resistors (say, 1 MΩ per phase) in the delta-connected source so that the neutral node of the wye-connected resistors serves as the ground node 0. Example 12.12 will illustrate this.

EXAMPLE 12.11

For the balanced Y-Δ circuit in Fig. 12.27, use *PSpice* to find the line current $\mathbf{I}_{aA}$, the phase voltage $\mathbf{V}_{AB}$, and the phase current $\mathbf{I}_{AC}$. Assume that the source frequency is 60 Hz.

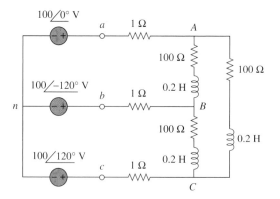

Figure 12.27   For Example 12.10.

Solution:

The schematic is shown in Fig. 12.28. The pseudocomponents IPRINT are inserted in the appropriate lines to obtain $\mathbf{I}_{aA}$ and $\mathbf{I}_{AC}$, while VPRINT2 is inserted between nodes A and B to print differential voltage $\mathbf{V}_{AB}$. We set the attributes of IPRINT and VPRINT2 each to $AC = yes$, $MAG = yes$, $PHASE = yes$, to print only the magnitude and phase of the currents and voltages. As a single-frequency analysis, we select **Analysis/Setup/ AC Sweep** and enter *Total Pts = 1, Start Freq = 60,* and *Final Freq = 60.* Once the circuit is saved, it is simulated by selecting **Analysis/Simulate**. The output file includes the following:

```
FREQ         V(A,B)      VP(A,B)
6.000E+01   1.699E+02   3.081E+01


FREQ         IM(V_PRINT2)  IP(V_PRINT2)
6.000E+01   2.350E+00     -3.620E+01


FREQ         IM(V_PRINT3)  IP(V_PRINT3)
6.000E+01   1.357E+00     -6.620E+01
```

From this, we obtain

$$\mathbf{I}_{aA} = 2.35\underline{/-36.2°}\ \text{A}$$

$$\mathbf{V}_{AB} = 169.9\underline{/30.81°}\ \text{V}, \qquad \mathbf{I}_{AC} = 1.357\underline{/-66.2°}\ \text{A}$$

Figure 12.28   Schematic for the circuit in Fig. 12.27.

PRACTICE PROBLEM 12.11

Refer to the balanced Y-Y circuit of Fig. 12.29. Use *PSpice* to find the line current $\mathbf{I}_{bB}$ and the phase voltage $\mathbf{V}_{AN}$. Take $f = 100$ Hz.

Figure 12.29   For Practice Prob. 12.11.

Answer: $100.9\underline{/60.87°}$ V, $8.547\underline{/-91.27°}$ A.

EXAMPLE 12.12

Consider the unbalanced Δ-Δ circuit in Fig. 12.30. Use *PSpice* to find the generator current $\mathbf{I}_{ab}$, the line current $\mathbf{I}_{bB}$, and the phase current $\mathbf{I}_{BC}$.

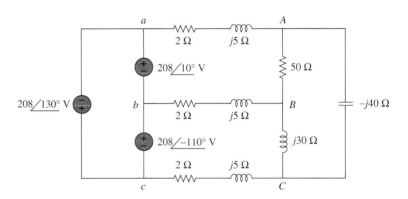

Figure 12.30   For Example 12.12.

Solution:

As mentioned above, we avoid the loop of voltage sources by inserting a 1-$\mu\Omega$ series resistor in the delta-connected source. To provide a ground node 0, we insert balanced wye-connected resistors (1 MΩ per phase) in the delta-connected source, as shown in the schematic in Fig. 12.31. Three IPRINT pseudocomponents with their attributes are inserted to be able to get the required currents $\mathbf{I}_{ab}$, $\mathbf{I}_{bB}$, and $\mathbf{I}_{BC}$. Since the operating frequency is not given and the inductances and capacitances should be specified instead of impedances, we assume $\omega = 1$ rad/s so that $f = 1/2\pi = 0.159155$ Hz. Thus,

$$L = \frac{X_L}{\omega} \qquad \text{and} \qquad C = \frac{1}{\omega X_C}$$

We select **Analysis/Setup/AC Sweep** and enter *Total Pts* = 1, *Start Freq* = 0.159155, and *Final Freq* = 0.159155. Once the schematic is saved, we select **Analysis/Simulate** to simulate the circuit. The output file includes:

```
FREQ          IM(V_PRINT1)    IP(V_PRINT1)
1.592E−01     9.106E+00       1.685E+02


FREQ          IM(V_PRINT2)    IP(V_PRINT2)
1.592E−01     5.959E+00       2.821E+00


FREQ          IM(V_PRINT3)    IP(V_PRINT3)
1.592E−01     5.500E+00       −7.532E+00
```

from which we get

$$\mathbf{I}_{ab} = 5.96\underline{/2.82°}\text{ A}$$

$$\mathbf{I}_{bB} = 9.106\underline{/168.5°}\text{ A}, \qquad \mathbf{I}_{BC} = 5.5\underline{/-7.53°}\text{ A}$$

Figure 12.31   Schematic for the circuit in Fig. 12.30.

PRACTICE PROBLEM 12.12

For the unbalanced circuit in Fig. 12.32, use *PSpice* to find the generator current $\mathbf{I}_{ca}$, the line current $\mathbf{I}_{cC}$, and the phase current $\mathbf{I}_{AB}$.

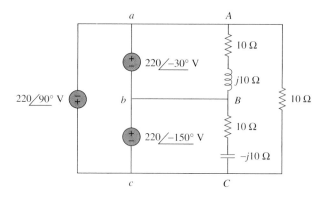

Figure 12.32   For Practice Prob. 12.12.

Answer: $24.68\underline{/-90°}$ A, $15.56\underline{/105°}$ A, $37.24\underline{/83.79°}$ A.

---

†12.10 APPLICATIONS

Both wye and delta source connections have important practical applications. The wye source connection is used for long distance transmission of electric power, where resistive losses (I^2R) should be minimal. This is due to the fact that the wye connection gives a line voltage that is $\sqrt{3}$ greater than the delta connection; hence, for the same power, the line current is $\sqrt{3}$ smaller. The delta source connection is used when three single-phase circuits are desired from a three-phase source. This conversion from three-phase to single-phase is required in residential wiring, because household lighting and appliances use single-phase power. Three-phase power is used in industrial wiring where a large power is required. In some applications, it is immaterial whether the load is wye- or delta-connected. For example, both connections are satisfactory with induction motors. In fact, some manufacturers connect a motor in delta for 220 V and in wye for 440 V so that one line of motors can be readily adapted to two different voltages.

Here we consider two practical applications of those concepts covered in this chapter: power measurement in three-phase circuits and residential wiring.

12.10.1 Three-Phase Power Measurement

Section 11.9 presented the wattmeter as the instrument for measuring the average (or real) power in single-phase circuits. A single wattmeter can also measure the average power in a three-phase system that is balanced, so that $P_1 = P_2 = P_3$; the total power is three times the reading of that one wattmeter. However, two or three single-phase wattmeters are necessary to measure power if the system is unbalanced. The *three-wattmeter method* of power measurement, shown in Fig. 12.33, will work regardless of whether the load is balanced or unbalanced, wye- or delta-connected.

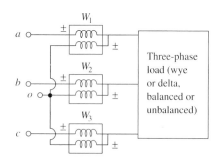

Figure 12.33   Three-wattmeter method for measuring three-phase power.

The three-wattmeter method is well suited for power measurement in a three-phase system where the power factor is constantly changing. The total average power is the algebraic sum of the three wattmeter readings,

$$P_T = P_1 + P_2 + P_3 \tag{12.61}$$

where P_1, P_2, and P_3 correspond to the readings of wattmeters W_1, W_2, and W_3, respectively. Notice that the common or reference point o in Fig. 12.33 is selected arbitrarily. If the load is wye-connected, point o can be connected to the neutral point n. For a delta-connected load, point o can be connected to any point. If point o is connected to point b, for example, the voltage coil in wattmeter W_2 reads zero and $P_2 = 0$, indicating that wattmeter W_2 is not necessary. Thus, two wattmeters are sufficient to measure the total power.

The *two-wattmeter method* is the most commonly used method for three-phase power measurement. The two wattmeters must be properly connected to any two phases, as shown typically in Fig. 12.34. Notice that the current coil of each wattmeter measures the line current, while the respective voltage coil is connected between the line and the third line and measures the line voltage. Also notice that the $\pm$ terminal of the voltage coil is connected to the line to which the corresponding current coil is connected. Although the individual wattmeters no longer read the power taken by any particular phase, the algebraic sum of the two wattmeter readings equals the total average power absorbed by the load, regardless of whether it is wye- or delta-connected, balanced or unbalanced. The total real power is equal to the algebraic sum of the two wattmeter readings,

$$P_T = P_1 + P_2 \tag{12.62}$$

We will show here that the method works for a balanced three-phase system.

Consider the balanced, wye-connected load in Fig. 12.35. Our objective is to apply the two-wattmeter method to find the average power absorbed by the load. Assume the source is in the abc sequence and the load impedance $\mathbf{Z}_Y = Z_Y\underline{/\theta}$. Due to the load impedance, each voltage coil leads its current coil by θ, so that the power factor is $\cos\theta$. We recall that each line voltage leads the corresponding phase voltage by $30°$. Thus, the total phase difference between the phase current $\mathbf{I}_a$ and line voltage

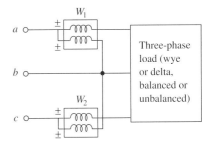

Figure 12.34   Two-wattmeter method for measuring three-phase power.

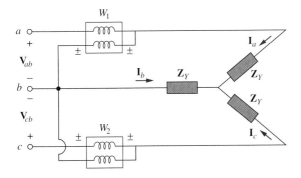

Figure 12.35   Two-wattmeter method applied to a balanced wye load.

$\mathbf{V}_{ab}$ is $\theta + 30°$, and the average power read by wattmeter W_1 is

$$P_1 = \text{Re}[\mathbf{V}_{ab}\mathbf{I}_a^*] = V_{ab}I_a \cos(\theta + 30°) = V_L I_L \cos(\theta + 30°) \quad (12.63)$$

Similarly, we can show that the average power read by wattmeter 2 is

$$P_2 = \text{Re}[\mathbf{V}_{cb}\mathbf{I}_c^*] = V_{cb}I_c \cos(\theta - 30°) = V_L I_L \cos(\theta - 30°) \quad (12.64)$$

We now use the trigonometric identities

$$\cos(A + B) = \cos A \cos B - \sin A \sin B$$
$$\cos(A - B) = \cos A \cos B + \sin A \sin B \quad (12.65)$$

to find the sum and the difference of the two wattmeter readings in Eqs. (12.63) and (12.64):

$$\begin{aligned}
P_1 + P_2 &= V_L I_L [\cos(\theta + 30°) + \cos(\theta - 30°)] \\
&= V_L I_L (\cos\theta \cos 30° - \sin\theta \sin 30° \\
&\quad + \cos\theta \cos 30° + \sin\theta \sin 30°) \\
&= V_L I_L 2 \cos 30° \cos\theta = \sqrt{3} V_L I_L \cos\theta \quad (12.66)
\end{aligned}$$

since $2\cos 30° = \sqrt{3}$. Comparing Eq. (12.66) with Eq. (12.50) shows that the sum of the wattmeter readings gives the total average power,

$$\boxed{P_T = P_1 + P_2} \quad (12.67)$$

Similarly,

$$\begin{aligned}
P_1 - P_2 &= V_L I_L [\cos(\theta + 30°) - \cos(\theta - 30°)] \\
&= V_l I_L (\cos\theta \cos 30° - \sin\theta \sin 30° \\
&\quad - \cos\theta \cos 30° - \sin\theta \sin 30°) \quad (12.68) \\
&= -V_L I_L 2 \sin 30° \sin\theta \\
P_2 - P_1 &= V_L I_L \sin\theta
\end{aligned}$$

since $2\sin 30° = 1$. Comparing Eq. (12.68) with Eq. (12.51) shows that the difference of the wattmeter readings is proportional to the total reactive power, or

$$\boxed{Q_T = \sqrt{3}(P_2 - P_1)} \quad (12.69)$$

From Eqs. (12.67) and (12.69), the total apparent power can be obtained as

$$S_T = \sqrt{P_T^2 + Q_T^2} \quad (12.70)$$

Dividing Eq. (12.69) by Eq. (12.67) gives the tangent of the power factor angle as

$$\tan\theta = \frac{Q_T}{P_T} = \sqrt{3}\frac{P_2 - P_1}{P_2 + P_1} \quad (12.71)$$

from which we can obtain the power factor as pf $= \cos\theta$. Thus, the two-wattmeter method not only provides the total real and reactive powers, it can also be used to compute the power factor. From Eqs. (12.67), (12.69), and (12.71), we conclude that:

1. If $P_2 = P_1$, the load is resistive.
2. If $P_2 > P_1$, the load is inductive.
3. If $P_2 < P_1$, the load is capacitive.

Although these results are derived from a balanced wye-connected load, they are equally valid for a balanced delta-connected load. However, the two-wattmeter method cannot be used for power measurement in a three-phase four-wire system unless the current through the neutral line is zero. We use the three-wattmeter method to measure the real power in a three-phase four-wire system.

EXAMPLE 12.13

Three wattmeters W_1, W_2, and W_3 are connected, respectively, to phases a, b, and c to measure the total power absorbed by the unbalanced wye-connected load in Example 12.9 (see Fig. 12.23). (a) Predict the wattmeter readings. (b) Find the total power absorbed.

Solution:

Part of the problem is already solved in Example 12.9. Assume that the wattmeters are properly connected as in Fig. 12.36.

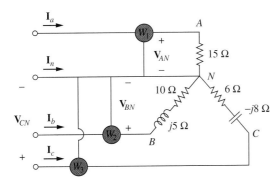

Figure 12.36   For Example 12.13.

(a) From Example 12.9,

$$\mathbf{V}_{AN} = 100\underline{/0°}, \qquad \mathbf{V}_{BN} = 100\underline{/120°}, \qquad \mathbf{V}_{CN} = 100\underline{/-120°} \text{ V}$$

while

$$\mathbf{I}_a = 6.67\underline{/0°}, \qquad \mathbf{I}_b = 8.94\underline{/93.44°}, \qquad \mathbf{I}_c = 10\underline{/-66.87°} \text{ A}$$

We calculate the wattmeter readings as follows:

$$P_1 = \text{Re}(\mathbf{V}_{AN}\mathbf{I}_a^*) = V_{AN}I_a\cos(\theta_{\mathbf{V}_{AN}} - \theta_{\mathbf{I}_a})$$
$$= 100 \times 6.67 \times \cos(0° - 0°) = 667 \text{ W}$$
$$P_2 = \text{Re}(\mathbf{V}_{BN}\mathbf{I}_b^*) = V_{BN}I_b\cos(\theta_{\mathbf{V}_{BN}} - \theta_{\mathbf{I}_b})$$
$$= 100 \times 8.94 \times \cos(120° - 93.44°) = 800 \text{ W}$$
$$P_3 = \text{Re}(\mathbf{V}_{CN}\mathbf{I}_c^*) = V_{CN}I_c\cos(\theta_{\mathbf{V}_{CN}} - \theta_{\mathbf{I}_c})$$
$$= 100 \times 10 \times \cos(-120° + 66.87°) = 600 \text{ W}$$

(b) The total power absorbed is

$$P_T = P_1 + P_2 + P_3 = 667 + 800 + 600 = 2067 \text{ W}$$

We can find the power absorbed by the resistors in Fig. 12.36 and use that to check or confirm this result.

$$\begin{aligned} P_T &= |I_a|^2(15) + |I_b|^2(10) + |I_c|^2(6) \\ &= 6.67^2(15) + 8.94^2(10) + 10^2(6) \\ &= 667 + 800 + 600 = 2067 \text{ W} \end{aligned}$$

which is exactly the same thing.

PRACTICE PROBLEM 12.13

Repeat Example 12.13 for the network in Fig. 12.24 (see Practice Prob. 12.9). *Hint:* Connect the reference point o in Fig. 12.33 to point B.

Answer: (a) 2722 W, 0 W, 6177, (b) 8899 W.

EXAMPLE 12.14

The two-wattmeter method produces wattmeter readings $P_1 = 1560$ W and $P_2 = 2100$ W when connected to a delta-connected load. If the line voltage is 220 V, calculate: (a) the per-phase average power, (b) the per-phase reactive power, (c) the power factor, and (d) the phase impedance.

Solution:

We can apply the given results to the delta-connected load.
(a) The total real or average power is

$$P_T = P_1 + P_2 = 1560 + 2100 = 3660 \text{ W}$$

The per-phase average power is then

$$P_p = \frac{1}{3}P_T = 1220 \text{ W}$$

(b) The total reactive power is

$$Q_T = \sqrt{3}(P_2 - P_1) = \sqrt{3}(2100 - 1560) = 935.3 \text{ VAR}$$

so that the per-phase reactive power is

$$Q_p = \frac{1}{3}Q_T = 311.77 \text{ VAR}$$

(c) The power angle is

$$\theta = \tan^{-1}\frac{Q_T}{P_T} = \tan^{-1}\frac{935.3}{3660} = 14.33°$$

Hence, the power factor is

$$\cos\theta = 0.9689 \text{ (leading)}$$

It is a lagging pf because Q_T is positive or $P_2 > P_1$.

(c) The phase impedance is $\mathbf{Z}_p = Z_p\underline{/\theta}$. We know that θ is the same as the pf angle; that is, $\theta = 14.57°$.

$$Z_p = \frac{V_p}{I_p}$$

We recall that for a delta-connected load, $V_p = V_L = 220$ V. From Eq. (12.46),

$$P_p = V_p I_p \cos\theta \quad\Longrightarrow\quad I_p = \frac{1220}{220 \times 0.9689} = 5.723 \text{ A}$$

Hence,

$$Z_p = \frac{V_p}{I_p} = \frac{220}{5.723} = 38.44 \ \Omega$$

and

$$\mathbf{Z}_p = 38.44\underline{/14.33°} \ \Omega$$

PRACTICE PROBLEM 12.14

Let the line voltage $V_L = 208$ V and the wattmeter readings of the balanced system in Fig. 12.35 be $P_1 = -560$ W and $P_2 = 800$ W. Determine:

(a) the total average power
(b) the total reactive power
(c) the power factor
(d) the phase impedance

Is the impedance inductive or capacitive?

Answer: (a) 240 W, (b) 2355.6 VAR, (c) 0.1014, (d) $18.25\underline{/84.18°} \ \Omega$, inductive.

EXAMPLE 12.15

The three-phase balanced load in Fig. 12.35 has impedance per phase of $\mathbf{Z}_Y = 8 + j6 \ \Omega$. If the load is connected to 208-V lines, predict the readings of the wattmeters W_1 and W_2. Find P_T and Q_T.

Solution:

The impedance per phase is

$$\mathbf{Z}_Y = 8 + j6 = 10\underline{/36.87°} \ \Omega$$

so that the pf angle is 36.87°. Since the line voltage $V_L = 208$ V, the line current is

$$I_L = \frac{V_p}{|\mathbf{Z}_Y|} = \frac{208/\sqrt{3}}{10} = 12 \text{ A}$$

Then

$$P_1 = V_L I_L \cos(\theta + 30°) = 208 \times 12 \times \cos(36.87° + 30°)$$

$$= 980.48 \text{ W}$$

$$P_2 = V_L I_L \cos(\theta - 30°) = 208 \times 12 \times \cos(36.87° - 30°)$$

$$= 2478.1 \text{ W}$$

Thus, wattmeter 1 reads 980.48 W, while wattmeter 2 reads 2478.1 W. Since $P_2 > P_1$, the load is inductive. This is evident from the load $\mathbf{Z}_Y$ itself. Next,

$$P_T = P_1 + P_2 = 3.4586 \text{ kW}$$

and

$$Q_T = \sqrt{3}(P_2 - P_1) = \sqrt{3}(1497.6) \text{ VAR} = 2.594 \text{ kVAR}$$

PRACTICE PROBLEM 12.15

If the load in Fig. 12.35 is delta-connected with impedance per phase of $\mathbf{Z}_p = 30 - j40 \ \Omega$ and $V_L = 440$ V, predict the readings of the wattmeters W_1 and W_2. Calculate P_T and Q_T.

Answer: 6.166 kW, 0.8021 kW, 6.968 kW, −9.291 kVAR.

12.10.2 Residential Wiring

In the United States, most household lighting and appliances operate on 120-V, 60-Hz, single-phase alternating current. (The electricity may also be supplied at 110, 115, or 117 V, depending on the location.) The local power company supplies the house with a three-wire ac system. Typically, as in Fig. 12.37, the line voltage of, say, 12,000 V is stepped

Figure 12.37   A 120/240 household power system.
(Source: A. Marcus and C. M. Thomson, Electricity for Technicians, 2nd ed. [Englewood Cliffs, NJ: Prentice Hall, 1975], p. 324.)

down to 120/240 V with a transformer (more details on transformers in the next chapter). The three wires coming from the transformer are typically colored red (hot), black (hot), and white (neutral). As shown in Fig. 12.38, the two 120-V voltages are opposite in phase and hence add up to zero. That is, $\mathbf{V}_W = 0\underline{/0°}$, $\mathbf{V}_B = 120\underline{/0°}$, $\mathbf{V}_R = 120\underline{/180°} = -\mathbf{V}_B$.

$$\mathbf{V}_{BR} = \mathbf{V}_B - \mathbf{V}_R = \mathbf{V}_B - (-\mathbf{V}_B) = 2\mathbf{V}_B = 240\underline{/0°} \qquad (12.72)$$

Since most appliances are designed to operate with 120 V, the lighting and appliances are connected to the 120-V lines, as illustrated in Fig. 12.39 for a room. Notice in Fig. 12.37 that all appliances are connected in parallel. Heavy appliances that consume large currents, such as air conditioners, dishwashers, ovens, and laundry machines, are connected to the 240-V power line.

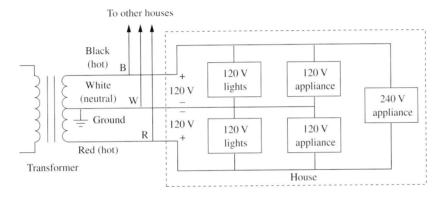

Figure 12.38   Single-phase three-wire residential wiring.

Because of the dangers of electricity, house wiring is carefully regulated by a code drawn by local ordinances and by the National Electrical Code (NEC). To avoid trouble, insulation, grounding, fuses, and circuit breakers are used. Modern wiring codes require a third wire for a separate ground. The ground wire does not carry power like the neutral wire but enables appliances to have a separate ground connection. Figure 12.40 shows the connection of the receptacle to a 120-V rms line and to the ground. As shown in the figure, the neutral line is connected to the ground (the earth) at many critical locations. Although the ground

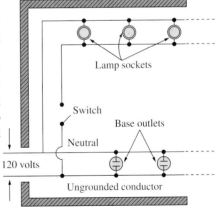

Figure 12.39   A typical wiring diagram of a room. *(Source: A. Marcus and C. M. Thomson, Electricity for Technicians, 2nd ed. [Englewood Cliffs, NJ: Prentice Hall, 1975], p. 325.)*

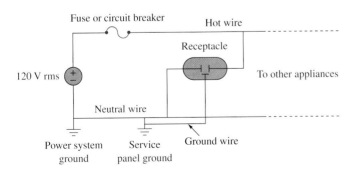

Figure 12.40   Connection of a receptacle to the hot line and to the ground.

line seems redundant, grounding is important for many reasons. First, it is required by NEC. Second, grounding provides a convenient path to ground for lightning that strikes the power line. Third, grounds minimize the risk of electric shock. What causes shock is the passage of current from one part of the body to another. The human body is like a big resistor R. If V is the potential difference between the body and the ground, the current through the body is determined by Ohm's law as

$$I = \frac{V}{R} \tag{12.73}$$

The value of R varies from person to person and depends on whether the body is wet or dry. How great or how deadly the shock is depends on the amount of current, the pathway of the current through the body, and the length of time the body is exposed to the current. Currents less than 1 mA may not be harmful to the body, but currents greater than 10 mA can cause severe shock. A modern safety device is the *ground-fault circuit interrupter* (GFCI), used in outdoor circuits and in bathrooms, where the risk of electric shock is greatest. It is essentially a circuit breaker that opens when the sum of the currents i_R, i_W, and i_B through the red, white, and the black lines is not equal to zero, or $i_R + i_W + i_B \neq 0$.

The best way to avoid electric shock is to follow safety guidelines concerning electrical systems and appliances. Here are some of them:

- Never assume that an electrical circuit is dead. Always check to be sure.

- Use safety devices when necessary, and wear suitable clothing (insulated shoes, gloves, etc.).

- Never use two hands when testing high-voltage circuits, since the current through one hand to the other hand has a direct path through your chest and heart.

- Do not touch an electrical appliance when you are wet. Remember that water conducts electricity.

- Be extremely careful when working with electronic appliances such as radio and TV because these appliances have large capacitors in them. The capacitors take time to discharge after the power is disconnected.

- Always have another person present when working on a wiring system, just in case of an accident.

12.11 SUMMARY

1. The phase sequence is the order in which the phase voltages of a three-phase generator occur with respect to time. In an *abc* sequence of balanced source voltages, $\mathbf{V}_{an}$ leads $\mathbf{V}_{bn}$ by 120°, which in turn leads $\mathbf{V}_{cn}$ by 120°. In an *acb* sequence of balanced voltages, $\mathbf{V}_{an}$ leads $\mathbf{V}_{cn}$ by 120°, which in turn leads $\mathbf{V}_{bn}$ by 120°.

2. A balanced wye- or delta-connected load is one in which the three-phase impedances are equal.

3. The easiest way to analyze a balanced three-phase circuit is to transform both the source and the load to a Y-Y system and then analyze the single-phase equivalent circuit. Table 12.1 presents a summary of the formulas for phase currents and voltages and line currents and voltages for the four possible configurations.

4. The line current I_L is the current flowing from the generator to the load in each transmission line in a three-phase system. The line voltage V_L is the voltage between each pair of lines, excluding the neutral line if it exists. The phase current I_p is the current flowing through each phase in a three-phase load. The phase voltage V_p is the voltage of each phase. For a wye-connected load,

$$V_L = \sqrt{3}V_p \qquad \text{and} \qquad I_L = I_p$$

For a delta-connected load,

$$V_L = V_p \qquad \text{and} \qquad I_L = \sqrt{3}I_p$$

5. The total instantaneous power in a balanced three-phase system is constant and equal to the average power.

6. The total complex power absorbed by a balanced three-phase Y-connected or Δ-connected load is

$$\mathbf{S} = P + jQ = \sqrt{3}V_L I_L \underline{/\theta}$$

where θ is the angle of the load impedances.

7. An unbalanced three-phase system can be analyzed using nodal or mesh analysis.

8. *PSpice* is used to analyze three-phase circuits in the same way as it is used for analyzing single-phase circuits.

9. The total real power is measured in three-phase systems using either the three-wattmeter method or the two-wattmeter method.

10. Residential wiring uses a 120/240-V, single-phase, three-wire system.

REVIEW QUESTIONS

12.1 What is the phase sequence of a three-phase motor for which $\mathbf{V}_{AN} = 220\underline{/-100°}$ V and $\mathbf{V}_{BN} = 220\underline{/140°}$ V?

(a) *abc* (b) *acb*

12.2 If in an *acb* phase sequence, $\mathbf{V}_{an} = 100\underline{/-20°}$, then $\mathbf{V}_{cn}$ is:

(a) $100\underline{/-140°}$ (b) $100\underline{/100°}$
(c) $100\underline{/-50°}$ (d) $100\underline{/10°}$

12.3 Which of these is not a required condition for a balanced system:

(a) $|\mathbf{V}_{an}| = |\mathbf{V}_{bn}| = |\mathbf{V}_{cn}|$

(b) $\mathbf{I}_a + \mathbf{I}_b + \mathbf{I}_c = 0$
(c) $V_{an} + V_{bn} + V_{cn} = 0$
(d) Source voltages are 120° out of phase with each other.
(e) Load impedances for the three phases are equal.

12.4 In a Y-connected load, the line current and phase current are equal.

(a) True (b) False

12.5 In a Δ-connected load, the line current and phase current are equal.

(a) True (b) False

12.6 In a Y-Y system, a line voltage of 220 V produces a phase voltage of:

(a) 381 V   (b) 311 V   (c) 220 V
(d) 156 V   (e) 127 V

12.7 In a Δ-Δ system, a phase voltage of 100 V produces a line voltage of:

(a) 58 V   (b) 71 V   (c) 100 V
(d) 173 V   (e) 141 V

12.8 When a Y-connected load is supplied by voltages in *abc* phase sequence, the line voltages lag the corresponding phase voltages by 30°.

(a) True   (b) False

12.9 In a balanced three-phase circuit, the total instantaneous power is equal to the average power.

(a) True   (b) False

12.10 The total power supplied to a balanced Δ-load is found in the same way as for a balanced Y-load.

(a) True   (b) False

Answers: 12.1a, 12.2a, 12.3c, 12.4a, 12.5b, 12.6e, 12.7c, 12.8b, 12.9a, 12.10a.

PROBLEMS[1]

Section 12.2   Balanced Three-Phase Voltages

12.1 If $\mathbf{V}_{ab} = 400$ V in a balanced Y-connected three-phase generator, find the phase voltages, assuming the phase sequence is:

(a) *abc*   (b) *acb*

12.2 What is the phase sequence of a balanced three-phase circuit for which $\mathbf{V}_{an} = 160\underline{/30°}$ V and $\mathbf{V}_{cn} = 160\underline{/-90°}$ V? Find $\mathbf{V}_{bn}$.

12.3 Determine the phase sequence of a balanced three-phase circuit in which $\mathbf{V}_{bn} = 208\underline{/130°}$ V and $\mathbf{V}_{cn} = 208\underline{/10°}$ V. Obtain $\mathbf{V}_{an}$.

12.4 Assuming the *abc* sequence, if $\mathbf{V}_{ca} = 208\underline{/20°}$ V in a balanced three-phase circuit, find $\mathbf{V}_{ab}$, $\mathbf{V}_{bc}$, $\mathbf{V}_{an}$, and $\mathbf{V}_{bn}$.

12.5 Given that the line voltages of a three-phase circuit are

$$\mathbf{V}_{ab} = 420\underline{/0°}, \qquad \mathbf{V}_{bc} = 420\underline{/-120°}$$

$$\mathbf{V}_{ac} = 420\underline{/120°} \text{ V}$$

find the phase voltages $\mathbf{V}_{an}$, $\mathbf{V}_{bn}$, and $\mathbf{V}_{cn}$.

Section 12.3   Balanced Wye-Wye Connection

12.6 For the Y-Y circuit of Fig. 12.41, find the line currents, the line voltages, and the load voltages.

Figure 12.41   For Prob. 12.6.

12.7 Obtain the line currents in the three-phase circuit of Fig. 12.42 on the next page.

12.8 A balanced Y-connected load with a phase impedance of $16 + j9\ \Omega$ is connected to a balanced three-phase source with a line voltage of 220 V. Calculate the line current I_L.

12.9 A balanced Y-Y four-wire system has phase voltages

$$\mathbf{V}_{an} = 120\underline{/0°}, \qquad \mathbf{V}_{bn} = 120\underline{/-120°}$$

$$\mathbf{V}_{cn} = 120\underline{/120°} \text{ V}$$

The load impedance per phase is $19 + j13\ \Omega$, and the line impedance per phase is $1 + j2\ \Omega$. Solve for the line currents and neutral current.

---

[1] Remember that unless stated otherwise, all given voltages and currents are rms values.

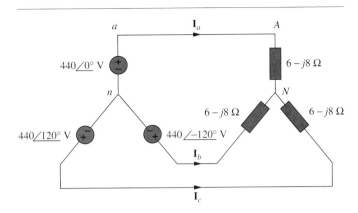

Figure 12.42   For Prob. 12.7.

12.10   For the circuit in Fig. 12.43, determine the current in the neutral line.

Figure 12.43   For Prob. 12.10.

Section 12.4   Balanced Wye-Delta Connection

12.11   For the three-phase circuit of Fig. 12.44, $\mathbf{I}_{bB} = 30\angle 60°$ A and $\mathbf{V}_{BC} = 220\angle 10°$ V. Find $\mathbf{V}_{an}$, $\mathbf{V}_{AB}$, $\mathbf{I}_{AC}$, and $\mathbf{Z}$.

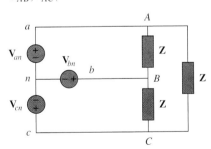

Figure 12.44   For Prob. 12.11.

12.12   Solve for the line currents in the Y-Δ circuit of Fig. 12.45. Take $\mathbf{Z}_\Delta = 60\angle 45°$ Ω.

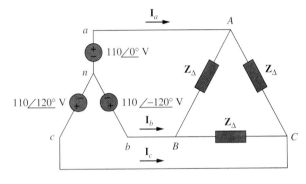

Figure 12.45   For Prob. 12.12.

12.13   In the circuit of Fig. 12.46 on the next page, calculate the line currents $\mathbf{I}_a$, $\mathbf{I}_b$, and $\mathbf{I}_c$. $\mathbf{Z}_L = 18 + j15$ Ω.

12.14   Obtain the line currents in the three-phase circuit of Fig. 12.47 on the next page.

12.15   The circuit in Fig. 12.48 is excited by a balanced three-phase source with a line voltage of 210 V. If $\mathbf{Z}_\ell = 1 + j1$ Ω, $\mathbf{Z}_\Delta = 24 - j30$ Ω, and $\mathbf{Z}_Y = 12 + j5$ Ω, determine the magnitude of the line current of the combined loads.

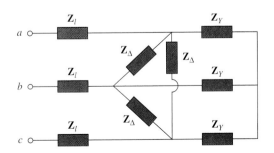

Figure 12.48   For Prob. 12.15.

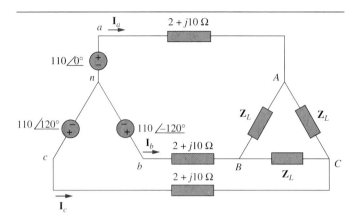

Figure 12.46   For Prob. 12.13.

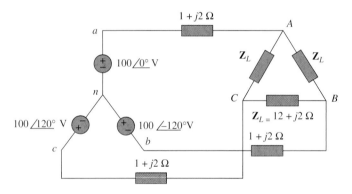

Figure 12.47   For Prob. 12.14.

12.16 A balanced delta-connected load has a phase current $\mathbf{I}_{AC} = 10\underline{/-30°}$ A.

(a) Determine the three line currents assuming that the circuit operates in the positive phase sequence.

(b) Calculate the load impedance if the line voltage is $\mathbf{V}_{AB} = 110\underline{/0°}$ V.

12.17 In a wye-delta three-phase circuit, the source is a balanced, positive phase sequence with $\mathbf{V}_{an} = 120\underline{/0°}$ V. It feeds a balanced load with $\mathbf{Z}_\Delta = 9 + j12$ Ω per phase through a balanced line with $\mathbf{Z}_\ell = 1 + j0.5$ Ω per phase. Calculate the phase voltages and currents in the load.

12.18 If $\mathbf{V}_{an} = 440\underline{/60°}$ V in the network of Fig. 12.49, find the load phase currents $\mathbf{I}_{AB}$, $\mathbf{I}_{BC}$, and $\mathbf{I}_{CA}$.

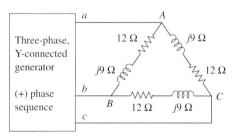

Figure 12.49   For Prob. 12.18.

Section 12.5   Balanced Delta-Delta Connection

12.19 For the Δ-Δ circuit of Fig. 12.50, calculate the phase and line currents.

Figure 12.50   For Prob. 12.19.

12.20 Refer to the Δ-Δ circuit in Fig. 12.51. Find the line and phase currents. Assume that the load impedance is $12 + j9$ Ω per phase.

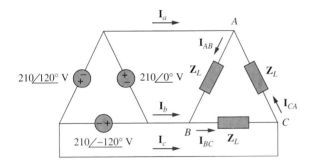

Figure 12.51   For Prob. 12.20.

12.21 Three 230-V generators form a delta-connected source that is connected to a balanced delta-connected load of $\mathbf{Z}_L = 10 + j8$ Ω per phase as shown in Fig. 12.52.

(a) Determine the value of $\mathbf{I}_{AC}$.

(b) What is the value of $\mathbf{I}_b$?

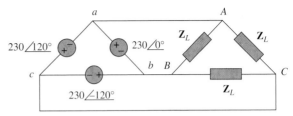

Figure 12.52   For Prob. 12.21.

12.22 Find the line currents $\mathbf{I}_a$, $\mathbf{I}_b$, and $\mathbf{I}_c$ in the three-phase network of Fig. 12.53 below. Take $\mathbf{Z}_\Delta = 12 - j15$ Ω, $\mathbf{Z}_Y = 4 + j6$ Ω, and $\mathbf{Z}_\ell = 2$ Ω.

12.23 A three-phase balanced system with a line voltage of 202 V rms feeds a delta-connected load with $\mathbf{Z}_P = 25\underline{/60°}$ Ω.

(a) Find the line current.

(b) Determine the total power supplied to the load using two wattmeters connected to the A and C lines.

12.24 A balanced delta-connected source has phase voltage $\mathbf{V}_{ab} = 416\underline{/30°}$ V and a positive phase sequence. If this is connected to a balanced delta-connected load, find the line and phase currents. Take the load impedance per phase as $60\underline{/30°}$ Ω and line impedance per phase as $1 + j1$ Ω.

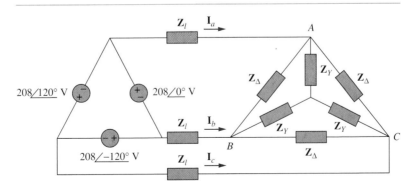

Figure 12.53   For Prob. 12.22.

548   PART 2   AC Circuits

Section 12.6   Balanced Delta-Wye Connection

12.25 In the circuit of Fig. 12.54, if $\mathbf{V}_{ab} = 440\underline{/10°}$,

$\mathbf{V}_{bc} = 440\underline{/250°}$, $\mathbf{V}_{ca} = 440\underline{/130°}$ V, find the line currents.

Figure 12.54   For Prob. 12.25.

12.26 For the balanced circuit in Fig. 12.55, $\mathbf{V}_{ab} = 125\underline{/0°}$ V. Find the line currents $\mathbf{I}_{aA}$, $\mathbf{I}_{bB}$, and $\mathbf{I}_{cC}$.

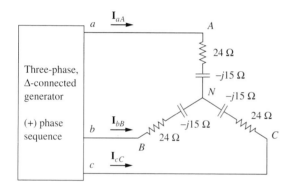

Figure 12.55   For Prob. 12.26.

12.27 In a balanced three-phase Δ-Y circuit, the source is connected in the positive sequence, with $\mathbf{V}_{ab} = 220\underline{/20°}$ V and $\mathbf{Z}_Y = 20 + j15$ Ω. Find the line currents.

12.28 A delta-connected generator supplies a balanced wye-connected load with an impedance of $30\underline{/-60°}$ Ω. If the line voltages of the generator have a magnitude of 400 V and are in the positive phase sequence, find the line current I_L and phase voltage V_p at the load.

Section 12.7   Power in a Balanced System

12.29 A balanced wye-connected load absorbs a total power of 5 kW at a leading power factor of 0.6 when connected to a line voltage of 240 V. Find the impedance of each phase and the total complex power of the load.

12.30 In Fig. 12.56, the rms value of the line voltage is 208 V. Find the average power delivered to the load.

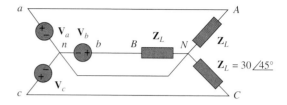

Figure 12.56   For Prob. 12.30.

12.31 A balanced delta-connected load is supplied by a 60-Hz three-phase source with a line voltage of 240 V. Each load phase draws 6 kW at a lagging power factor of 0.8. Find:

(a) the load impedance per phase
(b) the line current
(c) the value of capacitance needed to be connected in parallel with each load phase to minimize the current from the source

12.32 A balanced wye-connected load absorbs 50 kVA at a 0.6 lagging power factor when the line voltage is 440 V. Find the line current and the phase impedance.

12.33 A three-phase source delivers 4800 VA to a wye-connected load with a phase voltage of 208 V and a power factor of 0.9 lagging. Calculate the source line current and the source line voltage.

12.34 A balanced wye-connected load with a phase impedance of $10 - j16$ Ω is connected to a balanced three-phase generator with a line voltage of 220 V. Determine the line current and the complex power absorbed by the load.

12.35 Three equal impedances, $60 + j30$ Ω each, are delta-connected to a 230-V rms, three-phase circuit. Another three equal impedances, $40 + j10$ Ω each, are wye-connected across the same circuit at the same points. Determine:

(a) the line current
(b) the total complex power supplied to the two loads
(c) the power factor of the two loads combined

12.36 A 4200-V, three-phase transmission line has an impedance of $4 + j$ Ω per phase. If it supplies a load of 1 MVA at 0.75 power factor (lagging), find:

(a) the complex power
(b) the power loss in the line
(c) the voltage at the sending end

12.37 The total power measured in a three-phase system feeding a balanced wye-connected load is 12 kW at a power factor of 0.6 leading. If the line voltage is 208 V, calculate the line current I_L and the load impedance $\mathbf{Z}_Y$.

12.38 Given the circuit in Fig. 12.57 below, find the total complex power absorbed by the load.

12.39 Find the real power absorbed by the load in Fig. 12.58.

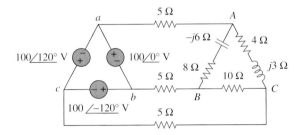

Figure 12.58   For Prob. 12.39.

12.40 For the three-phase circuit in Fig. 12.59, find the average power absorbed by the delta-connected load with $\mathbf{Z}_\Delta = 21 + j24\ \Omega$.

Figure 12.59   For Prob. 12.40.

12.41 A balanced delta-connected load draws 5 kW at a power factor of 0.8 lagging. If the three-phase system has an effective line voltage of 400 V, find the line current.

12.42 A balanced three-phase generator delivers 7.2 kW to a wye-connected load with impedance $30 - j40\ \Omega$ per phase. Find the line current I_L and the line voltage V_L.

12.43 Refer to Fig. 12.48. Obtain the complex power absorbed by the combined loads.

12.44 A three-phase line has an impedance of $1 + j3\ \Omega$ per phase. The line feeds a balanced delta-connected load, which absorbs a total complex power of $12 + j5$ kVA. If the line voltage at the load end has a magnitude of 240 V, calculate the magnitude of the line voltage at the source end and the source power factor.

12.45 A balanced wye-connected load is connected to the generator by a balanced transmission line with an impedance of $0.5 + j2\ \Omega$ per phase. If the load is rated at 450 kW, 0.708 power factor lagging, 440-V line voltage, find the line voltage at the generator.

12.46 A three-phase load consists of three 100-Ω resistors that can be wye- or delta-connected. Determine which connection will absorb the most average power from a three-phase source with a line voltage of 110 V. Assume zero line impedance.

12.47 The following three parallel-connected three-phase loads are fed by a balanced three-phase source.

> Load 1: 250 kVA, 0.8 pf lagging
>
> Load 2: 300 kVA, 0.95 pf leading
>
> Load 3: 450 kVA, unity pf

If the line voltage is 13.8 kV, calculate the line current and the power factor of the source. Assume that the line impedance is zero.

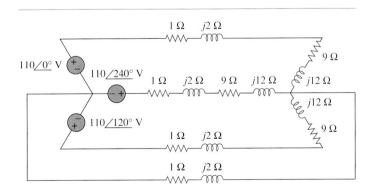

Figure 12.57   For Prob. 12.38.

12.48 A balanced, positive-sequence wye-connected source has $\mathbf{V}_{an} = 240\underline{/0^\circ}$ V rms and supplies an unbalanced delta-connected load via a transmission line with impedance $2 + j3$ Ω per phase.

(a) Calculate the line currents if $\mathbf{Z}_{AB} = 40 + j15$ Ω, $\mathbf{Z}_{BC} = 60$ Ω, $\mathbf{Z}_{CA} = 18 - j12$ Ω.

(b) Find the complex power supplied by the source.

12.49 Each phase load consists of a 20-Ω resistor and a 10-Ω inductive reactance. With a line voltage of 220 V rms, calculate the average power taken by the load if:

(a) the three phase loads are delta-connected

(b) the loads are wye-connected

12.50 A balanced three-phase source with $\mathbf{V}_L = 240$ V rms is supplying 8 kVA at 0.6 power factor lagging to two wye-connected parallel loads. If one load draws 3 kW at unity power factor, calculate the impedance per phase of the second load.

Section 12.8   Unbalanced Three-Phase Systems

12.51 For the circuit in Fig. 12.60, $\mathbf{Z}_a = 6 - j8$ Ω, $\mathbf{Z}_b = 12 + j9$ Ω, and $\mathbf{Z}_c = 15$ Ω. Find the line currents $\mathbf{I}_a$, $\mathbf{I}_b$, and $\mathbf{I}_c$.

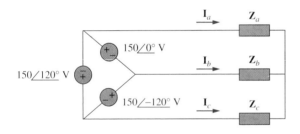

Figure 12.60   For Prob. 12.51.

12.52 A four-wire wye-wye circuit has

$$\mathbf{V}_{an} = 120\underline{/120^\circ}, \qquad \mathbf{V}_{bn} = 120\underline{/0^\circ}$$

$$\mathbf{V}_{cn} = 120\underline{/-120^\circ} \text{ V}$$

If the impedances are

$$\mathbf{Z}_{AN} = 20\underline{/60^\circ}, \qquad \mathbf{Z}_{BN} = 30\underline{/0^\circ}$$

$$\mathbf{Z}_{cn} = 40\underline{/30^\circ} \text{ }\Omega$$

find the current in the neutral line.

12.53 For the wye-connected load of Fig. 12.61, the line voltages all have a magnitude of 250 V and are in a positive phase sequence. Calculate the line currents and the neutral current.

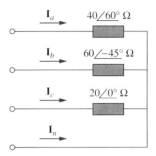

Figure 12.61   For Prob. 12.53.

12.54 A delta-connected load whose phase impedances are $\mathbf{Z}_{AB} = 50$ Ω, $\mathbf{Z}_{BC} = -j50$ Ω, and $\mathbf{Z}_{CA} = j50$ Ω is fed by a balanced wye-connected three-phase source with $V_p = 100$ V. Find the phase currents.

12.55 A balanced three-phase wye-connected generator with $V_p = 220$ V supplies an unbalanced wye-connected load with $\mathbf{Z}_{AN} = 60 + j80$ Ω, $\mathbf{Z}_{BN} = 100 - j120$ Ω, and $\mathbf{Z}_{CN} = 30 + j40$ Ω. Find the total complex power absorbed by the load.

12.56 Refer to the unbalanced circuit of Fig. 12.62. Calculate:

(a) the line currents

(b) the real power absorbed by the load

(c) the total complex power supplied by the source

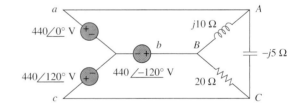

Figure 12.62   For Prob. 12.56.

12.57 Determine the line currents for the three-phase circuit of Fig. 12.63. Let $\mathbf{V}_a = 110\underline{/0^\circ}$, $\mathbf{V}_b = 110\underline{/-120^\circ}$, $\mathbf{V}_c = 110\underline{/120^\circ}$ V.

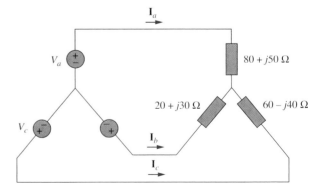

Figure 12.63   For Prob. 12.57.

Section 12.9   *PSpice* for Three-Phase Circuits

12.58   Solve Prob. 12.10 using *PSpice*.

12.59   The source in Fig. 12.64 is balanced and exhibits a positive phase sequence. If $f = 60$ Hz, use *PSpice* to find $\mathbf{V}_{AN}$, $\mathbf{V}_{BN}$, and $\mathbf{V}_{CN}$.

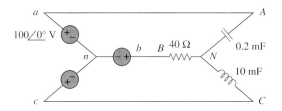

Figure 12.64   For Prob. 12.59.

12.60   Use *PSpice* to determine $\mathbf{I}_o$ in the single-phase, three-wire circuit of Fig. 12.65. Let $\mathbf{Z}_1 = 15 - j10\ \Omega$, $\mathbf{Z}_2 = 30 + j20\ \Omega$, and $\mathbf{Z}_3 = 12 + j5\ \Omega$.

Figure 12.65   For Prob. 12.60.

12.61   Given the circuit in Fig. 12.66, use *PSpice* to determine currents $\mathbf{I}_{aA}$ and voltage $\mathbf{V}_{BN}$.

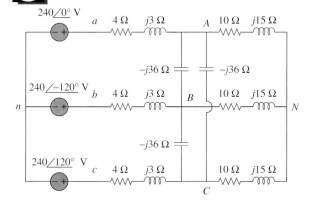

Figure 12.66   For Prob. 12.61.

12.62   The circuit in Fig. 12.67 operates at 60 Hz. Use *PSpice* to find the source current $\mathbf{I}_{ab}$ and the line current $\mathbf{I}_{bB}$.

Figure 12.67   For Prob. 12.62.

12.63   Use *PSpice* to find currents $\mathbf{I}_{aA}$ and $\mathbf{I}_{AC}$ in the unbalanced three-phase system shown in Fig. 12.68. Let

$$\mathbf{Z}_l = 2 + j, \qquad \mathbf{Z}_1 = 40 + j20\ \Omega,$$
$$\mathbf{Z}_2 = 50 - j30\ \Omega, \qquad \mathbf{Z}_3 = 25\ \Omega$$

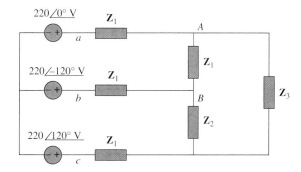

Figure 12.68   For Prob. 12.63.

12.64   For the circuit in Fig. 12.58, use *PSpice* to find the line currents and the phase currents.

12.65   A balanced three-phase circuit is shown in Fig. 12.69 on the next page. Use *PSpice* to find the line currents $\mathbf{I}_{aA}$, $\mathbf{I}_{bB}$, and $\mathbf{I}_{cC}$.

Section 12.10   Applications

12.66   A three-phase, four-wire system operating with a 208-V line voltage is shown in Fig. 12.70. The source voltages are balanced. The power absorbed by the resistive wye-connected load is measured by the three-wattmeter method. Calculate:

(a) the voltage to neutral

(b) the currents $\mathbf{I}_1$, $\mathbf{I}_2$, $\mathbf{I}_3$, and $\mathbf{I}_n$

(c) the readings of the wattmeters

(d) the total power absorbed by the load

Figure 12.69   For Prob. 12.65.

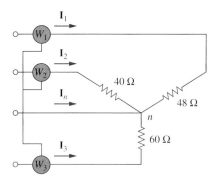

Figure 12.70   For Prob. 12.66.

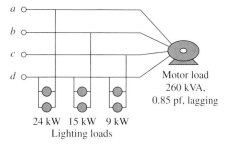

Figure 12.71   For Prob. 12.67.

12.68   Meter readings for a three-phase wye-connected alternator supplying power to a motor indicate that the line voltages are 330 V, the line currents are 8.4 A, and the total line power is 4.5 kW. Find:

(a) the load in VA

(b) the load pf

(c) the phase current

(d) the phase voltage

12.69   A factory is supplied with a three-phase 6.6-kV, 60-Hz transmission line. The factory has the following balanced loads:

Load 1: 1.2 MVA at 0.8 lagging pf

Load 2: 2 MVA at 0.75 leading pf

Load 3: 0.8 MW at unity pf

To correct the overall pf to 0.99 lagging at full load requires a star-connected capacitor bank. Determine the capacitance per phase of the bank.

*12.67   As shown in Fig. 12.71, a three-phase four-wire line with a phase voltage of 120 V supplies a balanced motor load at 260 kVA at 0.85 pf lagging. The motor load is connected to the three main lines marked *a*, *b*, and *c*. In addition, incandescent lamps (unity pf) are connected as follows: 24 kW from line *a* to the neutral, 15 kW from line *b* to the neutral, and 9 kW from line *a* to the neutral.

(a) If three wattmeters are arranged to measure the power in each line, calculate the reading of each meter.

(b) Find the current in the neutral line.

*An asterisk indicates a challenging problem.

12.70 The two-wattmeter method gives $P_1 = 1200$ W and $P_2 = -400$ W for a three-phase motor running on a 240-V line. Assume that the motor load is wye-connected and that it draws a line current of 6 A. Calculate the pf of the motor and its phase impedance.

12.71 In Fig. 12.72, two wattmeters are properly connected to the unbalanced load supplied by a balanced source such that $\mathbf{V}_{ab} = 208\underline{/0°}$ V with positive phase sequence.

    (a) Determine the reading of each wattmeter.

    (b) Calculate the total apparent power absorbed by the load.

Figure 12.72   For Prob. 12.71.

12.72 If wattmeters W_1 and W_2 are properly connected respectively between lines a and b and lines b and c to measure the power absorbed by the delta-connected load in Fig. 12.44, predict their readings.

12.73 For the circuit displayed in Fig. 12.73, find the wattmeter readings.

Figure 12.73   For Prob. 12.73.

12.74 Predict the wattmeter readings for the circuit in Fig. 12.74.

Figure 12.74   For Prob. 12.74.

12.75 A man has a body resistance of 600 Ω. How much current flows through his ungrounded body:

    (a) when he touches the terminals of a 12-V autobattery?

    (b) when he sticks his finger into a 120-V light socket?

12.76 Show that the I^2R losses will be higher for a 120-V appliance than for a 240-V appliance if both have the same power rating.

COMPREHENSIVE PROBLEMS

12.77 A three-phase generator supplied 3.6 kVA at a power factor of 0.85 lagging. If 2500 W are delivered to the load and line losses are 80 W per phase, what are the losses in the generator?

12.78 A three-phase 440-V, 51-kW, 60-kVA inductive load operates at 60 Hz and is wye-connected. It is desired to correct the power factor to 0.95 lagging. What

value of capacitor should be placed in parallel with each load impedance?

12.79 A balanced three-phase generator has an abc phase sequence with phase voltage $\mathbf{V}_{an} = 255\underline{/0°}$ V. The generator feeds an induction motor which may be represented by a balanced Y-connected load with an impedance of $12 + j5$ Ω per phase. Find the line currents and the load voltages. Assume a line impedance of 2 Ω per phase.

12.80 A balanced three-phase source furnishes power to the following three loads:

Load 1: 6 kVA at 0.83 pf lagging

Load 2: unknown

Load 3: 8 kW at 0.7071 pf leading

If the line current is 84.6 A rms, the line voltage at the load is 208 V rms, and the combined load has a 0.8 pf lagging, determine the unknown load.

12.81 A professional center is supplied by a balanced three-phase source. The center has four balanced three-phase loads as follows:

Load 1: 150 kVA at 0.8 pf leading

Load 2: 100 kW at unity pf

Load 3: 200 kVA at 0.6 pf lagging

Load 4: 80 kW and 95 kVAR (inductive)

If the line impedance is $0.02 + j0.05$ Ω per phase and the line voltage at the loads is 480 V, find the magnitude of the line voltage at the source.

12.82 A balanced three-phase system has a distribution wire with impedance $2 + j6$ Ω per phase. The system supplies two three-phase loads that are connected in parallel. The first is a balanced wye-connected load which absorbs 400 kVA at a power factor of 0.8 lagging. The second load is a balanced delta-connected load with impedance of $10 + j8$ Ω per phase. If the magnitude of the line voltage at the loads is 2400 V rms, calculate the magnitude of the line voltage at the source and the total complex power supplied to the two loads.

12.83 A commercially available three-phase inductive motor operates at a full load of 120 hp (1 hp = 746 W) at 95 percent efficiency at a lagging power factor of 0.707. The motor is connected in parallel to a 80-kW balanced three-phase heater at unity power factor. If the magnitude of the line voltage is 480 V rms, calculate the line current.

***12.84** Figure 12.75 displays a three-phase delta-connected motor load which is connected to a line voltage of 440 V and draws 4 kVA at a power factor of 72 percent lagging. In addition, a single 1.8 kVAR capacitor is connected between lines a and b, while a 800-W lighting load is connected between line c and neutral. Assuming the abc sequence and taking $\mathbf{V}_{an} = V_p\angle 0°$, find the magnitude and phase angle of currents $\mathbf{I}_a$, $\mathbf{I}_b$, $\mathbf{I}_c$, and $\mathbf{I}_n$.

Figure 12.75 For Prob. 12.84.

12.85 Design a three-phase heater with suitable symmetric loads using wye-connected pure resistance. Assume that the heater is supplied by a 240-V line voltage and is to give 27 kW of heat.

12.86 For the single-phase three-wire system in Fig. 12.76, find currents $\mathbf{I}_{aA}$, $\mathbf{I}_{bB}$, and $\mathbf{I}_{nN}$.

Figure 12.76 For Prob. 12.86.

12.87 Consider the single-phase three-wire system shown in Fig. 12.77. Find the current in the neutral wire and the complex power supplied by each source. Take $\mathbf{V}_s$ as a $115\angle 0°$-V, 60-Hz source.

Figure 12.77 For Prob. 12.87.

CHAPTER | 13

MAGNETICALLY COUPLED CIRCUITS

The scientist does not study nature because it is useful; he studies it because he delights in it, and he delights in it because it is beautiful. If nature were not beautiful, it would not be worth knowing, and if nature were not worth knowing, life would not be worth living.

—Jules Henri Poincaré

Enhancing Your Career

Career in Electromagnetics Electromagnetics is the branch of electrical engineering (or physics) that deals with the analysis and application of electric and magnetic fields. In electromagnetics, electric circuit analysis is applied at low frequencies.

The principles of electromagnetics (EM) are applied in various allied disciplines, such as electric machines, electromechanical energy conversion, radar meteorology, remote sensing, satellite communications, bioelectromagnetics, electromagnetic interference and compatibility, plasmas, and fiber optics. EM devices include electric motors and generators, transformers, electromagnets, magnetic levitation, antennas, radars, microwave ovens, microwave dishes, superconductors, and electrocardiograms. The design of these devices requires a thorough knowledge of the laws and principles of EM.

EM is regarded as one of the more difficult disciplines in electrical engineering. One reason is that EM phenomena are rather abstract. But if one enjoys working with mathematics and can visualize the invisible, one should consider being a specialist in EM, since few electrical engineers specialize in this area. Electrical engineers who specialize in EM are needed in microwave industries, radio/TV broadcasting stations, electromagnetic research laboratories, and several communications industries.

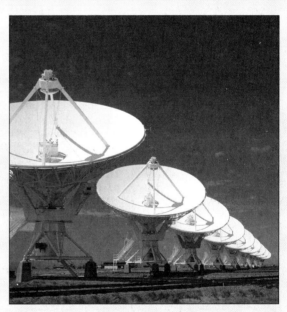

Telemetry receiving station for space satellites. (© Space Frontiers/Getty Images.)

13.1   INTRODUCTION

The circuits we have considered so far may be regarded as *conductively coupled*, because one loop affects the neighboring loop through current conduction. When two loops with or without contacts between them affect each other through the magnetic field generated by one of them, they are said to be *magnetically coupled*.

The transformer is an electrical device designed on the basis of the concept of magnetic coupling. It uses magnetically coupled coils to transfer energy from one circuit to another. Transformers are key circuit elements. They are used in power systems for stepping up or stepping down ac voltages or currents. They are used in electronic circuits such as radio and television receivers for such purposes as impedance matching, isolating one part of a circuit from another, and again for stepping up or down ac voltages and currents.

We will begin with the concept of mutual inductance and introduce the dot convention used for determining the voltage polarities of inductively coupled components. Based on the notion of mutual inductance, we then introduce the circuit element known as the *transformer*. We will consider the linear transformer, the ideal transformer, the ideal autotransformer, and the three-phase transformer. Finally, among their important applications, we look at transformers as isolating and matching devices and their use in power distribution.

13.2   MUTUAL INDUCTANCE

When two inductors (or coils) are in a close proximity to each other, the magnetic flux caused by current in one coil links with the other coil, thereby inducing voltage in the latter. This phenomenon is known as *mutual inductance*.

Let us first consider a single inductor, a coil with N turns. When current i flows through the coil, a magnetic flux ϕ is produced around it (Fig. 13.1). According to Faraday's law, the voltage v induced in the coil is proportional to the number of turns N and the time rate of change of the magnetic flux ϕ; that is,

$$v = N \frac{d\phi}{dt} \tag{13.1}$$

Figure 13.1 Magnetic flux produced by a single coil with N turns.

But the flux ϕ is produced by current i so that any change in ϕ is caused by a change in the current. Hence, Eq. (13.1) can be written as

$$v = N \frac{d\phi}{di} \frac{di}{dt} \tag{13.2}$$

or

$$v = L \frac{di}{dt} \tag{13.3}$$

which is the voltage-current relationship for the inductor. From Eqs. (13.2) and (13.3), the inductance L of the inductor is thus given by

$$L = N \frac{d\phi}{di} \tag{13.4}$$

This inductance is commonly called *self-inductance*, because it relates the voltage induced in a coil by a time-varying current in the same coil.

Now consider two coils with self-inductances L_1 and L_2 that are in close proximity with each other (Fig. 13.2). Coil 1 has N_1 turns, while coil 2 has N_2 turns. For the sake of simplicity, assume that the second inductor carries no current. The magnetic flux ϕ_1 emanating from coil 1 has two components: one component ϕ_{11} links only coil 1, and another component ϕ_{12} links both coils. Hence,

$$\phi_1 = \phi_{11} + \phi_{12} \tag{13.5}$$

Figure 13.2   Mutual inductance M_{21} of coil 2 with respect to coil 1.

Although the two coils are physically separated, they are said to be *magnetically coupled.* Since the entire flux ϕ_1 links coil 1, the voltage induced in coil 1 is

$$v_1 = N_1 \frac{d\phi_1}{dt} \tag{13.6}$$

Only flux ϕ_{12} links coil 2, so the voltage induced in coil 2 is

$$v_2 = N_2 \frac{d\phi_{12}}{dt} \tag{13.7}$$

Again, as the fluxes are caused by the current i_1 flowing in coil 1, Eq. (13.6) can be written as

$$v_1 = N_1 \frac{d\phi_1}{di_1} \frac{di_1}{dt} = L_1 \frac{di_1}{dt} \tag{13.8}$$

where $L_1 = N_1 \, d\phi_1/di_1$ is the self-inductance of coil 1. Similarly, Eq. (13.7) can be written as

$$v_2 = N_2 \frac{d\phi_{12}}{di_1} \frac{di_1}{dt} = M_{21} \frac{di_1}{dt} \tag{13.9}$$

where

$$M_{21} = N_2 \frac{d\phi_{12}}{di_1} \tag{13.10}$$

M_{21} is known as the *mutual inductance* of coil 2 with respect to coil 1. Subscript 21 indicates that the inductance M_{21} relates the voltage induced in coil 2 to the current in coil 1. Thus, the open-circuit *mutual voltage* (or induced voltage) across coil 2 is

$$\boxed{v_2 = M_{21} \frac{di_1}{dt}} \tag{13.11}$$

Suppose we now let current i_2 flow in coil 2, while coil 1 carries no current (Fig. 13.3). The magnetic flux ϕ_2 emanating from coil 2 comprises flux ϕ_{22} that links only coil 2 and flux ϕ_{21} that links both coils. Hence,

$$\phi_2 = \phi_{21} + \phi_{22} \tag{13.12}$$

The entire flux ϕ_2 links coil 2, so the voltage induced in coil 2 is

$$v_2 = N_2 \frac{d\phi_2}{dt} = N_2 \frac{d\phi_2}{di_2} \frac{di_2}{dt} = L_2 \frac{di_2}{dt} \tag{13.13}$$

Figure 13.3   Mutual inductance M_{12} of coil 1 with respect to coil 2.

where $L_2 = N_2 \, d\phi_2/di_2$ is the self-inductance of coil 2. Since only flux ϕ_{21} links coil 1, the voltage induced in coil 1 is

$$v_1 = N_1 \frac{d\phi_{21}}{dt} = N_1 \frac{d\phi_{21}}{di_2} \frac{di_2}{dt} = M_{12} \frac{di_2}{dt} \tag{13.14}$$

where

$$M_{12} = N_1 \frac{d\phi_{21}}{di_2} \tag{13.15}$$

which is the *mutual inductance* of coil 1 with respect to coil 2. Thus, the open-circuit *mutual voltage* across coil 1 is

$$\boxed{v_1 = M_{12} \frac{di_2}{dt}} \tag{13.16}$$

We will see in the next section that M_{12} and M_{21} are equal, that is,

$$M_{12} = M_{21} = M \tag{13.17}$$

and we refer to M as the mutual inductance between the two coils. Like self-inductance L, mutual inductance M is measured in henrys (H). Keep in mind that mutual coupling only exists when the inductors or coils are in close proximity, and the circuits are driven by time-varying sources. We recall that inductors act like short circuits to dc.

From the two cases in Figs. 13.2 and 13.3, we conclude that mutual inductance results if a voltage is induced by a time-varying current in another circuit. It is the property of an inductor to produce a voltage in reaction to a time-varying current in another inductor near it. Thus,

> Mutual inductance is the ability of one inductor to induce a voltage across a neighboring inductor, measured in henrys (H).

Although mutual inductance M is always a positive quantity, the mutual voltage $M \, di/dt$ may be negative or positive, just like the self-induced voltage $L \, di/dt$. However, unlike the self-induced $L \, di/dt$, whose polarity is determined by the reference direction of the current and the reference polarity of the voltage (according to the passive sign convention), the polarity of mutual voltage $M \, di/dt$ is not easy to determine, because four terminals are involved. The choice of the correct polarity for $M \, di/dt$ is made by examining the orientation or particular way in which both coils are physically wound and applying Lenz's law in conjunction with the right-hand rule. Since it is inconvenient to show the construction details of coils on a circuit schematic, we apply the *dot convention* in circuit analysis. By this convention, a dot is placed in the circuit at one end of each of the two magnetically coupled coils to indicate the direction of the magnetic flux if current enters that dotted terminal of the coil. This is illustrated in Fig. 13.4. Given a circuit, the dots are already placed beside the coils so that we need not bother about how to place them. The dots are used along with the dot convention to determine the polarity of the mutual voltage. The dot convention is stated as follows:

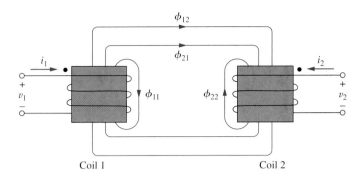

Figure 13.4   Illustration of the dot convention.

If a current enters the dotted terminal of one coil, the reference
polarity of the mutual voltage in the second coil is positive
at the dotted terminal of the second coil.

Alternatively,

If a current leaves the dotted terminal of one coil, the reference
polarity of the mutual voltage in the second coil is negative
at the dotted terminal of the second coil.

Thus, the reference polarity of the mutual voltage depends on the reference direction of the inducing current and the dots on the coupled coils. Application of the dot convention is illustrated in the four pairs of mutually coupled coils in Fig. 13.5. For the coupled coils in Fig. 13.5(a), the sign of the mutual voltage v_2 is determined by the reference polarity for v_2 and the direction of i_1. Since i_1 enters the dotted terminal of coil 1 and v_2 is positive at the dotted terminal of coil 2, the mutual voltage is $+M\,di_1/dt$. For the coils in Fig. 13.5(b), the current i_1 enters the dotted terminal of coil 1 and v_2 is negative at the dotted terminal of coil 2. Hence, the mutual voltage is $-M\,di_1/dt$. The same reasoning applies to the coils in Fig. 13.5(c) and 13.5(d).

Figure 13.6 shows the dot convention for coupled coils in series. For the coils in Fig. 13.6(a), the total inductance is

$$L = L_1 + L_2 + 2M \qquad \text{(Series-aiding connection)} \qquad (13.18)$$

For the coil in Fig. 13.6(b),

$$L = L_1 + L_2 - 2M \qquad \text{(Series-opposing connection)} \qquad (13.19)$$

Now that we know how to determine the polarity of the mutual voltage, we are prepared to analyze circuits involving mutual inductance.

Figure 13.5   Examples illustrating how to apply the dot convention.

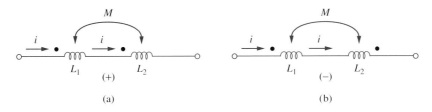

Figure 13.6   Dot convention for coils in series; the sign indicates the polarity of the mutual voltage: (a) series-aiding connection, (b) series-opposing connection.

As the first example, consider the circuit in Fig. 13.7. Applying KVL to coil 1 gives

$$v_1 = i_1 R_1 + L_1 \frac{di_1}{dt} + M \frac{di_2}{dt} \qquad (13.20\text{a})$$

For coil 2, KVL gives

$$v_2 = i_2 R_2 + L_2 \frac{di_2}{dt} + M \frac{di_1}{dt} \qquad (13.20\text{b})$$

We can write Eq. (13.20) in the frequency domain as

$$\mathbf{V}_1 = (R_1 + j\omega L_1)\mathbf{I}_1 + j\omega M \mathbf{I}_2 \qquad (13.21\text{a})$$

$$\mathbf{V}_2 = j\omega M \mathbf{I}_1 + (R_2 + j\omega L_2)\mathbf{I}_2 \qquad (13.21\text{b})$$

As a second example, consider the circuit in Fig. 13.8. We analyze this in the frequency domain. Applying KVL to coil 1, we get

$$\mathbf{V} = (\mathbf{Z}_1 + j\omega L_1)\mathbf{I}_1 - j\omega M \mathbf{I}_2 \qquad (13.22\text{a})$$

For coil 2, KVL yields

$$0 = -j\omega M \mathbf{I}_1 + (\mathbf{Z}_L + j\omega L_2)\mathbf{I}_2 \qquad (13.22\text{b})$$

Equations (13.21) and (13.22) are solved in the usual manner to determine the currents.

Figure 13.7   Time-domain analysis of a circuit containing coupled coils.

Figure 13.8   Frequency-domain analysis of a circuit containing coupled coils.

At this introductory level we are not concerned with the determination of the mutual inductances of the coils and their dot placements. Like R, L, and C, calculation of M would involve applying the theory of electromagnetics to the actual physical properties of the coils. In this text, we assume that the mutual inductance and the dots placement are the "givens" of the circuit problem, like the circuit components R, L, and C.

EXAMPLE 13.1

Calculate the phasor currents $\mathbf{I}_1$ and $\mathbf{I}_2$ in the circuit of Fig. 13.9.

Figure 13.9   For Example 13.1.

Solution:

For coil 1, KVL gives

$$-12 + (-j4 + j5)\mathbf{I}_1 - j3\mathbf{I}_2 = 0$$

or

$$j\mathbf{I}_1 - j3\mathbf{I}_2 = 12 \qquad (13.1.1)$$

For coil 2, KVL gives

$$-j3\mathbf{I}_1 + (12 + j6)\mathbf{I}_2 = 0$$

or

$$\mathbf{I}_1 = \frac{(12 + j6)\mathbf{I}_2}{j3} = (2 - j4)\mathbf{I}_2 \qquad (13.1.2)$$

Substituting this in Eq. (13.1.1), we get

$$(j2 + 4 - j3)\mathbf{I}_2 = (4 - j)\mathbf{I}_2 = 12$$

or

$$\mathbf{I}_2 = \frac{12}{4 - j} = 2.91\underline{/14.04^\circ} \text{ A} \qquad (13.1.3)$$

From Eqs. (13.1.2) and (13.1.3),

$$\mathbf{I}_1 = (2 - j4)\mathbf{I}_2 = (4.472\underline{/-63.43^\circ})(2.91\underline{/14.04^\circ})$$
$$= 13.01\underline{/-49.39^\circ} \text{ A}$$

PRACTICE PROBLEM 13.1

Determine the voltage $\mathbf{V}_o$ in the circuit of Fig. 13.10.

Figure 13.10   For Practice Prob. 13.1.

Answer: $0.6\underline{/-90^\circ}$ V.

EXAMPLE 13.2

Calculate the mesh currents in the circuit of Fig. 13.11.

Figure 13.11   For Example 13.2.

Solution:

The key to analyzing a magnetically coupled circuit is knowing the polarity of the mutual voltage. We need to apply the dot rule. In Fig. 13.11, suppose coil 1 is the one whose reactance is 6 Ω, and coil 2 is the one whose reactance is 8 Ω. To figure out the polarity of the mutual voltage in coil 1 due to current I_2, we observe that I_2 leaves the dotted terminal of coil 2. Since we are applying KVL in the clockwise direction, it implies that the mutual voltage is negative, that is, $-j2I_2$.

Alternatively, it might be best to figure out the mutual voltage by redrawing the relevant portion of the circuit, as shown in Fig. 13.12(a), where it becomes clear that the mutual voltage is $V_1 = -2jI_2$.

Thus, for mesh 1 in Fig. 13.11, KVL gives

$$-100 + I_1(4 - j3 + j6) - j6I_2 - j2I_2 = 0$$

or

$$100 = (4 + j3)I_1 - j8I_2 \qquad (13.2.1)$$

Similarly, to figure out the mutual voltage in coil 2 due to current I_1, consider the relevant portion of the circuit, as shown in Fig. 13.12(b). Applying the dot convention gives the mutual voltage as $V_2 = -2jI_1$. Also, current I_2 sees the two coupled coils in series in Fig. 13.11; since it leaves the dotted terminals in both coils, Eq. (13.18) applies. Therefore, for mesh 2 in Fig. 13.11, KVL gives

$$0 = -2jI_1 - j6I_1 + (j6 + j8 + j2 \times 2 + 5)I_2$$

or

$$0 = -j8I_1 + (5 + j18)I_2 \qquad (13.2.2)$$

Putting Eqs. (13.2.1) and (13.2.2) in matrix form, we get

$$\begin{bmatrix} 100 \\ 0 \end{bmatrix} = \begin{bmatrix} 4 + j3 & -j8 \\ -j8 & 5 + j18 \end{bmatrix} \begin{bmatrix} I_1 \\ I_2 \end{bmatrix}$$

(a) $V_1 = -2jI_2$

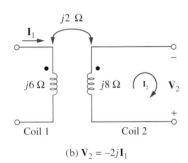

(b) $V_2 = -2jI_1$

Figure 13.12   For Example 13.2; redrawing the relevant portion of the circuit in Fig. 13.11 to find mutual voltages by the dot convention.

The determinants are

$$\Delta = \begin{vmatrix} 4+j3 & -j8 \\ -j8 & 5+j18 \end{vmatrix} = 30 + j87$$

$$\Delta_1 = \begin{vmatrix} 100 & -j8 \\ 0 & 5+j18 \end{vmatrix} = 100(5+j18)$$

$$\Delta_2 = \begin{vmatrix} 4+j3 & 100 \\ -j8 & 0 \end{vmatrix} = j800$$

Thus, we obtain the mesh currents as

$$\mathbf{I}_1 = \frac{\Delta_1}{\Delta} = \frac{100(5+j18)}{30+j87} = \frac{1{,}868.2\underline{/74.5^\circ}}{92.03\underline{/71^\circ}} = 20.3\underline{/3.5^\circ}\text{ A}$$

$$\mathbf{I}_2 = \frac{\Delta_2}{\Delta} = \frac{j800}{30+j87} = \frac{800\underline{/90^\circ}}{92.03\underline{/71^\circ}} = 8.693\underline{/19^\circ}\text{ A}$$

PRACTICE PROBLEM 13.2

Determine the phasor currents $\mathbf{I}_1$ and $\mathbf{I}_2$ in the circuit of Fig. 13.13.

Figure 13.13   For Practice Prob. 13.2.

Answer: $2.15\underline{/86.56^\circ}$, $3.23\underline{/86.56^\circ}$ A.

13.3 ENERGY IN A COUPLED CIRCUIT

In Chapter 6, we saw that the energy stored in an inductor is given by

$$w = \frac{1}{2}Li^2 \tag{13.23}$$

We now want to determine the energy stored in magnetically coupled coils.

Consider the circuit in Fig. 13.14. We assume that currents i_1 and i_2 are zero initially, so that the energy stored in the coils is zero. If we let i_1 increase from zero to I_1 while maintaining $i_2 = 0$, the power in coil 1 is

$$p_1(t) = v_1 i_1 = i_1 L_1 \frac{di_1}{dt} \tag{13.24}$$

and the energy stored in the circuit is

$$w_1 = \int p_1\,dt = L_1 \int_0^{I_1} i_1\,di_1 = \frac{1}{2}L_1 I_1^2 \tag{13.25}$$

Figure 13.14   The circuit for deriving energy stored in a coupled circuit.

If we now maintain $i_1 = I_1$ and increase i_2 from zero to I_2, the mutual voltage induced in coil 1 is $M_{12}\, di_2/dt$, while the mutual voltage induced in coil 2 is zero, since i_1 does not change. The power in the coils is now

$$p_2(t) = i_1 M_{12} \frac{di_2}{dt} + i_2 v_2 = I_1 M_{12} \frac{di_2}{dt} + i_2 L_2 \frac{di_2}{dt} \tag{13.26}$$

and the energy stored in the circuit is

$$w_2 = \int p_2\, dt = M_{12} I_1 \int_0^{I_2} di_2 + L_2 \int_0^{I_2} i_2\, di_2$$

$$= M_{12} I_1 I_2 + \frac{1}{2} L_2 I_2^2 \tag{13.27}$$

The total energy stored in the coils when both i_1 and i_2 have reached constant values is

$$w = w_1 + w_2 = \frac{1}{2} L_1 I_1^2 + \frac{1}{2} L_2 I_2^2 + M_{12} I_1 I_2 \tag{13.28}$$

If we reverse the order by which the currents reach their final values, that is, if we first increase i_2 from zero to I_2 and later increase i_1 from zero to I_1, the total energy stored in the coils is

$$w = \frac{1}{2} L_1 I_1^2 + \frac{1}{2} L_2 I_2^2 + M_{21} I_1 I_2 \tag{13.29}$$

Since the total energy stored should be the same regardless of how we reach the final conditions, comparing Eqs. (13.28) and (13.29) leads us to conclude that

$$M_{12} = M_{21} = M \tag{13.30a}$$

and

$$w = \frac{1}{2} L_1 I_1^2 + \frac{1}{2} L_2 I_2^2 + M I_1 I_2 \tag{13.30b}$$

This equation was derived based on the assumption that the coil currents both entered the dotted terminals. If one current enters one dotted terminal while the other current leaves the other dotted terminal, the mutual voltage is negative, so that the mutual energy $M I_1 I_2$ is also negative. In that case,

$$w = \frac{1}{2} L_1 I_1^2 + \frac{1}{2} L_2 I_2^2 - M I_1 I_2 \tag{13.31}$$

Also, since I_1 and I_2 are arbitrary values, they may be replaced by i_1 and i_2, which gives the instantaneous energy stored in the circuit the general expression

$$w = \frac{1}{2} L_1 i_1^2 + \frac{1}{2} L_2 i_2^2 \pm M i_1 i_2 \tag{13.32}$$

The positive sign is selected for the mutual term if both currents enter or leave the dotted terminals of the coils; the negative sign is selected otherwise.

We will now establish an upper limit for the mutual inductance M. The energy stored in the circuit cannot be negative because the circuit is passive. This means that the quantity $1/2L_1i_1^2 + 1/2L_2i_2^2 - Mi_1i_2$ must be greater than or equal to zero,

$$\frac{1}{2}L_1i_1^2 + \frac{1}{2}L_2i_2^2 - Mi_1i_2 \geq 0 \qquad (13.33)$$

To complete the square, we both add and subtract the term $i_1i_2\sqrt{L_1L_2}$ on the right-hand side of Eq. (13.33) and obtain

$$\frac{1}{2}(i_1\sqrt{L_1} - i_2\sqrt{L_2})^2 + i_1i_2(\sqrt{L_1L_2} - M) \geq 0 \qquad (13.34)$$

The squared term is never negative; at its least it is zero. Therefore, the second term on the right-hand side of Eq. (13.34) must be greater than zero; that is,

$$\sqrt{L_1L_2} - M \geq 0$$

or

$$M \leq \sqrt{L_1L_2} \qquad (13.35)$$

Thus, the mutual inductance cannot be greater than the geometric mean of the self-inductances of the coils. The extent to which the mutual inductance M approaches the upper limit is specified by the *coefficient of coupling* k, given by

$$k = \frac{M}{\sqrt{L_1L_2}} \qquad (13.36)$$

or

$$\boxed{M = k\sqrt{L_1L_2}} \qquad (13.37)$$

where $0 \leq k \leq 1$ or equivalently $0 \leq M \leq \sqrt{L_1L_2}$. The coupling coefficient is the fraction of the total flux emanating from one coil that links the other coil. For example, in Fig. 13.2,

$$k = \frac{\phi_{12}}{\phi_1} = \frac{\phi_{12}}{\phi_{11} + \phi_{12}} \qquad (13.38)$$

and in Fig. 13.3,

$$k = \frac{\phi_{21}}{\phi_2} = \frac{\phi_{21}}{\phi_{21} + \phi_{22}} \qquad (13.39)$$

If the entire flux produced by one coil links another coil, then $k = 1$ and we have 100 percent coupling, or the coils are said to be *perfectly coupled*. For $k < 0.5$, coils are said to be *loosely coupled*; and for $k > 0.5$, they are said to be *tightly coupled*. Thus,

> The coupling coefficient k is a measure of the magnetic coupling between two coils; $0 \leq k \leq 1$.

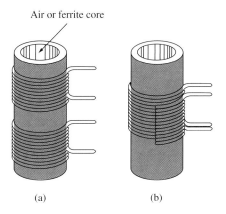

Air or ferrite core

(a)   (b)

Figure 13.15   Windings: (a) loosely coupled, (b) tightly coupled; cutaway view demonstrates both windings.

We expect k to depend on the closeness of the two coils, their core, their orientation, and their windings. Figure 13.15 shows loosely

coupled windings and tightly coupled windings. The air-core transformers used in radio frequency circuits are loosely coupled, whereas
iron-core transformers used in power systems are tightly coupled. The
linear transformers discussed in Section 3.4 are mostly air-core; the ideal
transformers discussed in Sections 13.5 and 13.6 are principally iron-core.

EXAMPLE 13.3

Figure 13.16   For Example 13.3.

Consider the circuit in Fig. 13.16. Determine the coupling coefficient.
Calculate the energy stored in the coupled inductors at time $t = 1$ s if
$v = 60 \cos(4t + 30°)$ V.

Solution:

The coupling coefficient is

$$k = \frac{M}{\sqrt{L_1 L_2}} = \frac{2.5}{\sqrt{20}} = 0.56$$

indicating that the inductors are tightly coupled. To find the energy stored,
we need to obtain the frequency-domain equivalent of the circuit.

$$
\begin{aligned}
60 \cos(4t + 30°) &\implies 60\underline{/30°}, \quad \omega = 4 \text{ rad/s} \\
5 \text{ H} &\implies j\omega L_1 = j20 \ \Omega \\
2.5 \text{ H} &\implies j\omega M = j10 \ \Omega \\
4 \text{ H} &\implies j\omega L_2 = j16 \ \Omega \\
\frac{1}{16} \text{ F} &\implies \frac{1}{j\omega C} = -j4 \ \Omega
\end{aligned}
$$

The frequency-domain equivalent is shown in Fig. 13.17. We now apply
mesh analysis. For mesh 1,

$$(10 + j20)\mathbf{I}_1 + j10\mathbf{I}_2 = 60\underline{/30°} \qquad (13.3.1)$$

For mesh 2,

$$j10\mathbf{I}_1 + (j16 - j4)\mathbf{I}_2 = 0$$

or

$$\mathbf{I}_1 = -1.2\mathbf{I}_2 \qquad (13.3.2)$$

Substituting this into Eq. (13.3.1) yields

$$\mathbf{I}_2(-12 - j14) = 60\underline{/30°} \implies \mathbf{I}_2 = 3.254\underline{/160.6°} \text{ A}$$

and

$$\mathbf{I}_1 = -1.2\mathbf{I}_2 = 3.905\underline{/-19.4°} \text{ A}$$

In the time-domain,

$$i_1 = 3.905 \cos(4t - 19.4°), \qquad i_2 = 3.254 \cos(4t + 160.6°)$$

At time $t = 1$ s, $4t = 4$ rad $= 229.2°$, and

$$i_1 = 3.905 \cos(229.2° - 19.4°) = -3.389 \text{ A}$$

$$i_2 = 3.254 \cos(229.2° + 160.6°) = 2.824 \text{ A}$$

The total energy stored in the coupled inductors is

$$w = \frac{1}{2}L_1 i_1^2 + \frac{1}{2}L_2 i_2^2 + M i_1 i_2$$

$$= \frac{1}{2}(5)(-3.389)^2 + \frac{1}{2}(4)(2.824)^2 + 2.5(-3.389)(2.824) = 20.73 \text{ J}$$

Figure 13.17   Frequency-domain equivalent of the circuit in Fig. 13.16.

PRACTICE PROBLEM 13.3

For the circuit in Fig. 13.18, determine the coupling coefficient and the energy stored in the coupled inductors at $t = 1.5$ s.

Figure 13.18   For Practice Prob. 13.3.

Answer: 0.7071, 9.85 J.

13.4 LINEAR TRANSFORMERS

Here we introduce the transformer as a new circuit element. A transformer is a magnetic device that takes advantage of the phenomenon of mutual inductance.

> A transformer is generally a four-terminal device comprising two (or more) magnetically coupled coils.

As shown in Fig. 13.19, the coil that is directly connected to the voltage source is called the *primary winding*. The coil connected to the load is called the *secondary winding*. The resistances R_1 and R_2 are included to account for the losses (power dissipation) in the coils. The transformer is said to be *linear* if the coils are wound on a magnetically linear

A linear transformer may also be regarded as one whose flux is proportional to the currents in its windings.

material—a material for which the magnetic permeability is constant. Such materials include air, plastic, Bakelite, and wood. In fact, most materials are magnetically linear. Linear transformers are sometimes called *air-core transformers*, although not all of them are necessarily air-core. They are used in radio and TV sets. Figure 13.20 portrays different types of transformers.

Primary coil   Secondary coil

Figure 13.19   A linear transformer.

(a)   (b)

Figure 13.20   Different types of transformers: (a) copper wound dry power transformer, (b) audio transformers. *(Courtesy of: (a) Electric Service Co., (b) Jensen Transformers.)*

We would like to obtain the input impedance $\mathbf{Z}_{in}$ as seen from the source, because $\mathbf{Z}_{in}$ governs the behavior of the primary circuit. Applying KVL to the two meshes in Fig. 13.19 gives

$$\mathbf{V} = (R_1 + j\omega L_1)\mathbf{I}_1 - j\omega M\mathbf{I}_2 \qquad (13.40a)$$

$$0 = -j\omega M\mathbf{I}_1 + (R_2 + j\omega L_2 + \mathbf{Z}_L)\mathbf{I}_2 \qquad (13.40b)$$

In Eq. (13.40b), we express $\mathbf{I}_2$ in terms of $\mathbf{I}_1$ and substitute it into Eq. (13.40a). We get the input impedance as

$$\mathbf{Z}_{\text{in}} = \frac{\mathbf{V}}{\mathbf{I}_1} = R_1 + j\omega L_1 + \frac{\omega^2 M^2}{R_2 + j\omega L_2 + \mathbf{Z}_L} \qquad (13.41)$$

Notice that the input impedance comprises two terms. The first term, $(R_1 + j\omega L_1)$, is the primary impedance. The second term is due to the coupling between the primary and secondary windings. It is as though this impedance is reflected to the primary. Thus, it is known as the *reflected impedance* $\mathbf{Z}_R$, and

Some authors call this the *coupled impedance*.

$$\boxed{\mathbf{Z}_R = \frac{\omega^2 M^2}{R_2 + j\omega L_2 + \mathbf{Z}_L}} \qquad (13.42)$$

It should be noted that the result in Eq. (13.41) or (13.42) is not affected by the location of the dots on the transformer, because the same result is produced when M is replaced by $-M$.

The little bit of experience gained in Sections 13.2 and 13.3 in analyzing magnetically coupled circuits is enough to convince anyone that analyzing these circuits is not as easy as circuits in previous chapters. For this reason, it is sometimes convenient to replace a magnetically coupled circuit by an equivalent circuit with no magnetic coupling. We want to replace the linear transformer in Fig. 13.19 by an equivalent T or Π circuit, a circuit that would have no mutual inductance.

The voltage-current relationships for the primary and secondary coils give the matrix equation

$$\begin{bmatrix} \mathbf{V}_1 \\ \mathbf{V}_2 \end{bmatrix} = \begin{bmatrix} j\omega L_1 & j\omega M \\ j\omega M & j\omega L_2 \end{bmatrix} \begin{bmatrix} \mathbf{I}_1 \\ \mathbf{I}_2 \end{bmatrix} \qquad (13.43)$$

Figure 13.21   Determining the equivalent circuit of a linear transformer.

By matrix inversion, this can be written as

$$\begin{bmatrix} \mathbf{I}_1 \\ \mathbf{I}_2 \end{bmatrix} = \begin{bmatrix} \dfrac{L_2}{j\omega(L_1 L_2 - M^2)} & \dfrac{-M}{j\omega(L_1 L_2 - M^2)} \\ \dfrac{-M}{j\omega(L_1 L_2 - M^2)} & \dfrac{L_1}{j\omega(L_1 L_2 - M^2)} \end{bmatrix} \begin{bmatrix} \mathbf{V}_1 \\ \mathbf{V}_2 \end{bmatrix} \qquad (13.44)$$

Our goal is to match Eqs. (13.43) and (13.44) with the corresponding equations for the T and Π networks.

For the T (or Y) network of Fig. 13.22, mesh analysis provides the terminal equations as

$$\begin{bmatrix} \mathbf{V}_1 \\ \mathbf{V}_2 \end{bmatrix} = \begin{bmatrix} j\omega(L_a + L_c) & j\omega L_c \\ j\omega L_c & j\omega(L_b + L_c) \end{bmatrix} \begin{bmatrix} \mathbf{I}_1 \\ \mathbf{I}_2 \end{bmatrix} \qquad (13.45)$$

Figure 13.22   An equivalent T circuit.

Figure 13.23   An equivalent Π circuit.

If the circuits in Figs. 13.21 and 13.22 are equivalents, Eqs. (13.43) and (13.45) must be identical. Equating terms in the impedance matrices of

Eqs. (13.43) and (13.45) leads to

$$L_a = L_1 - M, \qquad L_b = L_2 - M, \qquad L_c = M \qquad (13.46)$$

For the Π (or Δ) network in Fig. 13.23, nodal analysis gives the terminal equations as

$$\begin{bmatrix} \mathbf{I}_1 \\ \mathbf{I}_2 \end{bmatrix} = \begin{bmatrix} \dfrac{1}{j\omega L_A} + \dfrac{1}{j\omega L_C} & -\dfrac{1}{j\omega L_C} \\[3mm] -\dfrac{1}{j\omega L_C} & \dfrac{1}{j\omega L_B} + \dfrac{1}{j\omega L_C} \end{bmatrix} \begin{bmatrix} \mathbf{V}_1 \\ \mathbf{V}_2 \end{bmatrix} \qquad (13.47)$$

Equating terms in admittance matrices of Eqs. (13.44) and (13.47), we obtain

$$L_A = \frac{L_1 L_2 - M^2}{L_2 - M}, \qquad L_B = \frac{L_1 L_2 - M^2}{L_1 - M}$$
$$L_C = \frac{L_1 L_2 - M^2}{M} \qquad (13.48)$$

Note that in Figs. 13.23 and 13.24, the inductors are not magnetically coupled. Also note that changing the locations of the dots in Fig. 13.21 can cause M to become $-M$. As Example 13.6 illustrates, a negative value of M is physically unrealizable but the equivalent model is still mathematically valid.

Figure 13.24   For Example 13.4.

EXAMPLE 13.4

In the circuit of Fig. 13.24, calculate the input impedance and current $\mathbf{I}_1$. Take $\mathbf{Z}_1 = 60 - j100\ \Omega$, $\mathbf{Z}_2 = 30 + j40\ \Omega$, and $\mathbf{Z}_L = 80 + j60\ \Omega$.

Solution:

From Eq. (13.41),

$$\mathbf{Z}_{\text{in}} = \mathbf{Z}_1 + j20 + \frac{(5)^2}{j40 + \mathbf{Z}_2 + \mathbf{Z}_L}$$
$$= 60 - j100 + j20 + \frac{25}{110 + j140}$$
$$= 60 - j80 + 0.14\underline{/-51.84^\circ}$$
$$= 60.09 - j80.11 = 100.14\underline{/-53.1^\circ}\ \Omega$$

Thus,

$$\mathbf{I}_1 = \frac{\mathbf{V}}{\mathbf{Z}_{\text{in}}} = \frac{50\underline{/60°}}{100.14\underline{/-53.1°}} = 0.5\underline{/113.1°} \text{ A}$$

PRACTICE PROBLEM 13.4

Find the input impedance of the circuit of Fig. 13.25 and the current from the voltage source.

Figure 13.25   For Practice Prob. 13.4.

Answer: $8.58\underline{/58.05°}$ Ω, $1.165\underline{/-58.05°}$ A.

EXAMPLE 13.5

Determine the T-equivalent circuit of the linear transformer in Fig. 13.26(a).

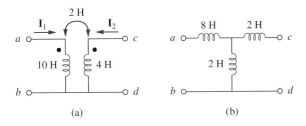

(a)   (b)

Figure 13.26   For Example 13.5: (a) a linear transformer, (b) its T-equivalent circuit.

Solution:

Given that $L_1 = 10$, $L_2 = 4$, and $M = 2$, the T equivalent network has the following parameters:

$$L_a = L_1 - M = 10 - 2 = 8 \text{ H}$$
$$L_b = L_2 - M = 4 - 2 = 2 \text{ H}, \qquad L_c = M = 2 \text{ H}$$

The T-equivalent circuit is shown in Fig. 13.26(b). We have assumed that reference directions for currents and voltage polarities in the primary and secondary windings conform to those in Fig. 13.21. Otherwise, we may need to replace M with $-M$, as Example 13.6 illustrates.

PRACTICE PROBLEM 13.5

For the linear transformer in Fig. 13.26 (a), find the Π equivalent network.

Answer: $L_A = 18$ H, $L_B = 4.5$ H, $L_C = 18$ H.

EXAMPLE 13.6

Solve for $\mathbf{I}_1$, $\mathbf{I}_2$, and $\mathbf{V}_o$ in Fig. 13.27 (the same circuit as for Practice Prob. 13.1) using the T-equivalent circuit for the linear transformer.

Figure 13.27   For Example 13.6.

Solution:

Notice that the circuit in Fig. 13.27 is the same as that in Fig. 13.10 except that the reference direction for current $\mathbf{I}_2$ has been reversed, just to make the reference directions for the currents for the magnetically coupled coils conform with those in Fig. 13.21.

We need to replace the magnetically coupled coils with the T-equivalent circuit. The relevant portion of the circuit in Fig. 13.27 is shown in Fig. 13.28(a). Comparing Fig. 13.28(a) with Fig. 13.21 shows that there are two differences. First, due to the current reference directions and voltage polarities, we need to replace M by $-M$ to make Fig. 13.28(a) conform with Fig. 13.21. Second, the circuit in Fig. 13.21 is in the time-domain, whereas the circuit in Fig. 13.28(a) is in the frequency-domain. The difference is the factor $j\omega$; that is, L in Fig. 13.21 has been replaced with $j\omega L$ and M with $j\omega M$. Since ω is not specified, we can assume $\omega = 1$ rad/s or any other value; it really does not matter. With these two differences in mind,

$$L_a = L_1 - (-M) = 8 + 1 = 9 \text{ H}$$
$$L_b = L_2 - (-M) = 5 + 1 = 6 \text{ H}, \qquad L_c = -M = -1 \text{ H}$$

Thus, the T-equivalent circuit for the coupled coils is as shown in Fig. 13.28(b).

Inserting the T-equivalent circuit in Fig. 13.28(b) to replace the two coils in Fig. 13.27 gives the equivalent circuit in Fig. 13.29, which can be solved using nodal or mesh analysis. Applying mesh analysis, we obtain

$$j6 = \mathbf{I}_1(4 + j9 - j1) + \mathbf{I}_2(-j1) \qquad (13.6.1)$$

and

$$0 = \mathbf{I}_1(-j1) + \mathbf{I}_2(10 + j6 - j1) \qquad (13.6.2)$$

From Eq. (13.6.2),

$$\mathbf{I}_1 = \frac{(10 + j5)}{j}\mathbf{I}_2 = (5 - j10)\mathbf{I}_2 \qquad (13.6.3)$$

(a)

(b)

Figure 13.28   For Example 13.6: (a) circuit for coupled coils of Fig. 13.27, (b) T-equivalent circuit.

Substituting Eq. (13.6.3) into Eq. (13.6.1) gives

$$j6 = (4 + j8)(5 - j10)\mathbf{I}_2 - j\mathbf{I}_2 = (100 - j)\mathbf{I}_2 \simeq 100\mathbf{I}_2$$

Since 100 is very large compared to 1, the imaginary part of $(100 - j)$ can be ignored so that $100 - j \simeq 100$. Hence,

$$\mathbf{I}_2 = \frac{j6}{100} = j0.06 = 0.06\underline{/90°} \text{ A}$$

From Eq. (13.6.3),

$$\mathbf{I}_1 = (5 - j10)\,j0.06 = 0.6 + j0.3 \text{ A}$$

and

$$\mathbf{V}_o = -10\mathbf{I}_2 = -j0.6 = 0.6\underline{/-90°} \text{ V}$$

This agrees with the answer to Practice Prob. 13.1. Of course, the direction of $\mathbf{I}_2$ in Fig. 13.10 is opposite to that in Fig. 13.27. This will not affect $\mathbf{V}_o$, but the value of $\mathbf{I}_2$ in this example is the negative of that of $\mathbf{I}_2$ in Practice Prob. 13.1. The advantage of using the T-equivalent model for the magnetically coupled coils is that in Fig. 13.29 we do not need to bother with the dot on the coupled coils.

Figure 13.29   For Example 13.6.

Solve the problem in Example 13.1 (see Fig. 13.9) using the T-equivalent model for the magnetically coupled coils.

Answer: $13\underline{/-49.4°}$ A, $2.91\underline{/14.04°}$ A.

13.5 IDEAL TRANSFORMERS

An ideal transformer is one with perfect coupling ($k = 1$). It consists of two (or more) coils with a large number of turns wound on a common core of high permeability. Because of this high permeability of the core, the flux links all the turns of both coils, thereby resulting in a perfect coupling.

To see how an ideal transformer is the limiting case of two coupled inductors where the inductances approach infinity and the coupling is perfect, let us reexamine the circuit in Fig. 13.14. In the frequency domain,

$$\mathbf{V}_1 = j\omega L_1\mathbf{I}_1 + j\omega M\mathbf{I}_2 \tag{13.49a}$$

$$\mathbf{V}_2 = j\omega M\mathbf{I}_1 + j\omega L_2\mathbf{I}_2 \tag{13.49b}$$

From Eq. (13.49a), $\mathbf{I}_1 = (\mathbf{V}_1 - j\omega M\mathbf{I}_2)/j\omega L_1$. Substituting this in Eq. (13.49b) gives

$$\mathbf{V}_2 = j\omega L_2\mathbf{I}_2 + \frac{M\mathbf{V}_1}{L_1} - \frac{j\omega M^2\mathbf{I}_2}{L_1}$$

But $M = \sqrt{L_1 L_2}$ for perfect coupling ($k = 1$). Hence,

$$\mathbf{V}_2 = j\omega L_2\mathbf{I}_2 + \frac{\sqrt{L_1 L_2}\mathbf{V}_1}{L_1} - \frac{j\omega L_1 L_2\mathbf{I}_2}{L_1} = \sqrt{\frac{L_2}{L_1}}\mathbf{V}_1 = n\mathbf{V}_1$$

where $n = \sqrt{L_2/L_1}$ and is called the *turns ratio*. As $L_1, L_2, M \rightarrow \infty$ such that n remains the same, the coupled coils become an ideal transformer. A transformer is said to be ideal if it has the following properties:

1. Coils have very large reactances ($L_1, L_2, M \rightarrow \infty$).
2. Coupling coefficient is equal to unity ($k = 1$).
3. Primary and secondary coils are lossless ($R_1 = 0 = R_2$).

An ideal transformer is a unity-coupled, lossless transformer in which the primary and secondary coils have infinite self-inductances.

Iron-core transformers are close approximations to ideal transformers. These are used in power systems and electronics.

Figure 13.30(a) shows a typical ideal transformer; the circuit symbol is in Fig. 13.30(b). The vertical lines between the coils indicate an iron core as distinct from the air core used in linear transformers. The primary winding has N_1 turns; the secondary winding has N_2 turns.

When a sinusoidal voltage is applied to the primary winding as shown in Fig. 13.31, the same magnetic flux ϕ goes through both windings. According to Faraday's law, the voltage across the primary winding is

$$v_1 = N_1\frac{d\phi}{dt} \tag{13.50a}$$

while that across the secondary winding is

$$v_2 = N_2\frac{d\phi}{dt} \tag{13.50b}$$

Dividing Eq. (13.50b) by Eq. (13.50a), we get

$$\frac{v_2}{v_1} = \frac{N_2}{N_1} = n \tag{13.51}$$

where n is, again, the *turns ratio* or *transformation ratio*. We can use the phasor voltages $\mathbf{V}_1$ and $\mathbf{V}_2$ rather than the instantaneous values v_1 and v_2. Thus, Eq. (13.51) may be written as

$$\boxed{\frac{\mathbf{V}_2}{\mathbf{V}_1} = \frac{N_2}{N_1} = n} \tag{13.52}$$

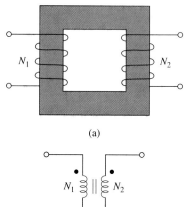

(a)

(b)

Figure 13.30   (a) Ideal transformer, (b) circuit symbol for ideal transformers.

Figure 13.31   Relating primary and secondary quantities in an ideal transformer.

For the reason of power conservation, the energy supplied to the primary must equal the energy absorbed by the secondary, since there are no losses in an ideal transformer. This implies that

$$v_1 i_1 = v_2 i_2 \tag{13.53}$$

In phasor form, Eq. (13.53) in conjunction with Eq. (13.52) becomes

$$\frac{\mathbf{I}_1}{\mathbf{I}_2} = \frac{\mathbf{V}_2}{\mathbf{V}_1} = n \tag{13.54}$$

showing that the primary and secondary currents are related to the turns ratio in the inverse manner as the voltages. Thus,

$$\boxed{\frac{\mathbf{I}_2}{\mathbf{I}_1} = \frac{N_1}{N_2} = \frac{1}{n}} \tag{13.55}$$

When $n = 1$, we generally call the transformer an *isolation transformer*. The reason will become obvious in Section 13.9.1. If $n > 1$, we have a *step-up transformer*, as the voltage is increased from primary to secondary ($\mathbf{V}_2 > \mathbf{V}_1$). On the other hand, if $n < 1$, the transformer is a *step-down transformer*, since the voltage is decreased from primary to secondary ($\mathbf{V}_2 < \mathbf{V}_1$).

A step-down transformer is one whose secondary voltage is less than its primary voltage.

A step-up transformer is one whose secondary voltage is greater than its primary voltage.

The ratings of transformers are usually specified as V_1/V_2. A transformer with rating 2400/120 V should have 2400 V on the primary and 120 in the secondary (i.e., a step-down transformer). Keep in mind that the voltage ratings are in rms.

Power companies often generate at some convenient voltage and use a step-up transformer to increase the voltage so that the power can be transmitted at very high voltage and low current over transmission lines, resulting in significant cost savings. Near residential consumer premises, step-down transformers are used to bring the voltage down to 120 V. Section 13.9.3 will elaborate on this.

It is important that we know how to get the proper polarity of the voltages and the direction of the currents for the transformer in Fig. 13.31. If the polarity of $\mathbf{V}_1$ or $\mathbf{V}_2$ or the direction of $\mathbf{I}_1$ or $\mathbf{I}_2$ is changed, n in Eqs. (13.51) to (13.55) may need to be replaced by $-n$. The two simple rules to follow are:

1. If $\mathbf{V}_1$ and $\mathbf{V}_2$ are *both* positive or both negative at the dotted terminals, use $+n$ in Eq. (13.52). Otherwise, use $-n$.

2. If $\mathbf{I}_1$ and $\mathbf{I}_2$ *both* enter into or both leave the dotted terminals, use $-n$ in Eq. (13.55). Otherwise, use $+n$.

The rules are demonstrated with the four circuits in Fig. 13.32.

Figure 13.32 Typical circuits illustrating proper voltage polarities and current directions in an ideal transformer.

Using Eqs. (13.52) and (13.55), we can always express $\mathbf{V}_1$ in terms of $\mathbf{V}_2$ and $\mathbf{I}_1$ in terms of $\mathbf{I}_2$, or vice versa:

$$\mathbf{V}_1 = \frac{\mathbf{V}_2}{n} \qquad \text{or} \qquad \mathbf{V}_2 = n\mathbf{V}_1 \tag{13.56}$$

$$\mathbf{I}_1 = n\mathbf{I}_2 \qquad \text{or} \qquad \mathbf{I}_2 = \frac{\mathbf{I}_1}{n} \tag{13.57}$$

The complex power in the primary winding is

$$\boxed{\mathbf{S}_1 = \mathbf{V}_1\mathbf{I}_1^* = \frac{\mathbf{V}_2}{n}(n\mathbf{I}_2)^* = \mathbf{V}_2\mathbf{I}_2^* = \mathbf{S}_2} \tag{13.58}$$

showing that the complex power supplied to the primary is delivered to the secondary without loss. The transformer absorbs no power. Of course, we should expect this, since the ideal transformer is lossless. The input impedance as seen by the source in Fig. 13.31 is found from Eqs. (13.56) and (13.57) as

$$\mathbf{Z}_{\text{in}} = \frac{\mathbf{V}_1}{\mathbf{I}_1} = \frac{1}{n^2}\frac{\mathbf{V}_2}{\mathbf{I}_2} \tag{13.59}$$

It is evident from Fig. 13.31 that $\mathbf{V}_2/\mathbf{I}_2 = \mathbf{Z}_L$, so that

$$\boxed{\mathbf{Z}_{\text{in}} = \frac{\mathbf{Z}_L}{n^2}} \tag{13.60}$$

The input impedance is also called the *reflected impedance*, since it appears as if the load impedance is reflected to the primary side. This ability of the transformer to transform a given impedance into another impedance provides us a means of *impedance matching* to ensure maximum power transfer. The idea of impedance matching is very useful in practice and will be discussed more in Section 13.9.2.

In analyzing a circuit containing an ideal transformer, it is common practice to eliminate the transformer by reflecting impedances and sources from one side of the transformer to the other. In the circuit of Fig. 13.33, suppose we want to reflect the secondary side of the circuit to the primary side. We find the Thevenin equivalent of the circuit to the right of the terminals a-b. We obtain $\mathbf{V}_{\text{Th}}$ as the open-circuit voltage at terminals a-b, as shown in Fig. 13.34(a). Since terminals a-b are open, $\mathbf{I}_1 = 0 = \mathbf{I}_2$ so that $\mathbf{V}_2 = \mathbf{V}_{s2}$. Hence, from Eq. (13.56),

$$\mathbf{V}_{\text{Th}} = \mathbf{V}_1 = \frac{\mathbf{V}_2}{n} = \frac{\mathbf{V}_{s2}}{n} \tag{13.61}$$

Notice that an ideal transformer reflects an impedance as the square of the turns ratio.

Figure 13.33   Ideal transformer circuit whose equivalent circuits are to be found.

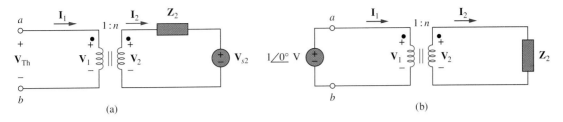

Figure 13.34   (a) Obtaining $\mathbf{V}_{Th}$ for the circuit in Fig. 13.33, (b) obtaining $\mathbf{Z}_{Th}$ for the circuit in Fig. 13.33.

To get $\mathbf{Z}_{Th}$, we remove the voltage source in the secondary winding and insert a unit source at terminals a-b, as in Fig. 13.34(b). From Eqs. (13.56) and (13.57), $\mathbf{I}_1 = n\mathbf{I}_2$ and $\mathbf{V}_1 = \mathbf{V}_2/n$, so that

$$\mathbf{Z}_{Th} = \frac{\mathbf{V}_1}{\mathbf{I}_1} = \frac{\mathbf{V}_2/n}{n\mathbf{I}_2} = \frac{\mathbf{Z}_2}{n^2}, \qquad \mathbf{V}_2 = \mathbf{Z}_2\mathbf{I}_2 \qquad (13.62)$$

which is what we should have expected from Eq. (13.60). Once we have $\mathbf{V}_{Th}$ and $\mathbf{Z}_{Th}$, we add the Thevenin equivalent to the part of the circuit in Fig. 13.33 to the left of terminals a-b. Figure 13.35 shows the result.

> The general rule for eliminating the transformer and reflecting the secondary circuit to the primary side is: divide the secondary impedance by n^2, divide the secondary voltage by n, and multiply the secondary current by n.

We can also reflect the primary side of the circuit in Fig. 13.33 to the secondary side. Figure 13.36 shows the equivalent circuit.

> The rule for eliminating the transformer and reflecting the primary circuit to the secondary side is: multiply the primary impedance by n^2, multiply the primary voltage by n, and divide the primary current by n.

According to Eq. (13.58), the power remains the same, whether calculated on the primary or the secondary side. But realize that this reflection approach only applies if there are no external connections between the primary and secondary windings. When we have external connections between the primary and secondary windings, we simply use regular mesh and nodal analysis. Examples of circuits where there are external connections between the primary and secondary windings are in Figs. 13.39 and 13.40. Also note that if the locations of the dots in Fig. 13.33 are changed, we might have to replace n by $-n$ in order to obey the dot rule, illustrated in Fig. 13.32.

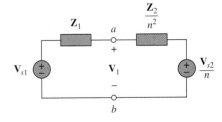

Figure 13.35   Equivalent circuit for Fig. 13.33 obtained by reflecting the secondary circuit to the primary side.

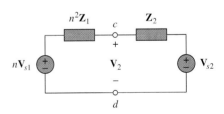

Figure 13.36   Equivalent circuit for Fig. 13.33 obtained by reflecting the primary circuit to the secondary side.

E X A M P L E   1 3 . 7

An ideal transformer is rated at 2400/120 V, 9.6 kVA, and has 50 turns on the secondary side. Calculate: (a) the turns ratio, (b) the number of turns on the primary side, and (c) the current ratings for the primary and secondary windings.

Solution:

(a) This is a step-down transformer, since $V_1 = 2{,}400 \text{ V} > V_2 = 120 \text{ V}$.

$$n = \frac{V_2}{V_1} = \frac{120}{2{,}400} = 0.05$$

(b)

$$n = \frac{N_2}{N_1} \implies 0.05 = \frac{50}{N_1}$$

or

$$N_1 = \frac{50}{0.05} = 1{,}000 \text{ turns}$$

(c) $S = V_1 I_1 = V_2 I_2 = 9.6 \text{ kVA}$. Hence,

$$I_1 = \frac{9{,}600}{V_1} = \frac{9{,}600}{2{,}400} = 4 \text{ A}$$

$$I_2 = \frac{9{,}600}{V_2} = \frac{9{,}600}{120} = 80 \text{ A} \qquad \text{or} \qquad I_2 = \frac{I_1}{n} = \frac{4}{0.05} = 80 \text{ A}$$

PRACTICE PROBLEM 13.7

The primary current to an ideal transformer rated at 3300/110 V is 3 A. Calculate: (a) the turns ratio, (b) the kVA rating, (c) the secondary current.

Answer: (a) 1/30, (b) 9.9 kVA, (c) 90 A.

EXAMPLE 13.8

For the ideal transformer circuit of Fig. 13.37, find: (a) the source current $\mathbf{I}_1$, (b) the output voltage $\mathbf{V}_o$, and (c) the complex power supplied by the source.

Figure 13.37   For Example 13.8.

Solution:

(a) The 20-Ω impedance can be reflected to the primary side and we get

$$\mathbf{Z}_R = \frac{20}{n^2} = \frac{20}{4} = 5 \ \Omega$$

Thus,

$$\mathbf{Z}_{\text{in}} = 4 - j6 + \mathbf{Z}_R = 9 - j6 = 10.82\underline{/-33.69°} \ \Omega$$

$$\mathbf{I}_1 = \frac{120\underline{/0°}}{\mathbf{Z}_{\text{in}}} = \frac{120\underline{/0°}}{10.82\underline{/-33.69°}} = 11.09\underline{/33.69°} \text{ A}$$

(b) Since both $\mathbf{I}_1$ and $\mathbf{I}_2$ leave the dotted terminals,

$$\mathbf{I}_2 = -\frac{1}{n}\mathbf{I}_1 = -5.545\underline{/33.69°}\ \text{A}$$

$$\mathbf{V}_o = 20\mathbf{I}_2 = 110.9\underline{/213.69°}\ \text{V}$$

(c) The complex power supplied is

$$\mathbf{S} = \mathbf{V}_s\mathbf{I}_1^* = (120\underline{/0°})(11.09\underline{/-33.69°}) = 1{,}330.8\underline{/-33.69°}\ \text{VA}$$

PRACTICE PROBLEM 13.8

In the ideal transformer circuit of Fig. 13.38, find $\mathbf{V}_o$ and the complex power supplied by the source.

Figure 13.38   For Practice Prob. 13.8.

Answer: $178.9\underline{/116.56°}\ \text{V}, 2{,}981.5\underline{/-26.56°}\ \text{VA}.$

EXAMPLE 13.9

Calculate the power supplied to the 10-Ω resistor in the ideal transformer circuit of Fig. 13.39.

Figure 13.39   For Example 13.9.

Solution:

Reflection to the secondary or primary side cannot be done with this circuit: there is direct connection between the primary and secondary sides due to the 30-Ω resistor. We apply mesh analysis. For mesh 1,

$$-120 + (20 + 30)\mathbf{I}_1 - 30\mathbf{I}_2 + \mathbf{V}_1 = 0$$

or

$$50\mathbf{I}_1 - 30\mathbf{I}_2 + \mathbf{V}_1 = 120 \qquad (13.9.1)$$

For mesh 2,

$$-\mathbf{V}_2 + (10 + 30)\mathbf{I}_2 - 30\mathbf{I}_1 = 0$$

or

$$-30\mathbf{I}_1 + 40\mathbf{I}_2 - \mathbf{V}_2 = 0 \qquad (13.9.2)$$

At the transformer terminals,

$$\mathbf{V}_2 = -\frac{1}{2}\mathbf{V}_1 \qquad (13.9.3)$$

$$\mathbf{I}_2 = -2\mathbf{I}_1 \qquad (13.9.4)$$

(Note that $n = 1/2$.) We now have four equations and four unknowns, but our goal is to get $\mathbf{I}_2$. So we substitute for $\mathbf{V}_1$ and $\mathbf{I}_1$ in terms of $\mathbf{V}_2$ and $\mathbf{I}_2$ in Eqs. (13.9.1) and (13.9.2). Equation (13.9.1) becomes

$$-55\mathbf{I}_2 - 2\mathbf{V}_2 = 120 \qquad (13.9.5)$$

and Eq. (13.9.2) becomes

$$15\mathbf{I}_2 + 40\mathbf{I}_2 - \mathbf{V}_2 = 0 \qquad \Longrightarrow \qquad \mathbf{V}_2 = 55\mathbf{I}_2 \qquad (13.9.6)$$

Substituting Eq. (13.9.6) in Eq. (13.9.5),

$$-165\mathbf{I}_2 = 120 \qquad \Longrightarrow \qquad \mathbf{I}_2 = -\frac{120}{165} = -0.7272 \text{ A}$$

The power absorbed by the 10-Ω resistor is

$$P = (-0.7272)^2(10) = 5.3 \text{ W}$$

PRACTICE PROBLEM 13.9

Find $\mathbf{V}_o$ in the circuit in Fig. 13.40.

Figure 13.40   For Practice Prob. 13.9.

Answer: 24 V.

13.6 IDEAL AUTOTRANSFORMERS

Unlike the conventional two-winding transformer we have considered so far, an *autotransformer* has a single continuous winding with a connection point called a *tap* between the primary and secondary sides. The tap is often adjustable so as to provide the desired turns ratio for stepping up or stepping down the voltage. This way, a variable voltage is provided to the load connected to the autotransformer.

An autotransformer is a transformer in which both the primary and the secondary are in a single winding.

Figure 13.41   A typical autotransformer. *(Courtesy of Todd Systems, Inc.)*

Figure 13.41 shows a typical autotransformer. As shown in Fig. 13.42, the autotransformer can operate in the step-down or step-up mode. The autotransformer is a type of power transformer. Its major advantage over the two-winding transformer is its ability to transfer larger apparent power. Example 13.10 will demonstrate this. Another advantage is that an autotransformer is smaller and lighter than an equivalent two-winding transformer. However, since both the primary and secondary windings are one winding, *electrical isolation* (no direct electrical connection) is lost. (We will see how the property of electrical isolation in the conventional transformer is practically employed in Section 13.9.1.) The lack of electrical isolation between the primary and secondary windings is a major disadvantage of the autotransformer.

Some of the formulas we derived for ideal transformers apply to ideal autotransformers as well. For the step-down autotransformer circuit of Fig. 13.42(a), Eq. (13.52) gives

$$\frac{\mathbf{V}_1}{\mathbf{V}_2} = \frac{N_1 + N_2}{N_2} = 1 + \frac{N_1}{N_2} \tag{13.63}$$

As an ideal autotransformer, there are no losses, so the complex power remains the same in the primary and secondary windings:

$$\mathbf{S}_1 = \mathbf{V}_1 \mathbf{I}_1^* = \mathbf{S}_2 = \mathbf{V}_2 \mathbf{I}_2^* \tag{13.64}$$

Equation (13.64) can also be expressed as

$$V_1 I_1 = V_2 I_2$$

or

$$\frac{V_2}{V_1} = \frac{I_1}{I_2} \tag{13.65}$$

Thus, the current relationship is

$$\frac{\mathbf{I}_1}{\mathbf{I}_2} = \frac{N_2}{N_1 + N_2} \tag{13.66}$$

For the step-up autotransformer circuit of Fig. 13.42(b),

$$\frac{\mathbf{V}_1}{N_1} = \frac{\mathbf{V}_2}{N_1 + N_2}$$

or

$$\frac{\mathbf{V}_1}{\mathbf{V}_2} = \frac{N_1}{N_1 + N_2} \tag{13.67}$$

(a)

(b)

Figure 13.42   (a) Step-down autotransformer, (b) step-up autotransformer.

The complex power given by Eq. (13.64) also applies to the step-up autotransformer so that Eq. (13.65) again applies. Hence, the current relationship is

$$\frac{\mathbf{I}_1}{\mathbf{I}_2} = \frac{N_1 + N_2}{N_1} = 1 + \frac{N_2}{N_1} \qquad (13.68)$$

A major difference between conventional transformers and autotransformers is that the primary and secondary sides of the autotransformer are not only coupled magnetically but also coupled conductively. The autotransformer can be used in place of a conventional transformer when electrical isolation is not required.

EXAMPLE 13.10

Compare the power ratings of the two-winding transformer in Fig. 13.43(a) and the autotransformer in Fig. 13.43(b).

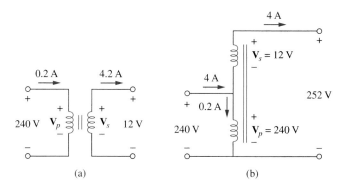

(a)   (b)

Figure 13.43   For Example 13.10.

Solution:

Although the primary and secondary windings of the autotransformer are together as a continuous winding, they are separated in Fig. 13.43(b) for clarity. We note that the current and voltage of each winding of the autotransformer in Fig. 13.43(b) are the same as those for the two-winding transformer in Fig. 13.43(a). This is the basis of comparing their power ratings.

For the two-winding transformer, the power rating is

$$S_1 = 0.2(240) = 48 \text{ VA} \qquad \text{or} \qquad S_2 = 4(12) = 48 \text{ VA}$$

For the autotransformer, the power rating is

$$S_1 = 4.2(240) = 1{,}008 \text{ VA} \qquad \text{or} \qquad S_2 = 4(252) = 1{,}008 \text{ VA}$$

which is 21 times the power rating of the two-winding transformer.

PRACTICE PROBLEM 13.10

Refer to Fig. 13.43. If the two-winding transformer is a 60-VA, 120 V/10 V transformer, what is the power rating of the autotransformer?

Answer: 780 VA.

EXAMPLE 13.11

Refer to the autotransformer circuit in Fig. 13.44. Calculate: (a) $\mathbf{I}_1$, $\mathbf{I}_2$, and $\mathbf{I}_o$ if $\mathbf{Z}_L = 8 + j6\ \Omega$, and (b) the complex power supplied to the load.

Figure 13.44   For Example 13.11.

Solution:

(a) This is a step-up autotransformer with $N_1 = 80$, $N_2 = 120$, $\mathbf{V}_1 = 120\underline{/30°}$, so Eq. (13.67) can be used to find $\mathbf{V}_2$ by

$$\frac{\mathbf{V}_1}{\mathbf{V}_2} = \frac{N_1}{N_1 + N_2} = \frac{80}{200}$$

or

$$\mathbf{V}_2 = \frac{200}{80}\mathbf{V}_1 = \frac{200}{80}(120\underline{/30°}) = 300\underline{/30°}\ \text{V}$$

$$\mathbf{I}_2 = \frac{\mathbf{V}_2}{\mathbf{Z}_L} = \frac{300\underline{/30°}}{8 + j6} = \frac{300\underline{/30°}}{10\underline{/36.87°}} = 30\underline{/-6.87°}\ \text{A}$$

But

$$\frac{\mathbf{I}_1}{\mathbf{I}_2} = \frac{N_1 + N_2}{N_1} = \frac{200}{80}$$

or

$$\mathbf{I}_1 = \frac{200}{80}\mathbf{I}_2 = \frac{200}{80}(30\underline{/-6.87°}) = 75\underline{/-6.87°}\ \text{A}$$

At the tap, KCL gives

$$\mathbf{I}_1 + \mathbf{I}_o = \mathbf{I}_2$$

or

$$\mathbf{I}_o = \mathbf{I}_2 - \mathbf{I}_1 = 30\underline{/-6.87°} - 75\underline{/-6.87°} = 45\underline{/173.13°}\ \text{A}$$

(b) The complex power supplied to the load is

$$\mathbf{S}_2 = \mathbf{V}_2\mathbf{I}_2^* = |\mathbf{I}_2|^2\mathbf{Z}_L = (30)^2(10\underline{/36.87°}) = 9\underline{/36.87°}\ \text{kVA}$$

PRACTICE PROBLEM 13.11

Figure 13.45   For Practice Prob. 13.11.

In the autotransformer circuit in Fig. 13.45, find currents $\mathbf{I}_1$, $\mathbf{I}_2$, and $\mathbf{I}_o$. Take $\mathbf{V}_1 = 1{,}250$ V, $\mathbf{V}_2 = 800$ V.

Answer: 12.8 A, 20 A, 7.2 A.

†13.7 THREE-PHASE TRANSFORMERS

To meet the demand for three-phase power transmission, transformer connections compatible with three-phase operations are needed. We can achieve the transformer connections in two ways: by connecting three single-phase transformers, thereby forming a so-called *transformer bank*, or by using a special three-phase transformer. For the same kVA rating, a three-phase transformer is always smaller and cheaper than three single-phase transformers. When single-phase transformers are used, one must ensure that they have the same turns ratio n to achieve a balanced three-phase system. There are four standard ways of connecting three single-phase transformers or a three-phase transformer for three-phase operations: Y-Y, Δ-Δ, Y-Δ, and Δ-Y.

For any of the four connections, the total apparent power S_T, real power P_T, and reactive power Q_T are obtained as

$$S_T = \sqrt{3}V_L I_L \tag{13.69a}$$

$$P_T = S_T \cos\theta = \sqrt{3}V_L I_L \cos\theta \tag{13.69b}$$

$$Q_T = S_T \sin\theta = \sqrt{3}V_L I_L \sin\theta \tag{13.69c}$$

where V_L and I_L are, respectively, equal to the line voltage V_{Lp} and the line current I_{Lp} for the primary side, or the line voltage V_{Ls} and the line current I_{Ls} for the secondary side. Notice from Eq. (13.69) that for each of the four connections, $V_{Ls}I_{Ls} = V_{Lp}I_{Lp}$, since power must be conserved in an ideal transformer.

For the Y-Y connection (Fig. 13.46), the line voltage V_{Lp} at the primary side, the line voltage V_{Ls} on the secondary side, the line current I_{Lp} on the primary side, and the line current I_{Ls} on the secondary side are related to the transformer per phase turns ratio n according to Eqs. (13.52) and (13.55) as

$$V_{Ls} = nV_{Lp} \tag{13.70a}$$

$$I_{Ls} = \frac{I_{Lp}}{n} \tag{13.70b}$$

For the Δ-Δ connection (Fig. 13.47), Eq. (13.70) also applies for the line voltages and line currents. This connection is unique in the sense that if one of the transformers is removed for repair or maintenance, the other two form an *open delta*, which can provide three-phase voltages at a reduced level of the original three-phase transformer.

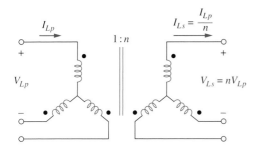

Figure 13.46   Y-Y three-phase transformer connection.

Figure 13.47   Δ-Δ three-phase transformer connection.

For the Y-Δ connection (Fig. 13.48), there is a factor of $\sqrt{3}$ arising from the line-phase values in addition to the transformer per phase turns ratio n. Thus,

$$V_{Ls} = \frac{nV_{Lp}}{\sqrt{3}} \tag{13.71a}$$

$$I_{Ls} = \frac{\sqrt{3}I_{Lp}}{n} \tag{13.71b}$$

Similarly, for the Δ-Y connection (Fig. 13.49),

$$V_{Ls} = n\sqrt{3}V_{Lp} \tag{13.72a}$$

$$I_{Ls} = \frac{I_{Lp}}{n\sqrt{3}} \tag{13.72b}$$

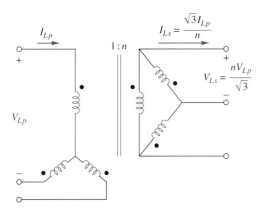

Figure 13.48   Y-Δ three-phase transformer connection.

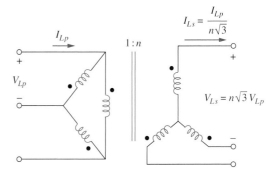

Figure 13.49   Δ-Y three-phase transformer connection.

EXAMPLE 13.12

The 42-kVA balanced load depicted in Fig. 13.50 is supplied by a three-phase transformer. (a) Determine the type of transformer connections. (b) Find the line voltage and current on the primary side. (c) Determine the kVA rating of each transformer used in the transformer bank. Assume that the transformers are ideal.

Figure 13.50   For Example 13.12.

Solution:

(a) A careful observation of Fig. 13.50 shows that the primary side is Y-connected, while the secondary side is Δ-connected. Thus, the three-phase transformer is Y-Δ, similar to the one shown in Fig. 13.48.

(b) Given a load with total apparent power $S_T = 42$ kVA, the turns ratio $n = 5$, and the secondary line voltage $V_{Ls} = 240$ V, we can find the secondary line current using Eq. (13.69a), by

$$I_{Ls} = \frac{S_T}{\sqrt{3}V_{Ls}} = \frac{42,000}{\sqrt{3}(240)} = 101 \text{ A}$$

From Eq. (13.71),

$$I_{Lp} = \frac{n}{\sqrt{3}}I_{Ls} = \frac{5 \times 101}{\sqrt{3}} = 292 \text{ A}$$

$$V_{Lp} = \frac{\sqrt{3}}{n}V_{Ls} = \frac{\sqrt{3} \times 240}{5} = 83.14 \text{ V}$$

(c) Because the load is balanced, each transformer equally shares the total load and since there are no losses (assuming ideal transformers), the kVA rating of each transformer is $S = S_T/3 = 14$ kVA. Alternatively, the transformer rating can be determined by the product of the phase current and phase voltage of the primary or secondary side. For the primary side, for example, we have a delta connection, so that the phase voltage is the same as the line voltage of 240 V, while the phase current is $I_{Lp}/\sqrt{3} = 58.34$ A. Hence, $S = 240 \times 58.34 = 14$ kVA.

PRACTICE PROBLEM 13.12

A three-phase Δ-Δ transformer is used to step down a line voltage of 625 kV, to supply a plant operating at a line voltage of 12.5 kV. The plant draws 40 MW with a lagging power factor of 85 percent. Find: (a) the current drawn by the plant, (b) the turns ratio, (c) the current on the primary side of the transformer, and (d) the load carried by each transformer.

Answer: (a) 2.1736 kA, (b) 0.02, (c) 43.47 A, (d) 15.69 MVA.

13.8 PSPICE ANALYSIS OF MAGNETICALLY COUPLED CIRCUITS

PSpice analyzes magnetically coupled circuits just like inductor circuits except that the dot convention must be followed. In *PSpice* Schematic, the dot (not shown) is always next to pin 1, which is the left-hand terminal of the inductor when the inductor with part name L is placed (horizontally) without rotation on a schematic. Thus, the dot or pin 1 will be at the bottom after one 90° counterclockwise rotation, since rotation is always about pin 1. Once the magnetically coupled inductors are arranged with the dot convention in mind and their value attributes are set in henries, we use the coupling symbol K_LINEAR to define the coupling. For each pair of coupled inductors, take the following steps:

1. Select **Draw/Get New Part** and type K_LINEAR.

2. Hit ⟨enter⟩ or click **OK** and place the K_LINEAR symbol on the schematic, as shown in Fig. 13.51. (Notice that K_LINEAR is not a component and therefore has no pins.)

3. **DCLICKL** on COUPLING and set the value of the coupling coefficient *k*.

4. **DCLICKL** on the boxed K (the coupling symbol) and enter the reference designator names for the coupled inductors as values of Li, i = 1, 2, . . . , 6. For example, if inductors L20 and L23 are coupled, we set L1 = L20 and L2 = L23. L1 and at least one other Li must be assigned values; other Li's may be left blank.

In step 4, up to six coupled inductors with equal coupling can be specified.

For the air-core transformer, the partname is XFRM_LINEAR. It can be inserted in a circuit by selecting **Draw/Get Part Name** and then typing in the part name or by selecting the part name from the analog.slb library. As shown typically in Fig. 13.52(a), the main attributes of the linear transformer are the coupling coefficient *k* and the inductance values L1 and L2 in henries. If the mutual inductance *M* is specified, its value must be used along with L1 and L2 to calculate *k*. Keep in mind that the value of *k* should lie between 0 and 1.

For the ideal transformer, the part name is XFRM_NONLINEAR and is located in the breakout.slb library. Select it by clicking **Draw/Get Part Name** and then typing in the part name. Its attributes are the coupling coefficient and the numbers of turns associated with L1 and L2, as illustrated typically in Fig. 13.52(b). The value of the coefficient of mutual coupling *k* = 1.

PSpice has some additional transformer configurations that we will not discuss here.

K K1
K_Linear
  COUPLING = 1

Figure 13.51
K_Linear for defining coupling.

TX2

COUPLING=0.5
L1_VALUE=1mH
L2_VALUE=25mH

(a)

TX4

kbreak
COUPLING = 0.5
L1_TURNS = 500
L2_TURNS = 1000

(b)

Figure 13.52
(a) Linear transformer XFRM_LINEAR
(b) ideal transformer XFRM_NONLINEAR.

EXAMPLE 13.13

Use *PSpice* to find i_1, i_2, and i_3 in the circuit displayed in Fig. 13.53.

Figure 13.53   For Example 13.13.

Solution:

The coupling coefficients of the three coupled inductors are determined as follows.

$$k_{12} = \frac{M_{12}}{\sqrt{L_1 L_2}} = \frac{1}{\sqrt{3 \times 3}} = 0.3333$$

$$k_{13} = \frac{M_{13}}{\sqrt{L_1 L_3}} = \frac{1.5}{\sqrt{3 \times 4}} = 0.433$$

$$k_{23} = \frac{M_{23}}{\sqrt{L_2 L_3}} = \frac{2}{\sqrt{3 \times 4}} = 0.5774$$

The operating frequency f is obtained from Fig. 13.53 as $\omega = 12\pi = 2\pi f \rightarrow f = 6$ Hz.

The schematic of the circuit is portrayed in Fig. 13.54. Notice how the dot convention is adhered to. For L2, the dot (not shown) is on pin 1 (the left-hand terminal) and is therefore placed without rotation. For L1, in order for the dot to be on the right-hand side of the inductor, the inductor must be rotated through 180°. For L3, the inductor must be rotated through 90° so that the dot will be at the bottom. Note that the 2-H inductor (L_4) is not coupled. To handle the three coupled inductors, we use three K_LINEAR parts provided in the analog library and set the following attributes (by double-clicking on the symbol K in the box):

```
K1 - K_LINEAR
L1 = L1
L2 = L2
COUPLING = 0.3333

K2 - K_LINEAR
L1 = L2
L2 = L3
COUPLING = 0.433
```

The right-hand values are the reference designators of the inductors on the schematic.

```
K3  -  K_LINEAR
L1  =  L1
L2  =  L3
COUPLING  =  0.5774
```

Three IPRINT pseudocomponents are inserted in the appropriate branches to obtain the required currents i_1, i_2, and i_3. As an AC single-frequency analysis, we select **Analysis/Setup/AC Sweep** and enter *Total Pts* = 1, *Start Freq* = 6, and *Final Freq* = 6. After saving the schematic, we select **Analysis/Simulate** to simulate it. The output file includes:

```
FREQ          IM(V_PRINT2)   IP(V_PRINT2)
6.000E+00     2.114E-01      -7.575E+01
FREQ          IM(V_PRINT1)   IP(V_PRINT1)
6.000E+00     4.654E-01      -7.025E+01
FREQ          IM(V_PRINT3)   IP(V_PRINT3)
6.000E+00     1.095E-01      1.715E+01
```

From this we obtain

$$\mathbf{I}_1 = 0.4654\underline{/-70.25°}$$

$$\mathbf{I}_2 = 0.2114\underline{/-75.75°}, \qquad \mathbf{I}_3 = 0.1095\underline{/17.15°}$$

Thus,

$$i_1 = 0.4654\cos(12\pi t - 70.25°)\ \text{A}$$
$$i_2 = 0.2114\cos(12\pi t - 75.75°)\ \text{A}$$
$$i_3 = 0.1095\cos(12\pi t + 17.15°)\ \text{A}$$

Figure 13.54   Schematic of the circuit of Fig. 13.53.

PRACTICE PROBLEM 13.13

Find i_o in the circuit of Fig. 13.55, using *PSpice*.

Figure 13.55   For Practice Prob. 13.13.

Answer: $0.1006 \cos(4t + 68.52°)$ A.

EXAMPLE 13.14

Find $\mathbf{V}_1$ and $\mathbf{V}_2$ in the ideal transformer circuit of Fig. 13.56 using *PSpice*.

Figure 13.56   For Example 13.14.

Solution:

As usual, we assume $\omega = 1$ and find the corresponding values of capacitance and inductance of the elements:

$$j10 = j\omega L \qquad \Longrightarrow \qquad L = 10 \text{ H}$$

$$-j40 = \frac{1}{j\omega C} \qquad \Longrightarrow \qquad C = 25 \text{ mF}$$

Reminder: For an ideal transformer, the inductances of both the primary and secondary windings are infinitely large.

Figure 13.57 shows the schematic. For the ideal transformer, we set the coupling factor to 0.999 and the numbers of turns to 400,000 and 100,000. The two VPRINT2 pseudocomponents are connected across the transformer terminals to obtain $\mathbf{V}_1$ and $\mathbf{V}_2$. As a single-frequency analysis, we select **Analysis/Setup/AC Sweep** and enter *Total Pts* = 1, *Start Freq* = 0.1592, and *Final Freq* = 0.1592. After saving the schematic, we select **Analysis/Simulate** to simulate it. The output file includes:

```
FREQ        VM(C,A)      VP(C,A)
1.592E−01   1.212E+02   −1.435E+02
```

```
FREQ          VM(B,C)          VP(B,C)
1.592E-01   2.775E+02       2.789E+01
```

From this we obtain

$$\mathbf{V}_1 = -\text{V(C,A)} = 121.1\underline{/36.5°}\text{ V}$$

$$\mathbf{V}_2 = \text{V(B,C)} = 27.75\underline{/27.89°}\text{ V}$$

Figure 13.57   The schematic for the circuit in Fig. 13.56.

PRACTICE PROBLEM 13.14

Obtain $\mathbf{V}_1$ and $\mathbf{V}_2$ in the circuit of Fig. 13.58 using *PSpice*.

Figure 13.58   For Practice Prob. 13.14.

Answer: $63.1\underline{/28.65°}\text{ V}$, $94.64\underline{/-151.4°}\text{ V}$.

†13.9 APPLICATIONS

Transformers are the largest, the heaviest, and often the costliest of circuit components. Nevertheless, they are indispensable passive devices in electric circuits. They are among the most efficient machines, 95 percent efficiency being common and 99 percent being achievable. They have numerous applications. For example, transformers are used:

- To step up or step down voltage and current, making them useful for power transmission and distribution.
- To isolate one portion of a circuit from another (i.e., to transfer power without any electrical connection).
- As an impedance-matching device for maximum power transfer.
- In frequency-selective circuits whose operation depends on the response of inductances.

Because of these diverse uses, there are many special designs for transformers (only some of which are discussed in this chapter): voltage transformers, current transformers, power transformers, distribution transformers, impedance-matching transformers, audio transformers, single-phase transformers, three-phase transformers, rectifier transformers, inverter transformers, and more. In this section, we consider three important applications: transformer as an isolation device, transformer as a matching device, and power distribution system.

For more information on the many kinds of transformers, a good text is W. M. Flanagan, *Handbook of Transformer Design and Applications*, 2nd ed. (New York: McGraw-Hill, 1993).

13.9.1   Transformer as an Isolation Device

Electrical isolation is said to exist between two devices when there is no physical connection between them. In a transformer, energy is transferred by magnetic coupling, without electrical connection between the primary circuit and secondary circuit. We now consider three simple practical examples of how we take advantage of this property.

First, consider the circuit in Fig. 13.59. A rectifier is an electronic circuit that converts an ac supply to a dc supply. A transformer is often used to couple the ac supply to the rectifier. The transformer serves two purposes. First, it steps up or steps down the voltage. Second, it provides electrical isolation between the ac power supply and the rectifier, thereby reducing the risk of shock hazard in handling the electronic device.

As a second example, a transformer is often used to couple two stages of an amplifier, to prevent any dc voltage in one stage from affecting the dc bias of the next stage. Biasing is the application of a dc voltage to a transistor amplifier or any other electronic device in order to produce a desired mode of operation. Each amplifier stage is biased separately to operate in a particular mode; the desired mode of operation will be compromised without a transformer providing dc isolation. As shown in Fig. 13.60, only the ac signal is coupled through the transformer from one stage to the next. We recall that magnetic coupling does not exist with a dc voltage source. Transformers are used in radio and TV receivers to couple stages of high-frequency amplifiers. When the sole purpose of a transformer is to provide isolation, its turns ratio n is made unity. Thus, an isolation transformer has $n = 1$.

As a third example, consider measuring the voltage across 13.2-kV lines. It is obviously not safe to connect a voltmeter directly to such high-voltage lines. A transformer can be used both to electrically isolate the line power from the voltmeter and to step down the voltage to a safe

Figure 13.59   A transformer used to isolate an ac supply from a rectifier.

level, as shown in Fig. 13.61. Once the voltmeter is used to measure the
secondary voltage, the turns ratio is used to determine the line voltage on
the primary side.

Figure 13.60   A transformer providing dc isolation between
two amplifier stages.

Figure 13.61   A transformer providing isolation between
the power lines and the voltmeter.

EXAMPLE 13.15

Determine the voltage across the load in Fig. 13.62.

Solution:

We can apply the superposition principle to find the load voltage. Let
$v_L = v_{L1} + v_{L2}$, where v_{L1} is due to the dc source and v_{L2} is due to
the ac source. We consider the dc and ac sources separately, as shown in
Fig. 13.63. The load voltage due to the dc source is zero, because a time-
varying voltage is necessary in the primary circuit to induce a voltage in
the secondary circuit. Thus, $v_{L1} = 0$. For the ac source,

$$\frac{V_2}{V_1} = \frac{V_2}{120} = \frac{1}{3} \quad \text{or} \quad V_2 = \frac{120}{3} = 40 \text{ V}$$

Hence, $V_{L2} = 40$ V ac or $v_{L2} = 40\cos\omega t$; that is, only the ac voltage
is passed to the load by the transformer. This example shows how the
transformer provides dc isolation.

Figure 13.62   For Example 13.15.

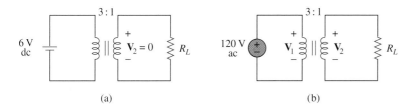

(a)   (b)

Figure 13.63   For Example 13.15: (a) dc source, (b) ac source.

PRACTICE PROBLEM 13.15

Refer to Fig. 13.61. Calculate the turns ratio required to step down the
13.2-kV line voltage to a safe level of 120 V.

Answer: 110.

13.9.2 Transformer as a Matching Device

We recall that for maximum power transfer, the load resistance R_L must be matched with the source resistance R_s. In most cases, the two resistances are not matched; both are fixed and cannot be altered. However, an iron-core transformer can be used to match the load resistance to the source resistance. This is called *impedance matching*. For example, to connect a loudspeaker to an audio power amplifier requires a transformer, because the speaker's resistance is only a few ohms while the internal resistance of the amplifier is several thousand ohms.

Consider the circuit shown in Fig. 13.64. We recall from Eq. (13.60) that the ideal transformer reflects its load back to the primary with a scaling factor of n^2. To match this reflected load R_L/n^2 with the source resistance R_s, we set them equal,

$$R_s = \frac{R_L}{n^2} \tag{13.73}$$

Equation (13.73) can be satisfied by proper selection of the turns ratio n. From Eq. (13.73), we notice that a step-down transformer ($n < 1$) is needed as the matching device when $R_s > R_L$, and a step-up ($n > 1$) is required when $R_s < R_L$.

Figure 13.64   Transformer used as a matching device.

EXAMPLE 13.16

Figure 13.65   Using an ideal transformer to match the speaker to the amplifier; for Example 13.16.

The ideal transformer in Fig. 13.65 is used to match the amplifier circuit to the loudspeaker to achieve maximum power transfer. The Thevenin (or output) impedance of the amplifier is 192 Ω, and the internal impedance of the speaker is 12 Ω. Determine the required turns ratio.

Solution:

We replace the amplifier circuit with the Thevenin equivalent and reflect the impedance $\mathbf{Z}_L = 12$ Ω of the speaker to the primary side of the ideal transformer. Figure 13.66 shows the result. For maximum power transfer,

$$\mathbf{Z}_{Th} = \frac{\mathbf{Z}_L}{n^2} \quad \text{or} \quad n^2 = \frac{\mathbf{Z}_L}{\mathbf{Z}_{Th}} = \frac{12}{192} = \frac{1}{16}$$

Thus, the turns ratio is $n = 1/4 = 0.25$.

Using $P = I^2 R$, we can show that indeed the power delivered to the speaker is much larger than without the ideal transformer. Without the ideal transformer, the amplifier is directly connected to the speaker. The power delivered to the speaker is

$$P_L = \left(\frac{\mathbf{V}_{Th}}{\mathbf{Z}_{Th} + \mathbf{Z}_L}\right)^2 \mathbf{Z}_L = 288 \, \mathbf{V}_{Th}^2 \, \mu W$$

With the transformer in place, the primary and secondary currents are

$$I_p = \frac{\mathbf{V}_{Th}}{\mathbf{Z}_{Th} + \mathbf{Z}_L/n^2}, \qquad I_s = \frac{I_p}{n}$$

Figure 13.66   Equivalent circuit of the circuit in Fig. 13.65, for Example 13.16.

Hence,

$$P_L = I_s^2 \mathbf{Z}_L = \left(\frac{\mathbf{V}_{\text{Th}}/n}{\mathbf{Z}_{\text{Th}} + \mathbf{Z}_L/n^2} \right)^2 \mathbf{Z}_L$$

$$= \left(\frac{n\mathbf{V}_{\text{Th}}}{n^2\mathbf{Z}_{\text{Th}} + \mathbf{Z}_L} \right)^2 \mathbf{Z}_L = 1,302\mathbf{V}_{\text{Th}}^2 \ \mu\text{W}$$

confirming what was said earlier.

PRACTICE PROBLEM 13.16

Calculate the turns ratio of an ideal transformer required to match a 100-Ω load to a source with internal impedance of 2.5 kΩ. Find the load voltage when the source voltage is 30 V.

Answer: 0.2, 3 V.

13.9.3 Power Distribution

A power system basically consists of three components: generation, transmission, and distribution. The local electric company operates a plant that generates several hundreds of megavolt-amperes (MVA), typically at about 18 kV. As Fig. 13.67 illustrates, three-phase step-up transformers are used to feed the generated power to the transmission line. Why do we need the transformer? Suppose we need to transmit 100,000 VA over a distance of 50 km. Since $S = VI$, using a line voltage of 1,000 V implies that the transmission line must carry 100 A and this requires a transmission line of a large diameter. If, on the other hand, we use a line voltage of 10,000 V, the current is only 10 A. The smaller current reduces the required conductor size, producing considerable savings as well as minimizing transmission line I^2R losses. To minimize losses requires a step-up transformer. Without the transformer, the majority of

One may ask, How would increasing the voltage not increase the current, thereby increasing I^2R losses? Keep in mind that $I = V_\ell/R$, where V_ℓ is the potential difference between the sending and receiving ends of the line. The voltage that is stepped up is the sending end voltage V, not V_ℓ. If the receiving end is V_R, then $V_\ell = V - V_R$. Since V and V_R are close to each other, V_ℓ is small even when V is stepped up.

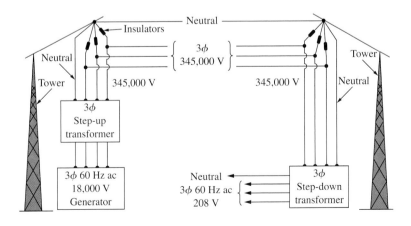

Figure 13.67   A typical power distribution system.
(Source: A. Marcus and C. M. Thomson, Electricity for Technicians, 2nd ed. [Englewood Cliffs, NJ: Prentice Hall, 1975], p. 337.)

the power generated would be lost on the transmission line. The ability of the transformer to step up or step down voltage and distribute power economically is one of the major reasons for generating ac rather than dc. Thus, for a given power, the larger the voltage, the better. Today, 1 MV is the largest voltage in use; the level may increase as a result of research and experiments.

Beyond the generation plant, the power is transmitted for hundreds of miles through an electric network called the *power grid.* The three-phase power in the power grid is conveyed by transmission lines hung overhead from steel towers which come in a variety of sizes and shapes. The (aluminum-conductor, steel-reinforced) lines typically have overall diameters up to about 40 mm and can carry current of up to 1,380 A.

At the substations, distribution transformers are used to step down the voltage. The step-down process is usually carried out in stages. Power may be distributed throughout a locality by means of either overhead or underground cables. The substations distribute the power to residential, commercial, and industrial customers. At the receiving end, a residential customer is eventually supplied with 120/240 V, while industrial or commercial customers are fed with higher voltages such as 460/208 V. Residential customers are usually supplied by distribution transformers often mounted on the poles of the electric utility company. When direct current is needed, the alternating current is converted to dc electronically.

EXAMPLE 13.17

A distribution transformer is used to supply a household as in Fig. 13.68. The load consists of eight 100-W bulbs, a 350-W TV, and a 15-kW kitchen range. If the secondary side of the transformer has 72 turns, calculate: (a) the number of turns of the primary winding, and (b) the current I_p in the primary winding.

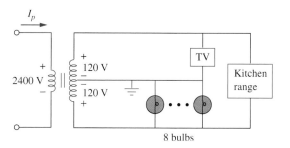

Figure 13.68   For Example 13.17.

Solution:

(a) The dot locations on the winding are not important, since we are only interested in the magnitudes of the variables involved. Since

$$\frac{N_p}{N_s} = \frac{V_p}{V_s}$$

we get

$$N_p = N_s \frac{V_p}{V_s} = 72 \frac{2{,}400}{240} = 720 \text{ turns}$$

(b) The total power absorbed by the load is

$$S = 8 \times 100 + 350 + 15{,}000 = 16.15 \text{ kW}$$

But $S = V_p I_p = V_s I_s$, so that

$$I_p = \frac{S}{V_p} = \frac{16{,}150}{2{,}400} = 6.729 \text{ A}$$

PRACTICE PROBLEM 13.17

In Example 13.17, if the eight 100-W bulbs are replaced by twelve 60-W bulbs and the kitchen range is replaced by a 4.5-kW air-conditioner, find: (a) the total power supplied, (b) the current I_p in the primary winding.

Answer: (a) 5.57 kW, (b) 2.321 A.

13.10 SUMMARY

1. Two coils are said to be mutually coupled if the magnetic flux ϕ emanating from one passes through the other. The mutual inductance between the two coils is given by

$$M = k\sqrt{L_1 L_2}$$

where k is the coupling coefficient, $0 < k < 1$.

2. If v_1 and i_1 are the voltage and current in coil 1, while v_2 and i_2 are the voltage and current in coil 2, then

$$v_1 = L_1 \frac{di_1}{dt} + M \frac{di_2}{dt} \qquad \text{and} \qquad v_2 = L_2 \frac{di_2}{dt} + M \frac{di_1}{dt}$$

Thus, the voltage induced in a coupled coil consists of self-induced voltage and mutual voltage.

3. The polarity of the mutually induced voltage is expressed in the schematic by the dot convention.

4. The energy stored in two coupled coils is

$$\frac{1}{2} L_1 i_1^2 + \frac{1}{2} L_2 i_2^2 \pm M i_1 i_2$$

5. A transformer is a four-terminal device containing two or more magnetically coupled coils. It is used in changing the current, voltage, or impedance level in a circuit.

6. A linear (or loosely coupled) transformer has its coils wound on a magnetically linear material. It can be replaced by an equivalent T or Π network for the purposes of analysis.

7. An ideal (or iron-core) transformer is a lossless ($R_1 = R_2 = 0$) transformer with unity coupling coefficient ($k = 1$) and infinite inductances ($L_1, L_2, M \to \infty$).

8. For an ideal transformer,

$$\mathbf{V}_2 = n\mathbf{V}_1, \qquad \mathbf{I}_2 = \frac{\mathbf{I}_1}{n}, \qquad \mathbf{S}_1 = \mathbf{S}_2, \qquad \mathbf{Z}_R = \frac{\mathbf{Z}_L}{n^2}$$

where $n = N_2/N_1$ is the turns ratio. N_1 is the number of turns of the primary winding and N_2 is the number of turns of the secondary winding. The transformer steps up the primary voltage when $n > 1$, steps it down when $n < 1$, or serves as a matching device when $n = 1$.

9. An autotransformer is a transformer with a single winding common to both the primary and the secondary circuits.

10. *PSpice* is a useful tool for analyzing magnetically coupled circuits.

11. Transformers are necessary in all stages of power distribution systems. Three-phase voltages may be stepped up or down by three-phase transformers.

12. Important uses of transformers in electronics applications are as electrical isolation devices and impedance-matching devices.

REVIEW QUESTIONS

13.1   Refer to the two magnetically coupled coils of Fig. 13.69(a). The polarity of the mutual voltage is:

(a) Positive   (b) Negative

(a)   (b)

Figure 13.69   For Review Questions 13.1 and 13.2.

13.2   For the two magnetically coupled coils of Fig. 13.69(b), the polarity of the mutual voltage is:

(a) Positive   (b) Negative

13.3   The coefficient of coupling for two coils having $L_1 = 2$ H, $L_2 = 8$ H, $M = 3$ H is:

(a) 0.1875   (b) 0.75
(c) 1.333   (d) 5.333

13.4   A transformer is used in stepping down or stepping up:

(a) dc voltages   (b) ac voltages
(c) both dc and ac voltages

13.5   The ideal transformer in Fig. 13.70(a) has $N_2/N_1 = 10$. The ratio V_2/V_1 is:

(a) 10   (b) 0.1   (c) −0.1   (d) −10

(a)   (b)

Figure 13.70   For Review Questions 13.5 and 13.6.

13.6   For the ideal transformer in Fig. 13.70(b), $N_2/N_1 = 10$. The ratio I_2/I_1 is:

(a) 10   (b) 0.1   (c) −0.1   (d) −10

13.7   A three-winding transformer is connected as portrayed in Fig. 13.71(a). The value of the output voltage V_o is:

(a) 10   (b) 6   (c) −6   (d) −10

(a)   (b)

Figure 13.71   For Review Questions 13.7 and 13.8.

13.8   If the three-winding transformer is connected as in Fig. 13.71(b), the value of the output voltage V_o is:

(a) 10   (b) 6   (c) −6   (d) −10

13.9   In order to match a source with internal impedance of 500 Ω to a 15-Ω load, what is needed is:

(a) step-up linear transformer

(b) step-down linear transformer

(c) step-up ideal transformer

(d) step-down ideal transformer

(e) autotransformer

13.10   Which of these transformers can be used as an isolation device?

(a) linear transformer   (b) ideal transformer

(c) autotransformer   (d) all of the above

Answers: 13.1b, 13.2a, 13.3b, 13.4b, 13.5d, 13.6b, 13.7c, 13.8a, 13.9d, 13.10b.

PROBLEMS

Section 13.2   Mutual Inductance

13.1   For the three coupled coils in Fig. 13.72, calculate the total inductance.

Figure 13.72   For Prob. 13.1.

13.2   Determine the inductance of the three series-connected inductors of Fig. 13.73.

Figure 13.73   For Prob. 13.2.

13.3   Two coils connected in series-aiding fashion have a total inductance of 250 mH. When connected in a series-opposing configuration, the coils have a total inductance of 150 mH. If the inductance of one coil (L_1) is three times the other, find L_1, L_2, and M. What is the coupling coefficient?

13.4   (a) For the coupled coils in Fig. 13.74(a), show that

$$L_{eq} = L_1 + L_2 + 2M$$

(b) For the coupled coils in Fig. 13.74(b), show that

$$L_{eq} = \frac{L_1 L_2 - M^2}{L_1 + L_2 - 2M}$$

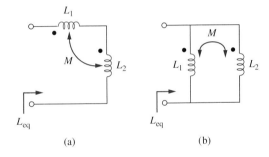

(a)   (b)

Figure 13.74   For Prob. 13.4.

13.5   Two coils are mutually coupled, with $L_1 = 25$ mH, $L_2 = 60$ mH, and $k = 0.5$. Calculate the maximum possible equivalent inductance if:

(a) the two coils are connected in series

(b) the coils are connected in parallel

13.6   Determine $\mathbf{V}_1$ and $\mathbf{V}_2$ in terms of $\mathbf{I}_1$ and $\mathbf{I}_2$ in the circuit in Fig. 13.75.

Figure 13.75   For Prob. 13.6.

13.7   Find $\mathbf{V}_o$ in the circuit of Fig. 13.76.

Figure 13.76   For Prob. 13.7.

13.8   Obtain $\mathbf{V}_o$ in the circuit of Fig. 13.77.

Figure 13.77   For Prob. 13.8.

13.9   Find $\mathbf{V}_x$ in the network shown in Fig. 13.78.

Figure 13.78   For Prob. 13.9.

13.10   Find $\mathbf{I}_o$ in the circuit of Fig. 13.79.

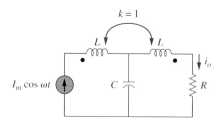

Figure 13.79   For Prob. 13.10.

13.11   Obtain the mesh equations for the circuit in Fig. 13.80.

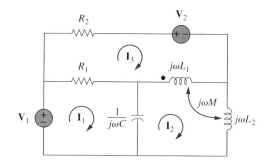

Figure 13.80   For Prob. 13.11.

13.12   Determine the equivalent L_{eq} in the circuit of Fig. 13.81.

Figure 13.81   For Prob. 13.12.

13.13   Calculate the equivalent impedance in the circuit of Fig. 13.82.

Figure 13.82   For Prob. 13.13.

13.14   Obtain the Thevenin equivalent circuit for the circuit in Fig. 13.83 at terminals a-b.

Figure 13.83   For Prob. 13.14.

13.15 Find the Norton equivalent for the circuit in Fig. 13.84 at terminals *a-b*.

Figure 13.84   For Prob. 13.15.

13.16 Obtain the Norton equivalent at terminals *a-b* of the circuit in Fig. 13.85.

Figure 13.85   For Prob. 13.16.

13.17 Determine the input impedance at terminals *a-b* of the circuit shown in Fig. 13.86.

Figure 13.86   For Prob. 13.17.

13.18 Find the Thevenin equivalent to the left of the load **Z** in the circuit in Fig. 13.87.

Figure 13.87   For Prob. 13.18.

13.19 Determine an equivalent T-section that can be used to replace the transformer in Fig. 13.88.

Figure 13.88   For Prob. 13.19.

Section 13.3   Energy in a Coupled Circuit

13.20 Determine currents I_1, I_2, and I_3 in the circuit of Fig. 13.89. Find the energy stored in the coupled coils at $t = 2$ ms. Take $\omega = 1,000$ rad/s.

Figure 13.89   For Prob. 13.20.

13.21 Find I_1 and I_2 in the circuit of Fig. 13.90. Calculate the power absorbed by the 4-Ω resistor.

Figure 13.90   For Prob. 13.21.

*13.22 Find current $\mathbf{I}_o$ in the circuit of Fig. 13.91.

Figure 13.91 For Prob. 13.22.

13.23 If $M = 0.2$ H and $v_s = 12 \cos 10t$ V in the circuit of Fig. 13.92, find i_1 and i_2. Calculate the energy stored in the coupled coils at $t = 15$ ms.

Figure 13.92 For Prob. 13.23.

13.24 In the circuit of Fig. 13.93,

(a) find the coupling coefficient,
(b) calculate v_o,
(c) determine the energy stored in the coupled inductors at $t = 2$ s.

Figure 13.93 For Prob. 13.24.

13.25 For the network in Fig. 13.94, find $\mathbf{Z}_{ab}$ and $\mathbf{I}_o$.

Figure 13.94 For Prob. 13.25.

13.26 Find $\mathbf{I}_o$ in the circuit of Fig. 13.95. Switch the dot on the winding on the right and calculate $\mathbf{I}_o$ again.

Figure 13.95 For Prob. 13.26.

13.27 Rework Example 13.1 using the concept of reflected impedance.

*13.28 In the circuit in Fig. 13.96, find the value of X that will give maximum power transfer to the 20-Ω load.

Figure 13.96 For Prob. 13.28.

Section 13.4 Linear Transformers

13.29 In the circuit of Fig. 13.97, find the value of the coupling coefficient k that will make the 10-Ω resistor dissipate 320 W. For this value of k, find the energy stored in the coupled coils at $t = 1.5$ s.

Figure 13.97 For Prob. 13.29.

---

*An asterisk indicates a challenging problem.

13.30 (a) Find the input impedance of the circuit in Fig. 13.98 using the concept of reflected impedance.

(b) Obtain the input impedance by replacing the linear transformer by its T equivalent.

Figure 13.98   For Prob. 13.30.

13.31 For the circuit in Fig. 13.99, find:

(a) the T-equivalent circuit,

(b) the Π-equivalent circuit.

Figure 13.99   For Prob. 13.31.

***13.32** Two linear transformers are cascaded as shown in Fig. 13.100. Show that

$$\mathbf{Z}_{in} = \frac{\omega^2 R(L_a^2 + L_a L_b - M_a^2) + j\omega^3(L_a^2 L_b + L_a L_b^2 - L_a M_b^2 - L_b M_a^2)}{\omega^2(L_a L_b + L_b^2 - M_b^2) - j\omega R(L_a + L_b)}$$

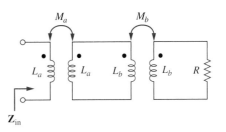

Figure 13.100   For Prob. 13.32.

13.33 Determine the input impedance of the air-core transformer circuit of Fig. 13.101.

Figure 13.101   For Prob. 13.33.

13.34 Find the input impedance of the circuit in Fig. 13.102.

Figure 13.102   For Prob. 13.34.

***13.35** Find currents $\mathbf{I}_1$, $\mathbf{I}_2$, and $\mathbf{I}_3$ in the circuit of Fig. 13.103.

Figure 13.103   For Prob. 13.35.

Section 13.5   Ideal Transformers

13.36 As done in Fig. 13.32, obtain the relationships between terminal voltages and currents for each of the ideal transformers in Fig. 13.104.

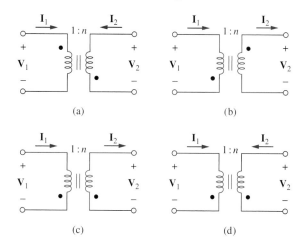

(a)   (b)

(c)   (d)

Figure 13.104   For Prob. 13.36.

13.37 A 480/2,400-V rms step-up ideal transformer delivers 50 kW to a resistive load. Calculate:

(a) the turns ratio

(b) the primary current

(c) the secondary current

13.38 A 4-kVA, 2,300/230-V rms transformer has an equivalent impedance of $2\underline{/10°}\ \Omega$ on the primary side. If the transformer is connected to a load with 0.6 power factor leading, calculate the input impedance.

13.39 A 1,200/240-V rms transformer has impedance $60\underline{/-30°}\ \Omega$ on the high-voltage side. If the transformer is connected to a $0.8\underline{/10°}$-Ω load on the low-voltage side, determine the primary and secondary currents.

13.40 A power transformer has a 2,000-turn primary and a 500-turn secondary and has a 12-Ω load connected across it. The primary is supplied by a 240-V, 60-Hz source. Find the power absorbed by the load.

13.41 Determine $\mathbf{I}_1$ and $\mathbf{I}_2$ in the circuit of Fig. 13.105.

Figure 13.105   For Prob. 13.41.

13.42 For the ideal transformer circuit of Fig. 13.106, find $\mathbf{V}_o$.

Figure 13.106   For Prob. 13.42.

13.43 Obtain $\mathbf{V}_1$ and $\mathbf{V}_2$ in the ideal transformer circuit of Fig. 13.107.

Figure 13.107   For Prob. 13.43.

13.44 In the ideal transformer circuit of Fig. 13.108, find $i_1(t)$ and $i_2(t)$.

Figure 13.108   For Prob. 13.44.

13.45 For the circuit shown in Fig. 13.109, find the value of the average power absorbed by the 8-Ω resistor.

Figure 13.109   For Prob. 13.45.

13.46 (a) Find $\mathbf{I}_1$ and $\mathbf{I}_2$ in the circuit of Fig. 13.110 on the next page.

(b) Switch the dot on one of the windings. Find $\mathbf{I}_1$ and $\mathbf{I}_2$ again.

13.47 For the circuit in Fig. 13.111, find $\mathbf{V}_o$. Switch the dot on the secondary side and find $\mathbf{V}_o$ again.

Figure 13.111   For Prob. 13.47.

13.48 Find $\mathbf{I}_x$ in the ideal transformer circuit of Fig. 13.112.

Figure 13.112   For Prob. 13.49.

13.49 Find current i_x in the ideal transformer circuit shown in Fig. 13.113.

Figure 13.113   For Prob. 13.49.

13.50 Calculate the input impedance for the network in Fig. 13.114 below.

13.51 Use the concept of reflected impedance to find the input impedance and current $\mathbf{I}_1$ in Fig. 13.115 below.

Figure 13.110   For Prob. 13.46.

Figure 13.114   For Prob. 13.50.

Figure 13.115   For Prob. 13.51.

13.52 For the circuit in Fig. 13.116, determine the turns ratio *n* that will cause maximum average power transfer to the load. Calculate that maximum average power.

Figure 13.116 For Prob. 13.52.

13.53 Refer to the network in Fig. 13.117.

(a) Find *n* for maximum power supplied to the 200-Ω load.

(b) Determine the power in the 200-Ω load if *n* = 10.

Figure 13.117 For Prob. 13.53.

13.54 A transformer is used to match an amplifier with an 8-Ω load as shown in Fig. 13.118. The Thevenin equivalent of the amplifier is: $V_{Th} = 10$ V, $Z_{Th} = 128$ Ω.

(a) Find the required turns ratio for maximum energy power transfer.

(b) Determine the primary and secondary currents.

(c) Calculate the primary and secondary voltages.

Figure 13.118 For Prob. 13.54.

13.55 In Fig. 13.119 below, determine the average power delivered to $\mathbf{Z}_s$.

13.56 Find the power absorbed by the 10-Ω resistor in the ideal transformer circuit of Fig. 13.120.

Figure 13.120 For Prob. 13.56.

13.57 For the ideal transformer circuit of Fig. 13.121 below, find:

(a) $\mathbf{I}_1$ and $\mathbf{I}_2$,

(b) $\mathbf{V}_1$, $\mathbf{V}_2$, and $\mathbf{V}_o$,

(c) the complex power supplied by the source.

Figure 13.119 For Prob. 13.55.

Figure 13.121 For Prob. 13.57.

13.58 Determine the average power absorbed by each resistor in the circuit of Fig. 13.122.

Figure 13.122   For Prob. 13.58.

13.59 Find the average power delivered to each resistor in the circuit of Fig. 13.123.

Figure 13.123   For Prob. 13.59.

13.60 Refer to the circuit in Fig. 13.124 below.

(a) Find currents $\mathbf{I}_1$, $\mathbf{I}_2$, and $\mathbf{I}_3$.

(b) Find the power dissipated in the 40-Ω resistor.

****13.61** For the circuit in Fig. 13.125 below, find $\mathbf{I}_1$, $\mathbf{I}_2$, and $\mathbf{V}_o$.

13.62 For the network in Fig. 13.126 below, find

(a) the complex power supplied by the source,

(b) the average power delivered to the 18-Ω resistor.

13.63 Find the mesh currents in the circuit of Fig. 13.127 on the next page.

13.64 For the ideal transformer circuit in Fig. 13.128, find the value of n that will cause maximum power to be delivered to the load $\mathbf{Z} = 7.5$ Ω.

Figure 13.128   For Prob. 13.64.

Figure 13.124   For Prob. 13.60.

Figure 13.125   For Prob. 13.61.

Figure 13.126   For Prob. 13.62.

Figure 13.127   For Prob. 13.63.

*13.65 Calculate the average power dissipated by the 20-Ω resistor in Fig. 13.129.

Figure 13.129   For Prob. 13.65.

Figure 13.130   For Prob. 31.68

*13.69 In the circuit of Fig. 13.131, $\mathbf{Z}_L$ is adjusted until maximum average power is delivered to $\mathbf{Z}_L$. Find $\mathbf{Z}_L$ and the maximum average power transferred to it. Take $N_1 = 600$ turns and $N_2 = 200$ turns.

Figure 13.131   For Prob. 13.69.

Section 13.6   Ideal Autotransformers

13.66 An ideal autotransformer with a 1:4 step-up turns ratio has its secondary connected to a 120-Ω load and the primary to a 420-V source. Determine the primary current.

13.67 An autotransformer with a 40 percent tap is supplied by a 400-V, 60-Hz source and is used for step-down operation. A 5-kVA load operating at unity power factor is connected to the secondary terminals. Find:

(a) the secondary voltage
(b) the secondary current
(c) the primary current

13.68 In the ideal autotransformer of Fig. 13.130, calculate $\mathbf{I}_1$, $\mathbf{I}_2$, and $\mathbf{I}_o$. Find the average power delivered to the load.

13.70 In the ideal transformer circuit shown in Fig. 13.132, determine the average power delivered to the load.

Figure 13.132   For Prob. 13.70.

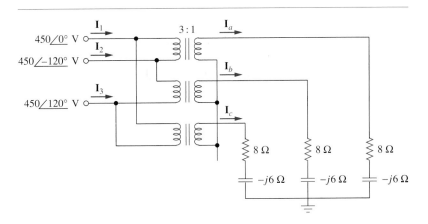

Figure 13.134   For Prob. 13.73.

13.71 In the autotransformer circuit in Fig. 13.133, show that

$$\mathbf{Z}_{\text{in}} = \left(1 + \frac{N_1}{N_2}\right)^2 \mathbf{Z}_L$$

Figure 13.133   For Prob. 13.71.

Section 13.7   Three-Phase Transformers

13.72 In order to meet an emergency, three single-phase transformers with 12,470/7,200 V rms are connected in Δ-Y to form a three-phase transformer which is fed by a 12,470-V transmission line. If the transformer supplies 60 MVA to a load, find:

(a) the turns ratio for each transformer,

(b) the currents in the primary and secondary windings of the transformer,

(c) the incoming and outgoing transmission line currents.

13.73 Figure 13.134 above shows a three-phase transformer that supplies a Y-connected load.

(a) Identify the transformer connection.

(b) Calculate currents $\mathbf{I}_2$ and $\mathbf{I}_c$.

(c) Find the average power absorbed by the load.

13.74 Consider the three-phase transformer shown in Fig. 13.135. The primary is fed by a three-phase source with line voltage of 2.4 kV rms, while the secondary supplies a three-phase 120-kW balanced load at pf of 0.8. Determine:

(a) the type of transformer connections,

(b) the values of I_{LS} and I_{PS},

(c) the values of I_{LP} and I_{PP},

(d) the kVA rating of each phase of the transformer.

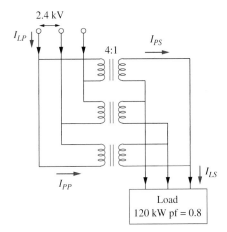

Figure 13.135   For Prob. 13.74.

13.75 A balanced three-phase transformer bank with the Δ-Y connection depicted in Fig. 13.136 on the next page is used to step down line voltages from 4,500 V rms to 900 V rms. If the transformer feeds a 120-kVA load, find:

(a) the turns ratio for the transformer,

(b) the line currents at the primary and secondary sides.

Figure 13.136   For Prob. 13.75.

13.76   A Y-Δ three-phase transformer is connected to a 60-kVA load with 0.85 power factor (leading) through a feeder whose impedance is $0.05 + j0.1 \ \Omega$ per phase, as shown in Fig. 13.137 below. Find the magnitude of:

(a) the line current at the load,

(b) the line voltage at the secondary side of the transformer,

(c) the line current at the primary side of the transformer.

13.77   The three-phase system of a town distributes power with a line voltage of 13.2 kV. A pole transformer connected to single wire and ground steps down the high-voltage wire to 120 V rms and serves a house as shown in Fig. 13.138.

(a) Calculate the turns ratio of the pole transformer to get 120 V.

(b) Determine how much current a 100-W lamp connected to the 120-V hot line draws from the high-voltage line.

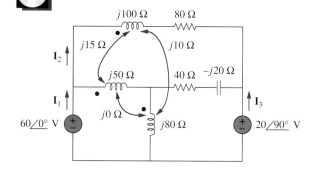

Figure 13.138   For Prob. 13.77.

Section 13.8   *PSpice* Analysis of Magnetically Coupled Circuits

13.78   Rework Prob. 13.21 using *PSpice*.

13.79   Use *PSpice* to find $\mathbf{I}_1$, $\mathbf{I}_2$, and $\mathbf{I}_3$ in the circuit of Fig. 13.139.

Figure 13.139   For Prob. 13.79.

13.80   Rework Prob. 13.22 using *PSpice*.

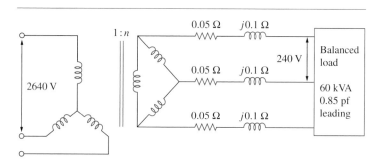

Figure 13.137   For Prob. 13.76.

13.81 Use *PSpice* to find $\mathbf{I}_1$, $\mathbf{I}_2$, and $\mathbf{I}_3$ in the circuit of Fig. 13.140.

Figure 13.140   For Prob. 13.81.

13.82 Use *PSpice* to find $\mathbf{V}_1$, $\mathbf{V}_2$, and $\mathbf{I}_o$ in the circuit of Fig. 13.141.

Figure 13.141   For Prob. 13.82.

13.83 Find $\mathbf{I}_x$ and $\mathbf{V}_x$ in the circuit of Fig. 13.142 below using *PSpice*.

13.84 Determine $\mathbf{I}_1$, $\mathbf{I}_2$, and $\mathbf{I}_3$ in the ideal transformer circuit of Fig. 13.143 using *PSpice*.

Figure 13.143   For Prob. 13.84.

Section 13.9   Applications

13.85 A stereo amplifier circuit with an output impedance of 7.2 kΩ is to be matched to a speaker with an input impedance of 8 Ω by a transformer whose primary side has 3,000 turns. Calculate the number of turns required on the secondary side.

13.86 A transformer having 2,400 turns on the primary and 48 turns on the secondary is used as an impedance-matching device. What is the reflected value of a 3-Ω load connected to the secondary?

13.87 A radio receiver has an input resistance of 300 Ω. When it is connected directly to an antenna system with a characteristic impedance of 75 Ω, an impedance mismatch occurs. By inserting an impedance-matching transformer ahead of the receiver, maximum power can be realized. Calculate the required turns ratio.

13.88 A step-down power transformer with a turns ratio of $n = 0.1$ supplies 12.6 V rms to a resistive load. If the primary current is 2.5 A rms, how much power is delivered to the load?

13.89 A 240/120-V rms power transformer is rated at 10 kVA. Determine the turns ratio, the primary current, and the secondary current.

Figure 13.142   For Prob. 13.83.

13.90 A 4-kVA, 2,400/240-V rms transformer has 250 turns on the primary side. Calculate:

(a) the turns ratio,

(b) the number of turns on the secondary side,

(c) the primary and secondary currents.

13.91 A 25,000/240-V rms distribution transformer has a primary current rating of 75 A.

(a) Find the transformer kVA rating.

(b) Calculate the secondary current.

13.92 A 4,800-V rms transmission line feeds a distribution transformer with 1,200 turns on the primary and 28 turns on the secondary. When a 10-Ω load is connected across the secondary, find:

(a) the secondary voltage,

(b) the primary and secondary currents,

(c) the power supplied to the load.

COMPREHENSIVE PROBLEMS

13.93 A four-winding transformer (Fig. 13.144) is often used in equipment (e.g., PCs, VCRs) that may be operated from either 110 V or 220 V. This makes the equipment suitable for both domestic and foreign use. Show which connections are necessary to provide:

(a) an output of 12 V with an input of 110 V,

(b) an output of 50 V with an input of 220 V.

are four possible connections, two of which are wrong. Find the output voltage of:

(a) a wrong connection,

(b) the right connection.

13.95 Ten bulbs in parallel are supplied by a 7,200/120-V transformer as shown in Fig. 13.145, where the bulbs are modeled by the 144-Ω resistors. Find:

(a) the turns ratio n,

(b) the current through the primary winding.

Figure 13.144   For Prob. 13.93.

*13.94 A 440/110-V ideal transformer can be connected to become a 550/440-V ideal autotransformer. There

Figure 13.145   For Prob. 13.95.

C H A P T E R 14

FREQUENCY RESPONSE

The most beautiful thing we can experience is the mysterious. It is the source of all true art and science.

—Albert Einstein

Enhancing Your Career

Career in Control Systems Control systems are another area of electrical engineering where circuit analysis is used. A control system is designed to regulate the behavior of one or more variables in some desired manner. Control systems play major roles in our everyday life. Household appliances such as heating and air-conditioning systems, switch-controlled thermostats, washers and dryers, cruise controllers in automobiles, elevators, traffic lights, manufacturing plants, navigation systems—all utilize control systems. In the aerospace field, precision guidance of space probes, the wide range of operational modes of the space shuttle, and the ability to maneuver space vehicles remotely from earth all require knowledge of control systems. In the manufacturing sector, repetitive production line operations are increasingly performed by robots, which are programmable control systems designed to operate for many hours without fatigue.

Control engineering integrates circuit theory and communication theory. It is not limited to any specific engineering discipline but may involve environmental, chemical, aeronautical, mechanical, civil, and electrical engineering. For example, a typical task for a control system engineer might be to design a speed regulator for a disk drive head.

A thorough understanding of control systems techniques is essential to the electrical engineer and is of great value for designing control systems to perform the desired task.

A welding robot. Source: (© Shela Terry/Science Photo Library/Photo Researchers.)

14.1 INTRODUCTION

In our sinusoidal circuit analysis, we have learned how to find voltages and currents in a circuit with a constant frequency source. If we let the amplitude of the sinusoidal source remain constant and vary the frequency, we obtain the circuit's *frequency response*. The frequency response may be regarded as a complete description of the sinusoidal steady-state behavior of a circuit as a function of frequency.

> The frequency response of a circuit is the variation in its behavior with change in signal frequency.

The sinusoidal steady-state frequency responses of circuits are of significance in many applications, especially in communications and control systems. A specific application is in electric filters that block out or eliminate signals with unwanted frequencies and pass signals of the desired frequencies. Filters are used in radio, TV, and telephone systems to separate one broadcast frequency from another.

We begin this chapter by considering the frequency response of simple circuits using their transfer functions. We then consider Bode plots, which are the industry-standard way of presenting frequency response. We also consider series and parallel resonant circuits and encounter important concepts such as resonance, quality factor, cutoff frequency, and bandwidth. We discuss different kinds of filters and network scaling. In the last section, we consider one practical application of resonant circuits and two applications of filters.

14.2 TRANSFER FUNCTION

The transfer function $\mathbf{H}(\omega)$ (also called the *network function*) is a useful analytical tool for finding the frequency response of a circuit. In fact, the frequency response of a circuit is the plot of the circuit's transfer function $\mathbf{H}(\omega)$ versus ω, with ω varying from $\omega = 0$ to $\omega = \infty$.

A transfer function is the frequency-dependent ratio of a forced function to a forcing function (or of an output to an input). The idea of a transfer function was implicit when we used the concepts of impedance and admittance to relate voltage and current. In general, a linear network can be represented by the block diagram shown in Fig. 14.1.

> The transfer function $\mathbf{H}(\omega)$ of a circuit is the frequency-dependent ratio of a phasor output $\mathbf{Y}(\omega)$ (an element voltage or current) to a phasor input $\mathbf{X}(\omega)$ (source voltage or current).

Thus,

$$\mathbf{H}(\omega) = \frac{\mathbf{Y}(\omega)}{\mathbf{X}(\omega)} \tag{14.1}$$

The frequency response of a circuit may also be considered as the variation of the gain and phase with frequency.

Figure 14.1   A block diagram representation of a linear network.

In this context, $\mathbf{X}(\omega)$ and $\mathbf{Y}(\omega)$ denote the input and output phasors of a network; they should not be confused with the same symbolism used for reactance and admittance. The multiple usage of symbols is conventionally permissible due to lack of enough letters in the English language to express all circuit variables distinctly.

assuming zero initial conditions. Since the input and output can be either voltage or current at any place in the circuit, there are four possible transfer functions:

Some authors use $\mathbf{H}(j\omega)$ for transfer instead of $\mathbf{H}(\omega)$, since ω and j are an inseparable pair.

$$\mathbf{H}(\omega) = \text{Voltage gain} = \frac{\mathbf{V}_o(\omega)}{\mathbf{V}_i(\omega)} \qquad (14.2\text{a})$$

$$\mathbf{H}(\omega) = \text{Current gain} = \frac{\mathbf{I}_o(\omega)}{\mathbf{I}_i(\omega)} \qquad (14.2\text{b})$$

$$\mathbf{H}(\omega) = \text{Transfer Impedance} = \frac{\mathbf{V}_o(\omega)}{\mathbf{I}_i(\omega)} \qquad (14.2\text{c})$$

$$\mathbf{H}(\omega) = \text{Transfer Admittance} = \frac{\mathbf{I}_o(\omega)}{\mathbf{V}_i(\omega)} \qquad (14.2\text{d})$$

where subscripts i and o denote input and output values. Being a complex quantity, $\mathbf{H}(\omega)$ has a magnitude $H(\omega)$ and a phase ϕ; that is, $\mathbf{H}(\omega) = H(\omega)\,\underline{/\phi}$.

To obtain the transfer function using Eq. (14.2), we first obtain the frequency-domain equivalent of the circuit by replacing resistors, inductors, and capacitors with their impedances R, $j\omega L$, and $1/j\omega C$. We then use any circuit technique(s) to obtain the appropriate quantity in Eq. (14.2). We can obtain the frequency response of the circuit by plotting the magnitude and phase of the transfer function as the frequency varies. A computer is a real time-saver for plotting the transfer function.

The transfer function $\mathbf{H}(\omega)$ can be expressed in terms of its numerator polynomial $\mathbf{N}(\omega)$ and denominator polynomial $\mathbf{D}(\omega)$ as

$$\boxed{\mathbf{H}(\omega) = \frac{\mathbf{N}(\omega)}{\mathbf{D}(\omega)}} \qquad (14.3)$$

where $\mathbf{N}(\omega)$ and $\mathbf{D}(\omega)$ are not necessarily the same expressions for the input and output functions, respectively. The representation of $\mathbf{H}(\omega)$ in Eq. (14.3) assumes that common numerator and denominator factors in $\mathbf{H}(\omega)$ have canceled, reducing the ratio to lowest terms. The roots of $\mathbf{N}(\omega) = 0$ are called the *zeros* of $\mathbf{H}(\omega)$ and are usually represented as $j\omega = z_1, z_2, \ldots$. Similarly, the roots of $\mathbf{D}(\omega) = 0$ are the *poles* of $\mathbf{H}(\omega)$ and are represented as $j\omega = p_1, p_2, \ldots$.

A zero, as a *root of the numerator polynomial*, is a value that results in a zero value of the function. A pole, as a *root of the denominator polynomial*, is a value for which the function is infinite.

A zero may also be regarded as the value of $s = j\omega$ that makes $\mathbf{H}(s)$ zero, and a pole as the value of $s = j\omega$ that makes $\mathbf{H}(s)$ infinite.

To avoid complex algebra, it is expedient to replace $j\omega$ temporarily with s when working with $\mathbf{H}(\omega)$ and replace s with $j\omega$ at the end.

EXAMPLE 14.1

For the *RC* circuit in Fig. 14.2(a), obtain the transfer function $\mathbf{V}_o/\mathbf{V}_s$ and its frequency response. Let $v_s = V_m \cos \omega t$.

Solution:

The frequency-domain equivalent of the circuit is in Fig. 14.2(b). By voltage division, the transfer function is given by

$$\mathbf{H}(\omega) = \frac{\mathbf{V}_o}{\mathbf{V}_s} = \frac{1/j\omega C}{R + 1/j\omega C} = \frac{1}{1 + j\omega RC}$$

Comparing this with Eq. (9.18e), we obtain the magnitude and phase of $\mathbf{H}(\omega)$ as

$$H = \frac{1}{\sqrt{1 + (\omega/\omega_0)^2}}, \qquad \phi = -\tan^{-1}\frac{\omega}{\omega_0}$$

where $\omega_0 = 1/RC$. To plot H and ϕ for $0 < \omega < \infty$, we obtain their values at some critical points and then sketch.

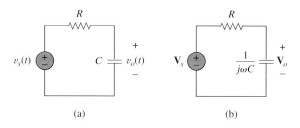

Figure 14.2 For Example 14.1: (a) time-domain RC circuit, (b) frequency-domain RC circuit.

At $\omega = 0$, $H = 1$ and $\phi = 0$. At $\omega = \infty$, $H = 0$ and $\phi = -90°$. Also, at $\omega = \omega_0$, $H = 1/\sqrt{2}$ and $\phi = -45°$. With these and a few more points as shown in Table 14.1, we find that the frequency response is as shown in Fig. 14.3. Additional features of the frequency response in Fig. 14.3 will be explained in Section 14.6.1 on lowpass filters.

(a)

(b)

Figure 14.3 Frequency response of the RC circuit: (a) amplitude response, (b) phase response.

TABLE 14.1 For Example 14.1.

ω/ω_0	H	ϕ	ω/ω_0	H	ϕ
0	1	0	10	0.1	$-84°$
1	0.71	$-45°$	20	0.05	$-87°$
2	0.45	$-63°$	100	0.01	$-89°$
3	0.32	$-72°$	∞	0	$-90°$

PRACTICE PROBLEM 14.1

Figure 14.4 RL circuit for Practice Prob. 14.1.

Obtain the transfer function $\mathbf{V}_o/\mathbf{V}_s$ of the RL circuit in Fig. 14.4, assuming $v_s = V_m \cos \omega t$. Sketch its frequency response.

Answer: $j\omega L/(R + j\omega L)$; see Fig. 14.5 for the response.

(a)   (b)

Figure 14.5   Frequency response of the *RL* circuit in Fig. 14.4.

EXAMPLE 14.2

For the circuit in Fig. 14.6, calculate the gain $\mathbf{I}_o(\omega)/\mathbf{I}_i(\omega)$ and its poles and zeros.

Solution:

By current division,

$$\mathbf{I}_o(\omega) = \frac{4 + j2\omega}{4 + j2\omega + 1/j0.5\omega}\mathbf{I}_i(\omega)$$

or

$$\frac{\mathbf{I}_o(\omega)}{\mathbf{I}_i(\omega)} = \frac{j0.5\omega(4 + j2\omega)}{1 + j2\omega + (j\omega)^2} = \frac{s(s + 2)}{s^2 + 2s + 1}, \qquad s = j\omega$$

Figure 14.6   For Example 14.2.

The zeros are at

$$s(s + 2) = 0 \qquad \Longrightarrow \qquad z_1 = 0, \; z_2 = -2$$

The poles are at

$$s^2 + 2s + 1 = (s + 1)^2 = 0$$

Thus, there is a repeated pole (or double pole) at $p = -1$.

PRACTICE PROBLEM 14.2

Find the transfer function $\mathbf{V}_o(\omega)/\mathbf{I}_i(\omega)$ for the circuit of Fig. 14.7. Obtain its zeros and poles.

Answer: $\dfrac{5(s + 2)(s + 1.5)}{s^2 + 4s + 5}$, $s = j\omega$; zeros: $-2, -1.5$;
poles: $-2 \pm j$.

Figure 14.7   For Practice Prob. 14.2.

†14.3 THE DECIBEL SCALE

It is not always easy to get a quick plot of the magnitude and phase of the transfer function as we did above. A more systematic way of obtaining the frequency response is to use Bode plots. Before we begin to construct Bode plots, we should take care of two important issues: the use of logarithms and decibels in expressing gain.

Since Bode plots are based on logarithms, it is important that we keep the following properties of logarithms in mind:

1. $\log P_1 P_2 = \log P_1 + \log P_2$
2. $\log P_1 / P_2 = \log P_1 - \log P_2$
3. $\log P^n = n \log P$
4. $\log 1 = 0$

Historical note: The *bel* is named after Alexander Graham Bell, the inventor of the telephone.

In communications systems, gain is measured in *bels*. Historically, the bel is used to measure the ratio of two levels of power or power gain G; that is,

$$G = \text{Number of bels} = \log_{10} \frac{P_2}{P_1} \qquad (14.4)$$

The *decibel* (dB) provides us with a unit of less magnitude. It is 1/10th of a bel and is given by

$$\boxed{G_{dB} = 10 \log_{10} \frac{P_2}{P_1}} \qquad (14.5)$$

When $P_1 = P_2$, there is no change in power and the gain is 0 dB. If $P_2 = 2P_1$, the gain is

$$G_{dB} = 10 \log_{10} 2 = 3 \text{ dB} \qquad (14.6)$$

and when $P_2 = 0.5 P_1$, the gain is

$$G_{dB} = 10 \log_{10} 0.5 = -3 \text{ dB} \qquad (14.7)$$

Equations (14.6) and (14.7) show another reason why logarithms are greatly used: The logarithm of the reciprocal of a quantity is simply negative the logarithm of that quantity.

Alternatively, the gain G can be expressed in terms of voltage or current ratio. To do so, consider the network shown in Fig. 14.8. If P_1 is the input power, P_2 is the output (load) power, R_1 is the input resistance, and R_2 is the load resistance, then $P_1 = 0.5 V_1^2 / R_1$ and $P_2 = 0.5 V_2^2 / R_2$, and Eq. (14.5) becomes

$$G_{dB} = 10 \log_{10} \frac{P_2}{P_1} = 10 \log_{10} \frac{V_2^2 / R_2}{V_1^2 / R_1}$$

$$= 10 \log_{10} \left(\frac{V_2}{V_1} \right)^2 + 10 \log_{10} \frac{R_1}{R_2} \qquad (14.8)$$

$$G_{dB} = 20 \log_{10} \frac{V_2}{V_1} - 10 \log_{10} \frac{R_2}{R_1} \qquad (14.9)$$

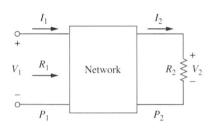

Figure 14.8   Voltage-current relationships for a four-terminal network.

For the case when $R_2 = R_1$, a condition that is often assumed when comparing voltage levels, Eq. (14.9) becomes

$$G_{dB} = 20 \log_{10} \frac{V_2}{V_1} \qquad (14.10)$$

Instead, if $P_1 = I_1^2 R_1$ and $P_2 = I_2^2 R_2$, for $R_1 = R_2$, we obtain

$$G_{dB} = 20 \log_{10} \frac{I_2}{I_1} \qquad (14.11)$$

Three things are important to note from Eqs. (14.5), (14.10), and (14.11):

1. That 10 log is used for power, while 20 log is used for voltage or current, because of the square relationship between them ($P = V^2/R = I^2 R$).

2. That the dB value is a logarithmic measurement of the *ratio* of one variable to another *of the same type*. Therefore, it applies in expressing the transfer function H in Eqs. (14.2a) and (14.2b), which are dimensionless quantities, but not in expressing H in Eqs. (14.2c) and (14.2d).

3. It is important to note that we only use voltage and current magnitudes in Eqs. (14.10) and (14.11). Negative signs and angles will be handled independently as we will see in section 14.4.

With this in mind, we now apply the concepts of logarithms and decibels to construct Bode plots.

14.4 BODE PLOTS

Obtaining the frequency response from the transfer function as we did in Section 14.2 is an uphill task. The frequency range required in frequency response is often so wide that it is inconvenient to use a linear scale for the frequency axis. Also, there is a more systematic way of locating the important features of the magnitude and phase plots of the transfer function. For these reasons, it has become standard practice to use a logarithmic scale for the frequency axis and a linear scale in each of the separate plots of magnitude and phase. Such semilogarithmic plots of the transfer function—known as *Bode plots*—have become the industry standard.

Historical note: Named after Hendrik W. Bode (1905–1982), an engineer with the Bell Telephone Laboratories, for his pioneering work in the 1930s and 1940s.

Bode plots are semilog plots of the magnitude (in decibels) and phase (in degrees) of a transfer function versus frequency.

Bode plots contain the same information as the nonlogarithmic plots discussed in the previous section, but they are much easier to construct, as we shall see shortly.

The transfer function can be written as

$$\mathbf{H} = H \underline{/\phi} = H e^{j\phi} \qquad (14.12)$$

Taking the natural logarithm of both sides,

$$\ln \mathbf{H} = \ln H + \ln e^{j\phi} = \ln H + j\phi \qquad (14.13)$$

TABLE 14.2   Specific gains and their decibel values.

Magnitude H	$20 \log_{10} H$ (dB)
0.001	−60
0.01	−40
0.1	−20
0.5	−6
$1/\sqrt{2}$	−3
1	0
$\sqrt{2}$	3
2	6
10	20
20	26
100	40
1000	60

The origin is where $\omega = 1$ or $\log \omega = 0$ and the gain is zero.

Thus, the real part of $\ln \mathbf{H}$ is a function of the magnitude while the imaginary part is the phase. In a Bode magnitude plot, the gain

$$H_{\mathrm{dB}} = 20 \log_{10} H \tag{14.14}$$

is plotted in decibels (dB) versus frequency. Table 14.2 provides a few values of H with the corresponding values in decibels. In a Bode phase plot, ϕ is plotted in degrees versus frequency. Both magnitude and phase plots are made on semilog graph paper.

A transfer function in the form of Eq. (14.3) may be written in terms of factors that have real and imaginary parts. One such representation might be

$$\mathbf{H}(\omega) = \frac{K(j\omega)^{\pm 1}(1 + j\omega/z_1)[1 + j2\zeta_1\omega/\omega_k + (j\omega/\omega_k)^2]\cdots}{(1 + j\omega/p_1)[1 + j2\zeta_2\omega/\omega_n + (j\omega/\omega_n)^2]\cdots} \tag{14.15}$$

which is obtained by dividing out the poles and zeros in $\mathbf{H}(\omega)$. The representation of $\mathbf{H}(\omega)$ as in Eq. (14.15) is called the *standard form*. In this particular case, $\mathbf{H}(\omega)$ has seven different factors that can appear in various combinations in a transfer function. These are:

1. A gain K
2. A pole $(j\omega)^{-1}$ or zero $(j\omega)$ at the origin
3. A simple pole $1/(1 + j\omega/p_1)$ or zero $(1 + j\omega/z_1)$
4. A quadratic pole $1/[1 + j2\zeta_2\omega/\omega_n + (j\omega/\omega_n)^2]$ or zero $[1 + j2\zeta_1\omega/\omega_k + (j\omega/\omega_k)^2]$

In constructing a Bode plot, we plot each factor separately and then combine them graphically. The factors can be considered one at a time and then combined additively because of the logarithms involved. It is this mathematical convenience of the logarithm that makes Bode plots a powerful engineering tool.

We will now make straight-line plots of the factors listed above. We shall find that these straight-line plots known as Bode plots approximate the actual plots to a surprising degree of accuracy.

Constant term: For the gain K, the magnitude is $20 \log_{10} K$ and the phase is $0°$; both are constant with frequency. Thus the magnitude and phase plots of the gain are shown in Fig. 14.9. If K is negative, the magnitude remains $20 \log_{10} |K|$ but the phase is $\pm 180°$.

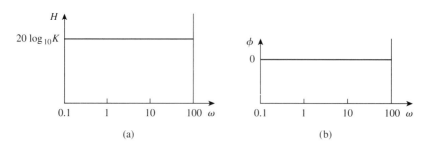

Figure 14.9   Bode plots for gain K: (a) magnitude plot, (b) phase plot.

Pole/zero at the origin: For the zero $(j\omega)$ at the origin, the magnitude is $20 \log_{10} \omega$ and the phase is $90°$. These are plotted in Fig. 14.10, where we notice that the slope of the magnitude plot is 20 dB/decade, while the phase is constant with frequency.

The Bode plots for the pole $(j\omega)^{-1}$ are similar except that the slope of the magnitude plot is -20 dB/decade while the phase is $-90°$. In general, for $(j\omega)^N$, where N is an integer, the magnitude plot will have a slope of $20N$ dB/decade, while the phase is $90N$ degrees.

Simple pole/zero: For the simple zero $(1 + j\omega/z_1)$, the magnitude is $20 \log_{10} |1 + j\omega/z_1|$ and the phase is $\tan^{-1} \omega/z_1$. We notice that

$$H_{dB} = 20 \log_{10} \left| 1 + \frac{j\omega}{z_1} \right| \quad \Longrightarrow \quad 20 \log_{10} 1 = 0 \qquad (14.16)$$
$$\text{as} \quad \omega \to 0$$

$$H_{dB} = 20 \log_{10} \left| 1 + \frac{j\omega}{z_1} \right| \quad \Longrightarrow \quad 20 \log_{10} \frac{\omega}{z_1} \qquad (14.17)$$
$$\text{as} \quad \omega \to \infty$$

showing that we can approximate the magnitude as zero (a straight line with zero slope) for small values of ω and by a straight line with slope 20 dB/decade for large values of ω. The frequency $\omega = z_1$ where the two asymptotic lines meet is called the *corner frequency* or *break frequency*. Thus the approximate magnitude plot is shown in Fig. 14.11(a), where the actual plot is also shown. Notice that the approximate plot is close to the actual plot except at the break frequency, where $\omega = z_1$ and the deviation is $20 \log_{10} |(1 + j1)| = 20 \log_{10} \sqrt{2} = 3$ dB.

The phase $\tan^{-1}(\omega/z_1)$ can be expressed as

$$\phi = \tan^{-1}\left(\frac{\omega}{z_1}\right) = \begin{cases} 0, & \omega = 0 \\ 45°, & \omega = z_1 \\ 90°, & \omega \to \infty \end{cases} \qquad (14.18)$$

As a straight-line approximation, we let $\phi \simeq 0$ for $\omega \le z_1/10$, $\phi \simeq 45°$ for $\omega = z_1$, and $\phi \simeq 90°$ for $\omega \ge 10z_1$. As shown in Fig. 14.11(b) along with the actual plot, the straight-line plot has a slope of 45° per decade.

The Bode plots for the pole $1/(1 + j\omega/p_1)$ are similar to those in Fig. 14.11 except that the corner frequency is at $\omega = p_1$, the magnitude

A decade is an interval between two frequencies with a ratio of 10; e.g., between ω_0 and $10\omega_0$, or between 10 and 100 Hz. Thus, 20 dB/decade means that the magnitude changes 20 dB whenever the frequency changes tenfold or one decade.

The special case of dc $(\omega = 0)$ does not appear on Bode plots because $\log 0 = -\infty$, implying that zero frequency is infinitely far to the left of the origin of Bode plots.

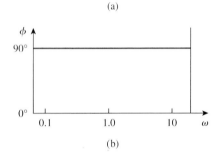

Figure 14.10   Bode plot for a zero $(j\omega)$ at the origin: (a) magnitude plot, (b) phase plot.

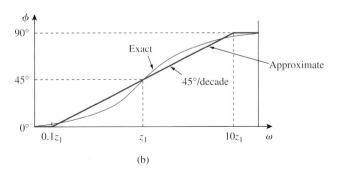

Figure 14.11   Bode plots of zero $(1 + j\omega/z_1)$: (a) magnitude plot, (b) phase plot.

has a slope of -20 dB/decade, and the phase has a slope of $-45°$ per decade.

Quadratic pole/zero: The magnitude of the quadratic pole $1/[1 + j2\zeta_2\omega/\omega_n + (j\omega/\omega_n)^2]$ is $-20\log_{10}|1 + j2\zeta_2\omega/\omega_n + (j\omega/\omega_n)^2|$ and the phase is $-\tan^{-1}(2\zeta_2\omega/\omega_n)/(1 - \omega^2/\omega_n^2)$. But

$$H_{\text{dB}} = -20\log_{10}\left|1 + \frac{j2\zeta_2\omega}{\omega_n} + \left(\frac{j\omega}{\omega_n}\right)^2\right| \implies 0$$

$$\text{as} \quad \omega \to 0$$

$$(14.19)$$

and

$$H_{\text{dB}} = -20\log_{10}\left|1 + \frac{j2\zeta_2\omega}{\omega_n} + \left(\frac{j\omega}{\omega_n}\right)^2\right| \implies -40\log_{10}\frac{\omega}{\omega_n}$$

$$\text{as} \quad \omega \to \infty$$

$$(14.20)$$

Thus, the amplitude plot consists of two straight asymptotic lines: one with zero slope for $\omega < \omega_n$ and the other with slope -40 dB/decade for $\omega > \omega_n$, with ω_n as the corner frequency. Figure 14.12(a) shows the approximate and actual amplitude plots. Note that the actual plot depends on the damping factor ζ_2 as well as the corner frequency ω_n. The significant peaking in the neighborhood of the corner frequency should be added to the straight-line approximation if a high level of accuracy is desired. However, we will use the straight-line approximation for the sake of simplicity.

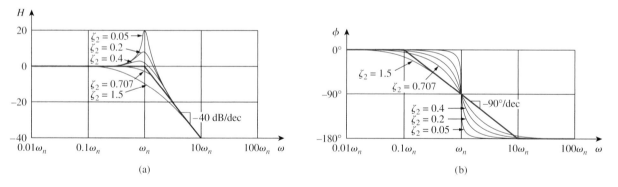

Figure 14.12   Bode plots of quadratic pole $[1 + j2\zeta\omega/\omega_n - \omega^2/\omega_n^2]^{-1}$: (a) magnitude plot, (b) phase plot.

The phase can be expressed as

$$\phi = -\tan^{-1}\frac{2\zeta_2\omega/\omega_n}{1 - \omega^2/\omega_n^2} = \begin{cases} 0, & \omega = 0 \\ -90°, & \omega = \omega_n \\ -180°, & \omega \to \infty \end{cases} \qquad (14.21)$$

The phase plot is a straight line with a slope of $90°$ per decade starting at $\omega_n/10$ and ending at $10\omega_n$, as shown in Fig. 14.12(b). We see again that the difference between the actual plot and the straight-line plot is due to the damping factor. Notice that the straight-line approximations for both magnitude and phase plots for the quadratic pole are the same as those for a double pole, i.e. $(1 + j\omega/\omega_n)^{-2}$. We should expect this because the double pole $(1 + j\omega/\omega_n)^{-2}$ equals the quadratic pole $1/[1 + j2\zeta_2\omega/\omega_n + (j\omega/\omega_n)^2]$ when $\zeta_2 = 1$. Thus, the quadratic pole can be treated as a double pole as far as straight-line approximation is concerned.

For the quadratic zero $[1 + j2\zeta_1\omega/\omega_k + (j\omega/\omega_k)^2]$, the plots in Fig. 14.12 are inverted because the magnitude plot has a slope of 40 dB/decade while the phase plot has a slope of 90° per decade.

Table 14.3 presents a summary of Bode plots for the seven factors. To sketch the Bode plots for a function $\mathbf{H}(\omega)$ in the form of Eq. (14.15), for example, we first record the corner frequencies on the semilog graph paper, sketch the factors one at a time as discussed above, and then combine additively the graphs of the factors. The combined graph is often drawn from left to right, changing slopes appropriately each time a corner frequency is encountered. The following examples illustrate this procedure.

There is another procedure for obtaining Bode plots that is faster and perhaps more efficient than the one we have just discussed. It consists in realizing that zeros cause an increase in slope, while poles cause a decrease. By starting with the low-frequency asymptote of the Bode plot, moving along the frequency axis, and increasing or decreasing the slope at each corner frequency, one can sketch the Bode plot immediately from the transfer function without the effort of making individual plots and adding them. This procedure can be used once you become proficient in the one discussed here.

Digital computers have rendered the procedure discussed here almost obsolete. Several software packages such as *PSpice*, *MATLAB*, Mathcad, and Micro-Cap can be used to generate frequency response plots. We will discuss *PSpice* later in the chapter.

TABLE 14.3   Summary of Bode straight-line magnitude and phase plots.

Factor	Magnitude	Phase
K	$20 \log_{10} K$	$0°$
$(j\omega)^N$	20N dB/decade	90N°
$\dfrac{1}{(j\omega)^N}$	−20N dB/decade	−90N°
$\left(1 + \dfrac{j\omega}{z}\right)^N$	20N dB/decade	90N°
$\dfrac{1}{(1 + j\omega/p)^N}$	−20N dB/decade	−90N°

continued

TABLE 14.3   *(continued)*

Factor	Magnitude	Phase

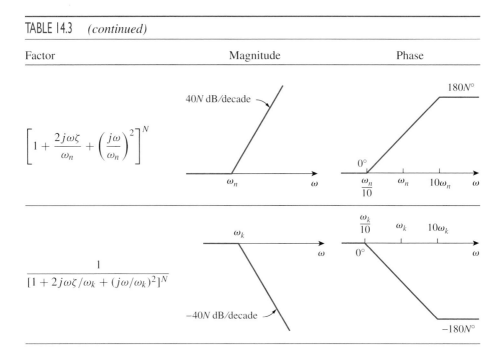

$$\left[1 + \frac{2j\omega\zeta}{\omega_n} + \left(\frac{j\omega}{\omega_n}\right)^2\right]^N$$

$$\frac{1}{[1 + 2j\omega\zeta/\omega_k + (j\omega/\omega_k)^2]^N}$$

EXAMPLE 14.3

Construct the Bode plots for the transfer function

$$\mathbf{H}(\omega) = \frac{200\,j\omega}{(j\omega + 2)(j\omega + 10)}$$

Solution:

We first put $\mathbf{H}(\omega)$ in the standard form by dividing out the poles and zeros. Thus,

$$\mathbf{H}(\omega) = \frac{10\,j\omega}{(1 + j\omega/2)(1 + j\omega/10)}$$

$$= \frac{10|j\omega|}{|1 + j\omega/2|\,|1 + j\omega/10|}\underline{/90° - \tan^{-1}\omega/2 - \tan^{-1}\omega/10}$$

Hence the magnitude and phase are

$$H_{\text{dB}} = 20\log_{10} 10 + 20\log_{10}|j\omega| - 20\log_{10}\left|1 + \frac{j\omega}{2}\right|$$

$$- 20\log_{10}\left|1 + \frac{j\omega}{10}\right|$$

$$\phi = 90° - \tan^{-1}\frac{\omega}{2} - \tan^{-1}\frac{\omega}{10}$$

We notice that there are two corner frequencies at $\omega = 2$, 10. For both the magnitude and phase plots, we sketch each term as shown by the dotted lines in Fig. 14.13. We add them up graphically to obtain the overall plots shown by the solid curves.

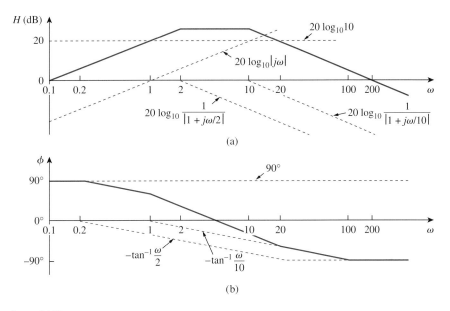

Figure 14.13   For Example 14.3: (a) magnitude plot, (b) phase plot.

PRACTICE PROBLEM 14.3

Draw the Bode plots for the transfer function

$$\mathbf{H}(\omega) = \frac{5(j\omega + 2)}{j\omega(j\omega + 10)}$$

Answer: See Fig. 14.14.

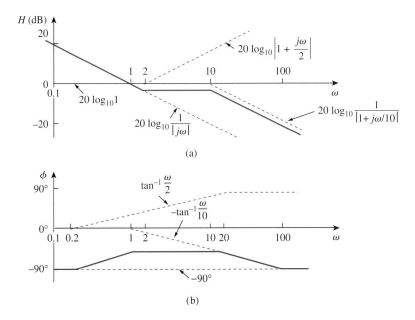

Figure 14.14   For Practice Prob. 14.3: (a) magnitude plot, (b) phase plot.

EXAMPLE 14.4

Obtain the Bode plots for

$$\mathbf{H}(\omega) = \frac{j\omega + 10}{j\omega(j\omega + 5)^2}$$

Solution:

Putting $\mathbf{H}(\omega)$ in the standard form, we get

$$\mathbf{H}(\omega) = \frac{0.4\,(1 + j\omega/10)}{j\omega\,(1 + j\omega/5)^2}$$

From this, we obtain the magnitude and phase as

$$H_{\text{dB}} = 20\log_{10} 0.4 + 20\log_{10}\left|1 + \frac{j\omega}{10}\right| - 20\log_{10}|j\omega|$$

$$- 40\log_{10}\left|1 + \frac{j\omega}{5}\right|$$

$$\phi = 0° + \tan^{-1}\frac{\omega}{10} - 90° - 2\tan^{-1}\frac{\omega}{5}$$

There are two corner frequencies at $\omega = 5$, 10 rad/s. For the pole with corner frequency at $\omega = 5$, the slope of the magnitude plot is -40 dB/decade and that of the phase plot is $-90°$ per decade due to the power of 2. The magnitude and the phase plots for the individual terms (in dotted lines) and the entire $\mathbf{H}(j\omega)$ (in solid lines) are in Fig. 14.15.

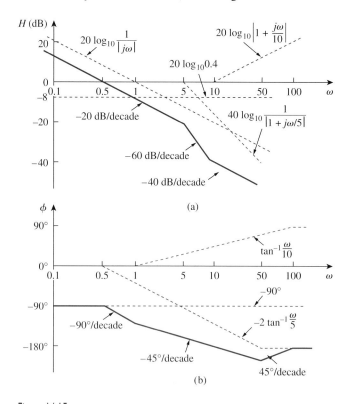

Figure 14.15 Bode plots for Example 14.4: (a) magnitude plot, (b) phase plot.

PRACTICE PROBLEM 14.4

Sketch the Bode plots for

$$\mathbf{H}(\omega) = \frac{50j\omega}{(j\omega + 4)(j\omega + 10)^2}$$

Answer: See Fig. 14.16.

(a)

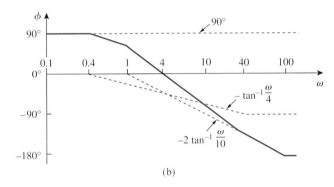

(b)

Figure 14.16   For Practice Prob. 14.4: (a) magnitude plot, (b) phase plot.

EXAMPLE 14.5

Draw the Bode plots for

$$\mathbf{H}(s) = \frac{s + 1}{s^2 + 60s + 100}$$

Solution:

We express $\mathbf{H}(s)$ as

$$\mathbf{H}(\omega) = \frac{1/100(1 + j\omega)}{1 + j\omega 6/10 + (j\omega/10)^2}$$

For the quadratic pole, $\omega_n = 10$ rad/s, which serves as the corner frequency. The magnitude and phase are

$$H_{dB} = -20\log_{10} 100 + 20\log_{10}|1 + j\omega|$$

$$- 20\log_{10}\left|1 + \frac{j\omega 6}{10} - \frac{\omega^2}{100}\right|$$

$$\phi = 0° + \tan^{-1}\omega - \tan^{-1}\left[\frac{\omega 6/10}{1 - \omega^2/100}\right]$$

Figure 14.17 shows the Bode plots. Notice that the quadratic pole is treated as a repeated pole at ω_k, that is, $(1 + j\omega/\omega_k)^2$, which is an approximation.

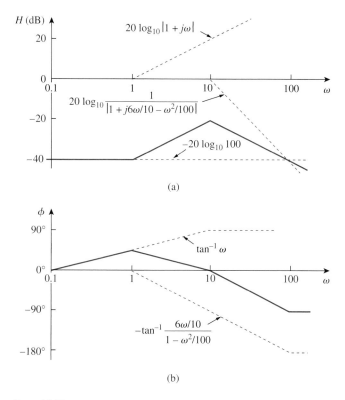

Figure 14.17　Bode plots for Example 14.5: (a) magnitude plot, (b) phase plot.

PRACTICE PROBLEM 1 4 . 5

Construct the Bode plots for

$$H(s) = \frac{10}{s(s^2 + 80s + 400)}$$

Answer:　See Fig. 14.18.

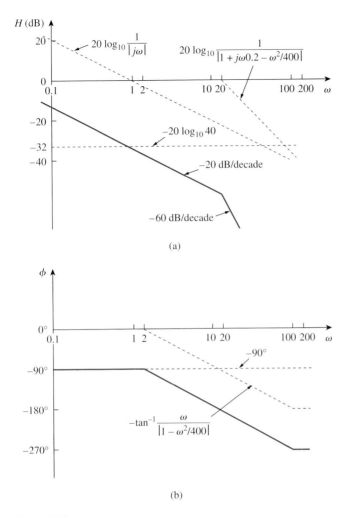

Figure 14.18   For Practice Prob. 14.5: (a) magnitude plot, (b) phase plot.

EXAMPLE 14.6

Given the Bode plot in Fig. 14.19, obtain the transfer function $\mathbf{H}(\omega)$.

Solution:

To obtain $\mathbf{H}(\omega)$ from the Bode plot, we keep in mind that a zero always causes an upward turn at a corner frequency, while a pole causes a downward turn. We notice from Fig. 14.19 that there is a zero $j\omega$ at the origin which should have intersected the frequency axis at $\omega = 1$. This is indicated by the straight line with slope $+20$ dB/decade. The fact that this straight line is shifted by 40 dB indicates that there is a 40-dB gain; that is,

$$40 = 20\log_{10} K \qquad \Longrightarrow \qquad \log_{10} K = 2$$

or

$$K = 10^2 = 100$$

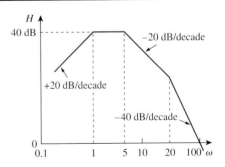

Figure 14.19   For Example 14.6.

In addition to the zero $j\omega$ at the origin, we notice that there are three factors with corner frequencies at $\omega = 1, 5$, and 20 rad/s. Thus, we have:

1. A pole at $p = 1$ with slope -20 dB/decade to cause a downward turn and counteract the pole at the origin. The pole at $p = 1$ is determined as $1/(1 + j\omega/1)$.
2. Another pole at $p = 5$ with slope -20 dB/decade causing a downward turn. The pole is $1/(1 + j\omega/5)$.
3. A third pole at $p = 20$ with slope -20 dB/decade causing a further downward turn. The pole is $1/(1 + j\omega/20)$.

Putting all these together gives the corresponding transfer function as

$$\mathbf{H}(\omega) = \frac{100 j\omega}{(1 + j\omega/1)(1 + j\omega/5)(1 + j\omega/20)}$$
$$= \frac{j\omega 10^4}{(j\omega + 1)(j\omega + 5)(j\omega + 20)}$$

or

$$\mathbf{H}(s) = \frac{10^4 s}{(s + 1)(s + 5)(s + 20)}, \qquad s = j\omega$$

PRACTICE PROBLEM 14.6

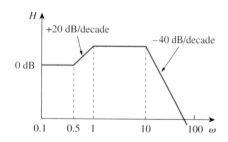

Figure 14.20   For Practice Prob. 14.6.

Obtain the transfer function $\mathbf{H}(\omega)$ corresponding to the Bode plot in Fig. 14.20.

Answer: $\mathbf{H}(\omega) = \dfrac{200(s + 0.5)}{(s + 1)(s + 10)^2}.$

14.5   SERIES RESONANCE

The most prominent feature of the frequency response of a circuit may be the sharp peak (or *resonant peak*) exhibited in its amplitude characteristic. The concept of resonance applies in several areas of science and engineering. Resonance occurs in any system that has a complex conjugate pair of poles; it is the cause of oscillations of stored energy from one form to another. It is the phenomenon that allows frequency discrimination in communications networks. Resonance occurs in any circuit that has at least one inductor and one capacitor.

Resonance is a condition in an *RLC* circuit in which the capacitive and inductive reactances are equal in magnitude, thereby resulting in a purely resistive impedance.

Resonant circuits (series or parallel) are useful for constructing filters, as their transfer functions can be highly frequency selective. They are used in many applications such as selecting the desired stations in radio and TV receivers.

Consider the series RLC circuit shown in Fig. 14.21 in the frequency domain. The input impedance is

$$\mathbf{Z} = \mathbf{H}(\omega) = \frac{\mathbf{V}_s}{\mathbf{I}} = R + j\omega L + \frac{1}{j\omega C} \qquad (14.22)$$

or

$$\mathbf{Z} = R + j\left(\omega L - \frac{1}{\omega C}\right) \qquad (14.23)$$

$\mathbf{V}_s = V_m \angle\theta$

Figure 14.21   The series resonant circuit.

Resonance results when the imaginary part of the transfer function is zero, or

$$\text{Im}(\mathbf{Z}) = \omega L - \frac{1}{\omega C} = 0 \qquad (14.24)$$

The value of ω that satisfies this condition is called the *resonant frequency* ω_0. Thus, the resonance condition is

$$\omega_0 L = \frac{1}{\omega_0 C} \qquad (14.25)$$

or

$$\boxed{\omega_0 = \frac{1}{\sqrt{LC}} \text{ rad/s}} \qquad (14.26)$$

Since $\omega_0 = 2\pi f_0$,

$$f_0 = \frac{1}{2\pi\sqrt{LC}} \text{ Hz} \qquad (14.27)$$

Note that at resonance:

1. The impedance is purely resistive, thus, $\mathbf{Z} = R$. In other words, the LC series combination acts like a short circuit, and the entire voltage is across R.

2. The voltage $\mathbf{V}_s$ and the current $\mathbf{I}$ are in phase, so that the power factor is unity.

3. The magnitude of the transfer function $\mathbf{H}(\omega) = \mathbf{Z}(\omega)$ is minimum.

4. The inductor voltage and capacitor voltage can be much more than the source voltage.

The frequency response of the circuit's current magnitude

$$I = |\mathbf{I}| = \frac{V_m}{\sqrt{R^2 + (\omega L - 1/\omega C)^2}} \qquad (14.28)$$

is shown in Fig. 14.22; the plot only shows the symmetry illustrated in this graph when the frequency axis is a logarithm. The average power

Note No. 4 becomes evident from the fact that

$$|\mathbf{V}_L| = \frac{V_m}{R}\omega_0 L = QV_m$$

$$|\mathbf{V}_C| = \frac{V_m}{R}\frac{1}{\omega_0 C} = QV_m$$

where Q is the quality factor, defined in Eq. (14.38).

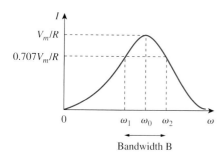

Figure 14.22 The current amplitude versus frequency for the series resonant circuit of Fig. 14.21.

dissipated by the RLC circuit is

$$P(\omega) = \frac{1}{2} I^2 R \tag{14.29}$$

The highest power dissipated occurs at resonance, when $I = V_m/R$, so that

$$P(\omega_0) = \frac{1}{2} \frac{V_m^2}{R} \tag{14.30}$$

At certain frequencies $\omega = \omega_1$, ω_2, the dissipated power is half the maximum value; that is,

$$P(\omega_1) = P(\omega_2) = \frac{(V_m/\sqrt{2})^2}{2R} = \frac{V_m^2}{4R} \tag{14.31}$$

Hence, ω_1 and ω_2 are called the *half-power frequencies*.

The half-power frequencies are obtained by setting Z equal to $\sqrt{2}R$, and writing

$$\sqrt{R^2 + \left(\omega L - \frac{1}{\omega C}\right)^2} = \sqrt{2}R \tag{14.32}$$

Solving for ω, we obtain

$$\omega_1 = -\frac{R}{2L} + \sqrt{\left(\frac{R}{2L}\right)^2 + \frac{1}{LC}}$$

$$\omega_2 = \frac{R}{2L} + \sqrt{\left(\frac{R}{2L}\right)^2 + \frac{1}{LC}} \tag{14.33}$$

We can relate the half-power frequencies with the resonant frequency. From Eqs. (14.26) and (14.33),

$$\omega_0 = \sqrt{\omega_1 \omega_2} \tag{14.34}$$

showing that the resonant frequency is the geometric mean of the half-power frequencies. Notice that ω_1 and ω_2 are in general not symmetrical around the resonant frequency ω_0, because the frequency response is not generally symmetrical. However, as will be explained shortly, symmetry of the half-power frequencies around the resonant frequency is often a reasonable approximation.

Although the height of the curve in Fig. 14.22 is determined by R, the width of the curve depends on other factors. The width of the response curve depends on the *bandwidth B*, which is defined as the difference between the two half-power frequencies,

$$B = \omega_2 - \omega_1 \tag{14.35}$$

This definition of bandwidth is just one of several that are commonly used. Strictly speaking, B in Eq. (14.35) is a half-power bandwidth, because it is the width of the frequency band between the half-power frequencies.

The "sharpness" of the resonance in a resonant circuit is measured quantitatively by the *quality factor Q*. At resonance, the reactive energy in the circuit oscillates between the inductor and the capacitor. The quality factor relates the maximum or peak energy stored to the energy dissipated in the circuit per cycle of oscillation:

$$Q = 2\pi \frac{\text{Peak energy stored in the circuit}}{\substack{\text{Energy dissipated by the circuit} \\ \text{in one period at resonance}}} \qquad (14.36)$$

Although the same symbol Q is used for the reactive power, the two are not equal and should not be confused. Q here is dimensionless, whereas reactive power Q is in VAR. This may help distinguish between the two.

It is also regarded as a measure of the energy storage property of a circuit in relation to its energy dissipation property. In the series RLC circuit, the peak energy stored is $\frac{1}{2}LI^2$, while the energy dissipated in one period is $\frac{1}{2}(I^2 R)(1/f_0)$. Hence,

$$Q = 2\pi \frac{\frac{1}{2}LI^2}{\frac{1}{2}I^2 R(1/f_0)} = \frac{2\pi f_0 L}{R} \qquad (14.37)$$

or

$$\boxed{Q = \frac{\omega_0 L}{R} = \frac{1}{\omega_0 C R}} \qquad (14.38)$$

Notice that the quality factor is dimensionless. The relationship between the bandwidth B and the quality factor Q is obtained by substituting Eq. (14.33) into Eq. (14.35) and utilizing Eq. (14.38).

$$\boxed{B = \frac{R}{L} = \frac{\omega_0}{Q}} \qquad (14.39)$$

or $B = \omega_0^2 C R$. Thus

> The quality factor of a resonant circuit is the ratio of its resonant frequency to its bandwidth.

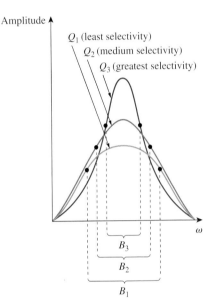

Figure 14.23   The higher the circuit Q, the smaller the bandwidth.

Keep in mind that Eqs. (14.26), (14.33), (14.38), and (14.39) only apply to a series RLC circuit.

As illustrated in Fig. 14.23, the higher the value of Q, the more selective the circuit is but the smaller the bandwidth. The *selectivity* of an RLC circuit is the ability of the circuit to respond to a certain frequency and discriminate against all other frequencies. If the band of frequencies to be selected or rejected is narrow, the quality factor of the resonant circuit must be high. If the band of frequencies is wide, the quality factor must be low.

The quality factor is a measure of the selectivity (or "sharpness" of resonance) of the circuit.

A resonant circuit is designed to operate at or near its resonant frequency. It is said to be a *high-Q circuit* when its quality factor is equal to or greater than 10. For high-Q circuits ($Q \geq 10$), the half-power frequencies are, for all practical purposes, symmetrical around the resonant frequency and can be approximated as

$$\omega_1 \simeq \omega_0 - \frac{B}{2}, \qquad \omega_2 \simeq \omega_0 + \frac{B}{2} \qquad (14.40)$$

High-Q circuits are used often in communications networks.

We see that a resonant circuit is characterized by five related parameters: the two half-power frequencies ω_1 and ω_2, the resonant frequency ω_0, the bandwidth B, and the quality factor Q.

EXAMPLE 14.7

Figure 14.24   For Example 14.7.

In the circuit in Fig. 14.24, $R = 2\,\Omega$, $L = 1$ mH, and $C = 0.4\,\mu$F. (a) Find the resonant frequency and the half-power frequencies. (b) Calculate the quality factor and bandwidth. (c) Determine the amplitude of the current at ω_0, ω_1, and ω_2.

Solution:

(a) The resonant frequency is

$$\omega_0 = \frac{1}{\sqrt{LC}} = \frac{1}{\sqrt{10^{-3} \times 0.4 \times 10^{-6}}} = 50 \text{ krad/s}$$

METHOD **1**   The lower half-power frequency is

$$\omega_1 = -\frac{R}{2L} + \sqrt{\left(\frac{R}{2L}\right)^2 + \frac{1}{LC}}$$

$$= -\frac{2}{2 \times 10^{-3}} + \sqrt{(10^3)^2 + (50 \times 10^3)^2}$$

$$= -1 + \sqrt{1 + 2500} \text{ krad/s} = 49 \text{ krad/s}$$

Similarly, the upper half-power frequency is

$$\omega_2 = 1 + \sqrt{1 + 2500} \text{ krad/s} = 51 \text{ krad/s}$$

(b) The bandwidth is

$$B = \omega_2 - \omega_1 = 2 \text{ krad/s}$$

or

$$B = \frac{R}{L} = \frac{2}{10^{-3}} = 2 \text{ krad/s}$$

The quality factor is

$$Q = \frac{\omega_0}{B} = \frac{50}{2} = 25$$

METHOD **2**   Alternatively, we could find

$$Q = \frac{\omega_0 L}{R} = \frac{50 \times 10^3 \times 10^{-3}}{2} = 25$$

From Q, we find

$$B = \frac{\omega_0}{Q} = \frac{50 \times 10^3}{25} = 2 \text{ krad/s}$$

Since $Q > 10$, this is a high-Q circuit and we can obtain the half-power frequencies as

$$\omega_1 = \omega_0 - \frac{B}{2} = 50 - 1 = 49 \text{ krad/s}$$

$$\omega_2 = \omega_0 + \frac{B}{2} = 50 + 1 = 51 \text{ krad/s}$$

as obtained earlier.

(c) At $\omega = \omega_0$,

$$I = \frac{V_m}{R} = \frac{20}{2} = 10 \text{ A}$$

At $\omega = \omega_1, \omega_2$,

$$I = \frac{V_m}{\sqrt{2}R} = \frac{10}{\sqrt{2}} = 7.071 \text{ A}$$

PRACTICE PROBLEM 14.7

A series-connected circuit has $R = 4 \; \Omega$ and $L = 25$ mH. (a) Calculate the value of C that will produce a quality factor of 50. (b) Find ω_1, ω_2, and B. (c) Determine the average power dissipated at $\omega = \omega_0$, ω_1, ω_2. Take $V_m = 100$ V.

Answer: (a) 0.625 μF, (b) 7920 rad/s, 8080 rad/s, 160 rad/s, (c) 1.25 kW, 0.625 kW, 0.625 kW.

14.6 PARALLEL RESONANCE

The parallel RLC circuit in Fig. 14.25 is the dual of the series RLC circuit. So we will avoid needless repetition. The admittance is

$$\mathbf{Y} = H(\omega) = \frac{\mathbf{I}}{\mathbf{V}} = \frac{1}{R} + j\omega C + \frac{1}{j\omega L} \qquad (14.41)$$

or

$$\mathbf{Y} = \frac{1}{R} + j\left(\omega C - \frac{1}{\omega L}\right) \qquad (14.42)$$

Resonance occurs when the imaginary part of $\mathbf{Y}$ is zero,

$$\omega C - \frac{1}{\omega L} = 0 \qquad (14.43)$$

or

$$\boxed{\omega_0 = \frac{1}{\sqrt{LC}} \text{ rad/s} \qquad (14.44)}$$

which is the same as Eq. (14.26) for the series resonant circuit. The voltage $|\mathbf{V}|$ is sketched in Fig. 14.26 as a function of frequency. Notice that at resonance, the parallel LC combination acts like an open circuit, so that the entire current flows through R. Also, the inductor and capacitor current can be much more than the source current at resonance.

Figure 14.25   The parallel resonant circuit.

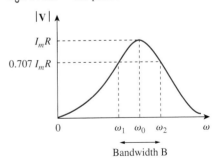

Figure 14.26   The current amplitude versus frequency for the series resonant circuit of Fig. 14.25.

We can see this from the fact that

$$|I_L| = \frac{I_m R}{\omega_0 L} = Q I_m$$

$$|I_C| = \omega_0 C I_m R = Q I_m$$

where Q is the quality factor, defined in Eq. (14.47).

We exploit the duality between Figs. 14.21 and 14.25 by comparing Eq. (14.42) with Eq. (14.23). By replacing R, L, and C in the expressions for the series circuit with $1/R$, C, and L respectively, we obtain for the parallel circuit

$$\omega_1 = -\frac{1}{2RC} + \sqrt{\left(\frac{1}{2RC}\right)^2 + \frac{1}{LC}}$$
$$\omega_2 = \frac{1}{2RC} + \sqrt{\left(\frac{1}{2RC}\right)^2 + \frac{1}{LC}}$$
(14.45)

$$B = \omega_2 - \omega_1 = \frac{1}{RC}$$
(14.46)

$$Q = \frac{\omega_0}{B} = \omega_0 RC = \frac{R}{\omega_0 L}$$
(14.47)

Using Eqs. (14.45) and (14.47), we can express the half-power frequencies in terms of the quality factor. The result is

$$\omega_1 = \omega_0 \sqrt{1 + \left(\frac{1}{2Q}\right)^2} - \frac{\omega_0}{2Q}, \qquad \omega_2 = \omega_0 \sqrt{1 + \left(\frac{1}{2Q}\right)^2} + \frac{\omega_0}{2Q}$$
(14.48)

Again, for high-Q circuits ($Q \geq 10$)

$$\omega_1 \simeq \omega_0 - \frac{B}{2}, \qquad \omega_2 \simeq \omega_0 + \frac{B}{2}$$
(14.49)

Table 14.4 presents a summary of the characteristics of the series and parallel resonant circuits. Besides the series and parallel RLC considered here, other resonant circuits exist. Example 14.9 treats a typical example.

TABLE 14.4   Summary of the characteristics of resonant RLC circuits.

Characteristic	Series circuit	Parallel circuit
Resonant frequency, ω_0	$\dfrac{1}{\sqrt{LC}}$	$\dfrac{1}{\sqrt{LC}}$
Quality factor, Q	$\dfrac{\omega_0 L}{R}$ or $\dfrac{1}{\omega_0 RC}$	$\dfrac{R}{\omega_0 L}$ or $\omega_0 RC$
Bandwidth, B	$\dfrac{\omega_0}{Q}$	$\dfrac{\omega_0}{Q}$
Half-power frequencies, ω_1, ω_2	$\omega_0 \sqrt{1 + \left(\dfrac{1}{2Q}\right)^2} \pm \dfrac{\omega_0}{2Q}$	$\omega_0 \sqrt{1 + \left(\dfrac{1}{2Q}\right)^2} \pm \dfrac{\omega_0}{2Q}$
For $Q \geq 10$, ω_1, ω_2	$\omega_0 \pm \dfrac{B}{2}$	$\omega_0 \pm \dfrac{B}{2}$

EXAMPLE 14.8

In the parallel RLC circuit in Fig. 14.27, let $R = 8\ k\Omega$, $L = 0.2\ mH$, and $C = 8\ \mu F$. (a) Calculate ω_0, Q, and B. (b) Find ω_1 and ω_2. (c) Determine the power dissipated at ω_0, ω_1, and ω_2.

Solution:

(a)

$$\omega_0 = \frac{1}{\sqrt{LC}} = \frac{1}{\sqrt{0.2 \times 10^{-3} \times 8 \times 10^{-6}}} = \frac{10^5}{4} = 25\ krad/s$$

Figure 14.27   For Example 14.8.

$$Q = \frac{R}{\omega_0 L} = \frac{8 \times 10^3}{25 \times 10^3 \times 0.2 \times 10^{-3}} = 1,600$$

$$B = \frac{\omega_0}{Q} = 15.625\ rad/s$$

(b) Due to the high value of Q, we can regard this as a high-Q circuit. Hence,

$$\omega_1 = \omega_0 - \frac{B}{2} = 25,000 - 7.812 = 24,992\ rad/s$$

$$\omega_2 = \omega_0 + \frac{B}{2} = 25,000 + 7.812 = 25,008\ rad/s$$

(c) At $\omega = \omega_0$, $\mathbf{Y} = 1/R$ or $\mathbf{Z} = R = 8\ k\Omega$. Then

$$\mathbf{I}_o = \frac{\mathbf{V}}{\mathbf{Z}} = \frac{10\underline{/-90°}}{8,000} = 1.25\underline{/-90°}\ mA$$

Since the entire current flows through R at resonance, the average power dissipated at $\omega = \omega_0$ is

$$P = \frac{1}{2}|\mathbf{I}_o|^2 R = \frac{1}{2}(1.25 \times 10^{-3})^2(8 \times 10^3) = 6.25\ mW$$

or

$$P = \frac{V_m^2}{2R} = \frac{100}{2 \times 8 \times 10^3} = 6.25\ mW$$

At $\omega = \omega_1,\ \omega_2$,

$$P = \frac{V_m^2}{4R} = 3.125\ mW$$

PRACTICE PROBLEM 14.8

A parallel resonant circuit has $R = 100\ k\Omega$, $L = 20\ mH$, and $C = 5\ nF$. Calculate ω_0, ω_1, ω_2, Q, and B.

Answer: 100 krad/s, 99 krad/s, 101 krad/s, 50, 2 krad/s.

EXAMPLE 14.9

Determine the resonant frequency of the circuit in Fig. 14.28.

Figure 14.28   For Example 14.9.

Solution:

The input admittance is

$$\mathbf{Y} = j\omega 0.1 + \frac{1}{10} + \frac{1}{2 + j\omega 2} = 0.1 + j\omega 0.1 + \frac{2 - j\omega 2}{4 + 4\omega^2}$$

At resonance, $\mathrm{Im}(\mathbf{Y}) = 0$ and

$$\omega_0 0.1 - \frac{2\omega_0}{4 + 4\omega_0^2} = 0 \quad \Longrightarrow \quad \omega_0 = 2 \text{ rad/s}$$

PRACTICE PROBLEM 14.9

Calculate the resonant frequency of the circuit in Fig. 14.29.

Answer: 2.179 rad/s.

Figure 14.29   For Practice Prob. 14.9.

14.7 PASSIVE FILTERS

The concept of filters has been an integral part of the evolution of electrical engineering from the beginning. Several technological achievements would not have been possible without electrical filters. Because of this prominent role of filters, much effort has been expended on the theory, design, and construction of filters and many articles and books have been written on them. Our discussion in this chapter should be considered introductory.

> A filter is a circuit that is designed to pass signals with desired frequencies and reject or attenuate others.

As a frequency-selective device, a filter can be used to limit the frequency spectrum of a signal to some specified band of frequencies. Filters are the circuits used in radio and TV receivers to allow us to select one desired signal out of a multitude of broadcast signals in the environment.

A filter is a *passive filter* if it consists of only passive elements R, L, and C. It is said to be an *active filter* if it consists of active elements (such as transistors and op amps) in addition to passive elements R, L, and C. We consider passive filters in this section and active filters in the next section. LC filters have been used in practical applications for more than eight decades. LC filter technology feeds related areas such as equalizers, impedance-matching networks, transformers, shaping networks, power dividers, attenuators, and directional couplers, and is continuously providing practicing engineers with oppurtunities to innovate and experiment. Besides the LC filters we study in these sections, there are other kinds of filters—such as digital filters, electromechanical filters, and microwave filters—which are beyond the level of the text.

As shown in Fig. 14.30, there are four types of filters whether passive or active:

1. A *lowpass filter* passes low frequencies and stops high frequencies, as shown ideally in Fig. 14.30(a).

2. A *highpass filter* passes high frequencies and rejects low frequencies, as shown ideally in Fig. 14.30(b).

3. A *bandpass filter* passes frequencies within a frequency band and blocks or attenuates frequencies outside the band, as shown ideally in Fig. 14.30(c).

4. A *bandstop filter* passes frequencies outside a frequency band and blocks or attenuates frequencies within the band, as shown ideally in Fig. 14.30(d).

Table 14.5 presents a summary of the characteristics of these filters. Be aware that the characteristics in Table 14.5 are only valid for first- or second-order filters—but one should not have the impression that only these kinds of filter exist. We now consider typical circuits for realizing the filters shown in Table 14.5.

(a)

(b)

(c)

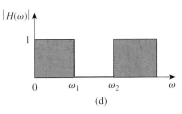
(d)

TABLE 14.5   Summary of the characteristics of ideal filters.

Type of Filter	$H(0)$	$H(\infty)$	$H(\omega_c)$ or $H(\omega_0)$
Lowpass	1	0	$1/\sqrt{2}$
Highpass	0	1	$1/\sqrt{2}$
Bandpass	0	0	1
Bandstop	1	1	0

ω_c is the cutoff frequency for lowpass and highpass filters; ω_0 is the center frequency for bandpass and bandstop filters.

Figure 14.30   Ideal frequency response of four types of filter: (a) lowpass filter, (b) highpass filter, (c) bandpass filter, (d) bandstop filter.

14.7.1 Lowpass Filter

A typical lowpass filter is formed when the output of an *RC* circuit is taken off the capacitor as shown in Fig. 14.31. The transfer function (see also Example 14.1) is

$$\mathbf{H}(\omega) = \frac{\mathbf{V}_o}{\mathbf{V}_i} = \frac{1/j\omega C}{R + 1/j\omega C}$$

$$\mathbf{H}(\omega) = \frac{1}{1 + j\omega RC} \qquad (14.50)$$

Note that $\mathbf{H}(0) = 1$, $\mathbf{H}(\infty) = 0$. Figure 14.32 shows the plot of $|H(\omega)|$, along with the ideal characteristic. The half-power frequency, which is equivalent to the corner frequency on the Bode plots but in the context of filters is usually known as the *cutoff frequency* ω_c, is obtained by setting the magnitude of $\mathbf{H}(\omega)$ equal to $1/\sqrt{2}$, thus

$$H(\omega_c) = \frac{1}{\sqrt{1 + \omega_c^2 R^2 C^2}} = \frac{1}{\sqrt{2}}$$

or

$$\omega_c = \frac{1}{RC} \qquad (14.51)$$

Figure 14.31   A lowpass filter.

Figure 14.32   Ideal and actual
frequency response of a lowpass filter.

The cutoff frequency is also called the *rolloff frequency*.

A lowpass filter is designed to pass only frequencies from dc up
to the cutoff frequency ω_c.

A lowpass filter can also be formed when the output of an RL
circuit is taken off the resistor. Of course, there are many other circuits
for lowpass filters.

14.7.2   Highpass Filter

A highpass filter is formed when the output of an RC circuit is taken off
the resistor as shown in Fig. 14.33. The transfer function is

$$\mathbf{H}(\omega) = \frac{\mathbf{V}_o}{\mathbf{V}_i} = \frac{R}{R + 1/j\omega C}$$

$$\mathbf{H}(\omega) = \frac{j\omega RC}{1 + j\omega RC} \tag{14.52}$$

Note that $\mathbf{H}(0) = 0$, $\mathbf{H}(\infty) = 1$. Figure 14.34 shows the plot of $|H(\omega)|$.
Again, the corner or cutoff frequency is

$$\omega_c = \frac{1}{RC} \tag{14.53}$$

A highpass filter is designed to pass all frequencies above its cutoff frequency ω_c.

A highpass filter can also be formed when the output of an RL
circuit is taken off the inductor.

14.7.3   Bandpass Filter

The RLC series resonant circuit provides a bandpass filter when the
output is taken off the resistor as shown in Fig. 14.35. The transfer
function is

$$\mathbf{H}(\omega) = \frac{\mathbf{V}_o}{\mathbf{V}_i} = \frac{R}{R + j(\omega L - 1/\omega C)} \tag{14.54}$$

The cutoff frequency is the frequency at which
the transfer function **H** drops in magnitude to
70.71% of its maximum value. It is also regarded
as the frequency at which the power dissipated
in a circuit is half of its maximum value.

Figure 14.33   A highpass filter.

Figure 14.34   Ideal and actual
frequency response of a highpass
filter.

Figure 14.35   A bandpass filter.

We observe that $\mathbf{H}(0) = 0$, $\mathbf{H}(\infty) = 0$. Figure 14.36 shows the plot of $|H(\omega)|$. The bandpass filter passes a band of frequencies ($\omega_1 < \omega < \omega_2$) centered on ω_0, the center frequency, which is given by

$$\omega_0 = \frac{1}{\sqrt{LC}} \tag{14.55}$$

A bandpass filter is designed to pass all frequencies within a band of frequencies, $\omega_1 < \omega < \omega_2$.

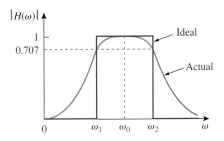

Figure 14.36   Ideal and actual frequency response of a bandpass filter.

Since the bandpass filter in Fig. 14.35 is a series resonant circuit, the half-power frequencies, the bandwidth, and the quality factor are determined as in Section 14.5. A bandpass filter can also be formed by cascading the lowpass filter (where $\omega_2 = \omega_c$) in Fig. 14.31 with the highpass filter (where $\omega_1 = \omega_c$) in Fig. 14.33.

14.7.4 Bandstop Filter

A filter that prevents a band of frequencies between two designated values (ω_1 and ω_2) from passing is variably known as a *bandstop, bandreject,* or *notch* filter. A bandstop filter is formed when the output RLC series resonant circuit is taken off the LC series combination as shown in Fig. 14.37. The transfer function is

$$\mathbf{H}(\omega) = \frac{\mathbf{V}_o}{\mathbf{V}_i} = \frac{j(\omega L - 1/\omega C)}{R + j(\omega L - 1/\omega C)} \tag{14.56}$$

Notice that $\mathbf{H}(0) = 1$, $\mathbf{H}(\infty) = 1$. Figure 14.38 shows the plot of $|H(\omega)|$. Again, the center frequency is given by

$$\omega_0 = \frac{1}{\sqrt{LC}} \tag{14.57}$$

Figure 14.37   A bandstop filter.

while the half-power frequencies, the bandwidth, and the quality factor are calculated using the formulas in Section 14.5 for a series resonant circuit. Here, ω_0 is called the *frequency of rejection*, while the corresponding bandwidth ($B = \omega_2 - \omega_1$) is known as the *bandwidth of rejection*. Thus,

A bandstop filter is designed to stop or eliminate all frequencies within a band of frequencies, $\omega_1 < \omega < \omega_2$.

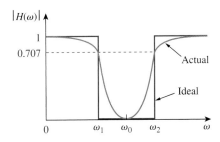

Figure 14.38   Ideal and actual frequency response of a bandstop filter.

Notice that adding the transfer functions of the bandpass and the bandstop gives unity at any frequency for the same values of R, L, and C. Of course, this is not true in general but true for the circuits treated here. This is due to the fact that the characteristic of one is the inverse of the other.

In concluding this section, we should note that:

1. From Eqs. (14.50), (14.52), (14.54), and (14.56), the maximum gain of a passive filter is unity. To generate a gain greater than unity, one should use an active filter as the next section shows.

2. There are other ways to get the types of filters treated in this section.

3. The filters treated here are the simple types. Many other filters have sharper and complex frequency responses.

EXAMPLE 14.10

Figure 14.39   For Example 14.10.

Determine what type of filter is shown in Fig. 14.39. Calculate the corner or cutoff frequency. Take $R = 2$ kΩ, $L = 2$ H, and $C = 2$ μF.

Solution:

The transfer function is

$$\mathbf{H}(s) = \frac{\mathbf{V}_o}{\mathbf{V}_i} = \frac{R \parallel 1/sC}{sL + R \parallel 1/sC}, \qquad s = j\omega \qquad (14.10.1)$$

But

$$R \parallel \frac{1}{sC} = \frac{R/sC}{R + 1/sC} = \frac{R}{1 + sRC}$$

Substituting this into Eq. (14.10.1) gives

$$\mathbf{H}(s) = \frac{R/(1+sRC)}{sL + R/(1+sRC)} = \frac{R}{s^2RLC + sL + R}, \qquad s = j\omega$$

or

$$\mathbf{H}(\omega) = \frac{R}{-\omega^2RLC + j\omega L + R} \qquad (14.10.2)$$

Since $\mathbf{H}(0) = 1$ and $\mathbf{H}(\infty) = 0$, we conclude from Table 14.5 that the circuit in Fig. 14.39 is a second-order lowpass filter. The magnitude of $\mathbf{H}$ is

$$H = \frac{R}{\sqrt{(R - \omega^2RLC)^2 + \omega^2L^2}} \qquad (14.10.3)$$

The corner frequency is the same as the half-power frequency, i.e., where $\mathbf{H}$ is reduced by a factor of $1\sqrt{2}$. Since the dc value of $H(\omega)$ is 1, at the corner frequency, Eq. (14.10.3) becomes after squaring

$$H^2 = \frac{1}{2} = \frac{R^2}{(R - \omega_c^2RLC)^2 + \omega_c^2L^2}$$

or

$$2 = (1 - \omega_c^2LC)^2 + \left(\frac{\omega_c L}{R}\right)^2$$

Substituting the values of R, L, and C, we obtain

$$2 = \left(1 - \omega_c^2\, 4 \times 10^{-6}\right)^2 + (\omega_c\, 10^{-3})^2$$

Assuming that ω_c is in krad/s,

$$2 = (1 - 4\omega_c)^2 + \omega_c^2 \qquad \text{or} \qquad 16\omega_c^4 - 7\omega_c^2 - 1 = 0$$

Solving the quadratic equation in ω_c^2, we get $\omega_c^2 = 0.5509$, or

$$\omega_c = 0.742 \text{ krad/s} = 742 \text{ rad/s}$$

PRACTICE PROBLEM 14.10

For the circuit in Fig. 14.40, obtain the transfer function $\mathbf{V}_o(\omega)/\mathbf{V}_i(\omega)$. Identify the type of filter the circuit represents and determine the corner frequency. Take $R_1 = 100\ \Omega = R_2$, $L = 2$ mH.

Answer: $\dfrac{R_2}{R_1 + R_2}\left(\dfrac{j\omega}{j\omega + \omega_c}\right)$, highpass filter

$\omega_c = \dfrac{R_1 R_2}{(R_1 + R_2)L} = 25$ krad/s.

Figure 14.40   For Practice Prob. 14.10.

EXAMPLE 14.11

If the bandstop filter in Fig. 14.37 is to reject a 200-Hz sinusoid while passing other frequencies, calculate the values of L and C. Take $R = 150\ \Omega$ and the bandwidth as 100 Hz.

Solution:

We use the formulas for a series resonant circuit in Section 14.5.

$$B = 2\pi(100) = 200\pi \text{ rad/s}$$

But

$$B = \frac{R}{L} \qquad \Longrightarrow \qquad L = \frac{R}{B} = \frac{150}{200\pi} = 0.2387 \text{ H}$$

Rejection of the 200-Hz sinusoid means that f_0 is 200 Hz, so that ω_0 in Fig. 14.38 is

$$\omega_0 = 2\pi f_0 = 2\pi(200) = 400\pi$$

Since $\omega_0 = 1/\sqrt{LC}$,

$$C = \frac{1}{\omega_0^2 L} = \frac{1}{(400\pi)^2(0.2387)} = 2.66\ \mu\text{F}$$

PRACTICE PROBLEM 14.11

Design a bandpass filter of the form in Fig. 14.35 with a lower cutoff frequency of 20.1 kHz and an upper cutoff frequency of 20.3 kHz. Take $R = 20$ kΩ. Calculate L, C, and Q.

Answer: 15.92 H, 3.9 pF, 101.

14.8 ACTIVE FILTERS

There are three major limitations to the passive filters considered in the previous section. First, they cannot generate gain greater than 1; passive elements cannot add energy to the network. Second, they may require bulky and expensive inductors. Third, they perform poorly at frequencies below the audio frequency range (300 Hz $< f <$ 3,000 Hz). Nevertheless, passive filters are useful at high frequencies.

Active filters consist of combinations of resistors, capacitors, and op amps. They offer some advantages over passive RLC filters. First, they are often smaller and less expensive, because they do not require inductors. This makes feasible the integrated circuit realizations of filters. Second, they can provide amplifier gain in addition to providing the same frequency response as RLC filters. Third, active filters can be combined with buffer amplifiers (voltage followers) to isolate each stage of the filter from source and load impedance effects. This isolation allows designing the stages independently and then cascading them to realize the desired transfer function. (Bode plots, being logarithmic, may be added when transfer functions are cascaded.) However, active filters are less reliable and less stable. The practical limit of most active filters is about 100 kHz— most active filters operate well below that frequency.

Filters are often classified according to their order (or number of poles) or their specific design type.

14.8.1 First-Order Lowpass Filter

One type of first-order filter is shown in Fig. 14.41. The components selected for Z_i and Z_f determine whether the filter is lowpass or highpass, but one of the components must be reactive.

Figure 14.41   A general first-order active filter.

Figure 14.42 shows a typical active lowpass filter. For this filter, the transfer function is

$$\mathbf{H}(\omega) = \frac{\mathbf{V}_o}{\mathbf{V}_i} = -\frac{\mathbf{Z}_f}{\mathbf{Z}_i} \qquad (14.58)$$

where $\mathbf{Z}_i = R_i$ and

$$\mathbf{Z}_f = R_f \left\| \frac{1}{j\omega C_f} = \frac{R_f/j\omega C_f}{R_f + 1/j\omega C_f} = \frac{R_f}{1 + j\omega C_f R_f} \right. \qquad (14.59)$$

Therefore,

$$\mathbf{H}(\omega) = -\frac{R_f}{R_i} \frac{1}{1 + j\omega C_f R_f} \qquad (14.60)$$

We notice that Eq. (14.60) is similar to Eq. (14.50), except that there is a low frequency ($\omega \to 0$) gain or dc gain of $-R_f/R_i$. Also, the corner frequency is

$$\omega_c = \frac{1}{R_f C_f} \qquad (14.61)$$

which does not depend on R_i. This means that several inputs with different R_i could be summed if required, and the corner frequency would remain the same for each input.

Figure 14.42   Active first-order lowpass filter.

14.8.2 First-Order Highpass Filter

Figure 14.43 shows a typical highpass filter. As before,

$$\mathbf{H}(\omega) = \frac{\mathbf{V}_o}{\mathbf{V}_i} = -\frac{\mathbf{Z}_f}{\mathbf{Z}_i} \qquad (14.62)$$

where $\mathbf{Z}_i = R_i + 1/j\omega C_i$ and $\mathbf{Z}_f = R_f$ so that

$$\mathbf{H}(\omega) = -\frac{R_f}{R_i + 1/j\omega C_i} = -\frac{j\omega C_i R_f}{1 + j\omega C_i R_i} \qquad (14.63)$$

Figure 14.43   Active first-order highpass filter.

This is similar to Eq. (14.52), except that at very high frequencies ($\omega \to \infty$), the gain tends to $-R_f/R_i$. The corner frequency is

$$\omega_c = \frac{1}{R_i C_i} \qquad (14.64)$$

14.8.3 Bandpass Filter

The circuit in Fig. 14.42 may be combined with that in Fig. 14.43 to form a bandpass filter that will have a gain K over the required range of frequencies. By cascading a unity-gain lowpass filter, a unity-gain highpass filter, and an inverter with gain $-R_f/R_i$, as shown in the block diagram of Fig. 14.44(a), we can construct a bandpass filter whose frequency response is that in Fig. 14.44(b). The actual construction of the bandpass filter is shown in Fig. 14.45.

This way of creating a bandpass filter, not necessarily the best, is perhaps the easiest to understand.

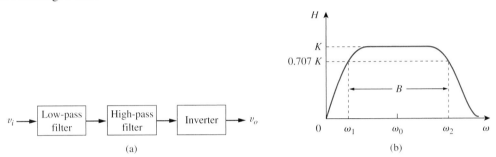

Figure 14.44   Active bandpass filter: (a) block diagram, (b) frequency response.

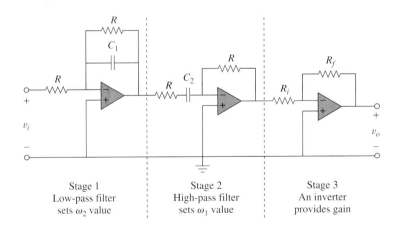

Figure 14.45   Active bandpass filter.

The analysis of the bandpass filter is relatively simple. Its transfer function is obtained by multiplying Eqs. (14.60) and (14.63) with the gain of the inverter; that is

$$\mathbf{H}(\omega) = \frac{\mathbf{V}_o}{\mathbf{V}_i} = \left(-\frac{1}{1 + j\omega C_1 R}\right)\left(-\frac{j\omega C_2 R}{1 + j\omega C_2 R}\right)\left(-\frac{R_f}{R_i}\right)$$

$$= -\frac{R_f}{R_i}\frac{1}{1 + j\omega C_1 R}\frac{j\omega C_2 R}{1 + j\omega C_2 R} \qquad (14.65)$$

The lowpass section sets the upper corner frequency as

$$\omega_2 = \frac{1}{RC_1} \tag{14.66}$$

while the highpass section sets the lower corner frequency as

$$\omega_1 = \frac{1}{RC_2} \tag{14.67}$$

With these values of ω_1 and ω_2, the center frequency, bandwidth, and quality factor are found as follows:

$$\omega_0 = \sqrt{\omega_1 \omega_2} \tag{14.68}$$

$$B = \omega_2 - \omega_1 \tag{14.69}$$

$$Q = \frac{\omega_0}{B} \tag{14.70}$$

To find the passband gain K, we write Eq. (14.65) in the standard form of Eq. (14.15),

$$\mathbf{H}(\omega) = -\frac{R_f}{R_i} \frac{j\omega/\omega_1}{(1 + j\omega/\omega_1)(1 + j\omega/\omega_2)} = -\frac{R_f}{R_i} \frac{j\omega\omega_2}{(\omega_1 + j\omega)(\omega_2 + j\omega)} \tag{14.71}$$

At the center frequency $\omega_0 = \sqrt{\omega_1 \omega_2}$, the magnitude of the transfer function is

$$|\mathbf{H}(\omega_0)| = \left| \frac{R_f}{R_i} \frac{j\omega_0\omega_2}{(\omega_1 + j\omega_0)(\omega_2 + j\omega_0)} \right| = \frac{R_f}{R_i} \frac{\omega_2}{\omega_1 + \omega_2} \tag{14.72}$$

Thus the passband gain is

$$K = \frac{R_f}{R_i} \frac{\omega_2}{\omega_1 + \omega_2} \tag{14.73}$$

14.8.4 Bandreject (or Notch) Filter

A bandreject filter may be constructed by parallel combination of a low-pass filter and a highpass filter and a summing amplifier, as shown in the block diagram of Fig. 14.46(a). The circuit is designed such that the

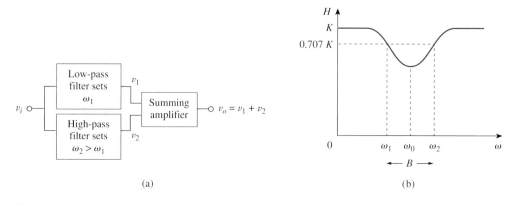

Figure 14.46 Active bandreject filter: (a) block diagram, (b) frequency response.

lower cutoff frequency ω_1 is set by the lowpass filter while the upper cut-off frequency ω_2 is set by the highpass filter. The gap between ω_1 and ω_2 is the bandwidth of the filter. As shown in Fig. 14.46(b), the filter passes frequencies below ω_1 and above ω_2. The block diagram in Fig. 14.46(a) is actually constructed as shown in Fig. 14.47. The transfer function is

$$\mathbf{H}(\omega) = \frac{\mathbf{V}_o}{\mathbf{V}_i} = -\frac{R_f}{R_i}\left(-\frac{1}{1 + j\omega C_1 R} - \frac{j\omega C_2 R}{1 + j\omega C_2 R}\right) \qquad (14.74)$$

The formulas for calculating the values of ω_1, ω_2, the center frequency, bandwidth, and quality factor are the same as in Eqs. (14.66) to (14.70).

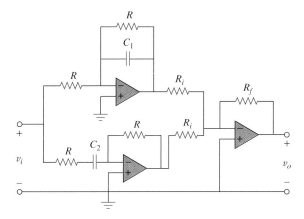

Figure 14.47   Active bandreject filter.

To determine the passband gain K of the filter, we can write Eq. (14.74) in terms of the upper and lower corner frequencies as

$$\begin{aligned}\mathbf{H}(\omega) &= \frac{R_f}{R_i}\left(\frac{1}{1 + j\omega/\omega_2} + \frac{j\omega/\omega_1}{1 + j\omega/\omega_1}\right)\\[2mm] &= \frac{R_f}{R_i}\frac{(1 + j2\omega/\omega_1 + (j\omega)^2/\omega_1\omega_1)}{(1 + j\omega/\omega_2)(1 + j\omega/\omega_1)}\end{aligned} \qquad (14.75)$$

Comparing this with the standard form in Eq. (14.15) indicates that in the two passbands ($\omega \to 0$ and $\omega \to \infty$) the gain is

$$K = \frac{R_f}{R_i} \qquad (14.76)$$

We can also find the gain at the center frequency by finding the magnitude of the transfer function at $\omega_0 = \sqrt{\omega_1\omega_2}$, writing

$$\begin{aligned}H(\omega_0) &= \left|\frac{R_f}{R_i}\frac{(1 + j2\omega_0/\omega_1 + (j\omega_0)^2/\omega_1\omega_1)}{(1 + j\omega_0/\omega_2)(1 + j\omega_0/\omega_1)}\right|\\[2mm] &= \frac{R_f}{R_i}\frac{2\omega_1}{\omega_1 + \omega_2}\end{aligned} \qquad (14.77)$$

Again, the filters treated in this section are only typical. There are many other active filters that are more complex.

EXAMPLE 14.12

Design a low-pass active filter with a dc gain of 4 and a corner frequency of 500 Hz.

Solution:

From Eq. (14.61), we find

$$\omega_c = 2\pi f_c = 2\pi(500) = \frac{1}{R_f C_f} \tag{14.12.1}$$

The dc gain is

$$H(0) = -\frac{R_f}{R_i} = -4 \tag{14.12.2}$$

We have two equations and three unknowns. If we select $C_f = 0.2 \ \mu F$, then

$$R_f = \frac{1}{2\pi(500)0.2 \times 10^{-6}} = 1.59 \ k\Omega$$

and

$$R_i = \frac{R_f}{4} = 397.5 \ \Omega$$

We use a 1.6-kΩ resistor for R_f and a 400-Ω resistor for R_i. Figure 14.42 shows the filter.

PRACTICE PROBLEM 14.12

Design a highpass filter with a high-frequency gain of 5 and a corner frequency of 2 kHz. Use a 0.1-μF capacitor in your design.

Answer: $R_i = 800 \ \Omega$ and $R_f = 4 \ k\Omega$.

EXAMPLE 14.13

Design a bandpass filter in the form of Fig. 14.45 to pass frequencies between 250 Hz and 3,000 Hz and with $K = 10$. Select $R = 20 \ k\Omega$.

Solution:

Since $\omega_1 = 1/RC_2$, we obtain

$$C_2 = \frac{1}{R\omega_1} = \frac{1}{2\pi f_1 R} = \frac{1}{2\pi \times 250 \times 20 \times 10^3} = 31.83 \ nF$$

Similarly, since $\omega_2 = 1/RC_1$,

$$C_1 = \frac{1}{R\omega_2} = \frac{1}{2\pi f_2 R} = \frac{1}{2\pi \times 3,000 \times 20 \times 10^3} = 2.65 \ nF$$

From Eq. (14.73),

$$\frac{R_f}{R_i} = K\frac{\omega_1 + \omega_2}{\omega_2} = K\frac{f_1 + f_2}{f_2} = \frac{10(3,250)}{3,000} = 10.83$$

If we select $R_i = 10 \ k\Omega$, then $R_f = 10.83R_i \simeq 108.3 \ k\Omega$.

PRACTICE PROBLEM 14.13

Design a notch filter based on Fig. 14.47 for $\omega_0 = 20$ krad/s, $K = 5$, and $Q = 10$. Use $R = R_i = 10$ kΩ.

Answer: $C_1 = 47.62$ nF, $C_2 = 52.63$ nF, and $R_f = 50$ kΩ.

†14.9 SCALING

In designing and analyzing filters and resonant circuits or in circuit analysis in general, it is sometimes convenient to work with element values of 1 Ω, 1 H, or 1 F, and then transform the values to realistic values by *scaling*. We have taken advantage of this idea by not using realistic element values in most of our examples and problems; mastering circuit analysis is made easy by using convenient component values. We have thus eased calculations, knowing that we could use scaling to then make the values realistic.

There are two ways of scaling a circuit: *magnitude* or *impedance scaling*, and *frequency scaling*. Both are useful in scaling responses and circuit elements to values within the practical ranges. While magnitude scaling leaves the frequency response of a circuit unaltered, frequency scaling shifts the frequency response up or down the frequency spectrum.

14.9.1   Magnitude Scaling

Magnitude scaling is the process of increasing all impedances in a network by a factor, the frequency response remaining unchanged.

Recall that impedances of individual elements R, L, and C are given by

$$\mathbf{Z}_R = R, \qquad \mathbf{Z}_L = j\omega L, \qquad \mathbf{Z}_C = \frac{1}{j\omega C} \qquad (14.78)$$

In magnitude scaling, we multiply the impedance of each circuit element by a factor K_m and let the frequency remain constant. This gives the new impedances as

$$\mathbf{Z}'_R = K_m \mathbf{Z}_R = K_m R, \qquad \mathbf{Z}'_L = K_m \mathbf{Z}_L = j\omega K_m L$$

$$\mathbf{Z}'_C = K_m \mathbf{Z}_C = \frac{1}{j\omega C/K_m} \qquad (14.79)$$

Comparing Eq. (14.79) with Eq. (14.78), we notice the following changes in the element values: $R \rightarrow K_m R$, $L \rightarrow K_m L$, and $C \rightarrow C/K_m$. Thus, in magnitude scaling, the new values of the elements and frequency are

$$
\begin{array}{ll}
R' = K_m R, & L' = K_m L \\[2mm]
C' = \dfrac{C}{K_m}, & \omega' = \omega
\end{array}
\qquad (14.80)
$$

The primed variables are the new values and the unprimed variables are the old values. Consider the series or parallel RLC circuit. We now have

$$\omega_0' = \frac{1}{\sqrt{L'C'}} = \frac{1}{\sqrt{K_m LC / K_m}} = \frac{1}{\sqrt{LC}} = \omega_0 \qquad (14.81)$$

showing that the resonant frequency, as expected, has not changed. Similarly, the quality factor and the bandwidth are not affected by magnitude scaling. Also, magnitude scaling does not affect transfer functions in the forms of Eqs. (14.2a) and (14.2b), which are dimensionless quantities.

14.9.2 Frequency Scaling

Frequency scaling is the process of shifting the frequency response of a network up or down the frequency axis while leaving the impedance the same.

Frequency scaling is equivalent to relabeling the frequency axis of a frequency response plot. It is needed when translating frequencies such as a resonant frequency, a corner frequency, a bandwidth, etc., to a realistic level. It can be used to bring capacitance and inductance values into a range that is convenient to work with.

We achieve frequency scaling by multiplying the frequency by a factor K_f while keeping the impedance the same.

From Eq. (14.78), we see that the impedances of L and C are frequency-dependent. If we apply frequency scaling to $\mathbf{Z}_L(\omega)$ and $\mathbf{Z}_C(\omega)$ in Eq. (14.78), we obtain

$$\mathbf{Z}_L = j(\omega K_f)L' = j\omega L \qquad \Longrightarrow \qquad L' = \frac{L}{K_f} \qquad (14.82a)$$

$$\mathbf{Z}_C = \frac{1}{j(\omega K_f)C'} = \frac{1}{j\omega C} \qquad \Longrightarrow \qquad C' = \frac{C}{K_f} \qquad (14.82b)$$

since the impedance of the inductor and capacitor must remain the same after frequency scaling. We notice the following changes in the element values: $L \to L/K_f$ and $C \to C/K_f$. The value of R is not affected, since its impedance does not depend on frequency. Thus, in frequency scaling, the new values of the elements and frequency are

$$\boxed{\begin{array}{cc} R' = R, & L' = \dfrac{L}{K_f} \\[3mm] C' = \dfrac{C}{K_f}, & \omega' = K_f \omega \end{array}} \qquad (14.83)$$

Again, if we consider the series or parallel RLC circuit, for the resonant frequency

$$\omega_0' = \frac{1}{\sqrt{L'C'}} = \frac{1}{\sqrt{(L/K_f)(C/K_f)}} = \frac{K_f}{\sqrt{LC}} = K_f \omega_0 \qquad (14.84)$$

and for the bandwidth

$$B' = K_f B \qquad (14.85)$$

but the quality factor remains the same ($Q' = Q$).

14.9.3 Magnitude and Frequency Scaling

If a circuit is scaled in magnitude and frequency at the same time, then

$$R' = K_m R, \qquad L' = \frac{K_m}{K_f} L$$

$$C' = \frac{1}{K_m K_f} C, \qquad \omega' = K_f \omega \tag{14.86}$$

These are more general formulas than those in Eqs. (14.80) and (14.83). We set $K_m = 1$ in Eq. (14.86) when there is no magnitude scaling or $K_f = 1$ when there is no frequency scaling.

EXAMPLE 14.14

A fourth-order Butterworth lowpass filter is shown in Fig. 14.48(a). The filter is designed such that the cutoff frequency $\omega_c = 1$ rad/s. Scale the circuit for a cutoff frequency of 50 kHz using 10-kΩ resistors.

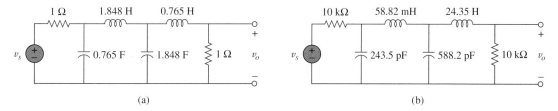

(a)   (b)

Figure 14.48   For Example 14.14: (a) Normalized Butterworth lowpass filter, (b) scaled version of the same lowpass filter.

Solution:

If the cutoff frequency is to shift from $\omega_c = 1$ rad/s to $\omega'_c = 2\pi(50)$ krad/s, then the frequency scale factor is

$$K_f = \frac{\omega'_c}{\omega_c} = \frac{100\pi \times 10^3}{1} = \pi \times 10^5$$

Also, if each 1-Ω resistor is to be replaced by a 10-kΩ resistor, then the magnitude scale factor must be

$$K_m = \frac{R'}{R} = \frac{10 \times 10^3}{1} = 10^4$$

Using Eq. (14.86),

$$L'_1 = \frac{K_m}{K_f} L_1 = \frac{10^4}{\pi \times 10^5}(1.848) = 58.82 \text{ mH}$$

$$L'_2 = \frac{K_m}{K_f} L_2 = \frac{10^4}{\pi \times 10^5}(0.765) = 24.35 \text{ mH}$$

$$C'_1 = \frac{C_1}{K_m K_f} = \frac{0.765}{\pi \times 10^9} = 243.5 \text{ pF}$$

$$C'_2 = \frac{C_2}{K_m K_f} = \frac{1.848}{\pi \times 10^9} = 588.2 \text{ pF}$$

The scaled circuit is as shown in Fig. 14.48(b). This circuit uses practical values and will provide the same transfer function as the prototype in Fig. 14.48(a), but shifted in frequency.

PRACTICE PROBLEM 14.14

Figure 14.49   For Practice Prob. 14.14.

A third-order Butterworth filter normalized to $\omega_c = 1$ rad/s is shown in Fig. 14.49. Scale the circuit to a cutoff frequency of 10 kHz. Use 15-nF capacitors.

Answer: $R_1' = R_2' = 1.061$ kΩ, $C_1' = C_2' = 15$ nF, $L' = 33.77$ mH.

14.10 FREQUENCY RESPONSE USING PSPICE

PSpice is a useful tool in the hands of the modern circuit designer for obtaining the frequency response of circuits. The frequency response is obtained using the AC Sweep as discussed in Section D.5 (Appendix D). This requires that we specify in the AC Sweep dialog box *Total Pts, Start Freq, End Freq*, and the sweep type. *Total Pts* is the number of points in the frequency sweep, and *Start Freq* and *End Freq* are, respectively, the starting and final frequencies, in hertz. In order to know what frequencies to select for *Start Freq* and *End Freq*, one must have an idea of the frequency range of interest by making a rough sketch of the frequency response. In a complex circuit where this may not be possible, one may use a trial-and-error approach.

There are three types of sweeps:

Linear: The frequency is varied linearly from *Start Freq* to *End Freq* with *Total Pts* equally spaced points (or responses).

Octave: The frequency is swept logarithmically by octaves from *Start Freq* to *End Freq* with *Total* points per octave. An octave is a factor of 2 (e.g., 2 to 4, 4 to 8, 8 to 16).

Decade: The frequency is varied logarithmically by decades from *Start Freq* to *End Freq* with *Total* points per decade. A decade is a factor of 10 (e.g., from 2 Hz to 20 Hz, 20 Hz to 200 Hz, 200 Hz to 2 kHz).

It is best to use a linear sweep when displaying a narrow frequency range of interest, as a linear sweep displays the frequency range well in a narrow range. Conversely, it is best to use a logarithmic (octave or decade) sweep for displaying a wide frequency range of interest—if a linear sweep is used for a wide range, all the data will be crowded at the high- or low-frequency end and insufficient data at the other end.

With the above specifications, *PSpice* performs a steady-state sinusoidal analysis of the circuit as the frequency of all the independent sources is varied (or swept) from *Start Freq* to *End Freq*.

The *PSpice* A/D program produces a graphical output. The output data type may be specified in the *Trace Command Box* by adding one of the following suffixes to V or I:

M   Amplitude of the sinusoid.

P   Phase of the sinusoid.

dB   Amplitude of the sinusoid in decibels, i.e., $20 \log_{10}$ (amplitude).

EXAMPLE 14.15

Determine the frequency response of the circuit shown in Fig. 14.50.

Solution:

We let the input voltage v_s be a sinusoid of amplitude 1 V and phase 0°. Figure 14.51 is the schematic for the circuit. The capacitor is rotated 270° counterclockwise to ensure that pin 1 (the positive terminal) is on top. The voltage marker is inserted to the output voltage across the capacitor. To perform a linear sweep for $1 < f < 1000$ Hz with 50 points, we select **Analysis/Setup/AC Sweep**, **DCLICK** *Linear*, type 50 in the *Total Pts* box, type 1 in the *Start Freq* box, and type 1000 in the *End Freq* box. After saving the file, we select **Analysis/Simulate** to simulate the circuit. If there are no errors, the *PSpice* A/D window will display the plot of V(C1:1), which is the same as V_o or $H(\omega) = V_o/1$, as shown in Fig. 14.52(a). This is the magnitude plot, since V(C1:1) is the same as VM(C1:1). To obtain the phase plot, select **Trace/Add** in the *PSpice* A/D menu and type VP(C1:1) in the **Trace Command** box. Figure 14.52(b) shows the result. By hand, the transfer function is

$$H(\omega) = \frac{V_o}{V_s} = \frac{1,000}{9,000 + j\omega 8}$$

or

$$H(\omega) = \frac{1}{9 + j16\pi \times 10^{-3}}$$

showing that the circuit is a lowpass filter as demonstrated in Fig. 14.52. Notice that the plots in Fig. 14.52 are similar to those in Fig. 14.3.

Figure 14.50   For Example 14.15.

Figure 14.51   The schematic for the circuit in Fig. 14.50.

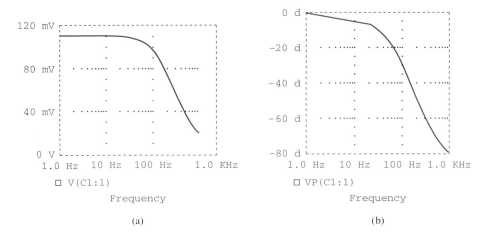

Figure 14.52   For Example 14.15: (a) magnitude plot, (b) phase plot of the frequency response.

PRACTICE PROBLEM 14.15

Obtain the frequency response of the circuit in Fig. 14.53 using *PSpice*. Use a linear frequency sweep and consider $1 < f < 1000$ Hz with 100 points.

Answer: See Fig. 14.54.

Figure 14.53   For Practice Prob. 14.15.

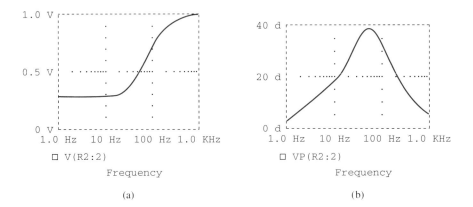

Figure 14.54   For Practice Problem 14.15: (a) magnitude plot, (b) phase plot of the frequency response.

EXAMPLE 14.16

Use *PSpice* to generate the gain and phase Bode plots of V_o in the circuit of Fig. 14.55.

Solution:

The circuit treated in Example 14.15 is first-order while the one in this example is second-order. Since we are interested in Bode plots, we use decade frequency sweep for $300 < f < 3{,}000$ Hz with 50 points per decade. We select this range because we know that the resonant frequency of the circuit is within the range. Recall that

$$\omega_0 = \frac{1}{\sqrt{LC}} = 5 \text{ krad/s} \qquad \text{or} \qquad f_0 = \frac{\omega}{2\pi} = 795.8 \text{ Hz}$$

After drawing the circuit as in Fig. 14.55, we select **Analysis/Setup/AC Sweep**, **DCLICK** *Decade*, enter 50 as the *Total Pts* box, 300 as the *Start Freq*, and 3,000 as the *End Freq* box. Upon saving the file, we simulate it by selecting **Analysis/Simulate**. This will automatically bring up the *PSpice* A/D window and display V(C1:1) if there are no errors. Since we are interested in the Bode plot, we select **Trace/Add** in the *PSpice* A/D menu and type dB(V(C1:1)) in the **Trace Command** box. The result is the Bode magnitude plot in Fig. 14.56(a). For the phase plot, we select **Trace/Add** in the *PSpice* A/D menu and type VP(C1:1) in the **Trace Command** box. The result is the Bode phase plot of Fig. 14.56(b). Notice that the plots confirm the resonant frequency of 795.8 Hz.

Figure 14.55   For Example 14.16.

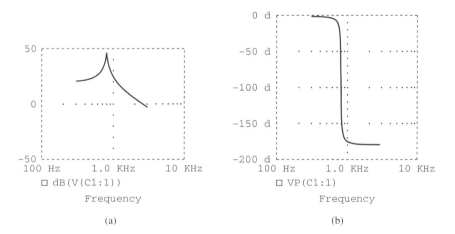

(a)   (b)

Figure 14.56   For Example 14.16: (a) Bode plot, (b) phase plot of the response.

PRACTICE PROBLEM 14.16

Consider the network in Fig. 14.57. Use *PSpice* to obtain the Bode plots for V_o over a frequency from 1 kHz to 100 kHz using 20 points per decade.

Figure 14.57   For Practice Prob. 14.16.

Answer: See Fig. 14.58.

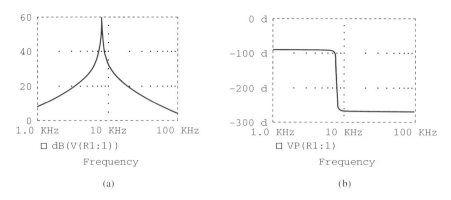

Figure 14.58   For Practice Prob. 14.16: Bode (a) magnitude plot, (b) phase plot.

†14.11 APPLICATIONS

Resonant circuits and filters are widely used, particularly in electronics, power systems, and communications systems. For example, a Notch filter with a cutoff frequency at 60 Hz may be used to eliminate the 60-Hz power line noise in various communications electronics. Filtering of signals in communications systems is necessary in order to select the desired signal from a host of others in the same range (as in the case of radio receivers discussed next) and also to minimize the effects of noise and interference on the desired signal. In this section, we consider one practical application of resonant circuits and two applications of filters. The focus of each application is not to understand the details of how each device works but to see how the circuits considered in this chapter are applied in the practical devices.

14.11.1   Radio Receiver

Series and parallel resonant circuits are commonly used in radio and TV receivers to tune in stations and to separate the audio signal from the radio-frequency carrier wave. As an example, consider the block diagram of an AM radio receiver shown in Fig. 14.59. Incoming amplitude-modulated radio waves (thousands of them at different frequencies from different broadcasting stations) are received by the antenna. A resonant circuit (or a bandpass filter) is needed to select just one of the incoming waves. The selected signal is very weak and is amplified in stages in order to generate an audible audio-frequency wave. Thus we have the radio frequency (RF) amplifier to amplify the selected broadcast signal, the intermediate frequency (IF) amplifier to amplify an internally generated signal based on the RF signal, and the audio amplifier to amplify the audio signal just before it reaches the loudspeaker. It is much easier to amplify the signal at three stages than to build an amplifier to provide the same amplification for the entire band.

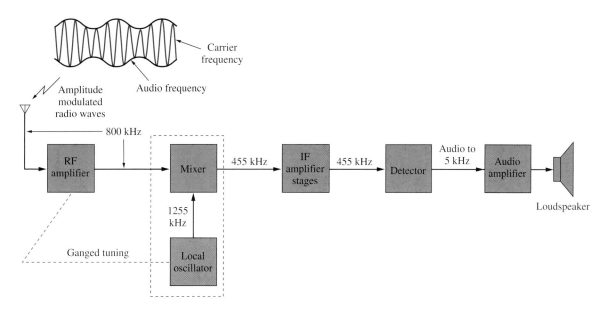

Figure 14.59   A simplified block diagram of a superheterodyne AM radio receiver.

The type of AM receiver shown in Fig. 14.59 is known as the *super-heterodyne receiver*. In the early development of radio, each amplification stage had to be tuned to the frequency of the incoming signal. This way, each stage must have several tuned circuits to cover the entire AM band (540 to 1600 kHz). To avoid the problem of having several resonant circuits, modern receivers use a *frequency mixer* or *heterodyne* circuit, which always produces the same IF signal (445 kHz) but retains the audio frequencies carried on the incoming signal. To produce the constant IF frequency, the rotors of two separate variable capacitors are mechanically coupled with one another so that they can be rotated simultaneously with a single control; this is called *ganged tuning*. A *local oscillator* ganged with the RF amplifier produces an RF signal that is combined with the incoming wave by the frequency mixer to produce an output signal that contains the sum and the difference frequencies of the two signals. For example, if the resonant circuit is tuned to receive an 800-kHz incoming signal, the local oscillator must produce a 1,255-kHz signal, so that the sum (1,255 + 800 = 2,055 kHz) and the difference (1,255 − 800 = 455 kHz) of frequencies are available at the output of the mixer. However, only the difference, 455 kHz, is used in practice. This is the only frequency to which all the IF amplifier stages are tuned, regardless of the station dialed. The original audio signal (containing the "intelligence") is extracted in the detector stage. The detector basically removes the IF signal, leaving the audio signal. The audio signal is amplified to drive the loudspeaker, which acts as a transducer converting the electrical signal to sound.

Our major concern here is the tuning circuit for the AM radio receiver. The operation of the FM radio receiver is different from that of the AM receiver discussed here, and in a much different range of frequencies, but the tuning is similar.

EXAMPLE 14.17

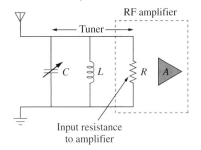

RF amplifier

Tuner

C L R A

Input resistance
to amplifier

Figure 14.60   The tuner circuit for
Example 14.17.

The resonant or tuner circuit of an AM radio is portrayed in Fig. 14.60. Given that $L = 1 \ \mu H$, what must be the range of C to have the resonant frequency adjustable from one end of the AM band to another?

Solution:

The frequency range for AM broadcasting is 540 to 1,600 kHz. We consider the low and high ends of the band. Since the resonant circuit in Fig. 14.60 is a parallel type, we apply the ideas in Section 14.6. From Eq. (14.44),

$$\omega_0 = 2\pi f_0 = \frac{1}{\sqrt{LC}}$$

or

$$C = \frac{1}{4\pi^2 f_0^2 L}$$

For the high end of the AM band, $f_0 = 1,600$ kHz, and the corresponding C is

$$C_1 = \frac{1}{4\pi^2 \times 1,600^2 \times 10^6 \times 10^{-6}} = 9.9 \text{ nF}$$

For the low end of the AM band, $f_0 = 540$ kHz, and the corresponding C is

$$C_2 = \frac{1}{4\pi^2 \times 540^2 \times 10^6 \times 10^{-6}} = 86.9 \text{ nF}$$

Thus, C must be an adjustable (gang) capacitor varying from 9.9 nF to 86.9 nF.

PRACTICE PROBLEM 14.17

For an FM radio receiver, the incoming wave is in the frequency range from 88 to 108 MHz. The tuner circuit is a parallel RLC circuit with a 4-μH coil. Calculate the range of the variable capacitor necessary to cover the entire band.

Answer: From 0.543 pF to 0.818 pF.

14.11.2 Touch-Tone Telephone

A typical application of filtering is the Touch-Tone telephone set shown in Fig. 14.61. The keypad has 12 buttons arranged in four rows and three columns. The arrangement provides 12 distinct signals by using seven tones divided into two groups: the low-frequency group (697 to 941 Hz) and the high-frequency group (1,209 to 1,477 Hz). Pressing a button generates a sum of two sinusoids corresponding to its unique pair of frequencies. For example, pressing the number 6 button generates sinusoidal tones with frequencies 770 Hz and 1,477 Hz.

When a caller dials a telephone number, a set of signals is transmitted to the telephone office, where the Touch-Tone signals are decoded by detecting the frequencies they contain. Figure 14.62 shows the block diagram for the detection scheme. The signals are first amplified and separated into their respective groups by the lowpass (LP) and highpass (HP) filters. The limiters (L) are used to convert the separated tones into

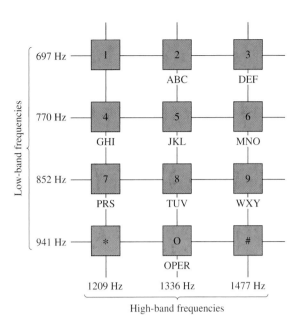

Figure 14.61   Frequency assignments for Touch-Tone dialing. (*Adapted from G. Daryanani,* Principles of Active Network Synthesis and Design *[New York: John Wiley & Sons], 1976, p. 79.*)

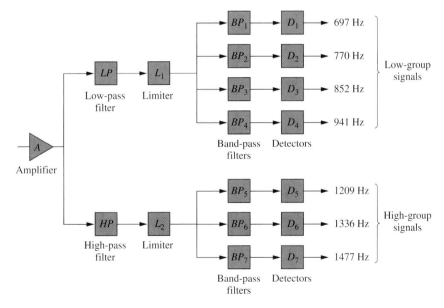

Figure 14.62   Block diagram of detection scheme. (*Source: G. Daryanani,* Principles of Active Network Synthesis and Design *[New York: John Wiley & Sons], 1976, p. 79.*)

square waves. The individual tones are identified using seven highpass (HP) filters, each filter passing one tone and rejecting other tones. Each filter is followed by a detector (D), which is energized when its input voltage exceeds a certain level. The outputs of the detectors provide the required dc signals needed by the switching system to connect the caller to the party being called.

EXAMPLE 14.18

Using the standard 600-Ω resistor used in telephone circuits and a series RLC circuit, design the bandpass filter BP_2 in Fig. 14.62.

Solution:

The bandpass filter is the series RLC circuit in Fig. 14.35. Since BP_2 passes frequencies 697 Hz to 852 Hz and is centered at $f_0 = 770$ Hz, its bandwidth is

$$B = 2\pi(f_2 - f_1) = 2\pi(852 - 697) = 973.89 \text{ rad/s}$$

From Eq. (14.39),

$$L = \frac{R}{B} = \frac{600}{973.89} = 0.616 \text{ H}$$

From Eq. (14.27) or (14.55),

$$C = \frac{1}{\omega_0^2 L} = \frac{1}{4\pi^2 f_0^2 L} = \frac{1}{4\pi^2 \times 770^2 \times 0.616} = 69.36 \text{ nF}$$

PRACTICE PROBLEM 14.18

Repeat Example 14.18 for bandpass filter BP_6.

Answer: 0.356 H, 39.83 nF.

14.11.3   Crossover Network

Another typical application of filters is the *crossover network* that couples an audio amplifier to woofer and tweeter speakers, as shown in Fig. 14.63(a). The network basically consists of one highpass RC filter and one lowpass RL filter. It routes frequencies higher than a prescribed crossover frequency f_c to the tweeter (high-frequency loudspeaker) and frequencies below f_c into the woofer (low-frequency loudspeaker). These loudspeakers have been designed to accommodate certain frequency responses. A woofer is a low-frequency loudspeaker designed to reproduce the lower part of the frequency range, up to about 3 kHz. A tweeter can reproduce audio frequencies from about 3 kHz to about 20 kHz. The two speaker types can be combined to reproduce the entire audio range of interest and provide the optimum in frequency response.

By replacing the amplifier with a voltage source, the approximate equivalent circuit of the crossover network is shown in Fig. 14.63(b), where the loudspeakers are modeled by resistors. As a highpass filter, the transfer function V_1/V_s is given by

$$H_1(\omega) = \frac{V_1}{V_s} = \frac{j\omega R_1 C}{1 + j\omega R_1 C} \tag{14.87}$$

Similarly, the transfer function of the lowpass filter is given by

$$H_2(\omega) = \frac{V_2}{V_s} = \frac{R_2}{R_2 + j\omega L} \tag{14.88}$$

(a)

(b)

Figure 14.63   (a) A crossover network for two loudspeakers, (b) equivalent model.

The values of R_1, R_2, L, and C may be selected such that the two filters have the same cutoff frequency, known as the *crossover frequency*, as shown in Fig. 14.64.

The principle behind the crossover network is also used in the resonant circuit for a TV receiver, where it is necessary to separate the video and audio bands of RF carrier frequencies. The lower-frequency band (picture information in the range from about 30 Hz to about 4 MHz) is channeled into the receiver's video amplifier, while the high-frequency band (sound information around 4.5 MHz) is channeled to the receiver's sound amplifier.

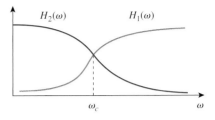

Figure 14.64   Frequency responses of the crossover network in Fig. 14.63.

EXAMPLE 14.19

In the crossover network of Fig. 14.63, suppose each speaker acts as a 6-Ω resistance. Find C and L if the crossover frequency is 2.5 kHz.

Solution:

For the highpass filter,

$$\omega_c = 2\pi f_c = \frac{1}{R_1 C}$$

or

$$C = \frac{1}{2\pi f_c R_1} = \frac{1}{2\pi \times 2.5 \times 10^3 \times 6} = 10.61 \ \mu\text{F}$$

For the lowpass filter,

$$\omega_c = 2\pi f_c = \frac{R_2}{L}$$

or

$$L = \frac{R_2}{2\pi f_c} = \frac{6}{2\pi \times 2.5 \times 10^3} = 382 \ \mu\text{H}$$

PRACTICE PROBLEM 14.19

If each speaker in Fig. 14.63 has an 8-Ω resistance and $C = 10 \ \mu\text{F}$, find L and the crossover frequency.

Answer: 0.64 mH, 1.989 kHz.

14.12 SUMMARY

1. The transfer function $\mathbf{H}(\omega)$ is the ratio of the output response $\mathbf{Y}(\omega)$ to the input excitation $\mathbf{X}(\omega)$; that is, $\mathbf{H}(\omega) = \mathbf{Y}(\omega)/\mathbf{X}(\omega)$.

2. The frequency response is the variation of the transfer function with frequency.

3. Zeros of a transfer function $\mathbf{H}(s)$ are the values of $s = j\omega$ that make $H(s) = 0$, while poles are the values of s that make $H(s) \to \infty$.

4. The decibel is the unit of logarithmic gain. For a gain G, its decibel equivalent is $G_{\text{dB}} = 20 \log_{10} G$.

5. Bode plots are semilog plots of the magnitude and phase of the transfer function as it varies with frequency. The straight-line approximations of H (in dB) and ϕ (in degrees) are constructed using the corner frequencies defined by the poles and zeros of $\mathbf{H}(\omega)$.

6. The resonant frequency is that frequency at which the imaginary part of a transfer function vanishes. For series and parallel RLC circuits,

$$\omega_0 = \frac{1}{\sqrt{LC}}$$

7. The half-power frequencies (ω_1, ω_2) are those frequencies at which the power dissipated is one-half of that dissipated at the resonant frequency. The geometric mean between the half-power frequencies is the resonant frequency, or

$$\omega_0 = \sqrt{\omega_1 \omega_2}$$

8. The bandwidth is the frequency band between half-power frequencies:

$$B = \omega_2 - \omega_1$$

9. The quality factor is a measure of the sharpness of the resonance peak. It is the ratio of the resonant (angular) frequency to the bandwidth,

$$Q = \frac{\omega_0}{B}$$

10. A filter is a circuit designed to pass a band of frequencies and reject others. Passive filters are constructed with resistors, capacitors, and inductors. Active filters are constructed with resistors, capacitors, and an active device, usually an op amp.

11. Four common types of filters are lowpass, highpass, bandpass, and bandstop. A lowpass filter passes only signals whose frequencies are below the cutoff frequency ω_c. A highpass filter passes only signals whose frequencies are above the cutoff frequency ω_c. A bandpass filter passes only signals whose frequencies are within a prescribed range ($\omega_1 < \omega < \omega_2$). A bandstop filter passes only signals whose frequencies are outside a prescribed range ($\omega_1 > \omega > \omega_2$).

12. Scaling is the process whereby unrealistic element values are magnitude-scaled by a factor K_m and/or frequency-scaled by a factor K_f to produce realistic values.

$$R' = K_m R, \qquad L' = \frac{K_m}{K_f} L, \qquad C' = \frac{1}{K_m K_f} C$$

13. *PSpice* can be used to obtain the frequency response of a circuit if a frequency range for the response and the desired number of points within the range are specified in the AC Sweep.

14. The radio receiver—one practical application of resonant circuits—employs a bandpass resonant circuit to tune in one frequency among all the broadcast signals picked up by the antenna.

15. The Touch-Tone telephone and the crossover network are two typical applications of filters. The Touch-Tone telephone system employs filters to separate tones of different frequencies to activate electronic switches. The crossover network separates signals in different frequency ranges so that they can be delivered to different devices such as tweeters and woofers in a loudspeaker system.

REVIEW QUESTIONS

14.1 A zero of the transfer function

$$H(s) = \frac{10(s+1)}{(s+2)(s+3)}$$

is at

(a) 10   (b) -1 (c) -2 (d) -3

14.2 On the Bode magnitude plot, the slope of the pole $1/(5+j\omega)^2$ is

(a) 20 dB/decade   (b) 40 dB/decade
(c) -40 dB/decade   (d) -20 dB/decade

14.3 On the Bode phase plot, the slope of $[1+j10\omega - \omega^2/25]^2$ is

(a) 45°/decade   (b) 90°/decade
(c) 135°/decade   (d) 180°/decade

14.4 How much inductance is needed to resonate at 5 kHz with a capacitance of 12 nF?

(a) 2,652 H   (b) 11.844 H
(c) 3.333 H   (d) 84.43 mH

14.5 The difference between the half-power frequencies is called the:

(a) quality factor   (b) resonant frequency
(c) bandwidth   (d) cutoff frequency

14.6 In a series RLC circuit, which of these quality factors has the steepest curve at resonance?

(a) $Q = 20$ (b) $Q = 12$
(c) $Q = 8$ (d) $Q = 4$

14.7 In a parallel RLC circuit, the bandwidth B is directly proportional to R.

(a) True   (b) False

14.8 When the elements of an RLC circuit are both magnitude-scaled and frequency-scaled, which quality is unaffected?

(a) resistor   (b) resonant frequency
(c) bandwidth   (d) quality factor

14.9 What kind of filter can be used to select a signal of one particular radio station?

(a) lowpass   (b) highpass
(c) bandpass   (d) bandstop

14.10 A voltage source supplies a signal of constant amplitude, from 0 to 40 kHz, to an RC lowpass filter. The load resistor experiences the maximum voltage at:

(a) dc   (b) 10 kHz
(c) 20 kHz   (d) 40 kHz

Answers: 14.1b, 14.2c, 14.3d, 14.4d, 14.5c, 14.6a, 14.7b, 14.8d, 14.9c, 14.10a.

PROBLEMS

Section 14.2   Transfer Function

14.1 Find the transfer function $\mathbf{V}_o/\mathbf{V}_i$ of the RC circuit in Fig. 14.65. Express it using $\omega_0 = 1/RC$.

Figure 14.65   For Prob. 14.1.

14.2 Obtain the transfer function $\mathbf{V}_o/\mathbf{V}_i$ of the RL circuit of Fig. 14.66. Express it using $\omega_0 = R/L$.

Figure 14.66   For Probs. 14.2 and 14.36.

14.3 (a) Given the circuit in Fig. 14.67, determine the transfer function $H(s) = V_o(s)/V_i(s)$.

(b) If $R = 40$ kΩ and $C = 2$ μF, specify the locations of the poles and zeros of $H(s)$.

Figure 14.67 For Prob. 14.3.

14.4 Find the transfer function $\mathbf{H}(\omega) = \mathbf{V}_o/\mathbf{V}_i$ of the circuits shown in Fig. 14.68.

(a)

(b)

Figure 14.68 For Prob. 14.4.

14.5 Repeat Prob. 14.4 for the circuits in Fig. 14.69.

(a)

(b)

Figure 14.69 For Prob. 14.5.

14.6 Obtain the transfer function $\mathbf{H}(\omega) = \mathbf{I}_o/\mathbf{I}_s$ of the circuits shown in Fig. 14.70.

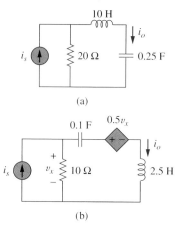

(a)

(b)

Figure 14.70 For Prob. 14.6.

Section 14.3 The Decibel Scale

14.7 Calculate $|\mathbf{H}(\omega)|$ if H_{dB} equals

(a) 0.05 dB   (b) -6.2 dB   (c) 104.7 dB

14.8 Determine the magnitude (in dB) and the phase (in degrees) of $\mathbf{H}(\omega)$ at $\omega = 1$ if $\mathbf{H}(\omega)$ equals

(a) 0.05   (b) 125

(c) $\dfrac{10j\omega}{2 + j\omega}$ (d) $\dfrac{3}{1 + j\omega} + \dfrac{6}{2 + j\omega}$

Section 14.4 Bode Plots

14.9 A ladder network has a voltage gain of

$$\mathbf{H}(\omega) = \frac{10}{(1 + j\omega)(10 + j\omega)}$$

Sketch the Bode plots for the gain.

14.10 Sketch the Bode magnitude and phase plots of:

$$\mathbf{H}(j\omega) = \frac{50}{j\omega(5 + j\omega)}$$

14.11 Sketch the Bode plots for

$$\mathbf{H}(\omega) = \frac{10 + j\omega}{j\omega(2 + j\omega)}$$

14.12 A transfer function is given by

$$T(s) = \frac{s + 1}{s(s + 10)}$$

Sketch the magnitude and phase Bode plots.

14.13 Construct the Bode plots for

$$G(s) = \frac{s + 1}{s^2(s + 10)}, \qquad s = j\omega$$

14.14 Draw the Bode plots for

$$\mathbf{H}(\omega) = \frac{50(j\omega + 1)}{j\omega(-\omega^2 + 10j\omega + 25)}$$

14.15 Construct the Bode magnitude and phase plots for

$$H(s) = \frac{40(s+1)}{(s+2)(s+10)}, \qquad s = j\omega$$

14.16 Sketch the Bode plots of the magnitude and phase of:

$$G(s) = \frac{s}{(s+1)(s+10)^2}$$

14.17 Sketch the Bode plots for

$$G(s) = \frac{s}{(s+2)^2(s+1)}, \qquad s = j\omega$$

14.18 Draw Bode plots for

$$G(s) = \frac{(s+2)^2}{s(s+5)(s+10)}, \qquad s = j\omega$$

14.19 A filter has

$$H(s) = \frac{s}{s^2 + 10s + 100}$$

Sketch the filter's Bode magnitude and phase plots.

14.20 Sketch Bode magnitude and phase plots for

$$N(s) = \frac{100(s^2 + s + 1)}{(s+1)(s+10)}, \qquad s = j\omega$$

Construct the straight-line approximate plots and the exact plots.

14.21 Construct Bode plots for

$$\mathbf{T}(\omega) = \frac{10j\omega(1 + j\omega)}{(10 + j\omega)(100 + 10j\omega - \omega^2)}$$

14.22 Find the transfer function $\mathbf{H}(\omega)$ with the Bode magnitude plot shown in Fig. 14.71.

Figure 14.71   For Prob. 14.22.

14.23 The Bode magnitude plot of $\mathbf{H}(\omega)$ is shown in Fig. 14.72. Find $\mathbf{H}(\omega)$.

Figure 14.72   For Prob. 14.23.

14.24 The Bode phase plot of $\mathbf{G}(\omega)$ of a network is depicted in Fig. 14.73. Find $\mathbf{G}(\omega)$.

Figure 14.73   For Prob. 14.24.

Section 14.5   Series Resonance

14.25 A series RLC network has $R = 2$ kΩ, $L = 40$ mH, and $C = 1$ μF. Calculate the impedance at resonance and at one-fourth, one-half, twice, and four times the resonant frequency.

14.26 A series RLC circuit has $R = 0.1$ kΩ, $L = 10$ mH, and $C = 5$ nF. Find:

(a) the resonant frequency

(b) the bandwidth

(c) the quality factor

14.27 Design a series RLC circuit that will have an impedance of 10 Ω at the resonant frequency of $\omega_0 = 50$ rad/s and a quality factor of 80. Find the bandwidth.

14.28 Design a series RLC circuit with $B = 20$ rad/s and $\omega_0 = 1,000$ rad/s. Find the circuit's Q. Let $R = 10\Omega$.

14.29 For the circuit in Fig. 14.74, find the frequency ω for which $v(t)$ and $i(t)$ are in phase.

Figure 14.74   For Prob. 14.29.

Section 14.6   Parallel Resonance

14.30 Design a parallel resonant RLC circuit with $\omega_0 = 10$ rad/s and $Q = 20$. Calculate the bandwidth of the circuit. Let $R = 10\,\Omega$.

14.31 At 10 MHz, a series circuit has $R = 5.6$ kΩ, $X_L = 40$ kΩ, $X_C = 40$ kΩ. Calculate the bandwidth.

14.32 A parallel resonant circuit with quality factor 120 has a resonant frequency of 6×10^6 rad/s. Calculate the bandwidth and half-power frequencies.

14.33 A parallel RLC circuit is resonant at 5.6 MHz, has a Q of 80, and has a resistive branch of 40 kΩ. Determine the values of L and C in the other two branches.

14.34 A parallel RLC circuit has $R = 5$ kΩ, $L = 8$ mH, and $C = 60$ μF. Determine:

(a) the resonant frequency

(b) the bandwidth

(c) the quality factor

14.35 It is expected that a parallel RLC resonant circuit has a midband admittance of 25×10^{-3} S, quality factor of 80, and a resonant frequency of 200 krad/s. Calculate the values of R, L, and C. Find the bandwidth and the half-power frequencies.

14.36 Rework Prob. 14.25 if the elements are connected in parallel.

14.37 Find the resonant frequency of the circuit in Fig. 14.75.

Figure 14.75   For Prob. 14.37.

14.38 For the "tank" circuit in Fig. 14.76, find the resonant frequency.

Figure 14.76   For Probs. 14.38 and 14.91.

14.39 A parallel resonance circuit has a resistance of 2 kΩ and half-power frequencies of 86 kHz and 90 kHz.

Determine:

(a) the capacitance

(b) the inductance

(c) the resonant frequency

(d) the bandwidth

(e) the quality factor

14.40 For the circuit shown in Fig. 14.77:

(a) Calculate the resonant frequency ω_0, the quality factor Q, and the bandwidth B.

(b) What value of capacitance must be connected in series with the 20-μF capacitor in order to double the bandwidth?

Figure 14.77   For Prob. 14.40.

14.41 For the circuits in Fig. 14.78, find the resonant frequency ω_0, the quality factor Q, and the bandwidth B.

Figure 14.78   For Prob. 14.41.

14.42 Calculate the resonant frequency of each of the circuits in Fig. 14.79.

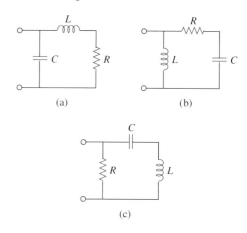

Figure 14.79   For Prob. 14.42.

*14.43 For the circuit in Fig. 14.80, find:

(a) the resonant frequency ω_0

(b) $\mathbf{Z}_{in}(\omega)$

Figure 14.80   For Prob. 14.43.

14.44 In the circuit of Fig. 14.81, $i(t) = 10 \sin t$ A. Calculate the value of C such that $v(t) = V_o \sin t$ V. Find V_o.

Figure 14.81   For Prob. 14.44.

14.45 For the network illustrated in Fig. 14.82, find

(a) the transfer function $\mathbf{H}(\omega) = \mathbf{V}_o(\omega)/\mathbf{I}(\omega)$,

(b) the magnitude of $\mathbf{H}$ at $\omega_0 = 1$ rad/s.

Figure 14.82   For Probs. 14.45, 14.78, and 14.92.

14.46 A circuit consisting of a coil with inductance 10 mH and resistance 20 Ω is connected in series with a capacitor and a generator with an rms voltage of 120 V. Find:

(a) the value of the capacitance that will cause the circuit to be in resonance at 15 kHz

(b) the current through the coil at resonance

(c) the Q of the circuit

Section 14.7   Passive Filters

14.47 Show that the circuit in Fig. 14.66 is a lowpass filter. Calculate the corner frequency f_c if $L = 2$ mH and $R = 10$ kΩ.

14.48 Find the transfer function $\mathbf{V}_o/\mathbf{V}_s$ of the circuit in Fig. 14.83. Show that the circuit is a lowpass filter.

Figure 14.83   For Prob. 14.48.

14.49 Determine the cutoff frequency of the lowpass filter described by

$$\mathbf{H}(\omega) = \frac{4}{2 + j\omega 10}$$

Find the gain in dB and phase of $\mathbf{H}(\omega)$ at $\omega = 2$ rad/s.

14.50 Determine what type of filter is in Fig. 14.84. Calculate the corner frequency f_c.

Figure 14.84   For Prob. 14.50.

14.51 Design an RL lowpass filter that uses a 40-mH coil and has a cutoff frequency of 5 kHz.

14.52 In a highpass RL filter with a cutoff frequency of 100 kHz, $L = 40$ mH. Find R.

14.53 Design a series RLC type bandpass filter with cutoff frequencies of 10 kHz and 11 kHz. Assuming $C = 80$ pF, find R, L, and Q.

14.54 Design an RC highpass filter that has a cutoff frequency of 2 kHz and uses a 300-pF capacitor.

14.55 Determine the range of frequencies that will be passed by a series RLC bandpass filter with $R = 10$ Ω, $L = 25$ mH, and $C = 0.4$ μF. Find the quality factor.

---

*An asterisk indicates a challenging problem.

14.56 (a) Show that for a bandpass filter,

$$\mathbf{H}(s) = \frac{sB}{s^2 + sB + \omega_0^2}, s = j\omega$$

where B = bandwidth of the filter and ω_0 is the center frequency.

(b) Similarly, show that for a bandstop filter,

$$\mathbf{H}(s) = \frac{s^2 + \omega_0^2}{s^2 + sB + \omega_0^2}, s = j\omega$$

14.57 Determine the center frequency and bandwidth of the bandpass filters in Fig. 14.85.

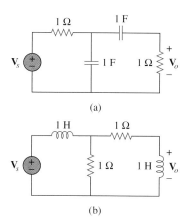

(a)

(b)

Figure 14.85   For Prob. 14.57.

14.58 The circuit parameters for a series RLC bandstop filter are $R = 2$ kΩ, $L = 0.1$ H, $C = 40$ pF. Calculate:

(a) the center frequency

(b) the half-power frequencies

(c) the quality factor

14.59 Find the bandwidth and center frequency of the bandstop filter of Fig. 14.86.

Figure 14.86   For Prob. 14.59.

Sections 14.8   Active Filters

14.60 Obtain the transfer function of a highpass filter with a passband gain of 10 and a cutoff frequency of 50 rad/s.

14.61 Find the transfer function for each of the active filters in Fig. 14.87.

(a)

(b)

Figure 14.87   For Probs. 14.61 and 14.62.

14.62 The filter in Fig. 14.85(b) has a 3-dB cutoff frequency at 1 kHz. If its input is connected to a 120-mV variable frequency signal, find the output voltage at:

(a) 200 Hz   (b) 2 kHz   (c) 10 kHz

14.63 Design an active first-order highpass filter with

$$\mathbf{H}(s) = -\frac{100s}{s + 10}, \qquad s = j\omega$$

Use a 1-μF capacitor.

14.64 Obtain the transfer function of the active filter in Fig. 14.88. What kind of filter is it?

Figure 14.88   For Prob. 14.64.

14.65   A highpass filter is shown in Fig. 14.89. Show that the transfer function is

$$\mathbf{H}(\omega) = \left(1 + \frac{R_f}{R_i}\right)\frac{j\omega RC}{1 + j\omega RC}$$

Figure 14.89   For Prob. 14.65.

14.66   A "general" first-order filter is shown in Fig. 14.90.

(a)   Show that the transfer function is

$$\mathbf{H}(s) = \frac{R_4}{R_3 + R_4} \times \frac{s + (1/R_1C)[R_1/R_2 - R_3/R_4]}{s + 1/R_2C},$$

$$s = j\omega$$

(b)   What condition must be satisfied for the circuit to operate as a highpass filter?

(c)   What condition must be satisfied for the circuit to operate as a lowpass filter?

Figure 14.90   For Prob. 14.66.

14.67   Design an active lowpass filter with dc gain of 0.25 and a corner frequency of 500 Hz.

14.68   Design an active highpass filter with a high-frequency gain of 5 and a corner frequency of 200 Hz.

14.69   Design the filter in Fig. 14.91 to meet the following requirements:

(a)   It must attenuate a signal at 2 kHz by 3 dB compared with its value at 10 MHz.

(b)   It must provide a steady-state output of $v_o(t) = 10\sin(2\pi \times 10^8 t + 180°)$ V for an input $v_s(t) = 4\sin(2\pi \times 10^8 t)$ V.

Figure 14.91   For Prob. 14.69.

*__14.70__   A second-order active filter known as a Butterworth filter is shown in Fig. 14.92.

(a)   Find the transfer function $\mathbf{V}_o/\mathbf{V}_i$.

(b)   Show that it is a lowpass filter.

Figure 14.92   For Prob. 14.70.

Section 14.9   Scaling

14.71   Use magnitude and frequency scaling on the circuit of Fig. 14.76 to obtain an equivalent circuit in which the inductor and capacitor have magnitude 1 H and 1 F respectively.

14.72   What values of K_m and K_f will scale a 4-mH inductor and a 20-μF capacitor to 1 H and 2 F respectively?

14.73   Calculate the values of R, L, and C that will result in $R = 12$ kΩ, $L = 40$ μH, and $C = 300$ nF respectively when magnitude-scaled by 800 and frequency-scaled by 1000.

14.74   A circuit has $R_1 = 3$ Ω, $R_2 = 10\Omega$, $L = 2$ H, and $C = 1/10$ F. After the circuit is magnitude-scaled by 100 and frequency-scaled by 10^6, find the new values of the circuit elements.

14.75   In an RLC circuit, $R = 20$ Ω, $L = 4$ H, and $C = 1$ F. The circuit is magnitude-scaled by 10 and frequency-scaled by 10^5. Calculate the new values of the elements.

14.76   Obtain the values of R, L, and C when magnitude-scaled by 10^3 and frequency-scaled by 10^6 that will result in $R' = 50$ kΩ, $L' = 10$ μH, and $C' = 40$ pF.

14.77 A series RLC circuit has $R = 10\ \Omega$, $\omega_0 = 40$ rad/s, and $B = 5$ rad/s. Find L and C when the circuit is scaled:

(a) in magnitude by a factor of 600,

(b) in frequency by a factor of 1,000,

(c) in magnitude by a factor of 400 and in frequency by a factor of 10^5.

14.78 Redesign the circuit in Fig. 14.82 so that all resistive elements are scaled by a factor of 1,000 and all frequency-sensitive elements are frequency-scaled by a factor of 10^4.

*14.79** Refer to the network in Fig. 14.93.

(a) Find $\mathbf{Z}_{in}(s)$.

(b) Scale the elements by $K_m = 10$ and $K_f = 100$. Find $\mathbf{Z}_{in}(s)$ and ω_0.

Figure 14.93   For Prob. 14.79.

14.80 (a) For the circuit in Fig. 14.94, draw the new circuit after it has been scaled by $K_m = 200$ and $K_f = 10^4$.

(b) Obtain the Thevenin equivalent impedance at terminals a-b of the scaled circuit at $\omega = 10^4$ rad/s.

Figure 14.94   For Prob. 14.80.

14.81 The circuit shown in Fig. 14.95 has the impedance

$$Z(s) = \frac{1,000(s+1)}{(s+1+j50)(s+1-j50)}, s = j\omega$$

Find:

(a) the values of R, L, C, and G

(b) the element values which will raise the resonant frequency by a factor of 10^3 by frequency scaling

Figure 14.95   For Prob. 14.81.

14.82 Scale the lowpass active filter in Fig. 14.96 so that its corner frequency increases from 1 rad/s to 200 rad/s. Use a 1-μF capacitor.

Figure 14.96   For Prob. 14.82.

14.83 The op amp circuit in Fig. 14.97 is to be magnitude-scaled by 100 and frequency-scaled by 10^5. Find the resulting element values.

Figure 14.97   For Prob. 14.83.

Section 14.10   Frequency Response Using *PSpice*

14.84 Obtain the frequency response of the circuit in Fig. 14.98 using *PSpice*.

Figure 14.98   For Prob. 14.84.

14.85 Use *PSpice* to obtain the magnitude and phase plots of $\mathbf{V}_o/\mathbf{I}_s$ of the circuit in Fig. 14.99.

Figure 14.99   For Prob. 14.85.

14.86 Use *PSpice* to provide the frequency response (magnitude and phase of i) of the circuit in Fig. 14.100. Use linear frequency sweep from 1 to 10,000 Hz.

Figure 14.100   For Prob. 14.86.

14.87 In the interval $0.1 < f < 100$ Hz, plot the response of the network in Fig. 14.101. Classify this filter and obtain ω_0.

Figure 14.101   For Prob. 14.87.

14.88 Use *PSpice* to generate the magnitude and phase Bode plots of $\mathbf{V}_o$ in the circuit of Fig. 14.102.

Figure 14.102   For Prob. 14.88.

14.89 Obtain the magnitude plot of the response $\mathbf{V}_o$ in the network of Fig. 14.103 for the frequency interval $100 < f < 1,000$ Hz.

Figure 14.103   For Prob. 14.89.

14.90 Obtain the frequency response of the circuit in Fig. 14.40 (see Practice Problem 14.10). Take $R_1 = R_2 = 100 \ \Omega$, $L = 2$ mH. Use $1 < f < 100,000$ Hz.

14.91 For the "tank" circuit of Fig. 14.76, obtain the frequency response (voltage across the capacitor) using *PSpice*. Determine the resonant frequency of the circuit.

14.92 Using *PSpice*, plot the magnitude of the frequency response of the circuit in Fig. 14.82.

Section 14.11   Applications

14.93 The resonant circuit for a radio broadcast consists of a 120-pF capacitor in parallel with a 240-μH inductor. If the inductor has an internal resistance of 400 Ω, what is the resonant frequency of the circuit? What would be the resonant frequency if the inductor resistance were reduced to 40 Ω?

14.94 For an emergency situation, an engineer needs to make an RC highpass filter. He has one 10-pF capacitor, one 30-pF capacitor, one 1.8-kΩ resistor, and one 3.3-kΩ resistor available. Find the greatest cutoff frequency possible using these elements.

14.95 A series-tuned antenna circuit consists of a variable capacitor (40 pF to 360 pF) and a 240-μH antenna coil which has a dc resistance of 12 Ω.

  (a) Find the frequency range of radio signals to which the radio is tunable.

  (b) Determine the value of Q at each end of the frequency range.

14.96 The crossover circuit in Fig. 14.104 is a lowpass filter that is connected to a woofer. Find the transfer function $\mathbf{H}(\omega) = \mathbf{V}_o(\omega)/\mathbf{V}_i(\omega)$.

Figure 14.104   For Prob. 14.96.

14.97 The crossover circuit in Fig. 14.105 is a highpass filter that is connected to a tweeter. Determine the

transfer function $\mathbf{H}(\omega) = \mathbf{V}_o(\omega)/\mathbf{V}_i(\omega)$.

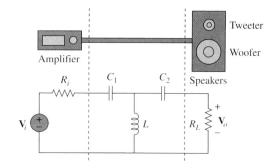

Figure 14.105   For Prob. 14.97.

COMPREHENSIVE PROBLEMS

14.98 A certain electronic test circuit produced a resonant curve with half-power points at 432 Hz and 454 Hz. If $Q = 20$, what is the resonant frequency of the circuit?

14.99 In an electronic device, a series circuit is employed that has a resistance of 100 Ω, a capacitive reactance of 5 kΩ, and an inductive reactance of 300 Ω when used at 2 MHz. Find the resonant frequency and bandwidth of the circuit.

14.100 In a certain application, a simple RC lowpass filter is designed to reduce high frequency noise. If the desired corner frequency is 20 kHz and $C = 0.5~\mu$F, find the value of R.

14.101 In an amplifier circuit, a simple RC highpass filter is needed to block the dc component while passing the time-varying component. If the desired rolloff frequency is 15 Hz and $C = 10~\mu$F, find the value of R.

14.102 Practical RC filter design should allow for source and load resistances as shown in Fig. 14.106. Let $R = 4$ kΩ and $C = 40$-nF. Obtain the cutoff frequency when:

(a) $R_s = 0, R_L = \infty$,
(b) $R_s = 1$ kΩ, $R_L = 5$ kΩ.

Figure 14.106   For Prob. 14.102.

14.103 The RC circuit in Fig. 14.107 is used for a lead compensator in a system design. Obtain the transfer function of the circuit.

Figure 14.107   For Prob. 14.103.

14.104 A low-quality factor, double-tuned bandpass filter is shown in Fig. 14.108. Use *PSpice* to generate the magnitude plot of $\mathbf{V}_o(\omega)$.

Figure 14.108   For Prob. 14.104.

PART 3

ADVANCED CIRCUIT ANALYSIS

Chapter **15** *Introduction to Laplace Transforms*

Chapter **16** *Applications of Laplace Transforms*

Chapter **17** *The Fourier Series*

Chapter **18** *Fourier Transform*

Chapter **19** *Two-Port Networks*

C H A P T E R | 1 5

INTRODUCTION TO LAPLACE TRANSFORMS

A good scientist is a person with original ideas. A good engineer is a person who makes a design that works with as few original ideas as possible.

—Freeman Dyson

Historical Profiles

Pierre Simon Laplace (1749–1827), a French astronomer and mathematician, first presented the transform that bears his name and its applications to differential equations in 1779.

Born of humble origins in Beaumont-en-Auge, Normandy, France, Laplace became a professor of mathematics at the age of 20. His mathematical abilities inspired the famous mathematician Simeon Poisson, who called Laplace the Isaac Newton of France. He made important contributions in potential theory, probability theory, astronomy, and celestial mechanics. He was widely known for his work, *Traite de Mecanique Celeste (Celestial Mechanics)*, which supplemented the work of Newton on astronomy. The Laplace transform, the subject of this chapter, is named after him.

Samuel F. B. Morse (1791–1872), an American painter, invented the telegraph, the first practical, commercialized application of electricity.

Morse was born in Charlestown, Massachusetts and studied at Yale and the Royal Academy of Arts in London to become an artist. In the 1830s, he became intrigued with developing a telegraph. He had a working model by 1836 and applied for a patent in 1838. The U.S. Senate appropriated funds for Morse to construct a telegraph line between Baltimore and Washington, D.C. On May 24, 1844, he sent the famous first message: "What hath God wrought!" Morse also developed a code of dots and dashes for letters and numbers, for sending messages on the telegraph. The development of the telegraph led to the invention of the telephone.

15.1   INTRODUCTION

Our frequency-domain analysis has been limited to circuits with sinusoidal inputs. In other words, we have assumed sinusoidal time-varying excitations in all our non-dc circuits. This chapter introduces the *Laplace transform*, a very powerful tool for analyzing circuits with sinusoidal *or* nonsinusoidal inputs.

The idea of transformation should be familiar by now. When using phasors for the analysis of circuits, we transform the circuit from the time domain to the frequency or phasor domain. Once we obtain the phasor result, we transform it back to the time domain. The Laplace transform method follows the same process: we use the Laplace transformation to transform the circuit from the time domain to the frequency domain, obtain the solution, and apply the inverse Laplace transform to the result to transform it back to the time domain.

The Laplace transform is significant for a number of reasons. First, it can be applied to a wider variety of inputs than phasor analysis. Second, it provides an easy way to solve circuit problems involving initial conditions, because it allows us to work with algebraic equations instead of differential equations. Third, the Laplace transform is capable of providing us, in one single operation, the total response of the circuit comprising both the natural and forced responses.

We begin with the definition of the Laplace transform and use it to derive the transforms of some basic, important functions. We consider some properties of the Laplace transform that are very helpful in circuit analysis. We then consider the inverse Laplace transform, transfer functions, and convolution. In this chapter, we will focus on the mechanics of the Laplace transformation. In Chapter 16 we will examine how the Laplace transform is applied in circuit analysis, network stability, and network synthesis.

15.2   DEFINITION OF THE LAPLACE TRANSFORM

Given a function $f(t)$, its Laplace transform, denoted by $F(s)$ or $\mathcal{L}[f(t)]$, is given by

$$\mathcal{L}[f(t)] = F(s) = \int_{0^-}^{\infty} f(t)e^{-st}\,dt \qquad (15.1)$$

where s is a complex variable given by

$$s = \sigma + j\omega \qquad (15.2)$$

Since the argument st of the exponent e in Eq. (15.1) must be dimensionless, it follows that s has the dimensions of frequency and units of inverse seconds (s^{-1}). In Eq. (15.1), the lower limit is specified as 0^- to indicate a time just before $t = 0$. We use 0^- as the lower limit to include the origin and capture any discontinuity of $f(t)$ at $t = 0$; this will accommodate functions—such as singularity functions—that may be discontinuous at $t = 0$.

For an ordinary function $f(t)$, the lower limit can be replaced by 0.

> The Laplace transform is an integral transformation of a function $f(t)$ from the time domain into the complex frequency domain, giving $F(s)$.

We assume in Eq. (15.1) that $f(t)$ is ignored for $t < 0$. To ensure that this is the case, a function is often multiplied by the unit step. Thus, $f(t)$ is written as $f(t)u(t)$ or $f(t), t \geq 0$.

The Laplace transform in Eq. (15.1) is known as the *one-sided* (or *unilateral*) Laplace transform. The *two-sided* (or *bilateral*) Laplace transform is given by

$$F(s) = \int_{-\infty}^{\infty} f(t)e^{-st}\,dt \qquad (15.3)$$

The one-sided Laplace transform in Eq. (15.1), being adequate for our purposes, is the only type of Laplace transform that we will treat in this book.

A function $f(t)$ may not have a Laplace transform. In order for $f(t)$ to have a Laplace transform, the integral in Eq. (15.1) must converge to a finite value. Since $|e^{j\omega t}| = 1$ for any value of t, the integral converges when

$$\int_{0^-}^{\infty} e^{-\sigma t}|f(t)|\,dt \;<\; \infty \qquad (15.4)$$

$$|e^{j\omega t}| = \sqrt{\cos^2 \omega t + \sin^2 \omega t} = 1$$

for some real value $\sigma = \sigma_c$. Thus, the region of convergence for the Laplace transform is $\text{Re}(s) = \sigma > \sigma_c$, as shown in Fig. 15.1. In this region, $|F(s)| < \infty$ and $F(s)$ exists. $F(s)$ is undefined outside the region of convergence. Fortunately, all functions of interest in circuit analysis satisfy the convergence criterion in Eq. (15.4) and have Laplace transforms. Therefore, it is not necessary to specify σ_c in what follows.

A companion to the direct Laplace transform in Eq. (15.1) is the *inverse* Laplace transform given by

$$\mathcal{L}^{-1}[F(s)] = f(t) = \frac{1}{2\pi j} \int_{\sigma_1 - j\infty}^{\sigma_1 + j\infty} F(s)e^{st}\,ds \qquad (15.5)$$

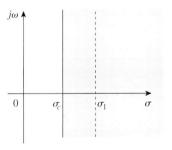

Figure 15.1   Region of convergence for the Laplace transform.

where the integration is performed along a straight line ($\sigma_1 + j\omega, -\infty < \omega < \infty$) in the region of convergence, $\sigma_1 > \sigma_c$. See Fig. 15.1. The direct application of Eq. (15.5) involves some knowledge about complex analysis beyond the scope of this book. For this reason, we will not use Eq. (15.5) to find the inverse Laplace transform. We will rather use a look-up table, to be developed in Section 15.3. The functions $f(t)$ and $F(s)$ are regarded as a Laplace transform pair where

$$f(t) \quad \Longleftrightarrow \quad F(s) \qquad (15.6)$$

meaning that there is one-to-one correspondence between $f(t)$ and $F(s)$. The following examples derive the Laplace transforms of some important functions.

EXAMPLE 15.1

Determine the Laplace transform of each of the following functions: (a) $u(t)$, (b) $e^{-at}u(t), a \geq 0$, and (c) $\delta(t)$.

Solution:

(a) For the unit step function $u(t)$, shown in Fig. 15.2(a), the Laplace transform is

$$\mathcal{L}[u(t)] = \int_{0^-}^{\infty} 1e^{-st}\, dt = -\frac{1}{s}e^{-st}\Big|_0^{\infty}$$

$$= -\frac{1}{s}(0) + \frac{1}{s}(1) = \frac{1}{s}$$

(15.1.1)

(b) For the exponential function, shown in Fig. 15.2(b), the Laplace transform is

$$\mathcal{L}[e^{-at}u(t)] = \int_{0^-}^{\infty} e^{-at}e^{-st}\, dt$$

$$= -\frac{1}{s+a}e^{-(s+a)t}\Big|_0^{\infty} = \frac{1}{s+a}$$

(15.1.2)

(c) For the unit impulse function, shown in Fig. 15.2(c),

$$\mathcal{L}[\delta(t)] = \int_{0^-}^{\infty} \delta(t)e^{-st}\, dt = e^{-0} = 1$$

(15.1.3)

since the impulse function $\delta(t)$ is zero everywhere except at $t = 0$. The sifting property in Eq. (7.33) has been applied in Eq. (15.1.3).

Figure 15.2   For Example 15.1: (a) unit step function, (b) exponential function, (c) unit impulse function.

PRACTICE PROBLEM 15.1

Find the Laplace transforms of these functions: $r(t) = tu(t)$, that is, the ramp function; and $e^{at}u(t)$.

Answer: $1/s^2$, $1/(s-a)$.

EXAMPLE 15.2

Determine the Laplace transform of $f(t) = \sin \omega t u(t)$.

Solution:

Using Eq. (B.27) in addition to Eq. (15.1), we obtain the Laplace transform of the sine function as

$$F(s) = \mathcal{L}[\sin \omega t] = \int_0^\infty (\sin \omega t)e^{-st} \, dt = \int_0^\infty \left(\frac{e^{j\omega t} - e^{-j\omega t}}{2j} \right) e^{-st} \, dt$$

$$= \frac{1}{2j} \int_0^\infty (e^{-(s-j\omega)t} - e^{-(s+j\omega)t}) \, dt$$

$$= \frac{1}{2j} \left(\frac{1}{s - j\omega} - \frac{1}{s + j\omega} \right) = \frac{\omega}{s^2 + \omega^2}$$

PRACTICE PROBLEM 15.2

Find the Laplace transform of $f(t) = \cos \omega t u(t)$.

Answer: $s/(s^2 + \omega^2)$.

15.3 PROPERTIES OF THE LAPLACE TRANSFORM

The properties of the Laplace transform help us to obtain transform pairs without directly using Eq. (15.1) as we did in Examples 15.1 and 15.2. As we derive each of these properties, we should keep in mind the definition of the Laplace transform in Eq. (15.1).

Linearity

If $F_1(s)$ and $F_2(s)$ are, respectively, the Laplace transforms of $f_1(t)$ and $f_2(t)$, then

$$\boxed{\mathcal{L}[a_1 f_1(t) + a_2 f_2(t)] = a_1 F_1(s) + a_2 F_2(s)} \qquad (15.7)$$

where a_1 and a_2 are constants. Equation 15.7 expresses the linearity property of the Laplace transform. The proof of Eq. (15.7) follows readily from the definition of the Laplace transform in Eq. (15.1).

For example, by the linearity property in Eq. (15.7), we may write

$$\mathcal{L}[\cos \omega t \, u(t)] = \mathcal{L} \left[\frac{1}{2}(e^{j\omega t} + e^{-j\omega t}) \right] = \frac{1}{2}\mathcal{L}[e^{j\omega t}] + \frac{1}{2}\mathcal{L}[e^{-j\omega t}] \quad (15.8)$$

But from Example 15.1(b), $\mathcal{L}[e^{-at}] = 1/(s + a)$. Hence,

$$\mathcal{L}[\cos \omega t \, u(t)] = \frac{1}{2} \left(\frac{1}{s - j\omega} + \frac{1}{s + j\omega} \right) = \frac{s}{s^2 + \omega^2} \qquad (15.9)$$

Scaling

If $F(s)$ is the Laplace transform of $f(t)$, then

$$\mathcal{L}[f(at)] = \int_{0^-}^\infty f(at)e^{-st} \, dt \qquad (15.10)$$

where a is a constant and $a > 0$. If we let $x = at$, $dx = a\,dt$, then

$$\mathcal{L}[f(at)] = \int_{0^-}^{\infty} f(x)e^{-x(s/a)}\frac{dx}{a} = \frac{1}{a}\int_{0^-}^{\infty} f(x)e^{-x(s/a)}\,dx \quad (15.11)$$

Comparing this integral with the definition of the Laplace transform in Eq. (15.1) shows that s in Eq. (15.1) must be replaced by s/a while the dummy variable t is replaced by x. Hence, we obtain the scaling property as

$$\mathcal{L}[f(at)] = \frac{1}{a}F\left(\frac{s}{a}\right) \quad (15.12)$$

For example, we know from Example 15.2 that

$$\mathcal{L}[\sin \omega t\, u(t)] = \frac{\omega}{s^2 + \omega^2} \quad (15.13)$$

Using the scaling property in Eq. (15.12),

$$\mathcal{L}[\sin 2\omega t\, u(t)] = \frac{1}{2}\frac{\omega}{(s/2)^2 + \omega^2} = \frac{2\omega}{s^2 + 4\omega^2} \quad (15.14)$$

which may also be obtained from Eq. (15.13) by replacing ω with 2ω.

Time Shift

If $F(s)$ is the Laplace transform of $f(t)$, then

$$\mathcal{L}[f(t-a)u(t-a)] = \int_{0^-}^{\infty} f(t-a)u(t-a)e^{-st}\,dt \quad (15.15)$$
$$a \geq 0$$

But $u(t-a) = 0$ for $t < a$ and $u(t-a) = 1$ for $t > a$. Hence,

$$\mathcal{L}[f(t-a)u(t-a)] = \int_{a}^{\infty} f(t-a)e^{-st}\,dt \quad (15.16)$$

If we let $x = t - a$, then $dx = dt$ and $t = x + a$. As $t \to a$, $x \to 0$ and as $t \to \infty$, $x \to \infty$. Thus,

$$\mathcal{L}[f(t-a)u(t-a)] = \int_{0^-}^{\infty} f(x)e^{-s(x+a)}\,dx$$

$$= e^{-as}\int_{0^-}^{\infty} f(x)e^{-sx}\,dx = e^{-as}F(s)$$

or

$$\mathcal{L}[f(t-a)u(t-a)] = e^{-as}F(s) \quad (15.17)$$

In other words, if a function is delayed in time by a, the result in the s domain is multiplying the Laplace transform of the function (without the delay) by e^{-as}. This is called the *time-delay* or *time-shift property* of the Laplace transform.

As an example, we know from Eq. (15.9) that

$$\mathcal{L}[\cos \omega t \, u(t)] = \frac{s}{s^2 + \omega^2}$$

Using the time-shift property in Eq. (15.17),

$$\mathcal{L}[\cos \omega(t - a)u(t - a)] = e^{-as} \frac{s}{s^2 + \omega^2} \tag{15.18}$$

Frequency Shift

If $F(s)$ is the Laplace transform of $f(t)$, then

$$\mathcal{L}[e^{-at} f(t) \, u(t)] = \int_0^\infty e^{-at} f(t) e^{-st} \, dt$$

$$= \int_0^\infty f(t) e^{-(s+a)t} \, dt = F(s + a)$$

or

$$\boxed{\mathcal{L}[e^{-at} f(t) \, u(t)] = F(s + a)} \tag{15.19}$$

That is, the Laplace transform of $e^{-at} f(t)$ can be obtained from the Laplace transform of $f(t)$ by replacing every s with $s + a$. This is known as *frequency shift* or *frequency translation*.

As an example, we know that

$$\cos \omega t \, u(t) \quad \Longleftrightarrow \quad \frac{s}{s^2 + \omega^2}$$

and $\tag{15.20}$

$$\sin \omega t \, u(t) \quad \Longleftrightarrow \quad \frac{\omega}{s^2 + \omega^2}$$

Using the shift property in Eq. (15.19), we obtain the Laplace transform of the damped sine and damped cosine functions as

$$\mathcal{L}[e^{-at} \cos \omega t \, u(t)] = \frac{s + a}{(s + a)^2 + \omega^2} \tag{15.21a}$$

$$\mathcal{L}[e^{-at} \sin \omega t \, u(t)] = \frac{\omega}{(s + a)^2 + \omega^2} \tag{15.21b}$$

Time Differentiation

Given that $F(s)$ is the Laplace transform of $f(t)$, the Laplace transform of its derivative is

$$\mathcal{L}\left[\frac{df}{dt} u(t)\right] = \int_{0^-}^\infty \frac{df}{dt} e^{-st} \, dt \tag{15.22}$$

To integrate this by parts, we let $u = e^{-st}$, $du = -se^{-st} \, dt$, and $dv = (df/dt) \, dt = df(t)$, $v = f(t)$. Then

$$\mathcal{L}\left[\frac{df}{dt} u(t)\right] = f(t) e^{-st} \Big|_{0^-}^\infty - \int_{0^-}^\infty f(t)[-se^{-st}] \, dt$$

$$= 0 - f(0^-) + s \int_{0^-}^\infty f(t) e^{-st} \, dt = sF(s) - f(0^-)$$

or

$$\mathcal{L}[f'(t)] = sF(s) - f(0^-) \qquad (15.23)$$

The Laplace transform of the second derivative of $f(t)$ is a repeated application of Eq. (15.23) as

$$\mathcal{L}\left[\frac{d^2 f}{dt^2}\right] = s\mathcal{L}[f'(t)] - f'(0^-) = s[sF(s) - f(0^-)] - f'(0^-)$$

$$= s^2 F(s) - sf(0^-) - f'(0^-)$$

or

$$\mathcal{L}[f''(t)] = s^2 F(s) - sf(0^-) - f'(0^-) \qquad (15.24)$$

Continuing in this manner, we can obtain the Laplace transform of the nth derivative of $f(t)$ as

$$\mathcal{L}\left[\frac{d^n f}{dt^n}\right] = s^n F(s) - s^{n-1} f(0^-)$$

$$- s^{n-2} f'(0^-) - \cdots - s^0 f^{(n-1)}(0^-) \qquad (15.25)$$

As an example, we can use Eq. (15.23) to obtain the Laplace transform of the sine from that of the cosine. If we let $f(t) = \cos \omega t \, u(t)$, then $f(0) = 1$ and $f'(t) = -\omega \sin \omega t \, u(t)$. Using Eq. (15.23) and the scaling property,

$$\mathcal{L}[\sin \omega t \, u(t)] = -\frac{1}{\omega}\mathcal{L}[f'(t)] = -\frac{1}{\omega}[sF(s) - f(0^-)]$$

$$= -\frac{1}{\omega}\left(s\frac{s}{s^2 + \omega^2} - 1\right) = \frac{\omega}{s^2 + \omega^2} \qquad (15.26)$$

as expected.

Time Integration

If $F(s)$ is the Laplace transform of $f(t)$, the Laplace transform of its integral is

$$\mathcal{L}\left[\int_0^t f(t)\, dt\right] = \int_{0^-}^{\infty}\left[\int_0^t f(x)\, dx\right] e^{-st}\, dt \qquad (15.27)$$

To integrate this by parts, we let

$$u = \int_0^t f(x)\, dx, \qquad du = f(t)\, dt$$

and

$$dv = e^{-st}\, dt, \qquad v = -\frac{1}{s} e^{-st}$$

Then

$$\mathcal{L}\left[\int_0^t f(t)\,dt\right] = \left[\int_0^t f(x)\,dx\right]\left(-\frac{1}{s}e^{-st}\right)\Bigg|_{0^-}^{\infty}$$
$$- \int_{0^-}^{\infty}\left(-\frac{1}{s}\right)e^{-st}f(t)\,dt$$

For the first term on the right-hand side of the equation, evaluating the term at $t = \infty$ yields zero due to $e^{-s\infty}$ and evaluating it at $t = 0$ gives $\frac{1}{s}\int_0^0 f(x)\,dx = 0$. Thus, the first term is zero, and

$$\mathcal{L}\left[\int_0^t f(t)\,dt\right] = \frac{1}{s}\int_{0^-}^{\infty} f(t)e^{-st}\,dt = \frac{1}{s}F(s)$$

or simply,

$$\boxed{\mathcal{L}\left[\int_0^t f(t)\,dt\right] = \frac{1}{s}F(s)} \qquad (15.28)$$

As an example, if we let $f(t) = u(t)$, from Example 15.1(a), $F(s) = 1/s$. Using Eq. (15.28),

$$\mathcal{L}\left[\int_0^t f(t)\,dt\right] = \mathcal{L}[t] = \frac{1}{s}\left(\frac{1}{s}\right)$$

Thus, the Laplace transform of the ramp function is

$$\mathcal{L}[t] = \frac{1}{s^2} \qquad (15.29)$$

Applying Eq. (15.28), this gives

$$\mathcal{L}\left[\int_0^t t\,dt\right] = \mathcal{L}\left[\frac{t^2}{2}\right] = \frac{1}{s}\frac{1}{s^2}$$

or

$$\mathcal{L}[t^2] = \frac{2}{s^3} \qquad (15.30)$$

Repeated applications of Eq. (15.28) lead to

$$\mathcal{L}[t^n] = \frac{n!}{s^{n+1}} \qquad (15.31)$$

Similarly, using integration by parts, we can show that

$$\mathcal{L}\left[\int_{-\infty}^t f(t)\,dt\right] = \frac{1}{s}F(s) + \frac{1}{s}f^{-1}(0^-) \qquad (15.32)$$

where

$$f^{-1}(0^-) = \int_{-\infty}^{0^-} f(t)\,dt$$

Frequency Differentiation

If $F(s)$ is the Laplace transform of $f(t)$, then

$$F(s) = \int_{0^-}^{\infty} f(t)e^{-st}\, dt$$

Taking the derivative with respect to s,

$$\frac{dF(s)}{ds} = \int_{0^-}^{\infty} f(t)(-te^{-st})\, dt = \int_{0^-}^{\infty} (-tf(t))e^{-st}\, dt = \mathcal{L}[-tf(t)]$$

and the frequency differentiation property becomes

$$\boxed{\mathcal{L}[tf(t)] = -\frac{dF(s)}{ds}} \tag{15.33}$$

Repeated applications of this equation lead to

$$\mathcal{L}[t^n f(t)] = (-1)^n \frac{d^n F(s)}{ds^n} \tag{15.34}$$

For example, we know from Example 15.1(b) that $\mathcal{L}[e^{-at}] = 1/(s+a)$. Using the property in Eq. (15.33),

$$\mathcal{L}[te^{-at}u(t)] = -\frac{d}{ds}\left(\frac{1}{s+a}\right) = \frac{1}{(s+a)^2} \tag{15.35}$$

Note that if $a = 0$, we obtain $\mathcal{L}[t] = 1/s^2$ as in Eq. (15.29), and repeated applications of Eq. (15.33) will yield Eq. (15.31).

Time Periodicity

If function $f(t)$ is a periodic function such as shown in Fig. 15.3, it can be represented as the sum of time-shifted functions shown in Fig. 15.4. Thus,

$$f(t) = f_1(t) + f_2(t) + f_3(t) + \cdots$$
$$= f_1(t) + f_1(t - T)u(t - T) \tag{15.36}$$
$$+ f_1(t - 2T)u(t - 2T) + \cdots$$

where $f_1(t)$ is the same as the function $f(t)$ gated over the interval $0 < t < T$, that is,

$$f_1(t) = f(t)[u(t) - u(t - T)] \tag{15.37a}$$

or

$$f_1(t) = \begin{cases} f(t), & 0 < t < T \\ 0, & \text{otherwise} \end{cases} \tag{15.37b}$$

We now transform each term in Eq. (15.36) and apply the time-shift property in Eq. (15.17). We obtain

$$F(s) = F_1(s) + F_1(s)e^{-Ts} + F_1(s)e^{-2Ts} + F_1(s)e^{-3Ts} + \cdots$$
$$= F_1(s)[1 + e^{-Ts} + e^{-2Ts} + e^{-3Ts} + \cdots] \tag{15.38}$$

But

$$1 + x + x^2 + x^3 + \cdots = \frac{1}{1-x} \tag{15.39}$$

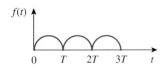

Figure 15.3   A periodic function.

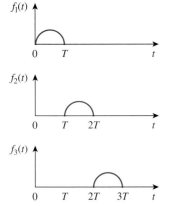

Figure 15.4   Decomposition of the periodic function in Fig. 15.2.

if $|x| < 1$. Hence,

$$F(s) = \frac{F_1(s)}{1 - e^{-Ts}} \qquad (15.40)$$

where $F_1(s)$ is the Laplace transform of $f_1(t)$; in other words, $F_1(s)$ is the transform $f(t)$ defined over its first period only. Equation (15.40) shows that the Laplace transform of a periodic function is the transform of the first period of the function divided by $1 - e^{-Ts}$.

Initial and Final Values

The initial-value and final-value properties allow us to find the initial value $f(0)$ and the final value $f(\infty)$ of $f(t)$ directly from its Laplace transform $F(s)$. To obtain these properties, we begin with the differentiation property in Eq. (15.23), namely,

$$sF(s) - f(0^+) = \mathcal{L}\left[\frac{df}{dt}\right] = \int_{0^-}^{\infty} \frac{df}{dt} e^{-st}\, dt \qquad (15.41)$$

If we let $s \to \infty$, the integrand in Eq. (15.41) vanishes due to the damping exponential factor, and Eq. (15.41) becomes

$$\lim_{s \to \infty} \left[sF(s) - f(0^+)\right] = 0$$

Since $f(0^+)$ is independent of s, we can write

$$f(0^+) = \lim_{s \to \infty} sF(s) \qquad (15.42)$$

This is known as the *initial-value theorem*. For example, we know from Eq. (15.21a) that

$$f(t) = e^{-2t} \cos 10t \qquad \Longleftrightarrow \qquad F(s) = \frac{s+2}{(s+2)^2 + 10^2} \qquad (15.43)$$

Using the initial-value theorem,

$$f(0^+) = \lim_{s \to \infty} sF(s) = \lim_{s \to \infty} \frac{s^2 + 2s}{s^2 + 4s + 104}$$

$$= \lim_{s \to \infty} \frac{1 + 2/s}{1 + 4/s + 104/s^2} = 1$$

which confirms what we would expect from the given $f(t)$.

In Eq. (15.41), we let $s \to 0$; then

$$\lim_{s \to 0} [sF(s) - f(0^-)] = \int_{0^-}^{\infty} \frac{df}{dt} e^{0t}\, dt = \int_{0^-}^{\infty} df = f(\infty) - f(0^-)$$

or

$$f(\infty) = \lim_{s \to 0} sF(s) \qquad (15.44)$$

This is referred to as the *final-value theorem*. In order for the final-value theorem to hold, all poles of $F(s)$ must be located in the left half of the

s plane (see Fig. 15.1 or Fig. 15.9); that is, the poles must have negative real parts. The only exception to this requirement is the case in which $F(s)$ has a simple pole at $s = 0$, because the effect of $1/s$ will be nullified by $sF(s)$ in Eq. (15.44). For example, from Eq. (15.21b),

$$f(t) = e^{-2t} \sin 5t \, u(t) \quad \Longleftrightarrow \quad F(s) = \frac{5}{(s+2)^2 + 5^2} \quad (15.45)$$

Applying the final-value theorem,

$$f(\infty) = \lim_{s \to 0} sF(s) = \lim_{s \to 0} \frac{5s}{s^2 + 4s + 29} = 0$$

as expected from the given $f(t)$. As another example,

$$f(t) = \sin t \, u(t) \quad \Longleftrightarrow \quad f(s) = \frac{1}{s^2 + 1} \quad (15.46)$$

so that

$$f(\infty) = \lim_{s \to 0} sF(s) = \lim_{s \to 0} \frac{s}{s^2 + 1} = 0$$

This is incorrect, because $f(t) = \sin t$ oscillates between $+1$ and -1 and does not have a limit as $t \to \infty$. Thus, the final-value theorem cannot be used to find the final value of $f(t) = \sin t$, because $F(s)$ has poles at $s = \pm j$, which are not in the left half of the s plane. In general, the final-value theorem does not apply in finding the final values of sinusoidal functions—these functions oscillate forever and do not have final values.

The initial-value and final-value theorems depict the relationship between the origin and infinity in the time domain and the s domain. They serve as useful checks on Laplace transforms.

Table 15.1 provides a list of the properties of the Laplace transform. The last property (on convolution) will be proved in Section 15.5. There are other properties, but these are enough for present purposes. Table 15.2 summarizes the Laplace transforms of some common functions. We have omitted the factor $u(t)$ except where it is necessary.

EXAMPLE 15.3

Obtain the Laplace transform of $f(t) = \delta(t) + 2u(t) - 3e^{-2t}, t \geq 0$.

Solution:

By the linearity property,

$$F(s) = \mathcal{L}[\delta(t)] + 2\mathcal{L}[u(t)] - 3\mathcal{L}[e^{-2t}u(t)]$$

$$= 1 + 2\frac{1}{s} - 3\frac{1}{s+2} = \frac{s^2 + s + 4}{s(s+2)}$$

PRACTICE PROBLEM 15.3

Find the Laplace transform of $f(t) = \cos 2t + e^{-3t}, t \geq 0$.

Answer: $\dfrac{2s^2 + 3s + 4}{(s+3)(s^2+4)}$.

TABLE 15.1   Properties of the Laplace transform.

Property	$f(t)$	$F(s)$
Linearity	$a_1 f_1(t) + a_2 f_2(t)$	$a_1 F_1(s) + a_2 F_2(s)$
Scaling	$f(at)$	$\frac{1}{a} F\left(\frac{s}{a}\right)$
Time shift	$f(t-a)u(t-a)$	$e^{-as} F(s)$
Frequency shift	$e^{-at} f(t)$	$F(s+a)$
Time differentiation	$\frac{df}{dt}$	$sF(s) - f(0^-)$
	$\frac{d^2 f}{dt^2}$	$s^2 F(s) - sf(0^-) - f'(0^-)$
	$\frac{d^3 f}{dt^3}$	$s^3 F(s) - s^2 f(0^-) - sf'(0^-) - f''(0^-)$
	$\frac{d^n f}{dt^n}$	$s^n F(s) - s^{n-1} f(0^-) - s^{n-2} f'(0^-) - \cdots - f^{(n-1)}(0^-)$
Time integration	$\int_0^t f(t)\,dt$	$\frac{1}{s} F(s)$
Frequency differentiation	$tf(t)$	$-\frac{d}{ds} F(s)$
Frequency integration	$\frac{f(t)}{t}$	$\int_s^\infty F(s)\,ds$
Time periodicity	$f(t) = f(t+nT)$	$\frac{F_1(s)}{1 - e^{-sT}}$
Initial value	$f(0^+)$	$\lim_{s \to \infty} sF(s)$
Final value	$f(\infty)$	$\lim_{s \to 0} sF(s)$
Convolution	$f_1(t) * f_1(t)$	$F_1(s) F_2(s)$

TABLE 15.2   Laplace transform pairs.*

$f(t)$	$F(s)$
$\delta(t)$	1
$u(t)$	$\frac{1}{s}$
e^{-at}	$\frac{1}{s+a}$
t	$\frac{1}{s^2}$
t^n	$\frac{n!}{s^{n+1}}$
te^{-at}	$\frac{1}{(s+a)^2}$
$t^n e^{-at}$	$\frac{n!}{(s+a)^{n+1}}$
$\sin \omega t$	$\frac{\omega}{s^2 + \omega^2}$
$\cos \omega t$	$\frac{s}{s^2 + \omega^2}$
$\sin(\omega t + \theta)$	$\frac{s \sin\theta + \omega\cos\theta}{s^2 + \omega^2}$
$\cos(\omega t + \theta)$	$\frac{s \cos\theta - \omega\sin\theta}{s^2 + \omega^2}$
$e^{-at} \sin \omega t$	$\frac{\omega}{(s+a)^2 + \omega^2}$
$e^{-at} \cos \omega t$	$\frac{s+a}{(s+a)^2 + \omega^2}$

*Defined for $t \geq 0$, $f(t) = 0$ for $t < 0$.

EXAMPLE 15.4

Determine the Laplace transform of $f(t) = t^2 \sin 2t\, u(t)$.

Solution:

We know that
$$\mathcal{L}[\sin 2t] = \frac{2}{s^2 + 2^2}$$

Using frequency differentiation in Eq. (15.34),

$$F(s) = \mathcal{L}[t^2 \sin 2t] = (-1)^2 \frac{d^2}{ds^2}\left(\frac{2}{s^2 + 4}\right)$$
$$= \frac{d}{ds}\left(\frac{-4s}{(s^2 + 4)^2}\right) = \frac{12s^2 - 16}{(s^2 + 4)^3}$$

PRACTICE PROBLEM 15.4

Find the Laplace transform of $f(t) = t^2 \cos 3t \, u(t)$.

Answer: $\dfrac{2s(s^2 - 27)}{(s^2 + 9)^3}$.

EXAMPLE 15.5

Figure 15.5   The gate function; for Example 15.5.

Find the Laplace transform of the gate function in Fig. 15.5.

Solution:

We can express the gate function in Fig. 15.5 as

$$g(t) = 10[u(t - 2) - u(t - 3)]$$

Since we know the Laplace transform of $u(t)$, we apply the time-shift property and obtain

$$G(s) = 10\left(\frac{e^{-2s}}{s} - \frac{e^{-3s}}{s}\right) = \frac{10}{s}(e^{-2s} - e^{-3s})$$

PRACTICE PROBLEM 15.5

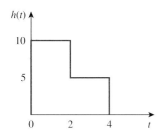

Figure 15.6   For Practice Prob. 15.5.

Find the Laplace transform of the function $h(t)$ in Fig. 15.6.

Answer: $\dfrac{5}{s}(2 - e^{-2s} - e^{-4s})$.

EXAMPLE 15.6

Figure 15.7   For Example 15.6.

Calculate the Laplace transform of the periodic function in Fig. 15.7.

Solution:

The period of the function is $T = 2$. To apply Eq. (15.40), we first obtain the transform of the first period of the function.

$$f_1(t) = 2t[u(t) - u(t - 1)] = 2tu(t) - 2tu(t - 1)$$
$$= 2tu(t) - 2(t - 1 + 1)u(t - 1)$$
$$= 2tu(t) - 2(t - 1)u(t - 1) - 2u(t - 1)$$

Using the time-shift property,

$$F_1(s) = \frac{2}{s^2} - 2\frac{e^{-s}}{s^2} - \frac{2}{s}e^{-s} = \frac{2}{s^2}(1 - e^{-s} - se^{-s})$$

Thus, the transform of the periodic function in Fig. 15.7 is

$$F(s) = \frac{F_1(s)}{1 - e^{-Ts}} = \frac{2}{s^2(1 - e^{-2s})}(1 - e^{-s} - se^{-s})$$

PRACTICE PROBLEM 15.6

Determine the Laplace transform of the periodic function in Fig. 15.8.

Answer: $\dfrac{1 - e^{-2s}}{s(1 - e^{-5s})}$.

Figure 15.8   For Practice Prob. 15.6.

EXAMPLE 15.7

Find the initial and final values of the function whose Laplace transform is

$$H(s) = \frac{20}{(s + 3)(s^2 + 8s + 25)}$$

Solution:

Applying the initial-value theorem,

$$h(0) = \lim_{s \to \infty} sH(s) = \lim_{s \to \infty} \frac{20s}{(s + 3)(s^2 + 8s + 25)}$$

$$= \lim_{s \to \infty} \frac{20/s^2}{(1 + 3/s)(1 + 8/s + 25/s^2)} = \frac{0}{(1 + 0)(1 + 0 + 0)} = 0$$

To be sure that the final-value theorem is applicable, we check where the poles of $H(s)$ are located. The poles of $H(s)$ are $s = -3, -4 \pm j3$, which all have negative real parts: they are all located on the left half of the s plane (Fig. 15.9). Hence the final-value theorem applies and

$$h(\infty) = \lim_{s \to 0} sH(s) = \lim_{s \to 0} \frac{20s}{(s + 3)(s^2 + 8s + 25)}$$

$$= \frac{0}{(0 + 3)(0 + 0 + 25)} = 0$$

Both the initial and final values could be determined from $h(t)$ if we knew it. See Example 15.11, where $h(t)$ is given.

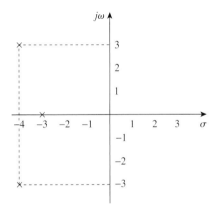

Figure 15.9   For Example 15.7: Poles of $H(s)$.

PRACTICE PROBLEM 15.7

Obtain the initial and the final values of

$$G(s) = \frac{s^3 + 2s + 6}{s(s + 1)^2(s + 3)}$$

Answer: 1, 2.

15.4 THE INVERSE LAPLACE TRANSFORM

Given $F(s)$, how do we transform it back to the time domain and obtain the corresponding $f(t)$? By matching entries in Table 15.2, we avoid using Eq. (15.5) to find $f(t)$.

Suppose $F(s)$ has the general form of

$$F(s) = \frac{N(s)}{D(s)} \tag{15.47}$$

where $N(s)$ is the numerator polynomial and $D(s)$ is the denominator polynomial. The roots of $N(s) = 0$ are called the *zeros* of $F(s)$, while the roots of $D(s) = 0$ are the *poles* of $F(s)$. Although Eq. (15.47) is similar in form to Eq. (14.3), here $F(s)$ is the Laplace transform of a function, which is not necessarily a transfer function. We use *partial fraction expansion* to break $F(s)$ down into simple terms whose inverse transform we obtain from Table 15.2. Thus, finding the inverse Laplace transform of $F(s)$ involves two steps.

> Software packages such as *MATLAB*, Mathcad, and Maple are capable of finding partial fraction expansions quite easily.

Steps to Find the Inverse Laplace Transform:

1. Decompose $F(s)$ into simple terms using partial fraction expansion.

2. Find the inverse of each term by matching entries in Table 15.2.

Let us consider the three possible forms $F(s)$ may take and how to apply the two steps to each form.

15.4.1 Simple Poles

Recall from Chapter 14 that a simple pole is a first-order pole. If $F(s)$ has only simple poles, then $D(s)$ becomes a product of factors, so that

$$F(s) = \frac{N(s)}{(s + p_1)(s + p_2) \cdots (s + p_n)} \tag{15.48}$$

where $s = -p_1, -p_2, \ldots, -p_n$ are the simple poles, and $p_i \neq p_j$ for all $i \neq j$ (i.e., the poles are distinct). Assuming that the degree of $N(s)$ is less than the degree of $D(s)$, we use partial fraction expansion to decompose $F(s)$ in Eq. (15.48) as

> Otherwise, we must first apply long division so that $F(s) = N(s)/D(s) = Q(s) + R(s)/D(s)$, where the degree of $R(s)$, the remainder of the long division, is less than the degree of $D(s)$.

$$F(s) = \frac{k_1}{s + p_1} + \frac{k_2}{s + p_2} + \cdots + \frac{k_n}{s + p_n} \tag{15.49}$$

The expansion coefficients $k_1, k_2, \ldots, k_n$ are known as the *residues* of $F(s)$. There are many ways of finding the expansion coefficients. One way is using the *residue method*. If we multiply both sides of Eq. (15.49) by $(s + p_1)$, we obtain

$$(s + p_1)F(s) = k_1 + \frac{(s + p_1)k_2}{s + p_2} + \cdots + \frac{(s + p_1)k_n}{s + p_n} \tag{15.50}$$

Since $p_i \neq p_j$, setting $s = -p_1$ in Eq. (15.50) leaves only k_1 on the right-hand side of Eq. (15.50). Hence,

$$(s + p_1)F(s) \Big|_{s=-p_1} = k_1 \tag{15.51}$$

Thus, in general,

$$k_i = (s + p_i)F(s) \Big|_{s=-p_i} \tag{15.52}$$

This is known as *Heaviside's theorem*. Once the values of k_i are known, we proceed to find the inverse of $F(s)$ using Eq. (15.49). Since the inverse transform of each term in Eq. (15.49) is $\mathcal{L}^{-1}[k/(s+a)] = ke^{-at}u(t)$, then, from Table 15.2,

$$f(t) = \left(k_1 e^{-p_1 t} + k_2 e^{-p_2 t} + \cdots + k_n e^{-p_n t}\right) u(t) \qquad (15.53)$$

Historical note: Named after Oliver Heaviside (1850–1925), an English engineer, the pioneer of operational calculus.

15.4.2 Repeated Poles

Suppose $F(s)$ has n repeated poles at $s = -p$. Then we may represent $F(s)$ as

$$F(s) = \frac{k_n}{(s+p)^n} + \frac{k_{n-1}}{(s+p)^{n-1}} + \cdots + \frac{k_2}{(s+p)^2}$$
$$+ \frac{k_1}{s+p} + F_1(s) \qquad (15.54)$$

where $F_1(s)$ is the remaining part of $F(s)$ that does not have a pole at $s = -p$. We determine the expansion coefficient k_n as

$$k_n = (s+p)^n F(s) \big|_{s=-p} \qquad (15.55)$$

as we did above. To determine k_{n-1}, we multiply each term in Eq. (15.54) by $(s+p)^n$ and differentiate to get rid of k_n, then evaluate the result at $s = -p$ to get rid of the other coefficients except k_{n-1}. Thus, we obtain

$$k_{n-1} = \frac{d}{ds}[(s+p)^n F(s)] \big|_{s=-p} \qquad (15.56)$$

Repeating this gives

$$k_{n-2} = \frac{1}{2!} \frac{d^2}{ds^2}[(s+p)^n F(s)] \big|_{s=-p} \qquad (15.57)$$

The mth term becomes

$$k_{n-m} = \frac{1}{m!} \frac{d^m}{ds^m}[(s+p)^n F(s)] \big|_{s=-p} \qquad (15.58)$$

where $m = 1, 2, \ldots, n-1$. One can expect the differentiation to be difficult to handle as m increases. Once we obtain the values of $k_1, k_2, \ldots, k_n$ by partial fraction expansion, we apply the inverse transform

$$\mathcal{L}^{-1}\left[\frac{1}{(s+a)^n}\right] = \frac{t^{n-1} e^{-at}}{(n-1)!} u(t) \qquad (15.59)$$

to each term in the right-hand side of Eq. (15.54) and obtain

$$f(t) = \left(k_1 e^{-pt} + k_2 t e^{-pt} + \frac{k_3}{2!} t^2 e^{-pt} \right.$$
$$\left. + \cdots + \frac{k_n}{(n-1)!} t^{n-1} e^{-pt}\right) u(t) + f_1(t) \qquad (15.60)$$

15.4.3 Complex Poles

A pair of complex poles is simple if it is not repeated; it is a double or multiple pole if repeated. Simple complex poles may be handled the same way as simple real poles, but because complex algebra is involved the result is always cumbersome. An easier approach is a method known as *completing the square*. The idea is to express each complex pole pair (or quadratic term) in $D(s)$ as a complete square such as $(s + \alpha)^2 + \beta^2$ and then use Table 15.2 to find the inverse of the term.

Since $N(s)$ and $D(s)$ always have real coefficients and we know that the complex roots of polynomials with real coefficients must occur in conjugate pairs, $F(s)$ may have the general form

$$F(s) = \frac{A_1 s + A_2}{s^2 + as + b} + F_1(s) \tag{15.61}$$

where $F_1(s)$ is the remaining part of $F(s)$ that does not have this pair of complex poles. If we complete the square by letting

$$s^2 + as + b = s^2 + 2\alpha s + \alpha^2 + \beta^2 = (s + \alpha)^2 + \beta^2 \tag{15.62}$$

and we also let

$$A_1 s + A_2 = A_1(s + \alpha) + B_1 \beta \tag{15.63}$$

then Eq. (15.61) becomes

$$F(s) = \frac{A_1(s + \alpha)}{(s + \alpha)^2 + \beta^2} + \frac{B_1 \beta}{(s + \alpha)^2 + \beta^2} + F_1(s) \tag{15.64}$$

From Table 15.2, the inverse transform is

$$\boxed{f(t) = \left(A_1 e^{-\alpha t} \cos \beta t + B_1 e^{-\alpha t} \sin \beta t\right) u(t) + f_1(t)} \tag{15.65}$$

The sine and cosine terms can be combined using Eq. (9.11).

Whether the pole is simple, repeated, or complex, a general approach that can always be used in finding the expansion coefficients is the *method of algebra*, illustrated in Examples 15.9 to 15.11. To apply the method, we first set $F(s) = N(s)/D(s)$ equal to an expansion containing unknown constants. We multiply the result through by a common denominator. Then we determine the unknown constants by equating coefficients (i.e., by algebraically solving a set of simultaneous equations for these coefficients at like powers of s).

Another general approach is to substitute specific, convenient values of s to obtain as many simultaneous equations as the number of unknown coefficients, and then solve for the unknown coefficients. We must make sure that each selected value of s is not one of the poles of $F(s)$. Example 15.11 illustrates this idea.

EXAMPLE 15.8

Find the inverse Laplace transform of

$$F(s) = \frac{3}{s} - \frac{5}{s+1} + \frac{6}{s^2+4}$$

Solution:

The inverse transform is given by

$$f(t) = \mathcal{L}^{-1}[F(s)] = \mathcal{L}^{-1}\left(\frac{3}{s}\right) - \mathcal{L}^{-1}\left(\frac{5}{s+1}\right) + \mathcal{L}^{-1}\left(\frac{6}{s^2+4}\right)$$

$$= (3 - 5e^{-t} + 3\sin 2t)u(t), \qquad t \geq 0$$

where Table 15.2 has been consulted for the inverse of each term.

PRACTICE PROBLEM 15.8

Determine the inverse Laplace transform of

$$F(s) = 1 + \frac{4}{s+3} - \frac{5s}{s^2+16}$$

Answer: $\delta(t) + (4e^{-3t} - 5\cos 4t)u(t), t \geq 0.$

EXAMPLE 15.9

Find $f(t)$ given that

$$F(s) = \frac{s^2 + 12}{s(s+2)(s+3)}$$

Solution:

Unlike in the previous example where the partial fractions have been provided, we first need to determine the partial fractions. Since there are three poles, we let

$$\frac{s^2 + 12}{s(s+2)(s+3)} = \frac{A}{s} + \frac{B}{s+2} + \frac{C}{s+3} \qquad (15.9.1)$$

where A, B, and C are the constants to be determined. We can find the constants using two approaches.

METHOD 1   **Residue method:**

$$A = sF(s)\,\Big|_{s=0} = \frac{s^2 + 12}{(s+2)(s+3)}\,\Big|_{s=0} = \frac{12}{(2)(3)} = 2$$

$$B = (s+2)F(s)\,\Big|_{s=-2} = \frac{s^2 + 12}{s(s+3)}\,\Big|_{s=-2} = \frac{4 + 12}{(-2)(1)} = -8$$

$$C = (s+3)F(s)\,\Big|_{s=-3} = \frac{s^2 + 12}{s(s+2)}\,\Big|_{s=-3} = \frac{9 + 12}{(-3)(-1)} = 7$$

METHOD **2** **Algebraic method:** Multiplying both sides of Eq. (15.9.1) by $s(s+2)(s+3)$ gives

$$s^2 + 12 = A(s+2)(s+3) + Bs(s+3) + Cs(s+2)$$

or

$$s^2 + 12 = A(s^2 + 5s + 6) + B(s^2 + 3s) + C(s^2 + 2s)$$

Equating the coefficients of like powers of s gives

Constant: $\quad 12 = 6A \quad \Longrightarrow \quad A = 2$

$s:\qquad\qquad 0 = 5A + 3B + 2C \quad \Longrightarrow \quad 3B + 2C = -10$

$s^2:\qquad\qquad 1 = A + B + C \quad \Longrightarrow \quad B + C = -1$

Thus $A = 2$, $B = -8$, $C = 7$, and Eq. (15.9.1) becomes

$$F(s) = \frac{2}{s} - \frac{8}{s+2} + \frac{7}{s+3}$$

By finding the inverse transform of each term, we obtain

$$f(t) = (2 - 8e^{-2t} + 7e^{-3t})u(t), \qquad t \geq 0.$$

PRACTICE PROBLEM 15.9

Find $f(t)$ if

$$F(s) = \frac{6(s+2)}{(s+1)(s+3)(s+4)}$$

Answer: $f(t) = (e^{-t} + 3e^{-3t} - 4e^{-4t})u(t), t \geq 0.$

EXAMPLE 15.10

Calculate $v(t)$ given that

$$V(s) = \frac{10s^2 + 4}{s(s+1)(s+2)^2}$$

Solution:

While the previous example is on simple roots, this example is on repeated roots. Let

$$V(s) = \frac{10s^2 + 4}{s(s+1)(s+2)^2}$$

$$= \frac{A}{s} + \frac{B}{s+1} + \frac{C}{(s+2)^2} + \frac{D}{s+2}$$

(15.10.1)

METHOD **1**   **Residue method:**

$$A = sV(s) \Big|_{s=0} = \frac{10s^2 + 4}{(s+1)(s+2)^2} \Big|_{s=0} = \frac{4}{(1)(2)^2} = 1$$

$$B = (s+1)V(s) \Big|_{s=-1} = \frac{10s^2 + 4}{s(s+2)^2} \Big|_{s=-1} = \frac{14}{(-1)(1)^2} = -14$$

$$C = (s+2)^2 V(s) \Big|_{s=-2} = \frac{10s^2 + 4}{s(s+1)} \Big|_{s=-2} = \frac{44}{(-2)(-1)} = 22$$

$$D = \frac{d}{ds}[(s+2)^2 V(s)] \Big|_{s=-2} = \frac{d}{ds}\left(\frac{10s^2 + 4}{s^2 + s}\right) \Big|_{s=-2}$$

$$= \frac{(s^2 + s)(20s) - (10s^2 + 4)(2s + 1)}{(s^2 + s)^2} \Big|_{s=-2} = \frac{52}{4} = 13$$

METHOD **2**   **Algebraic method:** Multiplying Eq. (15.10.1) by $s(s+1)(s+2)^2$, we obtain

$$10s^2 + 4 = A(s+1)(s+2)^2 + Bs(s+2)^2$$
$$+ Cs(s+1) + Ds(s+1)(s+2)$$

or

$$10s^2 + 4 = A(s^3 + 5s^2 + 8s + 4) + B(s^3 + 4s^2 + 4s)$$
$$+ C(s^2 + s) + D(s^3 + 3s^2 + 2s)$$

Equating coefficients,

Constant: $4 = 4A$ $\implies$ $A = 1$

s: $0 = 8A + 4B + C + 2D$ $\implies$ $4B + C + 2D = -8$

s^2: $10 = 5A + 4B + C + 3D$ $\implies$ $4B + C + 3D = 5$

s^3: $0 = A + B + D$ $\implies$ $B + D = -1$

Solving these simultaneous equations gives $A = 1$, $B = -14$, $C = 22$, $D = 13$, so that

$$V(s) = \frac{1}{s} - \frac{14}{s+1} + \frac{13}{s+2} + \frac{22}{(s+2)^2}$$

Taking the inverse transform of each term, we get

$$v(t) = (1 - 14e^{-t} + 13e^{-2t} + 22te^{-2t})u(t), \qquad t \geq 0$$

PRACTICE PROBLEM 15.10

Obtain $g(t)$ if

$$G(s) = \frac{s^3 + 2s + 6}{s(s+1)^2(s+3)}$$

Answer: $(2 - 3.25e^{-t} - 1.5te^{-t} + 2.25e^{-3t})u(t), t \geq 0.$

EXAMPLE 15.11

Find the inverse transform of the frequency-domain function in Example 15.7:

$$H(s) = \frac{20}{(s+3)(s^2+8s+25)}$$

Solution:

In this example, $H(s)$ has a pair of complex poles at $s^2+8s+25=0$ or $s = -4 \pm j3$. We let

$$H(s) = \frac{20}{(s+3)(s^2+8s+25)} = \frac{A}{s+3} + \frac{Bs+C}{(s^2+8s+25)} \quad (15.11.1)$$

We now determine the expansion coefficients in two ways.

METHOD 1 **Combination of methods:** We can obtain A using the method of residue,

$$A = (s+3)H(s)\Big|_{s=-3} = \frac{20}{s^2+8s+25}\Big|_{s=-3} = \frac{20}{10} = 2$$

Although B and C can be obtained using the method of residue, we will not do so, to avoid complex algebra. Rather, we can substitute two specific values of s [say $s = 0, 1$, which are not poles of $F(s)$] into Eq. (15.11.1). This will give us two simultaneous equations from which to find B and C. If we let $s = 0$ in Eq. (15.11.1), we obtain

$$\frac{20}{75} = \frac{A}{3} + \frac{C}{25}$$

or

$$20 = 25A + 3C \quad (15.11.2)$$

Since $A = 2$, Eq. (15.11.2) gives $C = -10$. Substituting $s = 1$ into Eq. (15.11.1) gives

$$\frac{20}{(4)(34)} = \frac{A}{4} + \frac{B+C}{34}$$

or

$$20 = 34A + 4B + 4C \quad (15.11.3)$$

But $A = 2$, $C = -10$, so that Eq. (15.11.3) gives $B = -2$.

METHOD 2 **Algebraic method:** Multiplying both sides of Eq. (15.11.1) by $(s+3)(s^2+8s+25)$ yields

$$\begin{aligned} 20 &= A(s^2+8s+25) + (Bs+C)(s+3) \\ &= A(s^2+8s+25) + B(s^2+3s) + C(s+3) \end{aligned} \quad (15.11.4)$$

Equating coefficients,

$$s^2: \qquad 0 = A + B \qquad \Longrightarrow \qquad A = -B$$
$$s: \qquad 0 = 8A + 3B + C = 5A + C \qquad \Longrightarrow \qquad C = -5A$$
$$\text{Constant:} \quad 20 = 25A + 3C = 25A - 15A \qquad \Longrightarrow \qquad A = 2$$

That is, $B = -2$, $C = -10$. Thus

$$H(s) = \frac{2}{s+3} - \frac{2s+10}{(s^2+8s+25)} = \frac{2}{s+3} - \frac{2(s+4)+2}{(s+4)^2+9}$$

$$= \frac{2}{s+3} - \frac{2(s+4)}{(s+4)^2+9} - \frac{2}{3}\frac{3}{(s+4)^2+9}$$

Taking the inverse of each term, we obtain

$$h(t) = (2e^{-3t} - 2e^{-4t}\cos 3t - \frac{2}{3}e^{-4t}\sin 3t)u(t) \qquad (15.11.5)$$

It is alright to leave the result this way. However, we can combine the cosine and sine terms as

$$h(t) = (2e^{-3t} - Re^{-4t}\cos(3t - \theta))u(t) \qquad (15.11.6)$$

To obtain Eq. (15.11.6) from Eq. (15.11.5), we apply Eq. (9.11). Next, we determine the coefficient R and the phase angle θ:

$$R = \sqrt{2^2 + \left(\frac{2}{3}\right)^2} = 2.108, \qquad \theta = \tan^{-1}\frac{\frac{2}{3}}{2} = 18.43°$$

Thus,

$$h(t) = (2e^{-3t} - 2.108e^{-4t}\cos(3t - 18.43°))u(t)$$

PRACTICE PROBLEM 15.11

Find $g(t)$ given that

$$G(s) = \frac{10}{(s+1)(s^2+4s+13)}$$

Answer: $e^{-t} - e^{-2t}\cos 3t + \frac{1}{3}e^{-2t}\sin 3t, t \geq 0$.

15.5 THE CONVOLUTION INTEGRAL

The term *convolution* means "folding." Convolution is an invaluable tool to the engineer because it provides a means of viewing and characterizing physical systems. For example, it is used in finding the response $y(t)$ of a system to an excitation $x(t)$, knowing the system impulse response $h(t)$. This is achieved through the *convolution integral*, defined as

$$y(t) = \int_{-\infty}^{\infty} x(\lambda)h(t - \lambda)\,d\lambda \qquad (15.66)$$

or simply

$$y(t) = x(t) * h(t) \qquad (15.67)$$

where λ is a dummy variable and the asterisk denotes convolution. Equation (15.66) or (15.67) states that the output is equal to the input convolved with the unit impulse response. The convolution process is commutative:

$$y(t) = x(t) * h(t) = h(t) * x(t) \qquad (15.68a)$$

or

$$y(t) = \int_{-\infty}^{\infty} x(\lambda)h(t - \lambda)\,d\lambda = \int_{-\infty}^{\infty} h(\lambda)x(t - \lambda)\,d\lambda \qquad (15.68b)$$

This implies that the order in which the two functions are convolved is immaterial. We will see shortly how to take advantage of this commutative property when performing graphical computation of the convolution integral.

> The convolution of two signals consists of time-reversing one of the signals, shifting it, and multiplying it point by point with the second signal, and integrating the product.

The convolution integral in Eq. (15.66) is the general one; it applies to any linear system. However, the convolution integral can be simplified if we assume that a system has two properties. First, if $x(t) = 0$ for $t < 0$, then

$$y(t) = \int_{-\infty}^{\infty} x(\lambda) h(t - \lambda) \, d\lambda = \int_{0}^{\infty} x(\lambda) h(t - \lambda) \, d\lambda \qquad (15.69)$$

Second, if the system's impulse response is *causal* (i.e., $h(t) = 0$ for $t < 0$), then $h(t - \lambda) = 0$ for $t - \lambda < 0$ or $\lambda > t$, so that Eq. (15.69) becomes

$$y(t) = h(t) * x(t) = \int_{0}^{t} x(\lambda) h(t - \lambda) \, d\lambda \qquad (15.70)$$

Here are some properties of the convolution integral.

1. $x(t) * h(t) = h(t) * x(t)$ (Commutative)
2. $f(t) * [x(t) + y(t)] = f(t) * x(t) + f(t) * y(t)$ (Distributive)
3. $f(t) * [x(t) * y(t)] = [f(t) * x(t)] * y(t)$ (Associative)
4. $f(t) * \delta(t) = \int_{-\infty}^{\infty} f(\lambda) \delta(t - \lambda) \, d\lambda = f(t)$
5. $f(t) * \delta(t - t_o) = f(t - t_o)$
6. $f(t) * \delta'(t) = \int_{-\infty}^{\infty} f(\lambda) \delta'(t - \lambda) \, d\lambda = f'(t)$
7. $f(t) * u(t) = \int_{-\infty}^{\infty} f(\lambda) u(t - \lambda) \, d\lambda = \int_{-\infty}^{t} f(\lambda) \, d\lambda$

Before learning how to evaluate the convolution integral in Eq. (15.70), let us establish the link between the Laplace transform and the convolution integral. Given two functions $f_1(t)$ and $f_2(t)$ with Laplace transforms $F_1(s)$ and $F_2(s)$, respectively, their convolution is

$$f(t) = f_1(t) * f_2(t) = \int_{0}^{t} f_1(\lambda) f_2(t - \lambda) \, d\lambda \qquad (15.71)$$

Taking the Laplace transform gives

$$F(s) = \mathcal{L}[f_1(t) * f_2(t)] = F_1(s) F_2(s) \qquad (15.72)$$

To prove that Eq. (15.72) is true, we begin with the fact that $F_1(s)$ is defined as

$$F_1(s) = \int_{0^-}^{\infty} f_1(\lambda)e^{-s\lambda} \, d\lambda \qquad (15.73)$$

Multiplying this with $F_2(s)$ gives

$$F_1(s)F_2(s) = \int_{0^-}^{\infty} f_1(\lambda)[F_2(s)e^{-s\lambda}] \, d\lambda \qquad (15.74)$$

We recall from the time shift property in Eq. (15.17) that the term in brackets can be written as

$$F_2(s)e^{-s\lambda} = \mathcal{L}[f_2(t - \lambda)u(t - \lambda)]$$

$$= \int_{0^-}^{\infty} f_2(t - \lambda)u(t - \lambda)e^{-s\lambda} \, dt \qquad (15.75)$$

Substituting Eq. (15.75) into Eq. (15.74) gives

$$F_1(s)F_2(s) = \int_{0^-}^{\infty} f_1(\lambda) \left[\int_{0^-}^{\infty} f_2(t - \lambda)u(t - \lambda)e^{-s\lambda} \, dt \right] d\lambda \quad (15.76)$$

Interchanging the order of integration results in

$$F_1(s)F_2(s) = \int_{0^-}^{\infty} \left[\int_{0^-}^{t} f_1(\lambda) f_2(t - \lambda) \, d\lambda \right] e^{-s\lambda} \, dt \qquad (15.77)$$

The integral in brackets extends only from 0 to t because the delayed unit step $u(t - \lambda) = 1$ for $\lambda < t$ and $u(t - \lambda) = 0$ for $\lambda > t$. We notice that the integral is the convolution of $f_1(t)$ and $f_2(t)$ as in Eq. (15.71). Hence,

$$\boxed{F_1(s)F_s(s) = \mathcal{L}[f_1(t) * f_2(t)]} \qquad (15.78)$$

as desired. This indicates that convolution in the time domain is equivalent to multiplication in the s domain. For example, if $x(t) = 4e^{-t}$ and $h(t) = 5e^{-2t}$, applying the property in Eq. (15.78), we get

$$h(t) * x(t) = \mathcal{L}^{-1}[H(s)X(s)] = \mathcal{L}^{-1} \left[\left(\frac{5}{s + 2} \right) \left(\frac{4}{s + 1} \right) \right]$$

$$= \mathcal{L}^{-1} \left[\frac{20}{s + 1} + \frac{-20}{s + 2} \right] \qquad (15.79)$$

$$= 20(e^{-t} - e^{-2t}), \qquad t \geq 0$$

Although we can find the convolution of two signals using Eq. (15.78), as we have just done, if the product $F_1(s)F_2(s)$ is very complicated, finding the inverse may be tough. Also, there are situations in which $f_1(t)$ and $f_2(t)$ are available in the form of experimental data and there are no explicit Laplace transforms. In these cases, one must do the convolution in the time domain.

The process of convolving two signals in the time domain is better appreciated from a graphical point of view. The graphical procedure for evaluating the convolution integral in Eq. (15.70) usually involves four steps.

Steps to evaluate the convolution integral:

1. Folding: Take the mirror image of $h(\lambda)$ about the ordinate axis to obtain $h(-\lambda)$.

2. Displacement: Shift or delay $h(-\lambda)$ by t to obtain $h(t - \lambda)$.

3. Multiplication: Find the product of $h(t - \lambda)$ and $x(\lambda)$.

4. Integration: For a given time t, calculate the area under the product $h(t - \lambda)x(\lambda)$ for $0 < \lambda < t$ to get $y(t)$ at t.

The folding operation in step 1 is the reason for the term *convolution*. The function $h(t - \lambda)$ scans or slides over $x(\lambda)$. In view of this superposition procedure, the convolution integral is also known as the *superposition integral*.

To apply the four steps, it is necessary to be able to sketch $x(\lambda)$ and $h(t - \lambda)$. To get $x(\lambda)$ from the original function $x(t)$ involves merely replacing t with λ. Sketching $h(t - \lambda)$ is the key to the convolution process. It involves reflecting $h(\lambda)$ about the vertical axis and shifting it by t. Analytically, we obtain $h(t - \lambda)$ by replacing every t in $h(t)$ by $t - \lambda$. Since convolution is commutative, it may be more convenient to apply steps 1 and 2 to $x(t)$ instead of $h(t)$. The best way to illustrate the procedure is with some examples.

EXAMPLE 15.12

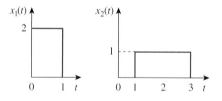

Figure 15.10   For Example 15.12.

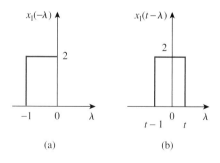

(a)   (b)

Figure 15.11   (a) Folding $x_1(\lambda)$, (b) shifting $x_1(-\lambda)$ by t.

Find the convolution of the two signals in Fig. 15.10.

Solution:

We follow the four steps to get $y(t) = x_1(t) * x_2(t)$. First, we fold $x_1(t)$ as shown in Fig. 15.11(a) and shift it by t as shown in Fig. 15.11(b). For different values of t, we now multiply the two functions and integrate to determine the area of the overlapping region.

For $0 < t < 1$, there is no overlap of the two functions, as shown in Fig. 15.12(a). Hence,

$$y(t) = x_1(t) * x_2(t) = 0, \qquad 0 < t < 1 \qquad (15.12.1)$$

For $1 < t < 2$, the two signals overlap between 1 and t, as shown in Fig. 15.12(b).

$$y(t) = \int_1^t (2)(1)\, d\lambda = 2\lambda \Big|_1^t = 2(t - 1), \qquad 1 < t < 2 \qquad (15.12.2)$$

For $2 < t < 3$, the two signals completely overlap between $(t - 1)$ and t, as shown in Fig. 15.12(c). It is easy to see that the area under the curve is 2. Or

$$y(t) = \int_{t-1}^t (2)(1)\, d\lambda = 2\lambda \Big|_{t-1}^t = 2, \qquad 2 < t < 3 \qquad (15.12.3)$$

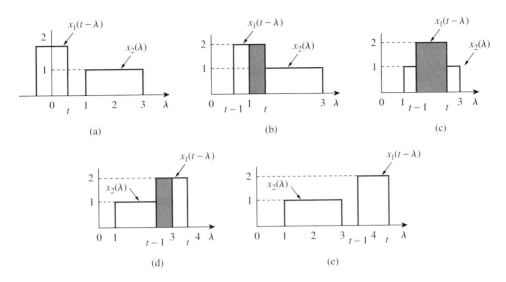

Figure 15.12   Overlapping of $x_1(t - \lambda)$ and $x_2(\lambda)$ for: (a) $0 < t < 1$, (b) $1 < t < 2$, (c) $2 < t < 3$, (d) $3 < t < 4$, (e) $t > 4$.

For $3 < t < 4$, the two signals overlap between $(t - 1)$ and 3, as shown in Fig. 15.12(d).

$$y(t) = \int_{t-1}^{3} (2)(1) \, d\lambda = 2\lambda \Big|_{t-1}^{3} \qquad (15.12.4)$$

$$= 2(3 - t + 1) = 8 - 2t, \qquad 3 < t < 4$$

For $t > 4$, the two signals do not overlap [Fig. 15.12(e)], and

$$y(t) = 0, \qquad t > 4 \qquad (15.12.5)$$

Combining Eqs. (15.12.1) to (15.12.5), we obtain

$$y(t) = \begin{cases} 0, & 0 \le t \le 1 \\ 2t - 2, & 1 \le t \le 2 \\ 2, & 2 \le t \le 3 \\ 8 - 2t, & 3 \le t \le 4 \\ 0, & t \ge 4 \end{cases} \qquad (15.12.6)$$

which is sketched in Fig. 15.13. Notice that $y(t)$ in this equation is continuous. This fact can be used to check the results as we move from one range of t to another. The result in Eq. (15.12.6) can be obtained without using the graphical procedure—by directly using Eq. (15.70) and the properties of step functions. This will be illustrated in Example 15.14.

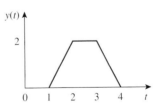

Figure 15.13   Convolution of signals $x_1(t)$ and $x_2(t)$ in Fig. 15.10.

PRACTICE PROBLEM 15.12

Graphically convolve the two functions in Fig. 15.14.

Answer: The result of the convolution $y(t)$ is shown in Fig. 15.15, where

$$y(t) = \begin{cases} t, & 0 \le t \le 2 \\ 6 - 2t, & 2 \le t \le 3 \\ 0, & \text{otherwise} \end{cases}$$

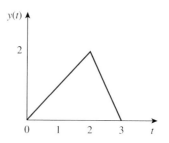

Figure 15.14   For Practice Prob. 15.12.

Figure 15.15   Convolution of the signals in Fig. 15.14.

EXAMPLE 15.13

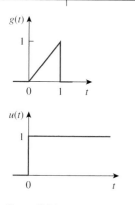

Figure 15.16   For Example 15.13.

Graphically convolve $g(t)$ and $u(t)$ shown in Fig. 15.16.

Solution:

Let $y(t) = g(t) * u(t)$. We can find $y(t)$ in two ways.

METHOD 1   Suppose we fold $g(t)$, as in Fig. 15.17(a), and shift it by t, as in Fig. 15.17(b). Since $g(t) = t, 0 < t < 1$ originally, we expect that $g(t - \lambda) = t - \lambda, 0 < t - \lambda < 1$ or $t - 1 < \lambda < t$. There is no overlap of the two functions when $t < 0$ so that $y(0) = 0$ for this case.

Figure 15.17   Convolution of $g(t)$ and $u(t)$ in Fig. 15.16 with $g(t)$ folded.

For $0 < t < 1$, $g(t - \lambda)$ and $u(\lambda)$ overlap from 0 to t, as evident in Fig. 15.17(b). Therefore,

$$y(t) = \int_0^t (1)(t - \lambda)\, d\lambda = \left(t\lambda - \frac{1}{2}\lambda^2\right)\bigg|_0^t$$

$$= t^2 - \frac{t^2}{2} = \frac{t^2}{2}, \qquad 0 \le t \le 1 \tag{15.13.1}$$

For $t > 1$, the two functions overlap completely between $(t - 1)$ and t [see Fig. 15.17(c)]. Hence,

$$y(t) = \int_{t-1}^t (1)(t - \lambda)\, d\lambda$$

$$= \left(t\lambda - \frac{1}{2}\lambda^2\right)\bigg|_{t-1}^t = \frac{1}{2}, \qquad t \ge 1 \tag{15.13.2}$$

Thus, from Eqs. (15.13.1) and (15.13.2),

$$y(t) = \begin{cases} \dfrac{1}{2}t^2, & 0 \le t \le 1 \\ \dfrac{1}{2}, & t \ge 1 \end{cases}$$

METHOD 2 Instead of folding g, suppose we fold the unit step function $u(t)$, as in Fig. 15.18(a), and then shift it by t, as in Fig. 15.18(b). Since $u(t) = 1$ for $t > 0$, $u(t - \lambda) = 1$ for $t - \lambda > 0$ or $\lambda < t$, the two functions overlap from 0 to t, so that

$$y(t) = \int_0^t (1)\lambda \, d\lambda = \frac{1}{2}\lambda^2 \Big|_0^t = \frac{t^2}{2}, \qquad 0 \le t \le 1 \qquad (15.13.3)$$

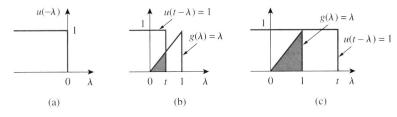

Figure 15.18   Convolution of $g(t)$ and $u(t)$ in Fig. 15.16 with $u(t)$ folded.

For $t > 1$, the two functions overlap between 0 and 1, as shown in Fig. 15.18(c). Hence,

$$y(t) = \int_0^1 (1)\lambda \, d\lambda = \frac{1}{2}\lambda^2 \Big|_0^1 = \frac{1}{2}, \qquad t \ge 1 \qquad (15.13.4)$$

And, from Eqs. (15.13.3) and (15.13.4),

$$y(t) = \begin{cases} \dfrac{1}{2}t^2, & 0 \le t \le 1 \\ \dfrac{1}{2}, & t \ge 1 \end{cases}$$

Although the two methods give the same result, as expected, notice that it is more convenient to fold the unit step function $u(t)$ than fold $g(t)$ in this example. Figure 15.19 shows $y(t)$.

Figure 15.19   Result of Example 15.13.

PRACTICE PROBLEM 15.13

Given $g(t)$ and $f(t)$ in Fig. 15.20, graphically find $y(t) = g(t) * f(t)$.

Answer: $y(t) = \begin{cases} 3(1 - e^{-t}), & 0 \le t \le 1 \\ 3(e - 1)e^{-t}, & t \ge 1 \\ 0, & \text{elsewhere} \end{cases}$

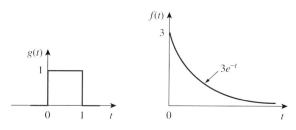

Figure 15.20   For Practice Prob. 15.13.

EXAMPLE 15.14

(a)

(b)

Figure 15.21   For Example 15.14.

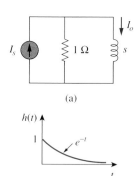

(a)

(b)

Figure 15.22   For the circuit in Fig. 15.21(a): (a) its s-domain equivalent, (b) its impulse response.

For the RL circuit in Fig. 15.21(a), use the convolution integral to find the response $i_o(t)$ due to the excitation shown in Fig. 15.21(b).

Solution:

This problem can be solved in two ways: directly using the convolution integral or using the graphical technique. To use either approach, we first need the unit impulse response $h(t)$ of the circuit. In the s domain, applying the current division principle to the circuit in Fig. 15.22(a) gives

$$I_o = \frac{1}{s+1} I_s$$

Hence,

$$H(s) = \frac{I_o}{I_s} = \frac{1}{s+1} \tag{15.14.1}$$

and the inverse Laplace transform of this gives

$$h(t) = e^{-t} u(t) \tag{15.14.2}$$

Figure 15.22(b) shows the impulse response $h(t)$ of the circuit.

METHOD 1   To use the convolution integral directly, recall that the response is given in the s domain as

$$I_o(s) = H(s) I_s(s)$$

With the given $i_s(t)$ in Fig. 15.21(b),

$$i_s(t) = u(t) - u(t-2)$$

so that

$$i_o(t) = h(t) * i_s(t) = \int_0^t i_s(\lambda) h(t-\lambda)\, d\lambda$$

$$= \int_0^t [u(\lambda) - u(\lambda - 2)] e^{-(t-\lambda)}\, d\lambda \tag{15.14.3}$$

Since $u(\lambda - 2) = 0$ for $0 < \lambda < 2$, the integrand involving $u(\lambda)$ is nonzero for all $\lambda > 0$, whereas the integrand involving $u(\lambda - 2)$ is nonzero only for $\lambda > 2$. The best way to handle the integral is to do the two parts separately. For $0 < t < 2$,

$$i_o'(t) = \int_0^t (1)e^{-(t-\lambda)}\,d\lambda = e^{-t}\int_0^t (1)e^{\lambda}\,d\lambda \tag{15.14.4}$$

$$= e^{-t}(e^t - 1) = 1 - e^{-t}, \qquad 0 < t < 2$$

For $t > 2$,

$$i_o''(t) = \int_2^t (1)e^{-(t-\lambda)}\,d\lambda = e^{-t}\int_2^t e^{\lambda}\,d\lambda \tag{15.14.5}$$

$$= e^{-t}(e^t - e^2) = 1 - e^2 e^{-t}, \qquad t > 2$$

Substituting Eqs. (15.14.4) and (15.14.5) into Eq. (15.14.3) gives

$$i_o(t) = i_o'(t) - i_o''(t)$$

$$= (1 - e^{-t})[u(t-2) - u(t)] - (1 - e^2 e^{-t})u(t-2) \tag{15.14.6}$$

$$= \begin{cases} 1 - e^{-t}\ \text{A}, & 0 < t < 2 \\ (e^2 - 1)e^{-t}\ \text{A}, & t > 2 \end{cases}$$

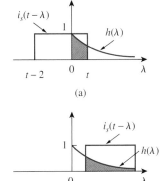

(a)

$\boxed{\text{METHOD } \mathbf{2}}$ To use the graphical technique, we may fold $i_s(t)$ in Fig. 15.21(b) and shift by t, as shown in Fig. 15.23(a). For $0 < t < 2$, the overlap between $i_s(t - \lambda)$ and $h(\lambda)$ is from 0 to t, so that

$$i_o(t) = \int_0^t (1)e^{-\lambda}\,d\lambda = -e^{-\lambda}\Big|_0^t = 1 - e^{-t}, \qquad 0 \le t \le 2 \tag{15.14.7}$$

For $t > 2$, the two functions overlap between $(t - 2)$ and t, as in Fig. 15.23(b). Hence

$$i_o(t) = \int_{t-2}^t (1)e^{-\lambda}\,d\lambda = -e^{-\lambda}\Big|_{t-2}^t = -e^{-t} + e^{-(t-2)} \tag{15.14.8}$$

$$= (e^2 - 1)e^{-t}, \qquad t \ge 0$$

(b)

Figure 15.23   For Example 15.14.

From Eqs. (15.14.7) and (15.14.8), the response is

$$i_o(t) = \begin{cases} 1 - e^{-t}\ \text{A}, & 0 \le t \le 2 \\ (e^2 - 1)e^{-t}\ \text{A}, & t \ge 2 \end{cases} \tag{15.14.9}$$

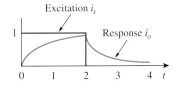

Figure 15.24   For Example 15.14; excitation and response.

which is the same as in Eq. (15.14.6). Thus, the response $i_o(t)$ along the excitation $i_s(t)$ is as shown in Fig. 15.24.

$\boxed{\text{PRACTICE PROBLEM}}$ $\mathsf{15.14}$

Use convolution to find $v_o(t)$ in the circuit of Fig. 15.25(a) when the excitation is the signal shown in Fig. 15.25(b).

Answer: $20(e^{-t} - e^{-2t})$ V.

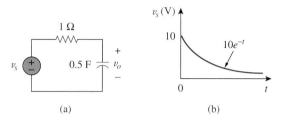

Figure 15.25   For Practice Prob. 15.14.

†15.6 APPLICATION TO INTEGRODIFFERENTIAL EQUATIONS

The Laplace transform is useful in solving linear integrodifferential equations. Using the differentiation and integration properties of Laplace transforms, each term in the integrodifferential equation is transformed. Initial conditions are automatically taken into account. We solve the resulting algebraic equation in the s domain. We then convert the solution back to the time domain by using the inverse transform. The following examples illustrate the process.

EXAMPLE 15.15

Use the Laplace transform to solve the differential equation

$$\frac{d^2v(t)}{dt^2} + 6\frac{dv(t)}{dt} + 8v(t) = 2u(t)$$

subject to $v(0) = 1$, $v'(0) = -2$.

Solution:

We take the Laplace transform of each term in the given differential equation and obtain

$$[s^2V(s) - sv(0) - v'(0)] + 6[sV(s) - v(0)] + 8V(s) = \frac{2}{s}$$

Substituting $v(0) = 1$, $v'(0) = -2$,

$$s^2V(s) - s + 2 + 6sV(s) - 6 + 8V(s) = \frac{2}{s}$$

or

$$(s^2 + 6s + 8)V(s) = s + 4 + \frac{2}{s} = \frac{s^2 + 4s + 2}{s}$$

Hence,

$$V(s) = \frac{s^2 + 4s + 2}{s(s + 2)(s + 4)} = \frac{A}{s} + \frac{B}{s + 2} + \frac{C}{s + 4}$$

where

$$A = sV(s)\,\big|_{s=0} = \frac{s^2 + 4s + 2}{(s + 2)(s + 4)}\bigg|_{s=0} = \frac{2}{(2)(4)} = \frac{1}{4}$$

$$B = (s + 2)V(s)\,\big|_{s=-2} = \frac{s^2 + 4s + 2}{s(s + 4)}\bigg|_{s=-2} = \frac{-2}{(-2)(2)} = \frac{1}{2}$$

$$C = (s + 4)V(s)\,\big|_{s=-4} = \frac{s^2 + 4s + 2}{s(s + 2)}\bigg|_{s=-4} = \frac{2}{(-4)(-2)} = \frac{1}{4}$$

Hence,

$$V(s) = \frac{\frac{1}{4}}{s} + \frac{\frac{1}{2}}{s + 2} + \frac{\frac{1}{4}}{s + 4}$$

By the inverse Laplace transform,

$$v(t) = \frac{1}{4}(1 + 2e^{-2t} + e^{-4t})u(t)$$

PRACTICE PROBLEM 15.15

Solve the following differential equation using the Laplace transform method.

$$\frac{d^2v(t)}{dt^2} + 4\frac{dv(t)}{dt} + 4v(t) = e^{-t}$$

if $v(0) = v'(0) = 1$.

Answer: $(e^{-t} + 2te^{-2t})u(t)$.

EXAMPLE 15.16

Solve for the response $y(t)$ in the following integrodifferential equation.

$$\frac{dy}{dt} + 5y(t) + 6\int_0^t y(\tau)\,d\tau = u(t), \qquad y(0) = 2$$

Solution:

Taking the Laplace transform of each term, we get

$$[sY(s) - y(0)] + 5Y(s) + \frac{6}{s}Y(s) = \frac{1}{s}$$

Substituting $y(0) = 2$ and multiplying through by s,

$$Y(s)(s^2 + 5s + 6) = 1 + 2s$$

or

$$Y(s) = \frac{2s + 1}{(s + 2)(s + 3)} = \frac{A}{s + 2} + \frac{B}{s + 3}$$

where

$$A = (s + 2)Y(s)\,\big|_{s=-2} = \frac{2s + 1}{s + 3}\bigg|_{s=-2} = \frac{-3}{1} = -3$$

$$B = (s + 3)Y(s)\,\big|_{s=-3} = \frac{2s + 1}{s + 2}\bigg|_{s=-3} = \frac{-5}{-1} = 5$$

Thus,

$$Y(s) = \frac{-3}{s+2} + \frac{5}{s+3}$$

Its inverse transform is

$$y(t) = (-3e^{-2t} + 5e^{-3t})u(t)$$

PRACTICE PROBLEM 15.16

Use the Laplace transform to solve the integrodifferential equation

$$\frac{dy}{dt} + 3y(t) + 2\int_0^t y(\tau)\,d\tau = 2e^{-3t}, \qquad y(0) = 0$$

Answer: $(-e^{-t} + 4e^{-2t} - 3e^{-3t})u(t)$.

15.7 SUMMARY

1. The Laplace transform allows a signal represented by a function in the time domain to be analyzed in the s domain (or complex frequency domain). It is defined as

$$\mathcal{L}[f(t)] = F(s) = \int_0^\infty f(t)e^{-st}\,dt$$

2. Properties of the Laplace transform are listed in Table 15.1, while the Laplace transforms of basic common functions are listed in Table 15.2.

3. The inverse Laplace transform can be found using partial fraction expansions and using the Laplace transform pairs in Table 15.2 as a look-up table. Real poles lead to exponential functions and complex poles to damped sinusoids.

4. The convolution of two signals consists of time-reversing one of the signals, shifting it, multiplying it point by point with the second signal, and integrating the product. The convolution integral relates the convolution of two signals in the time domain to the inverse of the product of their Laplace transforms:

$$\mathcal{L}^{-1}[F_1(s)F_2(s)] = f_1(t) * f_2(t) = \int_0^t f_1(\lambda)f_2(t-\lambda)\,d\lambda$$

5. In the time domain, the output $y(t)$ of the network is the convolution of the impulse response with the input $x(t)$,

$$y(t) = h(t) * x(t)$$

6. The Laplace transform can be used to solve a linear integrodifferential equation.

REVIEW QUESTIONS

15.1   Every function $f(t)$ has a Laplace transform.

    (a)   True   (b)   False

15.2   The variable s in the Laplace transform $H(s)$ is called

    (a)   complex frequency   (b)   transfer function
    (c)   zero   (d)   pole

15.3   The Laplace transform of $u(t-2)$ is:

    (a) $\dfrac{1}{s+2}$ (b) $\dfrac{1}{s-2}$

    (c) $\dfrac{e^{2s}}{s}$ (d) $\dfrac{e^{-2s}}{s}$

15.4   The zero of the function

$$F(s) = \frac{s+1}{(s+2)(s+3)(s+4)}$$

    is at

    (a) -4 (b) -3
    (c) -2 (d) -1

15.5   The poles of the function

$$F(s) = \frac{s+1}{(s+2)(s+3)(s+4)}$$

    are at

    (a) -4 (b) -3
    (c) -2 (d) -1

15.6   If $F(s) = 1/(s+2)$, then $f(t)$ is

    (a) $e^{2t}u(t)$ (b) $e^{-2t}u(t)$
    (c) $u(t-2)$ (d) $u(t+2)$

15.7   Given that $F(s) = e^{-2s}/(s+1)$, then $f(t)$ is

    (a) $e^{-2(t-1)}u(t-1)$ (b) $e^{-(t-2)}u(t-2)$
    (c) $e^{-t}u(t-2)$ (d) $e^{-t}u(t+1)$
    (e) $e^{-(t-2)}u(t)$

15.8   The initial value of $f(t)$ with transform

$$F(s) = \frac{s+1}{(s+2)(s+3)}$$

    is:

    (a)   nonexistent (b) ∞ (c)   0
    (d)   1   (e) $\frac{1}{6}$

15.9   The inverse Laplace transform of

$$\frac{s+2}{(s+2)^2+1}$$

    is:

    (a) $e^{-t}\cos 2t$ (b) $e^{-t}\sin 2t$ (c) $e^{-2t}\cos t$
    (d) $e^{-2t}\sin 2t$ (e)   none of the above

15.10   The result of $u(t) * u(t)$ is:

    (a) $u^2(t)$ (b) $tu(t)$
    (c) $t^2u(t)$ (d) $\delta(t)$

Answers: 15.1b, 15.2a, 15.3d, 15.4d, 15.5a,b,c, 15.6b, 15.7b, 15.8d, 15.9c, 15.10b.

PROBLEMS

Sections 15.2 and 15.3   Definition and Properties of the Laplace Transform

15.1   Find the Laplace transform of:

    (a) $\cosh at$ (b) $\sinh at$

    [*Hint:* $\cosh x = \frac{1}{2}(e^x + e^{-x})$,
    $\sinh x = \frac{1}{2}(e^x - e^{-x})$.]

15.2   Determine the Laplace transform of:

    (a) $\cos(\omega t + \theta)$ (b) $\sin(\omega t + \theta)$

15.3   Obtain the Laplace transform of each of the following functions:

    (a) $e^{-2t}\cos 3tu(t)$ (b) $e^{-2t}\sin 4tu(t)$
    (c) $e^{-3t}\cosh 2tu(t)$ (d) $e^{-4t}\sinh tu(t)$
    (e) $te^{-t}\sin 2tu(t)$

15.4   Find the Laplace transforms of the following:

    (a) $g(t) = 6\cos(4t-1)$
    (b) $f(t) = 2tu(t) + 5e^{-3(t-2)}u(t-2)$

15.5   Find the Laplace transform of each of the following functions:

    (a) $t^2\cos(2t+30°)u(t)$ (b) $3t^4e^{-2t}u(t)$
    (c) $2tu(t) - 4\dfrac{d}{dt}\delta(t)$ (d) $2e^{-(t-1)}u(t)$
    (e) $5u(t/2)$ (f) $6e^{-t/3}u(t)$
    (g) $\dfrac{d^n}{dt^n}\delta(t)$

15.6   Calculate the Laplace transforms of these functions:

(a) $2\delta(t-1)$ (b) $10u(t-2)$
(c) $(t+4)u(t)$ (d) $2e^{-t}u(t-4)$

15.7   Obtain the Laplace transform of

(a) $10\cos 4(t-1)u(t)$
(b) $t^2 e^{-2t}u(t) + u(t-3)$

15.8   Find the Laplace transforms of the following functions:

(a) $2\delta(3t) + 6u(2t) + 4e^{-2t} - 10e^{-3t}$
(b) $te^{-t}u(t-1)$
(c) $\cos 2(t-1)u(t-1)$
(d) $\sin 4t[u(t) - u(t-\pi)]$

15.9   Determine the Laplace transforms of these functions:

(a) $f(t) = (t-4)u(t-2)$
(b) $g(t) = 2e^{-4t}u(t-1)$
(c) $h(t) = 5\cos(2t-1)u(t)$
(d) $p(t) = 6[u(t-2) - u(t-4)]$

15.10   In two different ways, find the Laplace transform of

$$g(t) = \frac{d}{dt}(te^{-t}\cos t)$$

15.11   Find $F(s)$ if:

(a) $f(t) = 6e^{-t}\cosh 2t$ (b) $f(t) = 3te^{-2t}\sinh 4t$
(c) $f(t) = 8e^{-3t}\cosh tu(t-2)$

15.12   Find the Laplace transform of:

$$f(t) = te^{-2t}u(t-1)$$

15.13   Find the Laplace transform of the following functions:

(a) $t\cos t\, u(t)$ (b) $e^{-t}t\sin t\, u(t)$
(c) $\dfrac{\sin \beta t}{t}u(t)$

15.14   Calculate the Laplace transform of the function in Fig. 15.26.

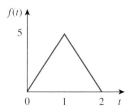

Figure 15.26   For Prob. 15.14.

15.15   Find the Laplace transform of the function in Fig. 15.27.

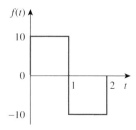

Figure 15.27   For Prob. 15.15.

15.16   Obtain the Laplace transform of $f(t)$ in Fig. 15.28.

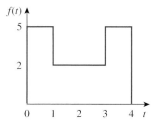

Figure 15.28   For Prob. 15.16.

15.17   Determine the Laplace transforms of the function in Fig. 15.29.

Figure 15.29   For Prob. 15.17.

15.18   Obtain the Laplace transforms of the functions in Fig. 15.30.

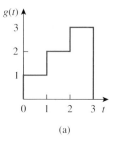

Figure 15.30   For Prob. 15.18.

15.19 Calculate the Laplace transform of the train of unit impulses in Fig. 15.31.

Figure 15.31   For Prob. 15.19.

15.20 The periodic function shown in Fig. 15.32 is defined over its period as

$$g(t) = \begin{cases} \sin \pi t, & 0 < t < 1 \\ 0, & 1 < t < 2 \end{cases}$$

Find $G(s)$.

Figure 15.32   For Prob. 15.20.

15.21 Obtain the Laplace transform of the periodic waveform in Fig. 15.33.

Figure 15.33   For Prob. 15.21.

15.22 Find the Laplace transforms of the functions in Fig. 15.34.

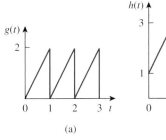

Figure 15.34   For Prob. 15.22.

15.23 Determine the Laplace transforms of the periodic functions in Fig. 15.35.

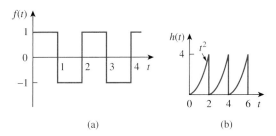

Figure 15.35   For Prob. 15.23.

15.24 Find the initial and final values, if they exist, of the following Laplace transforms:

(a) $F(s) = \dfrac{10s^3 + 1}{s^2 + 6s + 5}$

(b) $F(s) = \dfrac{s + 1}{s^2 - 4s + 6}$

(c) $F(s) = \dfrac{2s^2 + 7}{(s + 1)(s + 2)(s^2 + 2s + 5)}$

15.25 Find $f(0)$ and $f(\infty)$, if they exist, when:

(a) $F(s) = \dfrac{8(s + 1)(s + 3)}{s(s + 2)(s + 4)}$

(b) $F(s) = \dfrac{6(s - 1)}{s^4 - 1}$

15.26 Determine the initial and final values of $f(t)$, if they exist, given that:

(a) $F(s) = \dfrac{s^2 + 3}{s^3 + 4s^2 + 6}$

(b) $F(s) = \dfrac{s^2 - 2s + 1}{(s - 2)(s^2 + 2s + 4)}$

Section 15.4   The Inverse Laplace Transform

15.27 Determine the inverse Laplace transform of each of the following functions:

(a) $F(s) = \dfrac{1}{s} + \dfrac{2}{s + 1}$

(b) $G(s) = \dfrac{3s + 1}{s + 4}$

(c) $H(s) = \dfrac{4}{(s + 1)(s + 3)}$

(d) $J(s) = \dfrac{12}{(s + 2)^2(s + 4)}$

15.28 Determine the inverse Laplace transform of:

(a) $F(s) = \dfrac{2(s + 1)}{(s + 3)(s + 5)}$

(b) $H(s) = \dfrac{6s + 22}{(s + 1)(2s^2 + 4s + 10)}$

15.29 Find the inverse Laplace transform of:

$$V(s) = \frac{2s + 26}{s(s^2 + 4s + 13)}$$

15.30 Find the inverse Laplace transform of:

(a) $H_1(s) = \dfrac{2s + 6}{s^2 + 4s + 13}$

(b) $H_2(s) = \dfrac{s^2 + 4}{(s + 1)^2(s^2 + 2s + 5)}$

(c) $H_3(s) = \dfrac{(s + 2)e^{-s}}{(s + 1)(s + 3)}$

15.31 Find $f(t)$ for each $F(s)$:

(a) $\dfrac{10s}{(s + 1)(s + 2)(s + 3)}$

(b) $\dfrac{2s^2 + 4s + 1}{(s + 1)(s + 2)^3}$

(c) $\dfrac{s + 1}{(s + 2)(s^2 + 2s + 5)}$

15.32 Determine the inverse Laplace transform of each of the following functions:

(a) $\dfrac{8(s + 1)(s + 3)}{s(s + 2)(s + 4)}$ (b) $\dfrac{s^2 - 2s + 4}{(s + 1)(s + 2)^2}$

(c) $\dfrac{s^2 + 1}{(s + 3)(s^2 + 4s + 5)}$

15.33 Calculate the inverse Laplace transform of:

(a) $\dfrac{6(s - 1)}{s^4 - 1}$ (b) $\dfrac{se^{-\pi s}}{s^2 + 1}$ (c) $\dfrac{8}{s(s + 1)^3}$

15.34 Find the time functions that have the following Laplace transforms:

(a) $F(s) = 10 + \dfrac{s^2 + 1}{s^2 + 4}$

(b) $G(s) = \dfrac{e^{-s} + 4e^{-2s}}{s^2 + 6s + 8}$

(c) $H(s) = \dfrac{(s + 1)e^{-2s}}{s(s + 3)(s + 4)}$

15.35 Obtain $f(t)$ for the following transforms:

(a) $F(s) = \dfrac{(s + 3)e^{-6s}}{(s + 1)(s + 2)}$

(b) $F(s) = \dfrac{4 - e^{-2s}}{s^2 + 5s + 4}$

(c) $F(s) = \dfrac{se^{-s}}{(s + 3)(s^2 + 4)}$

15.36 Obtain the inverse Laplace transforms of the following functions:

(a) $X(s) = \dfrac{1}{s^2(s + 2)(s + 3)}$

(b) $Y(s) = \dfrac{1}{s(s + 1)^2}$

(c) $Z(s) = \dfrac{1}{s(s + 1)(s^2 + 6s + 10)}$

15.37 Obtain the inverse Laplace transforms of these functions:

(a) $\dfrac{12e^{-2s}}{s(s^2 + 4)}$ (b) $\dfrac{2s + 1}{(s^2 + 1)(s^2 + 9)}$

(c) $\dfrac{9s^2}{(s^2 + 4s + 13)}$

15.38 Find $f(t)$ given that:

(a) $F(s) = \dfrac{s^2 + 4s}{s^2 + 10s + 26}$

(b) $F(s) = \dfrac{5s^2 + 7s + 29}{s(s^2 + 4s + 29)}$

*__15.39__ Determine $f(t)$ if:

(a) $F(s) = \dfrac{2s^3 + 4s^2 + 1}{(s^2 + 2s + 17)(s^2 + 4s + 20)}$

(b) $F(s) = \dfrac{s^2 + 4}{(s^2 + 9)(s^2 + 6s + 3)}$

15.40 Show that

$$\mathcal{L}^{-1}\left[\frac{4s^2 + 7s + 13}{(s + 2)(s^2 + 2s + 5)}\right] =$$

$$\left[\sqrt{2}e^{-t}\cos(2t + 45°) + 3e^{-2t}\right]u(t)$$

Section 15.5   The Convolution Integral

15.41 Given $f(t)$ and $h(t)$ as in Fig. 15.36, find $f(t) * h(t)$.

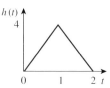

Figure 15.36   For Prob. 15.41.

---

*An asterisk indicates a challenging problem.

15.42 Graphically convolve the pairs of functions in Fig. 15.37.

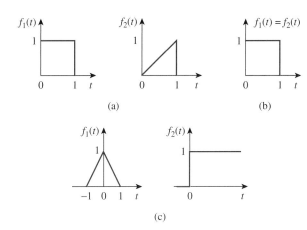

(a)

(b)

(c)

Figure 15.37   For Prob. 15.42.

15.43 Find $y(t) = x(t) * h(t)$ for each paired $x(t)$ and $h(t)$ in Fig. 15.38.

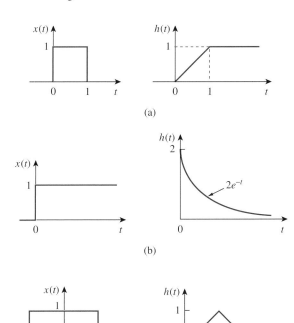

(a)

(b)

(c)

Figure 15.38   For Prob. 15.43.

15.44 Obtain the convolution of the pairs of signals in Fig. 15.39.

(a)

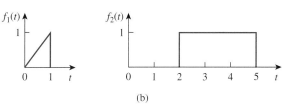

(b)

Figure 15.39   For Prob. 15.44.

15.45 Show that:

(a) $x(t) * \delta(t) = x(t)$

(b) $f(t) * u(t) = \int_0^t f(\lambda)\, d\lambda$

15.46 Determine the convolution for each of the following pairs of continuous signals:

(a) $x_1(t) = e^{-t}, t > 0, x_2(t) = 4e^{-2t}, 0 < t < 3$

(b) $x_1(t) = u(t-1) - u(t-3)$,
$x_2(t) = u(t) - u(t-1)$

(c) $x_1(t) = 4e^{-t}u(t)$,
$x_2(t) = u(t+1) - 2u(t) + u(t-1)$

15.47 Given that $F_1(s) = F_2(s) = s/(s^2 + 1)$, find $\mathcal{L}^{-1}[F_1(s)F_2(s)]$ by convolution.

15.48 Find $f(t)$ using convolution given that:

(a) $F(s) = \dfrac{4}{(s^2 + 2s + 5)^2}$

(b) $F(s) = \dfrac{2s}{(s+1)(s^2+4)}$

15.49 The impulse response of a circuit is

$$h(t) = \begin{cases} 4e^{-2t}, & t > 0 \\ 0, & t < 0 \end{cases}$$

For an input signal of $u(t) - u(t-1)$, find the corresponding output using convolution.

Section 15.6   Application to Integrodifferential Equations

15.50   Use the Laplace transform to solve the differential equation

$$\frac{d^2 v(t)}{dt^2} + 2\frac{dv(t)}{dt} + 10v(t) = 3\cos 2t$$

subject to $v(0) = 1$, $dv(0)/dt = -2$.

15.51   Given that $v(0) = 2$ and $dv(0)/dt = 4$, solve

$$\frac{d^2 v}{dt^2} + 5\frac{dv}{dt} + 6v = 10e^{-t}u(t)$$

15.52   Use the Laplace transform to find $i(t)$ for $t > 0$ if

$$\frac{d^2 i}{dt^2} + 3\frac{di}{dt} + 2i + \delta(t) = 0,$$

$$i(0) = 0, \qquad i'(0) = 3$$

15.53   Solve the following equation by means of the Laplace transform:

$$y'' + 5y' + 6y = \cos 2t$$

Let $y(0) = 1$, $y'(0) = 4$.

15.54   The voltage across a circuit is given by

$$v'' + 3v' + 2v = 5e^{-3t}$$

Find $v(t)$ if the initial conditions are $v(0) = 0$, $v'(0) = -1$.

15.55   Solve for $y(t)$ in the following differential equation if the initial conditions are zero.

$$\frac{d^3 y}{dt^3} + 6\frac{d^2 y}{dt^2} + 8\frac{dy}{dt} = e^{-t}\cos 2t$$

15.56   Solve for $v(t)$ in the integrodifferential equation

$$4\frac{dv}{dt} + 12\int_{-\infty}^{t} v\,dt = 0$$

given that $v(0) = 2$.

15.57   Solve the following integrodifferential equation using the Laplace transform method:

$$\frac{dy(t)}{dt} + 9\int_{0}^{t} y(\tau)\,d\tau = \cos 2t, \qquad y(0) = 1$$

15.58   Given the integrodifferential equation

$$6v + \frac{dv}{dt} + 10\int_{0}^{t} v(\tau)d\tau = u(t-2)$$

with $v(0) = 0$, find $v(t)$.

15.59   Solve the integrodifferential equation

$$\frac{dy}{dt} + 4y + 3\int_{0}^{t} y\,dt = 6e^{-2t}, \qquad y(0) = -1$$

15.60   Solve the following integrodifferential equation

$$2\frac{dx}{dt} + 5x + 3\int_{0}^{t} x\,dt + 4 = \sin 4t, \qquad x(0) = 1$$

APPLICATIONS OF LAPLACE TRANSFORMS

Communication skills are the most important skills any engineer can have. A very critical element in this tool set is the ability to ask a question and understand the answer, a very simple thing and yet it may make the difference between success and failure!

—James Watson

Enhancing Your Career

Asking Questions In over 30 years of teaching, I have struggled with determining how best to help students learn. Regardless of how much time students spend in studying for a course, the most helpful activity for students is learning how to ask questions in class and then asking those questions. The student, by asking questions, becomes actively involved in the learning process and no longer is merely a passive receptor of information. I think this active involvement contributes so much to the learning process that it is probably the single most important aspect to the development of a modern engineer. In fact, asking questions is the basis of science. As Charles P. Steinmetz rightly said, "No man really becomes a fool until he stops asking questions."

It seems very straightforward and quite easy to ask questions. Have we not been doing that all our lives? The truth is to ask questions in an appropriate manner and to maximize the learning process takes some thought and preparation.

I am sure that there are several models one could effectively use. Let me share what has worked for me. The most important thing to keep in mind is that you do not have to form a perfect question. Since the question-and-answer format allows the question to be developed in an iterative manner, the original question can easily be refined as you go. I frequently tell students that they are most welcome to read their questions in class.

Here are three things you should keep in mind when asking questions. First, prepare your question. If you are like many students who are either shy or have not learned to ask questions in class, you may wish to start with a question

you have written down outside of class. Second, wait for an appropriate time to ask the question. Simply use your judgment on that. Third, be prepared to clarify your question by paraphrasing it or saying it in a different way in case you are asked to repeat the question.

One last comment: not all professors like students to ask questions in class even though they may say they do. You need to find out which professors like classroom questions. Good luck in enhancing one of your most important skills as an engineer.

16.1 INTRODUCTION

Now that we have introduced the Laplace transform, let us see what we can do with it. Please keep in mind that with the Laplace transform we actually have one of the most powerful mathematical tools for analysis, synthesis, and design. Being able to look at circuits and systems in the s domain can help us to understand how our circuits and systems really function. In this chapter we will take an in-depth look at how easy it is to work with circuits in the s domain. In addition, we will briefly look at physical systems. We are sure you have studied some mechanical systems and may have used the same differential equations to describe them as we use to describe our electric circuits. Actually that is a wonderful thing about the physical universe in which we live; the same differential equations can be used to describe any linear circuit, system, or process. The key is the term *linear*.

> A **system** is a mathematical model of a physical process relating the input to the output.

It is entirely appropriate to consider circuits as systems. Historically, circuits have been discussed as a separate topic from systems, so we will actually talk about circuits and systems in this chapter realizing that circuits are nothing more than a class of electrical systems.

The most important thing to remember is that everything we discussed in the last chapter and in this chapter applies to any linear system. In the last chapter, we saw how we can use Laplace transforms to solve linear differential equations and integral equations. In this chapter, we introduce the concept of modeling circuits in the s domain. We can use that principle to help us solve just about any kind of linear circuit. We will take a quick look at how state variables can be used to analyze systems with multiple inputs and multiple outputs. Finally, we examine how the Laplace transform is used in network stability analysis and in network synthesis.

16.2 CIRCUIT ELEMENT MODELS

Having mastered how to obtain the Laplace transform and its inverse, we are now prepared to employ the Laplace transform to analyze circuits. This usually involves three steps.

> **Steps in applying the Laplace transform:**
>
> 1. Transform the circuit from the time domain to the s domain.
> 2. Solve the circuit using nodal analysis, mesh analysis, source transformation, superposition, or any circuit analysis technique with which we are familiar.
> 3. Take the inverse transform of the solution and thus obtain the solution in the time domain.

Only the first step is new and will be discussed here. As we did in phasor analysis, we transform a circuit in the time domain to the frequency or s domain by Laplace transforming each term in the circuit.

For a resistor, the voltage-current relationship in the time domain is

$$v(t) = Ri(t) \tag{16.1}$$

Taking the Laplace transform, we get

$$\boxed{V(s) = RI(s)} \tag{16.2}$$

For an inductor,

$$v(t) = L\frac{di(t)}{dt} \tag{16.3}$$

Taking the Laplace transform of both sides gives

$$V(s) = L[sI(s) - i(0^-)] = sLI(s) - Li(0^-) \tag{16.4}$$

or

$$\boxed{I(s) = \frac{1}{sL}V(s) + \frac{i(0^-)}{s}} \tag{16.5}$$

The s-domain equivalents are shown in Fig. 16.1, where the initial condition is modeled as a voltage or current source.

For a capacitor,

$$i(t) = C\frac{dv(t)}{dt} \tag{16.6}$$

which transforms into the s domain as

$$I(s) = C[sV(s) - v(0^-)] = sCV(s) - Cv(0^-) \tag{16.7}$$

or

$$\boxed{V(s) = \frac{1}{sC}I(s) + \frac{v(0^-)}{s}} \tag{16.8}$$

The s-domain equivalents are shown in Fig. 16.2. With the s-domain equivalents, the Laplace transform can be used readily to solve first- and second-order circuits such as those we considered in Chapters 7 and 8. We should observe from Eqs. (16.3) to (16.8) that the initial conditions are part of the transformation. This is one advantage of using the Laplace transform in circuit analysis. Another advantage is that a complete response—transient and steady state—of a network is obtained. We will illustrate this with Examples 16.2 and 16.3. Also, observe the duality of Eqs. (16.5) and (16.8), confirming what we already know from Chapter 8 (see Table 8.1), namely, that L and C, $I(s)$ and $V(s)$, and $v(0)$ and $i(0)$ are dual pairs.

As one can infer from step 2, all the circuit analysis techniques applied for dc circuits are applicable to the s domain.

(a)   (b)

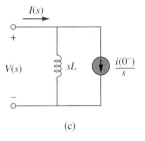

(c)

Figure 16.1   Representation of an inductor: (a) time-domain, (b,c) s-domain equivalents.

The elegance of using the Laplace transform in circuit analysis lies in the automatic inclusion of the initial conditions in the transformation process, thus providing a complete (transient and steady-state) solution.

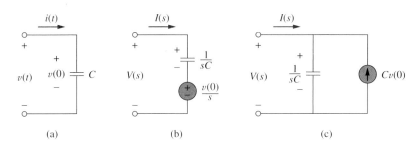

Figure 16.2   Representation of a capacitor: (a) time-domain, (b,c) s-domain equivalents.

Figure 16.3   Time-domain and s-domain representations of passive elements under zero initial conditions.

If we assume zero initial conditions for the inductor and the capacitor, the above equations reduce to:

Resistor: $V(s) = RI(s)$

Inductor: $V(s) = sLI(s)$

Capacitor: $V(s) = \dfrac{1}{sC}I(s)$

(16.9)

The s-domain equivalents are shown in Fig. 16.3.

We define the impedance in the s-domain as the ratio of the voltage transform to the current transform under zero initial conditions, that is,

$$Z(s) = \frac{V(s)}{I(s)}$$

(16.10)

Thus the impedances of the three circuit elements are

Resistor: $Z(s) = R$

Inductor: $Z(s) = sL$

Capacitor: $Z(s) = \dfrac{1}{sC}$

(16.11)

Table 16.1 summarizes these. The admittance in the s-domain is the reciprocal of the impedance, or

$$Y(s) = \frac{1}{Z(s)} = \frac{I(s)}{V(s)}$$

(16.12)

The use of the Laplace transform in circuit analysis facilitates the use of various signal sources such as impulse, step, ramp, exponential, and sinusoidal.

The models for dependent sources and op amps are easy to develop drawing from the simple fact that if the Laplace transform of $f(t)$ is $F(s)$, then the Laplace transform of $af(t)$ is $aF(s)$—the linearity property. The dependent source model is a little easier in that we deal with a single value. The dependent source can have only two controlling values, a constant times either a voltage or a current. Thus,

$$\mathcal{L}[av(t)] = aV(s)$$

(16.13)

$$\mathcal{L}[ai(t)] = aI(s)$$

(16.14)

TABLE 16.1   Impedance of an element in the s-domain.*

Element	$Z(s) = V(s)/I(s)$
Resistor	R
Inductor	sL
Capacitor	$1/sC$

*Assuming zero initial conditions

The ideal op amp can be treated just like a resistor. Nothing within an op amp, either real or ideal, does anything more than multiply a voltage by a constant. Thus, we only need to write the equations as we always do using the constraint that the input voltage to the op amp has to be zero and the input current has to be zero.

EXAMPLE 16.1

Find $v_o(t)$ in the circuit in Fig. 16.4, assuming zero initial conditions.

Solution:

We first transform the circuit from the time domain to the s domain.

$$u(t) \implies \frac{1}{s}$$

$$1\,H \implies sL = s$$

$$\frac{1}{3}\,F \implies \frac{1}{sC} = \frac{3}{s}$$

Figure 16.4   For Example 16.1.

The resulting s-domain circuit is in Fig. 16.5. We now apply mesh analysis. For mesh 1,

$$\frac{1}{s} = \left(1 + \frac{3}{s}\right) I_1 - \frac{3}{s} I_2 \qquad (16.1.1)$$

For mesh 2,

$$0 = -\frac{3}{s} I_1 + \left(s + 5 + \frac{3}{s}\right) I_2$$

or

$$I_1 = \frac{1}{3}(s^2 + 5s + 3) I_2 \qquad (16.1.2)$$

Figure 16.5   Mesh analysis of the frequency-domain equivalent of the same circuit.

Substituting this into Eq. (16.1.1),

$$\frac{1}{s} = \left(1 + \frac{3}{s}\right) \frac{1}{3}(s^2 + 5s + 3) I_2 - \frac{3}{s} I_2$$

Multiplying through by $3s$ gives

$$3 = (s^3 + 8s^2 + 18s) I_2 \quad \implies \quad I_2 = \frac{3}{s^3 + 8s^2 + 18s}$$

$$V_o(s) = s I_2 = \frac{3}{s^2 + 8s + 18} = \frac{3}{\sqrt{2}} \frac{\sqrt{2}}{(s+4)^2 + (\sqrt{2})^2}$$

Taking the inverse transform yields

$$v_o(t) = \frac{3}{\sqrt{2}} e^{-4t} \sin \sqrt{2}t\,\mathrm{V}, \qquad t \geq 0$$

PRACTICE PROBLEM 16.1

Figure 16.6   For Practice Prob. 16.1.

Determine $v_o(t)$ in the circuit of Fig. 16.6, assuming zero initial conditions.

Answer: $8(1 - e^{-2t} - 2te^{-2t})u(t)$ V.

EXAMPLE 16.2

Find $v_o(t)$ in the circuit of Fig. 16.7. Assume $v_o(0) = 5$ V.

Figure 16.7   For Example 16.2.

Solution:

We transform the circuit to the s domain as shown in Fig. 16.8. The initial condition is included in the form of the current source $Cv_o(0) = 0.1(5) = 0.5$ A. [See Fig. 16.2(c).] We apply nodal analysis. At the top node,

$$\frac{10/(s+1) - V_o}{10} + 2 + 0.5 = \frac{V_o}{10} + \frac{V_o}{10/s}$$

or

$$\frac{1}{s+1} + 2.5 = \frac{2V_o}{10} + \frac{sV_o}{10} = \frac{1}{10}V_o(s+2)$$

Multiplying through by 10,

$$\frac{10}{s+1} + 25 = V_o(s+2)$$

or

$$V_o = \frac{25s + 35}{(s+1)(s+2)} = \frac{A}{s+1} + \frac{B}{s+2}$$

Figure 16.8   Nodal analysis of the equivalent of the circuit in Fig. 16.7.

where

$$A = (s + 1)V_o(s) \big|_{s=-1} = \frac{25s + 35}{(s + 2)} \bigg|_{s=-1} = \frac{10}{1} = 10$$

$$B = (s + 2)V_o(s) \big|_{s=-2} = \frac{25s + 35}{(s + 1)} \bigg|_{s=-2} = \frac{-15}{-1} = 15$$

Thus,

$$V_o(s) = \frac{10}{s + 1} + \frac{15}{s + 2}$$

Taking the inverse Laplace transform, we obtain

$$v_o(t) = (10e^{-t} + 15e^{-2t})u(t) \text{ V}$$

PRACTICE PROBLEM 16.2

Find $v_o(t)$ in the circuit shown in Fig. 16.9. Note that, since the voltage input is multiplied by $u(t)$, the voltage source is a short for all $t < 0$ and $i < (0) = 0$.

Answer: $(\frac{4}{5}e^{-2t} + \frac{8}{15}e^{-t/3})u(t)$ V.

Figure 16.9   For Practice Prob. 16.2.

EXAMPLE 16.3

In the circuit in Fig. 16.10(a), the switch moves from position a to position b at $t = 0$. Find $i(t)$ for $t > 0$.

Solution:

The initial current through the inductor is $i(0) = I_o$. For $t > 0$, Fig. 16.10(b) shows the circuit transformed to the s domain. The initial condition is incorporated in the form of a voltage source as $Li(0) = LI_o$. Using mesh analysis,

$$I(s)(R + sL) - LI_o - \frac{V_o}{s} = 0 \qquad (16.3.1)$$

or

$$I(s) = \frac{LI_o}{R + sL} + \frac{V_o}{s(R + sL)} = \frac{I_o}{s + R/L} + \frac{V_o/L}{s(s + R/L)} \qquad (16.3.2)$$

Applying partial fraction expansion on the second term on the right-hand side of Eq. (16.3.2) yields

$$I(s) = \frac{I_o}{s + R/L} + \frac{V_o/R}{s} - \frac{V_o/R}{(s + R/L)} \qquad (16.3.3)$$

The inverse Laplace transform of this gives

$$i(t) = \left(I_o - \frac{V_o}{R}\right)e^{-t/\tau} + \frac{V_o}{R}, \qquad t \geq 0 \qquad (16.3.4)$$

where $\tau = R/L$. The term in fences is the transient response, while the second term is the steady-state response. In other words, the final value is

(a)

(b)

Figure 16.10   For Example 16.3.

$i(\infty) = V_o/R$, which we could have predicted by applying the final-value theorem on Eq. (16.3.2) or (16.3.3); that is,

$$\lim_{s \to 0} s I(s) = \lim_{s \to 0} \left(\frac{s I_o}{s + R/L} + \frac{V_o/L}{s + R/L} \right) = \frac{V_o}{R} \qquad (16.3.5)$$

Equation (16.3.4) may also be written as

$$i(t) = I_o e^{-t/\tau} + \frac{V_o}{R}(1 - e^{-t/\tau}), \qquad t \ge 0 \qquad (16.3.6)$$

The first term is the natural response, while the second term is the forced response. If the initial condition $I_o = 0$, Eq. (16.3.6) becomes

$$i(t) = \frac{V_o}{R}(1 - e^{-t/\tau}), \qquad t \ge 0 \qquad (16.3.7)$$

which is the step response, since it is due to the step input V_o with no initial energy.

PRACTICE PROBLEM 16.3

Figure 16.11   For Practice Prob. 16.3.

The switch in Fig. 16.11 has been in position b for a long time. It is moved to position a at $t = 0$. Determine $v(t)$ for $t > 0$.

Answer: $v(t) = (V_o - I_o R)e^{-t/\tau} + I_o R, t > 0$, where $\tau = RC$.

16.3 CIRCUIT ANALYSIS

Circuit analysis is again relatively easy to do when we are in the s domain. We merely need to transform a complicated set of mathematical relationships in the time domain into the s domain where we convert operators (derivatives and integrals) into simple multipliers of s and $1/s$. This now allows us to use algebra to set up and solve our circuit equations. The exciting thing about this is that *all* of the circuit theorems and relationships we developed for dc circuits are perfectly valid in the s domain.

> Remember, equivalent circuits, with capacitors and inductors, only exist in the s domain; they cannot be transformed back into the time domain.

EXAMPLE 16.4

Consider the circuit in Fig. 16.12(a). Find the value of the voltage across the capacitor assuming that the value of $v_s(t) = 10u(t)$ V and assume that at $t = 0$, -1 A flows through the inductor and $+5$ V is across the capacitor.

Solution:

Figure 16.12(b) represents the entire circuit in the s domain with the initial conditions incorporated. We now have a straightforward nodal analysis problem. Since the value of V_1 is also the value of the capacitor voltage in the time domain and is the only unknown node voltage, we only need to write one equation.

$$\frac{V_1 - V_s}{10/3} + \frac{V_1 - 0}{5s} - \frac{i(0)}{s} + \frac{V_1 - [v(0)/s]}{1/(0.1s)} = 0 \qquad (16.4.1)$$

or

$$0.1\left(s + 3 + \frac{2}{s}\right)V_1 = \frac{3}{s} + \frac{1}{s} + 0.5 \qquad (16.4.2)$$

where $v(0) = 5$ V and $i(0) = -1$ A. Simplifying we get

$$(s^2 + 3s + 2)V_1 = 40 + 5s$$

or

$$V_1 = \frac{40 + 5s}{(s+1)(s+2)} = \frac{35}{s+1} - \frac{30}{s+2} \qquad (16.4.3)$$

Taking the inverse Laplace transform yields

$$v_1(t) = (35e^{-t} - 30e^{-2t})u(t) \text{ V} \qquad (16.4.4)$$

(a)

(b)

Figure 16.12   For Example 16.4.

PRACTICE PROBLEM 16.4

For the circuit shown in Fig. 16.12 with the same initial conditions, find the current through the inductor for all time $t > 0$.

Answer: $i(t) = (3 - 7e^{-t} + 3e^{-2t})u(t)$ A.

EXAMPLE 16.5

For the circuit shown in Fig. 16.12, and the initial conditions used in Example 16.4, use superposition to find the value of the capacitor voltage.

Solution:

Since the circuit in the s domain actually has three independent sources, we can look at the solution one source at a time. Figure 16.13 presents the circuits in the s domain considering one source at a time. We now have three nodal analysis problems. First, let us solve for the capacitor voltage in the circuit shown in Fig. 16.13(a).

$$\frac{V_1 - V_s}{10/3} + \frac{V_1 - 0}{5s} - 0 + \frac{V_1 - 0}{1/(0.1s)} = 0$$

or

$$0.1\left(s + 3 + \frac{2}{s}\right)V_1 = \frac{3}{s}$$

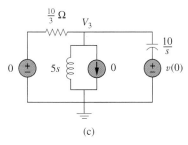

Figure 16.13   For Example 16.5.

Simplifying we get

$$(s^2 + 3s + 2)V_1 = 30$$

$$V_1 = \frac{30}{(s+1)(s+2)} = \frac{30}{s+1} - \frac{30}{s+2}$$

or

$$v_1(t) = (30e^{-t} - 30e^{-2t})u(t) \text{ V} \tag{16.5.1}$$

For Fig. 16.13(b) we get,

$$\frac{V_2 - 0}{10/3} + \frac{V_2 - 0}{5s} - \frac{1}{s} + \frac{V_2 - 0}{1/(0.1s)} = 0$$

or

$$0.1\left(s + 3 + \frac{2}{s}\right)V_2 = \frac{1}{s}$$

This leads to

$$V_2 = \frac{10}{(s+1)(s+2)} = \frac{10}{s+1} - \frac{10}{s+2}$$

Taking the inverse Laplace transform, we get

$$v_2(t) = (10e^{-t} - 10e^{-2t})u(t) \text{ V} \tag{16.5.2}$$

For Fig. 16.13(c),

$$\frac{V_3 - 0}{10/3} + \frac{V_3 - 0}{5s} - 0 + \frac{V_3 - 5/s}{1/(0.1s)} = 0$$

or

$$0.1\left(s + 3 + \frac{2}{s}\right)V_3 = 0.5$$

$$V_3 = \frac{5s}{(s+1)(s+2)} = \frac{-5}{s+1} + \frac{10}{s+2}$$

This leads to

$$v_3(t) = (-5e^{-t} + 10e^{-2t})u(t) \text{ V} \tag{16.5.3}$$

Now all we need to do is to add Eqs. (16.5.1), (16.5.2), and (16.5.3).

$$v(t) = v_1(t) + v_2(t) + v_3(t)$$

$$= \{(30 + 10 - 5)e^{-t} + (-30 + 10 - 10)e^{-2t}\}u(t) \text{ V}$$

or

$$v(t) = (35e^{-t} - 30e^{-2t})u(t) \text{ V}$$

which agrees with our answer in Example 16.4.

PRACTICE PROBLEM 16.5

For the circuit shown in Fig. 16.12, and the same initial conditions in Example 16.4, find the current through the inductor for all time $t > 0$ using superposition.

Answer: $i(t) = (3 - 7e^{-t} + 3e^{-2t})u(t) \text{ A}$.

EXAMPLE 16.6

Assume that there is no initial energy stored in the circuit of Fig. 16.14 at $t = 0$ and that $i_s = 10\,u(t)$ A. (a) Find $V_o(s)$ using Thevenin's theorem. (b) Apply the initial- and final-value theorems to find $v_o(0^+)$ and $v_o(\infty)$. (c) Determine $v_o(t)$.

Solution:

Since there is no initial energy stored in the circuit, we assume that the initial inductor current and initial capacitor voltage are zero at $t = 0$.

(a) To find the Thevenin equivalent circuit, we remove the 5-Ω resistor and then find V_{oc} (V_{Th}) and I_{sc}. To find V_{Th}, we use the Laplace-transformed circuit in Fig. 16.15(a). Since $I_x = 0$, the dependent voltage source contributes nothing, so

$$V_{oc} = V_{Th} = 5\left(\frac{10}{s}\right) = \frac{50}{s}$$

To find Z_{Th}, we consider the circuit in Fig. 16.15(b), where we first find I_{sc}. We can use nodal analysis to solve for V_1 which then leads to I_{sc} ($I_{sc} = I_x = V_1/2s$).

$$-\frac{10}{s} + \frac{(V_1 - 2I_x) - 0}{5} + \frac{V_1 - 0}{2s} = 0$$

along with

$$I_x = \frac{V_1}{2s}$$

leads to

$$V_1 = \frac{100}{2s + 3}$$

Hence,

$$I_{sc} = \frac{V_1}{2s} = \frac{100/(2s + 3)}{2s} = \frac{50}{s(2s + 3)}$$

and

$$Z_{Th} = \frac{V_{oc}}{I_{sc}} = \frac{50/s}{50/[s(2s + 3)]} = 2s + 3$$

The given circuit is replaced by its Thevenin equivalent at terminals a-b as shown in Fig. 16.16. From Fig. 16.16,

$$V_o = \frac{5}{5 + Z_{Th}} V_{Th} = \frac{5}{5 + 2s + 3}\left(\frac{50}{s}\right) = \frac{250}{s(2s + 8)} = \frac{125}{s(s + 4)}$$

(b) Using the initial-value theorem,

$$v_o(0) = \lim_{s \to \infty} s V_o(s) = \lim_{s \to \infty} \frac{125}{s + 4} = \lim_{s \to \infty} \frac{125/s}{1 + 4/s} = \frac{0}{1} = 0$$

Using the final-value theorem,

$$v_o(\infty) = \lim_{s \to 0} s V_o(s) = \lim_{s \to 0} \frac{125}{s + 4} = \frac{125}{4} = 31.25\text{ V}$$

Figure 16.14   For Example 16.6.

(a)

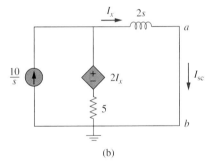

(b)

Figure 16.15   For Example 16.16: (a) finding V_{Th}, (b) determining Z_{Th}.

Figure 16.16   The Thevenin equivalent of the circuit in Fig. 16.14 in the s domain.

(c) By partial fraction,

$$V_o = \frac{125}{s(s+4)} = \frac{A}{s} + \frac{B}{s+4}$$

$$A = sV_o(s)\bigg|_{s=0} = \frac{125}{s+4}\bigg|_{s=0} = 31.25$$

$$B = (s+4)V_o(s)\bigg|_{s=-4} = \frac{125}{s}\bigg|_{s=-4} = -31.25$$

$$V_o = \frac{31.25}{s} - \frac{31.25}{s+4}$$

Taking the inverse Laplace transform gives

$$v_o(t) = 31.25(1 - e^{-4t})u(t) \text{ V}$$

Notice that the values of $v_o(0)$ and $v_o(\infty)$ obtained in part (b) are confirmed.

PRACTICE PROBLEM 16.6

Figure 16.17   For Practice Prob. 16.6.

The initial energy in the circuit in Fig. 16.17 is zero at $t = 0$. Assume that $v_s = 5u(t)$ V. (a) Find $V_o(s)$ using the Thevenin theorem. (b) Apply the initial- and final-value theorems to find $v_o(0)$ and $v_o(\infty)$. (c) Obtain $v_o(t)$.

Answer: (a) $V_o(s) = \frac{10(4s+1)}{s(10s+3)}$, (b) 4, 3.333 V,
(c) $(3.333 + 0.6667e^{-0.3t})u(t)$ V.

16.4   TRANSFER FUNCTIONS

For electrical networks, the transfer function is also known as the *network function*.

The *transfer function* is a key concept in signal processing because it indicates how a signal is processed as it passes through a network. It is a fitting tool for finding the network response, determining (or designing for) network stability, and network synthesis. The transfer function of a network describes how the output behaves with respect to the input. It specifies the transfer from the input to the output in the s domain, assuming no initial energy.

The transfer function $H(s)$ is the ratio of the output response $Y(s)$ to the input excitation $X(s)$, assuming all initial conditions are zero.

Thus,

$$H(s) = \frac{Y(s)}{X(s)} \tag{16.15}$$

The transfer function depends on what we define as input and output. Since the input and output can be either current or voltage at any place in the circuit, there are four possible transfer functions:

$$H(s) = \text{Voltage gain} = \frac{V_o(s)}{V_i(s)} \quad (16.16a)$$

$$H(s) = \text{Current gain} = \frac{I_o(s)}{I_i(s)} \quad (16.16b)$$

$$H(s) = \text{Impedance} = \frac{V(s)}{I(s)} \quad (16.16c)$$

$$H(s) = \text{Admittance} = \frac{I(s)}{V(s)} \quad (16.16d)$$

Some authors would not consider Eqs. (16.16c) and (16.16d) transfer functions.

Thus, a circuit can have many transfer functions. Note that $H(s)$ is dimensionless in Eqs. (16.16a) and (16.16b).

Each of the transfer functions in Eq. (16.16) can be found in two ways. One way is to assume any convenient input $X(s)$, use any circuit analysis technique (such as current or voltage division, nodal or mesh analysis) to find the output $Y(s)$, and then obtain the ratio of the two. The other approach is to apply the *ladder method*, which involves walking our way through the circuit. By this approach, we assume that the output is 1 V or 1 A as appropriate and use the basic laws of Ohm and Kirchhoff (KCL only) to obtain the input. The transfer function becomes unity divided by the input. This approach may be more convenient to use when the circuit has many loops or nodes so that applying nodal or mesh analysis becomes cumbersome. In the first method, we assume an input and find the output; in the second method, we assume the output and find the input. In both methods, we calculate $H(s)$ as the ratio of output to input transforms. The two methods rely on the linearity property, since we only deal with linear circuits in this book. Example 16.7 illustrates these methods.

Equation (16.15) assumes that both $X(s)$ and $Y(s)$ are known. Sometimes, we know the input $X(s)$ and the transfer function $H(s)$. We find the output $Y(s)$ as

$$Y(s) = H(s)X(s) \quad (16.17)$$

and take the inverse transform to get $y(t)$. A special case is when the input is the unit impulse function, $x(t) = \delta(t)$, so that $X(s) = 1$. For this case,

$$Y(s) = H(s) \quad \text{or} \quad y(t) = h(t) \quad (16.18)$$

where

$$h(t) = \mathcal{L}^{-1}[H(s)] \quad (16.19)$$

The term $h(t)$ represents the *unit impulse response*—it is the time-domain response of the network to a unit impulse. Thus, Eq. (16.19) provides a new interpretation for the transfer function: $H(s)$ is the Laplace transform of the unit impulse response of the network. Once we know the impulse response $h(t)$ of a network, we can obtain the response of the network to *any* input signal using Eq. (16.17) in the s domain or using the convolution integral (section 15.5) in the time domain.

The unit impulse response is the output response of a circuit when the input is a unit impulse.

EXAMPLE 16.7

The output of a linear system is $y(t) = 10e^{-t}\cos 4t u(t)$ when the input is $x(t) = e^{-t}u(t)$. Find the transfer function of the system and its impulse response.

Solution:

If $x(t) = e^{-t}u(t)$ and $y(t) = 10e^{-t}\cos 4t u(t)$, then

$$X(s) = \frac{1}{s+1} \quad \text{and} \quad Y(s) = \frac{10(s+1)}{(s+1)^2 + 4^2}$$

Hence,

$$H(s) = \frac{Y(s)}{X(s)} = \frac{10(s+1)^2}{(s+1)^2 + 16} = \frac{10(s^2 + 2s + 1)}{s^2 + 2s + 17}$$

To find $h(t)$, we write $H(s)$ as

$$H(s) = 10 - 40\frac{4}{(s+1)^2 + 4^2}$$

From Table 16.2, we obtain

$$h(t) = 10\delta(t) - 40e^{-t}\sin 4t\, u(t)$$

PRACTICE PROBLEM 16.7

The transfer function of a linear system is

$$H(s) = \frac{2s}{s+6}$$

Find the output $y(t)$ due to the input $e^{-3t}u(t)$ and its impulse response.

Answer: $-2e^{-3t} + 4e^{-6t}, t \geq 0, 2\delta(t) - 12e^{-6t}u(t)$.

EXAMPLE 16.8

Figure 16.18   For Example 16.8.

Determine the transfer function $H(s) = V_o(s)/I_o(s)$ of the circuit in Fig. 16.18.

Solution:

METHOD **1**   By current division,

$$I_2 = \frac{(s+4)I_o}{s+4+2+1/2s}$$

But

$$V_o = 2I_2 = \frac{2(s+4)I_o}{s+6+1/2s}$$

Hence,

$$H(s) = \frac{V_o(s)}{I_o(s)} = \frac{4s(s+4)}{2s^2 + 12s + 1}$$

METHOD 2 We can apply the ladder method. We let $V_o = 1$ V. By Ohm's law, $I_2 = V_o/2 = 1/2$ A. The voltage across the $(2 + 1/2s)$ impedance is

$$V_1 = I_2 \left(2 + \frac{1}{2s} \right) = 1 + \frac{1}{4s} = \frac{4s + 1}{4s}$$

This is the same as the voltage across the $(s + 4)$ impedance. Hence,

$$I_1 = \frac{V_1}{s + 4} = \frac{4s + 1}{4s(s + 4)}$$

Applying KCL at the top node yields

$$I_o = I_1 + I_2 = \frac{4s + 1}{4s(s + 4)} + \frac{1}{2} = \frac{2s^2 + 12s + 1}{4s(s + 4)}$$

Hence,

$$H(s) = \frac{V_o}{I_o} = \frac{1}{I_o} = \frac{4s(s + 4)}{2s^2 + 12s + 1}$$

as before.

PRACTICE PROBLEM 16.8

Find the transfer function $H(s) = I_1(s)/I_o(s)$ in the circuit of Fig. 16.18.

Answer: $\dfrac{4s + 1}{2s^2 + 12s + 1}$.

EXAMPLE 16.9

For the s-domain circuit in Fig. 16.19, find: (a) the transfer function $H(s) = V_o/V_i$, (b) the impulse response, (c) the response when $v_i(t) = u(t)$ V, (d) the response when $v_i(t) = 8 \cos 2t$ V.

Solution:

(a) Using voltage division,

$$V_o = \frac{1}{s + 1} V_{ab} \qquad (16.9.1)$$

But

$$V_{ab} = \frac{1 \parallel (s + 1)}{1 + 1 \parallel (s + 1)} V_i = \frac{(s + 1)/(s + 2)}{1 + (s + 1)/(s + 2)} V_i$$

or

$$V_{ab} = \frac{s + 1}{2s + 3} V_i \qquad (16.9.2)$$

Substituting Eq. (16.9.2) into Eq. (16.9.1) results in

$$V_o = \frac{V_i}{2s + 3}$$

Thus, the impulse response is

$$H(s) = \frac{V_o}{V_i} = \frac{1}{2s + 3}$$

Figure 16.19   For Example 16.9.

(b) We may write $H(s)$ as

$$H(s) = \frac{1}{2} \frac{1}{s + \frac{3}{2}}$$

Its inverse Laplace transform is the required impulse response:

$$h(t) = \frac{1}{2} e^{-3t/2} u(t)$$

(c) When $v_i(t) = u(t)$, $V_i(s) = 1/s$, and

$$V_o(s) = H(s)V_i(s) = \frac{1}{2s(s + \frac{3}{2})} = \frac{A}{s} + \frac{B}{s + \frac{3}{2}}$$

where

$$A = sV_o(s) \Big|_{s=0} = \frac{1}{2(s + \frac{3}{2})} \Big|_{s=0} = \frac{1}{3}$$

$$B = \left(s + \frac{3}{2}\right) V_o(s) \Big|_{s=-3/2} = \frac{1}{2s} \Big|_{s=-3/2} = -\frac{1}{3}$$

Hence, for $v_i(t) = u(t)$,

$$V_o(s) = \frac{1}{3} \left(\frac{1}{s} - \frac{1}{s + \frac{3}{2}}\right)$$

and its inverse Laplace transform is

$$v_o(t) = \frac{1}{3}(1 - e^{-3t/2})u(t) \text{ V}$$

(d) When $v_i(t) = 8\cos 2t$, then $V_i(s) = \dfrac{8s}{s^2 + 4}$, and

$$V_o(s) = H(s)V_i(s) = \frac{4s}{(s + \frac{3}{2})(s^2 + 4)}$$

$$= \frac{A}{s + \frac{3}{2}} + \frac{Bs + C}{s^2 + 4} \tag{16.9.3}$$

where

$$A = \left(s + \frac{3}{2}\right) V_o(s) \Big|_{s=-3/2} = \frac{4s}{s^2 + 4} \Big|_{s=-3/2} = -\frac{24}{25}$$

To get B and C, we multiply Eq. (16.9.3) by $(s + 3/2)(s^2 + 4)$. We get

$$4s = A(s^2 + 4) + B\left(s^2 + \frac{3}{2}s\right) + C\left(s + \frac{3}{2}\right)$$

Equating coefficients,

Constant:　$0 = 4A + \frac{3}{2}C \quad \Longrightarrow \quad C = -\frac{8}{3}A$

$s:$　$4 = \frac{3}{2}B + C$

$s^2:$　$0 = A + B \quad \Longrightarrow \quad B = -A$

Solving these gives $A = -24/25$, $B = 24/25$, $C = 64/25$. Hence, for $v_i(t) = 8\cos 2t$ V,

$$V_o(s) = \frac{-\frac{24}{25}}{s + \frac{3}{2}} + \frac{24}{25}\frac{s}{s^2 + 4} + \frac{32}{25}\frac{2}{s^2 + 4}$$

and its inverse is

$$v_o(t) = \frac{24}{25}\left(-e^{-3t/2} + \cos 2t + \frac{4}{3}\sin 2t\right)u(t)\ \text{V}$$

PRACTICE PROBLEM 16.9

Rework Example 16.9 for the circuit shown in Fig. 16.20.

Answer: (a) $2/(s + 4)$, (b) $2e^{-4t}u(t)$, (c) $\frac{1}{2}(1 - e^{-4t})u(t)$ V,
(d) $3.2(-e^{-4t} + \cos 2t + \frac{1}{2}\sin 2t)u(t)$ V.

Figure 16.20   For Practice Prob. 16.9.

16.5 STATE VARIABLES

Thus far in this book, we have considered techniques for analyzing systems with only one input and only one output. Many engineering systems have many inputs and many outputs, as shown in Fig. 16.21. The state variable method is a very important tool in analyzing systems and understanding such highly complex systems. Thus, the state variable model is more general than the single-input, single-output model, such as a transfer function. Although the topic cannot be adequately covered in one chapter, let alone one section of a chapter, we will cover it briefly at this point.

In the state variable model, we specify a collection of variables that describe the internal behavior of the system. These variables are known as the *state variables* of the system. They are the variables that determine the future behavior of a system when the present state of the system and the input signals are known. In other words, they are those variables which, if known, allow all other system parameters to be determined by using only algebraic equations.

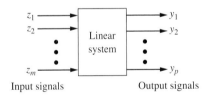

Figure 16.21   A linear system with m inputs and p outputs.

A state variable is a physical property which characterizes the state of a system, regardless of how the system got to that state.

Common examples of state variables are the pressure, volume, and temperature. In an electric circuit, the state variables are the inductor current and capacitor voltage since they collectively describe the energy state of the system.

The standard way to represent the state equations is to arrange them as a set of first-order differential equations:

$$\dot{\mathbf{x}} = \mathbf{A}x + \mathbf{B}z \tag{16.20}$$

where

$$\mathbf{x}(t) = \begin{bmatrix} x_1(t) \\ x_2(t) \\ \vdots \\ x_n(t) \end{bmatrix} = \text{state vector representing } n \text{ state vectors}$$

and the dot represents the first derivative with respect to time, i.e.,

$$\dot{\mathbf{x}}(t) = \begin{bmatrix} \dot{x}_1(t) \\ \dot{x}_2(t) \\ \vdots \\ \dot{x}_n(t) \end{bmatrix}$$

and

$$\mathbf{z}(t) = \begin{bmatrix} z_1(t) \\ z_2(t) \\ \vdots \\ z_m(t) \end{bmatrix} = \text{input vector representing } m \text{ inputs}$$

$\mathbf{A}$ and $\mathbf{B}$ are respectively $n \times n$ and $n \times m$ matrices. In addition to the state equation in Eq. (16.20), we need the output equation. The complete state model or state space is

$$\dot{\mathbf{x}} = \mathbf{A}x + \mathbf{B}z \tag{16.21a}$$

$$\mathbf{y} = \mathbf{C}x + \mathbf{D}z \tag{16.21b}$$

where $\mathbf{y}(t) = \begin{bmatrix} y_1(t) \\ y_2(t) \\ \vdots \\ y_p(t) \end{bmatrix} = \text{the output vector representing } p \text{ outputs. } \mathbf{C}$ and

$\mathbf{D}$ are, respectively, $p \times n$ and $p \times m$ matrices. For the special case of single-input single-output, $n = m = p = 1$.

Assuming zero initial conditions, the transfer function of the system is found by taking the Laplace transform of Eq. (16.21a); we obtain

$$s\mathbf{X}(s) = \mathbf{A}\mathbf{X}(s) + \mathbf{B}\mathbf{Z}(s) \qquad \longrightarrow \qquad (s\mathbf{I} - \mathbf{A})\mathbf{X}(s) = \mathbf{B}\mathbf{Z}(s)$$

or

$$\mathbf{X}(s) = (s\mathbf{I} - \mathbf{A})^{-1}\mathbf{B}\mathbf{Z}(s) \tag{16.22}$$

where $\mathbf{I}$ is the identity matrix. Taking the Laplace transform of Eq. (16.21b) yields

$$\mathbf{Y}(s) = \mathbf{C}\mathbf{X}(s) + \mathbf{D}\mathbf{Z}(s) \tag{16.23}$$

Substituting Eq. (16.22) into Eq. (16.23) and dividing by $Z(s)$ gives the transfer function as

$$\mathbf{H}(s) = \frac{\mathbf{Y}(s)}{\mathbf{Z}(s)} = \mathbf{C}(s\mathbf{I} - \mathbf{A})^{-1}\mathbf{B} + \mathbf{D} \tag{16.24}$$

where

$$\mathbf{A} = \text{system matrix}$$

$$\mathbf{B} = \text{input coupling matrix}$$

$$\mathbf{C} = \text{output matrix}$$

$$\mathbf{D} = \text{feedforward matrix}$$

In most cases, $\mathbf{D} = 0$, so the degree of the numerator of $H(s)$ in Eq. (16.24) is less than that of the denominator. Thus

$$\boxed{\mathbf{H}(s) = \mathbf{C}(s\mathbf{I} - \mathbf{A})^{-1}\mathbf{B}} \qquad (16.25)$$

Because of the matrix computation involved, *MATLAB* can be used to find the transfer function.

    To apply state variable analysis to a circuit, we follow the following three steps.

Steps to apply the state variable method to circuit analysis:

1. Select the inductor current i and capacitor voltage v as the state variables, making sure they are consistent with the passive sign convention.

2. Apply KCL and KVL to the circuit and obtain circuit variables (voltages and currents) in terms of the state variables. This should lead to a set of first-order differential equations necessary and sufficient to determine all state variables.

3. Obtain the output equation and put the final result in state-space representation.

    Steps 1 and 3 are usually straightforward; the major task is in step 2. We will illustrate this with examples.

EXAMPLE 16.10

Find the state-space representation of the circuit in Fig. 16.22. Determine the transfer function of the circuit when v_s is the input and i_x is the output. Take $R = 1\,\Omega$, $C = 0.25$ F, and $L = 0.5$ H.

Solution:

We select the inductor current i and capacitor voltage v as the state variables.

$$v_L = L\frac{di}{dt} \qquad (16.10.1)$$

$$i_C = C\frac{dv}{dt} \qquad (16.10.2)$$

Figure 16.22   For Example 16.10.

Applying KCL at node 1 gives

$$i = i_x + i_C \quad \longrightarrow \quad C\frac{dv}{dt} = i - \frac{v}{R}$$

or

$$\dot{v} = -\frac{v}{RC} + \frac{i}{C} \qquad (16.10.3)$$

since the same voltage v is across both R and C. Applying KVL around the outer loop yields

$$v_s = v_L + v \quad \longrightarrow \quad L\frac{di}{dt} = -v + v_s$$

$$\dot{i} = -\frac{v}{L} + \frac{v_s}{L} \qquad (16.10.4)$$

Equations (16.10.3) and (16.10.4) constitute the state equations. If we regard i_x as the output,

$$i_x = \frac{v}{R} \qquad (16.10.5)$$

Putting Eqs. (16.10.3) and (16.10.4) in the standard form leads to

$$\begin{bmatrix} \dot{v} \\ \dot{i} \end{bmatrix} = \begin{bmatrix} \frac{-1}{RC} & \frac{1}{C} \\ \frac{-1}{L} & 0 \end{bmatrix} \begin{bmatrix} v \\ i \end{bmatrix} + \begin{bmatrix} 0 \\ \frac{1}{L} \end{bmatrix} v_s \qquad (16.10.6a)$$

$$i_x = \begin{bmatrix} \frac{1}{R} & 0 \end{bmatrix} \begin{bmatrix} v \\ i \end{bmatrix} \qquad (16.10.6b)$$

If $R = 1$, $C = \frac{1}{4}$, and $L = \frac{1}{2}$, we obtain from Eq. (16.10.6) matrices

$$\mathbf{A} = \begin{bmatrix} \frac{-1}{RC} & \frac{1}{C} \\ \frac{-1}{L} & 0 \end{bmatrix} = \begin{bmatrix} -4 & 4 \\ -2 & 0 \end{bmatrix}, \qquad \mathbf{B} = \begin{bmatrix} 0 \\ \frac{1}{L} \end{bmatrix} = \begin{bmatrix} 0 \\ 2 \end{bmatrix},$$

$$\mathbf{C} = \begin{bmatrix} \frac{1}{R} & 0 \end{bmatrix} = \begin{bmatrix} 1 & 0 \end{bmatrix}$$

$$s\mathbf{I} - \mathbf{A} = \begin{bmatrix} s & 0 \\ 0 & s \end{bmatrix} - \begin{bmatrix} -4 & 4 \\ -2 & 0 \end{bmatrix} = \begin{bmatrix} s+4 & -4 \\ 2 & s \end{bmatrix}$$

Taking the inverse of this gives

$$(s\mathbf{I} - \mathbf{A})^{-1} = \frac{\text{adjoint of } \mathbf{A}}{\text{determinant of } \mathbf{A}} = \frac{\begin{bmatrix} s & 4 \\ -2 & s+4 \end{bmatrix}}{s^2 + 4s + 8}$$

Thus, the transfer function is given by

$$\mathbf{H}(s) = \mathbf{C}(s\mathbf{I} - \mathbf{A})^{-1}\mathbf{B} = \frac{\begin{bmatrix} 1 & 0 \end{bmatrix} \begin{bmatrix} s & 4 \\ -2 & s+4 \end{bmatrix} \begin{bmatrix} 0 \\ 2 \end{bmatrix}}{s^2 + 4s + 8} = \frac{\begin{bmatrix} 1 & 0 \end{bmatrix} \begin{bmatrix} 8 \\ 2s+8 \end{bmatrix}}{s^2 + 4s + 8}$$

$$= \frac{8}{s^2 + 4s + 8}$$

which is the same thing we would get by directly Laplace transforming the circuit and obtaining $\mathbf{H}(s) = I_x(s)/V_s(s)$. The real advantage of the state variable approach comes with multiple input and multiple outputs. In this case, we have one input v_s and one output i_x. In the next example, we will have two inputs and two outputs.

PRACTICE PROBLEM 16.10

Obtain the state variable model for the circuit shown in Fig. 16.23. Let $R_1 = 1$, $R_2 = 2$, $C = 0.5$, and $L = 0.2$ and obtain the transfer function.

Answer:

$$\begin{bmatrix} \dot{v} \\ \dot{i} \end{bmatrix} = \begin{bmatrix} \frac{-1}{R_1 C} & \frac{-1}{C} \\ \frac{-1}{L} & \frac{-R_2}{L} \end{bmatrix} \begin{bmatrix} v \\ i \end{bmatrix} + \begin{bmatrix} \frac{1}{R_1 C} \\ 0 \end{bmatrix} v_s, \qquad v_o = \begin{bmatrix} 0 & R_2 \end{bmatrix} \begin{bmatrix} v \\ i \end{bmatrix}$$

$$\mathbf{H}(s) = \frac{20}{s^2 + 12s + 30}$$

Figure 16.23   For Practice Prob. 16.10.

EXAMPLE 16.11

Consider the circuit in Fig. 16.24, which may be regarded as a two-input, two-output system. Determine the state variable model and find the transfer function of the system.

Figure 16.24   For Example 16.11.

Solution:

In this case, we have two inputs v_s and v_i and two outputs v_o and i_o. Again, we select the inductor current i and capacitor voltage v as the state variables. Applying KVL around the left-hand loop gives

$$-v_s + i_1 + \frac{1}{6}\dot{i} = 0 \qquad \longrightarrow \qquad \dot{i} = 6v_s - 6i_1 \qquad (16.11.1)$$

We need to eliminate i_1. Applying KVL around the loop containing v_s, 1-Ω resistor, 2-Ω resistor, and $\frac{1}{3}$-F capacitor yields

$$v_s = i_1 + v_o + v \qquad (16.11.2)$$

But at node 1, KCL gives

$$i_1 = i + \frac{v_o}{2} \qquad \longrightarrow \qquad v_o = 2(i_1 - i) \qquad (16.11.3)$$

Substituting this in Eq. (16.11.2),

$$v_s = 3i_1 + v - 2i \qquad \longrightarrow \qquad i_1 = \frac{2i - v + v_s}{3} \qquad (16.11.4)$$

Substituting this in Eq. (16.11.1),

$$\dot{i} = 2v - 4i + 4v_s \tag{16.11.5}$$

which is one state equation. To obtain the second one, we apply KCL at node 2.

$$\frac{v_o}{2} = \frac{1}{3}\dot{v} + i_o \quad \longrightarrow \quad \dot{v} = \frac{3}{2}v_o - 3i_o \tag{16.11.6}$$

We need to eliminate v_o and i_o. From the right-hand loop, it is evident that

$$i_o = \frac{v - v_i}{3} \tag{16.11.7}$$

Substituting Eq. (16.11.4) into Eq. (16.11.3) gives

$$v_o = 2\left(\frac{2i - v + v_s}{3} - i\right) = -\frac{2}{3}(v + i - v_s) \tag{16.11.8}$$

Substituting Eqs. (16.11.7) and (16.11.8) into Eq. (16.11.6) yields the second state equation as

$$\dot{v} = -2v - i + v_s + v_i \tag{16.11.9}$$

The two output equations are already obtained in Eqs. (16.11.7) and (16.11.8). Putting Eqs. (16.11.5) and (16.11.7) to (16.11.9) together in the standard form leads the state model for the circuit, namely,

$$\begin{bmatrix} \dot{v} \\ \dot{i} \end{bmatrix} = \begin{bmatrix} -2 & -1 \\ 2 & -4 \end{bmatrix} \begin{bmatrix} v \\ i \end{bmatrix} + \begin{bmatrix} 1 & 1 \\ 4 & 0 \end{bmatrix} \begin{bmatrix} v_s \\ v_i \end{bmatrix} \tag{16.11.10a}$$

$$\begin{bmatrix} v_o \\ i_o \end{bmatrix} = \begin{bmatrix} -\frac{2}{3} & -\frac{2}{3} \\ \frac{1}{3} & 0 \end{bmatrix} \begin{bmatrix} v \\ i \end{bmatrix} + \begin{bmatrix} \frac{2}{3} & 0 \\ 0 & -\frac{1}{3} \end{bmatrix} \begin{bmatrix} v_s \\ v_i \end{bmatrix} \tag{16.11.10b}$$

PRACTICE PROBLEM 16.11

For the electric circuit in Fig. 16.25, determine the state model. Take v_o and i_o as the output variables.

Answer:

$$\begin{bmatrix} \dot{v} \\ \dot{i} \end{bmatrix} = \begin{bmatrix} -2 & -2 \\ 4 & -8 \end{bmatrix} \begin{bmatrix} v \\ i \end{bmatrix} + \begin{bmatrix} 2 & 0 \\ 0 & -8 \end{bmatrix} \begin{bmatrix} i_1 \\ i_2 \end{bmatrix}$$

$$\begin{bmatrix} v_o \\ i_o \end{bmatrix} = \begin{bmatrix} 1 & 0 \\ 0 & 1 \end{bmatrix} \begin{bmatrix} v \\ i \end{bmatrix} + \begin{bmatrix} 0 & 0 \\ 0 & 1 \end{bmatrix} \begin{bmatrix} i_1 \\ i_2 \end{bmatrix}$$

Figure 16.25   For Practice Prob. 16.11.

EXAMPLE 16.12

Assume we have a system where the output is $y(t)$ and the input is $z(t)$. Let the following differential equation describe the relationship between the input and the output.

$$\frac{d^2 y(t)}{dt^2} + 3\frac{dy(t)}{dt} + 2y(t) = 5z(t) \qquad (16.12.1)$$

Obtain the state model and the transfer function of the system.

Solution:

First, we select the state variables. Let $x_1 = y(t)$, therefore

$$\dot{x}_1 = \dot{y}(t) \qquad (16.12.2)$$

Now let

$$x_2 = \dot{x}_1 = \dot{y}(t) \qquad (16.12.3)$$

Note that at this time we are looking at a second-order system that would normally have two first-order terms in the solution.

Now we have $\dot{x}_2 = \ddot{y}(t)$, where we can find the value $\dot{x}_2$ from Eq. (16.12.1), i.e.,

$$\dot{x}_2 = \ddot{y}(t) = -2y(t) - 3\dot{y}(t) + 5z(t) = -2x_1 - 3x_2 + 5z(t) \quad (16.12.4)$$

From Eqs. (16.12.2) to (16.12.4), we can now write the following matrix equations:

$$\begin{bmatrix} \dot{x}_1 \\ \dot{x}_2 \end{bmatrix} = \begin{bmatrix} 0 & 1 \\ -2 & -3 \end{bmatrix} \begin{bmatrix} x_1 \\ x_2 \end{bmatrix} + \begin{bmatrix} 0 \\ 5 \end{bmatrix} z(t) \qquad (16.12.5)$$

$$\mathbf{y}(t) = \begin{bmatrix} 1 & 0 \end{bmatrix} \begin{bmatrix} x_1 \\ x_2 \end{bmatrix} \qquad (16.12.6)$$

We now obtain the transfer function.

$$s\mathbf{I} - \mathbf{A} = s\begin{bmatrix} 1 & 0 \\ 0 & 1 \end{bmatrix} - \begin{bmatrix} 0 & 1 \\ -2 & -3 \end{bmatrix} = \begin{bmatrix} s & -1 \\ 2 & s+3 \end{bmatrix}$$

The inverse is

$$(s\mathbf{I} - \mathbf{A})^{-1} = \frac{\begin{bmatrix} s+3 & 1 \\ -2 & s \end{bmatrix}}{s(s+3) + 2}$$

The transfer function is

$$\mathbf{H}(s) = \mathbf{C}(s\mathbf{I} - \mathbf{A})^{-1}\mathbf{B} = \frac{\begin{pmatrix} 1 & 0 \end{pmatrix}\begin{bmatrix} s+3 & 1 \\ -2 & s \end{bmatrix}\begin{pmatrix} 0 \\ 5 \end{pmatrix}}{s(s+3) + 2} = \frac{\begin{pmatrix} 1 & 0 \end{pmatrix}\begin{pmatrix} 5 \\ 5s \end{pmatrix}}{s(s+3) + 2}$$

$$= \frac{5}{(s+1)(s+2)}$$

To check this, we directly apply the Laplace transfer to each term in Eq. (16.12.1). Since initial conditions are zero, we get

$$[s^2 + 3s + 2]Y(s) = 5Z(s) \quad \longrightarrow \quad H(s) = \frac{Y(s)}{Z(s)} = \frac{5}{s^2 + 3s + 2}$$

which is in agreement with what we got previously.

PRACTICE PROBLEM 16.12

Develop a set of state variable equations that represent the following differential equation.

$$\frac{d^3y}{dt^3} + 6\frac{d^2y}{dt^2} + 11\frac{dy}{dt} + 6y = z(t)$$

Answer:

$$\mathbf{A} = \begin{bmatrix} 0 & 1 & 0 \\ 0 & 0 & 1 \\ -6 & -11 & -6 \end{bmatrix}, \qquad \mathbf{B} = \begin{bmatrix} 0 \\ 0 \\ 1 \end{bmatrix}, \qquad \mathbf{C} = \begin{bmatrix} 1 & 0 & 0 \end{bmatrix}.$$

†16.6 APPLICATIONS

So far we have considered three applications of Laplace's transform: circuit analysis in general, obtaining transfer functions, and solving linear integrodifferential equations. The Laplace transform also finds application in other areas in circuit analysis, signal processing, and control systems. Here we will consider two more important applications: network stability and network synthesis.

16.6.1 Network Stability

A circuit is *stable* if its impulse response $h(t)$ is bounded (i.e., $h(t)$ converges to a finite value) as $t \to \infty$; it is *unstable* if $h(t)$ grows without bound as $t \to \infty$. In mathematical terms, a circuit is stable when

$$\lim_{t \to \infty} |h(t)| = \text{finite} \tag{16.26}$$

Since the transfer function $H(s)$ is the Laplace transform of the impulse response $h(t)$, $H(s)$ must meet certain requirements in order for Eq. (16.26) to hold. Recall that $H(s)$ may be written as

$$H(s) = \frac{N(s)}{D(s)} \tag{16.27}$$

where the roots of $N(s) = 0$ are called the *zeros* of $H(s)$ because they make $H(s) = 0$, while the roots of $D(s) = 0$ are called the *poles* of $H(s)$ since they cause $H(s) \to \infty$. The zeros and poles of $H(s)$ are often located in the s plane as shown in Fig. 16.26(a). Recall from Eqs. (15.47) and (15.48) that $H(s)$ may also be written in terms of its poles as

$$H(s) = \frac{N(s)}{D(s)} = \frac{N(s)}{(s + p_1)(s + p_2) \cdots (s + p_n)} \tag{16.28}$$

$H(s)$ must meet two requirements for the circuit to be stable. First, the degree of $N(s)$ must be less than the degree of $D(s)$; otherwise, long division would produce

$$H(s) = k_n s^n + k_{n-1} s^{n-1} + \cdots + k_1 s + k_0 + \frac{R(s)}{D(s)} \tag{16.29}$$

where the degree of $R(s)$, the remainder of the long division, is less than the degree of $D(s)$. The inverse of $H(s)$ in Eq. (16.26) does not meet

o Zero
x Pole

(a)

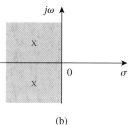

(b)

Figure 16.26 The complex s plane: (a) poles and zeros plotted, (b) left-half plane.

the condition in Eq. (16.26). Second, all the poles of $H(s)$ in Eq. (16.27) (i.e., all the roots of $D(s) = 0$) must have negative real parts; in other words, all the poles must lie in the left half of the s plane, as shown typically in Fig. 16.26(b). The reason for this will be apparent if we take the inverse Laplace transform of $H(s)$ in Eq. (16.27). Since Eq. (16.27) is similar to Eq. (15.48), its partial fraction expansion is similar to the one in Eq. (15.49) so that the inverse of $H(s)$ is similar to that in Eq. (15.53). Hence,

$$h(t) = (k_1 e^{-p_1 t} + k_2 e^{-p_2 t} + \cdots + k_n e^{-p_n t})u(t) \qquad (16.30)$$

We see from this equation that each pole p_i must be positive (i.e., pole $s = -p_i$ in the left-half plane) in order for $e^{-p_i t}$ to decrease with increasing t. Thus,

> A circuit is stable when all the poles of its transfer function $H(s)$ lie in the left half of the s plane.

An unstable circuit never reaches steady state because the transient response does not decay to zero. Consequently, steady-state analysis is only applicable to stable circuits.

A circuit made up exclusively of passive elements (R, L, and C) and independent sources cannot be unstable, because that would imply that some branch currents or voltages would grow indefinitely with sources set to zero. Passive elements cannot generate such indefinite growth. Passive circuits either are stable or have poles with zero real parts. To show that this is the case, consider the series RLC circuit in Fig. 16.27. The transfer function is given by

$$H(s) = \frac{V_o}{V_s} = \frac{1/sC}{R + sL + 1/sC}$$

or

$$H(s) = \frac{1/L}{s^2 + sR/L + 1/LC} \qquad (16.31)$$

Figure 16.27 A typical RLC circuit.

Notice that $D(s) = s^2 + sR/L + 1/LC = 0$ is the same as the characteristic equation obtained for the series RLC circuit in Eq. (8.8). The circuit has poles at

$$p_{1,2} = -\alpha \pm \sqrt{\alpha^2 - \omega_0^2} \qquad (16.32)$$

where

$$\alpha = \frac{R}{2L}, \qquad \omega_0 = \frac{1}{LC}$$

For $R, L, C > 0$, the two poles always lie in the left half of the s plane, implying that the circuit is always stable. However, when $R = 0$, $\alpha = 0$ and the circuit becomes unstable. Although ideally this is possible, it does not really happen, because R is never zero.

On the other hand, active circuits or passive circuits with controlled sources can supply energy, and they can be unstable. In fact, an oscillator is a typical example of a circuit designed to be unstable. An oscillator is designed such that its transfer function is of the form

$$H(s) = \frac{N(s)}{s^2 + \omega_0^2} = \frac{N(s)}{(s + j\omega_0)(s - j\omega_0)} \tag{16.33}$$

so that its output is sinusoidal.

EXAMPLE 16.13

Figure 16.28   For Example 16.13.

Determine the values of k for which the circuit in Fig. 16.28 is stable.

Solution:

Applying mesh analysis to the first-order circuit in Fig. 16.28 gives

$$V_i = \left(R + \frac{1}{sC}\right)I_1 - \frac{I_2}{sC} \tag{16.13.1}$$

and

$$0 = -kI_1 + \left(R + \frac{1}{sC}\right)I_2 - \frac{I_1}{sC}$$

or

$$0 = -\left(k + \frac{1}{sC}\right)I_1 + \left(R + \frac{1}{sC}\right)I_2 \tag{16.13.2}$$

We can write Eqs. (16.13.1) and (16.13.2) in matrix form as

$$\begin{bmatrix} V_i \\ 0 \end{bmatrix} = \begin{bmatrix} \left(R + \dfrac{1}{sC}\right) & -\dfrac{1}{sC} \\ -\left(k + \dfrac{1}{sC}\right) & \left(R + \dfrac{1}{sC}\right) \end{bmatrix} \begin{bmatrix} I_1 \\ I_2 \end{bmatrix}$$

The determinant is

$$\Delta = \left(R + \frac{1}{sC}\right)^2 - \frac{k}{sC} - \frac{1}{s^2C^2} = \frac{sR^2C + 2R - k}{sC} \tag{16.13.3}$$

The characteristic equation ($\Delta = 0$) gives the single pole as

$$p = \frac{k - 2R}{R^2C}$$

which is negative when $k < 2R$. Thus, we conclude the circuit is stable when $k < 2R$ and unstable for $k > 2R$.

PRACTICE PROBLEM 16.13

Figure 16.29   For Practice Prob. 16.13.

For what value of β is the circuit in Fig. 16.29 stable?

Answer: $\beta > 1/R$.

EXAMPLE 16.14

An active filter has the transfer function

$$H(s) = \frac{k}{s^2 + s(4 - k) + 1}$$

For what values of k is the filter stable?

Solution:

As a second-order circuit, $H(s)$ may be written as

$$H(s) = \frac{N(s)}{s^2 + bs + c}$$

where $b = 4 - k$, $c = 1$, and $N(s) = k$. This has poles at $p^2 + bp + c = 0$, that is,

$$p_{1,2} = \frac{-b \pm \sqrt{b^2 - 4c}}{2}$$

For the circuit to be stable, the poles must be located in the left half of the s plane. This implies that $b > 0$.

Applying this to the given $H(s)$ means that for the circuit to be stable, $4 - k > 0$ or $k < 4$.

PRACTICE PROBLEM 16.14

A second-order active circuit has the transfer function

$$H(s) = \frac{1}{s^2 + s(10 + \alpha) + 25}$$

Find the range of the values of α for which the circuit is stable. What is the value of α that will cause oscillation?

Answer: $\alpha > -10, \alpha = -10$.

16.6.2 Network Synthesis

Network synthesis may be regarded as the process of obtaining an appropriate network to represent a given transfer function. Network synthesis is easier in the s domain than in the time domain.

In network analysis, we find the transfer function of a given network. In network synthesis, we reverse the approach: given a transfer function, we are required to find a suitable network.

Network synthesis is finding a network that represents a given transfer function.

Keep in mind that in synthesis, there may be many different answers—or possibly no answers—because there are many circuits that can be used to represent the same transfer function; in network analysis, there is only one answer.

Network synthesis is an exciting field of prime engineering importance. Being able to look at a transfer function and come up with the type of circuit it represents is a great asset to a circuit designer. Although network synthesis constitutes a whole course by itself and requires some experience, the following examples are meant to whet your appetite.

EXAMPLE 16.15

Given the transfer function

$$H(s) = \frac{V_o(s)}{V_i(s)} = \frac{10}{s^2 + 3s + 10}$$

realize the function using the circuit in Fig. 16.30(a). (a) Select $R = 5\,\Omega$, and find L and C. (b) Select $R = 1\,\Omega$, and find L and C.

Solution:

The s-domain equivalent of the circuit in Fig. 16.30(a) is shown in Fig. 16.30(b). The parallel combination of R and C gives

$$R \left\| \frac{1}{sC} = \frac{R/sC}{R + 1/sC} = \frac{R}{1 + sRC} \right.$$

Using the voltage division principle,

$$V_o = \frac{R/(1 + sRC)}{sL + R/(1 + sRC)} V_i = \frac{R}{sL(1 + sRC) + R} V_i$$

or

$$\frac{V_o}{V_i} = \frac{R}{s^2 RLC + sL + R} = \frac{1/LC}{s^2 + s/RC + 1/LC}$$

Comparing this with the given transfer function $H(s)$ reveals that

$$\frac{1}{LC} = 10, \qquad \frac{1}{RC} = 3$$

There are several values of R, L, and C that satisfy these requirements. This is the reason for specifying one element value so that others can be determined.
(a) If we select $R = 5\,\Omega$, then

$$C = \frac{1}{3R} = 66.67 \text{ mF}, \qquad L = \frac{1}{10C} = 1.5 \text{ H}$$

(b) If we select $R = 1\,\Omega$, then

$$C = \frac{1}{3R} = 0.333 \text{ F}, \qquad L = \frac{1}{10C} = 0.3 \text{ H}$$

Making $R = 1\,\Omega$ can be regarded as *normalizing* the design.
In this example we have used passive elements to realize the given transfer function. The same goal can be achieved by using active elements, as the next example demonstrates.

(a)

(b)

Figure 16.30   For Example 16.15.

PRACTICE PROBLEM 16.15

Figure 16.31   For Practice Prob. 16.15.

Realize the function

$$G(s) = \frac{V_o(s)}{V_i(s)} = \frac{4s}{s^2 + 4s + 20}$$

using the circuit in Fig. 16.31. Select $R = 2\,\Omega$, and determine L and C.

Answer: 0.5 H, 0.1 F.

EXAMPLE 16.16

Synthesize the function

$$T(s) = \frac{V_o(s)}{V_s(s)} = \frac{10^6}{s^2 + 100s + 10^6}$$

using the topology in Fig. 16.32.

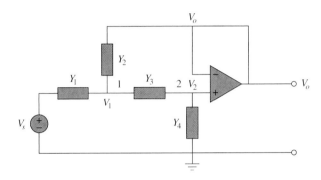

Figure 16.32   For Example 16.16.

Solution:

We apply nodal analysis to nodes 1 and 2. At node 1,

$$(V_s - V_1)Y_1 = (V_1 - V_o)Y_2 + (V_1 - V_2)Y_3 \qquad (16.16.1)$$

At node 2,

$$(V_1 - V_2)Y_3 = (V_2 - 0)Y_4 \qquad (16.16.2)$$

But $V_2 = V_o$, so Eq. (16.16.1) becomes

$$Y_1 V_s = (Y_1 + Y_2 + Y_3)V_1 - (Y_2 + Y_3)V_o \qquad (16.16.3)$$

and Eq. (16.16.2) becomes

$$V_1 Y_3 = (Y_3 + Y_4)V_o$$

or

$$V_1 = \frac{1}{Y_3}(Y_3 + Y_4)V_o \qquad (16.16.4)$$

Substituting Eq. (16.16.4) into Eq. (16.16.3) gives

$$Y_1 V_s = (Y_1 + Y_2 + Y_3)\frac{1}{Y_3}(Y_3 + Y_4)V_o - (Y_2 + Y_3)V_o$$

or

$$Y_1 Y_3 V_s = [Y_1 Y_3 + Y_4(Y_1 + Y_2 + Y_3)]V_o$$

Thus,

$$\frac{V_o}{V_s} = \frac{Y_1 Y_3}{Y_1 Y_3 + Y_4(Y_1 + Y_2 + Y_3)} \qquad (16.16.5)$$

To synthesize the given transfer function $T(s)$, compare it with the one in Eq. (16.16.5). Notice two things: (1) $Y_1 Y_3$ must not involve s because the numerator of $T(s)$ is constant; (2) the given transfer function is second-order, which implies that we must have two capacitors. Therefore, we must make Y_1 and Y_3 resistive, while Y_2 and Y_4 are capacitive. So we select

$$Y_1 = \frac{1}{R_1}, \qquad Y_2 = sC_1, \qquad Y_3 = \frac{1}{R_2}, \qquad Y_4 = sC_2 \qquad (16.16.6)$$

Substituting Eq. (16.16.6) into Eq. (16.16.5) gives

$$\frac{V_o}{V_s} = \frac{1/(R_1 R_2)}{1/(R_1 R_2) + sC_2(1/R_1 + 1/R_2 + sC_1)}$$

$$= \frac{1/(R_1 R_2 C_1 C_2)}{s^2 + s(R_1 + R_2)/(R_1 R_2 C_1) + 1/(R_1 R_2 C_1 C_2)}$$

Comparing this with the given transfer function $T(s)$, we notice that

$$\frac{1}{R_1 R_2 C_1 C_2} = 10^6, \qquad \frac{R_1 + R_2}{R_1 R_2 C_1} = 100$$

If we select $R_1 = R_2 = 10$ kΩ, then

$$C_1 = \frac{R_1 + R_2}{100 R_1 R_2} = \frac{20 \times 10^3}{100 \times 100 \times 10^6} = 2 \ \mu\text{F}$$

$$C_2 = \frac{10^{-6}}{R_1 R_2 C_1} = \frac{10^{-6}}{100 \times 10^6 \times 2 \times 10^{-6}} = 5 \ \text{nF}$$

Thus, the given transfer function is realized using the circuit shown in Fig. 16.33.

Figure 16.33   For Example 16.16.

PRACTICE PROBLEM 16.16

Synthesize the function

$$\frac{V_o(s)}{V_{\text{in}}} = \frac{-2s}{s^2 + 6s + 10}$$

using the op amp circuit shown in Fig. 16.34. Select

$$Y_1 = \frac{1}{R_1}, \qquad Y_2 = sC_1, \qquad Y_3 = sC_2, \qquad Y_4 = \frac{1}{R_2}$$

Let $R_1 = 1$ kΩ, and determine C_1, C_2, and R_2.

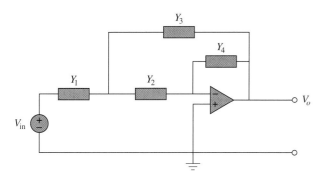

Figure 16.34   For Practice Prob. 16.16.

Answer: 0.1 mF, 0.5 mF, 2 kΩ.

16.7 COMPUTATION USING MATLAB

MATLAB is a software package that is widely used for engineering computation and simulation. A review of *MATLAB* is provided in Appendix E for the beginner. This section shows how to use the software to numerically perform most of these operations presented in this chapter and Chapter 15. The key to describing a system in *MATLAB* is to specify the numerator (num) and denominator (den) of the transfer function of the system. Once this is done, we can use several *MATLAB* commands to obtain the system's Bode plots (frequency response) and the system's response to a given input.

The command **bode** produces the Bode plots (both magnitude and phase) of a given transfer function $H(s)$. The format of the command is **bode** (num, den), where num is the numerator of $H(s)$ and den is its denominator. The frequency range and number of points are automatically selected. For example, consider the transfer function in Example 14.3. It is better to first write the numerator and denominator in polynomial forms. Thus,

$$H(s) = \frac{200 j\omega}{(j\omega + 2)(j\omega + 10)} = \frac{200s}{s^2 + 12s + 20}, \qquad s = j\omega \quad (16.34)$$

Using the following commands, the Bode plots are generated as shown in Fig. 16.35. If necessary, the command **logspace** can be included to generate a logarithmically spaced frequency and the command **semilogx** can be used to produce a semilog scale.

```
>> num = [200 0];    % specify the numerator of H(s)
>> den = [1 12 20];  % specify the denominator of H(s)
>> bode(num, den);   % determine and draw Bode plots
```

The step response $y(t)$ of a system is the output when the input $x(t)$ is the unit step function. The command **step** plots the step response of a system given the numerator and denominator of the transfer function of that system. The time range and number of points are automatically

Bode diagrams

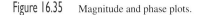

Figure 16.35   Magnitude and phase plots.

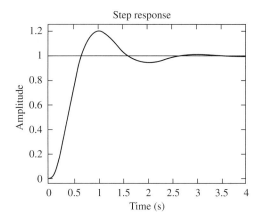

Step response

Figure 16.36   The step response of $H(s) = 12/(s^2 + 3s + 12)$.

selected. For example, consider a second-order system with the transfer function

$$H(s) = \frac{12}{s^2 + 3s + 12} \tag{16.35}$$

We obtain the step response of the system shown in Fig. 16.36 by using the following commands.

```
>> n = 12;
>> d = [1 3 12];
>> step(n,d);
```

We can verify the plot in Fig. 16.36 by obtaining $y(t) = x(t) * u(t)$ or $Y(s) = X(s)H(s)$.

The command **lsim** is a more general command than **step**. It calculates the time response of a system to any arbitrary input signal. The format of the command is $y = $ **lsim** (num, den, x, t), where $x(t)$ is the input signal, t is the time vector, and $y(t)$ is the output generated. For example, assume a system is described by the transfer function

$$H(s) = \frac{s + 4}{s^3 + 2s^2 + 5s + 10} \tag{16.36}$$

To find the response $y(t)$ of the system to input $x(t) = 10e^{-t}u(t)$, we use the following *MATLAB* commands. Both the response $y(t)$ and the input $x(t)$ are plotted in Fig. 16.37.

```
>> t = 0:0.02:5; % time vector 0 < t < 5 with increment 0.02
>> x = 10*exp(-t);
>> num = [1 4];
>> den = [1 2 5 10];
>> y = lsim(num,den,x,t);
>> plot(t,x,t,y)
```

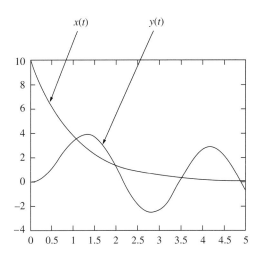

Figure 16.37   The response of the system described by $H(s) = (s+4)/(s^3 + 2s^2 + 5s + 10)$ to an exponential input.

16.8 SUMMARY

1. The Laplace transform can be used to analyze a circuit. We convert each element from the time domain to the s domain, solve the problem using any circuit analysis technique, and convert the result to the time domain using the inverse transform.

2. In the s domain, the circuit elements are replaced with the initial condition at $t = 0$ as follows. (Please note, voltage models are given below, but the corresponding current models work equally as well.):

   Resistor: $v_R = Ri \quad \longrightarrow \quad V_R = RI$

   Inductor: $v_L = L\dfrac{di}{dt} \quad \longrightarrow \quad V_L = sLI - Li(0^-)$

   Capacitor: $v_C = \displaystyle\int i\, dt \quad \longrightarrow \quad V_C = \dfrac{I}{sC} - \dfrac{v(0^-)}{s}$

3. Using the Laplace transform to analyze a circuit results in a complete (both transient and steady state) response because the initial conditions are incorporated in the transformation process.

4. The transfer function $H(s)$ of a network is the Laplace transform of the impulse response $h(t)$.

5. In the s domain, the transfer function $H(s)$ relates the output response $Y(s)$ and an input excitation $X(s)$; that is, $H(s) = Y(s)/X(s)$.

6. The state variable model is a useful tool for analyzing complex systems with several inputs and outputs. State variable analysis is a powerful technique that is most popularly used in circuit theory and control. The state of a system is the smallest set of quantities (known as state variables) that we must know in order to determine its future response to any given input. The state equation in state

variable form is

$$\dot{\mathbf{x}} = \mathbf{A}x + \mathbf{B}z$$

while the output equation is

$$\mathbf{y} = \mathbf{C}x + \mathbf{D}z$$

7. For an electric circuit, we first select capacitor voltages and inductor current as state variables. We then apply KCL and KVL to obtain the state equations.

8. Two other areas of applications of the Laplace transform covered in this chapter are circuit stability and synthesis. A circuit is stable when all the poles of its transfer function lie in the left half of the s plane. Network synthesis is the process of obtaining an appropriate network to represent a given transfer function for which analysis in the s domain is well suited.

9. *MATLAB* can be used to plot the frequency response (Bode plots) and determine the response of a system to a given input.

REVIEW QUESTIONS

16.1 The voltage through a resistor with current $i(t)$ in the s domain is $sRI(s)$.

(a) True   (b) False

16.2 The current through an RL series circuit with input voltage $v(t)$ is given in the s domain as:

(a) $V(s)\left[R + \dfrac{1}{sL}\right]$ (b) $V(s)(R + sL)$

(c) $\dfrac{V(s)}{R + 1/sL}$ (d) $\dfrac{V(s)}{R + sL}$

16.3 The impedance of a 10-F capacitor is:

(a) $10/s$ (b) $s/10$ (c) $1/10s$ (d) $10s$

16.4 We can usually obtain the Thevenin equivalent in the time domain.

(a) True   (b) False

16.5 A transfer function is defined only when all initial conditions are zero.

(a) True   (b) False

16.6 If the input to a linear system is $\delta(t)$ and the output is $e^{-2t}u(t)$, the transfer function of the system is:

(a) $\dfrac{1}{s + 2}$ (b) $\dfrac{1}{s - 2}$ (c) $\dfrac{s}{s + 2}$ (d) $\dfrac{s}{s - 2}$

(e) None of the above

16.7 If the transfer function of a system is

$$H(s) = \frac{s^2 + s + 2}{s^3 + 4s^2 + 5s + 1}$$

it follows that the input is $X(s) = s^3 + 4s^2 + 5s + 1$, while the output is $Y(s) = s^2 + s + 2$.

(a) True   (b) False

16.8 Which of the following equations is called the state equation?

(a) $\dot{x} = \mathbf{A}x + \mathbf{B}z$
(b) $\mathbf{y} = \mathbf{C}x + \mathbf{D}z$
(c) $\mathbf{H}(s) = \mathbf{Y}(s)/\mathbf{Z}(s)$
(d) $\mathbf{H}(s) = \mathbf{C}(s\mathbf{I} - \mathbf{A})^{-1}\mathbf{B}$

16.9 A single-input, single-output system is described by the state model as:

$$\dot{x}_1 = 2x_1 - x_2 + 3z$$
$$\dot{x}_2 = -4x_2 - z$$
$$y = 3x_1 - 2x_2 + z$$

Which of the following matrices is incorrect?

(a) $\mathbf{A} = \begin{bmatrix} 2 & -1 \\ 0 & -4 \end{bmatrix}$ (b) $\mathbf{B} = \begin{bmatrix} 3 \\ -1 \end{bmatrix}$

(c) $\mathbf{C} = \begin{bmatrix} 3 & -2 \end{bmatrix}$ (d) $\mathbf{D} = \mathbf{0}$

16.10 Which *MATLAB* command is used to obtain the frequency response of a system?

(a) **root** (b) **step** (c) **bode** (d) **lsim** (e) **rlocus**

Answers: 16.1b, 16.2d, 16.3c, 16.4b, 16.5b, 16.6a, 16.7b, 16.8a, 16.9d, 16.10c.

PROBLEMS

Sections 16.2 and 16.3   Circuit Element Models and Circuit Analysis

16.1   Determine $i(t)$ in the circuit of Fig. 16.38 by means of the Laplace transform.

Figure 16.38   For Prob. 16.1.

16.2   Find v_x in the circuit shown in Fig. 16.39 given $v_s = 4u(t)$ V.

Figure 16.39   For Prob. 16.2.

16.3   Find $v_o(t)$ in the circuit shown in Fig. 16.40 given $i_s(t) = 5u(t)$ A.

Figure 16.40   For Prob. 16.3.

16.4   Find $v_o(t)$ in the circuit in Fig. 16.41.

Figure 16.41   For Prob. 16.4.

16.5   If $i_s(t) = e^{-2t}u(t)$ A in the circuit shown in Fig. 16.42, find the value of $i_o(t)$.

Figure 16.42   For Prob. 16.5.

16.6   Determine $i_o(t)$ in the circuit shown in Fig. 16.43 given $i_s(t) = 5e^{-2t}$ A.

Figure 16.43   For Prob. 16.6.

16.7   Use the Laplace transform to find i_x in the circuit of Fig. 16.44.

Figure 16.44   For Prob. 16.7.

16.8   Find the input impedance of each of the networks in Fig. 16.45.

(a)

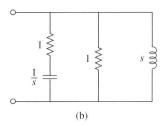

(b)

Figure 16.45   For Prob. 16.8.

16.9   Find the input impedance $Z_{in}(s)$ of each of the circuits in Fig. 16.46.

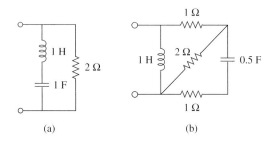

(a)   (b)

Figure 16.46   For Prob. 16.9.

16.10   At terminals a-b of the circuit in Fig. 16.47, find the Thevenin and Norton equivalent circuits.

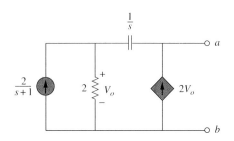

Figure 16.47   For Prob. 16.10.

16.11   Obtain the mesh currents in the circuit of Fig. 16.48.

Figure 16.48   For Prob. 16.11.

---

*An asterisk indicates a challenging problem.

16.12   Find $v_o(t)$ in the circuit in Fig. 16.49.

Figure 16.49   For Prob. 16.12.

16.13   Determine $i_o(t)$ in the circuit in Fig. 16.50.

Figure 16.50   For Prob. 16.13.

***16.14**   Determine $i_o(t)$ in the network shown in Fig. 16.51.

Figure 16.51   For Prob. 16.14.

16.15   Find $V_x(s)$ in the circuit shown in Fig. 16.52.

Figure 16.52   For Prob. 16.15.

***16.16**   Find $i_o(t)$ for $t > 0$ in the circuit in Fig. 16.53.

Figure 16.53   For Prob. 16.16.

16.17 Calculate $i_o(t)$ for $t > 0$ in the network of Fig. 16.54.

$2e^{-t}u(t)$ V

1 F i_o 1 H

1 Ω $4u(t)$ A   1 Ω

Figure 16.54   For Prob. 16.17.

16.18 (a) Find the Laplace transform of the voltage shown in Fig. 16.55(a). (b) Using that value of $v_s(t)$ in the circuit shown in Fig. 16.55(b), find the value of $v_o(t)$.

$v_s(t)$

3 V

0   1 s t

(a)

1 Ω

$v_s(t)$ 1 F $v_o(t)$ 2 Ω

(b)

Figure 16.55   For Prob. 16.18.

16.19 In the circuit of Fig. 16.56, let $i(0) = 1$ A, $v_o(0) = 2$ V, and $v_s = 4e^{-2t}u(t)$ V. Find $v_o(t)$ for $t > 0$.

2 Ω $2i$

v_s i 1 H   1 F v_o

Figure 16.56   For Prob. 16.19.

16.20 Find $v_o(t)$ in the circuit in Fig. 16.57 if $v_x(0) = 2$ V and $i(0) = 1$ A.

+ v_x − i

1 F

$e^{-t}u(t)$ A   1 Ω   1 Ω   1 H v_o

Figure 16.57   For Prob. 16.20.

16.21 Find the voltage $v_o(t)$ in the circuit of Fig. 16.58 by means of the Laplace transform.

1 Ω   1 H

$10u(t)$ V   0.5 F   2 Ω   1 F v_o

Figure 16.58   For Prob. 16.21.

16.22 Find the node voltages v_1 and v_2 in the circuit of Fig. 16.59 using the Laplace transform technique. Assume that $i_s = 12e^{-t}u(t)$ A and that all initial conditions are zero.

v_1 4 H v_2

i_s 1 Ω   2 Ω $\frac{1}{3}$ F

Figure 16.59   For Prob. 16.22.

16.23 Consider the parallel RLC circuit of Fig. 16.60. Find $v(t)$ and $i(t)$ given that $v(0) = 5$ and $i(0) = -2$ A.

$4u(t)$ A   10 Ω   4 H i $\frac{1}{80}$ F v

Figure 16.60   For Prob. 16.23.

16.24 The switch in the circuit of Fig. 16.61 has been closed for a long time. It is opened at $t = 0$. Determine $v_o(t)$ for $t > 0$ using the Laplace transform.

Figure 16.61   For Prob. 16.24.

16.25 For the RLC circuit shown in Fig. 16.62, find the complete response if $v(0) = 2$ V when the switch is closed.

Figure 16.62   For Prob. 16.25.

16.26 For the op amp circuit in Fig. 16.63, find $v_o(t)$ for $t > 0$. Take $v_s = 3e^{-5t}u(t)$ V.

10 kΩ

50 μF

20 kΩ

v_o

v_s

Figure 16.63   For Prob. 16.26.

16.27 Find $I_1(s)$ and $I_2(s)$ in the circuit of Fig. 16.64.

Figure 16.64   For Prob. 16.27.

16.28 For the circuit in Fig. 16.65, find $v_o(t)$ for $t > 0$.

Figure 16.65   For Prob. 16.28.

16.29 For the ideal transformer circuit in Fig. 16.66, determine $i_o(t)$.

Figure 16.66   For Prob. 16.29.

Section 16.4   Transfer Functions

16.30 The transfer function of a system is

$$H(s) = \frac{s^2}{3s + 1}$$

Find the output when the system has an input of $4e^{-t/3}u(t)$.

16.31 When the input to a system is a unit step function, the response is $10 \cos 2t\, u(t)$. Obtain the transfer function of the system.

16.32 A circuit is known to have its transfer function as

$$H(s) = \frac{s + 3}{s^2 + 4s + 5}$$

Find its output when:

(a) the input is a unit step function
(b) the input is $6te^{-2t}u(t)$.

16.33 When a unit step is applied to a system at $t = 0$, its response is

$$y(t) = \left[4 + \frac{1}{2}e^{-3t} - e^{-2t}(2 \cos 4t + 3 \sin 4t)\right]u(t)$$

What is the transfer function of the system?

16.34 For the circuit in Fig. 16.67, find $H(s) = V_o(s)/V_s(s)$. Assume zero initial conditions.

Figure 16.67   For Prob. 16.34.

16.35 Obtain the transfer function $H(s) = V_o/V_s$ for the circuit of Fig. 16.68.

Figure 16.68   For Prob. 16.35.

16.36 Repeat the previous problem for $H(s) = V_o/I$.

16.37 For the circuit in Fig. 16.69, find:

  (a) I_1/V_s (b) I_2/V_x

Figure 16.69   For Prob. 16.37.

16.38 Refer to the network in Fig. 16.70. Find the following transfer functions:

  (a) $H_1(s) = V_o(s)/V_s(s)$
  (b) $H_2(s) = V_o(s)/I_s(s)$
  (c) $H_3(s) = I_o(s)/I_s(s)$
  (d) $H_4(s) = I_o(s)/V_s(s)$

Figure 16.70   For Prob. 16.38.

16.39 Calculate the gain $H(s) = V_o/V_s$ in the op amp circuit of Fig. 16.71.

Figure 16.71   For Prob. 16.39.

16.40 Refer to the RL circuit in Fig. 16.72. Find:

  (a) the impulse response $h(t)$ of the circuit
  (b) the unit step response of the circuit.

Figure 16.72   For Prob. 16.40.

16.41 A network has the impulse response $h(t) = 2e^{-t}u(t)$. When the input signal $v_i(t) = 5u(t)$ is applied to it, find its output.

16.42 Obtain the impulse response of a system modeled by the differential equation

$$2\frac{dy}{dt} + y(t) = x(t)$$

where $x(t)$ is the input and $y(t)$ is the output.

16.43 Develop the state equations for Prob. 16.1.

16.44 Develop the state equations for Prob. 16.2.

16.45 Develop the state equations for the circuit shown in Fig. 16.73.

Figure 16.73   For Prob. 16.45.

16.46 Develop the state equations for the circuit shown in Fig. 16.74.

Figure 16.74   For Prob. 16.46.

16.47 Develop the state equations for the circuit shown in Fig. 16.75.

Figure 16.75   For Prob. 16.47.

16.48 Develop the state equations for the following differential equation.

$$\frac{d^2 y(t)}{dt^2} + \frac{4 \, dy(t)}{dt} = 3y(t) = z(t)$$

*16.49** Develop the state equations for the following differential equation.

$$\frac{d^2 y(t)}{dt^2} + \frac{5 \, dy(t)}{dt} = 6y(t) = \frac{dz(t)}{dt} + z(t)$$

*16.50** Develop the state equations for the following differential equation.

$$\frac{d^3 y(t)}{dt^3} + \frac{6 \, d^2 y(t)}{dt^2} + \frac{11 \, dy(t)}{dt} + 6y(t) = z(t)$$

*16.51** Given the following state equation, solve for $y(t)$.

$$\dot{\mathbf{x}} = \begin{bmatrix} -4 & 4 \\ -2 & 0 \end{bmatrix} x + \begin{bmatrix} 0 \\ 2 \end{bmatrix} u(t)$$

$$\mathbf{y}(t) = [1 \quad 0]x$$

*16.52** Given the following state equation, solve for $y_1(t)$ and $y_2(t)$.

$$\dot{\mathbf{x}} = \begin{bmatrix} -2 & -1 \\ 2 & -4 \end{bmatrix} x + \begin{bmatrix} 1 & 1 \\ 4 & 0 \end{bmatrix} \begin{bmatrix} u(t) \\ 2u(t) \end{bmatrix}$$

$$\mathbf{y} = \begin{bmatrix} -2 & -2 \\ 1 & 0 \end{bmatrix} x + \begin{bmatrix} 2 & 0 \\ 0 & -1 \end{bmatrix} \begin{bmatrix} u(t) \\ 2u(t) \end{bmatrix}$$

Section 16.6   Applications

16.53 Show that the parallel RLC circuit shown in Fig. 16.76 is stable.

Figure 16.76   For Prob. 16.53.

16.54 A system is formed by cascading two systems as shown in Fig. 16.77. Given that the impulse response of the systems are

$$h_1(t) = 3e^{-t} u(t), \qquad h_2(t) = e^{-4t} u(t)$$

(a) Obtain the impulse response of the overall system.

(b) Check if the overall system is stable.

Figure 16.77   For Prob. 16.54.

16.55 Determine whether the op amp circuit in Fig. 16.78 is stable.

Figure 16.78   For Prob. 16.55.

16.56 It is desired to realize the transfer function

$$\frac{V_2(s)}{V_1(s)} = \frac{2s}{s^2 + 2s + 6}$$

using the circuit in Fig. 16.79. Choose $R = 1 \text{ k}\Omega$ and find L and C.

Figure 16.79   For Prob. 16.56.

16.57   Realize the transfer function

$$\frac{V_o(s)}{V_i(s)} = \frac{5}{s^2 + 6s + 25}$$

using the circuit in Fig. 16.80. Choose $R_1 = 4\ \Omega$ and $R_2 = 1\ \Omega$, and determine L and C.

Figure 16.80   For Prob. 16.57.

16.58   Realize the transfer function

$$\frac{V_o(s)}{V_s(s)} = -\frac{s}{s + 10}$$

using the circuit in Fig. 16.81. Let $Y_1 = sC_1$, $Y_2 = 1/R_1$, $Y_3 = sC_2$. Choose $R_1 = 1\ \text{k}\Omega$ and determine C_1 and C_2.

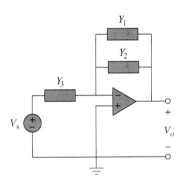

Figure 16.81   For Prob. 16.58.

16.59   Synthesize the transfer function

$$\frac{V_o(s)}{V_{in}(s)} = \frac{10^6}{s^2 + 100s + 10^6}$$

using the topology of Fig. 16.82. Let $Y_1 = 1/R_1$, $Y_2 = 1/R_2$, $Y_3 = sC_1$, $Y_4 = sC_2$. Choose $R_1 = 1\ \text{k}\Omega$ and determine C_1, C_2, and R_2.

Figure 16.82   For Prob. 16.59.

Section 16.7   Computation Using *MATLAB*

16.60   Determine the Bode plots for the following transfer function using *MATLAB*.

$$H(s) = \frac{s + 1}{s^2 + 5s + 6}$$

16.61   Determine the Bode plots for the following transfer function using *MATLAB*.

$$H(s) = \frac{s + 4}{s^3 + 6s^2 + 11s + 6}$$

16.62   Determine the Bode plots for the following transfer function using *MATLAB*.

$$H(s) = \frac{s + 1}{s^2 + 0.5s + 1}$$

16.63   Given the following transfer function, determine the response to a unit step input using *MATLAB*.

$$H(s) = \frac{s + 2}{s^2 + 4s + 3}$$

16.64   Given the following transfer function, determine the response to an input equal to $10e^{-t}u(t)$ using *MATLAB*.

$$H(s) = \frac{4}{s^2 + 5s + 6}$$

16.65   Given the following transfer function, determine the response to an input equal to $(1 + 3e^{-2t})u(t)$ using *MATLAB*.

$$H(s) = \frac{s}{s^3 + 6s^2 + 11s + 6}$$

16.66   Given the following transfer function, determine the response to an input equal to $5e^{-3t}u(t)$ using *MATLAB*.

$$H(s) = \frac{1}{s^2 + s + 4}$$

COMPREHENSIVE PROBLEMS

16.67 Obtain the transfer function of the op amp circuit in Fig. 16.83 in the form of

$$\frac{V_o(s)}{V_i(s)} = \frac{as}{s^2 + bs + c}$$

where a, b, and c are constants. Determine the constants.

10 kΩ

1 μF

0.5 ΩF   10 kΩ

v_i v_o

Figure 16.83   For Prob. 16.67.

16.68 A certain network has an input admittance $Y(s)$. The admittance has a pole at $s = -3$, a zero at $s = -1$, and $Y(\infty) = 0.25$ S.

(a) Find $Y(s)$.

(b) An 8-V battery is connected to the network via a switch. If the switch is closed at $t = 0$, find the current $i(t)$ through $Y(s)$ using the Laplace transform.

16.69 A gyrator is a device for simulating an inductor in a network. A basic gyrator circuit is shown in Fig. 16.84. By finding $V_i(s)/I_o(s)$, show that the inductance produced by the gyrator is $L = CR^2$.

R

C

R

R

v_i i_o

R

Figure 16.84   For Prob. 16.69.

C H A P T E R | 17

THE FOURIER SERIES

The human mind is not capable of grasping the Universe. We are like a little child entering a huge library. The walls are covered to the ceilings with books in many different tongues. The child knows that someone must have written these books. It does not know who or how. It does not understand the languages in which they are written. But the child notes a definite plan in the arrangement of the books—a mysterious order which it does not comprehend, but only dimly suspects.

—Albert Einstein

Historical Profiles

Jean Baptiste Joseph Fourier (1768–1830), a French mathematician, first presented the series and transform that bear his name. Fourier's results were not enthusiastically received by the scientific world. He could not even get his work published as a paper.

    Born in Auxerre, France, Fourier was orphaned at age 8. He attended a local military college run by Benedictine monks, where he demonstrated great proficiency in mathematics. Like most of his contemporaries, Fourier was swept into the politics of the French Revolution. He played an important role in Napoleon's expeditions to Egypt in the later 1790s. Due to his political involvement, he narrowly escaped death twice.

Alexander Graham Bell (1847–1922) inventor of the telephone, was a Scottish-American scientist.

    Bell was born in Edinburgh, Scotland, a son of Alexander Melville Bell, a well-known speech teacher. Alexander the younger also became a speech teacher after graduating from the University of Edinburgh and the University of London. In 1866 he became interested in transmitting speech electrically. After his older brother died of tuberculosis, his father decided to move to Canada. Alexander was asked to come to Boston to work at the School for the Deaf. There he met Thomas A. Watson, who became his assistant in his electromagnetic transmitter experiment. On March 10, 1876, Alexander sent the famous first telephone message: "Watson, come here I want you." The bel, the logarithmic unit introduced in Chapter 14, is named in his honor.

17.1 INTRODUCTION

We have spent a considerable amount of time on the analysis of circuits with sinusoidal sources. This chapter is concerned with a means of analyzing circuits with periodic, nonsinusoidal excitations. The notion of periodic functions was introduced in Chapter 9; it was mentioned there that the sinusoid is the most simple and useful periodic function. This chapter introduces the Fourier series, a technique for expressing a periodic function in terms of sinusoids. Once the source function is expressed in terms of sinusoids, we can apply the phasor method to analyze circuits.

The Fourier series is named after Jean Baptiste Joseph Fourier (1768–1830). In 1822, Fourier's genius came up with the insight that any practical periodic function can be represented as a sum of sinusoids. Such a representation, along with the superposition theorem, allows us to find the response of circuits to arbitrary periodic inputs using phasor techniques.

We begin with the trigonometric Fourier series. Later we consider the exponential Fourier series. We then apply Fourier series in circuit analysis. Finally, practical applications of Fourier series in spectrum analyzers and filters are demonstrated.

17.2 TRIGONOMETRIC FOURIER SERIES

While studying heat flow, Fourier discovered that a nonsinusoidal periodic function can be expressed as an infinite sum of sinusoidal functions. Recall that a periodic function is one that repeats every T seconds. In other words, a periodic function $f(t)$ satisfies

$$f(t) = f(t + nT) \tag{17.1}$$

where n is an integer and T is the period of the function.

According to the *Fourier theorem*, any practical periodic function of frequency ω_0 can be expressed as an infinite sum of sine or cosine functions that are integral multiples of ω_0. Thus, $f(t)$ can be expressed as

$$f(t) = a_0 + a_1 \cos \omega_0 t + b_1 \sin \omega_0 t + a_2 \cos 2\omega_0 t$$
$$+ b_2 \sin 2\omega_0 t + a_3 \cos 3\omega_0 t + b_3 \sin 3\omega_0 t + \cdots \tag{17.2}$$

or

$$f(t) = \underbrace{a_0}_{\text{dc}} + \underbrace{\sum_{n=1}^{\infty} (a_n \cos n\omega_0 t + b_n \sin n\omega_0 t)}_{\text{ac}} \tag{17.3}$$

where $\omega_0 = 2\pi/T$ is called the *fundamental frequency* in radians per second. The sinusoid $\sin n\omega_0 t$ or $\cos n\omega_0 t$ is called the nth harmonic of $f(t)$; it is an odd harmonic if n is odd and an even harmonic if n is even. Equation 17.3 is called the *trigonometric Fourier series* of $f(t)$. The constants a_n and b_n are the *Fourier coefficients*. The coefficient a_0

The harmonic frequency ω_n is an integral multiple of the fundamental frequency ω_0, i.e., $\omega_n = n\omega_0$.

is the dc component or the average value of $f(t)$. (Recall that sinusoids have zero average values.) The coefficients a_n and b_n (for $n \neq 0$) are the amplitudes of the sinusoids in the ac component. Thus,

> The Fourier series of a periodic function $f(t)$ is a representation that resolves $f(t)$ into a dc component and an ac component comprising an infinite series of harmonic sinusoids.

A function that can be represented by a Fourier series as in Eq. (17.3) must meet certain requirements, because the infinite series in Eq. (17.3) may or may not converge. These conditions on $f(t)$ to yield a convergent Fourier series are as follows:

1. $f(t)$ is single-valued everywhere.
2. $f(t)$ has a finite number of finite discontinuities in any one period.
3. $f(t)$ has a finite number of maxima and minima in any one period.
4. The integral $\displaystyle\int_{t_0}^{t_0+T} |f(t)|\, dt < \infty$ for any t_0.

These conditions are called *Dirichlet conditions*. Although they are not necessary conditions, they are sufficient conditions for a Fourier series to exist.

A major task in Fourier series is the determination of the Fourier coefficients a_0, a_n, and b_n. The process of determining the coefficients is called *Fourier analysis*. The following trigonometric integrals are very helpful in Fourier analysis. For any integers m and n,

$$\int_0^T \sin n\omega_0 t\, dt = 0 \qquad (17.4\text{a})$$

$$\int_0^T \cos n\omega_0 t\, dt = 0 \qquad (17.4\text{b})$$

$$\int_0^T \sin n\omega_0 t \cos m\omega_0 t\, dt = 0 \qquad (17.4\text{c})$$

$$\int_0^T \sin n\omega_0 t \sin m\omega_0 t\, dt = 0, \qquad (m \neq n) \qquad (17.4\text{d})$$

$$\int_0^T \cos n\omega_0 t \cos m\omega_0 t\, dt = 0, \qquad (m \neq n) \qquad (17.4\text{e})$$

$$\int_0^T \sin^2 n\omega_0 t\, dt = \frac{T}{2} \qquad (17.4\text{f})$$

$$\int_0^T \cos^2 n\omega_0 t\, dt = \frac{T}{2} \qquad (17.4\text{g})$$

Let us use these identities to evaluate the Fourier coefficients.

Historical note: Although Fourier published his theorem in 1822, it was P. G. L. Dirichlet (1805–1859) who later supplied an acceptable proof of the theorem.

A software package like *Mathcad* or *Maple* can be used to evaluate the Fourier coefficients.

We begin by finding a_0. We integrate both sides of Eq. (17.3) over one period and obtain

$$\int_0^T f(t)\,dt = \int_0^T \left[a_0 + \sum_{n=1}^{\infty}(a_n \cos n\omega_0 t + b_n \sin n\omega_0 t) \right] dt$$

$$= \int_0^T a_0\,dt + \sum_{n=1}^{\infty}\left[\int_0^T a_n \cos n\omega_0 t\,dt \right.$$

$$\left. + \int_0^T b_n \sin n\omega_0 t\,dt \right] dt \qquad (17.5)$$

Invoking the identities of Eqs. (17.4a) and (17.4b), the two integrals involving the ac terms vanish. Hence,

$$\int_0^T f(t)\,dt = \int_0^T a_0\,dt = a_0 T$$

or

$$\boxed{a_0 = \frac{1}{T}\int_0^T f(t)\,dt} \qquad (17.6)$$

showing that a_0 is the average value of $f(t)$.

To evaluate a_n, we multiply both sides of Eq. (17.3) by $\cos m\omega_0 t$ and integrate over one period:

$$\int_0^T f(t) \cos m\omega_0 t\,dt$$

$$= \int_0^T \left[a_0 + \sum_{n=1}^{\infty}(a_n \cos n\omega_0 t + b_n \sin n\omega_0 t) \right] \cos m\omega_0 t\,dt$$

$$= \int_0^T a_0 \cos m\omega_0 t\,dt + \sum_{n=1}^{\infty}\left[\int_0^T a_n \cos n\omega_0 t \cos m\omega_0 t\,dt \right.$$

$$\left. + \int_0^T b_n \sin n\omega_0 t \cos m\omega_0 t\,dt \right] dt \qquad (17.7)$$

The integral containing a_0 is zero in view of Eq. (17.4b), while the integral containing b_n vanishes according to Eq. (17.4c). The integral containing a_n will be zero except when $m = n$, in which case it is $T/2$, according to Eqs. (17.4e) and (17.4g). Thus,

$$\int_0^T f(t) \cos m\omega_0 t\,dt = a_n \frac{T}{2}, \qquad \text{for } m = n$$

or

$$\boxed{a_n = \frac{2}{T}\int_0^T f(t) \cos n\omega_0 t\,dt} \qquad (17.8)$$

In a similar vein, we obtain b_n by multiplying both sides of Eq. (17.3) by $\sin m\omega_0 t$ and integrating over the period. The result is

$$\boxed{b_n = \frac{2}{T}\int_0^T f(t) \sin n\omega_0 t\,dt} \qquad (17.9)$$

Be aware that since $f(t)$ is periodic, it may be more convenient to carry the integrations above from $-T/2$ to $T/2$ or generally from t_0 to $t_0 + T$ instead of 0 to T. The result will be the same.

An alternative form of Eq. (17.3) is the *amplitude-phase* form

$$f(t) = a_0 + \sum_{n=1}^{\infty} A_n \cos(n\omega_0 t + \phi_n) \qquad (17.10)$$

We can use Eqs. (9.11) and (9.12) to relate Eq. (17.3) to Eq. (17.10), or we can apply the trigonometric identity

$$\cos(\alpha + \beta) = \cos\alpha \cos\beta - \sin\alpha \sin\beta \qquad (17.11)$$

to the ac terms in Eq. (17.10) so that

$$a_0 + \sum_{n=1}^{\infty} A_n \cos(n\omega_0 t + \phi_n) = a_0 + \sum_{n=1}^{\infty} (A_n \cos\phi_n) \cos n\omega_0 t \\ - (A_n \sin\phi_n) \sin n\omega_0 t \qquad (17.12)$$

Equating the coefficients of the series expansions in Eqs. (17.3) and (17.12) shows that

$$a_n = A_n \cos\phi_n, \qquad b_n = -A_n \sin\phi_n \qquad (17.13a)$$

or

$$A_n = \sqrt{a_n^2 + b_n^2}, \qquad \phi_n = -\tan^{-1}\frac{b_n}{a_n} \qquad (17.13b)$$

To avoid any confusion in determining ϕ_n, it may be better to relate the terms in complex form as

$$A_n \underline{/\phi_n} = a_n - jb_n \qquad (17.14)$$

The convenience of this relationship will become evident in Section 17.6. The plot of the amplitude A_n of the harmonics versus $n\omega_0$ is called the *amplitude spectrum* of $f(t)$; the plot of the phase ϕ_n versus $n\omega_0$ is the *phase spectrum* of $f(t)$. Both the amplitude and phase spectra form the *frequency spectrum* of $f(t)$.

The frequency spectrum is also known as the line spectrum in view of the discrete frequency components.

> The frequency spectrum of a signal consists of the plots of the amplitudes and phases of the harmonics versus frequency.

Thus, the Fourier analysis is also a mathematical tool for finding the spectrum of a periodic signal. Section 17.6 will elaborate more on the spectrum of a signal.

To evaluate the Fourier coefficients a_0, a_n, and b_n, we often need to apply the following integrals:

$$\int \cos at\, dt = \frac{1}{a}\sin at \qquad (17.15a)$$

$$\int \sin at\, dt = -\frac{1}{a}\cos at \qquad (17.15b)$$

$$\int t \cos at \, dt = \frac{1}{a^2} \cos at + \frac{1}{a} t \sin at \qquad (17.15c)$$

$$\int t \sin at \, dt = \frac{1}{a^2} \sin at - \frac{1}{a} t \cos at \qquad (17.15d)$$

It is also useful to know the values of the cosine, sine, and exponential functions for integral multiples of π. These are given in Table 17.1, where n is an integer.

TABLE 17.1   Values of cosine, sine, and exponential functions for integral multiples of π.

Function	Value
$\cos 2n\pi$	1
$\sin 2n\pi$	0
$\cos n\pi$	$(-1)^n$
$\sin n\pi$	0
$\cos \dfrac{n\pi}{2}$	$\begin{cases} (-1)^{n/2}, & n = \text{even} \\ 0, & n = \text{odd} \end{cases}$
$\sin \dfrac{n\pi}{2}$	$\begin{cases} (-1)^{(n-1)/2}, & n = \text{odd} \\ 0, & n = \text{even} \end{cases}$
$e^{j2n\pi}$	1
$e^{jn\pi}$	$(-1)^n$
$e^{jn\pi/2}$	$\begin{cases} (-1)^{n/2}, & n = \text{even} \\ j(-1)^{(n-1)/2}, & n = \text{odd} \end{cases}$

EXAMPLE 17.1

Figure 17.1   For Example 17.1; a square wave.

Determine the Fourier series of the waveform shown in Fig. 17.1. Obtain the amplitude and phase spectra.

Solution:

The Fourier series is given by Eq. (17.3), namely,

$$f(t) = a_0 + \sum_{n=1}^{\infty} (a_n \cos n\omega_0 t + b_n \sin n\omega_0 t) \qquad (17.1.1)$$

Our goal is to obtain the Fourier coefficients $a_0, a_n,$ and b_n using Eqs. (17.6), (17.8), and (17.9). First, we describe the waveform as

$$f(t) = \begin{cases} 1, & 0 < t < 1 \\ 0, & 1 < t < 2 \end{cases} \qquad (17.1.2)$$

and $f(t) = f(t + T)$. Since $T = 2$, $\omega_0 = 2\pi/T = \pi$. Thus,

$$a_0 = \frac{1}{T} \int_0^T f(t) \, dt = \frac{1}{2} \left[\int_0^1 1 \, dt + \int_1^2 0 \, dt \right] = \frac{1}{2} t \Big|_0^1 = \frac{1}{2} \qquad (17.1.3)$$

Using Eq. (17.8) along with Eq. (17.15a),

$$
\begin{aligned}
a_n &= \frac{2}{T} \int_0^T f(t) \cos n\omega_0 t \, dt \\
&= \frac{2}{2} \left[\int_0^1 1 \cos n\pi t \, dt + \int_1^2 0 \cos n\pi t \, dt \right] \\
&= \frac{1}{n\pi} \sin n\pi t \, \Big|_0^1 = \frac{1}{n\pi} \sin n\pi = 0
\end{aligned}
\tag{17.1.4}
$$

From Eq. (17.9) with the aid of Eq. (17.15b),

$$
\begin{aligned}
b_n &= \frac{2}{T} \int_0^T f(t) \sin n\omega_0 t \, dt \\
&= \frac{2}{2} \left[\int_0^1 1 \sin n\pi t \, dt + \int_1^2 0 \sin n\pi t \, dt \right] \\
&= -\frac{1}{n\pi} \cos n\pi t \, \Big|_0^1 \\
&= -\frac{1}{n\pi}(\cos n\pi - 1), \qquad \cos n\pi = (-1)^n \\
&= \frac{1}{n\pi}[1 - (-1)^n] = \begin{cases} \dfrac{2}{n\pi}, & n = \text{odd} \\ 0, & n = \text{even} \end{cases}
\end{aligned}
\tag{17.1.5}
$$

Substituting the Fourier coefficients in Eqs. (17.1.3) to (17.1.5) into Eq. (17.1.1) gives the Fourier series as

$$
f(t) = \frac{1}{2} + \frac{2}{\pi} \sin \pi t + \frac{2}{3\pi} \sin 3\pi t + \frac{2}{5\pi} \sin 5\pi t + \cdots
\tag{17.1.6}
$$

Since $f(t)$ contains only the dc component and the sine terms with the fundamental component and odd harmonics, it may be written as

$$
f(t) = \frac{1}{2} + \frac{2}{\pi} \sum_{k=1}^{\infty} \frac{1}{n} \sin n\pi t, \qquad n = 2k - 1
\tag{17.1.7}
$$

By summing the terms one by one as demonstrated in Fig. 17.2, we notice how superposition of the terms can evolve into the original square. As more and more Fourier components are added, the sum gets closer and closer to the square wave. However, it is not possible in practice to sum the series in Eq. (17.1.6) or (17.1.7) to infinity. Only a partial sum ($n = 1, 2, 3, \ldots, N$, where N is finite) is possible. If we plot the partial sum (or truncated series) over one period for a large N as in Fig. 17.3, we notice that the partial sum oscillates above and below the actual value of $f(t)$. At the neighborhood of the points of discontinuity ($x = 0, 1, 2, \ldots$), there is overshoot and damped oscillation. In fact, an overshoot of about 9 percent of the peak value is always present, regardless of the number of terms used to approximate $f(t)$. This is called the *Gibbs phenomenon*.

Summing the Fourier terms by hand calculation may be tedious. A computer is helpful to compute the terms and plot the sum like those shown in Fig. 17.2.

Historical note: Named after the mathematical physicist Josiah Willard Gibbs, who first observed it in 1899.

dc component

Fundamental ac component

(a)

Sum of first two ac components

Sum of first three ac components

Sum of first four ac components

Sum of first five ac components

(b)

Figure 17.2   Evolution of a square wave from its Fourier components.

Figure 17.3   Truncating the Fourier series at $N = 11$; Gibbs phenomenon.

Finally, let us obtain the amplitude and phase spectra for the signal in Fig. 17.1. Since $a_n = 0$,

$$A_n = \sqrt{a_n^2 + b_n^2} = |b_n| = \begin{cases} \dfrac{2}{n\pi}, & n = \text{odd} \\ 0, & n = \text{even} \end{cases} \qquad (17.1.8)$$

and

$$\phi_n = -\tan^{-1}\frac{b_n}{a_n} = \begin{cases} -90°, & n = \text{odd} \\ 0, & n = \text{even} \end{cases} \qquad (17.1.9)$$

The plots of A_n and ϕ_n for different values of $n\omega_0 = n\pi$ provide the amplitude and phase spectra in Fig. 17.4. Notice that the amplitudes of the harmonics decay very fast with frequency.

(a)

(b)

Figure 17.4   For Example 17.1: (a) amplitude and (b) phase spectrum of the function shown in Fig. 17.1.

PRACTICE PROBLEM 17.1

Find the Fourier series of the square wave in Fig. 17.5. Plot the amplitude and phase spectra.

Answer: $f(t) = \dfrac{4}{\pi} \displaystyle\sum_{k=1}^{\infty} \dfrac{1}{n} \sin n\pi t, n = 2k - 1$. See Fig. 17.6 for the spectra.

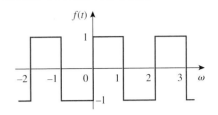

Figure 17.5   For Practice Prob. 17.1.

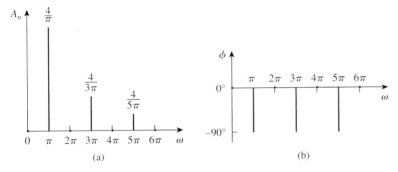

Figure 17.6   For Practice Prob. 17.1: amplitude and phase spectra for the function shown in Fig. 17.5.

EXAMPLE 17.2

Obtain the Fourier series for the periodic function in Fig. 17.7 and plot the amplitude and phase spectra.

Figure 17.7   For Example 17.2.

Solution:

The function is described as

$$f(t) = \begin{cases} t, & 0 < t < 1 \\ 0, & 1 < t < 2 \end{cases}$$

Since $T = 2$, $\omega_0 = 2\pi/T = \pi$. Then

$$a_0 = \frac{1}{T} \int_0^T f(t)\,dt = \frac{1}{2}\left[\int_0^1 t\,dt + \int_1^2 0\,dt \right] = \frac{1}{2}\frac{t^2}{2}\Big|_0^1 = \frac{1}{4} \quad (17.2.1)$$

To evaluate a_n and b_n, we need the integrals in Eq. (17.15):

$$a_n = \frac{2}{T} \int_0^T f(t) \cos n\omega_0 t\,dt$$

$$= \frac{2}{2}\left[\int_0^1 t \cos n\pi t\,dt + \int_1^2 0 \cos n\pi t\,dt \right] \quad (17.2.2)$$

$$= \left[\frac{1}{n^2\pi^2} \cos n\pi t + \frac{t}{n\pi} \sin n\pi t \right]\Big|_0^1$$

$$= \frac{1}{n^2\pi^2}(\cos n\pi - 1) + 0 = \frac{(-1)^n - 1}{n^2\pi^2}$$

since $\cos n\pi = (-1)^n$; and

$$
\begin{aligned}
b_n &= \frac{2}{T} \int_0^T f(t) \sin n\omega_0 t \, dt \\
&= \frac{2}{2} \left[\int_0^1 t \sin n\pi t \, dt + \int_1^2 0 \sin n\pi t \, dt \right] \\
&= \left[\frac{1}{n^2\pi^2} \sin n\pi t - \frac{t}{n\pi} \cos n\pi t \right]\Big|_0^1 \\
&= 0 - \frac{\cos n\pi}{n\pi} = \frac{(-1)^{n+1}}{n\pi}
\end{aligned}
\tag{17.2.3}
$$

Substituting the Fourier coefficients just found into Eq. (17.3) yields

$$
f(t) = \frac{1}{4} + \sum_{n=1}^{\infty} \left[\frac{[(-1)^n - 1]}{(n\pi)^2} \cos n\pi t + \frac{(-1)^{n+1}}{n\pi} \sin n\pi t \right]
$$

To obtain the amplitude and phase spectra, we notice that, for even harmonics, $a_n = 0, b_n = -1/n\pi$, so that

$$
A_n \underline{/\phi_n} = a_n - jb_n = 0 + j\frac{1}{n\pi}
\tag{17.2.4}
$$

Hence,

$$
A_n = |b_n| = \frac{1}{n\pi}, \qquad n = 2, 4, \ldots
$$
$$
\phi_n = 90°, \qquad n = 2, 4, \ldots
\tag{17.2.5}
$$

For odd harmonics, $a_n = -2/(n^2\pi^2)$, $b_n = 1/(n\pi)$ so that

$$
A_n \underline{/\phi_n} = a_n - jb_n = -\frac{2}{n^2\pi^2} - j\frac{1}{n\pi}
\tag{17.2.6}
$$

That is,

$$
\begin{aligned}
A_n &= \sqrt{a_n^2 + b_n^2} = \sqrt{\frac{4}{n^4\pi^4} + \frac{1}{n^2\pi^2}} \\
&= \frac{1}{n^2\pi^2}\sqrt{4 + n^2\pi^2}, \qquad n = 1, 3, \ldots
\end{aligned}
\tag{17.2.7}
$$

From Eq. (17.2.6), we observe that ϕ lies in the third quadrant, so that

$$
\phi_n = 180° + \tan^{-1}\frac{n\pi}{2}, \qquad n = 1, 3, \ldots
\tag{17.2.8}
$$

From Eqs. (17.2.5), (17.2.7), and (17.2.8), we plot A_n and ϕ_n for different values of $n\omega_0 = n\pi$ to obtain the amplitude spectrum and phase spectrum as shown in Fig. 17.8.

(a)

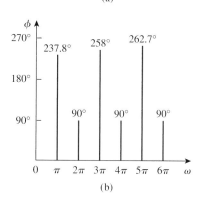

(b)

Figure 17.8   For Example 17.2: (a) amplitude spectrum, (b) phase spectrum.

PRACTICE PROBLEM 17.2

Determine the Fourier series of the sawtooth waveform in Fig. 17.9.

Answer: $f(t) = \dfrac{1}{2} - \dfrac{1}{\pi} \sum_{n=1}^{\infty} \dfrac{1}{n} \sin 2\pi n t.$

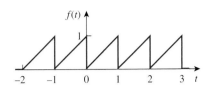

Figure 17.9   For Practice Prob. 17.2.

17.3 SYMMETRY CONSIDERATIONS

We noticed that the Fourier series of Example 17.1 consisted only of the sine terms. One may wonder if a method exists whereby one can know in advance that some Fourier coefficients would be zero and avoid the unnecessary work involved in the tedious process of calculating them. Such a method does exist; it is based on recognizing the existence of symmetry. Here we discuss three types of symmetry: (1) even symmetry, (2) odd symmetry, (3) half-wave symmetry.

17.3.1 Even Symmetry

A function $f(t)$ is *even* if its plot is symmetrical about the vertical axis; that is,

$$f(t) = f(-t) \qquad (17.16)$$

Examples of even functions are t^2, t^4, and $\cos t$. Figure 17.10 shows more examples of periodic even functions. Note that each of these examples satisfies Eq. (17.16). A main property of an even function $f_e(t)$ is that:

$$\int_{-T/2}^{T/2} f_e(t)\,dt = 2 \int_{0}^{T/2} f_e(t)\,dt \qquad (17.17)$$

because integrating from $-T/2$ to 0 is the same as integrating from 0 to $T/2$. Utilizing this property, the Fourier coefficients for an even function become

$$
\begin{aligned}
a_0 &= \frac{2}{T} \int_{0}^{T/2} f(t)\,dt \\[6pt]
a_n &= \frac{4}{T} \int_{0}^{T/2} f(t) \cos n\omega_0 t\,dt \\[6pt]
b_n &= 0
\end{aligned}
\qquad (17.18)
$$

Since $b_n = 0$, Eq. (17.3) becomes a *Fourier cosine series*. This makes sense because the cosine function is itself even. It also makes intuitive sense that an even function contains no sine terms since the sine function is odd.

To confirm Eq. (17.18) quantitatively, we apply the property of an even function in Eq. (17.17) in evaluating the Fourier coefficients in Eqs. (17.6), (17.8), and (17.9). It is convenient in each case to integrate over the interval $-T/2 < t < T/2$, which is symmetrical about the

(a)

(b)

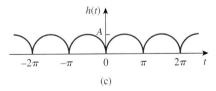

(c)

Figure 17.10   Typical examples of even periodic functions.

origin. Thus,

$$a_0 = \frac{1}{T} \int_{-T/2}^{T/2} f(t)\, dt = \frac{1}{T} \left[\int_{-T/2}^{0} f(t)\, dt + \int_{0}^{T/2} f(t)\, dt \right] \quad (17.19)$$

We change variables for the integral over the interval $-T/2 < t < 0$ by letting $t = -x$, so that $dt = -dx$, $f(t) = f(-t) = f(x)$, since $f(t)$ is an even function, and when $t = -T/2$, $x = T/2$. Then,

$$\begin{aligned} a_0 &= \frac{1}{T} \left[\int_{T/2}^{0} f(x)(-dx) + \int_{0}^{T/2} f(t)\, dt \right] \\ &= \frac{1}{T} \left[\int_{0}^{T/2} f(x)\, dx + \int_{0}^{T/2} f(t)\, dt \right] \end{aligned} \quad (17.20)$$

showing that the two integrals are identical. Hence,

$$a_0 = \frac{2}{T} \int_{0}^{T/2} f(t)\, dt \quad (17.21)$$

as expected. Similarly, from Eq. (17.8),

$$a_n = \frac{2}{T} \left[\int_{-T/2}^{0} f(t) \cos n\omega_0 t\, dt + \int_{0}^{T/2} f(t) \cos n\omega_0 t\, dt \right] \quad (17.22)$$

We make the same change of variables that led to Eq. (17.20) and note that both $f(t)$ and $\cos n\omega_0 t$ are even functions, implying that $f(-t) = f(t)$ and $\cos(-n\omega_0 t) = \cos n\omega_0 t$. Equation (17.22) becomes

$$\begin{aligned} a_n &= \frac{2}{T} \left[\int_{T/2}^{0} f(-x) \cos(-n\omega_0 x)(-dx) + \int_{0}^{T/2} f(t) \cos n\omega_0 t\, dt \right] \\ &= \frac{2}{T} \left[\int_{T/2}^{0} f(x) \cos(n\omega_0 x)(-dx) + \int_{0}^{T/2} f(t) \cos n\omega_0 t\, dt \right] \\ &= \frac{2}{T} \left[\int_{0}^{T/2} f(x) \cos(n\omega_0 x)\, dx + \int_{0}^{T/2} f(t) \cos n\omega_0 t\, dt \right] \end{aligned} \quad (17.23a)$$

or

$$a_n = \frac{4}{T} \int_{0}^{T/2} f(t) \cos n\omega_0 t\, dt \quad (17.23b)$$

as expected. For b_n, we apply Eq. (17.9),

$$b_n = \frac{2}{T} \left[\int_{-T/2}^{0} f(t) \sin n\omega_0 t\, dt + \int_{0}^{T/2} f(t) \sin n\omega_0 t\, dt \right] \quad (17.24)$$

We make the same change of variables but keep in mind that $f(-t) = f(t)$ but $\sin(-n\omega_0 t) = -\sin n\omega_0 t$. Equation (17.24) yields

$$\begin{aligned} b_n &= \frac{2}{T} \left[\int_{T/2}^{0} f(-x) \sin(-n\omega_0 x)(-dx) + \int_{0}^{T/2} f(t) \sin n\omega_0 t\, dt \right] \\ &= \frac{2}{T} \left[\int_{T/2}^{0} f(x) \sin n\omega_0 x\, dx + \int_{0}^{T/2} f(t) \sin n\omega_0 t\, dt \right] \\ &= \frac{2}{T} \left[-\int_{0}^{T/2} f(x) \sin(n\omega_0 x)\, dx + \int_{0}^{T/2} f(t) \sin n\omega_0 t\, dt \right] \\ &= 0 \end{aligned} \quad (17.25)$$

confirming Eq. (17.18).

17.3.2 Odd Symmetry

A function $f(t)$ is said to be *odd* if its plot is antisymmetrical about the vertical axis:

$$f(-t) = -f(t) \tag{17.26}$$

Examples of odd functions are t, t^3, and $\sin t$. Figure 17.11 shows more examples of periodic odd functions. All these examples satisfy Eq. (17.26). An odd function $f_o(t)$ has this major characteristic:

$$\int_{-T/2}^{T/2} f_o(t)\, dt = 0 \tag{17.27}$$

because integration from $-T/2$ to 0 is the negative of that from 0 to $T/2$. With this property, the Fourier coefficients for an odd function become

$$\begin{aligned} a_0 &= 0, \qquad a_n = 0 \\ b_n &= \frac{4}{T}\int_0^{T/2} f(t)\sin n\omega_0 t\, dt \end{aligned} \tag{17.28}$$

which give us a *Fourier sine series*. Again, this makes sense because the sine function is itself an odd function. Also, note that there is no dc term for the Fourier series expansion of an odd function.

The quantitative proof of Eq. (17.28) follows the same procedure taken to prove Eq. (17.18) except that $f(t)$ is now odd, so that $f(t) = -f(t)$. With this fundamental but simple difference, it is easy to see that $a_0 = 0$ in Eq. (17.20), $a_n = 0$ in Eq. (17.23a), and b_n in Eq. (17.24) becomes

$$b_n = \frac{2}{T}\left[\int_{T/2}^0 f(-x)\sin(-n\omega_0 x)(-dx) + \int_0^{T/2} f(t)\sin n\omega_0 t\, dt\right]$$

$$= \frac{2}{T}\left[-\int_{T/2}^0 f(x)\sin n\omega_0 x\, dx + \int_0^{T/2} f(t)\sin n\omega_0 t\, dt\right]$$

$$= \frac{2}{T}\left[\int_0^{T/2} f(x)\sin(n\omega_0 x)\, dx + \int_0^{T/2} f(t)\sin n\omega_0 t\, dt\right]$$

$$b_n = \frac{4}{T}\int_0^{T/2} f(t)\sin n\omega_0 t\, dt \tag{17.29}$$

as expected.

It is interesting to note that any periodic function $f(t)$ with neither even nor odd symmetry may be decomposed into even and odd parts. Using the properties of even and odd functions from Eqs. (17.16) and (17.26), we can write

$$f(t) = \underbrace{\frac{1}{2}[f(t) + f(-t)]}_{\text{even}} + \underbrace{\frac{1}{2}[f(t) - f(-t)]}_{\text{odd}} = f_e(t) + f_o(t) \tag{17.30}$$

Notice that $f_e(t) = \frac{1}{2}[f(t) + f(-t)]$ satisfies the property of an even function in Eq. (17.16), while $f_o(t) = \frac{1}{2}[f(t) - f(-t)]$ satisfies the

Figure 17.11   Typical examples of odd periodic functions.

property of an odd function in Eq. (17.26). The fact that $f_e(t)$ contains only the dc term and the cosine terms, while $f_o(t)$ has only the sine terms, can be exploited in grouping the Fourier series expansion of $f(t)$ as

$$f(t) = a_0 + \underbrace{\sum_{n=1}^{\infty} a_n \cos n\omega_0 t}_{\text{even}} + \underbrace{\sum_{n=1}^{\infty} b_n \sin n\omega_0 t}_{\text{odd}} = f_e(t) + f_o(t) \quad (17.31)$$

It follows readily from Eq. (17.31) that when $f(t)$ is even, $b_n = 0$, and when $f(t)$ is odd, $a_0 = 0 = a_n$.

Also, note the following properties of odd and even functions:

1. The product of two even functions is also an even function.

2. The product of two odd functions is an even function.

3. The product of an even function and an odd function is an odd function.

4. The sum (or difference) of two even functions is also an even function.

5. The sum (or difference) of two odd functions is an odd function.

6. The sum (or difference) of an even function and an odd function is neither even nor odd.

Each of these properties can be proved using Eqs. (17.16) and (17.26).

17.3.3 Half-Wave Symmetry

A function is half-wave (odd) symmetric if

$$f\left(t - \frac{T}{2}\right) = -f(t) \qquad (17.32)$$

which means that each half-cycle is the mirror image of the next half-cycle. Notice that functions $\cos n\omega_0 t$ and $\sin n\omega_0 t$ satisfy Eq. (17.32) for odd values of n and therefore possess half-wave symmetry when n is odd. Figure 17.12 shows other examples of half-wave symmetric functions. The functions in Figs. 17.11(a) and 17.11(b) are also half-wave symmetric. Notice that for each function, one half-cycle is the inverted

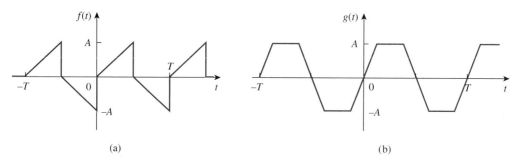

Figure 17.12   Typical examples of half-wave odd symmetric functions.

version of the adjacent half-cycle. The Fourier coefficients become

$$
\begin{aligned}
a_0 &= 0 \\[6pt]
a_n &= \begin{cases} \dfrac{4}{T}\displaystyle\int_0^{T/2} f(t)\cos n\omega_0 t\, dt, & \text{for } n \text{ odd} \\[10pt] 0, & \text{for } n \text{ even} \end{cases} \\[14pt]
b_n &= \begin{cases} \dfrac{4}{T}\displaystyle\int_0^{T/2} f(t)\sin n\omega_0 t\, dt, & \text{for } n \text{ odd} \\[10pt] 0, & \text{for } n \text{ even} \end{cases}
\end{aligned}
\qquad (17.33)
$$

showing that the Fourier series of a half-wave symmetric function contains only odd harmonics.

To derive Eq. (17.33), we apply the property of half-wave symmetric functions in Eq. (17.32) in evaluating the Fourier coefficients in Eqs. (17.6), (17.8), and (17.9). Thus,

$$
a_0 = \frac{1}{T}\int_{-T/2}^{T/2} f(t)\, dt = \frac{1}{T}\left[\int_{-T/2}^{0} f(t)\, dt + \int_0^{T/2} f(t)\, dt\right] \quad (17.34)
$$

We change variables for the integral over the interval $-T/2 < t < 0$ by letting $x = t + T/2$, so that $dx = dt$; when $t = -T/2, x = 0$; and when $t = 0, x = T/2$. Also, we keep Eq. (17.32) in mind; that is, $f(x - T/2) = -f(x)$. Then,

$$
\begin{aligned}
a_0 &= \frac{1}{T}\left[\int_0^{T/2} f\left(x - \frac{T}{2}\right) dx + \int_0^{T/2} f(t)\, dt\right] \\[8pt]
&= \frac{1}{T}\left[-\int_0^{T/2} f(x)\, dx + \int_0^{T/2} f(t)\, dt\right] = 0
\end{aligned}
\qquad (17.35)
$$

confirming the expression for a_0 in Eq. (17.33). Similarly,

$$
a_n = \frac{2}{T}\left[\int_{-T/2}^{0} f(t)\cos n\omega_0 t\, dt + \int_0^{T/2} f(t)\cos n\omega_0 t\, dt\right] \quad (17.36)
$$

We make the same change of variables that led to Eq. (17.35) so that Eq. (17.36) becomes

$$
\begin{aligned}
a_n = \frac{2}{T}\Bigg[&\int_0^{T/2} f\left(x - \frac{T}{2}\right)\cos n\omega_0\left(x - \frac{T}{2}\right) dx \\[8pt]
&+ \int_0^{T/2} f(t)\cos n\omega_0 t\, dt\Bigg]
\end{aligned}
\qquad (17.37)
$$

Since $f(x - T/2) = -f(x)$ and

$$
\begin{aligned}
\cos n\omega_0\left(x - \frac{T}{2}\right) &= \cos(n\omega_0 t - n\pi) \\[6pt]
&= \cos n\omega_0 t \cos n\pi + \sin n\omega_0 t \sin n\pi \\[6pt]
&= (-1)^n \cos n\omega_0 t
\end{aligned}
\qquad (17.38)
$$

substituting these in Eq. (17.37) leads to

$$a_n = \frac{2}{T}[1 - (-1)^n] \int_0^{T/2} f(t) \cos n\omega_0 t \, dt$$

$$= \begin{cases} \dfrac{4}{T} \displaystyle\int_0^{T/2} f(t) \cos n\omega_0 t \, dt, & \text{for } n \text{ odd} \\ 0, & \text{for } n \text{ even} \end{cases} \tag{17.39}$$

confirming Eq. (17.33). By following a similar procedure, we can derive b_n as in Eq. (17.33).

Table 17.2 summarizes the effects of these symmetries on the Fourier coefficients. Table 17.3 provides the Fourier series of some common periodic functions.

TABLE 17.2   Effects of symmetry on Fourier coefficients.

Symmetry	a_0	a_n	b_n	Remarks
Even	$a_0 \neq 0$	$a_n \neq 0$	$b_n = 0$	Integrate over $T/2$ and multiply by 2 to get the coefficients.
Odd	$a_0 = 0$	$a_n = 0$	$b_n \neq 0$	Integrate over $T/2$ and multiply by 2 to get the coefficients.
Half-wave	$a_0 = 0$	$a_{2n} = 0$ $a_{2n+1} \neq 0$	$b_{2n} = 0$ $b_{2n+1} \neq 0$	Integrate over $T/2$ and multiply by 2 to get the coefficients.

TABLE 17.3   The Fourier series of common functions.

Function	Fourier series

1. Square wave

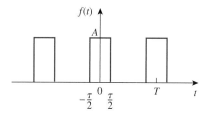

$$f(t) = \frac{4A}{\pi} \sum_{n=1}^{\infty} \frac{1}{2n-1} \sin(2n-1)\omega_0 t$$

2. Rectangular pulse train

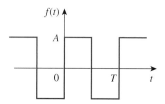

$$f(t) = \frac{A\tau}{T} + \frac{2A}{T} \sum_{n=1}^{\infty} \frac{1}{n} \sin \frac{n\pi\tau}{T} \cos n\omega_0 t$$

3. Sawtooth wave

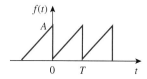

$$f(t) = \frac{A}{2} - \frac{A}{\pi} \sum_{n=1}^{\infty} \frac{\sin n\omega_0 t}{n}$$

TABLE 17.3   *(continued)*

Function	Fourier series

4. Triangular wave

$$f(t) = \frac{A}{2} - \frac{4A}{\pi^2} \sum_{n=1}^{\infty} \frac{1}{(2n+1)^2} \cos(2n-1)\omega_0 t$$

5. Half-wave rectified sine

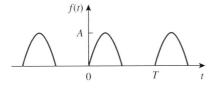

$$f(t) = \frac{A}{\pi} + \frac{A}{2} \sin \omega_0 t - \frac{2A}{\pi} \sum_{n=1}^{\infty} \frac{1}{4n^2 - 1} \cos 2n\omega_0 t$$

6. Full-wave rectified sine

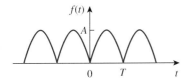

$$f(t) = \frac{2A}{\pi} - \frac{4A}{\pi} \sum_{n=1}^{\infty} \frac{1}{4n^2 - 1} \cos n\omega_0 t$$

E X A M P L E   1 7 . 3

Find the Fourier series expansion of $f(t)$ given in Fig. 17.13.

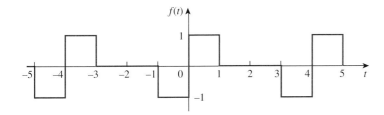

Figure 17.13   For Example 17.3.

Solution:

The function $f(t)$ is an odd function. Hence $a_0 = 0 = a_n$. The period is $T = 4$, and $\omega_0 = 2\pi/T = \pi/2$, so that

$$b_n = \frac{4}{T} \int_0^{T/2} f(t) \sin n\omega_0 t \, dt$$

$$= \frac{4}{4} \left[\int_0^1 1 \sin \frac{n\pi}{2} t \, dt + \int_1^2 0 \sin \frac{n\pi}{2} t \, dt \right]$$

$$= -\frac{2}{n\pi} \cos \frac{n\pi t}{2} \bigg|_0^1 = \frac{2}{n\pi} \left(1 - \cos \frac{n\pi}{2} \right)$$

Hence,

$$f(t) = \frac{2}{\pi} \sum_{n=1}^{\infty} \frac{1}{n} \left(1 - \cos \frac{n\pi}{2} \right) \sin \frac{n\pi}{2} t$$

which is a Fourier sine series.

PRACTICE PROBLEM 17.3

Find the Fourier series of the function $f(t)$ in Fig. 17.14.

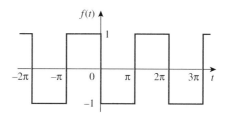

Figure 17.14   For Practice Prob. 17.3.

Answer: $f(t) = -\frac{4}{\pi} \sum_{k=1}^{\infty} \frac{1}{n} \sin nt, n = 2k - 1.$

EXAMPLE 17.4

Determine the Fourier series for the half-wave rectified cosine function shown in Fig. 17.15.

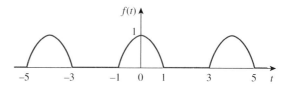

Figure 17.15   A half-wave rectified cosine function; for Example 17.4.

Solution:

This is an even function so that $b_n = 0$. Also, $T = 4$, $\omega_0 = 2\pi/T = \pi/2$. Over a period,

$$f(t) = \begin{cases} 0, & -2 < t < -1 \\ \cos\dfrac{\pi}{2}t, & -1 < t < 1 \\ 0, & 1 < t < 2 \end{cases}$$

$$a_0 = \frac{2}{T}\int_0^{T/2} f(t)\, dt = \frac{2}{4}\left[\int_0^1 \cos\frac{\pi}{2}t\, dt + \int_1^2 0\, dt\right]$$

$$= \frac{1}{2}\frac{2}{\pi}\sin\frac{\pi}{2}t\Big|_0^1 = \frac{1}{\pi}$$

$$a_n = \frac{4}{T}\int_0^{T/2} f(t)\cos n\omega_0 t\, dt = \frac{4}{4}\left[\int_0^1 \cos\frac{\pi}{2}t\cos\frac{n\pi t}{2}\, dt + 0\right]$$

But $\cos A \cos B = \frac{1}{2}[\cos(A+B) + \cos(A-B)]$. Then

$$a_n = \frac{1}{2}\int_0^1\left[\cos\frac{\pi}{2}(n+1)t + \cos\frac{\pi}{2}(n-1)t\right]dt$$

For $n = 1$,

$$a_1 = \frac{1}{2}\int_0^1 [\cos\pi t + 1]\, dt = \frac{1}{2}\left[\frac{\sin\pi t}{\pi} + t\right]\Big|_0^1 = \frac{1}{2}$$

For $n > 1$,

$$a_n = \frac{1}{\pi(n+1)}\sin\frac{\pi}{2}(n+1) + \frac{1}{\pi(n-1)}\sin\frac{\pi}{2}(n-1)$$

For $n =$ odd ($n = 1, 3, 5, \ldots$), $(n+1)$ and $(n-1)$ are both even, so

$$\sin\frac{\pi}{2}(n+1) = 0 = \sin\frac{\pi}{2}(n-1), \qquad n = \text{odd}$$

For $n =$ even ($n = 2, 4, 6, \ldots$), $(n+1)$ and $(n-1)$ are both odd. Also,

$$\sin\frac{\pi}{2}(n+1) = -\sin\frac{\pi}{2}(n-1) = \cos\frac{n\pi}{2} = (-1)^{n/2}, \qquad n = \text{even}$$

Hence,

$$a_n = \frac{(-1)^{n/2}}{\pi(n+1)} + \frac{-(-1)^{n/2}}{\pi(n-1)} = \frac{-2(-1)^{n/2}}{\pi(n^2-1)}, \qquad n = \text{even}$$

Thus,

$$f(t) = \frac{1}{\pi} + \frac{1}{2}\cos\frac{\pi}{2}t - \frac{2}{\pi}\sum_{n=\text{even}}^{\infty}\frac{(-1)^{n/2}}{(n^2-1)}\cos\frac{n\pi}{2}t$$

To avoid using $n = 2, 4, 6, \ldots$ and also to ease computation, we can replace n by $2k$, where $k = 1, 2, 3, \ldots$ and obtain

$$f(t) = \frac{1}{\pi} + \frac{1}{2}\cos\frac{\pi}{2}t - \frac{2}{\pi}\sum_{k=1}^{\infty}\frac{(-1)^k}{(4k^2-1)}\cos k\pi t$$

which is a Fourier cosine series.

PRACTICE PROBLEM 17.4

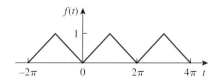

Figure 17.16   For Practice Prob. 17.4.

Find the Fourier series expansion of the function in Fig. 17.16.

Answer: $f(t) = \dfrac{1}{2} - \dfrac{4}{\pi^2} \displaystyle\sum_{k=1}^{\infty} \dfrac{1}{n^2} \cos nt, \ n = 2k - 1.$

EXAMPLE 17.5

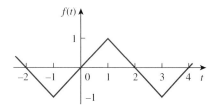

Figure 17.17   For Example 17.5.

Calculate the Fourier series for the function in Fig. 17.17.

Solution:

The function in Fig. 17.17 is half-wave odd symmetric, so that $a_0 = 0 = a_n$. It is described over half the period as

$$f(t) = t, \qquad -1 < t < 1$$

$T = 4, \omega_0 = 2\pi/T = \pi/2$. Hence,

$$b_n = \frac{4}{T} \int_0^{T/2} f(t) \sin n\omega_0 t \, dt$$

Instead of integrating $f(t)$ from 0 to 2, it is more convenient to integrate from -1 to 1. Applying Eq. (17.15d),

$$b_n = \frac{4}{4} \int_{-1}^{1} t \sin \frac{n\pi t}{2} \, dt = \left[\frac{\sin n\pi t/2}{n^2\pi^2/4} - \frac{t \cos n\pi t/2}{n\pi/2} \right]\Bigg|_{-1}^{1}$$

$$= \frac{4}{n^2\pi^2} \left[\sin \frac{n\pi}{2} - \sin\left(-\frac{n\pi}{2}\right) \right] - \frac{2}{n\pi} \left[\cos \frac{n\pi}{2} + \cos\left(-\frac{n\pi}{2}\right) \right]$$

$$= \frac{8}{n^2\pi^2} \sin \frac{n\pi}{2} - \frac{4}{n\pi} \cos \frac{n\pi}{2}$$

since $\sin(-x) = -\sin x$ is an odd function, while $\cos(-x) = \cos x$ is an even function. Using the identities for $\sin n\pi/2$ and $\cos n\pi/2$ in Table 17.1,

$$b_n = \begin{cases} \dfrac{8}{n^2\pi^2}(-1)^{(n-1)/2}, & n = \text{odd} = 1, 3, 5, \ldots \\[2mm] \dfrac{4}{n\pi}(-1)^{(n+2)/2}, & n = \text{even} = 2, 4, 6, \ldots \end{cases}$$

Thus,

$$f(t) = \sum_{n=1}^{\infty} b_n \sin \frac{n\pi}{2} t$$

where b_n is given above.

PRACTICE PROBLEM 17.5

Determine the Fourier series of the function in Fig. 17.12(a). Take $A = 1$ and $T = 2\pi$.

Answer: $f(t) = \dfrac{2}{\pi} \displaystyle\sum_{k=1}^{\infty} \left(\dfrac{-2}{n^2\pi} \cos nt + \dfrac{1}{n} \sin nt \right), n = 2k - 1.$

17.4   CIRCUIT APPLICATIONS

We find that in practice, many circuits are driven by nonsinusoidal periodic functions. To find the steady-state response of a circuit to a nonsinusoidal periodic excitation requires the application of a Fourier series, ac phasor analysis, and the superposition principle. The procedure usually involves three steps.

> **Steps for Applying Fourier Series:**
>
> 1. Express the excitation as a Fourier series.
> 2. Transform the circuit from the time domain to the frequency domain.
> 3. Find the response of the dc and ac components in the Fourier series.
> 4. Add the individual dc and ac responses using the superposition principle.

The first step is to determine the Fourier series expansion of the excitation. For the periodic voltage source shown in Fig. 17.18(a), for example, the Fourier series is expressed as

$$v(t) = V_0 + \sum_{n=1}^{\infty} V_n \cos(n\omega_0 t + \theta_n) \tag{17.40}$$

(The same could be done for a periodic current source.) Equation (17.40) shows that $v(t)$ consists of two parts: the dc component V_0 and the ac component $\mathbf{V}_n = V_n \underline{/\theta_n}$ with several harmonics. This Fourier series representation may be regarded as a set of series-connected sinusoidal sources, with each source having its own amplitude and frequency, as shown in Fig. 17.18(b).

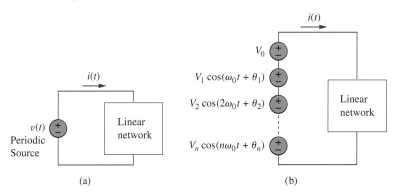

Figure 17.18   (a) Linear network excited by a periodic voltage source, (b) Fourier series representation (time-domain).

The second step is finding the response to each term in the Fourier series. The response to the dc component can be determined in the frequency domain by setting $n = 0$ or $\omega = 0$ as in Fig. 17.19(a), or in the time domain by replacing all inductors with short circuits and all capacitors with open circuits. The response to the ac component is obtained by applying the phasor techniques covered in Chapter 9, as shown in Fig. 17.19(b). The network is represented by its impedance $\mathbf{Z}(n\omega_0)$ or admittance $\mathbf{Y}(n\omega_0)$. $\mathbf{Z}(n\omega_0)$ is the input impedance at the source when ω is everywhere replaced by $n\omega_0$, and $\mathbf{Y}(n\omega_0)$ is the reciprocal of $\mathbf{Z}(n\omega_0)$.

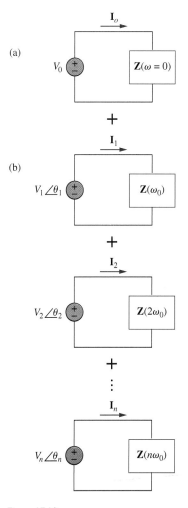

Figure 17.19   Steady-state responses: (a) dc component, (b) ac component (frequency domain).

Finally, following the principle of superposition, we add all the individual responses. For the case shown in Fig. 17.19,

$$i(t) = i_0(t) + i_1(t) + i_2(t) + \cdots$$

$$= \mathbf{I}_0 + \sum_{n=1}^{\infty} |\mathbf{I}_n| \cos(n\omega_0 t + \psi_n) \tag{17.41}$$

where each component $\mathbf{I}_n$ with frequency $n\omega_0$ has been transformed to the time domain to get $i_n(t)$, and ψ_n is the argument of $\mathbf{I}_n$.

EXAMPLE 17.6

Figure 17.20   For Example 17.6.

Let the function $f(t)$ in Example 17.1 be the voltage source $v_s(t)$ in the circuit of Fig. 17.20. Find the response $v_o(t)$ of the circuit.

Solution:

From Example 17.1,

$$v_s(t) = \frac{1}{2} + \frac{2}{\pi} \sum_{k=1}^{\infty} \frac{1}{n} \sin n\pi t, \qquad n = 2k - 1$$

where $\omega_n = n\omega_0 = n\pi$ rad/s. Using phasors, we obtain the response $\mathbf{V}_o$ in the circuit of Fig. 17.20 by voltage division:

$$\mathbf{V}_o = \frac{j\omega_n L}{R + j\omega_n L}\mathbf{V}_s = \frac{j2n\pi}{5 + j2n\pi}\mathbf{V}_s$$

For the dc component ($\omega_n = 0$ or $n = 0$)

$$\mathbf{V}_s = \frac{1}{2} \qquad \Longrightarrow \qquad \mathbf{V}_o = 0$$

This is expected, since the inductor is a short circuit to dc. For the nth harmonic,

$$\mathbf{V}_s = \frac{2}{n\pi}\angle{-90°} \tag{17.6.1}$$

and the corresponding response is

$$\mathbf{V}_o = \frac{2n\pi\angle{90°}}{\sqrt{25 + 4n^2\pi^2}\angle{\tan^{-1} 2n\pi/5}} \left(\frac{2}{n\pi}\angle{-90°}\right)$$

$$= \frac{4\angle{-\tan^{-1} 2n\pi/5}}{\sqrt{25 + 4n^2\pi^2}} \tag{17.6.2}$$

In the time domain,

$$v_o(t) = \sum_{k=1}^{\infty} \frac{4}{\sqrt{25 + 4n^2\pi^2}} \cos\left(n\pi t - \tan^{-1}\frac{2n\pi}{5}\right), \qquad n = 2k - 1$$

The first three terms ($k = 1, 2, 3$ or $n = 1, 3, 5$) of the odd harmonics in the summation give us

$$v_o(t) = 0.4981 \cos(\pi t - 51.49°) + 0.2051 \cos(3\pi t - 75.14°)$$
$$+ 0.1257 \cos(5\pi t - 80.96°) + \cdots \text{ V}$$

Figure 17.21 shows the amplitude spectrum for output voltage $v_o(t)$, while that of the input voltage $v_s(t)$ is in Fig. 17.4(a). Notice that the two

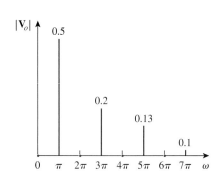

Figure 17.21   For Example 17.6: Amplitude spectrum of the output voltage.

spectra are close. Why? We observe that the circuit in Fig. 17.20 is a highpass filter with the corner frequency $\omega_c = R/L = 2.5$ rad/s, which is less than the fundamental frequency $\omega_0 = \pi$ rad/s. The dc component is not passed and the first harmonic is slightly attenuated, but higher harmonics are passed. In fact, from Eqs. (17.6.1) and (17.6.2), $\mathbf{V}_o$ is identical to $\mathbf{V}_s$ for large n, which is characteristic of a highpass filter.

PRACTICE PROBLEM 17.6

If the sawtooth waveform in Fig. 17.9 (see Practice Prob. 17.2) is the voltage source $v_s(t)$ in the circuit of Fig. 17.22, find the response $v_o(t)$.

Answer: $v_o(t) = \dfrac{1}{2} - \dfrac{1}{\pi} \displaystyle\sum_{n=1}^{\infty} \dfrac{\sin(2\pi nt - \tan^{-1} 4n\pi)}{n\sqrt{1 + 16n^2\pi^2}}$ V.

Figure 17.22   For Practice Prob. 17.6.

EXAMPLE 17.7

Find the response $i_o(t)$ in the circuit in Fig. 17.23 if the input voltage $v(t)$ has the Fourier series expansion

$$v(t) = 1 + \sum_{n=1}^{\infty} \frac{2(-1)^n}{1 + n^2} (\cos nt - n \sin nt)$$

Figure 17.23   For Example 17.7.

Solution:

Using Eq. (17.13), we can express the input voltage as

$$v(t) = 1 + \sum_{n=1}^{\infty} \frac{2(-1)^n}{\sqrt{1 + n^2}} \cos(nt + \tan^{-1} n)$$

$$= 1 - 1.414 \cos(t + 45°) + 0.8944 \cos(2t + 63.45°)$$
$$- 0.6345 \cos(3t + 71.56°) - 0.4851 \cos(4t + 78.7°) + \cdots$$

We notice that $\omega_0 = 1$, $\omega_n = n$ rad/s. The impedance at the source is

$$\mathbf{Z} = 4 + j\omega_n 2 \parallel 4 = 4 + \frac{j\omega_n 8}{4 + j\omega_n 2} = \frac{8 + j\omega_n 8}{2 + j\omega_n}$$

The input current is

$$\mathbf{I} = \frac{\mathbf{V}}{\mathbf{Z}} = \frac{2 + j\omega_n}{8 + j\omega_n 8} \mathbf{V}$$

where $\mathbf{V}$ is the phasor form of the source voltage $v(t)$. By current division,

$$\mathbf{I}_o = \frac{4}{4 + j\omega_n 2} \mathbf{I} = \frac{\mathbf{V}}{4 + j\omega_n 4}$$

Since $\omega_n = n$, $\mathbf{I}_o$ can be expressed as

$$\mathbf{I}_o = \frac{\mathbf{V}}{4\sqrt{1 + n^2}\underline{/\tan^{-1} n}}$$

For the dc component ($\omega_n = 0$ or $n = 0$)

$$\mathbf{V} = 1 \quad \Longrightarrow \quad \mathbf{I}_o = \frac{\mathbf{V}}{4} = \frac{1}{4}$$

For the nth harmonic,

$$\mathbf{V} = \frac{2(-1)^n}{\sqrt{1+n^2}} \big/ \tan^{-1} n$$

so that

$$\mathbf{I}_o = \frac{1}{4\sqrt{1+n^2} \big/ \tan^{-1} n} \frac{2(-1)^n}{\sqrt{1+n^2}} \big/ \tan^{-1} n = \frac{(-1)^n}{2(1+n^2)}$$

In the time domain,

$$i_o(t) = \frac{1}{4} + \sum_{n=1}^{\infty} \frac{(-1)^n}{2(1+n^2)} \cos nt \ \text{A}$$

PRACTICE PROBLEM 17.7

Figure 17.24   For Practice Prob. 17.7.

If the input voltage in the circuit of Fig. 17.24 is

$$v(t) = \frac{1}{3} + \frac{1}{\pi^2} \sum_{n=1}^{\infty} \left(\frac{1}{n^2} \cos nt - \frac{\pi}{n} \sin nt \right) \ \text{V}$$

determine the response $i_o(t)$.

Answer: $\dfrac{1}{9} + \displaystyle\sum_{n=1}^{\infty} \dfrac{\sqrt{1+n^2\pi^2}}{n^2\pi^2\sqrt{9+4n^2}} \cos\left(nt - \tan^{-1}\dfrac{2n}{3} + \tan^{-1} n\pi \right) \ \text{A}.$

17.5 AVERAGE POWER AND RMS VALUES

Recall the concepts of average power and rms value of a periodic signal that we discussed in Chapter 11. To find the average power absorbed by a circuit due to a periodic excitation, we write the voltage and current in amplitude-phase form [see Eq. (17.10)] as

$$v(t) = V_{\text{dc}} + \sum_{n=1}^{\infty} V_n \cos(n\omega_0 t - \theta_n) \tag{17.42}$$

$$i(t) = I_{\text{dc}} + \sum_{m=1}^{\infty} I_m \cos(m\omega_0 t - \phi_m) \tag{17.43}$$

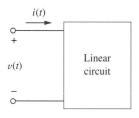

Figure 17.25   The voltage polarity reference and current reference direction.

Following the passive sign convention (Fig. 17.25), the average power is

$$P = \frac{1}{T} \int_0^T vi \, dt \tag{17.44}$$

Substituting Eqs. (17.42) and (17.43) into Eq. (17.44) gives

$$P = \frac{1}{T} \int_0^T V_{\text{dc}} I_{\text{dc}} \, dt + \sum_{m=1}^{\infty} \frac{I_m V_{\text{dc}}}{T} \int_0^T \cos(m\omega_0 t - \phi_m) \, dt$$

$$+ \sum_{n=1}^{\infty} \frac{V_n I_{\text{dc}}}{T} \int_0^T \cos(n\omega_0 t - \theta_n) \, dt \tag{17.45}$$

$$+ \sum_{m=1}^{\infty} \sum_{n=1}^{\infty} \frac{V_n I_m}{T} \int_0^T \cos(n\omega_0 t - \theta_n) \cos(m\omega_0 t - \phi_m) \, dt$$

The second and third integrals vanish, since we are integrating the cosine over its period. According to Eq. (17.4e), all terms in the fourth integral are zero when $m \neq n$. By evaluating the first integral and applying Eq. (17.4g) to the fourth integral for the case $m = n$, we obtain

$$P = V_{dc} I_{dc} + \frac{1}{2} \sum_{n=1}^{\infty} V_n I_n \cos(\theta_n - \phi_n) \qquad (17.46)$$

This shows that in average-power calculation involving periodic voltage and current, the total average power is the sum of the average powers in each harmonically related voltage and current.

Given a periodic function $f(t)$, its rms value (or the effective value) is given by

$$F_{rms} = \sqrt{\frac{1}{T} \int_0^T f^2(t)\, dt} \qquad (17.47)$$

Substituting $f(t)$ in Eq. (17.10) into Eq. (17.47) and noting that $(a+b)^2 = a^2 + 2ab + b^2$, we obtain

$$
\begin{aligned}
F_{rms}^2 = \frac{1}{T} \int_0^T &\left[a_0^2 + 2 \sum_{n=1}^{\infty} a_0 A_n \cos(n\omega_0 t + \phi_n) \right. \\
&\left. + \sum_{n=1}^{\infty} \sum_{m=1}^{\infty} A_n A_m \cos(n\omega_0 t + \phi_n) \cos(m\omega_0 t + \phi_m) \right] dt \\
= \frac{1}{T} \int_0^T &a_0^2\, dt + 2 \sum_{n=1}^{\infty} a_0 A_n \frac{1}{T} \int_0^T \cos(n\omega_0 t + \phi_n)\, dt \\
+ \sum_{n=1}^{\infty} \sum_{m=1}^{\infty} &A_n A_m \frac{1}{T} \int_0^T \cos(n\omega_0 t + \phi_n) \cos(m\omega_0 t + \phi_m)\, dt
\end{aligned}
$$

$$(17.48)$$

Distinct integers n and m have been introduced to handle the product of the two series summations. Using the same reasoning as above, we get

$$F_{rms}^2 = a_0^2 + \frac{1}{2} \sum_{n=1}^{\infty} A_n^2$$

or

$$F_{rms} = \sqrt{a_0^2 + \frac{1}{2} \sum_{n=1}^{\infty} A_n^2} \qquad (17.49)$$

In terms of Fourier coefficients a_n and b_n, Eq. (17.49) may be written as

$$F_{rms} = \sqrt{a_0^2 + \frac{1}{2} \sum_{n=1}^{\infty} (a_n^2 + b_n^2)} \qquad (17.50)$$

If $f(t)$ is the current through a resistor R, then the power dissipated in the resistor is

$$P = R F_{rms}^2 \qquad (17.51)$$

Or if $f(t)$ is the voltage across a resistor R, the power dissipated in the resistor is

$$P = \frac{F_{\text{rms}}^2}{R} \tag{17.52}$$

One can avoid specifying the nature of the signal by choosing a 1-Ω resistance. The power dissipated by the 1-Ω resistance is

$$P_{1\Omega} = F_{\text{rms}}^2 = a_0^2 + \frac{1}{2}\sum_{n=1}^{\infty}(a_n^2 + b_n^2) \tag{17.53}$$

Historical note: Named after the French mathematician Marc-Antoine Parseval Deschemes (1755–1836).

This result is known as *Parseval's theorem*. Notice that a_0^2 is the power in the dc component, while $1/2(a_n^2 + b_n^2)$ is the ac power in the nth harmonic. Thus, Parseval's theorem states that the average power in a periodic signal is the sum of the average power in its dc component and the average powers in its harmonics.

EXAMPLE 17.8

Figure 17.26   For Example 17.8.

Determine the average power supplied to the circuit in Fig. 17.26 if $i(t) = 2 + 10\cos(t + 10°) + 6\cos(3t + 35°)$ A.

Solution:

The input impedance of the network is

$$\mathbf{Z} = 10 \left\| \frac{1}{j2\omega} = \frac{10(1/j2\omega)}{10 + 1/j2\omega} = \frac{10}{1 + j20\omega} \right.$$

Hence,

$$\mathbf{V} = \mathbf{IZ} = \frac{10\mathbf{I}}{\sqrt{1 + 400\omega^2}\underline{/\tan^{-1} 20\omega}}$$

For the dc component, $\omega = 0$,

$$\mathbf{I} = 2 \text{ A} \quad \Longrightarrow \quad \mathbf{V} = 10(2) = 20 \text{ V}$$

This is expected, because the capacitor is an open circuit to dc and the entire 2-A current flows through the resistor. For $\omega = 1$ rad/s,

$$\mathbf{I} = 10\underline{/10°} \quad \Longrightarrow \quad \mathbf{V} = \frac{10(10\underline{/10°})}{\sqrt{1 + 400}\underline{/\tan^{-1} 20}}$$

$$= 5\underline{/-77.14°}$$

For $\omega = 3$ rad/s,

$$\mathbf{I} = 6\underline{/35°} \quad \Longrightarrow \quad \mathbf{V} = \frac{10(6\underline{/35°})}{\sqrt{1 + 3600}\underline{/\tan^{-1} 60}}$$

$$= 1\underline{/-54.04°}$$

Thus, in the time domain,

$$v(t) = 20 + 5\cos(t - 77.14°) + 1\cos(3t - 54.04°) \text{ V}$$

We obtain the average power supplied to the circuit by applying Eq. (17.46), as

$$P = V_{\text{dc}} I_{\text{dc}} + \frac{1}{2} \sum_{n=1}^{\infty} V_n I_n \cos(\theta_n - \phi_n)$$

To get the proper signs of θ_n and ϕ_n, we have to compare v and i in this example with Eqs. (17.42) and (17.43). Thus,

$$P = 20(2) + \frac{1}{2}(5)(10)\cos[77.14° - (-10°)]$$

$$+ \frac{1}{2}(1)(6)\cos[44.05° - (-35°)]$$

$$= 40 + 1.247 + 0.05 = 41.5 \text{ W}$$

Alternatively, we can find the average power absorbed by the resistor as

$$P = \frac{V_{\text{dc}}^2}{R} + \frac{1}{2} \sum_{n=1}^{\infty} \frac{|V_n|^2}{R} = \frac{20^2}{10} + \frac{1}{2} \cdot \frac{5^2}{10} + \frac{1}{2} \cdot \frac{1^2}{10}$$

$$= 40 + 1.25 + 0.05 = 41.5 \text{ W}$$

which is the same as the power supplied, since the capacitor absorbs no average power.

PRACTICE PROBLEM 17.8

The voltage and current at the terminals of a circuit are

$$v(t) = 80 + 120\cos 120\pi t + 60\cos(360\pi t - 30°)$$
$$i(t) = 5\cos(120\pi t - 10°) + 2\cos(360\pi t - 60°)$$

Find the average power absorbed by the circuit.

Answer: 347.4 W.

EXAMPLE 17.9

Find an estimate for the rms value of the voltage in Example 17.7.

Solution:

From Example 17.7, $v(t)$ is expressed as

$$v(t) = 1 - 1.414\cos(t + 45°) + 0.8944\cos(2t + 63.45°)$$
$$- 0.6345\cos(3t + 71.56°)$$
$$- 0.4851\cos(4t + 78.7°) + \cdots \text{ V}$$

Using Eq. (17.49),

$$V_{\text{rms}} = \sqrt{a_0^2 + \frac{1}{2} \sum_{n=1}^{\infty} A_n^2}$$

$$= \sqrt{1^2 + \frac{1}{2}\left[(-1.414)^2 + (0.8944)^2 + (-0.6345)^2 + (-0.4851)^2 + \cdots\right]}$$

$$= \sqrt{2.7186} = 1.649 \text{ V}$$

This is only an estimate, as we have not taken enough terms of the series. The actual function represented by the Fourier series is

$$v(t) = \frac{\pi e^t}{\sinh \pi}, \qquad -\pi < t < \pi$$

with $v(t) = v(t + T)$. The exact rms value of this is 1.776 V.

17.9

Find the rms value of the periodic current

$$i(t) = 8 + 30 \cos 2t - 20 \sin 2t + 15 \cos 4t - 10 \sin 4t \ \text{A}$$

Answer: 29.61 A.

17.6 EXPONENTIAL FOURIER SERIES

A compact way of expressing the Fourier series in Eq. (17.3) is to put it in exponential form. This requires that we represent the sine and cosine functions in the exponential form using Euler's identity:

$$\cos n\omega_0 t = \frac{1}{2}[e^{jn\omega_0 t} + e^{-jn\omega_0 t}] \qquad (17.54\text{a})$$

$$\sin n\omega_0 t = \frac{1}{2j}[e^{jn\omega_0 t} - e^{-jn\omega_0 t}] \qquad (17.54\text{b})$$

Substituting Eq. (17.54) into Eq. (17.3) and collecting terms, we obtain

$$f(t) = a_0 + \frac{1}{2}\sum_{n=1}^{\infty}[(a_n - jb_n)e^{jn\omega_0 t} + (a_n + jb_n)e^{-jn\omega_0 t}] \qquad (17.55)$$

If we define a new coefficient c_n so that

$$c_0 = a_0, \qquad c_n = \frac{(a_n - jb_n)}{2}, \qquad c_{-n} = c_n^* = \frac{(a_n + jb_n)}{2} \qquad (17.56)$$

then $f(t)$ becomes

$$f(t) = c_0 + \sum_{n=1}^{\infty}(c_n e^{jn\omega_0 t} + c_{-n}e^{-jn\omega_0 t}) \qquad (17.57)$$

or

$$f(t) = \sum_{n=-\infty}^{\infty} c_n e^{jn\omega_0 t} \qquad (17.58)$$

This is the *complex* or *exponential Fourier series* representation of $f(t)$. Note that this exponential form is more compact than the sine-cosine form in Eq. (17.3). Although the exponential Fourier series coefficients c_n can also be obtained from a_n and b_n using Eq. (17.56), they can also be obtained directly from $f(t)$ as

$$c_n = \frac{1}{T}\int_0^T f(t)e^{-jn\omega_0 t}\,dt \qquad (17.59)$$

where $\omega_0 = 2\pi/T$, as usual. The plots of the magnitude and phase of c_n versus $n\omega_0$ are called the *complex amplitude spectrum* and *complex phase spectrum* of $f(t)$, respectively. The two spectra form the complex frequency spectrum of $f(t)$.

> The exponential Fourier series of a periodic function $f(t)$ describes the spectrum of $f(t)$ in terms of the amplitude and phase angle of ac components at positive and negative harmonic frequencies.

The coefficients of the three forms of Fourier series (sine-cosine form, amplitude-phase form, and exponential form) are related by

$$A_n \underline{/\phi_n} = a_n - jb_n = 2c_n \tag{17.60}$$

or

$$c_n = |c_n| \underline{/\theta_n} = \frac{\sqrt{a_n^2 + b_n^2}}{2} \underline{/-\tan^{-1} b_n/a_n} \tag{17.61}$$

if only $a_n > 0$. Note that the phase θ_n of c_n is equal to ϕ_n.

In terms of the Fourier complex coefficients c_n, the rms value of a periodic signal $f(t)$ can be found as

$$
\begin{aligned}
F_{\text{rms}}^2 &= \frac{1}{T} \int_0^T f^2(t)\, dt = \frac{1}{T} \int_0^T f(t) \left[\sum_{n=-\infty}^{\infty} c_n e^{jn\omega_0 t} \right] dt \\
&= \sum_{n=-\infty}^{\infty} c_n \left[\frac{1}{T} \int_0^T f(t) e^{jn\omega_0 t}\, dt \right] \\
&= \sum_{n=-\infty}^{\infty} c_n c_n^* = \sum_{n=-\infty}^{\infty} |c_n|^2
\end{aligned}
\tag{17.62}
$$

or

$$F_{\text{rms}} = \sqrt{\sum_{n=-\infty}^{\infty} |c_n|^2} \tag{17.63}$$

Equation (17.62) can be written as

$$F_{\text{rms}}^2 = |c_0|^2 + 2 \sum_{n=1}^{\infty} |c_n|^2 \tag{17.64}$$

Again, the power dissipated by a 1-Ω resistance is

$$P_{1\Omega} = F_{\text{rms}}^2 = \sum_{n=-\infty}^{\infty} |c_n|^2 \tag{17.65}$$

which is a restatement of Parseval's theorem. The *power spectrum* of the signal $f(t)$ is the plot of $|c_n|^2$ versus $n\omega_0$. If $f(t)$ is the voltage across a resistor R, the average power absorbed by the resistor is F_{rms}^2/R; if $f(t)$ is the current through R, the power is $F_{\text{rms}}^2 R$.

Figure 17.27   The periodic pulse train.

The sinc function is called the *sampling function* in communication theory, where it is very useful.

As an illustration, consider the periodic pulse train of Fig. 17.27. Our goal is to obtain its amplitude and phase spectra. The period of the pulse train is $T = 10$, so that $\omega_0 = 2\pi/T = \pi/5$. Using Eq. (17.59),

$$
\begin{aligned}
c_n &= \frac{1}{T} \int_{-T/2}^{T/2} f(t) e^{-jn\omega_0 t} \, dt = \frac{1}{10} \int_{-1}^{1} 10 e^{-jn\omega_0 t} \, dt \\
&= \frac{1}{-jn\omega_0} e^{-jn\omega_0 t} \Big|_{-1}^{1} = \frac{1}{-jn\omega_0} (e^{-jn\omega_0} - e^{jn\omega_0}) \\
&= \frac{2}{n\omega_0} \frac{e^{jn\omega_0} - e^{-jn\omega_0}}{2j} = 2 \frac{\sin n\omega_0}{n\omega_0}, \qquad \omega_0 = \frac{\pi}{5} \\
&= 2 \frac{\sin n\pi/5}{n\pi/5}
\end{aligned}
\tag{17.66}
$$

and

$$
f(t) = 2 \sum_{n=-\infty}^{\infty} \frac{\sin n\pi/5}{n\pi/5} e^{jn\pi t/5}
\tag{17.67}
$$

Notice from Eq. (17.66) that c_n is the product of 2 and a function of the form $\sin x/x$. This function is known as the *sinc function*; we write it as

$$
\text{sinc}(x) = \frac{\sin x}{x}
\tag{17.68}
$$

Some properties of the sinc function are important here. For zero argument, the value of the sinc function is unity,

$$
\text{sinc}(0) = 1
\tag{17.69}
$$

This is obtained applying L'Hopital's rule to Eq. (17.68). For an integral multiple of π, the value of the sinc function is zero,

$$
\text{sinc}(n\pi) = 0, \qquad n = 1, 2, 3, \ldots
\tag{17.70}
$$

Also, the sinc function shows even symmetry. With all this in mind, we can obtain the amplitude and phase spectra of $f(t)$. From Eq. (17.66), the magnitude is

$$
|c_n| = 2 \left| \frac{\sin n\pi/5}{n\pi/5} \right|
\tag{17.71}
$$

while the phase is

$$
\theta_n = \begin{cases} 0°, & \sin \dfrac{n\pi}{5} > 0 \\[2mm] 180°, & \sin \dfrac{n\pi}{5} < 0 \end{cases}
\tag{17.72}
$$

Figure 17.28 shows the plot of $|c_n|$ versus n for n varying from -10 to 10, where $n = \omega/\omega_0$ is the normalized frequency. Figure 17.29 shows the plot of θ_n versus n. Both the amplitude spectrum and phase spectrum are called *line spectra*, because the value of $|c_n|$ and θ_n occur only at discrete values of frequencies. The spacing between the lines is ω_0. The power spectrum, which is the plot of $|c_n|^2$ versus $n\omega_0$, can also be plotted. Notice that the sinc function forms the envelope of the amplitude spectrum.

Examining the input and output spectra allows visualization of the effect of a circuit on a periodic signal.

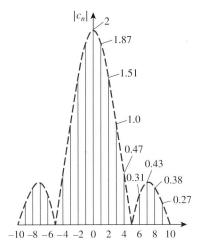

Figure 17.28   The amplitude of a periodic pulse train.

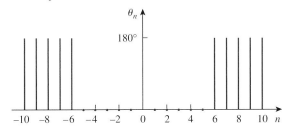

Figure 17.29   The phase spectrum of a periodic pulse train.

EXAMPLE 17.10

Find the exponential Fourier series expansion of the periodic function
$f(t) = e^t, 0 < t < 2\pi$ with $f(t + 2\pi) = f(t)$.

Solution:

Since $T = 2\pi$, $\omega_0 = 2\pi/T = 1$. Hence,

$$c_n = \frac{1}{T} \int_0^T f(t)e^{-jn\omega_0 t}\, dt = \frac{1}{2\pi} \int_0^{2\pi} e^t e^{-jnt}\, dt$$

$$= \frac{1}{2\pi} \frac{1}{1 - jn} e^{(1-jn)t} \bigg|_0^{2\pi} = \frac{1}{2\pi(1 - jn)}[e^{2\pi}e^{-j2\pi n} - 1]$$

But by Euler's identity,

$$e^{-j2\pi n} = \cos 2\pi n - j \sin 2\pi n = 1 - j0 = 1$$

Thus,

$$c_n = \frac{1}{2\pi(1 - jn)}[e^{2\pi} - 1] = \frac{85}{1 - jn}$$

The complex Fourier series is

$$f(t) = \sum_{n=-\infty}^{\infty} \frac{85}{1 - jn} e^{jnt}$$

We may want to plot the complex frequency spectrum of $f(t)$. If we let $c_n = |c_n| \underline{/\theta_n}$, then

$$|c_n| = \frac{85}{\sqrt{1 + n^2}}, \qquad \theta_n = \tan^{-1} n$$

By inserting in negative and positive values of n, we obtain the amplitude and the phase plots of c_n versus $n\omega_0 = n$, as in Fig. 17.30.

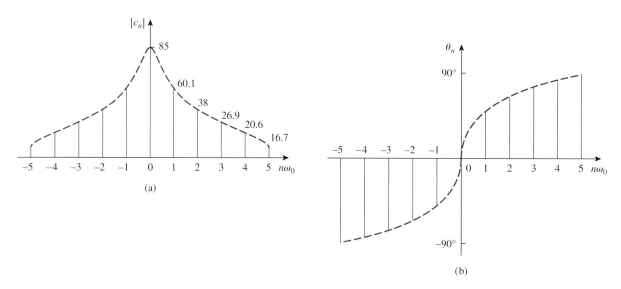

Figure 17.30   The complex frequency spectrum of the function in Example 17.10: (a) amplitude spectrum, (b) phase spectrum.

PRACTICE PROBLEM 17.10

Obtain the complex Fourier series of the function in Fig. 17.1.

Answer: $f(t) = \frac{1}{2} - \sum_{\substack{n=-\infty \\ n \neq 0 \\ n=\text{odd}}}^{\infty} \frac{j}{n\pi} e^{jn\pi t}.$

EXAMPLE 17.11

Find the complex Fourier series of the sawtooth wave in Fig. 17.9. Plot the amplitude and the phase spectra.

Solution:

From Fig. 17.9, $f(t) = t, 0 < t < 1, T = 1$ so that $\omega_0 = 2\pi/T = 2\pi$. Hence,

$$c_n = \frac{1}{T} \int_0^T f(t)e^{-jn\omega_0 t}\, dt = \frac{1}{1} \int_0^1 t e^{-j2n\pi t}\, dt \qquad (17.11.1)$$

But

$$\int te^{at}\,dt = \frac{e^{at}}{a^2}(ax-1)+C$$

Applying this to Eq. (17.11.1) gives

$$
\begin{aligned}
c_n &= \frac{e^{-j2n\pi t}}{(-j2n\pi)^2}(-j2n\pi t - 1)\,\Big|_0^1 \\
&= \frac{e^{-j2n\pi}(-j2n\pi - 1)+1}{-4n^2\pi^2}
\end{aligned}
\tag{17.11.2}
$$

Again,

$$e^{-j2\pi n} = \cos 2\pi n - j\sin 2\pi n = 1 - j0 = 1$$

so that Eq. (17.11.2) becomes

$$c_n = \frac{-j2n\pi}{-4n^2\pi^2} = \frac{j}{2n\pi} \tag{17.11.3}$$

This does not include the case when $n = 0$. When $n = 0$,

$$c_0 = \frac{1}{T}\int_0^T f(t)\,dt = \frac{1}{1}\int_0^1 t\,dt = \frac{t^2}{2}\Big|_1^0 = 0.5 \tag{17.11.4}$$

Hence,

$$f(t) = 0.5 + \sum_{\substack{n=-\infty \\ n\neq 0}}^{\infty} \frac{j}{2n\pi}e^{j2n\pi t} \tag{17.11.5}$$

and

$$|c_n| = \begin{cases} \dfrac{1}{2|n|\pi}, & n\neq 0 \\[2mm] 0.5, & n=0 \end{cases}, \qquad \theta_n = 90^\circ, \quad n\neq 0 \tag{17.11.6}$$

By plotting $|c_n|$ and θ_n for different n, we obtain the amplitude spectrum and the phase spectrum shown in Fig. 17.31.

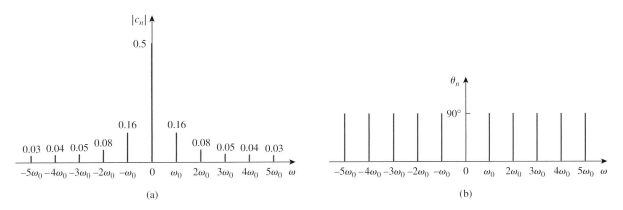

Figure 17.31   For Example 17.11: (a) amplitude spectrum, (b) phase spectrum.

PRACTICE PROBLEM 17.11

Obtain the complex Fourier series expansion of $f(t)$ in Fig. 17.17. Show the amplitude and phase spectra.

Answer: $f(t) = -\sum_{\substack{n=-\infty \\ n \neq 0}}^{\infty} \frac{j(-1)^n}{n\pi} e^{jn\pi t}$. See Fig. 17.32 for the spectra.

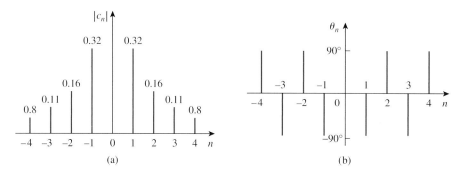

Figure 17.32   For Practice Prob. 17.11: (a) amplitude spectrum, (b) phase spectrum.

17.7 FOURIER ANALYSIS WITH PSPICE

Fourier analysis is usually performed with *PSpice* in conjunction with transient analysis. Therefore, we must do a transient analysis in order to perform a Fourier analysis.

To perform the Fourier analysis of a waveform, we need a circuit whose input is the waveform and whose output is the Fourier decomposition. A suitable circuit is a current (or voltage) source in series with a 1-Ω resistor as shown in Fig. 17.33. The waveform is inputted as $v_s(t)$ using VPULSE for a pulse or VSIN for a sinusoid, and the attributes of the waveform are set over its period T. The output V(1) from node 1 is the dc level (a_0) and the first nine harmonics (A_n) with their corresponding phases ψ_n; that is,

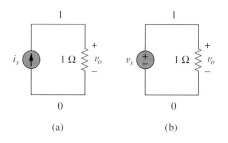

Figure 17.33   Fourier analysis with *PSpice* using: (a) a current source, (b) a voltage source.

$$v_o(t) = a_0 + \sum_{n=1}^{9} A_n \sin(n\omega_0 t + \psi_n) \qquad (17.73)$$

where

$$A_n = \sqrt{a_n^2 + b_n^2}, \qquad \psi_n = \phi_n - \frac{\pi}{2}, \qquad \phi_n = \tan^{-1}\frac{b_n}{a_n} \qquad (17.74)$$

Notice in Eq. (17.74) that the *PSpice* output is in the sine and angle form rather than the cosine and angle form in Eq. (17.10). The *PSpice* output also includes the normalized Fourier coefficients. Each coefficient a_n is normalized by dividing it by the magnitude of the fundamental a_1, so that the normalized component is a_n/a_1. The corresponding phase ψ_n is normalized by subtracting from it the phase ψ_1 of the fundamental, so that the normalized phase is $\psi_n - \psi_1$.

There are two types of Fourier analyses offered by *PSpice for Windows: Discrete Fourier Transform* (DFT) performed by the *PSpice* program and *Fast Fourier Transform* (FFT) performed by the *PSpice A/D* program. While DFT is an approximation of the exponential Fourier series, FTT is an algorithm for rapid efficient numerical computation of DFT. A full discussion of DFT and FTT is beyond the scope of this book.

17.7.1 Discrete Fourier Transform

A discrete Fourier transform (DFT) is performed by the *PSpice* program, which tabulates the harmonics in an output file. To enable a Fourier analysis, we select **Analysis/Setup/Transient** and bring up the Transient dialog box, shown in Fig. 17.34. The *Print Step* should be a small fraction of the period T, while the *Final Time* could be $6T$. The *Center Frequency* is the fundamental frequency $f_0 = 1/T$. The particular variable whose DFT is desired, V(1) in Fig. 17.34, is entered in the **Output Vars** command box. In addition to filling in the Transient dialog box, **DCLICK** *Enable Fourier*. With the Fourier analysis enabled and the schematic saved, run *PSpice* by selecting **Analysis/Simulate** as usual. The program executes a harmonic decomposition into Fourier components of the result of the transient analysis. The results are sent to an output file which can be retrieved by selecting **Analysis/Examine Output**. The output file includes the dc value and the first nine harmonics by default, although you can specify more in the *Number of harmonics* box (see Fig. 17.34).

17.7.2 Fast Fourier Transform

A fast Fourier transform (FFT) is performed by the *PSpice A/D* program and displays as a *PSpice A/D* plot the complete spectrum of a transient expression. As explained above, we first construct the schematic in Fig. 17.33(b) and enter the attributes of the waveform. We also need to enter the *Print Step* and the *Final Time* in the Transient dialog box. Once this is done, we can obtain the FFT of the waveform in two ways.

One way is to insert a voltage marker at node 1 in the schematic of the circuit in Fig. 17.33(b). After saving the schematic and selecting **Analysis/Simulate**, the waveform V(1) will be displayed in the *PSpice A/D* window. Double clicking the FFT icon in the *PSpice A/D* menu will automatically replace the waveform with its FFT. From the FFT-generated graph, we can obtain the harmonics. In case the FFT-generated graph is crowded, we can use the *User Defined* data range (see Fig. 17.35) to specify a smaller range.

Another way of obtaining the FFT of V(1) is to not insert a voltage marker at node 1 in the schematic. After selecting **Analysis/Simulate**, the *PSpice A/D* window will come up with no graph on it. We select **Trace/Add** and type V(1) in the **Trace Command** box and **DCLICKL OK**. We now select **Plot/X-Axis Settings** to bring up the *X Axis Setting* dialog box shown in Fig. 17.35 and then select **Fourier/OK**. This will cause the FFT of the selected trace (or traces) to be displayed. This second approach is useful for obtaining the FFT of any trace associated with the circuit.

A major advantage of the FFT method is that it provides graphical output. But its major disadvantage is that some of the harmonics may be too small to see.

Figure 17.34   Transient dialog box.

Figure 17.35   *X* axis settings dialog box.

In both DFT and FFT, we should let the simulation run for a large number of cycles and use a small value of *Step Ceiling* (in the Transient dialog box) to ensure accurate results. The *Final Time* in the Transient dialog box should be at least five times the period of the signal to allow the simulation to reach steady state.

EXAMPLE 17.12

Use *PSpice* to determine the Fourier coefficients of the signal in Fig. 17.1.

Solution:

Figure 17.36 shows the schematic for obtaining the Fourier coefficients. With the signal in Fig. 17.1 in mind, we enter the attributes of the voltage source VPULSE as shown in Fig. 17.36. We will solve this example using both the DFT and FFT approaches.

V1=0
V2=1
TD=0
TF=1u
TR=1u
PW=1
PER=2

Figure 17.36   Schematic for Example 17.12.

METHOD 1   **DFT Approach:** (The voltage marker in Fig. 17.36 is not needed for this method.) From Fig. 17.1, it is evident that $T = 2$ s,

$$f_0 = \frac{1}{T} = \frac{1}{2} = 0.5 \text{ Hz}$$

So, in the transient dialog box, we select the *Final Time* as $6T = 12$ s, the *Print Step* as 0.01 s, the *Step Ceiling* as 10 ms, the *Center Frequency* as 0.5 Hz, and the output variable as V(1). (In fact, Fig. 17.34 is for this particular example.) When *PSpice* is run, the output file contains the following result.

```
FOURIER COEFFICIENTS OF TRANSIENT RESPONSE V(1)

DC COMPONENT = 4.989950E-01
```

HARMONIC NO	FREQUENCY (HZ)	FOURIER COMPONENT	NORMALIZED COMPONENT	PHASE (DEG)	NORMALIZED PHASE (DEG)
1	5.000E-01	6.366E-01	1.000E+00	-1.809E-01	0.000E+00
2	1.000E+00	2.012E-03	3.160E-03	-9.226E+01	-9.208E+01
3	1.500E+00	2.122E-01	3.333E-01	-5.427E-01	-3.619E-01

(continued)

(continued)

4	2.000E+00	2.016E-03	3.167E-03	-9.451E+01	-9.433E+01
5	2.500E+00	1.273E-01	1.999E-01	-9.048E-01	-7.239E-01
6	3.000E+00	2.024E-03	3.180E-03	-9.676E+01	-9.658E+01
7	3.500E+00	9.088E-02	1.427E-01	-1.267E+00	-1.086E+00
8	4.000E+00	2.035E-03	3.197E-03	-9.898E+01	-9.880E+01
9	4.500E+00	7.065E-02	1.110E-01	-1.630E+00	-1.449E+00

Comparing the result with that in Eq. (17.1.7) (see Example 17.1) or with the spectra in Fig. 17.4 shows a close agreement. From Eq. (17.1.7), the dc component is 0.5 while *PSpice* gives 0.498995. Also, the signal has only odd harmonics with phase $\psi_n = -90°$, whereas *PSpice* seems to indicate that the signal has even harmonics although the magnitudes of the even harmonics are small.

METHOD **2** **FFT Approach:** With voltage marker in Fig. 17.36 in place, we run *PSpice* and obtain the waveform V(1) shown in Fig. 17.37(a) on the *PSpice A/D* window. By double clicking the FFT icon in the *PSpice A/D* menu and changing the X-axis setting to 0 to 10 Hz, we obtain the FFT of V(1) as shown in Fig. 17.37(b). The FFT-generated graph contains the dc and harmonic components within the selected frequency range. Notice that the magnitudes and frequencies of the harmonics agree with the DFT-generated tabulated values.

Figure 17.37   (a) Original waveform of Fig. 17.1, (b) FFT of the waveform.

PRACTICE PROBLEM 17.12

Obtain the Fourier coefficients of the function in Fig. 17.7 using *PSpice*.

Answer:

```
FOURIER COEFFICIENTS OF TRANSIENT RESPONSE V(1)

DC COMPONENT = 4.950000E-01
```

HARMONIC NO	FREQUENCY (HZ)	FOURIER COMPONENT	NORMALIZED COMPONENT	PHASE (DEG)	NORMALIZED PHASE (DEG)
1	1.000E+00	3.184E-01	1.000E+00	-1.782E+02	0.000E+00
2	2.000E+00	1.593E-01	5.002E-01	-1.764E+02	1.800E+00
3	3.000E+00	1.063E-01	3.338E-01	-1.746E+02	3.600E+00
4	4.000E+00	7.979E-02	2.506E-03	-1.728E+02	5.400E+00
5	5.000E+00	6.392E-01	2.008E-01	-1.710E+02	7.200E+00
6	6.000E+00	5.337E-02	1.676E-03	-1.692E+02	9.000E+00
7	7.000E+00	4.584E-02	1.440E-01	-1.674E+02	1.080E+01
8	8.000E+00	4.021E-02	1.263E-01	-1.656E+02	1.260E+01
9	9.000E+00	3.584E-02	1.126E-01	-1.638E+02	1.440E+01

EXAMPLE 17.13

Figure 17.38   For Example 17.13.

If v_s in the circuit of Fig. 17.38 is a sinusoidal voltage source of amplitude 12 V and frequency 100 Hz, find current $i(t)$.

Solution:

The schematic is shown in Fig. 17.39. We may use the DFT approach to obtain the Fourier coeffcents of $i(t)$. Since the period of the input waveform is $T = 1/100 = 10$ ms, in the Transient dialog box we select *Print Step:* 0.1 ms, *Final Time:* 100 ms, *Center Frequency:* 100 Hz, *Number of harmonics:* 4, and *Output Vars:* I(L1). When the circuit is simulated, the output file includes the following.

```
FOURIER COEFFICIENTS OF TRANSIENT RESPONSE I(VD)

DC COMPONENT = 8.583269E-03
```

HARMONIC NO	FREQUENCY (HZ)	FOURIER COMPONENT	NORMALIZED COMPONENT	PHASE (DEG)	NORMALIZED PHASE (DEG)
1	1.000E+02	8.730E-03	1.000E+00	-8.984E+01	0.000E+00
2	2.000E+02	1.017E-04	1.165E-02	-8.306E+01	6.783E+00
3	3.000E+02	6.811E-05	7.802E-03	-8.235E+01	7.490E+00
4	4.000E+02	4.403E-05	5.044E-03	-8.943E+01	4.054E+00

With the Fourier coefficients, the Fourier series describing the current $i(t)$ can be obtained using Eq. (17.73); that is,

$$i(t) = 8.5833 + 8.73 \sin(2\pi \cdot 100t - 89.84°)$$
$$+ 0.1017 \sin(2\pi \cdot 200t - 83.06°)$$
$$+ 0.068 \sin(2\pi \cdot 300t - 82.35°) + \cdots \text{ mA}$$

We can also use the FFT approach to cross-check our result. The current marker is inserted at pin 1 of the inductor as shown in Fig. 17.39. Running *PSpice* will automatically produce the plot of I(L1) in the *PSpice A/D* window, as shown in Fig. 17.40(a). By double clicking the FFT icon and setting the range of the X-axis from 0 to 200 Hz, we generate the FFT of I(L1) shown in Fig. 17.40(b). It is clear from the FFT-generated plot that only the dc component and the first harmonic are visible. Higher harmonics are negligibly small.

Figure 17.39   Schematic of the circuit in Fig. 17.38.

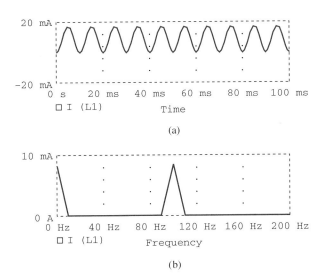

(a)

(b)

Figure 17.40   For Example 17.13: (a) plot of $i(t)$, (b) the FFT of $i(t)$.

A sinusoidal current source of amplitude 4 A and frequency 2 kHz is applied to the circuit in Fig. 17.41. Use *PSpice* to find $v(t)$.

Answer: $v(t) = -150.72 + 145.5 \sin(4\pi \cdot 10^3 t + 90°) + \cdots \ \mu V$. The Fourier components are shown below.

Figure 17.41   For Practice Prob. 17.14.

```
FOURIER COEFFICIENTS OF TRANSIENT RESPONSE V(R1:1)


DC COMPONENT =  -1.507169E-04
```

HARMONIC NO	FREQUENCY (HZ)	FOURIER COMPONENT	NORMALIZED COMPONENT	PHASE (DEG)	NORMALIZED PHASE (DEG)
1	2.000E+03	1.455E-04	1.000E+00	9.006E+01	0.000E+00
2	4.000E+03	1.851E-06	1.273E-02	9.597E+01	5.910E+00
3	6.000E+03	1.406E-06	9.662E-03	9.323E+01	3.167E+00
4	8.000E+03	1.010E-06	6.946E-02	8.077E+01	-9.292E+00

†17.8 APPLICATIONS

We demonstrated in Section 17.4 that the Fourier series expansion permits the application of the phasor techniques used in ac analysis to circuits containing nonsinusoidal periodic excitations. The Fourier series has many other practical applications, particularly in communications and signal processing. Typical applications include spectrum analysis, filtering, rectification, and harmonic distortion. We will consider two of these: spectrum analyzers and filters.

17.8.1 Spectrum Analyzers

The Fourier series provides the spectrum of a signal. As we have seen, the spectrum consists of the amplitudes and phases of the harmonics versus frequency. By providing the spectrum of a signal $f(t)$, the Fourier series helps us identify the pertinent features of the signal. It demonstrates which frequencies are playing an important role in the shape of the output and which ones are not. For example, audible sounds have significant components in the frequency range of 20 Hz to 15 kHz, while visible light signals range from 10^5 GHz to 10^6 GHz. Table 17.4 presents some other signals and the frequency ranges of their components. A periodic function is said to be *band-limited* if its amplitude spectrum contains only a finite number of coefficients A_n or c_n. In this case, the Fourier series becomes

$$f(t) = \sum_{n=-N}^{N} c_n e^{jn\omega_0 t} = a_0 + \sum_{n=1}^{N} A_n \cos(n\omega_0 t + \phi_n) \qquad (17.75)$$

This shows that we need only $2N + 1$ terms (namely, $a_0, A_1, A_2, \ldots, A_N$, $\phi_1, \phi_2, \ldots, \phi_N$) to completely specify $f(t)$ if ω_0 is known. This leads to the *sampling theorem*: a band-limited periodic function whose Fourier series contains N harmonics is uniquely specified by its values at $2N + 1$ instants in one period.

A *spectrum analyzer* is an instrument that displays the amplitude of the components of a signal versus frequency. It shows the various frequency components (spectral lines) that indicate the amount of energy at each frequency.

It is unlike an oscilloscope, which displays the entire signal (all components) versus time. An oscilloscope shows the signal in the time domain, while the spectrum analyzer shows the signal in the frequency domain. There is perhaps no instrument more useful to a circuit analyst than the spectrum analyzer. An analyzer can conduct noise and spurious signal analysis, phase checks, electromagnetic interference and filter examinations, vibration measurements, radar measurements, and more. Spectrum analyzers are commercially available in various sizes and shapes. Figure 17.42 displays a typical one.

17.8.2 Filters

Filters are an important component of electronics and communications systems. Chapter 14 presented a full discussion on passive and active filters. Here, we investigate how to design filters to select the fundamental

TABLE 17.4   Frequency ranges of typical signals.

Signal	Frequency Range
Audible sounds	20 Hz to 15 kHz
AM radio	540–1600 kHz
Short-wave radio	3–36 MHz
Video signals (U.S. standards)	dc to 4.2 MHz
VHF television, FM radio	54–216 MHz
UHF television	470–806 MHz
Cellular telephone	824–891.5 MHz
Microwaves	2.4–300 GHz
Visible light	10^5–10^6 GHz
X-rays	10^8–10^9 GHz

Figure 17.42   A typical spectrum analyzer. *(Courtesy of Hewlett-Packard.)*

component (or any desired harmonic) of the input signal and reject other harmonics. This filtering process cannot be accomplished without the Fourier series expansion of the input signal. For the purpose of illustration, we will consider two cases, a lowpass filter and a bandpass filter. In Example 17.6, we already looked at a highpass RL filter.

The output of a lowpass filter depends on the input signal, the transfer function $H(\omega)$ of the filter, and the corner or half-power frequency ω_c. We recall that $\omega_c = 1/RC$ for an RC passive filter. As shown in Fig. 17.43(a), the lowpass filter passes the dc and low-frequency components, while blocking the high-frequency components. By making ω_c

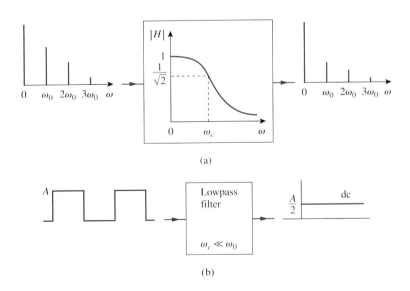

Figure 17.43   (a) Input and output spectra of a lowpass filter, (b) the lowpass filter passes only the dc component when $\omega_c \ll \omega_0$.

In this section, we have used ω_c for the center frequency of the bandpass filter instead of ω_0 as in Chapter 14, to avoid confusing ω_0 with the fundamental frequency of the input signal.

sufficiently large ($\omega_c \gg \omega_0$, e.g., making C small), a large number of the harmonics can be passed. On the other hand, by making ω_c sufficiently small ($\omega_c \ll \omega_0$), we can block out all the ac components and pass only dc, as shown typically in Fig. 17.43(b). (See Fig. 17.2(a) for the Fourier series expansion of the square wave.)

Similarly, the output of a bandpass filter depends on the input signal, the transfer function of the filter $H(\omega)$, its bandwidth B, and its center frequency ω_c. As illustrated in Fig. 17.44(a), the filter passes all the harmonics of the input signal within a band of frequencies ($\omega_1 < \omega < \omega_2$) centered around ω_c. We have assumed that ω_0, $2\omega_0$, and $3\omega_0$ are within that band. If the filter is made highly selective ($B \ll \omega_0$) and $\omega_c = \omega_0$, where ω_0 is the fundamental frequency of the input signal, the filter passes only the fundamental component ($n = 1$) of the input and blocks out all higher harmonics. As shown in Fig. 17.44(b), with a square wave as input, we obtain a sine wave of the same frequency as the output. (Again, refer to Fig. 17.2(a).)

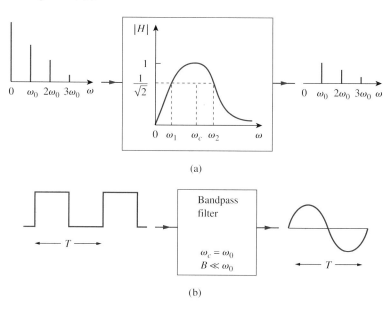

(a)

(b)

Figure 17.44   (a) Input and output spectra of a bandpass filter, (b) the bandpass filter passes only the fundamental component when $B \ll \omega_0$.

EXAMPLE 17.14

If the sawtooth waveform in Fig. 17.45(a) is applied to an ideal lowpass filter with the transfer function shown in Fig. 17.45(b), determine the output.

Solution:

The input signal in Fig. 17.45(a) is the same as the signal in Fig. 17.9. From Practice Prob. 17.2, we know that the Fourier series expansion is

$$x(t) = \frac{1}{2} - \frac{1}{\pi}\sin \omega_0 t - \frac{1}{2\pi}\sin 2\omega_0 t - \frac{1}{3\pi}\sin 3\omega_0 t - \cdots$$

where the period is $T = 1$ s and the fundamental frequency is $\omega_0 = 2\pi$ rad/s. Since the corner frequency of the filter is $\omega_c = 10$ rad/s, only the dc component and harmonics with $n\omega_0 < 10$ will be passed. For $n = 2$, $n\omega_0 = 4\pi = 12.566$ rad/s, which is higher than 10 rad/s, meaning that second and higher harmonics will be rejected. Thus, only the dc and fundamental components will be passed. Hence the output of the filter is

$$y(t) = \frac{1}{2} - \frac{1}{\pi} \sin 2\pi t$$

(a)   (b)

Figure 17.45   For Example 17.14.

PRACTICE PROBLEM 17.14

Rework Example 17.14 if the lowpass filter is replaced by the ideal bandpass filter shown in Fig. 17.46.

Answer: $y(t) = -\dfrac{1}{3\pi} \sin 3\omega_0 t - \dfrac{1}{4\pi} \sin 4\omega_0 t - \dfrac{1}{5\pi} \sin 5\omega_0 t.$

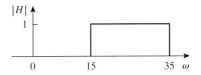

Figure 17.46   For Practice Prob. 17.14.

17.9 SUMMARY

1. A periodic function is one that repeats itself every T seconds; that is, $f(t \pm nT) = f(t), n = 1, 2, 3, \ldots$.

2. Any nonsinusoidal periodic function $f(t)$ that we encounter in electrical engineering can be expressed in terms of sinusoids using Fourier series:

$$f(t) = \underbrace{a_0}_{\text{dc}} + \underbrace{\sum_{n=1}^{\infty}(a_n \cos n\omega_0 t + b_n \sin n\omega_0 t)}_{\text{ac}}$$

where $\omega_0 = 2\pi/T$ is the fundamental frequency. The Fourier series resolves the function into the dc component a_0 and an ac component containing infinitely many harmonically related sinusoids. The Fourier coefficients are determined as

$$a_0 = \frac{1}{T}\int_0^T f(t)\, dt, \qquad a_n = \frac{2}{T}\int_0^T f(t) \cos n\omega_0 t\, dt$$

$$b_n = \frac{2}{T}\int_0^T f(t) \sin n\omega_0 t\, dt$$

If $f(t)$ is an even function, $b_n = 0$, and when $f(t)$ is odd, $a_0 = 0$ and $a_n = 0$. If $f(t)$ is half-wave symmetric, $a_0 = a_n = b_n = 0$ for even values of n.

3. An alternative to the trigonometric (or sine-cosine) Fourier series is the amplitude-phase form

$$f(t) = a_0 + \sum_{n=1}^{\infty} A_n \cos(n\omega_0 t + \phi_n)$$

where

$$A_n = \sqrt{a_n^2 + b_n^2}, \qquad \phi_n = -\tan^{-1}\frac{b_n}{a_n}$$

4. Fourier series representation allows us to apply the phasor method in analyzing circuits when the source function is a nonsinusoidal periodic function. We use phasor technique to determine the response of each harmonic in the series, transform the responses to the time domain, and add them up.

5. The average-power of periodic voltage and current is

$$P = V_{\text{dc}}I_{\text{dc}} + \frac{1}{2}\sum_{n=1}^{\infty} V_n I_n \cos(\theta_n - \phi_n)$$

In other words, the total average power is the sum of the average powers in each harmonically related voltage and current.

6. A periodic function can also be represented in terms of an exponential (or complex) Fourier series as

$$f(t) = \sum_{n=-\infty}^{\infty} c_n e^{jn\omega_0 t}$$

where

$$c_n = \frac{1}{T}\int_0^T f(t) e^{-jn\omega_0 t}\, dt$$

and $\omega_0 = 2\pi/T$. The exponential form describes the spectrum of $f(t)$ in terms of the amplitude and phase of ac components at positive and negative harmonic frequencies. Thus, there are three basic forms of Fourier series representation: the trigonometric form, the amplitude-phase form, and the exponential form.

7. The frequency (or line) spectrum is the plot of A_n and ϕ_n or $|c_n|$ and θ_n versus frequency.

8. The rms value of a periodic function is given by

$$F_{\text{rms}} = \sqrt{a_0^2 + \frac{1}{2}\sum_{n=1}^{\infty} A_n^2}$$

The power dissipated by a 1-Ω resistance is

$$P_{1\Omega} = F_{\text{rms}}^2 = a_0^2 + \frac{1}{2}\sum_{n=1}^{\infty}(a_n^2 + b_n^2) = \sum_{n=-\infty}^{\infty}|c_n|^2$$

This relationship is known as *Parseval's theorem*.

9. Using *PSpice*, a Fourier analysis of a circuit can be performed in conjunction with the transient analysis.

10. Fourier series find application in spectrum analyzers and filters. The spectrum analyzer is an instrument that displays the discrete Fourier spectra of an input signal, so that an analyst can determine the frequencies and relative energies of the signal's components. Because the Fourier spectra are discrete spectra, filters can be designed for great effectiveness in blocking frequency components of a signal that are outside a desired range.

REVIEW QUESTIONS

17.1 Which of the following cannot be a Fourier series?

(a) $t - \dfrac{t^2}{2} + \dfrac{t^3}{3} - \dfrac{t^4}{4} + \dfrac{t^5}{5}$

(b) $5 \sin t + 3 \sin 2t - 2 \sin 3t + \sin 4t$

(c) $\sin t - 2 \cos 3t + 4 \sin 4t + \cos 4t$

(d) $\sin t + 3 \sin 2.7t - \cos \pi t + 2 \tan \pi t$

(e) $1 + e^{-j\pi t} + \dfrac{e^{-j2\pi t}}{2} + \dfrac{e^{-j3\pi t}}{3}$

17.2 If $f(t) = t, 0 < t < \pi, f(t + n\pi) = f(t)$, the value of ω_0 is

(a) 1   (b) 2   (c) π (d) 2π

17.3 Which of the following are even functions?

(a) $t + t^2$ (b) $t^2 \cos t$ (c) e^{t^2}
(d) $t^2 + t^4$ (e) $\sinh t$

17.4 Which of the following are odd functions?

(a) $\sin t + \cos t$ (b) $t \sin t$
(c) $t \ln t$ (d) $t^3 \cos t$
(e) $\sinh t$

17.5 If $f(t) = 10 + 8 \cos t + 4 \cos 3t + 2 \cos 5t + \cdots$, the magnitude of the dc component is:

(a) 10   (b) 8   (c) 4
(d) 2   (e) 0

17.6 If $f(t) = 10 + 8 \cos t + 4 \cos 3t + 2 \cos 5t + \cdots$, the angular frequency of the 6th harmonic is

(a) 12   (b) 11   (c) 9
(d) 6   (e) 1

17.7 The function in Fig. 17.14 is half-wave symmetric.

(a) True   (b) False

17.8 The plot of $|c_n|$ versus $n\omega_0$ is called:

(a) complex frequency spectrum

(b) complex amplitude spectrum

(c) complex phase spectrum

17.9 When the periodic voltage $2 + 6 \sin \omega_0 t$ is applied to a 1-Ω resistor, the integer closest to the power (in watts) dissipated in the resistor is:

(a) 5   (b) 8   (c) 20
(d) 22   (e) 40

17.10 The instrument for displaying the spectrum of a signal is known as:

(a) oscilloscope   (b) spectrogram
(c) spectrum analyzer   (d) Fourier spectrometer

Answers: 17.1a,d, 17.2b, 17.3b,c,d, 17.4d,e, 17.5a, 17.6d, 17.7a, 17.8b, 17.9d ,17.10c.

PROBLEMS

Section 17.2   Trigonometric Fourier Series

17.1 Evaluate each of the following functions and see if it is periodic. If periodic, find its period.

(a) $f(t) = \cos \pi t + 2 \cos 3\pi t + 3 \cos 5\pi t$

(b) $y(t) = \sin t + 4 \cos 2\pi t$

(c) $g(t) = \sin 3t \cos 4t$

(d) $h(t) = \cos^2 t$

(e) $z(t) = 4.2 \sin(0.4\pi t + 10°)$
$\qquad\qquad + 0.8 \sin(0.6\pi t + 50°)$

(f) $p(t) = 10$

(g) $q(t) = e^{-\pi t}$

17.2 Determine the period of these periodic functions:

(a) $f_1(t) = 4 \sin 5t + 3 \sin 6t$

(b) $f_2(t) = 12 + 5 \cos 2t + 2 \cos(4t + 45°)$

(c) $f_3(t) = 4 \sin^2 600\pi t$

(d) $f_4(t) = e^{j10t}$

17.3 Give the Fourier coefficients a_0, a_n, and b_n of the waveform in Fig. 17.47. Plot the amplitude and phase spectra.

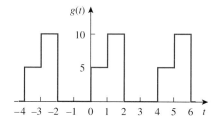

Figure 17.47   For Prob. 17.3.

17.4 Find the Fourier series expansion of the backward sawtooth waveform of Fig. 17.48. Obtain the amplitude and phase spectra.

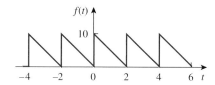

Figure 17.48   For Probs. 17.4 and 17.66.

17.5 Obtain the Fourier series expansion for the waveform shown in Fig. 17.49.

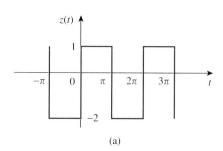

(a)

Figure 17.49   For Prob. 17.5.

17.6 Find the Fourier series expansion of the periodic waveform shown in Fig. 17.50.

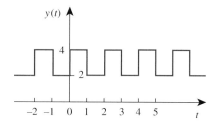

Figure 17.50   For Prob. 17.6.

17.7 Determine the Fourier series for the function in Fig 17.51.

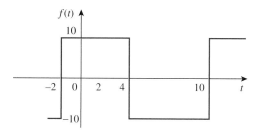

Figure 17.51   For Prob. 17.7.

17.8 Determine the Fourier series of the signal in Fig. 17.52.

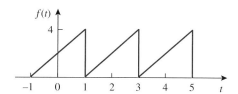

Figure 17.52   For Prob. 17.8.

17.9 Determine the Fourier coefficients a_n and b_n of the first three harmonic terms of the rectified cosine wave in Fig. 17.53.

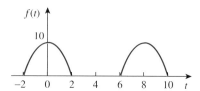

Figure 17.53   For Prob. 17.9.

17.10 Find the exponential Fourier series for the periodic function shown in Fig. 17.54.

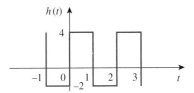

Figure 17.54   For Prob. 17.10.

17.11 Obtain the exponential Fourier series for the signal in Fig. 17.55.

Figure 17.55   For Prob. 17.11.

*__17.12__ A voltage source has a periodic waveform defined over its period as

$$v(t) = t(2\pi - t) \text{ V}, \qquad 0 < t < 2\pi$$

Find the Fourier series for this voltage.

17.13 A periodic function is defined over its period as

$$h(t) = \begin{cases} 10 \sin t, & 0 < t < \pi \\ 20 \sin(t - \pi), & \pi < t < 2\pi \end{cases}$$

Find the Fourier series of $h(t)$.

17.14 Find the quadrature (cosine and sine) form of the Fourier series

$$f(t) = 2 + \sum_{n=1}^{\infty} \frac{10}{n^3 + 1} \cos\left(2nt + \frac{n\pi}{4}\right)$$

17.15 Express the Fourier series

$$f(t) = 10 + \sum_{n=1}^{\infty} \frac{4}{n^2 + 1} \cos 10nt + \frac{1}{n^3} \sin 10nt$$

(a) in a cosine and angle form,
(b) in a sine and angle form.

17.16 The waveform in Fig. 17.56(a) has the following Fourier series:

$$v_1(t) = \frac{1}{2} - \frac{4}{\pi^2}\left(\cos \pi t + \frac{1}{9} \cos 3\pi t + \frac{1}{25} \cos 5\pi t + \cdots\right) \text{ V}$$

Obtain the Fourier series of $v_2(t)$ in Fig. 17.56(b).

(a)

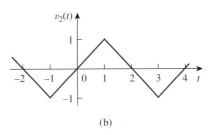

(b)

Figure 17.56   For Probs. 17.16 and 17.69.

Section 17.3   Symmetry Considerations

17.17 Determine if these functions are even, odd, or neither.

(a) $1 + t$ (b) $t^2 - 1$ (c) $\cos n\pi t \sin n\pi t$
(d) $\sin^2 \pi t$ (e) e^{-t}

17.18 Determine the fundamental frequency and specify the type of symmetry present in the functions in Fig. 17.57.

(a)

(b)

---

*An asterisk indicates a challenging problem.

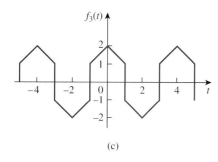

(c)

Figure 17.57   For Probs. 17.18 and 17.63.

17.19   Obtain the Fourier series expansion of the function in Fig. 17.58.

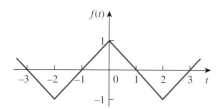

Figure 17.58   For Prob. 17.19.

17.20   Find the Fourier series for the signal in Fig. 17.59. Evaluate $f(t)$ at $t = 2$ using the first three nonzero harmonics.

Figure 17.59   For Probs. 17.20 and 17.67.

17.21   Determine the trigonometric Fourier series of the signal in Fig. 17.60.

Figure 17.60   For Prob. 17.21.

17.22   Calculate the Fourier coefficients for the function in Fig. 17.61.

Figure 17.61   For Prob. 17.22.

17.23   Find the Fourier series of the function shown in Fig. 17.62.

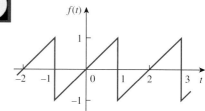

Figure 17.62   For Prob. 17.23.

17.24   In the periodic function of Fig. 17.63,

(a)   find the trigonometric Fourier series coefficients a_2 and b_2,

(b)   calculate the magnitude and phase of the component of $f(t)$ that has $\omega_n = 10$ rad/s,

(c)   use the first four nonzero terms to estimate $f(\pi/2)$,

(d)   show that

$$\frac{\pi}{4} = \frac{1}{1} - \frac{1}{3} + \frac{1}{5} - \frac{1}{7} + \frac{1}{9} - \frac{1}{11} + \cdots$$

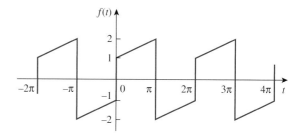

Figure 17.63   For Prob. 17.24.

17.25   Determine the Fourier series representation of the function in Fig. 17.64.

Figure 17.64   For Prob. 17.25.

17.26 Find the Fourier series representation of the signal shown in Fig. 17.65.

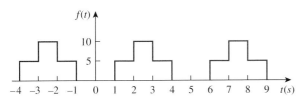

Figure 17.65   For Prob. 17.26.

17.27 For the waveform shown in Fig. 17.66 below,

(a) specify the type of symmetry it has,

(b) calculate a_3 and b_3,

(c) find the rms value using the first five nonzero harmonics.

17.28 Obtain the trigonometric Fourier series for the voltage waveform shown in Fig. 17.67.

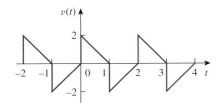

Figure 17.67   For Prob. 17.28.

17.29 Determine the Fourier series expansion of the sawtooth function in Fig. 17.68.

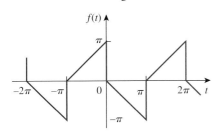

Figure 17.68   For Prob. 17.29.

17.30 (a) If $f(t)$ is an even function, show that

$$c_n = \frac{2}{T} \int_0^{T/2} f(t) \cos n\omega_o t \, dt$$

(b) If $f(t)$ is an odd function, show that

$$c_n = -\frac{j2}{T} \int_0^{T/2} f(t) \sin n\omega_o t \, dt$$

17.31 Let a_n and b_n be the Fourier series coefficients of $f(t)$ and let ω_o be its fundamental frequency. Suppose $f(t)$ is time-scaled to give $h(t) = f(\alpha t)$. Express the a_n' and b_n', and ω_o', of $h(t)$ in terms of a_n, b_n, and ω_o of $f(t)$.

Section 17.4   Circuit Applications

17.32 Find $i(t)$ in the circuit of Fig. 17.69 given that

$$i_s(t) = 1 + \sum_{n=1}^{\infty} \frac{1}{n^2} \cos 3nt \text{ A}$$

Figure 17.69   For Prob. 17.32.

17.33 In the circuit shown in Fig. 17.70, the Fourier series expansion of $v_s(t)$ is

$$v_s(t) = 3 + \frac{4}{\pi} \sum_{n=1}^{\infty} \frac{1}{n} \sin(n\pi t)$$

Find $v_o(t)$.

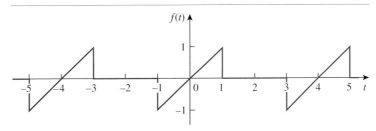

Figure 17.66   For Prob. 17.27.

Figure 17.70   For Prob. 17.33.

17.34   Obtain $v_o(t)$ in the network of Fig. 17.71 if

$$v(t) = \sum_{n=1}^{\infty} \frac{10}{n^2} \cos\left(nt + \frac{n\pi}{4}\right) \text{ V}$$

Figure 17.71   For Prob. 17.34.

17.35   If v_s in the circuit of Fig. 17.72 is the same as function $f_2(t)$ in Fig. 17.57(b), determine the dc component and the first three nonzero harmonics of $v_o(t)$.

Figure 17.72   For Prob. 17.35.

17.36   Determine $i_o(t)$ in the circuit of Fig. 17.73 if

$$v_s(t) = \sum_{\substack{n=1 \\ n=\text{odd}}}^{\infty} \left(\frac{-1}{n\pi} \sin\frac{n\pi}{2} \cos nt + \frac{3}{n\pi} \sin nt \right)$$

Figure 17.73   For Prob. 17.36.

17.37   The periodic voltage waveform in Fig. 17.35(a) is applied to the circuit in Fig. 17.74(b). Find the voltage $v_o(t)$ across the capacitor.

(a)

(b)

Figure 17.74   For Prob. 17.37.

17.38   If the square wave shown in Fig. 17.75(a) is applied to the circuit in Fig. 17.75(b), find the Fourier series for $v_o(t)$.

(a)

(b)

Figure 17.75   For Prob. 17.38.

17.39   If the periodic voltage in Fig. 17.76(a) is applied to the circuit in Fig. 17.76(b), find $i_o(t)$.

(a)

(b)

Figure 17.76   For Prob. 17.39.

*17.40 The signal in Fig. 17.77(a) is applied to the circuit in Fig. 17.77(b). Find $v_o(t)$.

(a)

(b)

Figure 17.77   For Prob. 17.40.

17.41 The full-wave rectified sinusoidal voltage in Fig. 17.78(a) is applied to the lowpass filter in Fig. 17.78(b). Obtain the output voltage $v_o(t)$ of the filter.

(a)

(b)

Figure 17.78   For Prob. 17.41.

17.42 The square wave in Fig. 17.79(a) is applied to the circuit in Fig. 17.79(b). Find the Fourier series of $v_o(t)$.

(a)

(b)

Figure 17.79   For Prob. 17.42.

Section 17.5   Average Power and RMS Values

17.43 The voltage across the terminals of a circuit is

$$v(t) = 30 + 20\cos(60\pi t + 45°) + 10\cos(60\pi t - 45°) \text{ V}$$

If the current entering the terminal at higher potential is

$$i(t) = 6 + 4\cos(60\pi t + 10°) - 2\cos(120\pi t - 60°) \text{ A}$$

find:

(a) the rms value of the voltage,
(b) the rms value of the current,
(c) the average power absorbed by the circuit.

17.44 The voltage and current through an element are, respectively,

$$v(t) = 30\cos(t + 25°) + 10\cos(2t + 35°) + 4\cos(3t - 10°) \text{ V}$$
$$i(t) = 2\cos t + \cos(2t - 10°) \text{ A}$$

(a) Find the average power delivered to the element.
(b) Plot the power spectrum.

17.45 A series RLC circuit has $R = 10\ \Omega$, $L = 2$ mH, and $C = 40\ \mu$F. Determine the effective current and average power absorbed when the applied voltage is

$$v(t) = 100\cos 1000t + 50\cos 2000t + 25\cos 3000t \text{ V}$$

17.46 Consider the periodic signal in Fig. 17.41. (a) Find the actual rms value of $f(t)$. (b) Use the first five nonzero harmonics of the Fourier series to obtain an estimate for the rms value.

17.47 Calculate the average power dissipated by the 10-Ω resistor in the circuit of Fig. 17.80 if

$$i_s(t) = 3 + 2\cos(50t - 60°)$$
$$+ 0.5\cos(100t - 120°) \text{ A}$$

Figure 17.80 For Prob. 17.47.

17.48 For the circuit in Fig. 17.81,

$$i(t) = 20 + 16\cos(10t + 45°)$$
$$+ 12\cos(20t - 60°) \text{ mA}$$

(a) find $v(t)$, and

(b) calculate the average power dissipated in the resistor.

Figure 17.81 For Prob. 17.48.

17.49 (a) For the periodic waveform in Prob. 17.5, find the rms value.

(b) Use the first five harmonic terms of the Fourier series in Prob. 17.5 to determine the effective value of the signal.

(c) Calculate the percentage error in the estimated rms value of $z(t)$ if

$$\% \text{ error} = \left(\frac{\text{estimated value}}{\text{exact value}} - 1\right) \times 100$$

Section 17.6 Exponential Fourier Series

17.50 Obtain the exponential Fourier series for $f(t) = t$, $-1 < t < 1$, with $f(t + 2n) = f(t)$.

17.51 Given the periodic function

$$f(t) = t^2, \qquad 0 < t < T$$

obtain the exponential Fourier series for the special case $T = 2$.

17.52 Calculate the complex Fourier series for $f(t) = e^t$, $-\pi < t < \pi$, with $f(t + 2\pi n) = f(t)$.

17.53 Find the complex Fourier series for $f(t) = e^{-t}$, $0 < t < 1$, with $f(t + n) = f(t)$.

17.54 Find the exponential Fourier series for the function in Fig. 17.82.

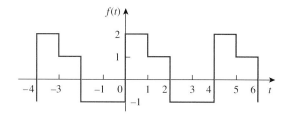

Figure 17.82 For Prob. 17.54.

17.55 Obtain the exponential Fourier series expansion of the half-wave rectified sinusoidal current of Fig. 17.83.

Figure 17.83 For Prob. 17.55.

17.56 The Fourier series trigonometric representation of a periodic function is

$$f(t) = 10 + \sum_{n=1}^{\infty}\left(\frac{1}{n^2+1}\cos n\pi t + \frac{n}{n^2+1}\sin n\pi t\right)$$

Find the exponential Fourier series representation of $f(t)$.

17.57 The coefficients of the trigonometric Fourier series representation of a function are:

$$b_n = 0, \qquad a_n = \frac{6}{n^3 - 2}, \qquad n = 0, 1, 2, \ldots$$

If $\omega_n = 50n$, find the exponential Fourier series for the function.

17.58 Find the exponential Fourier series of a function which has the following trigonometric Fourier series coefficients

$$a_0 = \frac{\pi}{4}, \qquad b_n = \frac{(-1)^n}{n}, \qquad a_n = \frac{(-1)^n - 1}{\pi n^2}$$

Take $T = 2\pi$.

17.59 The complex Fourier series of the function in Fig. 17.84(a) is

$$f(t) = \frac{1}{2} - \sum_{n=-\infty}^{\infty} \frac{je^{-j(2n+1)t}}{(2n+1)\pi}$$

Find the complex Fourier series of the function $h(t)$ in Fig. 17.84(b).

(a)

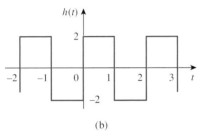

(b)

Figure 17.84   For Prob. 17.59.

17.60 Obtain the complex Fourier coefficients of the signal in Fig. 17.63.

17.61 The spectra of the Fourier series of a function are shown in Fig. 17.85. (a) Obtain the trigonometric Fourier series. (b) Calculate the rms value of the function.

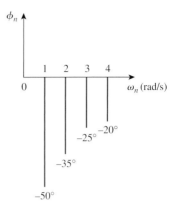

Figure 17.85   For Prob. 17.61.

17.62 A certain periodic function $f(t)$ is represented by a Fourier series with a limited number of terms. The discrete line spectrum for the periodic function is depicted in Fig. 17.86, where $A_n = \sqrt{a_n^2 + b_n^2}$.

(a) Determine the period of $f(t)$.

(b) Obtain the trigonometric form of the Fourier series for $f(t)$.

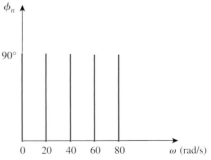

Figure 17.86   For Prob. 17.62.

17.63 Plot the amplitude spectrum for the signal $f_2(t)$ in Fig. 17.57(b). Consider the first five terms.

17.64 Given that

$$v(t) = \frac{10}{\pi}\left[1 + \frac{1}{2}\cos 2\pi t + \frac{2}{3}\cos 4\pi t\right.$$
$$\left. - \frac{2}{15}\cos 6\pi t + \cdots\right]$$

draw the amplitude and phase spectra for $v(t)$.

17.65 Given that

$$f(t) = \sum_{\substack{n=1 \\ n=\text{odd}}}^{\infty}\left(\frac{20}{n^2\pi^2}\cos 2nt - \frac{3}{n\pi}\sin 2nt\right)$$

plot the first five terms of the amplitude and phase spectra for the function.

Section 17.7   Fourier Analysis with *PSpice*

17.66 Determine the Fourier coefficients for the waveform in Fig. 17.48 using *PSpice*.

17.67 Calculate the Fourier coefficients of the signal in Fig. 17.59 using *PSpice*.

17.68 Use *PSpice* to find the Fourier series for the waveform in Prob. 17.8.

17.69 Use *PSpice* to obtain the Fourier coefficients of the waveform in Fig. 17.56(a).

17.70 Rework Prob. 17.40 using *PSpice*.

17.71 Use *PSpice* to solve Prob. 17.39.

Section 17.8   Applications

17.72 The signal displayed by a medical device can be approximated by the waveform shown in Fig. 17.87. Find the Fourier series representation of the signal.

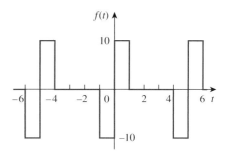

Figure 17.87   For Prob. 17.72.

17.73 A spectrum analyzer indicates that a signal is made up of three components only: 640 kHz at 2 V, 644 kHz at 1 V, 636 kHz at 1 V. If the signal is applied across a 10-Ω resistor, what is the average power absorbed by the resistor?

17.74 A certain band-limited periodic current has only three frequencies in its Fourier series representation: dc, 50 Hz, and 100 Hz. The current may be represented as

$$i(t) = 4 + 6\sin 100\pi t + 8\cos 100\pi t$$
$$- 3\sin 200\pi t - 4\cos 200\pi t \text{ A}$$

(a) Express $i(t)$ in amplitude-phase form.

(b) If $i(t)$ flows through a 2-Ω resistor, how many watts of average power will be dissipated?

17.75 Design a lowpass RC filter with a resistance $R = 2\,k\Omega$. The input to the filter is a periodic rectangular pulse train (see Table 17.3) with $A = 1V$, $T = 10$ ms, and $\tau = 1$ ms. Select C such that the dc component of the output is 50 times greater than the fundamental component of the output.

17.76 The signal in Fig. 17.74(a) is applied to the high-pass filter in Fig. 17.88. Determine the value of R such that the output signal $v_o(t)$ has an average power of at least 70 percent of the average power of the input signal.

Figure 17.88   For Prob. 17.76.

COMPREHENSIVE PROBLEMS

17.77 The voltage across a device is given by

$$v(t) = -2 + 10\cos 4t + 8\cos 6t + 6\cos 8t$$
$$- 5\sin 4t - 3\sin 6t - \sin 8t \text{ V}$$

Find:

(a) the period of $v(t)$,

(b) the average value of $v(t)$,

(c) the effective value of $v(t)$.

17.78 A certain band-limited periodic voltage has only three harmonics in its Fourier series representation. The harmonics have the following rms values: fundamental 40 V, third harmonic 20 V, fifth harmonic 10 V.

(a) If the voltage is applied across a 5-Ω resistor, find the average power dissipated by the resistor.

(b) If a dc component is added to the periodic voltage and the measured power dissipated increases by 5 percent, determine the value of the dc component added.

17.79 Write a program to compute the Fourier coefficients (up to the 10th harmonic) of the square wave in Table 17.3 with $A = 10$ and $T = 2$.

17.80 Write a computer program to calculate the exponential Fourier series of the half-wave rectified sinusoidal current of Fig. 17.83. Consider terms up to the 10th harmonic.

17.81 Consider the full-wave rectified sinusoidal current in Table 17.3. Assume that the current is passed through a 1-Ω resistor.

(a) Find the average power absorbed by the resistor.

(b) Obtain c_n for $n = 1, 2, 3$, and 4.

(c) What fraction of the total power is carried by the dc component?

(d) What fraction of the total power is carried by the second harmonic $(n = 2)$?

17.82 A band-limited voltage signal is found to have the complex Fourier coefficients presented in the table below. Calculate the average power that the signal would supply a 4-Ω resistor.

$n\omega_0$	$|c_n|$	θ_n
0	10.0	0°
ω	8.5	15°
2ω	4.2	30°
3ω	2.1	45°
4ω	0.5	60°
5ω	0.2	75°

FOURIER TRANSFORM

The science of today is the technology of tomorrow.

—Edward Teller

Enhancing Your Career

Career in Communications Systems Communications systems apply the principles of circuit analysis. A communication system is designed to convey information from a source (the transmitter) to a destination (the receiver) via a channel (the propagation medium). Communications engineers design systems for transmitting and receiving information. The information can be in the form of voice, data, or video.

We live in the information age—news, weather, sports, shopping, financial, business inventory, and other sources make information available to us almost instantly via communications systems. Some obvious examples of communications systems are the telephone network, mobile cellular telephones, radio, cable TV, satellite TV, fax, and radar. Mobile radio, used by police and fire departments, aircraft, and various businesses is another example.

The field of communications is perhaps the fastest growing area in electrical engineering. The merging of the communications field with computer technology in recent years has led to digital data communications networks such as local area networks, metropolitan area networks, and broadband integrated services digital networks. For example, the Internet (the "information superhighway") allows educators, business people, and others to send electronic mail from their computers worldwide, log onto remote databases, and transfer files. The Internet has hit the world like a tidal wave and is drastically changing the way people do business, communicate, and get information. This trend will continue.

A communications engineer designs systems that provide high-quality information services. The systems include hardware for generating, transmitting, and receiving information signals. Communications engineers are employed in numerous communications industries and places where communications systems are routinely used. More and more government agencies, academic departments, and businesses are demanding faster and more accurate transmission of information. To meet these needs, communications

Cordless phone.
© *Volume 86/PhotoDisc, Inc.*

engineers are in high demand. Therefore, the future is in communications and every electrical engineer must prepare accordingly.

18.1   INTRODUCTION

Fourier series enable us to represent a periodic function as a sum of sinusoids and to obtain the frequency spectrum from the series. The Fourier transform allows us to extend the concept of a frequency spectrum to nonperiodic functions. The transform assumes that a nonperiodic function is a periodic function with an infinite period. Thus, the Fourier transform is an integral representation of a nonperiodic function that is analogous to a Fourier series representation of a periodic function.

The Fourier transform is an *integral transform* like the Laplace transform. It transforms a function in the time domain into the frequency domain. The Fourier transform is very useful in communications systems and digital signal processing, in situations where the Laplace transform does not apply. While the Laplace transform can only handle circuits with inputs for $t > 0$ with initial conditions, the Fourier transform can handle circuits with inputs for $t < 0$ as well as those for $t > 0$.

We begin by using a Fourier series as a stepping stone in defining the Fourier transform. Then we develop some of the properties of the Fourier transform. Next, we apply the Fourier transform in analyzing circuits. We discuss Parseval's theorem, compare the Laplace and Fourier transforms, and see how the Fourier transform is applied in amplitude modulation and sampling.

18.2   DEFINITION OF THE FOURIER TRANSFORM

We saw in the previous chapter that a nonsinusoidal periodic function can be represented by a Fourier series, provided that it satisfies the Dirichlet conditions. What happens if a function is not periodic? Unfortunately, there are many important nonperiodic functions—such as a unit step or an exponential function—that we cannot represent by a Fourier series. As we shall see, the Fourier transform allows a transformation from the time to the frequency domain, even if the function is not periodic.

Suppose we want to find the Fourier transform of a nonperiodic function $p(t)$, shown in Fig. 18.1(a). We consider a periodic function $f(t)$ whose shape over one period is the same as $p(t)$, as shown in Fig. 18.1(b). If we let the period $T \to \infty$, only a single pulse of width τ [the desired nonperiodic function in Fig. 18.1(a)] remains, because the adjacent pulses have been moved to infinity. Thus, the function $f(t)$ is no longer periodic. In other words, $f(t) = p(t)$ as $T \to \infty$. It is interesting to consider the spectrum of $f(t)$ for $A = 10$ and $\tau = 0.2$ (see Section 17.6). Figure 18.2 shows the effect of increasing T on the spectrum. First, we notice that the general shape of the spectrum remains the same, and the frequency at which the envelope first becomes zero remains the same. However, the amplitude of the spectrum and the spacing between adjacent components both decrease, while the number of harmonics increases. Thus, over a range of frequencies, the sum of the amplitudes of the harmonics remains almost constant. As the total "strength" or energy of the components within a band must remain unchanged, the amplitudes of the harmonics

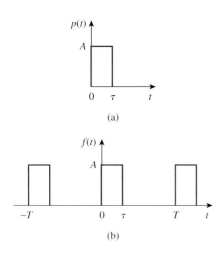

Figure 18.1   (a) A nonperiodic function, (b) increasing T to infinity makes $f(t)$ become the nonperiodic function in (a).

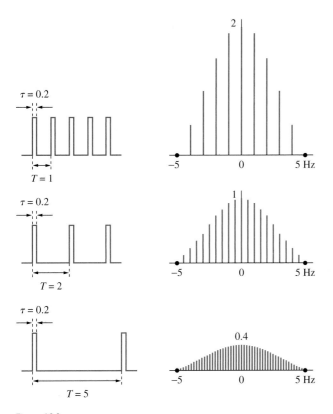

Figure 18.2   Effect of increasing T on the spectrum of the periodic pulse trains in Fig. 18.1(b). *(Source: L. Balmer, Signals and Systems: An Introduction [London: Prentice-Hall, 1991], p. 229.)*

must decrease as T increases. Since $f = 1/T$, as T increases, f or ω decreases, so that the discrete spectrum ultimately becomes continuous.

To further understand this connection between a nonperiodic function and its periodic counterpart, consider the exponential form of a Fourier series in Eq. (17.58), namely,

$$f(t) = \sum_{n=-\infty}^{\infty} c_n e^{jn\omega_0 t} \tag{18.1}$$

where

$$c_n = \frac{1}{T} \int_{-T/2}^{T/2} f(t) e^{-jn\omega_0 t} \, dt \tag{18.2}$$

The fundamental frequency is

$$\omega_0 = \frac{2\pi}{T} \tag{18.3}$$

and the spacing between adjacent harmonics is

$$\Delta\omega = (n+1)\omega_0 - n\omega_0 = \omega_0 = \frac{2\pi}{T} \tag{18.4}$$

Substituting Eq. (18.2) into Eq. (18.1) gives

$$
\begin{aligned}
f(t) &= \sum_{n=-\infty}^{\infty} \left[\frac{1}{T} \int_{-T/2}^{T/2} f(t) e^{-jn\omega_0 t} \, dt \right] e^{jn\omega_0 t} \\
&= \sum_{n=-\infty}^{\infty} \left[\frac{\Delta\omega}{2\pi} \int_{-T/2}^{T/2} f(t) e^{-jn\omega_0 t} \, dt \right] e^{jn\omega_0 t} \\
&= \frac{1}{2\pi} \sum_{n=-\infty}^{\infty} \left[\int_{-T/2}^{T/2} f(t) e^{-jn\omega_0 t} \, dt \right] \Delta\omega e^{jn\omega_0 t}
\end{aligned}
\tag{18.5}
$$

If we let $T \to \infty$, the summation becomes integration, the incremental spacing $\Delta\omega$ becomes the differential separation $d\omega$, and the discrete harmonic frequency $n\omega_0$ becomes a continuous frequency ω. Thus, as $T \to \infty$,

$$
\begin{aligned}
\sum_{n=-\infty}^{\infty} &\implies \int_{-\infty}^{\infty} \\
\Delta\omega &\implies d\omega \\
n\omega_0 &\implies \omega
\end{aligned}
\tag{18.6}
$$

so that Eq. (18.5) becomes

$$
f(t) = \frac{1}{2\pi} \int_{-\infty}^{\infty} \left[\int_{-\infty}^{\infty} f(t) e^{-j\omega t} \, dt \right] e^{j\omega t} \, d\omega
\tag{18.7}
$$

Some authors use $F(j\omega)$ instead of $F(\omega)$ to represent the Fourier transform.

The term in the brackets is known as the *Fourier transform* of $f(t)$ and is represented by $F(\omega)$. Thus

$$
\boxed{F(\omega) = \mathcal{F}[f(t)] = \int_{-\infty}^{\infty} f(t) e^{-j\omega t} \, dt}
\tag{18.8}
$$

where $\mathcal{F}$ is the Fourier transform operator. It is evident from Eq. (18.8) that:

> The Fourier transform is an integral transformation of $f(t)$ from the time domain to the frequency domain.

In general, $F(\omega)$ is a complex function; its magnitude is called the *amplitude spectrum*, while its phase is called the *phase spectrum*. Thus $F(\omega)$ is the *spectrum*.

Equation (18.7) can be written in terms of $F(\omega)$, and we obtain the *inverse Fourier transform* as

$$
\boxed{f(t) = \mathcal{F}^{-1}[F(\omega)] = \frac{1}{2\pi} \int_{-\infty}^{\infty} F(\omega) e^{j\omega t} \, d\omega}
\tag{18.9}
$$

The function $f(t)$ and its transform $F(\omega)$ form the Fourier transform pairs:

$$
f(t) \quad \Longleftrightarrow \quad F(\omega)
\tag{18.10}
$$

since one can be derived from the other.

The Fourier transform $F(\omega)$ exists when the Fourier integral in Eq. (18.8) converges. A sufficient but not necessary condition that $f(t)$ has a Fourier transform is that it be completely integrable in the sense that

$$\int_{-\infty}^{\infty} |f(t)|\, dt < \infty \qquad (18.11)$$

For example, the Fourier transform of the unit ramp function $tu(t)$ does not exist, because the function does not satisfy the condition above.

To avoid the complex algebra that explicitly appears in the Fourier transform, it is sometimes expedient to temporarily replace $j\omega$ with s and then replace s with $j\omega$ at the end.

EXAMPLE 18.1

Find the Fourier transform of the following functions: (a) $\delta(t - t_0)$, (b) $e^{j\omega_0 t}$, (c) $\cos \omega_0 t$.

Solution:

(a) For the impulse function,

$$F(\omega) = \mathcal{F}[\delta(t - t_0)] = \int_{-\infty}^{\infty} \delta(t - t_0)e^{-j\omega t}\, dt = e^{-j\omega t_0} \qquad (18.1.1)$$

where the sifting property of the impulse function in Eq. (7.32) has been applied. For the special case $t_0 = 0$, we obtain

$$\mathcal{F}[\delta(t)] = 1 \qquad (18.1.2)$$

This shows that the magnitude of the spectrum of the impulse function is constant; that is, all frequencies are equally represented in the impulse function.

(b) We can find the Fourier transform of $e^{j\omega_0 t}$ in two ways. If we let

$$F(\omega) = \delta(\omega - \omega_0)$$

then we can find $f(t)$ using Eq. (18.9), writing

$$f(t) = \frac{1}{2\pi} \int_{-\infty}^{\infty} \delta(\omega - \omega_0)e^{j\omega t}\, d\omega$$

Using the sifting property of the impulse function gives

$$f(t) = \frac{1}{2\pi} e^{j\omega_0 t}$$

Since $F(\omega)$ and $f(t)$ constitute a Fourier transform pair, so too must $2\pi\delta(\omega - \omega_0)$ and $e^{j\omega_0 t}$,

$$\mathcal{F}[e^{j\omega_0 t}] = 2\pi\delta(\omega - \omega_0) \qquad (18.1.3)$$

Alternatively, from Eq. (18.1.2),

$$\delta(t) = \mathcal{F}^{-1}[1]$$

Using the inverse Fourier transform formula in Eq. (18.9),

$$\delta(t) = \mathcal{F}^{-1}[1] = \frac{1}{2\pi} \int_{-\infty}^{\infty} 1 e^{j\omega t}\, d\omega$$

or

$$\int_{-\infty}^{\infty} e^{j\omega t}\, d\omega = 2\pi\, \delta(t) \tag{18.1.4}$$

Interchanging variables t and ω results in

$$\int_{-\infty}^{\infty} e^{j\omega t}\, dt = 2\pi\, \delta(\omega) \tag{18.1.5}$$

Using this result, the Fourier transform of the given function is

$$\mathcal{F}[e^{j\omega_0 t}] = \int_{-\infty}^{\infty} e^{j\omega_0 t} e^{-j\omega t}\, dt = \int_{-\infty}^{\infty} e^{j(\omega_0 - \omega)}\, dt = 2\pi\, \delta(\omega_0 - \omega)$$

Since the impulse function is an even function, with $\delta(\omega_0 - \omega) = \delta(\omega - \omega_0)$,

$$\mathcal{F}[e^{j\omega_0 t}] = 2\pi\, \delta(\omega - \omega_0) \tag{18.1.6}$$

By simply changing the sign of ω_0, we readily obtain

$$\mathcal{F}[e^{-j\omega_0 t}] = 2\pi\, \delta(\omega + \omega_0) \tag{18.1.7}$$

Also, by setting $\omega_0 = 0$,

$$\mathcal{F}[1] = 2\pi\, \delta(\omega) \tag{18.1.8}$$

(c) By using the result in Eqs. (18.1.6) and (18.1.7), we get

$$\begin{aligned}
\mathcal{F}[\cos \omega_0 t] &= \mathcal{F}\left[\frac{e^{j\omega_0 t} + e^{-j\omega_0 t}}{2}\right] \\
&= \frac{1}{2}\mathcal{F}[e^{j\omega_0 t}] + \frac{1}{2}\mathcal{F}[e^{-j\omega_0 t}] \\
&= \pi\, \delta(\omega - \omega_0) + \pi\, \delta(\omega + \omega_0)
\end{aligned} \tag{18.1.9}$$

The Fourier transform of the cosine signal is shown in Fig. 18.3.

Figure 18.3   Fourier transform of $f(t) = \cos \omega_0 t$.

PRACTICE PROBLEM 18.1

Determine the Fourier transforms of the following functions: (a) gate function $g(t) = u(t - 1) - u(t - 2)$, (b) $4\delta(t + 2)$, (c) $\sin \omega_0 t$.

Answer: (a) $(e^{-j\omega} - e^{-j2\omega})/j\omega$, (b) $4e^{j2\omega}$,
(c) $j\pi[\delta(\omega + \omega_0) - \pi\delta(\omega - \omega_0)]$.

EXAMPLE 18.2

Derive the Fourier transform of a single rectangular pulse of width τ and height A, shown in Fig. 18.4.

Solution:

$$F(\omega) = \int_{-\tau/2}^{\tau/2} A e^{-j\omega t} \, dt = -\frac{A}{j\omega} e^{-j\omega t} \Big|_{-\tau/2}^{\tau/2}$$

$$= \frac{2A}{\omega} \left(\frac{e^{j\omega\tau/2} - e^{-j\omega\tau/2}}{2j} \right)$$

$$= A\tau \frac{\sin \omega\tau/2}{\omega\tau/2} = A\tau \text{ sinc } \frac{\omega\tau}{2}$$

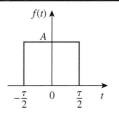

Figure 18.4   A rectangular pulse; for Example 18.2.

If we make $A = 10$ and $\tau = 2$ as in Fig. 17.27 (like in Section 17.6), then

$$F(\omega) = 20 \text{ sinc } \omega$$

whose amplitude spectrum is shown in Fig. 18.5. Comparing Fig. 18.4 with the frequency spectrum of the rectangular pulses in Fig. 17.28, we notice that the spectrum in Fig. 17.28 is discrete and its envelope has the same shape as the Fourier transform of a single rectangular pulse.

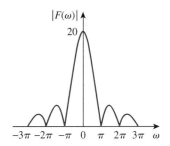

Figure 18.5   Amplitude spectrum of the rectangular pulse in Fig. 18.4: for Example 18.2.

PRACTICE PROBLEM 18.2

Obtain the Fourier transform of the function in Fig. 18.6.

Answer: $\dfrac{2(\cos \omega - 1)}{j\omega}$.

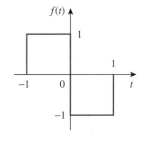

Figure 18.6   For Practice Prob. 18.2.

EXAMPLE 18.3

Obtain the Fourier transform of the "switched-on" exponential function shown in Fig. 18.7.

Solution:

From Fig. 18.7,

$$f(t) = e^{-at} u(t) = \begin{cases} e^{-at}, & t > 0 \\ 0, & t < 0 \end{cases}$$

Figure 18.7   For Example 18.3.

Hence,

$$F(\omega) = \int_{-\infty}^{\infty} f(t)e^{-j\omega t}\, dt = \int_{0}^{\infty} e^{-at}e^{-j\omega t}\, dt = \int_{0}^{\infty} e^{-(a+j\omega)t}\, dt$$

$$= \frac{-1}{a+j\omega}e^{-(a+j\omega)t}\Big|_{0}^{\infty} = \frac{1}{a+j\omega}$$

PRACTICE PROBLEM 18.3

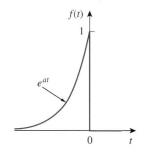

Figure 18.8   For Practice Prob. 18.3.

Determine the Fourier transform of the "switched-off" exponential function in Fig. 18.8.

Answer: $\dfrac{1}{a-j\omega}$.

18.3 PROPERTIES OF THE FOURIER TRANSFORM

We now develop some properties of the Fourier transform that are useful in finding the transforms of complicated functions from the transforms of simple functions. For each property, we will first state and derive it, and then illustrate it with some examples.

Linearity

If $F_1(\omega)$ and $F_2(\omega)$ are the Fourier transforms of $f_1(t)$ and $f_2(t)$, respectively, then

$$\boxed{\mathcal{F}[a_1 f_1(t) + a_2 f_2(t)] = a_1 F_1(\omega) + a_2 F_2(\omega)} \tag{18.12}$$

where a_1 and a_2 are constants. This property simply states that the Fourier transform of a linear combination of functions is the same as the linear combination of the transforms of the individual functions. The proof of the linearity property in Eq. (18.12) is straightforward. By definition,

$$\mathcal{F}[a_1 f_1(t) + a_2 f_2(t)] = \int_{-\infty}^{\infty} [a_1 f_1(t) + a_2 f_2(t)]e^{-j\omega t}\, dt$$

$$= \int_{-\infty}^{\infty} a_1 f_1(t)e^{-j\omega t}\, dt + \int_{-\infty}^{\infty} a_2 f_2(t)e^{-j\omega t}\, dt$$

$$= a_1 F_1(\omega) + a_2 F_2(\omega)$$

$$\tag{18.13}$$

For example, $\sin \omega_0 t = \frac{1}{2j}(e^{j\omega_0 t} - e^{-j\omega_0 t})$. Using the linearity property,

$$
\begin{aligned}
F[\sin \omega_0 t] &= \frac{1}{2j}[\mathcal{F}(e^{j\omega_0 t}) - \mathcal{F}(e^{-j\omega_0 t})] \\
&= \frac{\pi}{j}[\delta(\omega - \omega_0) - \delta(\omega + \omega_0)]
\end{aligned}
\tag{18.14}
$$

Time Scaling

If $F(\omega) = \mathcal{F}[f(t)]$, then

$$
\mathcal{F}[f(at)] = \frac{1}{|a|}F\left(\frac{\omega}{a}\right)
\tag{18.15}
$$

where a is a constant. Equation (18.15) shows that time expansion ($|a| > 1$) corresponds to frequency compression, or conversely, time compression ($|a| < 1$) implies frequency expansion. The proof of the time-scaling property proceeds as follows.

$$
\mathcal{F}[f(at)] = \int_{-\infty}^{\infty} f(at)e^{-j\omega t}\, dt
\tag{18.16}
$$

If we let $x = at$, so that $dx = a\, dt$, then

$$
\mathcal{F}[f(at)] = \int_{-\infty}^{\infty} f(x)e^{-j\omega x/a}\, \frac{dx}{a} = \frac{1}{a}F\left(\frac{\omega}{a}\right)
\tag{18.17}
$$

For example, for the rectangular pulse $p(t)$ in Example 18.2.

$$
\mathcal{F}[p(t)] = A\tau \, \text{sinc} \, \frac{\omega \tau}{2}
\tag{18.18a}
$$

Using Eq. (18.15),

$$
\mathcal{F}[p(2t)] = \frac{A\tau}{2} \, \text{sinc} \, \frac{\omega \tau}{4}
\tag{18.18b}
$$

It may be helpful to plot $p(t)$ and $p(2t)$ and their Fourier transforms. Since

$$
p(t) = \begin{cases} A, & -\dfrac{\tau}{2} < t < \dfrac{\tau}{2} \\ 0, & \text{otherwise} \end{cases}
\tag{18.19a}
$$

then replacing every t with $2t$ gives

$$
p(2t) = \begin{cases} A, & -\dfrac{\tau}{2} < 2t < \dfrac{\tau}{2} \\ 0, & \text{otherwise} \end{cases} = \begin{cases} A, & -\dfrac{\tau}{4} < t < \dfrac{\tau}{4} \\ 0, & \text{otherwise} \end{cases}
\tag{18.19b}
$$

showing that $p(2t)$ is time compressed, as shown in Fig. 18.9(b). To plot both Fourier transforms in Eq. (18.18), we recall that the sinc function has zeros when its argument is $n\pi$, where n is an integer. Hence, for the transform of $p(t)$ in Eq. (18.18a), $\omega\tau/2 = 2\pi f\tau/2 = n\pi \rightarrow f = n/\tau$, and for the transform of $p(2t)$ in Eq. (18.18b), $\omega\tau/4 = 2\pi f\tau/4 = n\pi \rightarrow f = 2n/\tau$. The plots of the Fourier transforms are shown in Fig. 18.9, which shows that time compression corresponds with frequency expansion. We should expect this intuitively, because when the signal is squashed in time, we expect it to change more rapidly, thereby causing higher-frequency components to exist.

Figure 18.9   The effect of time scaling: (a) transform of the pulse, (b) time compression of the pulse causes frequency expansion.

Time Shifting

If $F(\omega) = \mathcal{F}[f(t)]$, then

$$\mathcal{F}[f(t - t_0)] = e^{-j\omega t_0} F(\omega) \qquad (18.20)$$

that is, a delay in the time domain corresponds to a phase shift in the frequency domain. To derive the time shifting property, we note that

$$\mathcal{F}[f(t - t_0)] = \int_{-\infty}^{\infty} f(t - t_0)e^{-j\omega t}\, dt \qquad (18.21)$$

If we let $x = t - t_0$ so that $dx = dt$ and $t = x + t_0$, then

$$\mathcal{F}[f(t - t_0)] = \int_{-\infty}^{\infty} f(x)e^{-j\omega(x + t_0)}\, dx$$

$$= e^{-j\omega t_0} \int_{-\infty}^{\infty} f(x)e^{-j\omega x}\, dx = e^{-j\omega t_0} F(\omega) \qquad (18.22)$$

Similarly, $\mathcal{F}[f(t + t_0)] = e^{j\omega t_0} F(\omega)$.

For example, from Example 18.3,

$$\mathcal{F}[e^{-at}u(t)] = \frac{1}{a + j\omega} \qquad (18.23)$$

The transform of $f(t) = e^{-(t-2)}u(t-2)$ is

$$F(\omega) = \mathcal{F}[e^{-(t-2)}u(t-2)] = \frac{e^{-j2\omega}}{1 + j\omega} \qquad (18.24)$$

Frequency Shifting (or Amplitude Modulation)

This property states that if $F(\omega) = \mathcal{F}[f(t)]$, then

$$\boxed{\mathcal{F}[f(t)e^{j\omega_0 t}] = F(\omega - \omega_0)} \qquad (18.25)$$

meaning, a frequency shift in the frequency domain adds a phase shift to the time function. By definition,

$$
\begin{aligned}
\mathcal{F}[f(t)e^{j\omega_0 t}] &= \int_{-\infty}^{\infty} f(t)e^{j\omega_0 t}e^{-j\omega t}\, dt \\
&= \int_{-\infty}^{\infty} f(t)e^{-j(\omega-\omega_0)t}\, dt = F(\omega - \omega_0)
\end{aligned}
\qquad (18.26)
$$

For example, $\cos \omega_0 t = \frac{1}{2}(e^{j\omega_0 t} + e^{-j\omega_0 t})$. Using the property in Eq. (18.25),

$$
\begin{aligned}
\mathcal{F}[f(t)\cos \omega_0 t] &= \frac{1}{2}\mathcal{F}\left[f(t)e^{j\omega_0 t}\right] + \frac{1}{2}\mathcal{F}\left[f(t)e^{-j\omega_0 t}\right] \\
&= \frac{1}{2}F(\omega - \omega_0) + \frac{1}{2}F(\omega + \omega_0)
\end{aligned}
\qquad (18.27)
$$

This is an important result in modulation where frequency components of a signal are shifted. If, for example, the amplitude spectrum of $f(t)$ is as shown in Fig. 18.10(a), then the amplitude spectrum of $f(t)\cos \omega_0 t$ will be as shown in Fig. 18.10(b). We will elaborate on amplitude modulation in Section 18.7.1.

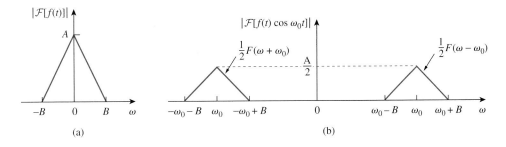

Figure 18.10   Amplitude spectra of: (a) signal $f(t)$, (b) modulated signal $f(t)\cos \omega_0 t$.

Time Differentiation

Given that $F(\omega) = \mathcal{F}[f(t)]$, then

$$\boxed{\mathcal{F}[f'(t)] = j\omega F(\omega)} \qquad (18.28)$$

In other words, the transform of the derivative of $f(t)$ is obtained by multiplying the transform of $f(t)$ by $j\omega$. By definition,

$$f(t) = \mathcal{F}^{-1}[F(\omega)] = \frac{1}{2\pi}\int_{-\infty}^{\infty} F(\omega)e^{j\omega t}\, d\omega \qquad (18.29)$$

Taking the derivative of both sides with respect to t gives

$$f'(t) = \frac{j\omega}{2\pi} \int_{-\infty}^{\infty} F(\omega)e^{j\omega t}\, d\omega = j\omega \mathcal{F}^{-1}[F(\omega)]$$

or

$$\mathcal{F}[f'(t)] = j\omega F(\omega) \tag{18.30}$$

Repeated applications of Eq. (18.30) give

$$\boxed{\mathcal{F}[f^{(n)}(t)] = (j\omega)^n F(\omega)} \tag{18.31}$$

For example, if $f(t) = e^{-at}u(t)$, then

$$f'(t) = -ae^{-at}u(t) = -af(t) \tag{18.32}$$

Taking the Fourier transforms of the first and last terms, we obtain

$$j\omega F(\omega) = -aF(\omega) \quad \Longrightarrow \quad F(\omega) = \frac{1}{a + j\omega} \tag{18.33}$$

which agrees with the result in Example 18.3.

Time Integration

Given that $F(\omega) = \mathcal{F}[f(t)]$, then

$$\boxed{\mathcal{F}\left[\int_{-\infty}^{t} f(t)\, dt\right] = \frac{F(\omega)}{j\omega} + \pi F(0)\delta(\omega)} \tag{18.34}$$

that is, the transform of the integral of $f(t)$ is obtained by dividing the transform of $f(t)$ by $j\omega$ and adding the result to the impulse term that reflects the dc component $F(0)$. Someone might ask, "How do we know that when we take the Fourier transform for time integration, we should integrate over the interval $[-\infty, t]$ and not $[-\infty, \infty]$?" When we integrate over $[-\infty, \infty]$, the result does not depend on time anymore, and the Fourier transform of a constant is what we will eventually get. But when we integrate over $[-\infty, t]$, we get the integral of the function from the past to time t, so that the result depends on t and we can take the Fourier transform of that.

If ω is replaced by 0 in Eq. (18.8),

$$F(0) = \int_{-\infty}^{\infty} f(t)\, dt \tag{18.35}$$

indicating that the dc component is zero when the integral of $f(t)$ over all time vanishes. The proof of the time integration in Eq. (18.34) will be given later when we consider the convolution property.

For example, we know that $\mathcal{F}[\delta(t)] = 1$ and that integrating the impulse function gives the unit step function [see Eq. (7.39a)]. By applying the property in Eq. (18.34), we obtain the Fourier transform of the unit step function as

$$\mathcal{F}[u(t)] = \mathcal{F}\left[\int_{-\infty}^{t} \delta(t)\, dt\right] = \frac{1}{j\omega} + \pi\delta(\omega) \tag{18.36}$$

Reversal

If $F(\omega) = \mathcal{F}[f(t)]$, then

$$\boxed{\mathcal{F}[f(-t)] = F(-\omega) = F^*(\omega)} \qquad (18.37)$$

where the asterisk denotes the complex conjugate. This property states that reversing $f(t)$ about the time axis reverses $F(\omega)$ about the frequency axis. This may be regarded as a special case of time scaling for which $a = -1$ in Eq. (18.15).

For example, $1 = u(t) + u(-t)$. Hence,

$$\mathcal{F}[1] = \mathcal{F}[u(t)] + \mathcal{F}[u(-t)]$$

$$= \frac{1}{j\omega} + \pi\delta(\omega)$$

$$-\frac{1}{j\omega} + \pi\delta(-\omega)$$

$$= 2\pi\delta(\omega)$$

Duality

This property states that if $F(\omega)$ is the Fourier transform of $f(t)$, then the Fourier transform of $F(t)$ is $2\pi f(-\omega)$; we write

$$\boxed{\mathcal{F}[f(t)] = F(\omega) \qquad \Longrightarrow \qquad \mathcal{F}[F(t)] = 2\pi f(-\omega)} \qquad (18.38)$$

This expresses the symmetry property of the Fourier transform. To derive this property, we recall that

$$f(t) = \mathcal{F}^{-1}[F(\omega)] = \frac{1}{2\pi}\int_{-\infty}^{\infty} F(\omega)e^{j\omega t}\, d\omega$$

or

$$2\pi f(t) = \int_{-\infty}^{\infty} F(\omega)e^{j\omega t}\, d\omega \qquad (18.39)$$

Replacing t by $-t$ gives

$$2\pi f(-t) = \int_{-\infty}^{\infty} F(\omega)e^{-j\omega t}\, d\omega$$

If we interchange t and ω, we obtain

$$2\pi f(-\omega) = \int_{-\infty}^{\infty} F(t)e^{-j\omega t}\, dt = \mathcal{F}[F(t)] \qquad (18.40)$$

as expected.

For example, if $f(t) = e^{-|t|}$, then

$$F(\omega) = \frac{2}{\omega^2 + 1} \qquad (18.41)$$

By the duality property, the Fourier transform of $F(t) = 2/(t^2 + 1)$ is

$$2\pi f(\omega) = 2\pi e^{-|\omega|} \qquad (18.42)$$

Figure 18.11 shows another example of the duality property. It illustrates the fact that if $f(t) = \delta(t)$ so that $F(\omega) = 1$, as in Fig. 18.11(a), then the Fourier transform of $F(t) = 1$ is $2\pi f(\omega) = 2\pi\delta(\omega)$ as shown in Fig. 18.11(b).

Since $f(t)$ is the sum of the signals in Figs. 18.7 and 18.8, $F(\omega)$ is the sum of the results in Example 18.3 and Practice Prob. 18.3.

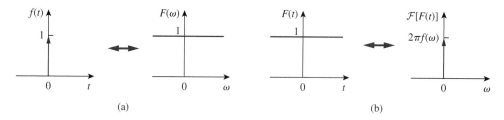

Figure 18.11   A typical illustration of the duality property of the Fourier transform: (a) transform of impulse, (b) transform of unit dc level.

Convolution

Recall from Chapter 15 that if $x(t)$ is the input excitation to a circuit with an impulse function of $h(t)$, then the output response $y(t)$ is given by the convolution integral

$$y(t) = h(t) * x(t) = \int_{-\infty}^{\infty} h(\lambda)x(t - \lambda)\, d\lambda \qquad (18.43)$$

If $X(\omega)$, $H(\omega)$, and $Y(\omega)$ are the Fourier transforms of $x(t), h(t)$, and $y(t)$, respectively, then

$$\boxed{Y(\omega) = \mathcal{F}[h(t) * x(t)] = H(\omega)X(\omega)} \qquad (18.44)$$

which indicates that convolution in the time domain corresponds with multiplication in the frequency domain.

To derive the convolution property, we take the Fourier transform of both sides of Eq. (18.43) to get

$$Y(\omega) = \int_{-\infty}^{\infty} \left[\int_{-\infty}^{\infty} h(\lambda)x(t - \lambda)\, d\lambda \right] e^{-j\omega t}\, dt \qquad (18.45)$$

Exchanging the order of integration and factoring $h(\lambda)$, which does not depend on t, we have

$$Y(\omega) = \int_{-\infty}^{\infty} h(\lambda) \left[\int_{-\infty}^{\infty} x(t - \lambda)e^{-j\omega t}\, dt \right] d\lambda$$

For the integral within the brackets, let $\tau = t - \lambda$ so that $t = \tau + \lambda$ and $dt = d\tau$. Then,

$$Y(\omega) = \int_{-\infty}^{\infty} h(\lambda) \left[\int_{-\infty}^{\infty} x(\tau)e^{-j\omega(\tau+\lambda)}\, d\tau \right] d\lambda$$

$$= \int_{-\infty}^{\infty} h(\lambda)e^{-j\omega\lambda}\, d\lambda \int_{-\infty}^{\infty} x(\tau)e^{-j\omega\tau}\, d\tau = H(\omega)X(\omega)$$

$$(18.46)$$

The important relationship in Eq. (18.46) is the key reason for using the Fourier transform in the analysis of linear systems.

as expected. This result expands the phasor method beyond what was done with the Fourier series in the previous chapter.

To illustrate the convolution property, suppose both $h(t)$ and $x(t)$ are identical rectangular pulses, as shown in Fig. 18.12(a) and 18.12(b). We recall from Example 18.2 and Fig. 18.5 that the Fourier transforms of the rectangular pulses are sinc functions, as shown in Fig. 18.12(c) and 18.12(d). According to the convolution property, the product of the sinc functions should give us the convolution of the rectangular pulses in the time domain. Thus, the convolution of the pulses in Fig. 18.12(e) and the product of the sinc functions in Fig. 18.12(f) form a Fourier pair.

In view of the duality property, we expect that if convolution in the time domain corresponds with multiplication in the frequency

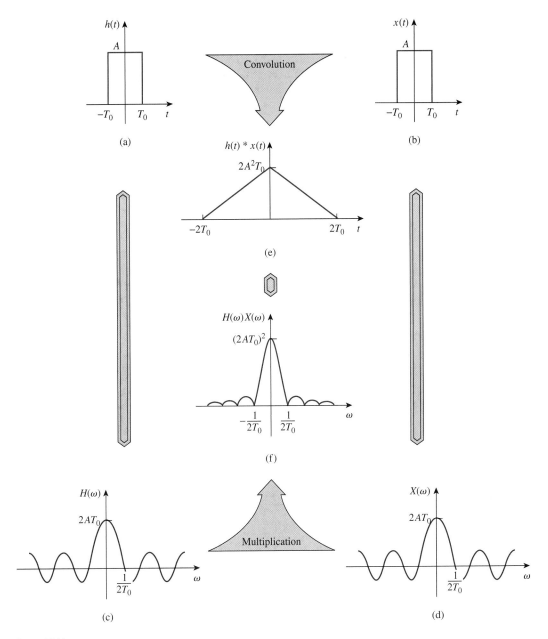

Figure 18.12   Graphical illustration of the convolution property. *(Source: E. O. Brigham, The Fast Fourier Transform [Englewood Cliffs, NJ: Prentice Hall, 1974], p. 60.)*

domain, then multiplication in the time domain should have a correspondence in the frequency domain. This happens to be the case. If $f(t) = f_1(t) f_2(t)$, then

$$F(\omega) = \mathcal{F}[f_1(t) f_2(t)] = \frac{1}{2\pi} F_1(\omega) * F_2(\omega) \qquad (18.47)$$

or

$$F(\omega) = \frac{1}{2\pi} \int_{-\infty}^{\infty} F_1(\lambda) F_2(\omega - \lambda) \, d\lambda \qquad (18.48)$$

which is convolution in the frequency domain. The proof of Eq. (18.48) readily follows from the duality property in Eq. (18.38).

Let us now derive the time integration property in Eq. (18.34). If we replace $x(t)$ with the unit step function $u(t)$ and $h(t)$ with $f(t)$ in Eq. (18.43), then

$$\int_{-\infty}^{\infty} f(\lambda)u(t - \lambda)\,d\lambda = f(t) * u(t) \tag{18.49}$$

But by the definition of the unit step function,

$$u(t - \lambda) = \begin{cases} 1, & t - \lambda > 0 \\ 0, & t - \lambda > 0 \end{cases}$$

We can write this as

$$u(t - \lambda) = \begin{cases} 1, & \lambda < t \\ 0, & \lambda > t \end{cases}$$

Substituting this into Eq. (18.49) makes the interval of integration change from $[-\infty, \infty]$ to $[-\infty, t]$, and thus Eq. (18.49) becomes

$$\int_{-\infty}^{t} f(\lambda)\,d\lambda = u(t) * f(t)$$

Taking the Fourier transform of both sides yields

$$\mathcal{F}\left[\int_{-\infty}^{t} f(\lambda)\,d\lambda\right] = U(\omega)F(\omega) \tag{18.50}$$

But from Eq. (18.36), the Fourier transform of the unit step function is

$$U(\omega) = \frac{1}{j\omega} + \pi\delta(\omega)$$

Substituting this into Eq. (18.50) gives

$$\mathcal{F}\left[\int_{-\infty}^{t} f(\lambda)\,d\lambda\right] = \left(\frac{1}{j\omega} + \pi\delta(\omega)\right)F(\omega)$$

$$= \frac{F(\omega)}{j\omega} + \pi F(0)\delta(\omega) \tag{18.51}$$

which is the time integration property of Eq. (18.34). Note that in Eq. (18.51), $F(\omega)\delta(\omega) = F(0)\delta(\omega)$, since $\delta(\omega)$ is only nonzero at $\omega = 0$.

Table 18.1 lists these properties of the Fourier transform. Table 18.2 presents the transform pairs of some common functions. Note the similarities between these tables and Tables 15.1 and 15.2.

TABLE 18.1   Properties of the Fourier transform.

Property	$f(t)$	$F(\omega)$
Linearity	$a_1 f_1(t) + a_2 f_2(t)$	$a_1 F_1(\omega) + a_2 F_2(\omega)$
Scaling	$f(at)$	$\dfrac{1}{\lvert a\rvert}F\left(\dfrac{\omega}{a}\right)$
Time shift	$f(t - a)$	$e^{-j\omega a}F(\omega)$
Frequency shift	$e^{j\omega_0 t}f(t)$	$F(\omega - \omega_0)$
Modulation	$\cos(\omega_0 t)\,f(t)$	$\dfrac{1}{2}[F(\omega + \omega_0) + F(\omega - \omega_0)]$

TABLE 18.1   *(continued)*

Property	$f(t)$	$F(\omega)$
Time differentiation	$\dfrac{df}{dt}$	$j\omega F(\omega)$
	$\dfrac{d^n f}{dt^n}$	$(j\omega)^n F(\omega)$
Time integration	$\displaystyle\int_{-\infty}^{t} f(t)\,dt$	$\dfrac{F(\omega)}{j\omega} + \pi F(0)\,\delta(\omega)$
Frequency differentiation	$t^n f(t)$	$(j)^n \dfrac{d^n}{d\omega^n} F(\omega)$
Reversal	$f(-t)$	$F(-\omega)$ or $F^*(\omega)$
Duality	$F(t)$	$2\pi f(-\omega)$
Convolution in t	$f_1(t) * f_1(t)$	$F_1(\omega)F_2(\omega)$
Convolution in ω	$f_1(t)f_1(t)$	$\dfrac{1}{2\pi} F_1(\omega) * F_2(\omega)$

TABLE 18.2   Fourier transform pairs.

$f(t)$	$F(\omega)$
$\delta(t)$	1
1	$2\pi\,\delta(\omega)$
$u(t)$	$\pi\,\delta(\omega) + \dfrac{1}{j\omega}$
$u(t+\tau) - u(t-\tau)$	$2\dfrac{\sin\omega\tau}{\omega}$
$|t|$	$\dfrac{-2}{\omega^2}$
$\operatorname{sgn}(t)$	$\dfrac{2}{j\omega}$
$e^{-at}u(t)$	$\dfrac{1}{a+j\omega}$
$e^{at}u(-t)$	$\dfrac{1}{a-j\omega}$
$t^n e^{-at}u(t)$	$\dfrac{n!}{(a+j\omega)^{n+1}}$
$e^{-a|t|}$	$\dfrac{2a}{a^2+\omega^2}$
$e^{j\omega_0 t}$	$2\pi\,\delta(\omega-\omega_0)$
$\sin\omega_0 t$	$j\pi[\delta(\omega+\omega_0) - \delta(\omega-\omega_0)]$
$\cos\omega_0 t$	$\pi[\delta(\omega+\omega_0) + \delta(\omega-\omega_0)]$
$e^{-at}\sin\omega_0 t\,u(t)$	$\dfrac{\omega_0}{(a+j\omega)^2+\omega_0^2}$
$e^{-at}\cos\omega_0 t\,u(t)$	$\dfrac{a+j\omega}{(a+j\omega)^2+\omega_0^2}$

EXAMPLE 18.4

Figure 18.13   The signum function of Example 18.4.

Find the Fourier transforms of the following functions: (a) signum function sgn(t), shown in Fig. 18.13, (b) the double-sided exponential $e^{-a|t|}$, and (c) the sinc function $(\sin t)/t$.

Solution:

(a) We can obtain the Fourier transform of the *signum* function in three ways.

METHOD **1**   We can write the signum function in terms of the unit step function as

$$sgn(t) = f(t) = u(t) - u(-t)$$

But from Eq. (18.36),

$$U(\omega) = \mathcal{F}[u(t)] = \pi\delta(\omega) + \frac{1}{j\omega}$$

Applying this and the reversal property, we obtain

$$\mathcal{F}[sgn(t)] = U(\omega) - U(-\omega)$$

$$= \left(\pi\delta(\omega) + \frac{1}{j\omega}\right) - \left(\pi\delta(-\omega) + \frac{1}{-j\omega}\right) = \frac{2}{j\omega}$$

METHOD **2**   Since $\delta(\omega) = \delta(-\omega)$, we have the next method. Another way of writing the signum function in terms of the unit step function is

$$f(t) = sgn(t) = -1 + 2u(t)$$

Taking the Fourier transform of each term gives

$$F(\omega) = -2\pi\delta(\omega) + 2\left(\pi\delta(\omega) + \frac{1}{j\omega}\right) = \frac{2}{j\omega}$$

METHOD **3**   We can take the derivative of the signum function in Fig. 18.13 and obtain

$$f'(t) = 2\delta(t)$$

Taking the transform of this,

$$j\omega F(\omega) = 2 \quad\Longrightarrow\quad F(\omega) = \frac{2}{j\omega}$$

as obtained previously.

(b) The double-sided exponential can be expressed as

$$f(t) = e^{-a|t|} = e^{-at}u(t) + e^{at}u(-t) = y(t) + y(-t)$$

where $y(t) = e^{-at}u(t)$ so that $Y(\omega) = 1/(a+j\omega)$. Applying the reversal property,

$$\mathcal{F}[e^{-a|t|}] = Y(\omega) + Y(-\omega) = \left(\frac{1}{a+j\omega} + \frac{1}{a-j\omega}\right) = \frac{2a}{a^2+\omega^2}$$

(c) From Example 18.2,

$$\mathcal{F}\left[u\left(t+\frac{\tau}{2}\right) - u\left(t-\frac{\tau}{2}\right)\right] = \tau\frac{\sin(\omega\tau/2)}{\omega\tau/2} = \tau\text{ sinc }\frac{\omega\tau}{2}$$

Setting $\tau/2 = 1$ gives

$$\mathcal{F}[u(t+1) - u(t-1)] = 2\frac{\sin \omega}{\omega}$$

Applying the duality property,

$$\mathcal{F}\left[2\frac{\sin t}{t}\right] = 2\pi[U(\omega+1) - U(\omega-1)]$$

or

$$\mathcal{F}\left[\frac{\sin t}{t}\right] = \pi[U(\omega+1) - U(\omega-1)]$$

PRACTICE PROBLEM 18.4

Determine the Fourier transforms of these functions: (a) gate function $g(t) = u(t) - u(t-1)$, (b) $f(t) = te^{-2t}u(t)$, and (c) sawtooth pulse $p(t) = 10t[u(t) - u(t-2)]$.

Answer: (a) $(1 - e^{-j\omega})\left[\pi\delta(\omega) + \dfrac{1}{j\omega}\right]$, (b) $\dfrac{1}{(2+j\omega)^2}$,

(c) $\dfrac{10(e^{-j2\omega} - 1)}{\omega^2} + \dfrac{20j}{\omega}e^{-j2\omega}$.

EXAMPLE 18.5

Find the Fourier transform of the function in Fig. 18.14.

Solution:

The Fourier transform can be found directly using Eq. (18.8), but it is much easier to find it using the derivative property. We can express the function as

$$f(t) = \begin{cases} 1+t, & -1 < t < 0 \\ 1-t, & 0 < t < 1 \end{cases}$$

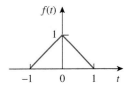

Figure 18.14   For Example 18.5.

Its first derivative is shown in Fig. 18.15(a) and is given by

$$f'(t) = \begin{cases} 1, & -1 < t < 0 \\ -1, & 0 < t < 1 \end{cases}$$

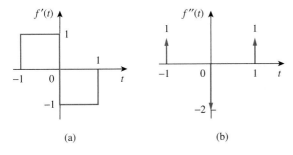

(a)   (b)

Figure 18.15   First and second derivatives of $f(t)$ in Fig. 18.14; for Example 18.5.

Its second derivative is in Fig. 18.15(b) and is given by

$$f''(t) = \delta(t+1) - 2\delta(t) + \delta(t-1)$$

Taking the Fourier transform of both sides,

$$(j\omega)^2 F(\omega) = e^{j\omega} - 2 + e^{-j\omega} = -2 + 2\cos\omega$$

or

$$F(\omega) = \frac{2(1-\cos\omega)}{\omega^2}$$

PRACTICE PROBLEM 18.5

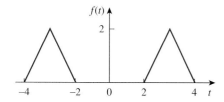

$f(t)$

Figure 18.16   For Practice Prob. 18.5.

Determine the Fourier transform of the function in Fig. 18.16.

Answer: $(8\cos 3\omega - 4\cos 4\omega - 4\cos 2\omega)/\omega^2$.

EXAMPLE 18.6

Obtain the inverse Fourier transform of:

(a) $F(\omega) = \dfrac{10j\omega + 4}{(j\omega)^2 + 6j\omega + 8}$ (b) $G(\omega) = \dfrac{\omega^2 + 21}{\omega^2 + 9}$

Solution:

(a) To avoid complex algebra, we can replace $j\omega$ with s for the moment. Using partial fraction expansion,

$$F(s) = \frac{10s + 4}{s^2 + 6s + 8} = \frac{10s + 4}{(s+4)(s+2)} = \frac{A}{s+4} + \frac{B}{s+2}$$

where

$$A = (s+4)F(s)\Big|_{s=-4} = \frac{10s+4}{(s+2)}\bigg|_{s=-4} = \frac{-36}{-2} = 18$$

$$B = (s+2)F(s)\Big|_{s=-2} = \frac{10s+4}{(s+4)}\bigg|_{s=-2} = \frac{-16}{2} = -8$$

Substituting $A = 18$ and $B = -8$ in $F(s)$ and s with $j\omega$ gives

$$F(j\omega) = \frac{18}{j\omega + 4} + \frac{-8}{j\omega + 2}$$

With the aid of Table 18.2, we obtain the inverse transform as

$$f(t) = (18e^{-4t} - 8e^{-2t})u(t)$$

(b) We simplify $G(\omega)$ as

$$G(\omega) = \frac{\omega^2 + 21}{\omega^2 + 9} = 1 + \frac{12}{\omega^2 + 9}$$

With the aid of Table 18.2, the inverse transform is obtained as

$$g(t) = \delta(t) + 2e^{-3|t|}$$

PRACTICE PROBLEM 18.6

Find the inverse Fourier transform of:

(a) $H(\omega) = \dfrac{6(3 + j2\omega)}{(1 + j\omega)(4 + j\omega)(2 + j\omega)}$

(b) $Y(\omega) = \pi\delta(\omega) + \dfrac{1}{j\omega} + \dfrac{2(1 + j\omega)}{(1 + j\omega)^2 + 16}$

Answer: (a) $h(t) = (2e^{-t} + 3e^{-2t} - 5e^{-4t})u(t)$,
(b) $y(t) = (1 + 2e^{-t}\cos 4t)u(t)$.

18.4 CIRCUIT APPLICATIONS

The Fourier transform generalizes the phasor technique to nonperiodic functions. Therefore, we apply Fourier transforms to circuits with non-sinusoidal excitations in exactly the same way we apply phasor techniques to circuits with sinusoidal excitations. Thus, Ohm's law is still valid:

$$V(\omega) = Z(\omega)I(\omega) \tag{18.52}$$

where $V(\omega)$ and $I(\omega)$ are the Fourier transforms of the voltage and current and $Z(\omega)$ is the impedance. We get the same expressions for the impedances of resistors, inductors, and capacitors as in phasor analysis, namely,

$$\begin{array}{ccc} R & \Longrightarrow & R \\[1mm] L & \Longrightarrow & j\omega L \\[1mm] C & \Longrightarrow & \dfrac{1}{j\omega C} \end{array} \tag{18.53}$$

Once we transform the functions for the circuit elements into the frequency domain and take the Fourier transforms of the excitations, we can use circuit techniques such as voltage division, source transformation, mesh analysis, node analysis, or Thevenin's theorem, to find the unknown response (current or voltage). Finally, we take the inverse Fourier transform to obtain the response in the time domain.

Although the Fourier transform method produces a response that exists for $-\infty < t < \infty$, Fourier analysis cannot handle circuits with initial conditions.

The transfer function is again defined as the ratio of the output response $Y(\omega)$ to the input excitation $X(\omega)$, that is,

$$H(\omega) = \dfrac{Y(\omega)}{X(\omega)} \tag{18.54}$$

Figure 18.17   Input-output relationship of a circuit in the frequency-domain.

or

$$Y(\omega) = H(\omega)X(\omega) \qquad (18.55)$$

The frequency-domain input-output relationship is portrayed in Fig. 18.17. Equation (18.55) shows that if we know the transfer function and the input, we can readily find the output. The relationship in Eq. (18.54) is the principal reason for using the Fourier transform in circuit analysis. Notice that $H(\omega)$ is identical to $H(s)$ with $s = j\omega$. Also, if the input is an impulse function [i.e., $x(t) = \delta(t)$], then $X(\omega) = 1$, so that the response is

$$Y(\omega) = H(\omega) = \mathcal{F}[h(t)] \qquad (18.56)$$

indicating that $H(\omega)$ is the Fourier transform of the impulse response $h(t)$.

EXAMPLE 18.7

Figure 18.18   For Example 18.7.

Find $v_o(t)$ in the circuit of Fig. 18.18 for $v_i(t) = 2e^{-3t}u(t)$.

Solution:

The Fourier transform of the input voltage is

$$V_i(\omega) = \frac{2}{3 + j\omega}$$

and the transfer function obtained by voltage division is

$$H(\omega) = \frac{V_o(\omega)}{V_i(\omega)} = \frac{1/j\omega}{2 + 1/j\omega} = \frac{1}{1 + j2\omega}$$

Hence,

$$V_o(\omega) = V_i(\omega)H(\omega) = \frac{2}{(3 + j\omega)(1 + j2\omega)}$$

or

$$V_o(\omega) = \frac{1}{(3 + j\omega)(0.5 + j\omega)}$$

By partial fractions,

$$V_o(\omega) = \frac{-0.4}{3 + j\omega} + \frac{0.4}{0.5 + j\omega}$$

Taking the inverse Fourier transform yields

$$v_o(t) = 0.4(e^{-0.5t} - e^{-3t})u(t)$$

PRACTICE PROBLEM 18.7

Figure 18.19   For Practice Prob. 18.7.

Determine $v_o(t)$ in Fig. 18.19 if $v_i(t) = 2\operatorname{sgn}(t) = -2 + 4u(t)$.

Answer: $-2 + 4(1 - e^{-4t})u(t)$.

EXAMPLE 18.8

Using the Fourier transform method, find $i_o(t)$ in Fig. 18.20 when $i_s(t) = 10 \sin 2t$ A.

Figure 18.20   For Example 18.8.

Solution:

By current division,

$$H(\omega) = \frac{I_o(\omega)}{I_s(\omega)} = \frac{2}{2 + 4 + 2/j\omega} = \frac{j\omega}{1 + j\omega 3}$$

If $i_s(t) = 10 \sin 2t$, then

$$I_s(\omega) = j\pi 10[\delta(\omega + 2) - \delta(\omega - 2)]$$

Hence,

$$I_o(\omega) = H(\omega)I_s(\omega) = \frac{10\pi \omega[\delta(\omega - 2) - \delta(\omega + 2)]}{1 + j\omega 3}$$

The inverse Fourier transform of $I_o(\omega)$ cannot be found using Table 18.2. We resort to the inverse Fourier transform formula in Eq. (18.9) and write

$$i_o(t) = \mathcal{F}^{-1}[I_o(\omega)] = \frac{1}{2\pi} \int_{-\infty}^{\infty} \frac{10\pi \omega[\delta(\omega - 2) - \delta(\omega + 2)]}{1 + j\omega 3} e^{j\omega t}\, d\omega$$

We apply the sifting property of the impulse function, namely,

$$\delta(\omega - \omega_0)f(\omega) = f(\omega_0)$$

or

$$\int_{-\infty}^{\infty} \delta(\omega - \omega_0)f(\omega)\, d\omega = f(\omega_0)$$

and obtain

$$i_o(t) = \frac{10\pi}{2\pi}\left[\frac{2}{1 + j6}e^{j2t} - \frac{-2}{1 - j6}e^{-j2t}\right]$$

$$= 10\left[\frac{e^{j2t}}{6.082e^{j80.54°}} + \frac{e^{-j2t}}{6.082e^{-j80.54°}}\right]$$

$$= 1.644[e^{j(2t - 80.54°)} + e^{-j(2t - 80.54°)}]$$

$$= 3.288 \cos(2t - 80.54°)\ \text{A}$$

PRACTICE PROBLEM 18.8

Find the current $i_o(t)$ in the circuit in Fig. 18.21, given that $i_s(t) = 20 \cos 4t$ A.

Answer: $11.8 \cos(4t + 26.57°)$ A.

Figure 18.21   For Practice Prob. 18.8.

18.5   PARSEVAL'S THEOREM

Parseval's theorem demonstrates one practical use of the Fourier transform. It relates the energy carried by a signal to the Fourier transform of the signal. If $p(t)$ is the power associated with the signal, the energy carried by the signal is

$$W = \int_{-\infty}^{\infty} p(t)\,dt \tag{18.57}$$

In order to be able compare the energy content of current and voltage signals, it is convenient to use a 1-Ω resistor as the base for energy calculation. For a 1-Ω resistor, $p(t) = v^2(t) = i^2(t) = f^2(t)$, where $f(t)$ stands for either voltage or current. The energy delivered to the 1-Ω resistor is

$$W_{1\Omega} = \int_{-\infty}^{\infty} f^2(t)\,dt \tag{18.58}$$

Parseval's theorem states that this same energy can be calculated in the frequency domain as

$$W_{1\Omega} = \int_{-\infty}^{\infty} f^2(t)\,dt = \frac{1}{2\pi} \int_{-\infty}^{\infty} |F(\omega)|^2\,d\omega \tag{18.59}$$

> Parseval's theorem states that the total energy delivered to a 1-Ω resistor equals the total area under the square of $f(t)$ or $1/2\pi$ times the total area under the square of the magnitude of the Fourier transform of $f(t)$.

Parseval's theorem relates energy associated with a signal to its Fourier transform. It provides the physical significance of $F(\omega)$, namely, that $|F(\omega)|^2$ is a measure of the energy density (in joules per hertz) corresponding to $f(t)$.

To derive Eq. (18.59), we begin with Eq. (18.58) and substitute Eq. (18.9) for one of the $f(t)$'s. We obtain

$$W_{1\Omega} = \int_{-\infty}^{\infty} f^2(t)\,dt = \int_{-\infty}^{\infty} f(t)\left[\frac{1}{2\pi}\int_{-\infty}^{\infty} F(\omega)e^{j\omega t}\,d\omega\right]dt \tag{18.60}$$

The function $f(t)$ can be moved inside the integral within the brackets, since the integral does not involve time:

$$W_{1\Omega} = \frac{1}{2\pi}\int_{-\infty}^{\infty}\int_{-\infty}^{\infty} f(t)F(\omega)e^{j\omega t}\,d\omega\,dt \tag{18.61}$$

Reversing the order of integration,

$$W_{1\Omega} = \frac{1}{2\pi}\int_{-\infty}^{\infty} F(\omega)\left[\int_{-\infty}^{\infty} f(t)e^{-j(-\omega)t}\,dt\right]d\omega$$

$$= \frac{1}{2\pi}\int_{-\infty}^{\infty} F(\omega)F(-\omega)\,d\omega = \frac{1}{2\pi}\int_{-\infty}^{\infty} F(\omega)F^*(\omega)\,d\omega \tag{18.62}$$

But if $z = x + jy$, $zz^* = (x + jy)(x - jy) = x^2 + y^2 = |z|^2$. Hence,

$$W_{1\Omega} = \int_{-\infty}^{\infty} f^2(t)\,dt = \frac{1}{2\pi}\int_{-\infty}^{\infty} |F(\omega)|^2\,d\omega \tag{18.63}$$

In fact, $|F(\omega)|^2$ is sometimes known as the energy spectral density of signal $f(t)$.

as expected. Equation (18.63) indicates that the energy carried by a signal can be found by integrating either the square of $f(t)$ in the time domain or $1/2\pi$ times the square of $F(\omega)$ in the frequency domain.

Since $|F(\omega)|^2$ is an even function, we may integrate from 0 to ∞ and double the result, that is,

$$W_{1\Omega} = \int_{-\infty}^{\infty} f^2(t)\, dt = \frac{1}{\pi} \int_0^{\infty} |F(\omega)|^2 \, d\omega \qquad (18.64)$$

We may also calculate the energy in any frequency band $\omega_1 < \omega < \omega_2$ as

$$W_{1\Omega} = \frac{1}{\pi} \int_{\omega_1}^{\omega_2} |F(\omega)|^2 \, d\omega \qquad (18.65)$$

Notice that Parseval's theorem as stated here applies to nonperiodic functions. Parseval's theorem for periodic functions was presented in Sections 17.5 and 17.6. As evident in Eq. (18.63), Parseval's theorem shows that the energy associated with a nonperiodic signal is spread over the entire frequency spectrum, whereas the energy of the periodic signal is concentrated at the frequencies of its harmonic components.

EXAMPLE 18.9

The voltage across a 10-Ω resistor is $v(t) = 5e^{-3t}u(t)$ V. Find the total energy dissipated in the resistor.

Solution:

We can find the energy using either $f(t) = v(t)$ or $F(\omega) = V(\omega)$.

METHOD 1 In the time domain,

$$W_{10\Omega} = 10 \int_{-\infty}^{\infty} f^2(t)\, dt = 10 \int_0^{\infty} 25 e^{-6t}\, dt$$

$$= 250 \frac{e^{-6t}}{-6} \Big|_0^{\infty} = \frac{250}{6} = 41.67 \text{ J}$$

METHOD 2 In the frequency domain,

$$F(\omega) = V(\omega) = \frac{5}{3 + j\omega}$$

so that

$$|F(\omega)|^2 = F(\omega)F^*(\omega) = \frac{25}{9 + \omega^2}$$

Hence, the energy dissipated is

$$W_{10\Omega} = \frac{10}{2\pi} \int_{-\infty}^{\infty} |F(\omega)|^2 \, d\omega = \frac{10}{\pi} \int_0^{\infty} \frac{25}{9 + \omega^2} \, d\omega$$

$$= \frac{250}{\pi} \left(\frac{1}{3} \tan^{-1} \frac{\omega}{3} \right) \Big|_0^{\infty} = \frac{250}{\pi} \left(\frac{1}{3} \right) \left(\frac{\pi}{2} \right) = \frac{250}{6} = 41.67 \text{ J}$$

PRACTICE PROBLEM 18.9

(a) Calculate the total energy absorbed by a 1-Ω resistor with $i(t) = 10e^{-2|t|}$ A in the time domain. (b) Repeat (a) in the frequency domain.

Answer: (a) 50 J, (b) 50 J.

EXAMPLE 18.10

Calculate the fraction of the total energy dissipated by a 1-Ω resistor in the frequency band $-10 < \omega < 10$ rad/s when the voltage across it is $v(t) = e^{-2t}u(t)$.

Solution:

Given that $f(t) = v(t) = e^{-2t}u(t)$, then

$$F(\omega) = \frac{1}{2 + j\omega} \implies |F(\omega)|^2 = \frac{1}{4 + \omega^2}$$

The total energy dissipated by the resistor is

$$W_{1\Omega} = \frac{1}{\pi} \int_0^\infty |F(\omega)|^2 \, d\omega = \frac{1}{\pi} \int_0^\infty \frac{d\omega}{4 + \omega^2}$$

$$= \frac{1}{\pi} \left(\frac{1}{2} \tan^{-1} \frac{\omega}{2} \Big|_0^\infty \right) = \frac{1}{\pi} \left(\frac{1}{2} \right) \frac{\pi}{2} = 0.25 \text{ J}$$

The energy in the frequencies $-10 < \omega < 10$ rad/s is

$$W = \frac{1}{\pi} \int_0^{10} |F(\omega)|^2 d\omega = \frac{1}{\pi} \int_0^{10} \frac{d\omega}{4 + \omega^2} = \frac{1}{\pi} \left(\frac{1}{2} \tan^{-1} \frac{\omega}{2} \Big|_0^{10} \right)$$

$$= \frac{1}{2\pi} \tan^{-1} 5 = \frac{1}{2\pi} \left(\frac{78.69°}{180°} \pi \right) = 0.218 \text{ J}$$

Its percentage of the total energy is

$$\frac{W}{W_{1\Omega}} = \frac{0.218}{0.25} = 87.4 \%$$

PRACTICE PROBLEM 18.10

A 2-Ω resistor has $i(t) = e^{-t}u(t)$. What percentage of the total energy is in the frequency band $-4 < \omega < 4$ rad/s?

Answer: 84.4 percent.

18.6 COMPARING THE FOURIER AND LAPLACE TRANSFORMS

It is worthwhile to take some moments to compare the Laplace and Fourier transforms. The following similarities and differences should be noted:

1. The Laplace transform defined in Chapter 15 is one-sided in that the integral is over $0 < t < \infty$, making it only useful for positive-time functions, $f(t)$, $t > 0$. The Fourier transform is applicable to functions defined for all time.

2. For a function $f(t)$ that is nonzero for positive time only (i.e., $f(t) = 0, \; t < 0$) and $\displaystyle\int_0^\infty |f(t)|\,dt < \infty$, the two transforms are related by

$$F(\omega) = F(s)\big|_{s=j\omega} \qquad (18.66)$$

This equation also shows that the Fourier transform can be regarded as a special case of the Laplace transform with $s = j\omega$. Recall that $s = \sigma + j\omega$. Therefore, Eq. (18.66) shows that the Laplace transform is related to the entire s plane, whereas the Fourier transform is restricted to the $j\omega$ axis. See Fig. 15.1.

> In other words, if all the poles of $F(s)$ lie in the left-hand side of the s plane, then one can obtain the Fourier transform $F(\omega)$ from the corresponding Laplace transform $F(s)$ by merely replacing s by $j\omega$. Note that this is not the case, for example, for $u(t)$ or $\cos \omega t u(t)$.

3. The Laplace transform is applicable to a wider range of functions than the Fourier transform. For example, the function $tu(t)$ has a Laplace transform but no Fourier transform. But Fourier transforms exist for signals that are not physically realizable and have no Laplace transforms.

4. The Laplace transform is better suited for the analysis of transient problems involving initial conditions, since it permits the inclusion of the initial conditions, whereas the Fourier transform does not. The Fourier transform is especially useful for problems in the steady state.

5. The Fourier transform provides greater insight into the frequency characteristics of signals than does the Laplace transform.

Some of the similarities and differences can be observed by comparing Tables 15.1 and 15.2 with Tables 18.1 and 18.2.

†18.7 APPLICATIONS

Besides its usefulness for circuit analysis, the Fourier transform is used extensively in a variety of fields such as optics, spectroscopy, acoustics, computer science, and electrical engineering. In electrical engineering, it is applied in communications systems and signal processing, where frequency response and frequency spectra are vital. Here we consider two simple applications: amplitude modulation (AM) and sampling.

18.7.1 Amplitude Modulation

Electromagnetic radiation or transmission of information through space has become an indispensable part of a modern technological society. However, transmission through space is only efficient and economical at high frequencies (above 20 kHz). To transmit intelligent signals—such as for speech and music—contained in the low-frequency range of 50 Hz to 20 kHz is expensive; it requires a huge amount of power and large antennas. A common method of transmitting low-frequency audio information is to transmit a high-frequency signal, called a *carrier*, which is controlled in some way to correspond to the audio information. Three characteristics (amplitude, frequency, or phase) of a carrier can be controlled so as to allow it to carry the intelligent signal, called the *modulating signal*. Here we will only consider the control of the carrier's amplitude. This is known as *amplitude modulation*.

> Amplitude modulation (AM) is a process whereby the amplitude of the carrier is controlled by the modulating signal.

AM is used in ordinary commercial radio bands and the video portion of commercial television.

Suppose the audio information, such as voice or music (or the modulating signal in general) to be transmitted is $m(t) = V_m \cos \omega_m t$, while the high-frequency carrier is $c(t) = V_c \cos \omega_c t$, where $\omega_c \gg \omega_m$. Then an AM signal $f(t)$ is given by

$$f(t) = V_c[1 + m(t)] \cos \omega_c t \tag{18.67}$$

Figure 18.22 illustrates the modulating signal $m(t)$, the carrier $c(t)$, and the AM signal $f(t)$. We can use the result in Eq. (18.27) together with the Fourier transform of the cosine function (see Example 18.1 or Table 18.1) to determine the spectrum of the AM signal:

$$
\begin{aligned}
F(\omega) &= \mathcal{F}[V_c \cos \omega_c t] + \mathcal{F}[V_c m(t) \cos \omega_c t] \\
&= V_c \pi [\delta(\omega - \omega_c) + \delta(\omega + \omega_c)] \\
&\quad + \frac{V_c}{2}[M(\omega - \omega_c) + M(\omega + \omega_c)]
\end{aligned}
\tag{18.68}
$$

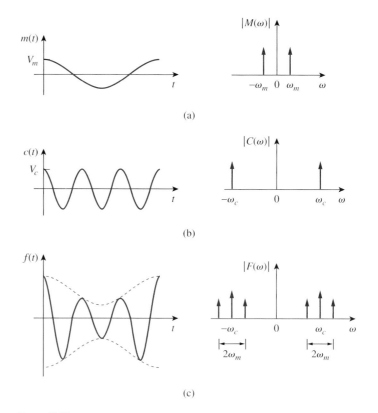

(a)

(b)

(c)

Figure 18.22 Time domain and frequency display of: (a) modulating signal, (b) carrier signal, (c) AM signal.

where $M(\omega)$ is the Fourier transform of the modulating signal $m(t)$. Shown in Fig. 18.23 is the frequency spectrum of the AM signal. Figure 18.23 indicates that the AM signal consists of the carrier and two other sinusoids. The sinusoid with frequency $\omega_c - \omega_m$ is known as the *lower sideband*, while the one with frequency $\omega_c + \omega_m$ is known as the *upper sideband*.

Notice that we have assumed that the modulating signal is sinusoidal to make the analysis easy. In real life, $m(t)$ is a nonsinusoidal, band-limited signal—its frequency spectrum is within the range between 0 and $\omega_u = 2\pi f_u$ (i.e., the signal has an upper frequency limit). Typically, $f_u = 5$ kHz for AM radio. If the frequency spectrum of the modulating signal is as shown in Fig. 18.24(a), then the frequency spectrum of the AM signal is shown in Fig. 18.24(b). Thus, to avoid any interference, carriers for AM radio stations are spaced 10 kHz apart.

At the receiving end of the transmission, the audio information is recovered from the modulated carrier by a process known as *demodulation*.

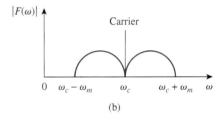

Figure 18.23   Frequency spectrum of AM signal.

Figure 18.24   Frequency spectrum of: (a) modulating signal, (b) AM signal.

EXAMPLE 18.11

A music signal has frequency components from 15 Hz to 30 kHz. If this signal could be used to amplitude modulate a 1.2-MHz carrier, find the range of frequencies for the lower and upper sidebands.

Solution:

The lower sideband is the difference of the carrier and modulating frequencies. It will include the frequencies from

$$1{,}200{,}000 - 30{,}000 \text{ Hz} = 1{,}170{,}000 \text{ Hz}$$

to

$$1{,}200{,}000 - 15 \text{ Hz} = 1{,}199{,}985 \text{ Hz}$$

The upper sideband is the sum of the carrier and modulating frequencies. It will include the frequencies from

$$1{,}200{,}000 + 15 \text{ Hz} = 1{,}200{,}015 \text{ Hz}$$

to

$$1{,}200{,}000 + 30{,}000 \text{ Hz} = 1{,}230{,}000 \text{ Hz}$$

PRACTICE PROBLEM 18.11

If a 2-MHz carrier is modulated by a 4-kHz intelligent signal, determine the frequencies of the three components of the AM signal that results.

Answer: 2,004,000 Hz, 2,000,000 Hz, 1,996,000 Hz.

(a)

(b)

(c)

Figure 18.25   (a) Continuous (analog) signal to be sampled, (b) train of impulses, (c) sampled (digital) signal.

18.7.2 Sampling

In analog systems, signals are processed in their entirety. However, in modern digital systems, only samples of signals are required for processing. This is possible as a result of the sampling theorem given in Section 17.8.1. The sampling can be done by using a train of pulses or impulses. We will use impulse sampling here.

Consider the continuous signal $g(t)$ shown in Fig. 18.25(a). This can be multiplied by a train of impulses $\delta(t - nT_s)$ shown in Fig. 18.25(b), where T_s is the *sampling interval* and $f_s = 1/T_s$ is the *sampling frequency* or the *sampling rate*. The sampled signal $g_s(t)$ is therefore

$$g_s(t) = g(t) \sum_{n=-\infty}^{\infty} \delta(t - nT_s) = \sum_{n=-\infty}^{\infty} g(nT_s)\delta(t - nT_s) \qquad (18.69)$$

The Fourier transform of this is

$$G_s(\omega) = \sum_{n=-\infty}^{\infty} g(nT_s)\mathcal{F}[\delta(t - nT_s)] = \sum_{n=-\infty}^{\infty} g(nT_s)e^{-jn\omega T_s} \qquad (18.70)$$

It can be shown that

$$\sum_{n=-\infty}^{\infty} g(nT_s)e^{-jn\omega T_s} = \frac{1}{T_s} \sum_{n=-\infty}^{\infty} G(\omega + n\omega_s) \qquad (18.71)$$

where $\omega_s = 2\pi/T_s$. Thus, Eq. (18.70) becomes

$$G_s(\omega) = \frac{1}{T_s} \sum_{n=-\infty}^{\infty} G(\omega + n\omega_s) \qquad (18.72)$$

This shows that the Fourier transform $G_s(\omega)$ of the sampled signal is a sum of translates of the Fourier transform of the original signal at a rate of $1/T_s$.

In order to ensure optimum recovery of the original signal, what must be the sampling interval? This fundamental question in sampling is answered by an equivalent part of the sampling theorem:

> A band-limited signal, with no frequency component higher than W hertz, may be completely recovered from its samples taken at a frequency at least twice as high as $2W$ samples per second.

In other words, for a signal with bandwidth W hertz, there is no loss of information or overlapping if the sampling frequency is at least twice the highest frequency in the modulating signal. Thus,

$$\frac{1}{T_s} = f_s \geq 2W \qquad (18.73)$$

The sampling frequency $f_s = 2W$ is known as the *Nyquist* frequency or rate, and $1/f_s$ is the Nyquist interval.

EXAMPLE 18.12

A telephone signal with a cutoff frequency of 5 kHz is sampled at a rate 60 percent higher than the minimum allowed rate. Find the sampling rate.

Solution:

The minimum sample rate is the Nyquist rate $= 2W = 2 \times 5 = 10$ kHz. Hence,

$$f_s = 1.60 \times 2W = 16 \text{ kHz}$$

PRACTICE PROBLEM 18.12

An audio signal that is band-limited to 12.5 kHz is digitized into 8-bit samples. What is the maximum sampling interval that must be used to ensure complete recovery?

Answer: 40 μs.

18.8 SUMMARY

1. The Fourier transform converts a nonperiodic function $f(t)$ into a transform $F(\omega)$, where

$$F(\omega) = \mathcal{F}[f(t)] = \int_{-\infty}^{\infty} f(t)e^{-j\omega t}\, dt$$

2. The inverse Fourier transform of $F(\omega)$ is

$$f(t) = \mathcal{F}^{-1}[F(\omega)] = \frac{1}{2\pi} \int_{-\infty}^{\infty} F(\omega)e^{j\omega t}\, d\omega$$

3. Important Fourier transform properties and pairs are summarized in Tables 18.1 and 18.2, respectively.

4. Using the Fourier transform method to analyze a circuit involves finding the Fourier transform of the excitation, transforming the circuit element into the frequency domain, solving for the unknown response, and transforming the response to the time domain using the inverse Fourier transform.

5. If $H(\omega)$ is the transfer function of a network, then $H(\omega)$ is the Fourier transform of the network's impulse response; that is,

$$H(\omega) = \mathcal{F}[h(t)]$$

   The output $V_o(\omega)$ of the network can be obtained from the input $V_i(\omega)$ using

$$V_o(\omega) = H(\omega)V_i(\omega)$$

6. Parseval's theorem gives the energy relationship between a function $f(t)$ and its Fourier transform $F(\omega)$. The 1-Ω energy is

$$W_{1\Omega} = \int_{-\infty}^{\infty} f^2(t)\, dt = \frac{1}{2\pi} \int_{-\infty}^{\infty} |F(\omega)|^2\, d\omega$$

   The theorem is useful in calculating energy carried by a signal either in the time domain or in the frequency domain.

7. Typical applications of the Fourier transform are found in amplitude modulation (AM) and sampling. For AM application, a way of determining the sidebands in an amplitude-modulated wave is derived from the modulation property of the Fourier transform. For sampling application, we found that no information is lost in sampling (required for digital transmission) if the sampling frequency is at least twice equal to the Nyquist rate.

REVIEW QUESTIONS

18.1 Which of these functions does not have a Fourier transform?

(a) $e^t u(-t)$ (b) $te^{-3t}u(t)$
(c) $1/t$ (d) $|t|u(t)$

18.2 The Fourier transform of e^{j2t} is:

(a) $\dfrac{1}{2 + j\omega}$ (b) $\dfrac{1}{-2 + j\omega}$

(c) $2\pi\delta(\omega - 2)$ (d) $2\pi\delta(\omega + 2)$

18.3 The inverse Fourier transform of $\dfrac{e^{-j\omega}}{2 + j\omega}$ is

(a) e^{-2t} (b) $e^{-2t}u(t - 1)$

(c) $e^{-2(t-1)}$ (d) $e^{-2(t-1)}u(t - 1)$

18.4 The inverse Fourier transform of $\delta(\omega)$ is:

(a) $\delta(t)$ (b) $u(t)$ (c) 1 (d) $1/2\pi$

18.5 The inverse Fourier transform of $j\omega$ is:

(a) $\delta'(t)$ (b) $u'(t)$
(c) $1/t$ (d) undefined

18.6 Evaluating the integral $\displaystyle\int_{-\infty}^{\infty} \dfrac{10\delta(\omega)}{4 + \omega^2}\, d\omega$ results in:

(a) 0 (b) 2 (c) 2.5 (d) ∞

18.7 The integral $\displaystyle\int_{-\infty}^{\infty} \dfrac{10\delta(\omega - 1)}{4 + \omega^2}\, d\omega$ gives:

(a) 0 (b) 2 (c) 2.5 (d) ∞

18.8 The current through a 1-F capacitor is $\delta(t)$ A. The voltage across the capacitor is:

(a) $u(t)$ (b) $-1/2 + u(t)$
(c) $e^{-t}u(t)$ (d) $\delta(t)$

18.9 A unit step current is applied through a 1-H inductor. The voltage across the inductor is:

(a) $u(t)$ (b) $\text{sgn}(t)$
(c) $e^{-t}u(t)$ (d) $\delta(t)$

18.10 Parseval's theorem is only for nonperiodic functions.

(a) True   (b) False

Answers: 18.1c, 18.2c, 18.3d, 18.4d, 18.5a, 18.6c, 18.7b, 18.8b, 18.9d, 18.10b

---

PROBLEMS

**Sections 18.2 and 18.3   Fourier Transform
                             and its Properties**

18.1 Obtain the Fourier transform of the function in Fig. 18.26.

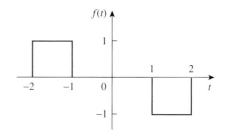

Figure 18.26   For Prob. 18.1.

18.2 What is the Fourier transform of the triangular pulse in Fig. 18.27?

Figure 18.27   For Prob. 18.2.

18.3 Calculate the Fourier transform of the signal in Fig. 18.28.

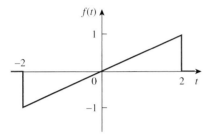

Figure 18.28   For Prob. 18.3.

18.4 Find the Fourier transform of the waveform shown in Fig. 18.29.

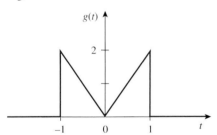

Figure 18.29   For Prob. 18.4.

18.5 Obtain the Fourier transform of the signal shown in Fig. 18.30.

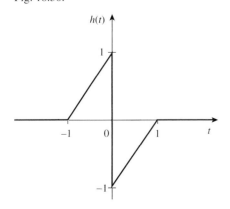

Figure 18.30   For Prob. 18.5.

18.6 For the signal in Fig. 18.31, determine the real part of the Fourier transform.

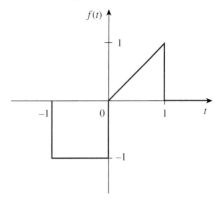

Figure 18.31   For Prob. 18.6.

18.7 Find the Fourier transforms of the signals in Fig. 18.32.

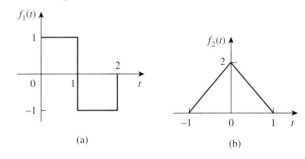

(a)   (b)

Figure 18.32   For Prob. 18.7.

18.8 Obtain the Fourier transform of the signals shown in Fig. 18.33.

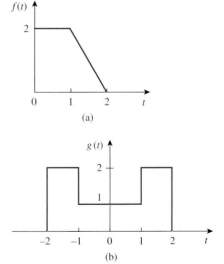

(a)

(b)

Figure 18.33   For Prob. 18.8.

18.9   Determine the Fourier transforms of the signals in Fig. 18.34.

(a)

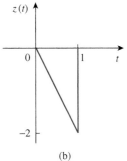

(b)

Figure 18.34   For Prob. 18.9.

18.10   Obtain the Fourier transforms of the signals shown in Fig. 18.35.

(a)   (b)

Figure 18.35   For Prob. 18.10.

18.11   Find the Fourier transform of the "sine-wave pulse" shown in Fig. 18.36.

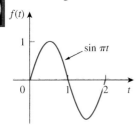

Figure 18.36   For Prob. 18.11.

18.12   Determine the Fourier transforms of these functions:

(a) $f(t) = e^t[u(t) - u(t-1)]$
(b) $g(t) = te^{-t}u(t)$
(c) $h(t) = u(t+1) - 2u(t) + u(t-1)$

18.13   Find the Fourier transform of the following signals:

(a) $f(t) = \cos(at - \pi/3)$, $-\infty < t < \infty$
(b) $g(t) = u(t+1)\sin \pi t$, $-\infty < t < \infty$
(c) $h(t) = (1 + A\sin at)\cos bt$, $-\infty < t < \infty$, where A, a, and b are constants
(d) $i(t) = 1 - t$, $0 < t < 4$

18.14   Find the Fourier transforms of these functions:

(a) $f(t) = e^{-t}\cos(3t + \pi)u(t)$
(b) $g(t) = \sin \pi t[u(t+1) - u(t-1)]$
(c) $h(t) = e^{-2t}\cos \pi t u(t-1)$
(d) $p(t) = e^{-2t}\sin 4t u(-t)$
(e) $q(t) = 4\,\text{sgn}(t-2) + 3\delta(t) - 2u(t-2)$

18.15   Find the Fourier transforms of the following functions:

(a) $f(t) = \delta(t+3) - \delta(t-3)$
(b) $f(t) = \int_{-\infty}^{\infty} 2\delta(t-1)\,dt$
(c) $f(t) = \delta(3t) - \delta'(2t)$

***18.16**   Determine the Fourier transforms of these functions:

(a) $f(t) = 4/t^2$ (b) $g(t) = 8/(4 + t^2)$

18.17   Find the Fourier transforms of:

(a) $\cos 2t u(t)$ (b) $\sin 10t u(t)$

18.18   Obtain the Fourier transform of $y(t) = e^{-t}\cos t u(t)$.

18.19   Find the Fourier transform of $f(t) = \cos 2\pi t[u(t) - u(t-1)]$.

18.20   (a) Show that a periodic signal with exponential Fourier series

$$f(t) = \sum_{n=-\infty}^{\infty} c_n e^{jn\omega_0 t}$$

has the Fourier transform

$$F(\omega) = \sum_{n=-\infty}^{\infty} c_n \delta(\omega - n\omega_0)$$

where $\omega_0 = 2\pi/T$.

(b) Find the Fourier transform of the signal in Fig. 18.37.

---

*An asterisk indicates a challenging problem.

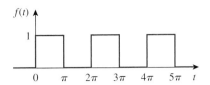

Figure 18.37   For Prob. 18.20(b).

18.21 Show that

$$\int_{-\infty}^{\infty} \left(\frac{\sin a\omega}{a\omega} \right)^2 d\omega = \frac{\pi}{a}$$

Hint: Use the fact that
$$\mathcal{F}[u(t+a) - u(t-a)] = 2a \left(\frac{\sin a\omega}{a\omega} \right).$$

18.22 Prove that if $F(\omega)$ is the Fourier transform of $f(t)$,

$$\mathcal{F}[f(t)\sin \omega_0 t] = \frac{j}{2}[F(\omega + \omega_0) - F(\omega - \omega_0)]$$

18.23 If the Fourier transform of $f(t)$ is

$$F(\omega) = \frac{10}{(2+j\omega)(5+j\omega)}$$

determine the transforms of the following:

(a) $f(-3t)$ (b) $f(2t-1)$ (c) $f(t)\cos 2t$
(d) $\dfrac{d}{dt} f(t)$ (e) $\displaystyle\int_{-\infty}^{t} f(t)\, dt$

18.24 Given that $\mathcal{F}[f(t)] = (j/\omega)(e^{-j\omega} - 1)$, find the Fourier transforms of:

(a) $x(t) = f(t) + 3$ (b) $y(t) = f(t-2)$
(c) $h(t) = f'(t)$
(d) $g(t) = 4f\left(\frac{2}{3}t\right) + 10f\left(\frac{5}{3}t\right)$

18.25 Obtain the inverse Fourier transforms of:

(a) $F(\omega) = \dfrac{10}{j\omega(j\omega + 2)}$

(b) $F(\omega) = \dfrac{4 - j\omega}{\omega^2 - 3j\omega - 2}$

18.26 Determine the inverse Fourier transforms of the following:

(a) $F(\omega) = \dfrac{e^{-j2\omega}}{1 + j\omega}$

(b) $H(\omega) = \dfrac{1}{(j\omega + 4)^2}$

(c) $G(\omega) = 2u(\omega + 1) - 2u(\omega - 1)$

18.27 Find the inverse Fourier transforms of the following functions:

(a) $F(\omega) = \dfrac{100}{j\omega(j\omega + 10)}$

(b) $G(\omega) = \dfrac{10j\omega}{(-j\omega + 2)(\omega + 3)}$

(c) $H(\omega) = \dfrac{60}{-\omega^2 + j40\omega + 1300}$

(d) $Y(\omega) = \dfrac{\delta(\omega)}{(j\omega + 1)(j\omega + 2)}$

18.28 Find the inverse Fourier transforms of:

(a) $\dfrac{\pi\delta(\omega)}{(5 + j\omega)(2 + j\omega)}$

(b) $\dfrac{10\delta(\omega + 2)}{j\omega(j\omega + 1)}$

(c) $\dfrac{20\delta(\omega - 1)}{(2 + j\omega)(3 + j\omega)}$

(d) $\dfrac{5\pi\delta(\omega)}{5 + j\omega} + \dfrac{5}{j\omega(5 + j\omega)}$

*18.29 Determine the inverse Fourier transforms of:

(a) $F(\omega) = 4\delta(\omega + 3) + \delta(\omega) + 4\delta(\omega - 3)$
(b) $G(\omega) = 4u(\omega + 2) - 4u(\omega - 2)$
(c) $H(\omega) = 6\cos 2\omega$

18.30 For a linear system with input $x(t)$ and output $y(t)$, find the impulse response for the following cases:

(a) $x(t) = e^{-at}u(t),$ $y(t) = u(t) - u(-t)$
(b) $x(t) = e^{-t}u(t),$ $y(t) = e^{-2t}u(t)$
(c) $x(t) = \delta(t),$ $y(t) = e^{-at}\sin bt\, u(t)$

18.31 Given a linear system with output $y(t)$ and impulse response $h(t)$, find the corresponding input $x(t)$ for the following cases:

(a) $y(t) = te^{-at}u(t),$ $h(t) = e^{-at}u(t)$
(b) $y(t) = u(t+1) - u(t-1),$ $h(t) = \delta(t)$
(c) $y(t) = e^{-at}u(t),$ $h(t) = \text{sgn}(t)$

*18.32 Determine the functions corresponding to the following Fourier transforms:

(a) $F_1(\omega) = \dfrac{e^{j\omega}}{-j\omega + 1}$ (b) $F_2(\omega) = 2e^{|\omega|}$

(c) $F_3(\omega) = \dfrac{1}{(1 + \omega^2)^2}$ (d) $F_4(\omega) = \dfrac{\delta(\omega)}{1 + j2\omega}$

*18.33 Find $f(t)$ if:

(a) $F(\omega) = 2\sin \pi\omega[u(\omega + 1) - u(\omega - 1)]$

(b) $F(\omega) = \dfrac{1}{\omega}(\sin 2\omega - \sin \omega) + \dfrac{j}{\omega}(\cos 2\omega - \cos \omega)$

18.34 Determine the signal $f(t)$ whose Fourier transform is shown in Fig. 18.38. (*Hint:* Use the duality property.)

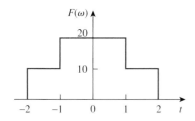

Figure 18.38   For Prob. 18.34.

18.35 A signal $f(t)$ has Fourier transform

$$F(\omega) = \frac{1}{2 + j\omega}$$

Determine the Fourier transform of the following signals:

(a) $x(t) = f(3t - 1)$
(b) $y(t) = f(t)\cos 5t$
(c) $z(t) = \dfrac{d}{dt}f(t)$
(d) $h(t) = f(t)*f(t)$
(e) $i(t) = tf(t)$

Section 18.4   Circuit Applications

18.36 A linear system has a transfer function

$$H(\omega) = \frac{10}{2 + j\omega}$$

Determine the output $v_o(t)$ at $t = 2$ s if the input $v_i(t)$ equals:

(a) $4\delta(t)$ V   (b) $6e^{-t}u(t)$ V   (c) $3\cos 2t$ V

18.37 Find the transfer function $I_o(\omega)/I_s(\omega)$ for the circuit in Fig. 18.39.

Figure 18.39   For Prob. 18.37.

18.38 Obtain $v_o(t)$ in the circuit of Fig. 18.40 when $v_i(t) = u(t)$ V.

Figure 18.40   For Prob. 18.38.

18.39 Given the circuit in Fig. 18.41, with its excitation, determine the Fourier transform of $i(t)$.

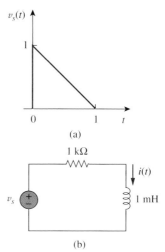

Figure 18.41   For Prob. 18.39.

18.40 Determine the current $i(t)$ in the circuit of Fig. 18.42(b), given the voltage source shown in Fig. 18.42(a).

Figure 18.42   For Prob. 18.40.

18.41 Determine the Fourier transform of $v(t)$ in the circuit shown in Fig. 18.43.

Figure 18.43   For Prob. 18.41.

18.42 Obtain the current $i_o(t)$ in the circuit in Fig. 18.44.

(a) Let $i(t) = \text{sgn}(t)$ A.
(b) Let $i(t) = 4[u(t) - u(t - 1)]$ A.

Figure 18.44   For Prob. 18.42.

18.43 Find $v_o(t)$ in the circuit of Fig. 18.45, where $i_s = 5e^{-t}u(t)$ A.

Figure 18.45   For Prob. 18.43.

18.44 If the rectangular pulse in Fig. 18.46(a) is applied to the circuit in Fig. 18.46(b), find v_o at $t = 1$ s.

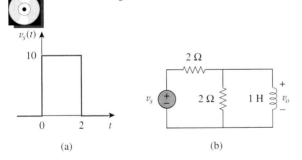

(a)   (b)

Figure 18.46   For Prob. 18.44.

18.45 Determine $v_o(t)$ in the circuit of Fig. 18.47.

Figure 18.47   For Prob. 18.45.

18.46 Determine the Fourier transform of $i_o(t)$ in the circuit of Fig. 18.48.

Figure 18.48   For Prob. 18.46.

18.47 In the circuit of Fig. 18.49, let $i_s = 4\delta(t)$ A. Find $V_o(\omega)$.

Figure 18.49   For Prob. 18.47.

18.48 Find $i_o(t)$ in the op amp circuit of Fig. 18.50.

Figure 18.50   For Prob. 18.48.

18.49 Use the Fourier transform method to obtain $v_o(t)$ in the circuit of Fig. 18.51.

Figure 18.51   For Prob. 18.49.

18.50 Determine $v_o(t)$ in the transformer circuit of Fig. 18.52.

Figure 18.52   For Prob. 18.50.

18.51 For the circuit in Fig. 18.53, given that $v_s = 2e^{-t}u(t)$ V, calculate the total 1-Ω energy content of $v_o(t)$.

Figure 18.53   For Prob. 18.51.

Section 18.5   Parseval's Theorem

18.52 For $F(\omega) = \dfrac{1}{3 + j\omega}$, find $J = \displaystyle\int_{-\infty}^{\infty} f^2(t)\, dt$.

18.53 If $f(t) = e^{-2|t|}$, find $J = \displaystyle\int_{-\infty}^{\infty} |F(\omega)|^2\, d\omega$.

18.54 Given the signal $f(t) = 4e^{-t}u(t)$, what is the total energy in $f(t)$?

18.55 Let $f(t) = 5e^{-(t-2)}u(t)$. Find $F(\omega)$ and use it to find the total energy in $f(t)$.

18.56 A voltage source $v_s(t) = e^{-t}\sin 2t\, u(t)$ V is applied to a 1-Ω resistor. Calculate the energy delivered to the resistor.

18.57 Let $i(t) = 2e^t u(-t)$ A. Find the total energy carried by $i(t)$ and the percentage of the 1-Ω energy in the frequency range of $-5 < \omega < 5$ rad/s.

Section 18.6   Applications

18.58 An AM signal is specified by

$$f(t) = 10(1 + 4\cos 200\pi t)\cos \pi \times 10^4 t$$

Determine the following:

(a) the carrier frequency,
(b) the lower sideband frequency,
(c) the upper sideband frequency.

18.59 For the linear system in Fig. 18.54, when the input voltage is $v_i(t) = 2\delta(t)$ V, the output is $v_o(t) = 10e^{-2t} - 6e^{-4t}$ V. Find the output when the input is $v_i(t) = 4e^{-t}u(t)$ V.

Figure 18.54   For Prob. 18.9.

18.60 A band-limited signal has the following Fourier series representation:

$$i_s(t) = 10 + 8\cos(2\pi t + 30°) + 5\cos(4\pi t - 150°)\text{mA}$$

If the signal is applied to the circuit in Fig. 18.55, find $v(t)$.

Figure 18.55   For Prob. 18.60.

18.61 A carrier wave of frequency 8 MHz is amplitude-modulated by a 5-kHz signal. Determine the lower and upper sidebands.

18.62 A voice signal occupying the frequency band of 0.4 to 3.5 kHz is used to amplitude-modulate a 10-MHz carrier. Determine the range of frequencies for the lower and upper sidebands.

18.63 For a given locality, calculate the number of stations allowable in the AM broadcasting band (540 to 1600 kHz) without interference with one another.

18.64 Repeat the previous problem for the FM broadcasting band (88 to 108 MHz), assuming that the carrier frequencies are spaced 200 kHz apart.

18.65 The highest-frequency component of a voice signal is 3.4 kHz. What is the Nyquist rate of the sampler of the voice signal?

18.66 A TV signal is band-limited to 4.5 MHz. If samples are to be reconstructed at a distant point, what is the maximum sampling interval allowable?

*__18.67__ Given a signal $g(t) = \text{sinc}\,(200\pi t)$, find the Nyquist rate and the Nyquist interval for the signal.

COMPREHENSIVE PROBLEMS

18.68 The voltage signal at the input of a filter is $v(t) = 50e^{-2|t|}$ V. What percentage of the total 1-Ω energy content lies in the frequency range of $1 < \omega < 5$ rad/s?

18.69 A signal with Fourier transform

$$F(\omega) = \frac{20}{4 + j\omega}$$

is passed through a filter whose cutoff frequency is 2 rad/s (i.e., $0 < \omega < 2$). What fraction of the energy in the input signal is contained in the output signal?

CHAPTER 19

TWO-PORT NETWORKS

Engineers Creed:
I take the vision which comes from dreams and apply the magic of science and mathematics, adding the heritage of my profession and my knowledge of nature's materials to create a design. I organize the efforts and skills of my fellow workers employing the capital of the thrifty and the products of many industries, and together we work toward our goal undaunted by hazards and obstacles. And when we have completed our task all can see that the dreams and plans have materialized for the comfort and welfare of all. I am an Engineer. I serve mankind by making dreams come true.

—Anonymous

Enhancing Your Career

Career in Education While two thirds of all engineers work in private industry, some work in academia and prepare students for engineering careers. The course on circuit analysis you are studying is an important part of the preparation process. If you enjoy teaching others, you may want to consider becoming an engineering educator.

Engineering professors work on state-of-the-art research projects, teach courses at graduate and undergraduate levels, and provide services to their professional societies and the community at large. They are expected to make original contributions in their areas of specialty. This requires a broad-based education in the fundamentals of electrical engineering and a mastery of the skills necessary for communicating their efforts to others.

If you like to do research, to work at the frontiers of engineering, to make contributions to technological advancement, to invent, consult, and/or teach, consider a career in engineering education. The best way to start is by talking with your professors and benefiting from their experience.

A solid understanding of mathematics and physics at the undergraduate level is vital to your success as an engineering professor. If you are having difficulty in solving your engineering textbook problems, start correcting any weaknesses you have in your mathematics and physics fundamentals.

Most universities these days require that engineering professors have a Ph.D. degree. In addition, some universities require that they be actively involved in research

The lecture method is still regarded as the most effective mode of teaching because of the personal contact with instructor and opportunity to ask questions. Source: © PhotoDisc, Inc. Copyright 1999.

leading to publications in reputable journals. To prepare yourself for a career in engineering education, get as broad an education as possible, because electrical engineering is changing rapidly and becoming interdisciplinary. Without doubt, engineering education is a rewarding career. Professors get a sense of satisfaction and fulfillment as they see their students graduate, become leaders in the professions, and contribute significantly to the betterment of humanity.

19.1   INTRODUCTION

A pair of terminals through which a current may enter or leave a network is known as a *port*. Two-terminal devices or elements (such as resistors, capacitors, and inductors) result in one-port networks. Most of the circuits we have dealt with so far are two-terminal or one-port circuits, represented in Fig. 19.1(a). We have considered the voltage across or current through a single pair of terminals—such as the two terminals of a resistor, a capacitor, or an inductor. We have also studied four-terminal or two-port circuits involving op amps, transistors, and transformers, as shown in Fig. 19.1(b). In general, a network may have *n* ports. A port is an access to the network and consists of a pair of terminals; the current entering one terminal leaves through the other terminal so that the net current entering the port equals zero.

In this chapter, we are mainly concerned with *two-port* networks (or, simply, *two-ports*).

> A two-port network is an electrical network with two separate ports for input and output.

Thus, a two-port network has two terminal pairs acting as access points. As shown in Fig. 19.1(b), the current entering one terminal of a pair leaves the other terminal in the pair. Three-terminal devices such as transistors can be configured into two-port networks.

Our study of two-port networks is for at least two reasons. First, such networks are useful in communications, control systems, power systems, and electronics. For example, they are used in electronics to model transistors and to facilitate cascaded design. Second, knowing the parameters of a two-port network enables us to treat it as a "black box" when embedded within a larger network.

To characterize a two-port network requires that we relate the terminal quantities V_1, V_2, I_1, and I_2 in Fig. 19.1(b), out of which two are independent. The various terms that relate these voltages and currents are called *parameters*. Our goal in this chapter is to derive six sets of these parameters. We will show the relationship between these parameters and how two-port networks can be connected in series, parallel, or cascade. As with op amps, we are only interested in the terminal behavior of the circuits. And we will assume that the two-port circuits contain no independent sources, although they can contain dependent sources. Finally, we will apply some of the concepts developed in this chapter to the analysis of transistor circuits and synthesis of ladder networks.

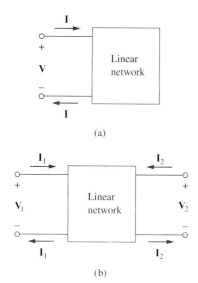

Figure 19.1   (a) One-port network, (b) two-port network.

19.2   IMPEDANCE PARAMETERS

Impedance and admittance parameters are commonly used in the synthesis of filters. They are also useful in the design and analysis of impedance-matching networks and power distribution networks. We discuss impedance parameters in this section and admittance parameters in the next section.

A two-port network may be voltage-driven as in Fig. 19.2(a) or current-driven as in Fig. 19.2(b). From either Fig. 19.2(a) or (b), the terminal voltages can be related to the terminal currents as

$$\mathbf{V}_1 = \mathbf{z}_{11}\mathbf{I}_1 + \mathbf{z}_{12}\mathbf{I}_2$$
$$\mathbf{V}_2 = \mathbf{z}_{21}\mathbf{I}_1 + \mathbf{z}_{22}\mathbf{I}_2$$

(19.1)

or in matrix form as

$$\begin{bmatrix} \mathbf{V}_1 \\ \mathbf{V}_2 \end{bmatrix} = \begin{bmatrix} \mathbf{z}_{11} & \mathbf{z}_{12} \\ \mathbf{z}_{21} & \mathbf{z}_{22} \end{bmatrix} \begin{bmatrix} \mathbf{I}_1 \\ \mathbf{I}_2 \end{bmatrix} = [\mathbf{z}] \begin{bmatrix} \mathbf{I}_1 \\ \mathbf{I}_2 \end{bmatrix}$$

(19.2)

Reminder: Only two of the four variables ($\mathbf{V}_1$, $\mathbf{V}_2$, $\mathbf{I}_1$, and $\mathbf{I}_2$) are independent. The other two can be found using Eq. (19.1).

where the **z** terms are called the *impedance parameters*, or simply *z parameters*, and have units of ohms.

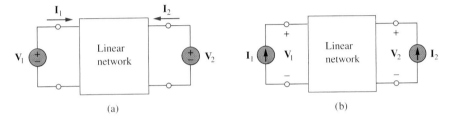

Figure 19.2   The linear two-port network: (a) driven by voltage sources, (b) driven by current sources.

The values of the parameters can be evaluated by setting $\mathbf{I}_1 = 0$ (input port open-circuited) or $\mathbf{I}_2 = 0$ (output port open-circuited). Thus,

$$\mathbf{z}_{11} = \left.\frac{\mathbf{V}_1}{\mathbf{I}_1}\right|_{\mathbf{I}_2=0}, \qquad \mathbf{z}_{12} = \left.\frac{\mathbf{V}_1}{\mathbf{I}_2}\right|_{\mathbf{I}_1=0}$$
$$\mathbf{z}_{21} = \left.\frac{\mathbf{V}_2}{\mathbf{I}_1}\right|_{\mathbf{I}_2=0}, \qquad \mathbf{z}_{22} = \left.\frac{\mathbf{V}_2}{\mathbf{I}_2}\right|_{\mathbf{I}_1=0}$$

(19.3)

Since the *z* parameters are obtained by open-circuiting the input or output port, they are also called the *open-circuit impedance parameters*. Specifically,

$\mathbf{z}_{11}$ = Open-circuit input impedance
$\mathbf{z}_{12}$ = Open-circuit transfer impedance from port 1 to port 2
$\mathbf{z}_{21}$ = Open-circuit transfer impedance from port 2 to port 1
$\mathbf{z}_{22}$ = Open-circuit output impedance

(19.4)

According to Eq. (19.3), we obtain $\mathbf{z}_{11}$ and $\mathbf{z}_{21}$ by connecting a voltage $\mathbf{V}_1$ (or a current source $\mathbf{I}_1$) to port 1 with port 2 open-circuited as in Fig. 19.3(a) and finding $\mathbf{I}_1$ and $\mathbf{V}_2$; we then get

$$\mathbf{z}_{11} = \frac{\mathbf{V}_1}{\mathbf{I}_1}, \qquad \mathbf{z}_{21} = \frac{\mathbf{V}_2}{\mathbf{I}_1}$$

(19.5)

(a)

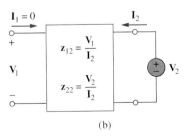

(b)

Figure 19.3   Determination of the *z* parameters: (a) finding $\mathbf{z}_{11}$ and $\mathbf{z}_{21}$, (b) finding $\mathbf{z}_{12}$ and $\mathbf{z}_{22}$.

Similarly, we obtain $\mathbf{z}_{12}$ and $\mathbf{z}_{22}$ by connecting a voltage $\mathbf{V}_2$ (or a current source $\mathbf{I}_2$) to port 2 with port 1 open-circuited as in Fig. 19.3(b) and finding $\mathbf{I}_2$ and $\mathbf{V}_1$; we then get

$$\mathbf{z}_{12} = \frac{\mathbf{V}_1}{\mathbf{I}_2}, \qquad \mathbf{z}_{22} = \frac{\mathbf{V}_2}{\mathbf{I}_2} \tag{19.6}$$

The above procedure provides us with a means of calculating or measuring the z parameters.

Sometimes $\mathbf{z}_{11}$ and $\mathbf{z}_{22}$ are called *driving-point impedances*, while $\mathbf{z}_{21}$ and $\mathbf{z}_{12}$ are called *transfer impedances*. A driving-point impedance is the input impedance of a two-terminal (one-port) device. Thus, $\mathbf{z}_{11}$ is the input driving-point impedance with the output port open-circuited, while $\mathbf{z}_{22}$ is the output driving-point impedance with the input port open-circuited.

When $\mathbf{z}_{11} = \mathbf{z}_{22}$, the two-port network is said to be *symmetrical*. This implies that the network has mirrorlike symmetry about some center line; that is, a line can be found that divides the network into two similar halves.

When the two-port network is linear and has no dependent sources, the transfer impedances are equal ($\mathbf{z}_{12} = \mathbf{z}_{21}$), and the two-port is said to be *reciprocal*. This means that if the points of excitation and response are interchanged, the transfer impedances remain the same. As illustrated in Fig. 19.4, a two-port is reciprocal if interchanging an ideal voltage source at one port with an ideal ammeter at the other port gives the same ammeter reading. The reciprocal network yields $\mathbf{V} = \mathbf{z}_{12}\mathbf{I}$ according to Eq. (19.1) when connected as in Fig. 19.4(a), but yields $\mathbf{V} = \mathbf{z}_{21}\mathbf{I}$ when connected as in Fig. 19.4(b). This is possible only if $\mathbf{z}_{12} = \mathbf{z}_{21}$. Any two-port that is made entirely of resistors, capacitors, and inductors must be reciprocal. A reciprocal network can be replaced by the T-equivalent circuit in Fig. 19.5(a) can be used. If the network is not reciprocal, a more general equivalent network is shown in Fig. 19.5(b); notice that this figure follows directly from Eq. (19.1).

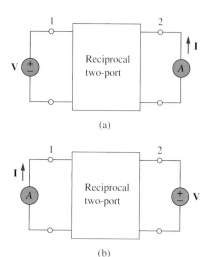

Figure 19.4   Interchanging a voltage source at one port with an ideal ammeter at the other port produces the same reading in a reciprocal two-port.

(a)

(b)

Figure 19.5   (a) T-equivalent circuit (for reciprocal case only), (b) general equivalent circuit.

Figure 19.6   An ideal transformer has no z parameters.

It should be mentioned that for some two-port networks, the z parameters do not exist because they cannot be described by Eq. (19.1). As an example, consider the ideal transformer of Fig. 19.6. The defining equations for the two-port network are:

$$\mathbf{V}_1 = \frac{1}{n}\mathbf{V}_2, \qquad \mathbf{I}_1 = -n\mathbf{I}_2 \tag{19.7}$$

Observe that it is impossible to express the voltages in terms of the currents, and vice versa, as Eq. (19.1) requires. Thus, the ideal transformer has no z parameters. However, it does have hybrid parameters, as we shall see in Section 19.4.

EXAMPLE 19.1

Determine the z parameters for the circuit in Fig. 19.7.

Solution:

METHOD 1   To determine $\mathbf{z}_{11}$ and $\mathbf{z}_{21}$, we apply a voltage source $\mathbf{V}_1$ to the input port and leave the output port open as in Fig. 19.8(a). Then,

$$\mathbf{z}_{11} = \frac{\mathbf{V}_1}{\mathbf{I}_1} = \frac{(20+40)\mathbf{I}_1}{\mathbf{I}_1} = 60 \ \Omega$$

that is, $\mathbf{z}_{11}$ is the input impedance at port 1.

$$\mathbf{z}_{21} = \frac{\mathbf{V}_2}{\mathbf{I}_1} = \frac{40\mathbf{I}_1}{\mathbf{I}_1} = 40 \ \Omega$$

To find $\mathbf{z}_{12}$ and $\mathbf{z}_{22}$, we apply a voltage source $\mathbf{V}_2$ to the output port and leave the input port open as in Fig. 19.8(b). Then,

$$\mathbf{z}_{12} = \frac{\mathbf{V}_1}{\mathbf{I}_2} = \frac{40\mathbf{I}_2}{\mathbf{I}_2} = 40 \ \Omega, \qquad \mathbf{z}_{22} = \frac{\mathbf{V}_2}{\mathbf{I}_2} = \frac{(30+40)\mathbf{I}_2}{\mathbf{I}_2} = 70 \ \Omega$$

Thus,

$$[\mathbf{z}] = \begin{bmatrix} 60 \ \Omega & 40 \ \Omega \\ 40 \ \Omega & 70 \ \Omega \end{bmatrix}$$

METHOD 2   Alternatively, since there is no dependent source in the given circuit, $\mathbf{z}_{12} = \mathbf{z}_{21}$ and we can use Fig. 19.5(a). Comparing Fig. 19.7 with Fig. 19.5(a), we get

$$\mathbf{z}_{12} = 40 \ \Omega = \mathbf{z}_{21}$$

$$\mathbf{z}_{11} - \mathbf{z}_{12} = 20 \quad \Longrightarrow \quad \mathbf{z}_{11} = 20 + \mathbf{z}_{12} = 60 \ \Omega$$

$$\mathbf{z}_{22} - \mathbf{z}_{12} = 30 \quad \Longrightarrow \quad \mathbf{z}_{22} = 30 + \mathbf{z}_{12} = 70 \ \Omega$$

Figure 19.7   For Example 19.1.

(a)

(b)

Figure 19.8   For Example 19.1: (a) finding $\mathbf{z}_{11}$ and $\mathbf{z}_{21}$, (b) finding $\mathbf{z}_{12}$ and $\mathbf{z}_{22}$.

PRACTICE PROBLEM 19.1

Find the z parameters of the two-port network in Fig. 19.9.

Answer: $\mathbf{z}_{11} = 14, \mathbf{z}_{12} = \mathbf{z}_{21} = \mathbf{z}_{22} = 6 \ \Omega$.

Figure 19.9   For Practice Prob. 19.1.

EXAMPLE 19.2

Find $\mathbf{I}_1$ and $\mathbf{I}_2$ in the circuit in Fig. 19.10.

Figure 19.10   For Example 19.2.

Solution:

This is not a reciprocal network. We may use the equivalent circuit in Fig. 19.5(b) but we can also use Eq. (19.1) directly. Substituting the given z parameters into Eq. (19.1),

$$\mathbf{V}_1 = 40\mathbf{I}_1 + j20\mathbf{I}_2 \tag{19.2.1}$$

$$\mathbf{V}_2 = j30\mathbf{I}_1 + 50\mathbf{I}_2 \tag{19.2.2}$$

Since we are looking for $\mathbf{I}_1$ and $\mathbf{I}_2$, we substitute

$$\mathbf{V}_1 = 100\underline{/0^\circ}, \qquad \mathbf{V}_2 = -10\mathbf{I}_2$$

into Eqs. (19.2.1) and (19.2.2), which become

$$100 = 40\mathbf{I}_1 + j20\mathbf{I}_2 \tag{19.2.3}$$

$$-10\mathbf{I}_2 = j30\mathbf{I}_1 + 50\mathbf{I}_2 \quad \Longrightarrow \quad \mathbf{I}_1 = j2\mathbf{I}_2 \tag{19.2.4}$$

Substituting Eq. (19.2.4) into Eq. (19.2.3) gives

$$100 = j80\mathbf{I}_2 + j20\mathbf{I}_2 \quad \Longrightarrow \quad \mathbf{I}_2 = \frac{100}{j100} = -j$$

From Eq. (19.2.4), $\mathbf{I}_1 = j2(-j) = 2$. Thus,

$$\mathbf{I}_1 = 2\underline{/0^\circ} \text{ A}, \qquad \mathbf{I}_2 = 1\underline{/-90^\circ} \text{ A}$$

PRACTICE PROBLEM 1 9 . 2

Calculate $\mathbf{I}_1$ and $\mathbf{I}_2$ in the two-port of Fig. 19.11.

Figure 19.11   For Practice Prob. 19.2.

Answer: $2\underline{/20^\circ}$ A, $1\underline{/-60^\circ}$ A.

19.3 ADMITTANCE PARAMETERS

In the previous section we saw that impedance parameters may not exist for a two-port network. So there is a need for an alternative means of describing such a network. This need may be met by the second set of parameters, which we obtain by expressing the terminal currents in terms of the terminal voltages. In either Fig. 19.12(a) or (b), the terminal currents can be expressed in terms of the terminal voltages as

$$
\begin{aligned}
\mathbf{I}_1 &= \mathbf{y}_{11}\mathbf{V}_1 + \mathbf{y}_{12}\mathbf{V}_2 \\
\mathbf{I}_2 &= \mathbf{y}_{21}\mathbf{V}_1 + \mathbf{y}_{22}\mathbf{V}_2
\end{aligned}
\tag{19.8}
$$

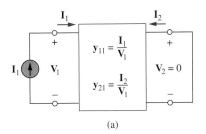

(a)

or in matrix form as

$$
\begin{bmatrix} \mathbf{I}_1 \\ \mathbf{I}_2 \end{bmatrix} = \begin{bmatrix} \mathbf{y}_{11} & \mathbf{y}_{12} \\ \mathbf{y}_{21} & \mathbf{y}_{22} \end{bmatrix} \begin{bmatrix} \mathbf{V}_1 \\ \mathbf{V}_2 \end{bmatrix} = [\mathbf{y}] \begin{bmatrix} \mathbf{V}_1 \\ \mathbf{V}_2 \end{bmatrix}
\tag{19.9}
$$

The **y** terms are known as the *admittance parameters* (or, simply, *y parameters*) and have units of siemens.

The values of the parameters can be determined by setting $\mathbf{V}_1 = 0$ (input port short-circuited) or $\mathbf{V}_2 = 0$ (output port short-circuited). Thus,

$$
\begin{aligned}
\mathbf{y}_{11} &= \left.\frac{\mathbf{I}_1}{\mathbf{V}_1}\right|_{\mathbf{V}_2=0}, & \mathbf{y}_{12} &= \left.\frac{\mathbf{I}_1}{\mathbf{V}_2}\right|_{\mathbf{V}_1=0} \\
\mathbf{y}_{21} &= \left.\frac{\mathbf{I}_2}{\mathbf{V}_1}\right|_{\mathbf{V}_2=0}, & \mathbf{y}_{22} &= \left.\frac{\mathbf{I}_2}{\mathbf{V}_2}\right|_{\mathbf{V}_1=0}
\end{aligned}
\tag{19.10}
$$

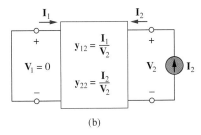

(b)

Figure 19.12   Determination of the *y* parameters: (a) finding y_{11} and y_{21}, (b) finding y_{12} and y_{22}.

Since the *y* parameters are obtained by short-circuiting the input or output port, they are also called the *short-circuit admittance parameters*. Specifically,

$\mathbf{y}_{11}$ = Short-circuit input admittance

$\mathbf{y}_{12}$ = Short-circuit transfer admittance from port 2 to port 1

$\mathbf{y}_{21}$ = Short-circuit transfer admittance from port 1 to port 2

$\mathbf{y}_{22}$ = Short-circuit output admittance

(19.11)

Following Eq. (19.10), we obtain $\mathbf{y}_{11}$ and $\mathbf{y}_{21}$ by connecting a current $\mathbf{I}_1$ to port 1 and short-circuiting port 2 as in Fig. 19.12(a), finding $\mathbf{V}_1$ and $\mathbf{I}_2$, and then calculating

$$
\mathbf{y}_{11} = \frac{\mathbf{I}_1}{\mathbf{V}_1}, \qquad \mathbf{y}_{21} = \frac{\mathbf{I}_2}{\mathbf{V}_1}
\tag{19.12}
$$

Similarly, we obtain $\mathbf{y}_{12}$ and $\mathbf{y}_{22}$ by connecting a current source $\mathbf{I}_2$ to port 2 and short-circuiting port 1 as in Fig. 19.12(b), finding $\mathbf{I}_1$ and $\mathbf{V}_2$, and then getting

$$
\mathbf{y}_{12} = \frac{\mathbf{I}_1}{\mathbf{V}_2}, \qquad \mathbf{y}_{22} = \frac{\mathbf{I}_2}{\mathbf{V}_2}
\tag{19.13}
$$

This procedure provides us with a means of calculating or measuring the *y* parameters. The impedance and admittance parameters are collectively referred to as *immittance* parameters.

For a two-port network that is linear and has no dependent sources, the transfer admittances are equal ($\mathbf{y}_{12} = \mathbf{y}_{21}$). This can be proved in the same way as for the z parameters. A reciprocal network ($\mathbf{y}_{12} = \mathbf{y}_{21}$) can be modeled by the Π-equivalent circuit in Fig. 19.13(a). If the network is not reciprocal, a more general equivalent network is shown in Fig. 19.13(b).

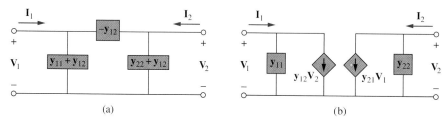

(a)   (b)

Figure 19.13   (a) Π-equivalent circuit (for reciprocal case only), (b) general equivalent circuit.

EXAMPLE 19.3

Obtain the y parameters for the Π network shown in Fig. 19.14.

Solution:

METHOD **1**   To find $\mathbf{y}_{11}$ and $\mathbf{y}_{21}$, short-circuit the output port and connect a current source $\mathbf{I}_1$ to the input port as in Fig. 19.15(a). Since the 8-Ω resistor is short-circuited, the 2-Ω resistor is in parallel with the 4-Ω resistor. Hence,

$$\mathbf{V}_1 = \mathbf{I}_1(4 \parallel 2) = \frac{4}{3}\mathbf{I}_1, \qquad \mathbf{y}_{11} = \frac{\mathbf{I}_1}{\mathbf{V}_1} = \frac{\mathbf{I}_1}{\frac{4}{3}\mathbf{I}_1} = 0.75 \text{ S}$$

By current division,

$$-\mathbf{I}_2 = \frac{4}{4+2}\mathbf{I}_1 = \frac{2}{3}\mathbf{I}_1, \qquad \mathbf{y}_{21} = \frac{\mathbf{I}_2}{\mathbf{V}_1} = \frac{-\frac{2}{3}\mathbf{I}_1}{\frac{4}{3}\mathbf{I}_1} = -0.5 \text{ S}$$

To get $\mathbf{y}_{12}$ and $\mathbf{y}_{22}$, short-circuit the input port and connect a current source $\mathbf{I}_2$ to the output port as in Fig. 19.15(b). The 4-Ω resistor is short-circuited so that the 2-Ω and 8-Ω resistors are in parallel.

$$\mathbf{V}_2 = \mathbf{I}_2(8 \parallel 2) = \frac{8}{5}\mathbf{I}_2, \qquad \mathbf{y}_{22} = \frac{\mathbf{I}_2}{\mathbf{V}_2} = \frac{\mathbf{I}_2}{\frac{8}{5}\mathbf{I}_2} = \frac{5}{8} = 0.625 \text{ S}$$

By current division,

$$-\mathbf{I}_1 = \frac{8}{8+2}\mathbf{I}_2 = \frac{4}{5}\mathbf{I}_2, \qquad \mathbf{y}_{12} = \frac{\mathbf{I}_1}{\mathbf{V}_2} = \frac{-\frac{4}{5}\mathbf{I}_2}{\frac{8}{5}\mathbf{I}_2} = -0.5 \text{ S}$$

METHOD **2**   Alternatively, comparing Fig. 19.14 with Fig. 19.13(a),

$$\mathbf{y}_{12} = -\frac{1}{2} \text{ S} = \mathbf{y}_{21}$$

$$\mathbf{y}_{11} + \mathbf{y}_{12} = \frac{1}{4} \qquad \Longrightarrow \qquad \mathbf{y}_{11} = \frac{1}{4} - \mathbf{y}_{12} = 0.75 \text{ S}$$

$$\mathbf{y}_{22} + \mathbf{y}_{12} = \frac{1}{8} \qquad \Longrightarrow \qquad \mathbf{y}_{22} = \frac{1}{8} - \mathbf{y}_{12} = 0.625 \text{ S}$$

as obtained previously.

Figure 19.14   For Example 19.3.

(a)

(b)

Figure 19.15   For Example 19.3: (a) finding $\mathbf{y}_{11}$ and $\mathbf{y}_{21}$, (b) finding $\mathbf{y}_{12}$ and $\mathbf{y}_{22}$.

PRACTICE PROBLEM 19.3

Obtain the y parameters for the T network shown in Fig. 19.16.

Answer: $y_{11} = 0.2273$ S, $y_{12} = y_{21} = -0.0909$ S, $y_{22} = 0.1364$ S.

Figure 19.16   For Practice Prob. 19.3.

EXAMPLE 19.4

Determine the y parameters for the two-port shown in Fig. 19.17.

Solution:

We follow the same procedure as in the previous example. To get y_{11} and y_{21}, we use the circuit in Fig. 19.18(a), in which port 2 is short-circuited and a current source is applied to port 1. At node 1,

$$\frac{\mathbf{V}_1 - \mathbf{V}_o}{8} = 2\mathbf{I}_1 + \frac{\mathbf{V}_o}{2} + \frac{\mathbf{V}_o - 0}{4}$$

But $\mathbf{I}_1 = \dfrac{\mathbf{V}_1 - \mathbf{V}_o}{8}$; therefore,

$$0 = \frac{\mathbf{V}_1 - \mathbf{V}_o}{8} + \frac{3\mathbf{V}_o}{4}$$

$$0 = \mathbf{V}_1 - \mathbf{V}_o + 6\mathbf{V}_o \qquad \Longrightarrow \qquad \mathbf{V}_1 = -5\mathbf{V}_o$$

Hence,

$$\mathbf{I}_1 = \frac{-5\mathbf{V}_o - \mathbf{V}_o}{8} = -0.75\mathbf{V}_o$$

and

$$y_{11} = \frac{\mathbf{I}_1}{\mathbf{V}_1} = \frac{-0.75\mathbf{V}_o}{-5\mathbf{V}_o} = 0.15 \text{ S}$$

At node 2,

$$\frac{\mathbf{V}_o - 0}{4} + 2\mathbf{I}_1 + \mathbf{I}_2 = 0$$

Figure 19.17   For Example 19.4.

(a)

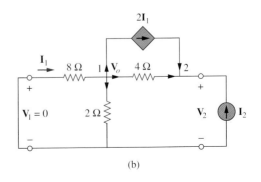

(b)

Figure 19.18   Solution of Example 19.4: (a) finding y_{11} and y_{21}, (b) finding y_{12} and y_{22}.

or

$$-\mathbf{I}_2 = 0.25\mathbf{V}_o - 1.5\mathbf{V}_o = -1.25\mathbf{V}_o$$

Hence,

$$\mathbf{y}_{21} = \frac{\mathbf{I}_2}{\mathbf{V}_1} = \frac{1.25\mathbf{V}_o}{-5\mathbf{V}_o} = -0.25 \text{ S}$$

Similarly, we get $\mathbf{y}_{12}$ and $\mathbf{y}_{22}$ using Fig. 19.18(b). At node 1,

$$\frac{0 - \mathbf{V}_o}{8} = 2\mathbf{I}_1 + \frac{\mathbf{V}_o}{2} + \frac{\mathbf{V}_o - \mathbf{V}_2}{4}$$

But $\mathbf{I}_1 = \dfrac{0 - \mathbf{V}_o}{8}$; therefore,

$$0 = -\frac{\mathbf{V}_o}{8} + \frac{\mathbf{V}_o}{2} + \frac{\mathbf{V}_o - \mathbf{V}_2}{4}$$

or

$$0 = -\mathbf{V}_o + 4\mathbf{V}_o + 2\mathbf{V}_o - 2\mathbf{V}_2 \qquad \Longrightarrow \qquad \mathbf{V}_2 = 2.5\mathbf{V}_o$$

Hence,

$$\mathbf{y}_{12} = \frac{\mathbf{I}_1}{\mathbf{V}_2} = \frac{-\mathbf{V}_o/8}{2.5\mathbf{V}_o} = -0.05 \text{ S}$$

At node 2,

$$\frac{\mathbf{V}_o - \mathbf{V}_2}{4} + 2\mathbf{I}_1 + \mathbf{I}_2 = 0$$

or

$$-\mathbf{I}_2 = 0.25\mathbf{V}_o - \frac{1}{4}(2.5\mathbf{V}_o) - \frac{2\mathbf{V}_o}{8} = -0.625\mathbf{V}_o$$

Thus,

$$\mathbf{y}_{22} = \frac{\mathbf{I}_2}{\mathbf{V}_2} = \frac{0.625\mathbf{V}_o}{2.5\mathbf{V}_o} = 0.25 \text{ S}$$

Notice that $\mathbf{y}_{12} \neq \mathbf{y}_{21}$ in this case, since the network is not reciprocal.

PRACTICE PROBLEM 19.4

Figure 19.19   For Practice Prob. 19.4.

Obtain the y parameters for the circuit in Fig. 19.19.

Answer: $\mathbf{y}_{11} = 0.625 \text{ S}$, $\mathbf{y}_{12} = -0.125 \text{ S}$, $\mathbf{y}_{21} = 0.375 \text{ S}$, $\mathbf{y}_{22} = 0.125 \text{ S}$.

19.4 HYBRID PARAMETERS

The z and y parameters of a two-port network do not always exist. So there is a need for developing another set of parameters. This third set of parameters is based on making $\mathbf{V}_1$ and $\mathbf{I}_2$ the dependent variables. Thus, we obtain

$$\begin{aligned} \mathbf{V}_1 &= \mathbf{h}_{11}\mathbf{I}_1 + \mathbf{h}_{12}\mathbf{V}_2 \\ \mathbf{I}_2 &= \mathbf{h}_{21}\mathbf{I}_1 + \mathbf{h}_{22}\mathbf{V}_2 \end{aligned}$$

(19.14)

or in matrix form,

$$\begin{bmatrix} \mathbf{V}_1 \\ \mathbf{I}_2 \end{bmatrix} = \begin{bmatrix} \mathbf{h}_{11} & \mathbf{h}_{12} \\ \mathbf{h}_{21} & \mathbf{h}_{22} \end{bmatrix} \begin{bmatrix} \mathbf{I}_1 \\ \mathbf{V}_2 \end{bmatrix} = [\mathbf{h}] \begin{bmatrix} \mathbf{I}_1 \\ \mathbf{V}_2 \end{bmatrix}$$

(19.15)

The **h** terms are known as the *hybrid parameters* (or, simply, *h parameters*) because they are a hybrid combination of ratios. They are very useful for describing electronic devices such as transistors (see Section 19.9); it is much easier to measure experimentally the *h* parameters of such devices than to measure their *z* or *y* parameters. In fact, we have seen that the ideal transformer in Fig. 19.6, described by Eq. (19.7), does not have *z* parameters. The ideal transformer can be described by the hybrid parameters, because Eq. (19.7) conforms with Eq. (19.14).

The values of the parameters are determined as

$$\mathbf{h}_{11} = \left.\frac{\mathbf{V}_1}{\mathbf{I}_1}\right|_{\mathbf{V}_2=0}, \qquad \mathbf{h}_{12} = \left.\frac{\mathbf{V}_1}{\mathbf{V}_2}\right|_{\mathbf{I}_1=0}$$

$$\mathbf{h}_{21} = \left.\frac{\mathbf{I}_2}{\mathbf{I}_1}\right|_{\mathbf{V}_2=0}, \qquad \mathbf{h}_{22} = \left.\frac{\mathbf{I}_2}{\mathbf{V}_2}\right|_{\mathbf{I}_1=0}$$

(19.16)

It is evident from Eq. (19.16) that the parameters $\mathbf{h}_{11}$, $\mathbf{h}_{12}$, $\mathbf{h}_{21}$, and $\mathbf{h}_{22}$ represent an impedance, a voltage gain, a current gain, and an admittance, respectively. This is why they are called the hybrid parameters. To be specific,

$\mathbf{h}_{11}$ = Short-circuit input impedance

$\mathbf{h}_{12}$ = Open-circuit reverse voltage gain

$\mathbf{h}_{21}$ = Short-circuit forward current gain

$\mathbf{h}_{22}$ = Open-circuit output admittance

(19.17)

The procedure for calculating the *h* parameters is similar to that used for the *z* or *y* parameters. We apply a voltage or current source to the appropriate port, short-circuit or open-circuit the other port, depending on the parameter of interest, and perform regular circuit analysis. For reciprocal networks, $\mathbf{h}_{12} = -\mathbf{h}_{21}$. This can be proved in the same way as we proved that $\mathbf{z}_{12} = \mathbf{z}_{21}$. Figure 19.20 shows the hybrid model of a two-port network.

A set of parameters closely related to the *h* parameters are the *g parameters* or *inverse hybrid parameters*. These are used to describe the terminal currents and voltages as

$$\begin{aligned} \mathbf{I}_1 &= \mathbf{g}_{11}\mathbf{V}_1 + \mathbf{g}_{12}\mathbf{I}_2 \\ \mathbf{V}_2 &= \mathbf{g}_{21}\mathbf{V}_1 + \mathbf{g}_{22}\mathbf{I}_2 \end{aligned}$$

(19.18)

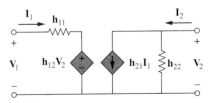

Figure 19.20   The *h*-parameter equivalent network of a two-port network.

or

$$\begin{bmatrix} \mathbf{I}_1 \\ \mathbf{V}_2 \end{bmatrix} = \begin{bmatrix} \mathbf{g}_{11} & \mathbf{g}_{12} \\ \mathbf{g}_{21} & \mathbf{g}_{22} \end{bmatrix} \begin{bmatrix} \mathbf{V}_1 \\ \mathbf{I}_2 \end{bmatrix} = [\mathbf{g}] \begin{bmatrix} \mathbf{V}_1 \\ \mathbf{I}_2 \end{bmatrix} \qquad (19.19)$$

The values of the g parameters are determined as

$$\mathbf{g}_{11} = \frac{\mathbf{I}_1}{\mathbf{V}_1}\bigg|_{\mathbf{I}_2=0}, \qquad \mathbf{g}_{12} = \frac{\mathbf{I}_1}{\mathbf{I}_2}\bigg|_{\mathbf{V}_1=0}$$

$$\mathbf{g}_{21} = \frac{\mathbf{V}_2}{\mathbf{V}_1}\bigg|_{\mathbf{I}_2=0}, \qquad \mathbf{g}_{22} = \frac{\mathbf{V}_2}{\mathbf{I}_2}\bigg|_{\mathbf{V}_1=0} \qquad (19.20)$$

Thus, the inverse hybrid parameters are specifically called

$\mathbf{g}_{11}$ = Open-circuit input admittance

$\mathbf{g}_{12}$ = Short-circuit reverse current gain

$\mathbf{g}_{21}$ = Open-circuit forward voltage gain

$\mathbf{g}_{22}$ = Short-circuit output impedance

$\qquad (19.21)$

Figure 19.21 shows the inverse hybrid model of a two-port network.

Figure 19.21   The g-parameter model of a two-port network.

EXAMPLE 19.5

Figure 19.22   For Example 19.5.

Find the hybrid parameters for the two-port network of Fig. 19.22.

Solution:

To find $\mathbf{h}_{11}$ and $\mathbf{h}_{21}$, we short-circuit the output port and connect a current source $\mathbf{I}_1$ to the input port as shown in Fig. 19.23(a). From Fig. 19.23(a),

$$\mathbf{V}_1 = \mathbf{I}_1(2 + 3 \parallel 6) = 4\mathbf{I}_1$$

Hence,

$$\mathbf{h}_{11} = \frac{\mathbf{V}_1}{\mathbf{I}_1} = 4\ \Omega$$

Also, from Fig. 19.23(a) we obtain, by current division,

$$-\mathbf{I}_2 = \frac{6}{6+3}\mathbf{I}_1 = \frac{2}{3}\mathbf{I}_1$$

Hence,

$$\mathbf{h}_{21} = \frac{\mathbf{I}_2}{\mathbf{I}_1} = -\frac{2}{3}$$

To obtain $\mathbf{h}_{12}$ and $\mathbf{h}_{22}$, we open-circuit the input port and connect a voltage source $\mathbf{V}_2$ to the output port as in Fig. 19.23(b). By voltage division,

$$\mathbf{V}_1 = \frac{6}{6+3}\mathbf{V}_2 = \frac{2}{3}\mathbf{V}_2$$

Hence,

$$\mathbf{h}_{12} = \frac{\mathbf{V}_1}{\mathbf{V}_2} = \frac{2}{3}$$

Also,

$$\mathbf{V}_2 = (3+6)\mathbf{I}_2 = 9\mathbf{I}_2$$

(a)

(b)

Figure 19.23   For Example 19.5:
(a) computing $\mathbf{h}_{11}$ and $\mathbf{h}_{21}$, (b) computing $\mathbf{h}_{12}$ and $\mathbf{h}_{22}$.

Thus,

$$h_{22} = \frac{I_2}{V_2} = \frac{1}{9} \ S$$

19.5

Determine the *h* parameters for the circuit in Fig. 19.24.

Answer: $h_{11} = 1.2 \ \Omega$, $h_{12} = 0.4$, $h_{21} = -0.4$, $h_{22} = 0.4 \ S$.

Figure 19.24   For Practice Prob. 19.5.

19.6

Determine the Thevenin equivalent at the output port of the circuit in Fig. 19.25.

Solution:

To find Z_{Th} and V_{Th}, we apply the normal procedure, keeping in mind the formulas relating the input and output ports of the *h* model. To obtain Z_{Th}, remove the 60-V voltage source at the input port and apply a 1-V voltage source at the output port, as shown in Fig. 19.26(a). From Eq. (19.14),

$$V_1 = h_{11}I_1 + h_{12}V_2 \qquad (19.6.1)$$

$$I_2 = h_{21}I_1 + h_{22}V_2 \qquad (19.6.2)$$

But $V_2 = 1$, and $V_1 = -40I_1$. Substituting these into Eqs. (19.6.1) and (19.6.2), we get

$$-40I_1 = h_{11}I_1 + h_{12} \quad \Longrightarrow \quad I_1 = -\frac{h_{12}}{40 + h_{11}} \quad (19.6.3)$$

$$I_2 = h_{21}I_1 + h_{22} \qquad (19.6.4)$$

Substituting Eq. (19.6.3) into Eq. (19.6.4) gives

$$I_2 = h_{22} - \frac{h_{21}h_{12}}{h_{11} + 40} = \frac{h_{11}h_{22} - h_{21}h_{12} + h_{22}40}{h_{11} + 40}$$

Therefore,

$$Z_{Th} = \frac{V_2}{I_2} = \frac{1}{I_2} = \frac{h_{11} + 40}{h_{11}h_{22} - h_{21}h_{12} + h_{22}40}$$

Substituting the values of the *h* parameters,

$$Z_{Th} = \frac{1000 + 40}{10^3 \times 200 \times 10^{-6} + 20 + 40 \times 200 \times 10^{-6}}$$

$$= \frac{1040}{20.21} = 51.46 \ \Omega$$

To get V_{Th}, we find the open-circuit voltage V_2 in Fig. 19.26(b). At the input port,

$$-60 + 40I_1 + V_1 = 0 \quad \Longrightarrow \quad V_1 = 60 - 40I_1 \quad (19.6.5)$$

At the output,

$$I_2 = 0 \qquad (19.6.6)$$

Figure 19.25   For Example 19.6.

(a)

(b)

Figure 19.26   For Example 19.6: (a) finding Z_{Th}, (b) finding V_{Th}.

Substituting Eqs. (19.6.5) and (19.6.6) into Eqs. (19.6.1) and (19.6.2), we obtain

$$60 - 40\mathbf{I}_1 = \mathbf{h}_{11}\mathbf{I}_1 + \mathbf{h}_{12}\mathbf{V}_2$$

or

$$60 = (\mathbf{h}_{11} + 40)\mathbf{I}_1 + \mathbf{h}_{12}\mathbf{V}_2 \qquad (19.6.7)$$

and

$$0 = \mathbf{h}_{21}\mathbf{I}_1 + \mathbf{h}_{22}\mathbf{V}_2 \qquad \Longrightarrow \qquad \mathbf{I}_1 = -\frac{\mathbf{h}_{22}}{\mathbf{h}_{21}}\mathbf{V}_2 \qquad (19.6.8)$$

Now substituting Eq. (19.6.8) into Eq. (19.6.7) gives

$$60 = \left[-(\mathbf{h}_{11} + 40)\frac{\mathbf{h}_{22}}{\mathbf{h}_{21}} + \mathbf{h}_{12}\right]\mathbf{V}_2$$

or

$$\mathbf{V}_{\text{Th}} = \mathbf{V}_2 = \frac{60}{-(\mathbf{h}_{11} + 40)\mathbf{h}_{22}/\mathbf{h}_{21} + \mathbf{h}_{12}} = \frac{60\mathbf{h}_{21}}{\mathbf{h}_{12}\mathbf{h}_{21} - \mathbf{h}_{11}\mathbf{h}_{22} - 40\mathbf{h}_{22}}$$

Substituting the values of the h parameters,

$$\mathbf{V}_{\text{Th}} = \frac{60 \times 10}{-20.21} = -29.69 \text{ V}$$

PRACTICE PROBLEM 19.6

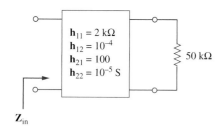

$\mathbf{h}_{11} = 2 \text{ k}\Omega$
$\mathbf{h}_{12} = 10^{-4}$
$\mathbf{h}_{21} = 100$
$\mathbf{h}_{22} = 10^{-5} \text{ S}$

50 kΩ

$\mathbf{Z}_{\text{in}}$

Find the impedance at the input port of the circuit in Fig. 19.27.

Answer: 1667 Ω.

Figure 19.27   For Practice Prob. 19.6.

EXAMPLE 19.7

1 H   1 F

1 Ω

Figure 19.28   For Example 19.7.

Find the g parameters as functions of s for the circuit in Fig. 19.28.

Solution:

In the s domain,

$$1 \text{ H} \qquad \Longrightarrow \qquad sL = s, \qquad 1 \text{ F} \qquad \Longrightarrow \qquad \frac{1}{sC} = \frac{1}{s}$$

To get $\mathbf{g}_{11}$ and $\mathbf{g}_{21}$, we open-circuit the output port and connect a voltage source $\mathbf{V}_1$ to the input port as in Fig. 19.29(a). From the figure,

$$\mathbf{I}_1 = \frac{\mathbf{V}_1}{s + 1}$$

or

$$\mathbf{g}_{11} = \frac{\mathbf{I}_1}{\mathbf{V}_1} = \frac{1}{s + 1}$$

By voltage division,

$$\mathbf{V}_2 = \frac{1}{s+1}\mathbf{V}_1$$

or

$$\mathbf{g}_{21} = \frac{\mathbf{V}_2}{\mathbf{V}_1} = \frac{1}{s+1}$$

To obtain $\mathbf{g}_{12}$ and $\mathbf{g}_{22}$, we short-circuit the input port and connect a current source $\mathbf{I}_2$ to the output port as in Fig. 19.29(b). By current division,

$$\mathbf{I}_1 = -\frac{1}{s+1}\mathbf{I}_2$$

or

$$\mathbf{g}_{12} = \frac{\mathbf{I}_1}{\mathbf{I}_2} = -\frac{1}{s+1}$$

Also,

$$\mathbf{V}_2 = \mathbf{I}_2\left(\frac{1}{s} + s \parallel 1\right)$$

Figure 19.29   Determining the g parameters in the s domain for the circuit in Fig. 19.28.

or

$$\mathbf{g}_{22} = \frac{\mathbf{V}_2}{\mathbf{I}_2} = \frac{1}{s} + \frac{s}{s+1} = \frac{s^2+s+1}{s(s+1)}$$

Thus,

$$[\mathbf{g}] = \begin{bmatrix} \dfrac{1}{s+1} & -\dfrac{1}{s+1} \\[2mm] \dfrac{1}{s+1} & \dfrac{s^2+s+1}{s(s+1)} \end{bmatrix}$$

PRACTICE PROBLEM 19.7

For the ladder network in Fig. 19.30, determine the g parameters in the s domain.

Answer: $[\mathbf{g}] = \begin{bmatrix} \dfrac{s+2}{s^2+3s+1} & -\dfrac{1}{s^2+3s+1} \\[2mm] \dfrac{1}{s^2+3s+1} & \dfrac{s(s+2)}{s^2+3s+1} \end{bmatrix}$.

Figure 19.30   For Practice Prob. 19.7.

19.5 TRANSMISSION PARAMETERS

Since there are no restrictions on which terminal voltages and currents should be considered independent and which should be dependent variables, we expect to be able to generate many sets of parameters. Another set of parameters relates the variables at the input port to those at the output port. Thus,

$$\boxed{\begin{aligned} \mathbf{V}_1 &= \mathbf{A}\mathbf{V}_2 - \mathbf{B}\mathbf{I}_2 \\ \mathbf{I}_1 &= \mathbf{C}\mathbf{V}_2 - \mathbf{D}\mathbf{I}_2 \end{aligned}}$$ (19.22)

or

$$\begin{bmatrix} \mathbf{V}_1 \\ \mathbf{I}_1 \end{bmatrix} = \begin{bmatrix} \mathbf{A} & \mathbf{B} \\ \mathbf{C} & \mathbf{D} \end{bmatrix} \begin{bmatrix} \mathbf{V}_2 \\ -\mathbf{I}_2 \end{bmatrix} = [\mathbf{T}] \begin{bmatrix} \mathbf{V}_2 \\ -\mathbf{I}_2 \end{bmatrix} \qquad (19.23)$$

Figure 19.31   Terminal variables used to define the **ABCD** parameters.

Equations (19.22) and (19.23) relate the input variables ($\mathbf{V}_1$ and $\mathbf{I}_1$) to the output variables ($\mathbf{V}_2$ and $-\mathbf{I}_2$). Notice that in computing the transmission parameters, $-\mathbf{I}_2$ is used rather than $\mathbf{I}_2$, because the current is considered to be leaving the network, as shown in Fig. 19.31, as opposed to entering the network as in Fig. 19.1(b). This is done merely for conventional reasons; when you cascade two-ports (output to input), it is most logical to think of $\mathbf{I}_2$ as leaving the two-port. It is also customary in the power industry to consider $\mathbf{I}_2$ as leaving the two-port.

The two-port parameters in Eqs. (19.22) and (19.23) provide a measure of how a circuit transmits voltage and current from a source to a load. They are useful in the analysis of transmission lines (such as cable and fiber) because they express sending-end variables ($\mathbf{V}_1$ and $\mathbf{I}_1$) in terms of the receiving-end variables ($\mathbf{V}_2$ and $-\mathbf{I}_2$). For this reason, they are called *transmission parameters*. They are also known as **ABCD** parameters. They are used in the design of telephone systems, microwave networks, and radars.

The transmission parameters are determined as

$$\mathbf{A} = \left.\frac{\mathbf{V}_1}{\mathbf{V}_2}\right|_{\mathbf{I}_2=0}, \qquad \mathbf{B} = \left.-\frac{\mathbf{V}_1}{\mathbf{I}_2}\right|_{\mathbf{V}_2=0}$$
$$\mathbf{C} = \left.\frac{\mathbf{I}_1}{\mathbf{V}_2}\right|_{\mathbf{I}_2=0}, \qquad \mathbf{D} = \left.-\frac{\mathbf{I}_1}{\mathbf{I}_2}\right|_{\mathbf{V}_2=0} \qquad (19.24)$$

Thus, the transmission parameters are called, specifically,

$$\mathbf{A} = \text{Open-circuit voltage ratio}$$
$$\mathbf{B} = \text{Negative short-circuit transfer impedance}$$
$$\mathbf{C} = \text{Open-circuit transfer admittance} \qquad (19.25)$$
$$\mathbf{D} = \text{Negative short-circuit current ratio}$$

A and **D** are dimensionless, **B** is in ohms, and **C** is in siemens. Since the transmission parameters provide a direct relationship between input and output variables, they are very useful in cascaded networks.

Our last set of parameters may be defined by expressing the variables at the output port in terms of the variables at the input port. We obtain

$$\mathbf{V}_2 = \mathbf{a}\mathbf{V}_1 - \mathbf{b}\mathbf{I}_1$$
$$\mathbf{I}_2 = \mathbf{c}\mathbf{V}_1 - \mathbf{d}\mathbf{I}_1 \qquad (19.26)$$

or

$$\begin{bmatrix} \mathbf{V}_2 \\ \mathbf{I}_2 \end{bmatrix} = \begin{bmatrix} \mathbf{a} & \mathbf{b} \\ \mathbf{c} & \mathbf{d} \end{bmatrix} \begin{bmatrix} \mathbf{V}_1 \\ -\mathbf{I}_1 \end{bmatrix} = [\mathbf{t}] \begin{bmatrix} \mathbf{V}_1 \\ -\mathbf{I}_1 \end{bmatrix} \qquad (19.27)$$

The parameters **a**, **b**, **c**, and **d** are called the *inverse transmission parameters*. They are determined as follows:

$$a = \frac{V_2}{V_1}\bigg|_{I_1=0}, \qquad b = -\frac{V_2}{I_1}\bigg|_{V_1=0}$$

$$c = \frac{I_2}{V_1}\bigg|_{I_1=0}, \qquad d = -\frac{I_2}{I_1}\bigg|_{V_1=0} \qquad (19.28)$$

From Eq. (19.28) and from our experience so far, it is evident that these parameters are known individually as

> **a** = Open-circuit voltage gain
> **b** = Negative short-circuit transfer impedance
> **c** = Open-circuit transfer admittance   (19.29)
> **d** = Negative short-circuit current gain

While **a** and **d** are dimensionless, **b** and **c** are in ohms and siemens, respectively.

In terms of the transmission or inverse transmission parameters, a network is reciprocal if

$$\mathbf{AD} - \mathbf{BC} = 1, \qquad \mathbf{ad} - \mathbf{bc} = 1 \qquad (19.30)$$

These relations can be proved in the same way as the transfer impedance relations for the z parameters. Alternatively, we will be able to use Table 19.1 a little later to derive Eq. (19.30) from the fact that $\mathbf{z}_{12} = \mathbf{z}_{21}$ for reciprocal networks.

EXAMPLE 19.8

Find the transmission parameters for the two-port network in Fig. 19.32.

Solution:

To determine **A** and **C**, we leave the output port open as in Fig. 19.33(a) so that $I_2 = 0$ and place a voltage source V_1 at the input port. We have

$$V_1 = (10 + 20)I_1 = 30I_1 \qquad \text{and} \qquad V_2 = 20I_1 - 3I_1 = 17I_1$$

Thus,

$$\mathbf{A} = \frac{V_1}{V_2} = \frac{30I_1}{17I_1} = 1.765, \qquad \mathbf{C} = \frac{I_1}{V_2} = \frac{I_1}{17I_1} = 0.0588 \text{ S}$$

Figure 19.32   For Example 19.8.

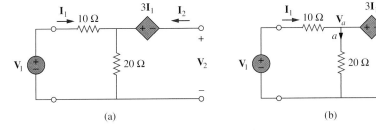

(a)   (b)

Figure 19.33   For Example 19.8: (a) finding **A** and **C**, (b) finding **B** and **D**.

To obtain **B** and **D**, we short-circuit the output port so that $\mathbf{V}_2 = 0$ as shown in Fig. 19.33(b) and place a voltage source $\mathbf{V}_1$ at the input port. At node a in the circuit of Fig. 19.33(b), KCL gives

$$\frac{\mathbf{V}_1 - \mathbf{V}_a}{10} - \frac{\mathbf{V}_a}{20} + \mathbf{I}_2 = 0 \qquad (19.8.1)$$

But $\mathbf{V}_a = 3\mathbf{I}_1$ and $\mathbf{I}_1 = (\mathbf{V}_1 - \mathbf{V}_a)/10$. Combining these gives

$$\mathbf{V}_a = 3\mathbf{I}_1 \qquad \mathbf{V}_1 = 13\mathbf{I}_1 \qquad (19.8.2)$$

Substituting $\mathbf{V}_a = 3\mathbf{I}_1$ into Eq. (19.8.1) and replacing the first term with $\mathbf{I}_1$,

$$\mathbf{I}_1 - \frac{3\mathbf{I}_1}{20} + \mathbf{I}_2 = 0 \qquad \Longrightarrow \qquad \frac{17}{20}\mathbf{I}_1 = -\mathbf{I}_2$$

Therefore,

$$\mathbf{D} = -\frac{\mathbf{I}_1}{\mathbf{I}_2} = \frac{20}{17} = 1.176, \qquad \mathbf{B} = -\frac{\mathbf{V}_1}{\mathbf{I}_2} = \frac{-13\mathbf{I}_1}{(-17/20)\,\mathbf{I}_1} = 15.29 \ \Omega$$

PRACTICE PROBLEM 19.8

Find the transmission parameters for the circuit in Fig. 19.16 (see Practice Prob. 19.3).

Answer: $\mathbf{A} = 1.5$, $\mathbf{B} = 11 \ \Omega$, $\mathbf{C} = 0.25$ S, $\mathbf{D} = 2.5$.

EXAMPLE 19.9

Figure 19.34   For Example 19.9.

The **ABCD** parameters of the two-port network in Fig. 19.34 are

$$\begin{bmatrix} 4 & 20 \ \Omega \\ 0.1 \ \text{S} & 2 \end{bmatrix}$$

The output port is connected to a variable load for maximum power transfer. Find R_L and the maximum power transferred.

Solution:

What we need is to find the Thevenin equivalent ($\mathbf{Z}_{Th}$ and $\mathbf{V}_{Th}$) at the load or output port. We find $\mathbf{Z}_{Th}$ using the circuit in Fig. 19.35(a). Our goal is to get $\mathbf{Z}_{Th} = \mathbf{V}_2/\mathbf{I}_2$. Substituting the given **ABCD** parameters into Eq. (19.22), we obtain

$$\mathbf{V}_1 = 4\mathbf{V}_2 - 20\mathbf{I}_2 \qquad (19.9.1)$$

$$\mathbf{I}_1 = 0.1\mathbf{V}_2 - 2\mathbf{I}_2 \qquad (19.9.2)$$

(a)

(b)

(c)

Figure 19.35   Solution of Example 19.9: (a) finding $\mathbf{Z}_{Th}$, (b) finding $\mathbf{V}_{Th}$, (c) finding R_L for maximum power transfer.

At the input port, $\mathbf{V}_1 = -10\mathbf{I}_1$. Substituting this into Eq. (19.9.1) gives

$$-10\mathbf{I}_1 = 4\mathbf{V}_2 - 20\mathbf{I}_2$$

or

$$\mathbf{I}_1 = -0.4\mathbf{V}_2 + 2\mathbf{I}_2 \qquad (19.9.3)$$

Setting the right-hand sides of Eqs. (19.9.2) and (19.9.3) equal,

$$0.1\mathbf{V}_2 - 2\mathbf{I}_2 = -0.4\mathbf{V}_2 + 2\mathbf{I}_2 \quad \Longrightarrow \quad 0.5\mathbf{V}_2 = 4\mathbf{I}_2$$

Hence,

$$\mathbf{Z}_{Th} = \frac{\mathbf{V}_2}{\mathbf{I}_2} = \frac{4}{0.5} = 8\ \Omega$$

To find $\mathbf{V}_{Th}$, we use the circuit in Fig. 19.35(b). At the output port $\mathbf{I}_2 = 0$ and at the input port $\mathbf{V}_1 = 50 - 10\mathbf{I}_1$. Substituting these into Eqs. (19.9.1) and (19.9.2),

$$50 - 10\mathbf{I}_1 = 4\mathbf{V}_2 \qquad (19.9.4)$$

$$\mathbf{I}_1 = 0.1\mathbf{V}_2 \qquad (19.9.5)$$

Substituting Eq. (19.9.5) into Eq. (19.9.4),

$$50 - \mathbf{V}_2 = 4\mathbf{V}_2 \quad \Longrightarrow \quad \mathbf{V}_2 = 10$$

Thus,

$$\mathbf{V}_{Th} = \mathbf{V}_2 = 10\ \text{V}$$

The equivalent circuit is shown in Fig. 19.35(c). For maximum power transfer,

$$R_L = \mathbf{Z}_{Th} = 8\ \Omega$$

From Eq. (4.24), the maximum power is

$$P = I^2 R_L = \left(\frac{\mathbf{V}_{Th}}{2R_L}\right)^2 R_L = \frac{\mathbf{V}_{Th}^2}{4R_L} = \frac{100}{4 \times 8} = 3.125\ \text{W}$$

PRACTICE PROBLEM 19.9

Find $\mathbf{I}_1$ and $\mathbf{I}_2$ if the transmission parameters for the two-port in Fig. 19.36 are

$$\begin{bmatrix} 5 & 10\ \Omega \\ 0.4\ \text{S} & 1 \end{bmatrix}$$

Figure 19.36   For Practice Prob. 19.9.

Answer: 1 A, -0.2 A.

†19.6 RELATIONSHIPS BETWEEN PARAMETERS

Since the six sets of parameters relate the same input and output terminal variables of the same two-port network, they should be interrelated. If two sets of parameters exist, we can relate one set to the other set. Let us demonstrate the process with two examples.

Given the z parameters, let us obtain the y parameters. From Eq. (19.2),

$$\begin{bmatrix} \mathbf{V}_1 \\ \mathbf{V}_2 \end{bmatrix} = \begin{bmatrix} \mathbf{z}_{11} & \mathbf{z}_{12} \\ \mathbf{z}_{21} & \mathbf{z}_{22} \end{bmatrix} \begin{bmatrix} \mathbf{I}_1 \\ \mathbf{I}_2 \end{bmatrix} = [\mathbf{z}] \begin{bmatrix} \mathbf{I}_1 \\ \mathbf{I}_2 \end{bmatrix} \tag{19.31}$$

or

$$\begin{bmatrix} \mathbf{I}_1 \\ \mathbf{I}_2 \end{bmatrix} = [\mathbf{z}]^{-1} \begin{bmatrix} \mathbf{V}_1 \\ \mathbf{V}_2 \end{bmatrix} \tag{19.32}$$

Also, from Eq. (19.9),

$$\begin{bmatrix} \mathbf{I}_1 \\ \mathbf{I}_2 \end{bmatrix} = \begin{bmatrix} \mathbf{y}_{11} & \mathbf{y}_{12} \\ \mathbf{y}_{21} & \mathbf{y}_{22} \end{bmatrix} \begin{bmatrix} \mathbf{V}_1 \\ \mathbf{V}_2 \end{bmatrix} = [\mathbf{y}] \begin{bmatrix} \mathbf{V}_1 \\ \mathbf{V}_2 \end{bmatrix} \tag{19.33}$$

Comparing Eqs. (19.32) and (19.33), we see that

$$[\mathbf{y}] = [\mathbf{z}]^{-1} \tag{19.34}$$

The adjoint of the $[\mathbf{z}]$ matrix is

$$\begin{bmatrix} \mathbf{z}_{22} & -\mathbf{z}_{12} \\ -\mathbf{z}_{21} & \mathbf{z}_{11} \end{bmatrix}$$

and its determinant is

$$\Delta_z = \mathbf{z}_{11}\mathbf{z}_{22} - \mathbf{z}_{12}\mathbf{z}_{21}$$

Substituting these into Eq. (19.34), we get

$$\begin{bmatrix} \mathbf{y}_{11} & \mathbf{y}_{12} \\ \mathbf{y}_{21} & \mathbf{y}_{22} \end{bmatrix} = \frac{\begin{bmatrix} \mathbf{z}_{22} & -\mathbf{z}_{12} \\ -\mathbf{z}_{21} & \mathbf{z}_{11} \end{bmatrix}}{\Delta_z} \tag{19.35}$$

Equating terms yields

$$\mathbf{y}_{11} = \frac{\mathbf{z}_{22}}{\Delta_z}, \qquad \mathbf{y}_{12} = -\frac{\mathbf{z}_{12}}{\Delta_z}, \qquad \mathbf{y}_{21} = -\frac{\mathbf{z}_{21}}{\Delta_z}, \qquad \mathbf{y}_{22} = \frac{\mathbf{z}_{11}}{\Delta_z} \tag{19.36}$$

As a second example, let us determine the h parameters from the z parameters. From Eq. (19.1),

$$\mathbf{V}_1 = \mathbf{z}_{11}\mathbf{I}_1 + \mathbf{z}_{12}\mathbf{I}_2 \tag{19.37a}$$

$$\mathbf{V}_2 = \mathbf{z}_{21}\mathbf{I}_1 + \mathbf{z}_{22}\mathbf{I}_2 \tag{19.37b}$$

Making $\mathbf{I}_2$ the subject of Eq. (19.37b),

$$\mathbf{I}_2 = -\frac{\mathbf{z}_{21}}{\mathbf{z}_{22}}\mathbf{I}_1 + \frac{1}{\mathbf{z}_{22}}\mathbf{V}_2 \tag{19.38}$$

Substituting this into Eq. (19.37a),

$$\mathbf{V}_1 = \frac{\mathbf{z}_{11}\mathbf{z}_{22} - \mathbf{z}_{12}\mathbf{z}_{21}}{\mathbf{z}_{22}}\mathbf{I}_1 + \frac{\mathbf{z}_{12}}{\mathbf{z}_{22}}\mathbf{V}_2 \tag{19.39}$$

Putting Eqs. (19.38) and (19.39) in matrix form,

$$\begin{bmatrix} \mathbf{V}_1 \\ \mathbf{I}_2 \end{bmatrix} = \begin{bmatrix} \dfrac{\Delta_z}{\mathbf{z}_{22}} & \dfrac{\mathbf{z}_{12}}{\mathbf{z}_{22}} \\ -\dfrac{\mathbf{z}_{21}}{\mathbf{z}_{22}} & \dfrac{1}{\mathbf{z}_{22}} \end{bmatrix} \begin{bmatrix} \mathbf{I}_1 \\ \mathbf{V}_2 \end{bmatrix} \tag{19.40}$$

From Eq. (19.15),

$$\begin{bmatrix} \mathbf{V}_1 \\ \mathbf{I}_2 \end{bmatrix} = \begin{bmatrix} \mathbf{h}_{11} & \mathbf{h}_{12} \\ \mathbf{h}_{21} & \mathbf{h}_{22} \end{bmatrix} \begin{bmatrix} \mathbf{I}_1 \\ \mathbf{V}_2 \end{bmatrix}$$

Comparing this with Eq. (19.40), we obtain

$$\mathbf{h}_{11} = \frac{\Delta_z}{\mathbf{z}_{22}}, \qquad \mathbf{h}_{12} = \frac{\mathbf{z}_{12}}{\mathbf{z}_{22}}, \qquad \mathbf{h}_{21} = -\frac{\mathbf{z}_{21}}{\mathbf{z}_{22}}, \qquad \mathbf{h}_{22} = \frac{1}{\mathbf{z}_{22}} \quad (19.41)$$

Table 19.1 provides the conversion formulas for the six sets of two-port parameters. Given one set of parameters, Table 19.1 can be used to find other parameters. For example, given the T parameters, we find the corresponding h parameters in the fifth column of the third row. Also, given that $\mathbf{z}_{21} = \mathbf{z}_{12}$ for a reciprocal network, we can use the table to express this condition in terms of other parameters. It can also be shown that

$$[\mathbf{g}] = [\mathbf{h}]^{-1} \quad (19.42)$$

but

$$[\mathbf{t}] \neq [\mathbf{T}]^{-1} \quad (19.43)$$

TABLE 19.1   Conversion of two-port parameters.

	z		y		h		g		T		t	
z	$\mathbf{z}_{11}$	$\mathbf{z}_{12}$	$\dfrac{\mathbf{y}_{22}}{\Delta_y}$	$-\dfrac{\mathbf{y}_{12}}{\Delta_y}$	$\dfrac{\Delta_h}{\mathbf{h}_{22}}$	$\dfrac{\mathbf{h}_{12}}{\mathbf{h}_{22}}$	$\dfrac{1}{\mathbf{g}_{11}}$	$-\dfrac{\mathbf{g}_{12}}{\mathbf{g}_{11}}$	$\dfrac{\mathbf{A}}{\mathbf{C}}$	$\dfrac{\Delta_T}{\mathbf{C}}$	$\dfrac{\mathbf{d}}{\mathbf{c}}$	$\dfrac{1}{\mathbf{c}}$
	$\mathbf{z}_{21}$	$\mathbf{z}_{22}$	$-\dfrac{\mathbf{y}_{21}}{\Delta_y}$	$\dfrac{\mathbf{y}_{11}}{\Delta_y}$	$\dfrac{\mathbf{h}_{21}}{\mathbf{h}_{22}}$	$\dfrac{1}{\mathbf{h}_{22}}$	$\dfrac{\mathbf{g}_{21}}{\mathbf{g}_{11}}$	$\dfrac{\Delta_g}{\mathbf{g}_{11}}$	$\dfrac{1}{\mathbf{C}}$	$\dfrac{\mathbf{D}}{\mathbf{C}}$	$\dfrac{\Delta_t}{\mathbf{c}}$	$\dfrac{\mathbf{a}}{\mathbf{c}}$
y	$\dfrac{\mathbf{z}_{22}}{\Delta_z}$	$-\dfrac{\mathbf{z}_{12}}{\Delta_z}$	$\mathbf{y}_{11}$	$\mathbf{y}_{12}$	$\dfrac{1}{\mathbf{h}_{11}}$	$-\dfrac{\mathbf{h}_{12}}{\mathbf{h}_{11}}$	$\dfrac{\Delta_g}{\mathbf{g}_{22}}$	$\dfrac{\mathbf{g}_{12}}{\mathbf{g}_{22}}$	$\dfrac{\mathbf{D}}{\mathbf{B}}$	$-\dfrac{\Delta_T}{\mathbf{B}}$	$\dfrac{\mathbf{a}}{\mathbf{b}}$	$-\dfrac{1}{\mathbf{b}}$
	$-\dfrac{\mathbf{z}_{21}}{\Delta_z}$	$\dfrac{\mathbf{z}_{11}}{\Delta_z}$	$\mathbf{y}_{21}$	$\mathbf{y}_{22}$	$\dfrac{\mathbf{h}_{21}}{\mathbf{h}_{11}}$	$\dfrac{\Delta_h}{\mathbf{h}_{11}}$	$\dfrac{\mathbf{g}_{21}}{\mathbf{g}_{22}}$	$\dfrac{1}{\mathbf{g}_{22}}$	$-\dfrac{1}{\mathbf{B}}$	$\dfrac{\mathbf{A}}{\mathbf{B}}$	$-\dfrac{\Delta_t}{\mathbf{b}}$	$\dfrac{\mathbf{d}}{\mathbf{b}}$
h	$\dfrac{\Delta_z}{\mathbf{z}_{22}}$	$\dfrac{\mathbf{z}_{12}}{\mathbf{z}_{22}}$	$\dfrac{1}{\mathbf{y}_{11}}$	$-\dfrac{\mathbf{y}_{12}}{\mathbf{y}_{11}}$	$\mathbf{h}_{11}$	$\mathbf{h}_{12}$	$\dfrac{\mathbf{g}_{22}}{\Delta_g}$	$-\dfrac{\mathbf{g}_{12}}{\Delta_g}$	$\dfrac{\mathbf{B}}{\mathbf{D}}$	$\dfrac{\Delta_T}{\mathbf{D}}$	$\dfrac{\mathbf{b}}{\mathbf{a}}$	$\dfrac{1}{\mathbf{a}}$
	$-\dfrac{\mathbf{z}_{21}}{\mathbf{z}_{22}}$	$\dfrac{1}{\mathbf{z}_{22}}$	$\dfrac{\mathbf{y}_{21}}{\mathbf{y}_{11}}$	$\dfrac{\Delta_y}{\mathbf{y}_{11}}$	$\mathbf{h}_{21}$	$\mathbf{h}_{22}$	$-\dfrac{\mathbf{g}_{21}}{\Delta_g}$	$\dfrac{\mathbf{g}_{11}}{\Delta_g}$	$-\dfrac{1}{\mathbf{D}}$	$\dfrac{\mathbf{C}}{\mathbf{D}}$	$\dfrac{\Delta_t}{\mathbf{a}}$	$\dfrac{\mathbf{c}}{\mathbf{a}}$
g	$\dfrac{1}{\mathbf{z}_{11}}$	$-\dfrac{\mathbf{z}_{12}}{\mathbf{z}_{11}}$	$\dfrac{\Delta_y}{\mathbf{y}_{22}}$	$\dfrac{\mathbf{y}_{12}}{\mathbf{y}_{22}}$	$\dfrac{\mathbf{h}_{22}}{\Delta_h}$	$\dfrac{\mathbf{h}_{12}}{\Delta_h}$	$\mathbf{g}_{11}$	$\mathbf{g}_{12}$	$\dfrac{\mathbf{C}}{\mathbf{A}}$	$-\dfrac{\Delta_T}{\mathbf{A}}$	$\dfrac{\mathbf{c}}{\mathbf{d}}$	$\dfrac{1}{\mathbf{d}}$
	$\dfrac{\mathbf{z}_{21}}{\mathbf{z}_{11}}$	$\dfrac{\Delta_z}{\mathbf{z}_{11}}$	$-\dfrac{\mathbf{y}_{21}}{\mathbf{y}_{22}}$	$\dfrac{1}{\mathbf{y}_{22}}$	$-\dfrac{\mathbf{h}_{21}}{\Delta_h}$	$\dfrac{\mathbf{h}_{11}}{\Delta_h}$	$\mathbf{g}_{21}$	$\mathbf{g}_{22}$	$\dfrac{1}{\mathbf{A}}$	$\dfrac{\mathbf{B}}{\mathbf{A}}$	$\dfrac{\Delta_t}{\mathbf{d}}$	$-\dfrac{\mathbf{b}}{\mathbf{d}}$
T	$\dfrac{\mathbf{z}_{11}}{\mathbf{z}_{21}}$	$\dfrac{\Delta_z}{\mathbf{z}_{21}}$	$-\dfrac{\mathbf{y}_{22}}{\mathbf{y}_{21}}$	$-\dfrac{1}{\mathbf{y}_{21}}$	$-\dfrac{\Delta_h}{\mathbf{h}_{21}}$	$-\dfrac{\mathbf{h}_{11}}{\mathbf{h}_{21}}$	$\dfrac{1}{\mathbf{g}_{21}}$	$\dfrac{\mathbf{g}_{22}}{\mathbf{g}_{21}}$	$\mathbf{A}$	$\mathbf{B}$	$\dfrac{\mathbf{d}}{\Delta_t}$	$\dfrac{\mathbf{b}}{\Delta_t}$
	$\dfrac{1}{\mathbf{z}_{21}}$	$\dfrac{\mathbf{z}_{22}}{\mathbf{z}_{21}}$	$-\dfrac{\Delta_y}{\mathbf{y}_{21}}$	$-\dfrac{\mathbf{y}_{11}}{\mathbf{y}_{21}}$	$-\dfrac{\mathbf{h}_{22}}{\mathbf{h}_{21}}$	$-\dfrac{1}{\mathbf{h}_{21}}$	$\dfrac{\mathbf{g}_{11}}{\mathbf{g}_{21}}$	$\dfrac{\Delta_g}{\mathbf{g}_{21}}$	$\mathbf{C}$	$\mathbf{D}$	$\dfrac{\mathbf{c}}{\Delta_t}$	$\dfrac{\mathbf{a}}{\Delta_t}$
t	$\dfrac{\mathbf{z}_{22}}{\mathbf{z}_{12}}$	$\dfrac{\Delta_z}{\mathbf{z}_{12}}$	$-\dfrac{\mathbf{y}_{11}}{\mathbf{y}_{12}}$	$-\dfrac{1}{\mathbf{y}_{12}}$	$\dfrac{1}{\mathbf{h}_{12}}$	$\dfrac{\mathbf{h}_{11}}{\mathbf{h}_{12}}$	$-\dfrac{\Delta_g}{\mathbf{g}_{12}}$	$-\dfrac{\mathbf{g}_{22}}{\mathbf{g}_{12}}$	$\dfrac{\mathbf{D}}{\Delta_T}$	$\dfrac{\mathbf{B}}{\Delta_T}$	$\mathbf{a}$	$\mathbf{b}$
	$\dfrac{1}{\mathbf{z}_{12}}$	$\dfrac{\mathbf{z}_{11}}{\mathbf{z}_{12}}$	$-\dfrac{\Delta_y}{\mathbf{y}_{12}}$	$-\dfrac{\mathbf{y}_{22}}{\mathbf{y}_{12}}$	$\dfrac{\mathbf{h}_{22}}{\mathbf{h}_{12}}$	$\dfrac{\Delta_h}{\mathbf{h}_{12}}$	$-\dfrac{\mathbf{g}_{11}}{\mathbf{g}_{12}}$	$-\dfrac{1}{\mathbf{g}_{12}}$	$\dfrac{\mathbf{C}}{\Delta_T}$	$\dfrac{\mathbf{A}}{\Delta_T}$	$\mathbf{c}$	$\mathbf{d}$

$\Delta_z = \mathbf{z}_{11}\mathbf{z}_{22} - \mathbf{z}_{12}\mathbf{z}_{21}, \qquad \Delta_h = \mathbf{h}_{11}\mathbf{h}_{22} - \mathbf{h}_{12}\mathbf{h}_{21}, \qquad \Delta_T = \mathbf{AD} - \mathbf{BC}$

$\Delta_y = \mathbf{y}_{11}\mathbf{y}_{22} - \mathbf{y}_{12}\mathbf{y}_{21}, \qquad \Delta_g = \mathbf{g}_{11}\mathbf{g}_{22} - \mathbf{g}_{12}\mathbf{g}_{21}, \qquad \Delta_t = \mathbf{ad} - \mathbf{bc}$

EXAMPLE 19.10

Find $[\mathbf{z}]$ and $[\mathbf{g}]$ of a two-port network if

$$[\mathbf{T}] = \begin{bmatrix} 10 & 1.5\ \Omega \\ 2\ \text{S} & 4 \end{bmatrix}$$

Solution:

If $\mathbf{A} = 10$, $\mathbf{B} = 1.5$, $\mathbf{C} = 2$, $\mathbf{D} = 4$, the determinant of the matrix is

$$\Delta_T = \mathbf{AD} - \mathbf{BC} = 40 - 3 = 37$$

From Table 19.1,

$$\mathbf{z}_{11} = \frac{\mathbf{A}}{\mathbf{C}} = \frac{10}{2} = 5, \qquad \mathbf{z}_{12} = \frac{\Delta_T}{\mathbf{C}} = \frac{37}{2} = 18.5$$

$$\mathbf{z}_{21} = \frac{1}{\mathbf{C}} = \frac{1}{2} = 0.5, \qquad \mathbf{z}_{22} = \frac{\mathbf{D}}{\mathbf{C}} = \frac{4}{2} = 2$$

$$\mathbf{g}_{11} = \frac{\mathbf{C}}{\mathbf{A}} = \frac{2}{10} = 0.2, \qquad \mathbf{g}_{12} = -\frac{\Delta_T}{\mathbf{A}} = -\frac{37}{10} = -3.7$$

$$\mathbf{g}_{21} = \frac{1}{\mathbf{A}} = \frac{1}{10} = 0.1, \qquad \mathbf{g}_{22} = \frac{\mathbf{B}}{\mathbf{A}} = \frac{1.5}{10} = 0.15$$

Thus,

$$[\mathbf{z}] = \begin{bmatrix} 5 & 18.5 \\ 0.5 & 2 \end{bmatrix} \Omega, \qquad [\mathbf{g}] = \begin{bmatrix} 0.2\ \text{S} & -3.7 \\ 0.1 & 0.15\ \Omega \end{bmatrix}$$

PRACTICE PROBLEM 19.10

Determine $[\mathbf{y}]$ and $[\mathbf{T}]$ of a two-port network whose z parameters are

$$[\mathbf{z}] = \begin{bmatrix} 6 & 4 \\ 4 & 6 \end{bmatrix} \Omega$$

Answer: $[\mathbf{y}] = \begin{bmatrix} 0.3 & -0.2 \\ -0.2 & 0.3 \end{bmatrix} \text{S}, \quad [\mathbf{T}] = \begin{bmatrix} 1.5 & 5\ \Omega \\ 0.25\ \text{S} & 1.5 \end{bmatrix}.$

EXAMPLE 19.11

Figure 19.37   For Example 19.11.

Obtain the y parameters of the op amp circuit in Fig. 19.37. Show that the circuit has no z parameters.

Solution:

Since no current can enter the input terminals of the op amp, $\mathbf{I}_1 = 0$, which can be expressed in terms of $\mathbf{V}_1$ and $\mathbf{V}_2$ as

$$\mathbf{I}_1 = 0\mathbf{V}_1 + 0\mathbf{V}_2 \qquad (19.11.1)$$

Comparing this with Eq. (19.8) gives

$$\mathbf{y}_{11} = 0 = \mathbf{y}_{12}$$

Also,

$$\mathbf{V}_2 = R_3\mathbf{I}_2 + \mathbf{I}_o(R_1 + R_2)$$

where $\mathbf{I}_o$ is the current through R_1 and R_2. But $\mathbf{I}_o = \mathbf{V}_1/R_1$. Hence,

$$\mathbf{V}_2 = R_3\mathbf{I}_2 + \frac{\mathbf{V}_1(R_1 + R_2)}{R_1}$$

which can be written as

$$\mathbf{I}_2 = -\frac{(R_1 + R_2)}{R_1 R_3}\mathbf{V}_1 + \frac{\mathbf{V}_2}{R_3}$$

Comparing this with Eq. (19.8) shows that

$$\mathbf{y}_{21} = -\frac{(R_1 + R_2)}{R_1 R_3}, \qquad \mathbf{y}_{22} = \frac{1}{R_3}$$

The determinant of the $[\mathbf{y}]$ matrix is

$$\Delta_y = \mathbf{y}_{11}\mathbf{y}_{22} - \mathbf{y}_{12}\mathbf{y}_{21} = 0$$

Since $\Delta_y = 0$, the $[\mathbf{y}]$ matrix has no inverse; therefore, the $[\mathbf{z}]$ matrix does not exist according to Eq. (19.34). Note that the circuit is not reciprocal because of the active element.

PRACTICE PROBLEM 19.11

Find the z parameters of the op amp circuit in Fig. 19.38. Show that the circuit has no y parameters.

Answer: $[\mathbf{z}] = \begin{bmatrix} R_1 & 0 \\ -R_2 & 0 \end{bmatrix}$. Since $[\mathbf{z}]^{-1}$ does not exist, $[\mathbf{y}]$ does not exist.

Figure 19.38   For Practice Prob. 19.11.

19.7 INTERCONNECTION OF NETWORKS

A large, complex network may be divided into subnetworks for the purposes of analysis and design. The subnetworks are modeled as two-port networks, interconnected to form the original network. The two-port networks may therefore be regarded as building blocks that can be interconnected to form a complex network. The interconnection can be in series, in parallel, or in cascade. Although the interconnected network can be described by any of the six parameter sets, a certain set of parameters may have a definite advantage. For example, when the networks are in series, their individual z parameters add up to give the z parameters of the larger network. When they are in parallel, their individual y parameters add up to give the y parameters of the larger network. When they are cascaded, their individual transmission parameters can be multiplied together to get the transmission parameters of the larger network.

Consider the series connection of two two-port networks shown in Fig. 19.39. The networks are regarded as being in series because their

Figure 19.39 Series connection of two two-port networks.

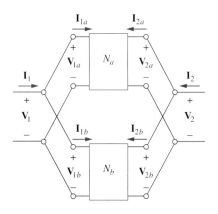

Figure 19.40 Parallel connection of two two-port networks.

input currents are the same and their voltages add. In addition, each network has a common reference, and when the circuits are placed in series, the common reference points of each circuit are connected together. For network N_a,

$$\begin{aligned}\mathbf{V}_{1a} &= \mathbf{z}_{11a}\mathbf{I}_{1a} + \mathbf{z}_{12a}\mathbf{I}_{2a}\\ \mathbf{V}_{2a} &= \mathbf{z}_{21a}\mathbf{I}_{1a} + \mathbf{z}_{22a}\mathbf{I}_{2a}\end{aligned} \tag{19.44}$$

and for network N_b,

$$\begin{aligned}\mathbf{V}_{1b} &= \mathbf{z}_{11b}\mathbf{I}_{1b} + \mathbf{z}_{12b}\mathbf{I}_{2b}\\ \mathbf{V}_{2b} &= \mathbf{z}_{21b}\mathbf{I}_{1b} + \mathbf{z}_{22b}\mathbf{I}_{2b}\end{aligned} \tag{19.45}$$

We notice from Fig. 19.39 that

$$\mathbf{I}_1 = \mathbf{I}_{1a} = \mathbf{I}_{1b}, \qquad \mathbf{I}_2 = \mathbf{I}_{2a} = \mathbf{I}_{2b} \tag{19.46}$$

and that

$$\begin{aligned}\mathbf{V}_1 &= \mathbf{V}_{1a} + \mathbf{V}_{1b} = (\mathbf{z}_{11a} + \mathbf{z}_{11b})\mathbf{I}_1 + (\mathbf{z}_{12a} + \mathbf{z}_{12b})\mathbf{I}_2\\ \mathbf{V}_2 &= \mathbf{V}_{2a} + \mathbf{V}_{2b} = (\mathbf{z}_{21a} + \mathbf{z}_{21b})\mathbf{I}_1 + (\mathbf{z}_{22a} + \mathbf{z}_{22b})\mathbf{I}_2\end{aligned} \tag{19.47}$$

Thus, the z parameters for the overall network are

$$\begin{bmatrix}\mathbf{z}_{11} & \mathbf{z}_{12}\\ \mathbf{z}_{21} & \mathbf{z}_{22}\end{bmatrix} = \begin{bmatrix}\mathbf{z}_{11a} + \mathbf{z}_{11b} & \mathbf{z}_{12a} + \mathbf{z}_{12b}\\ \mathbf{z}_{21a} + \mathbf{z}_{21b} & \mathbf{z}_{22a} + \mathbf{z}_{22b}\end{bmatrix} \tag{19.48}$$

or

$$\boxed{[\mathbf{z}] = [\mathbf{z}_a] + [\mathbf{z}_b]} \tag{19.49}$$

showing that the z parameters for the overall network are the sum of the z parameters for the individual networks. This can be extended to n networks in series. If two two-port networks in the [**h**] model, for example, are connected in series, we use Table 19.1 to convert the **h** to **z** and then apply Eq. (19.49). We finally convert the result back to **h** using Table 19.1.

Two two-port networks are in parallel when their port voltages are equal and the port currents of the larger network are the sums of the individual port currents. In addition, each circuit must have a common reference and when the networks are connected together, they must all have their common references tied together. The parallel connection of two two-port networks is shown in Fig. 19.40. For the two networks,

$$\begin{aligned}\mathbf{I}_{1a} &= \mathbf{y}_{11a}\mathbf{V}_{1a} + \mathbf{y}_{12a}\mathbf{V}_{2a}\\ \mathbf{I}_{2a} &= \mathbf{y}_{21a}\mathbf{V}_{1a} + \mathbf{y}_{22a}\mathbf{V}_{2a}\end{aligned} \tag{19.50}$$

and

$$\begin{aligned}\mathbf{I}_{1b} &= \mathbf{y}_{11b}\mathbf{V}_{1b} + \mathbf{y}_{12b}\mathbf{V}_{2b}\\ \mathbf{I}_{2a} &= \mathbf{y}_{21b}\mathbf{V}_{1b} + \mathbf{y}_{22b}\mathbf{V}_{2b}\end{aligned} \tag{19.51}$$

But from Fig. 19.40,

$$\mathbf{V}_1 = \mathbf{V}_{1a} = \mathbf{V}_{1b}, \qquad \mathbf{V}_2 = \mathbf{V}_{2a} = \mathbf{V}_{2b} \tag{19.52a}$$

$$\mathbf{I}_1 = \mathbf{I}_{1a} + \mathbf{I}_{1b}, \qquad \mathbf{I}_2 = \mathbf{I}_{2a} + \mathbf{I}_{2b} \tag{19.52b}$$

Substituting Eqs. (19.50) and (19.51) into Eq. (19.52b) yields

$$\begin{aligned}\mathbf{I}_1 &= (\mathbf{y}_{11a} + \mathbf{y}_{11b})\mathbf{V}_1 + (\mathbf{y}_{12a} + \mathbf{y}_{12b})\mathbf{V}_2\\ \mathbf{I}_2 &= (\mathbf{y}_{21a} + \mathbf{y}_{21b})\mathbf{V}_1 + (\mathbf{y}_{22a} + \mathbf{y}_{22b})\mathbf{V}_2\end{aligned} \tag{19.53}$$

Thus, the y parameters for the overall network are

$$\begin{bmatrix} \mathbf{y}_{11} & \mathbf{y}_{12} \\ \mathbf{y}_{21} & \mathbf{y}_{22} \end{bmatrix} = \begin{bmatrix} \mathbf{y}_{11a} + \mathbf{y}_{11b} & \mathbf{y}_{12a} + \mathbf{y}_{12b} \\ \mathbf{y}_{21a} + \mathbf{y}_{21b} & \mathbf{y}_{22a} + \mathbf{y}_{22b} \end{bmatrix} \qquad (19.54)$$

or

$$\boxed{[\mathbf{y}] = [\mathbf{y}_a] + [\mathbf{y}_b]} \qquad (19.55)$$

showing that the y parameters of the overall network are the sum of the y parameters of the individual networks. The result can be extended to n two-port networks in parallel.

Two networks are said to be *cascaded* when the output of one is the input of the other. The connection of two two-port networks in cascade is shown in Fig. 19.41. For the two networks,

$$\begin{bmatrix} \mathbf{V}_{1a} \\ \mathbf{I}_{1a} \end{bmatrix} = \begin{bmatrix} \mathbf{A}_a & \mathbf{B}_a \\ \mathbf{C}_a & \mathbf{D}_a \end{bmatrix} \begin{bmatrix} \mathbf{V}_{2a} \\ -\mathbf{I}_{2a} \end{bmatrix} \qquad (19.56)$$

$$\begin{bmatrix} \mathbf{V}_{1b} \\ \mathbf{I}_{1b} \end{bmatrix} = \begin{bmatrix} \mathbf{A}_b & \mathbf{B}_b \\ \mathbf{C}_b & \mathbf{D}_b \end{bmatrix} \begin{bmatrix} \mathbf{V}_{2b} \\ -\mathbf{I}_{2b} \end{bmatrix} \qquad (19.57)$$

From Fig. 19.41,

$$\begin{bmatrix} \mathbf{V}_1 \\ \mathbf{I}_1 \end{bmatrix} = \begin{bmatrix} \mathbf{V}_{1a} \\ \mathbf{I}_{1a} \end{bmatrix}, \qquad \begin{bmatrix} \mathbf{V}_{2a} \\ -\mathbf{I}_{2a} \end{bmatrix} = \begin{bmatrix} \mathbf{V}_{1b} \\ \mathbf{I}_{1b} \end{bmatrix}, \qquad \begin{bmatrix} \mathbf{V}_{2b} \\ -\mathbf{I}_{2b} \end{bmatrix} = \begin{bmatrix} \mathbf{V}_2 \\ -\mathbf{I}_2 \end{bmatrix} \qquad (19.58)$$

Substituting these into Eqs. (19.56) and (19.57),

$$\begin{bmatrix} \mathbf{V}_1 \\ \mathbf{I}_1 \end{bmatrix} = \begin{bmatrix} \mathbf{A}_a & \mathbf{B}_a \\ \mathbf{C}_a & \mathbf{D}_a \end{bmatrix} \begin{bmatrix} \mathbf{A}_b & \mathbf{B}_b \\ \mathbf{C}_b & \mathbf{D}_b \end{bmatrix} \begin{bmatrix} \mathbf{V}_2 \\ -\mathbf{I}_2 \end{bmatrix} \qquad (19.59)$$

Thus, the transmission parameters for the overall network are the product of the transmission parameters for the individual transmission parameters:

$$\begin{bmatrix} \mathbf{A} & \mathbf{B} \\ \mathbf{C} & \mathbf{D} \end{bmatrix} = \begin{bmatrix} \mathbf{A}_a & \mathbf{B}_a \\ \mathbf{C}_a & \mathbf{D}_a \end{bmatrix} \begin{bmatrix} \mathbf{A}_b & \mathbf{B}_b \\ \mathbf{C}_b & \mathbf{D}_b \end{bmatrix} \qquad (19.60)$$

or

$$\boxed{[\mathbf{T}] = [\mathbf{T}_a][\mathbf{T}_b]} \qquad (19.61)$$

It is this property that makes the transmission parameters so useful. Keep in mind that the multiplication of the matrices must be in the order in which the networks N_a and N_b are cascaded.

Figure 19.41   Cascade connection of two two-port networks.

EXAMPLE 19.12

Evaluate $\mathbf{V}_2/\mathbf{V}_s$ in the circuit in Fig. 19.42.

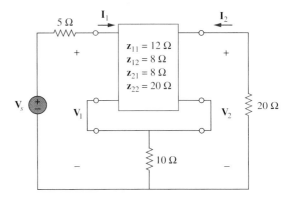

Figure 19.42   For Example 19.12.

Solution:

This may be regarded as two two-ports in series. For N_b,

$$\mathbf{z}_{12b} = \mathbf{z}_{21b} = 10 = \mathbf{z}_{11} = \mathbf{z}_{22}$$

Thus,

$$[\mathbf{z}] = [\mathbf{z}_a] + [\mathbf{z}_b] = \begin{bmatrix} 12 & 8 \\ 8 & 20 \end{bmatrix} + \begin{bmatrix} 10 & 10 \\ 10 & 10 \end{bmatrix} = \begin{bmatrix} 22 & 18 \\ 18 & 30 \end{bmatrix}$$

But

$$\mathbf{V}_1 = \mathbf{z}_{11}\mathbf{I}_1 + \mathbf{z}_{12}\mathbf{I}_2 = 22\mathbf{I}_1 + 18\mathbf{I}_2 \tag{19.12.1}$$

$$\mathbf{V}_2 = \mathbf{z}_{21}\mathbf{I}_1 + \mathbf{z}_{22}\mathbf{I}_2 = 18\mathbf{I}_1 + 30\mathbf{I}_2 \tag{19.12.2}$$

Also, at the input port

$$\mathbf{V}_1 = \mathbf{V}_s - 5\mathbf{I}_1 \tag{19.12.3}$$

and at the output port

$$\mathbf{V}_2 = -20\mathbf{I}_2 \qquad \Longrightarrow \qquad \mathbf{I}_2 = -\frac{\mathbf{V}_2}{20} \tag{19.12.4}$$

Substituting Eqs. (19.12.3) and (19.12.4) into Eq. (19.12.1) gives

$$\mathbf{V}_s - 5\mathbf{I}_1 = 22\mathbf{I}_1 - \frac{18}{20}\mathbf{V}_2 \qquad \Longrightarrow \qquad \mathbf{V}_s = 27\mathbf{I}_1 - 0.9\mathbf{V}_2 \tag{19.12.5}$$

while substituting Eq. (19.12.4) into Eq. (19.12.2) yields

$$\mathbf{V}_2 = 18\mathbf{I}_1 - \frac{30}{20}\mathbf{V}_2 \qquad \Longrightarrow \qquad \mathbf{I}_1 = \frac{2.5}{18}\mathbf{V}_2 \tag{19.12.6}$$

Substituting Eq. (19.12.6) into Eq. (19.12.5), we get

$$\mathbf{V}_s = 27 \times \frac{2.5}{18}\mathbf{V}_2 - 0.9\mathbf{V}_2 = 2.85\mathbf{V}_2$$

And so,

$$\frac{\mathbf{V}_2}{\mathbf{V}_s} = \frac{1}{2.85} = 0.3509$$

PRACTICE PROBLEM 19.12

Find $\mathbf{V}_2/\mathbf{V}_s$ in the circuit in Fig. 19.43.

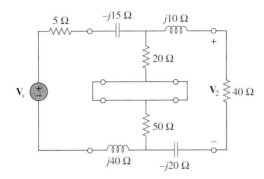

Figure 19.43   For Practice Prob. 19.12.

Answer: $0.58\underline{/-40°}$.

EXAMPLE 19.13

Find the y parameters of the two-port in Fig. 19.44.

Solution:

Let us refer to the upper network as N_a and the lower one as N_b. The two networks are connected in parallel. Comparing N_a and N_b with the circuit in Fig. 19.13(a), we obtain

$$\mathbf{y}_{12a} = -j4 = \mathbf{y}_{21a}, \qquad \mathbf{y}_{11a} = 2 + j4, \qquad \mathbf{y}_{22a} = 3 + j4$$

or

$$[\mathbf{y}_a] = \begin{bmatrix} 2 + j4 & -j4 \\ -j4 & 3 + j4 \end{bmatrix} \text{S}$$

Figure 19.44   For Example 19.13.

and

$$\mathbf{y}_{12b} = -4 = \mathbf{y}_{21b}, \qquad \mathbf{y}_{11b} = 4 - j2, \qquad \mathbf{y}_{22b} = 4 - j6$$

or

$$[\mathbf{y}_b] = \begin{bmatrix} 4 - j2 & -4 \\ -4 & 4 - j6 \end{bmatrix} \text{S}$$

The overall y parameters are

$$[\mathbf{y}] = [\mathbf{y}_a] + [\mathbf{y}_b] = \begin{bmatrix} 6 + j2 & -4 - j4 \\ -4 - j4 & 7 - j2 \end{bmatrix} \text{S}$$

PRACTICE PROBLEM 19.13

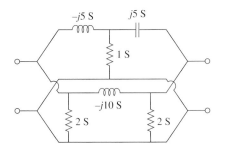

Figure 19.45   For Practice Prob. 19.13.

Obtain the y parameters for the network in Fig. 19.45.

Answer: $\begin{bmatrix} 27 - j15 & -25 + j10 \\ -25 + j10 & 27 - j5 \end{bmatrix}$ S.

EXAMPLE 19.14

Figure 19.46   For Example 19.14.

Find the transmission parameters for the circuit in Fig. 19.46.

Solution:

We can regard the given circuit in Fig. 19.46 as a cascade connection of two T networks as shown in Fig. 19.47(a). We can show that a T network, shown in Fig. 19.47(b), has the following transmission parameters [see Prob. 19.52(b)]:

$$\mathbf{A} = 1 + \frac{R_1}{R_2}, \qquad \mathbf{B} = R_3 + \frac{R_1(R_2 + R_3)}{R_2}$$

$$\mathbf{C} = \frac{1}{R_2}, \qquad \mathbf{D} = 1 + \frac{R_3}{R_2}$$

Applying this to the cascaded networks N_a and N_b in Fig. 19.47(a), we get

$$\mathbf{A}_a = 1 + 4 = 5, \qquad \mathbf{B}_a = 8 + 4 \times 9 = 44 \ \Omega$$
$$\mathbf{C}_a = 1 \ \text{S}, \qquad \mathbf{D}_a = 1 + 8 = 9$$

or in matrix form,

$$[\mathbf{T}_a] = \begin{bmatrix} 5 & 44 \ \Omega \\ 1 \ \text{S} & 9 \end{bmatrix}$$

and

$$\mathbf{A}_b = 1, \qquad \mathbf{B}_b = 6 \ \Omega, \qquad \mathbf{C}_b = 0.5 \ \text{S}, \qquad \mathbf{D}_b = 1 + \frac{6}{2} = 4$$

i.e.,

$$[\mathbf{T}_b] = \begin{bmatrix} 1 & 6 \ \Omega \\ 0.5 \ \text{S} & 4 \end{bmatrix}$$

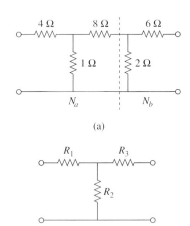

Figure 19.47   For Example 19.14: (a) Breaking the circuit in Fig. 19.46 into two two-ports, (b) a general T two-port.

Thus, for the total network in Fig. 19.46,

$$[\mathbf{T}] = [\mathbf{T}_a][\mathbf{T}_b] = \begin{bmatrix} 5 & 44 \\ 1 & 9 \end{bmatrix}\begin{bmatrix} 1 & 6 \\ 0.5 & 4 \end{bmatrix}$$

$$= \begin{bmatrix} 5 \times 1 + 44 \times 0.5 & 5 \times 6 + 44 \times 4 \\ 1 \times 1 + 9 \times 0.5 & 1 \times 6 + 9 \times 4 \end{bmatrix}$$

$$= \begin{bmatrix} 27 & 206\ \Omega \\ 5.5\ \text{S} & 42 \end{bmatrix}$$

Notice that

$$\Delta_{T_a} = \Delta_{T_b} = \Delta_T = 1$$

showing that the network is reciprocal.

PRACTICE PROBLEM 19.14

Obtain the **ABCD** parameter representation of the circuit in Fig. 19.48.

Answer: $[\mathbf{T}] = \begin{bmatrix} 29.25 & 2200\ \Omega \\ 0.425\ \text{S} & 32 \end{bmatrix}$.

Figure 19.48   For Practice Prob. 19.14.

19.8 COMPUTING TWO-PORT PARAMETERS USING *PSPICE*

Hand calculation of the two-port parameters may become difficult when the two-port is complicated. We resort to *PSpice* in such situations. If the circuit is purely resistive, *PSpice* dc analysis may be used; otherwise, *PSpice* ac analysis is required at a specific frequency. The key to using *PSpice* in computing a particular two-port parameter is to remember how that parameter is defined and to constrain the appropriate port variable with a 1-A or 1-V source while using an open or short circuit to impose the other necessary constraints. The following two examples illustrate the idea.

EXAMPLE 19.15

Find the *h* parameters of the network in Fig. 19.49.

Solution:

From Eq. (19.16),

$$\mathbf{h}_{11} = \left.\frac{\mathbf{V}_1}{\mathbf{I}_1}\right|_{\mathbf{V}_2=0}, \qquad \mathbf{h}_{21} = \left.\frac{\mathbf{I}_2}{\mathbf{I}_1}\right|_{\mathbf{V}_2=0}$$

showing that $\mathbf{h}_{11}$ and $\mathbf{h}_{21}$ can be found by setting $\mathbf{V}_2 = 0$. Also by setting $\mathbf{I}_1 = 1$ A, $\mathbf{h}_{11}$ becomes $\mathbf{V}_1/1$ while $\mathbf{h}_{21}$ becomes $\mathbf{I}_2/1$. With this in mind, we draw the schematic in Fig. 19.50(a). We insert a 1-A dc current source

Figure 19.49   For Example 19.15.

IDC to take care of $\mathbf{I}_1 = 1$ A, the pseudocomponent VIEWPOINT to display $\mathbf{V}_1$ and pseudocomponent IPROBE to display $\mathbf{I}_2$. After saving the schematic, we run *PSpice* by selecting **Analysis/Simulate** and note the values displayed on the pseudocomponents. We obtain

$$\mathbf{h}_{11} = \frac{\mathbf{V}_1}{1} = 10 \; \Omega, \qquad \mathbf{h}_{21} = \frac{\mathbf{I}_2}{1} = -0.5$$

(a)

(b)

Figure 19.50   For Example 19.15: (a) computing $\mathbf{h}_{11}$ and $\mathbf{h}_{21}$, (b) computing $\mathbf{h}_{12}$ and $\mathbf{h}_{22}$.

Similarly, from Eq. (19.16),

$$\mathbf{h}_{12} = \left.\frac{\mathbf{V}_1}{\mathbf{V}_2}\right|_{\mathbf{I}_1=0}, \qquad \mathbf{h}_{22} = \left.\frac{\mathbf{I}_2}{\mathbf{V}_2}\right|_{\mathbf{I}_1=0}$$

indicating that we obtain $\mathbf{h}_{12}$ and $\mathbf{h}_{22}$ by open-circuiting the input port ($\mathbf{I}_1 = 0$). By making $\mathbf{V}_2 = 1$ V, $\mathbf{h}_{12}$ becomes $\mathbf{V}_1/1$ while $\mathbf{h}_{22}$ becomes $\mathbf{I}_2/1$. Thus, we use the schematic in Fig. 19.50(b) with a 1-V dc voltage source VDC inserted at the output terminal to take care of $\mathbf{V}_2 = 1$ V. The pseudocomponents VIEWPOINT and IPROBE are inserted to display the values of $\mathbf{V}_1$ and $\mathbf{I}_2$, respectively. (Notice that in Fig. 19.50(b), the 5-Ω resistor is ignored because the input port is open-circuited and *PSpice* will not allow such. We may include the 5-Ω resistor if we replace the open circuit with a very large resistor, say, 10 MΩ.) After simulating the schematic, we obtain the values displayed on the pseudocomponents as shown in Fig. 19.50(b). Thus,

$$\mathbf{h}_{12} = \frac{\mathbf{V}_1}{1} = 0.8333, \qquad \mathbf{h}_{22} = \frac{\mathbf{I}_2}{1} = 0.1833 \; \text{S}$$

PRACTICE PROBLEM 19.15

Obtain the *h* parameters for the network in Fig. 19.51 using *PSpice*.

Answer: $h_{11} = 4.238 \; \Omega$, $h_{21} = -0.6190$, $h_{12} = -0.7143$, $h_{22} = -0.1429$ S.

Figure 19.51   For Practice Prob. 19.15.

EXAMPLE 19.16

Find the z parameters for the circuit in Fig. 19.52 at $\omega = 10^6$ rad/s.

Solution:

Notice that we used dc analysis in Example 19.15 because the circuit in Fig. 19.49 is purely resistive. Here, we use ac analysis at $f = \omega/2\pi = 0.15915$ MHz, because L and C are frequency dependent.

In Eq. (19.3), we defined the z parameters as

$$\mathbf{z}_{11} = \left.\frac{\mathbf{V}_1}{\mathbf{I}_1}\right|_{\mathbf{I}_2=0}, \qquad \mathbf{z}_{21} = \left.\frac{\mathbf{V}_2}{\mathbf{I}_1}\right|_{\mathbf{I}_2=0}$$

This suggests that if we let $\mathbf{I}_1 = 1$ A and open-circuit the output port so that $\mathbf{I}_2 = 0$, then we obtain

$$\mathbf{z}_{11} = \frac{\mathbf{V}_1}{1} \quad \text{and} \quad \mathbf{z}_{21} = \frac{\mathbf{V}_2}{1}$$

We realize this with the schematic in Fig. 19.53(a). We insert a 1-A ac current source IAC at the input terminal of the circuit and two VPRINT1 pseudocomponents to obtain $\mathbf{V}_1$ and $\mathbf{V}_2$. The attributes of each VPRINT1 are set as $AC = yes$, $MAG = yes$, and $PHASE = yes$ to print the magnitude and phase values of the voltages. We select **Analysis/Setup/AC Sweep** and enter 1 as *Total Pts*, 0.1519MEG as *Start Freq*, and 0.1519MEG as *Final Freq* in the **AC Sweep and Noise Analysis** dialog box. After saving

Figure 19.52   For Example 19.16.

(a)

(b)

Figure 19.53   For Example 19.16: (a) circuit for determining $\mathbf{z}_{11}$ and $\mathbf{z}_{21}$, (b) circuit for determining $\mathbf{z}_{12}$ and $\mathbf{z}_{22}$.

the schematic, we select **Analysis/Simulate** to simulate it. We obtain $\mathbf{V}_1$ and $\mathbf{V}_2$ from the output file. Thus,

$$\mathbf{z}_{11} = \frac{\mathbf{V}_1}{1} = 19.70\underline{/175.7^\circ}\ \Omega, \qquad \mathbf{z}_{21} = \frac{\mathbf{V}_2}{1} = 19.79\underline{/170.2^\circ}\ \Omega$$

In a similar manner, from Eq. (19.3),

$$\mathbf{z}_{12} = \frac{\mathbf{V}_1}{\mathbf{I}_2}\bigg|_{\mathbf{I}_1=0}, \qquad \mathbf{z}_{22} = \frac{\mathbf{V}_2}{\mathbf{I}_2}\bigg|_{\mathbf{I}_1=0}$$

suggesting that if we let $\mathbf{I}_2 = 1$ A and open-circuit the input port,

$$\mathbf{z}_{12} = \frac{\mathbf{V}_1}{1} \qquad \text{and} \qquad \mathbf{z}_{22} = \frac{\mathbf{V}_2}{1}$$

This leads to the schematic in Fig. 19.53(b). The only difference between this schematic and the one in Fig. 19.53(a) is that the 1-A ac current source IAC is now at the output terminal. We run the schematic in Fig. 19.53(b) and obtain $\mathbf{V}_1$ and $\mathbf{V}_2$ from the output file. Thus,

$$\mathbf{z}_{12} = \frac{\mathbf{V}_1}{1} = 19.70\underline{/175.7^\circ}\ \Omega, \qquad \mathbf{z}_{22} = \frac{\mathbf{V}_2}{1} = 19.56\underline{/175.7^\circ}\ \Omega$$

PRACTICE PROBLEM 19.16

Figure 19.54   For Practice Prob. 19.16.

Obtain the z parameters of the circuit in Fig. 19.54 at $f = 60$ Hz.

Answer: $z_{11} = 3.987\underline{/175.5^\circ}$, $z_{21} = 0.0175\underline{/-2.65^\circ}$, $z_{12} = 0$, $z_{22} = 0.2651\underline{/91.9^\circ}\ \Omega$.

†19.9 APPLICATIONS

We have seen how the six sets of network parameters can be used to characterize a wide range of two-port networks. Depending on the way two-ports are interconnected to form a larger network, a particular set of parameters may have advantages over others, as we noticed in Section 19.7. In this section, we will consider two important application areas of two-port parameters: transistor circuits and synthesis of ladder networks.

19.9.1 Transistor Circuits

The two-port network is often used to isolate a load from the excitation of a circuit. For example, the two-port in Fig. 19.55 may represent an amplifier, a filter, or some other network. When the two-port represents an amplifier, expressions for the voltage gain A_v, the current gain A_i, the input impedance Z_{in}, and the output impedance Z_{out} can be derived with

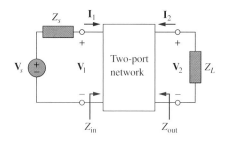

Figure 19.55   Two-port network isolating source and load.

ease. They are defined as follows:

$$A_v = \frac{V_2(s)}{V_1(s)} \tag{19.62}$$

$$A_i = \frac{I_2(s)}{I_1(s)} \tag{19.63}$$

$$Z_{\text{in}} = \frac{V_1(s)}{I_1(s)} \tag{19.64}$$

$$Z_{\text{out}} = \frac{V_2(s)}{I_2(s)}\bigg|_{V_s=0} \tag{19.65}$$

Any of the six sets of two-port parameters can be used to derive the expressions in Eqs. (19.62) to (19.65). However, the hybrid (h) parameters are the most useful for transistors; they are easily measured and are often provided in the manufacturer's data or spec sheets for transistors. The h parameters provide a quick estimate of the performance of transistor circuits. They are used for finding the exact voltage gain, input impedance, and output impedance of a transistor.

The h parameters for transistors have specific meanings expressed by their subscripts. They are listed by the first subscript and related to the general h parameters as follows:

$$h_i = h_{11}, \qquad h_r = h_{12}, \qquad h_f = h_{21}, \qquad h_o = h_{22} \tag{19.66}$$

The subscripts i, r, f, and o stand for input, reverse, forward, and output. The second subscript specifies the type of connection used: e for common emitter (CE), c for common collector (CC), and b for common base (CB). Here we are mainly concerned with the common-emitter connection. Thus, the four h parameters for the common-emitter amplifier are:

$$
\begin{aligned}
h_{ie} &= \text{Base input impedance} \\
h_{re} &= \text{Reverse voltage feedback ratio} \\
h_{fe} &= \text{Base-collector current gain} \\
h_{oe} &= \text{Output admittance}
\end{aligned}
\tag{19.67}
$$

These are calculated or measured in the same way as the general h parameters. Typical values are $h_{ie} = 6 \text{ k}\Omega$, $h_{re} = 1.5 \times 10^{-4}$, $h_{fe} = 200$, $h_{oe} = 8 \ \mu\text{S}$. We must keep in mind that these values represent ac characteristics of the transistor, measured under specific circumstances.

Figure 19.56 shows the circuit schematic for the common-emitter amplifier and the equivalent hybrid model. From the figure, we see that

$$\mathbf{V}_b = h_{ie}\mathbf{I}_b + h_{re}\mathbf{V}_c \tag{19.68a}$$

$$\mathbf{I}_c = h_{fe}\mathbf{I}_b + h_{oe}\mathbf{V}_c \tag{19.68b}$$

Consider the transistor amplifier connected to an ac source and a load as in Fig. 19.57. This is an example of a two-port network embedded within a larger network. We can analyze the hybrid equivalent circuit as usual with Eq. (19.68) in mind. (See Example 19.6.) Recognizing from Fig. 19.57 that $\mathbf{V}_c = -R_L\mathbf{I}_c$ and substituting this into Eq. (19.68b) gives

$$\mathbf{I}_c = h_{fe}\mathbf{I}_b - h_{oe}R_L\mathbf{I}_c$$

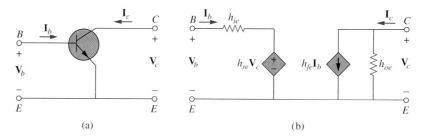

Figure 19.56   Common emitter amplifier: (a) circuit schematic, (b) hybrid model.

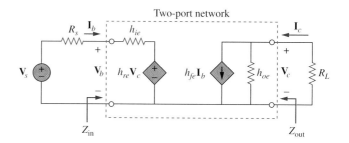

Figure 19.57   Transistor amplifier with source and load resistance.

or

$$(1 + h_{oe}R_L)\mathbf{I}_c = h_{fe}\mathbf{I}_b \tag{19.69}$$

From this, we obtain the current gain as

$$\boxed{A_i = \frac{\mathbf{I}_c}{\mathbf{I}_b} = \frac{h_{fe}}{1 + h_{oe}R_L}} \tag{19.70}$$

From Eqs. (19.68b) and (19.70), we can express $\mathbf{I}_b$ in terms of $\mathbf{V}_c$:

$$\mathbf{I}_c = \frac{h_{fe}}{1 + h_{oe}R_L}\mathbf{I}_b = h_{fe}\mathbf{I}_b + h_{oe}\mathbf{V}_c$$

or

$$\mathbf{I}_b = \frac{h_{oe}\mathbf{V}_c}{\dfrac{h_{fe}}{1 + h_{oe}R_L} - h_{fe}} \tag{19.71}$$

Substituting Eq. (19.71) into Eq. (19.68a) and dividing by $\mathbf{V}_c$ gives

$$\frac{\mathbf{V}_b}{\mathbf{V}_c} = \frac{h_{oe}h_{ie}}{\dfrac{h_{fe}}{1 + h_{oe}R_L} - h_{fe}} + h_{re}$$

$$= \frac{h_{ie} + h_{ie}h_{oe}R_L - h_{re}h_{fe}R_L}{-h_{fe}R_L} \tag{19.72}$$

Thus, the voltage gain is

$$\boxed{A_v = \frac{\mathbf{V}_c}{\mathbf{V}_b} = \frac{-h_{fe}R_L}{h_{ie} + (h_{ie}h_{oe} - h_{re}h_{fe})R_L}} \tag{19.73}$$

Substituting $\mathbf{V}_c = -R_L\mathbf{I}_c$ into Eq. (19.68a) gives

$$\mathbf{V}_b = h_{ie}\mathbf{I}_b - h_{re}R_L\mathbf{I}_c$$

or

$$\frac{\mathbf{V}_b}{\mathbf{I}_b} = h_{ie} - h_{re}R_L\frac{\mathbf{I}_c}{\mathbf{I}_b} \qquad (19.74)$$

Replacing $\mathbf{I}_c/\mathbf{I}_b$ by the current gain in Eq. (19.70) yields the input impedance as

$$\boxed{Z_{\text{in}} = \frac{\mathbf{V}_b}{\mathbf{I}_b} = h_{ie} - \frac{h_{re}h_{fe}R_L}{1 + h_{oe}R_L}} \qquad (19.75)$$

The output impedance Z_{out} is the same as the Thevenin equivalent at the output terminals. As usual, by removing the voltage source and placing a 1-V source at the output terminals, we obtain the circuit in Fig. 19.58, from which Z_{out} is determined as $1/\mathbf{I}_c$. Since $\mathbf{V}_c = 1$ V, the input loop gives

$$h_{re}(1) = -\mathbf{I}_b(R_s + h_{ie}) \qquad \Longrightarrow \qquad \mathbf{I}_b = -\frac{h_{re}}{R_s + h_{ie}} \qquad (19.76)$$

For the output loop,

$$\mathbf{I}_c = h_{oe}(1) + h_{fe}\mathbf{I}_b \qquad (19.77)$$

Substituting Eq. (19.76) into Eq. (19.77) gives

$$\mathbf{I}_c = \frac{(R_s + h_{ie})h_{oe} - h_{re}h_{fe}}{R_s + h_{ie}} \qquad (19.78)$$

From this, we obtain the output impedance Z_{out} as $1/\mathbf{I}_c$; that is,

$$\boxed{Z_{\text{out}} = \frac{R_s + h_{ie}}{(R_s + h_{ie})h_{oe} - h_{re}h_{fe}}} \qquad (19.79)$$

Figure 19.58   Finding the output impedance of the amplifier circuit in Fig. 19.57.

EXAMPLE 19.17

Consider the common-emitter amplifier circuit of Fig. 19.59. (a) Determine the voltage gain, current gain, input impedance, and output impedance using these h parameters:

$$h_{ie} = 1 \text{ k}\Omega, \qquad h_{re} = 2.5 \times 10^{-4}, \qquad h_{fe} = 50, \qquad h_{oe} = 20 \text{ }\mu\text{S}$$

(b) Find the output voltage $\mathbf{V}_o$.

Figure 19.59   For Example 19.17.

Solution:

(a) We note that $R_s = 0.8$ kΩ and $R_L = 1.2$ kΩ. We treat the transistor of Fig. 19.59 as a two-port network and apply Eqs. (19.70) to (19.79).

$$h_{ie}h_{oe} - h_{re}h_{fe} = 10^3 \times 20 \times 10^{-6} - 2.5 \times 10^{-4} \times 50$$
$$= 7.5 \times 10^{-3}$$

$$A_v = \frac{-h_{fe}R_L}{h_{ie} + (h_{ie}h_{oe} - h_{re}h_{fe})R_L} = \frac{-50 \times 1200}{1000 + 7.5 \times 10^{-3} \times 1200}$$
$$= -59.46$$

$$A_i = \frac{h_{fe}}{1 + h_{oe}R_L} = \frac{50}{1 + 20 \times 10^{-6} \times 1200} = 48.83$$

$$Z_{in} = h_{ie} - h_{re}A_i R_L = 1000 - 2.5 \times 10^{-4} \times 48.83 \times 1200 = 985.4\ \Omega$$

$$(R_s + h_{ie})h_{oe} - h_{re}h_{fe}$$
$$= (800 + 1000) \times 20 \times 10^{-6} - 2.5 \times 10^{-4} \times 50 = 23.5 \times 10^{-3}$$

$$Z_{out} = \frac{R_s + h_{ie}}{(R_s + h_{ie})h_{oe} - h_{re}h_{fe}} = \frac{800 + 1000}{23.5 \times 10^{-3}} = 76.6\ \text{k}\Omega$$

(b) The output voltage is

$$\mathbf{V}_o = A_v\mathbf{V}_s = -59.46(3.2\underline{/0°})\ \text{mV} = 0.19\underline{/180°}\ \text{V}$$

PRACTICE PROBLEM 19.17

Figure 19.60   For Practice Prob. 19.17.

For the transistor amplifier of Fig. 19.60, find the voltage gain, current gain, input impedance, and output impedance. Assume that

$$h_{ie} = 6\ \text{k}\Omega, \qquad h_{re} = 1.5 \times 10^{-4}, \qquad h_{fe} = 200, \qquad h_{oe} = 8\ \mu\text{S}$$

Answer: $-123.61, 194.17, 6$ kΩ, 128.08 kΩ.

19.9.2   Ladder Network Synthesis

Another application of two-port parameters is the synthesis (or building) of ladder networks which are found frequently in practice and have particular use in designing passive lowpass filters. Based on our discussion of second-order circuits in Chapter 8, the order of the filter is the order of the characteristic equation describing the filter and is determined by the number of reactive elements that cannot be combined into single elements (e.g., through series or parallel combination). Figure 19.61(a) shows an LC ladder network with an odd number of elements (to realize an odd-order filter), while Fig. 19.61(b) shows one with an even number of elements (for realizing an even-order filter). When either network is terminated by the load impedance Z_L and the source impedance Z_s, we obtain the structure in Fig. 19.62. To make the design less complicated, we will assume that $Z_s = 0$. Our goal is to synthesize the transfer function of the LC ladder network. We begin by characterizing the ladder network by its admittance parameters, namely,

$$\mathbf{I}_1 = \mathbf{y}_{11}\mathbf{V}_1 + \mathbf{y}_{12}\mathbf{V}_2 \tag{19.80a}$$

$$\mathbf{I}_2 = \mathbf{y}_{21}\mathbf{V}_1 + \mathbf{y}_{22}\mathbf{V}_2 \tag{19.80b}$$

(Of course, the impedance parameters could be used instead of the admittance parameters.) At the input port, $\mathbf{V}_1 = \mathbf{V}_s$ since $\mathbf{Z}_s = 0$. At the output port, $\mathbf{V}_2 = \mathbf{V}_o$ and $\mathbf{I}_2 = -\mathbf{V}_2/\mathbf{Z}_L = -\mathbf{V}_o\mathbf{Y}_L$. Thus Eq. (19.80b) becomes

$$-\mathbf{V}_o\mathbf{Y}_L = \mathbf{y}_{21}\mathbf{V}_s + \mathbf{y}_{22}\mathbf{V}_o$$

or

$$\mathbf{H}(s) = \frac{\mathbf{V}_o}{\mathbf{V}_s} = \frac{-\mathbf{y}_{21}}{\mathbf{Y}_L + \mathbf{y}_{22}} \tag{19.81}$$

We can write this as

$$\boxed{\mathbf{H}(s) = -\frac{\mathbf{y}_{21}/\mathbf{Y}_L}{1 + \mathbf{y}_{22}/\mathbf{Y}_L}} \tag{19.82}$$

We may ignore the negative sign in Eq. (19.82) because filter requirements are often stated in terms of the magnitude of the transfer function. The main objective in filter design is to select capacitors and inductors so that the parameters $\mathbf{y}_{21}$ and $\mathbf{y}_{22}$ are synthesized, thereby realizing the desired transfer function. To achieve this, we take advantage of an important property of the LC ladder network: all z and y parameters are ratios of polynomials that contain only even powers of s or odd powers of s—that is, they are ratios of either Od(s)/Ev(s) or Ev(s)/Od(s), where Od and Ev are odd and even functions, respectively. Let

$$\mathbf{H}(s) = \frac{\mathbf{N}(s)}{\mathbf{D}(s)} = \frac{\mathbf{N}_o + \mathbf{N}_e}{\mathbf{D}_o + \mathbf{D}_e} \tag{19.83}$$

where $\mathbf{N}(s)$ and $\mathbf{D}(s)$ are the numerator and denominator of the transfer function $\mathbf{H}(s)$; $\mathbf{N}_o$ and $\mathbf{N}_e$ are the odd and even parts of $\mathbf{N}$; $\mathbf{D}_o$ and $\mathbf{D}_e$ are

Figure 19.61 LC ladder networks for lowpass filters of: (a) odd order, (b) even order.

Figure 19.62 LC ladder network with terminating impedances.

the odd and even parts of **D**. Since **N**(s) must be either odd or even, we can write Eq. (19.83) as

$$\mathbf{H}(s) = \begin{cases} \dfrac{\mathbf{N}_o}{\mathbf{D}_o + \mathbf{D}_e}, & (\mathbf{N}_e = 0) \\[3mm] \dfrac{\mathbf{N}_e}{\mathbf{D}_o + \mathbf{D}_e}, & (\mathbf{N}_o = 0) \end{cases} \qquad (19.84)$$

and can rewrite this as

$$\mathbf{H}(s) = \begin{cases} \dfrac{\mathbf{N}_o/\mathbf{D}_e}{1 + \mathbf{D}_o/\mathbf{D}_e}, & (\mathbf{N}_e = 0) \\[3mm] \dfrac{\mathbf{N}_e/\mathbf{D}_o}{1 + \mathbf{D}_e/\mathbf{D}_o}, & (\mathbf{N}_o = 0) \end{cases} \qquad (19.85)$$

Comparing this with Eq. (19.82), we obtain the y parameters of the network as

$$\frac{\mathbf{y}_{21}}{\mathbf{Y}_L} = \begin{cases} \dfrac{\mathbf{N}_o}{\mathbf{D}_e}, & (\mathbf{N}_e = 0) \\[3mm] \dfrac{\mathbf{N}_e}{\mathbf{D}_o}, & (\mathbf{N}_o = 0) \end{cases} \qquad (19.86)$$

and

$$\frac{\mathbf{y}_{22}}{\mathbf{Y}_L} = \begin{cases} \dfrac{\mathbf{D}_o}{\mathbf{D}_e}, & (\mathbf{N}_e = 0) \\[3mm] \dfrac{\mathbf{D}_e}{\mathbf{D}_o}, & (\mathbf{N}_o = 0) \end{cases} \qquad (19.87)$$

The following example illustrates the procedure.

EXAMPLE 19.18

Design the LC ladder network terminated with a 1-Ω resistor that has the normalized transfer function

$$\mathbf{H}(s) = \frac{1}{s^3 + 2s^2 + 2s + 1}$$

(This transfer function is for a Butterworth lowpass filter.)

Solution:

The denominator shows that this is a third-order network, so that the LC ladder network is shown in Fig. 19.63(a), with two inductors and one capacitor. Our goal is to determine the values of the inductors and capacitor. To achieve this, we group the terms in the denominator into odd or even parts:

$$\mathbf{D}(s) = (s^3 + 2s) + (2s^2 + 1)$$

so that

$$\mathbf{H}(s) = \frac{1}{(s^3 + 2s) + (2s^2 + 1)}$$

Divide the numerator and denominator by the odd part of the denominator to get

$$\mathbf{H}(s) = \frac{\dfrac{1}{s^3 + 2s}}{1 + \dfrac{2s^2 + 1}{s^3 + 2s}} \qquad (19.18.1)$$

From Eq. (19.82), when $\mathbf{Y}_L = 1$,

$$\mathbf{H}(s) = \frac{-y_{21}}{1 + y_{22}} \qquad (19.18.2)$$

(a)

Comparing Eqs. (19.19.1) and (19.19.2), we obtain

$$y_{21} = -\frac{1}{s^3 + 2s}, \qquad y_{22} = \frac{2s^2 + 1}{s^3 + 2s}$$

Any realization of y_{22} will automatically realize y_{21}, since y_{22} is the output driving-point admittance, that is, the output admittance of the network with the input port short-circuited. We determine the values of L and C in Fig. 19.63(a) that will give us y_{22}. Recall that y_{22} is the short-circuit output admittance. So we short-circuit the input port as shown in Fig. 19.63(b). First we get L_3 by letting

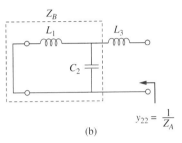

$$Z_A = \frac{1}{y_{22}} = \frac{s^3 + 2s}{2s^2 + 1} = sL_3 + Z_B \qquad (19.18.3)$$

By long division,

(b)

$$Z_A = 0.5s + \frac{1.5s}{2s^2 + 1} \qquad (19.18.4)$$

Comparing Eqs. (19.18.3) and (19.18.4) shows that

$$L_3 = 0.5\text{H}, \qquad Z_B = \frac{1.5s}{2s^2 + 1}$$

Next, we seek to get C_2 as in Fig. 19.63(c) and let

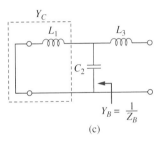

$$Y_B = \frac{1}{Z_B} = \frac{2s^2 + 1}{1.5s} = 1.333s + \frac{1}{1.5s} = sC_2 + Y_C$$

from which $C_2 = 1.33$ F and

(c)

$$Y_C = \frac{1}{1.5s} = \frac{1}{sL_1} \qquad \Longrightarrow \qquad L_1 = 1.5\text{H}$$

Figure 19.63   For Example 19.18.

Thus, the LC ladder network in Fig. 19.63(a) with $L_1 = 1.5$ H, $C_2 = 1.333$ F, and $L_3 = 0.5$ H has been synthesized to provide the given transfer function $\mathbf{H}(s)$. This result can be confirmed by finding $\mathbf{H}(s) = \mathbf{V}_2/\mathbf{V}_1$ in Fig. 19.63(a) or by confirming the required y_{21}.

PRACTICE PROBLEM 19.18

Realize the following transfer function using an LC ladder network terminated in a 1-Ω resistor:

$$H(s) = \frac{2}{s^3 + s^2 + 4s + 2}$$

Answer: Ladder network in Fig. 19.63(a) with $L_1 = L_3 = 1.0$ H and $C_2 = 0.5$ F.

19.10 SUMMARY

1. A two-port network is one with two ports (or two pairs of access terminals), known as input and output ports.

2. The six parameters used to model a two-port network are the impedance [z], admittance [y], hybrid [h], inverse hybrid [g], transmission [T], and inverse transmission [t] parameters.

3. The parameters relate the input and output port variables as

$$\begin{bmatrix} \mathbf{V}_1 \\ \mathbf{V}_2 \end{bmatrix} = [\mathbf{z}] \begin{bmatrix} \mathbf{I}_1 \\ \mathbf{I}_2 \end{bmatrix}, \qquad \begin{bmatrix} \mathbf{I}_1 \\ \mathbf{I}_2 \end{bmatrix} = [\mathbf{y}] \begin{bmatrix} \mathbf{V}_1 \\ \mathbf{V}_2 \end{bmatrix}, \qquad \begin{bmatrix} \mathbf{V}_1 \\ \mathbf{I}_2 \end{bmatrix} = [\mathbf{h}] \begin{bmatrix} \mathbf{I}_1 \\ \mathbf{V}_2 \end{bmatrix}$$

$$\begin{bmatrix} \mathbf{I}_1 \\ \mathbf{V}_2 \end{bmatrix} = [\mathbf{g}] \begin{bmatrix} \mathbf{V}_1 \\ \mathbf{I}_2 \end{bmatrix}, \qquad \begin{bmatrix} \mathbf{V}_1 \\ \mathbf{I}_1 \end{bmatrix} = [\mathbf{T}] \begin{bmatrix} \mathbf{V}_2 \\ -\mathbf{I}_2 \end{bmatrix}, \qquad \begin{bmatrix} \mathbf{V}_2 \\ \mathbf{I}_2 \end{bmatrix} = [\mathbf{t}] \begin{bmatrix} \mathbf{V}_1 \\ -\mathbf{I}_1 \end{bmatrix}$$

4. The parameters can be calculated or measured by short-circuiting or open-circuiting the appropriate input or output port.

5. A two-port network is reciprocal if $\mathbf{z}_{12} = \mathbf{z}_{21}$, $\mathbf{y}_{12} = \mathbf{y}_{21}$, $\mathbf{h}_{12} = -\mathbf{h}_{21}$, $\mathbf{g}_{12} = -\mathbf{g}_{21}$, $\Delta_T = 1$ or $\Delta_t = 1$. Networks that have dependent sources are not reciprocal.

6. Table 19.1 provides the relationships between the six sets of parameters. Three important relationships are

$$[\mathbf{y}] = [\mathbf{z}]^{-1}, \qquad [\mathbf{g}] = [\mathbf{h}]^{-1}, \qquad [\mathbf{t}] \neq [\mathbf{T}]^{-1}$$

7. Two-port networks may be connected in series, in parallel, or in cascade. In the series connection the z parameters are added, in the parallel connection the y parameters are added, and in the cascade connection the transmission parameters are multiplied in the correct order.

8. One can use *PSpice* to compute the two-port parameters by constraining the appropriate port variables with a 1-A or 1-V source while using an open or short circuit to impose the other necessary constraints.

9. The network parameters are specifically applied in the analysis of transistor circuits and the synthesis of ladder LC networks. Network parameters are especially useful in the analysis of transistor circuits because these circuits are easily modeled as two-port networks. LC ladder networks, important in the design of passive lowpass filters, resemble cascaded T networks and are therefore best analyzed as two-ports.

REVIEW QUESTIONS

19.1 For the single-element two-port network in Fig. 19.64(a), $\mathbf{z}_{11}$ is:

(a) 0   (b) 5   (c) 10
(d) 20   (e) nonexistent

19.2 For the single-element two-port network in Fig. 19.64(b), $\mathbf{z}_{11}$ is:

(a) 0   (b) 5   (c) 10
(d) 20   (e) nonexistent

(a)   (b)

Figure 19.64   For Review Questions.

19.3   For the single-element two-port network in
Fig. 19.64(a), y_{11} is:

(a) 0   (b) 5   (c) 10
(d) 20   (e) nonexistent

19.4   For the single-element two-port network in
Fig. 19.64(b), h_{21} is:

(a) −0.1   (b) −1   (c) 0
(d) 10   (e) nonexistent

19.5   For the single-element two-port network in
Fig. 19.64(a), **B** is:

(a) 0   (b) 5   (c) 10
(d) 20   (e) nonexistent

19.6   For the single-element two-port network in
Fig. 19.64(b), **B** is:

(a) 0   (b) 5   (c) 10
(d) 20   (e) nonexistent

19.7   When port 1 of a two-port circuit is short-circuited,
$I_1 = 4I_2$ and $V_2 = 0.25I_2$. Which of the following is
true?

(a) $y_{11} = 4$ (b) $y_{12} = 16$
(c) $y_{21} = 16$ (d) $y_{22} = 0.25$

19.8   A two-port is described by the following equations:

$$\mathbf{V}_1 = 50\mathbf{I}_1 + 10\mathbf{I}_2$$
$$\mathbf{V}_2 = 30\mathbf{I}_1 + 20\mathbf{I}_2$$

Which of the following is *not* true?

(a) $\mathbf{z}_{12} = 10$ (b) $\mathbf{y}_{12} = -0.0143$
(c) $\mathbf{h}_{12} = 0.5$ (d) $\mathbf{A} = 50$

19.9   If a two-port is reciprocal, which of the following is
not true?

(a) $\mathbf{z}_{21} = \mathbf{z}_{12}$ (b) $\mathbf{y}_{21} = \mathbf{y}_{12}$
(c) $\mathbf{h}_{21} = \mathbf{h}_{12}$ (d) $AD = BC + 1$

19.10 If the two single-element two-port networks in
Fig. 19.64 are cascaded, then **D** is:

(a) 0   (b) 0.1   (c) 2
(d) 10   (e) nonexistent

----

*Answers: 19.1c, 19.2e, 19.3e, 19.4b, 19.5a, 19.6c, 19.7b,
19.8d, 19.9c, 19.10c.*

PROBLEMS

Section 19.2   Impedance Parameters

19.1   Obtain the z parameters for the network in Fig. 19.65.

Figure 19.65   For Probs. 19.1 and 19.28

*19.2   Find the impedance parameter equivalent of the
network in Fig. 19.66.

Figure 19.66   For Prob. 19.2.

19.3   Determine the z parameters of the two-ports shown
in Fig. 19.67.

(a)

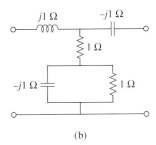

(b)

Figure 19.67   For Prob. 19.3.

---

*An asterisk indicates a challenging problem.

19.4   Calculate the z parameters for the circuit in Fig. 19.68.

Figure 19.68   For Prob. 19.4.

19.5   Obtain the z parameters for the network in Fig. 19.69 as functions of s.

Figure 19.69   For Prob. 19.5.

19.6   Obtain the z parameters for the circuit in Fig. 19.70.

Figure 19.70   For Prob. 19.6.

19.7   Calculate the impedance-parameter equivalent of the circuit in Fig. 19.71.

Figure 19.71   For Prob. 19.7.

19.8   Find the z parameters of the two-port in Fig. 19.72.

Figure 19.72   For Prob. 19.8.

19.9   Construct a circuit that realizes the following z parameters

$$[\mathbf{z}] = \begin{bmatrix} 10 & 4 \\ 4 & 6 \end{bmatrix}$$

19.10   Construct a two-port that realizes each of the following z parameters.

(a) $[\mathbf{z}] = \begin{bmatrix} 25 & 20 \\ 5 & 10 \end{bmatrix} \Omega$

(b) $[\mathbf{z}] = \begin{bmatrix} 1 + \dfrac{3}{s} & \dfrac{1}{s} \\ \dfrac{1}{s} & 2s + \dfrac{1}{s} \end{bmatrix} \Omega$

19.11   Determine a two-port network that is represented by the following z parameters.

$$[\mathbf{z}] = \begin{bmatrix} 6 + j3 & 5 - j2 \\ 5 - j2 & 8 - j \end{bmatrix} \Omega$$

19.12   For a two-port network,

$$[\mathbf{z}] = \begin{bmatrix} 12 & 4 \\ 4 & 6 \end{bmatrix} \Omega$$

find V_2/V_1 if the network is terminated with a 2-Ω resistor.

19.13   If $[\mathbf{z}] = \begin{bmatrix} 50 & 10 \\ 30 & 20 \end{bmatrix} \Omega$ in the two-port of Fig. 19.73, calculate the average power delivered to the 100-Ω resistor.

Figure 19.73   For Prob. 19.13.

19.14 For the two-port network shown in Fig. 19.74, show that at the output terminals,

$$\mathbf{Z}_{Th} = \mathbf{z}_{22} - \frac{\mathbf{z}_{12}\mathbf{z}_{21}}{\mathbf{z}_{11} + \mathbf{Z}_s}$$

and

$$\mathbf{V}_{Th} = \frac{\mathbf{z}_{21}}{\mathbf{z}_{11} + \mathbf{Z}_s}\mathbf{V}_s$$

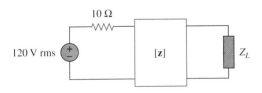

Figure 19.74   For Probs. 19.14 and 19.41.

19.15 For the two-port circuit in Fig. 19.75,

$$[\mathbf{z}] = \begin{bmatrix} 40 & 60 \\ 80 & 120 \end{bmatrix} \Omega$$

(a) Find $\mathbf{Z}_L$ for maximum power transfer to the load.
(b) Calculate the maximum power delivered to the load.

Figure 19.75   For Prob. 19.15.

19.16 For the circuit in Fig. 19.76, at $\omega = 2$ rad/s, $\mathbf{z}_{11} = 10\ \Omega$, $\mathbf{z}_{12} = \mathbf{z}_{21} = j6\ \Omega$, $\mathbf{z}_{22} = 4\ \Omega$. Obtain the Thevenin equivalent circuit at terminals a-b and calculate v_o.

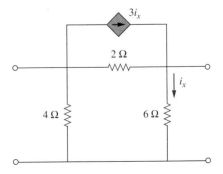

Figure 19.76   For Prob. 19.16.

Section 19.3   Admittance Parameters

*19.17 Determine the z and y parameters for the circuit in Fig. 19.77.

Figure 19.77   For Prob. 19.17.

19.18 Calculate the y parameters for the two-port in Fig. 19.78.

Figure 19.78   For Probs. 19.18 and 19.37.

19.19 Find the y parameters of the two-port in Fig. 19.79 in terms of s.

Figure 19.79   For Prob. 19.19.

19.20 Find the y parameters for the circuit in Fig. 19.80.

Figure 19.80   For Prob. 19.20.

19.21 Obtain the admittance parameter equivalent circuit of the two-port in Fig. 19.81.

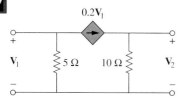

Figure 19.81   For Prob. 19.21.

19.22 Determine the y parameters for the two-ports in Fig. 19.82.

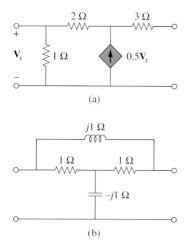

(a)

(b)

Figure 19.82   For Prob. 19.22.

19.23 (a) Find the y parameters of the two-port in Fig. 19.83.
(b) Determine $\mathbf{V}_2(s)$ for $v_s = 2u(t)\text{V}$.

Figure 19.83   For Prob. 19.23.

19.24 Find the resistive circuit that represents these y parameters:

$$[\mathbf{y}] = \begin{bmatrix} \dfrac{1}{2} & -\dfrac{1}{4} \\ -\dfrac{1}{4} & \dfrac{3}{8} \end{bmatrix}$$

19.25 Draw the two-port network that has the following y parameters:

$$[\mathbf{y}] = \begin{bmatrix} 1 & -0.5 \\ -0.5 & 1.5 \end{bmatrix} \text{S}$$

19.26 Calculate $[\mathbf{y}]$ for the two-port in Fig. 19.84.

Figure 19.84   For Prob. 19.26.

19.27 Find the y parameters for the circuit in Fig. 19.85.

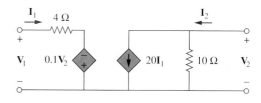

Figure 19.85   For Prob. 19.27.

19.28 In the circuit of Fig. 19.65, the input port is connected to a 1-A dc current source. Calculate the power dissipated by the 2-Ω resistor by using the y parameters. Confirm your result by direct circuit analysis.

19.29 In the bridge circuit of Fig. 19.86, $I_1 = 10$ A and $I_2 = -4$ A.

(a) Find V_1 and V_2 using y parameters.

(b) Confirm the results in part (a) by direct circuit analysis.

Figure 19.86   For Prob. 19.29.

Section 19.4   Hybrid Parameters

19.30   Find the h parameters for the networks in Fig. 19.87.

(a)   (b)

Figure 19.87   For Prob. 19.30.

19.31   Determine the hybrid parameters for the network in Fig. 19.88.

Figure 19.88   For Prob. 19.31.

19.32   Find the h and g parameters of the two-port network in Fig. 19.89 as functions of s.

Figure 19.89   For Prob. 19.32.

19.33   Obtain the h parameters for the two-port of Fig. 19.90.

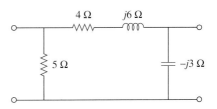

Figure 19.90   For Prob. 19.33.

19.34   Obtain the h and g parameters of the two-port in Fig. 19.91.

Figure 19.91   For Prob. 19.34.

19.35   Determine the h parameters for the network in Fig. 19.92.

Figure 19.92   For Prob. 19.35.

19.36   For the two-port in Fig. 19.93,

$$[\mathbf{h}] = \begin{bmatrix} 16\ \Omega & 3 \\ -2 & 0.01\ \text{S} \end{bmatrix}$$

Find:

(a) V_2/V_1 (b) I_2/I_1
(c) I_1/V_1 (d) V_2/I_1

Figure 19.93   For Prob. 19.36.

19.37 The input port of the circuit in Fig. 19.78 is connected to a 10-V dc voltage source while the output port is terminated by a 5-Ω resistor. Find the voltage across the 5-Ω resistor by using h parameters of the circuit. Confirm your result by using direct circuit analysis.

19.38 For the circuit in Fig. 19.94, $\mathbf{h}_{11} = 800\ \Omega$, $\mathbf{h}_{12} = 10^{-4}$, $\mathbf{h}_{21} = 50$, $\mathbf{h}_{22} = 0.5 \times 10^{-5}$ S. Find the input impedance Z_{in}.

Figure 19.94   For Prob. 19.38.

19.39 Obtain the g parameters for the bridged-tee network in Fig. 19.95.

Figure 19.95   For Prob. 19.39.

19.40 Find the g parameters for the circuit in Fig. 19.96.

Figure 19.96   For Prob. 19.40.

19.41 For the two-port in Fig. 19.74, show that

$$\frac{\mathbf{I}_2}{\mathbf{I}_1} = \frac{-\mathbf{g}_{21}}{\mathbf{g}_{11}\mathbf{Z}_L + \Delta_g}$$

$$\frac{\mathbf{V}_2}{\mathbf{V}_s} = \frac{\mathbf{g}_{21}\mathbf{Z}_L}{(1 + \mathbf{g}_{11}\mathbf{Z}_s)(\mathbf{g}_{22} + \mathbf{Z}_L) - \mathbf{g}_{21}\mathbf{g}_{12}\mathbf{Z}_s}$$

where Δ_g is the determinant of [$\mathbf{g}$] matrix.

19.42 Find the network which realizes each of the following g parameters:

(a) $\begin{bmatrix} 0.01 & -0.5 \\ 0.5 & 20 \end{bmatrix}$ (b) $\begin{bmatrix} 0.1 & 0 \\ 12 & s+2 \end{bmatrix}$

Section 19.5   Transmission Parameters

19.43 Find the transmission parameters for the single-element two-port networks in Fig. 19.97.

(a)   (b)

Figure 19.97   For Prob. 19.43.

19.44 Determine the transmission parameters of the circuit in Fig. 19.98.

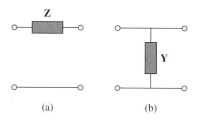

Figure 19.98   For Prob. 19.44.

19.45 Find the **ABCD** parameters for the network in Fig. 19.99.

Figure 19.99   For Prob. 19.45.

19.46   Find the transmission parameters for the circuit in Fig. 19.100.

Figure 19.100   For Prob. 19.46.

19.47   Obtain the **ABCD** parameters for the network in Fig. 19.101.

Figure 19.101   For Prob. 19.47.

19.48   For a two-port, let $\mathbf{A} = 4$, $\mathbf{B} = 30\ \Omega$, $\mathbf{C} = 0.1$ S, and $\mathbf{D} = 1.5$. Calculate the input impedance $\mathbf{Z}_{\text{in}} = \mathbf{V}_1/\mathbf{I}_1$, when:

(a) the output terminals are short-circuited,
(b) the output port is open-circuited,
(c) the output port is terminated by a 10-Ω load.

19.49   Using impedances in the s domain, obtain the transmission parameters for the circuit in Fig. 19.102.

Figure 19.102   For Prob. 19.49.

19.50   Derive the s-domain expression for the t parameters of the circuit in Fig. 19.103.

Figure 19.103   For Prob. 19.50.

19.51   Obtain the t parameters for the network in Fig. 19.104.

Figure 19.104   For Prob. 19.51.

Section 19.6   Relationships between Parameters

19.52   (a) For the T network in Fig. 19.105, show that the h parameters are:

$$\mathbf{h}_{11} = R_1 + \frac{R_2 R_3}{R_1 + R_3}, \qquad \mathbf{h}_{12} = \frac{R_2}{R_2 + R_3}$$

$$\mathbf{h}_{21} = -\frac{R_2}{R_2 + R_3}, \qquad \mathbf{h}_{22} = \frac{1}{R_2 + R_3}$$

(b) For the same network, show that the transmission parameters are:

$$\mathbf{A} = 1 + \frac{R_1}{R_2}, \qquad \mathbf{B} = R_3 + \frac{R_1}{R_2}(R_2 + R_3)$$

$$\mathbf{C} = \frac{1}{R_2}, \qquad \mathbf{D} = 1 + \frac{R_3}{R_2}$$

Figure 19.105   For Prob. 19.52.

19.53   Through derivation, express the z parameters in terms of the **ABCD** parameters.

19.54 Show that the transmission parameters of a two-port may be obtained from the y parameters as:

$$A = -\frac{\mathbf{y}_{22}}{\mathbf{y}_{21}}, \qquad B = -\frac{1}{\mathbf{y}_{21}}$$

$$C = -\frac{\Delta_y}{\mathbf{y}_{21}}, \qquad D = -\frac{\mathbf{y}_{11}}{\mathbf{y}_{21}}$$

19.55 Prove that the g parameters can be obtained from the z parameters as

$$\mathbf{g}_{11} = \frac{1}{\mathbf{z}_{11}}, \qquad \mathbf{g}_{12} = -\frac{\mathbf{z}_{12}}{\mathbf{z}_{11}}$$

$$\mathbf{g}_{21} = \frac{\mathbf{z}_{21}}{\mathbf{z}_{11}}, \qquad \mathbf{g}_{22} = \frac{\Delta_z}{\mathbf{z}_{11}}$$

19.56 If

$$[\mathbf{y}] = \begin{bmatrix} 2+j & j4 \\ -1 & 3-j \end{bmatrix} \text{ S,}$$

find:

(a) [z]   (b) [h]   (c) [t]

19.57 Given the transmission parameters

$$[\mathbf{T}] = \begin{bmatrix} 3 & 20 \\ 1 & 7 \end{bmatrix}$$

obtain the other five two-port parameters.

19.58 A two-port is described by

$$\mathbf{V}_1 = \mathbf{I}_1 + 2\mathbf{V}_2, \qquad \mathbf{I}_2 = -2\mathbf{I}_1 + 0.4\mathbf{V}_2$$

Find: (a) the y parameters, (b) the transmission parameters.

19.59 Given that

$$[\mathbf{g}] = \begin{bmatrix} 0.06 \text{ S} & -0.4 \\ 0.2 & 2 \text{ }\Omega \end{bmatrix}$$

determine:

(a) [z]   (b) [y]   (c) [h]   (d) [T]

19.60 Let $[\mathbf{y}] = \begin{bmatrix} 0.6 & -0.2 \\ -0.1 & 0.5 \end{bmatrix}$ (S). Find:

(a) [z]   (b) [h]   (c) [t]

19.61 For the bridge circuit in Fig. 19.106, obtain:

(a) the z parameters
(b) the h parameters
(c) the transmission parameters

Figure 19.106   For Prob. 19.61.

19.62 Find the z parameters of the op amp circuit in Fig. 19.107. Obtain the transmission parameters.

Figure 19.107   For Prob. 19.62.

19.63 Determine the z parameters of the two-port in Fig. 19.108.

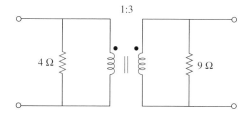

Figure 19.108   For Prob. 19.63.

19.64 Determine the y parameters at $\omega = 1,000$ rad/s for the op amp circuit in Fig. 19.109. Find the corresponding h parameters.

Figure 19.109   For Prob. 19.64.

Section 19.7   Interconnection of Networks

19.65 What is the y parameter presentation of the circuit in Fig. 19.110?

Figure 19.110   For Prob. 19.65.

19.66 In the two-port of Fig. 19.111, let $\mathbf{y}_{12} = \mathbf{y}_{21} = 0$, $\mathbf{y}_{11} = 2$ mS, and $\mathbf{y}_{22} = 10$ mS. Find $\mathbf{V}_o/\mathbf{V}_s$.

Figure 19.111   For Prob. 19.66.

19.67 Figure 19.112 shows two two-ports in series. Find the transmission parameters.

Figure 19.112   For Prob. 19.67.

19.68 Obtain the h parameters for the network in Fig. 19.113.

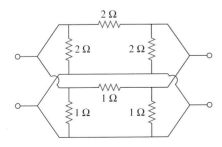

Figure 19.113   For Prob. 19.68.

19.69 The circuit in Fig. 19.114 may be regarded as two two-ports connected in parallel. Obtain the y parameters as functions of s.

Figure 19.114   For Prob. 19.69.

19.70 For the parallel-series connection of the two two-ports in Fig. 19.115, find the g parameters.

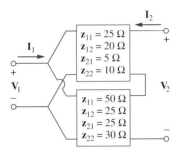

Figure 19.115   For Prob. 19.70.

19.71 Determine the z parameters for the network in Fig. 19.116.

Figure 19.116   For Prob. 19.71.

*19.72 A series-parallel connection of two two-ports is shown in Fig. 19.117. Determine the z parameter representation of the network.

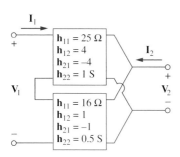

Figure 19.117   For Prob. 19.72.

19.73 Find the transmission parameters for the cascaded two-ports shown in Fig. 19.118. Obtain $\mathbf{Z}_{in} = \mathbf{V}_1/\mathbf{I}_1$ when the output is short-circuited.

Figure 19.118   For Prob. 19.73.

*19.74 Determine the **ABCD** parameters of the circuit in Fig. 19.119 as functions of s. (*Hint:* Partition the circuit into subcircuits and cascade them using the results of Prob. 19.43.)

Figure 19.119   For Prob. 19.74.

*19.75 For the individual two-ports shown in Fig. 19.120 where,

$$[\mathbf{z}_a] = \begin{bmatrix} 8 & 6 \\ 4 & 5 \end{bmatrix} \ \Omega \quad [\mathbf{y}_b] = \begin{bmatrix} 8 & -4 \\ 2 & 10 \end{bmatrix} \ S$$

(a) Determine the y parameters of the overall two-port.

(b) Find the voltage ratio $\mathbf{V}_o/\mathbf{V}_i$ when $\mathbf{Z}_L = 2\Omega$.

Figure 19.120   For Prob. 19.75.

Section 19.8   Computing Two-Port Parameters Using *PSpice*

19.76 Use *PSpice* to obtain the z parameters of the network in Fig. 19.121.

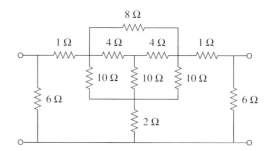

Figure 19.121   For Prob. 19.76.

19.77 Using *PSpice*, find the h parameters of the network in Fig. 19.122. Take $\omega = 1$ rad/s.

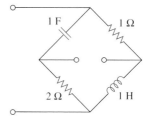

Figure 19.122   For Prob. 19.77.

19.78 Obtain the h parameters at $\omega = 4$ rad/s for the circuit in Fig. 19.123 using *PSpice*.

Figure 19.123   For Prob. 19.78.

19.79 Use *PSpice* to determine the z parameters of the circuit in Fig. 19.124. Take $\omega = 2$ rad/s.

Figure 19.124   For Prob. 19.79.

19.80 Use *PSpice* to find the z parameters of the circuit in Prob. 19.7.

19.81 Repeat Prob. 19.26 using *PSpice*.

19.82 Use *PSpice* to rework Prob. 19.31.

19.83 Rework Prob. 19.47 using *PSpice*.

19.84 Using *PSpice*, find the transmission parameters for the network in Fig. 19.125.

Figure 19.125   For Prob. 19.84.

19.85 At $\omega = 1$ rad/s, find the transmission parameters of the network in Fig. 19.126 using *PSpice*.

Figure 19.126   For Prob. 19.85.

19.86 Obtain the g parameters for the network in Fig. 19.127 using *PSpice*.

Figure 19.127   For Prob. 19.86.

19.87 For the circuit shown in Fig. 19.128, use *PSpice* to obtain the t parameters. Assume $\omega = 1$ rad/s.

Figure 19.128   For Prob. 19.87.

Section 19.9   Applications

19.88 Using the y parameters, derive formulas for Z_{in}, Z_{out}, A_i, and A_v for the common-emitter transistor circuit.

19.89 A transistor has the following parameters in a common-emitter circuit:

$$h_{ie} = 2640 \ \Omega, \qquad h_{re} = 2.6 \times 10^{-4}$$
$$h_{fe} = 72, \qquad h_{oe} = 16 \ \mu\text{S}, \qquad R_L = 100 \ \text{k}\Omega$$

What is the voltage amplification of the transistor? How many decibels gain is this?

19.90 A transistor with

$$h_{fe} = 120, \qquad h_{ie} = 2 \ \text{k}\Omega$$
$$h_{re} = 10^{-4}, \qquad h_{oe} = 20 \ \mu\text{S}$$

is used for a CE amplifier to provide an input resistance of 1.5 kΩ.

(a) Determine the necessary load resistance R_L.
(b) Calculate A_v, A_i, and Z_{out} if the amplifier is driven by a 4 mV source having an internal resistance of 600 Ω.
(c) Find the voltage across the load.

19.91 For the transistor network of Fig. 19.129,

$$h_{fe} = 80, \qquad h_{ie} = 1.2 \ \text{k}\Omega$$
$$h_{re} = 1.5 \times 10^{-4}, \qquad h_{oe} = 20 \ \mu\text{S}$$

Determine the following:

(a) voltage gain $A_v = V_o/V_s$,
(b) current gain $A_i = I_o/I_i$,
(c) input impedance Z_{in},
(d) output impedance Z_{out}.

Figure 19.129   For Prob. 19.91.

*19.92 Determine A_v, A_i, Z_{in}, and Z_{out} for the amplifier shown in Fig. 19.130. Assume that

$$h_{ie} = 4 \ \text{k}\Omega, \qquad h_{re} = 10^{-4}$$
$$h_{fe} = 100, \qquad h_{oe} = 30 \ \mu\text{S}$$

Figure 19.130   For Prob. 19.92.

*19.93 Calculate A_v, A_i, Z_{in}, and Z_{out} for the transistor network in Fig. 19.131. Assume that

$$h_{ie} = 2 \text{ k}\Omega, \qquad h_{re} = 2.5 \times 10^{-4}$$
$$h_{fe} = 150, \qquad h_{oe} = 10 \text{ }\mu\text{S}$$

Figure 19.131   For Prob. 19.93.

19.94 A transistor in its common-emitter mode is specified by

$$[\mathbf{h}] = \begin{bmatrix} 200 \text{ }\Omega & 0 \\ 100 & 10^{-6} \text{ S} \end{bmatrix}$$

Two such identical transistors are connected in cascade to form a two-stage amplifier used at audio frequencies. If the amplifier is terminated by a 4-kΩ resistor, calculate the overall A_v and Z_{in}.

19.95 Realize an LC ladder network such that

$$y_{22} = \frac{s^3 + 5s}{s^4 + 10s^2 + 8}$$

19.96 Design an LC ladder network to realize a lowpass filter with transfer function

$$H(s) = \frac{1}{s^4 + 2.613s^2 + 3.414s^2 + 2.613s + 1}$$

19.97 Synthesize the transfer function

$$H(s) = \frac{V_o}{V_s} = \frac{s^3}{s^3 + 6s + 12s + 24}$$

using the LC ladder network in Fig. 19.132.

Figure 19.132   For Prob. 19.97.

19.98 A two-stage amplifier in Fig. 19.133 contains two identical stages with

$$[\mathbf{h}] = \begin{bmatrix} 2 \text{ k}\Omega & 0.004 \\ 200 & 500 \text{ }\mu\text{S} \end{bmatrix}$$

If $\mathbf{Z}_L = 20 \text{ k}\Omega$, find the required value of $\mathbf{V}_s$ to produce $\mathbf{V}_o = 16$ V.

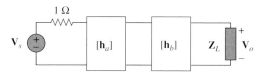

Figure 19.133   For Prob. 19.98.

COMPREHENSIVE PROBLEMS

19.99 Assume that the two circuits in Fig. 19.134 are equivalent. The parameters of the two circuits must be equal. Using this factor and the z parameters, derive Eqs. (9.67) and (9.68).

(a)

(b)

Figure 19.134   For Prob. 19.99.

Appendix A

Simultaneous Equations and Matrix Inversion

In circuit analysis, we often encounter a set of simultaneous equations having the form

$$
\begin{aligned}
a_{11}x_1 + a_{12}x_2 + \cdots + a_{1n}x_n &= b_1 \\
a_{21}x_1 + a_{22}x_2 + \cdots + a_{2n}x_n &= b_2 \\
&\vdots \\
a_{n1}x_1 + a_{n2}x_2 + \cdots + a_{nn}x_n &= b_n
\end{aligned}
\tag{A.1}
$$

where there are n unknown $x_1, x_2, \ldots, x_n$ to be determined. Equation (A.1) can be written in matrix form as

$$
\begin{bmatrix}
a_{11} & a_{12} & \cdots & a_{1n} \\
a_{21} & a_{22} & \cdots & a_{2n} \\
\vdots & \vdots & \cdots & \vdots \\
a_{n1} & a_{n2} & \cdots & a_{nn}
\end{bmatrix}
\begin{bmatrix}
x_1 \\ x_2 \\ \vdots \\ x_n
\end{bmatrix}
=
\begin{bmatrix}
b_2 \\ b_2 \\ \vdots \\ b_n
\end{bmatrix}
\tag{A.2}
$$

This matrix equation can be put in a compact form as

$$
\mathbf{AX} = \mathbf{B}
\tag{A.3}
$$

where

$$
\mathbf{A} =
\begin{bmatrix}
a_{11} & a_{12} & \cdots & a_{1n} \\
a_{21} & a_{22} & \cdots & a_{2n} \\
\vdots & \vdots & \cdots & \vdots \\
a_{n1} & a_{n2} & \cdots & a_{nn}
\end{bmatrix},
\qquad
\mathbf{X} =
\begin{bmatrix}
x_1 \\ x_2 \\ \vdots \\ x_n
\end{bmatrix},
\qquad
\mathbf{B} =
\begin{bmatrix}
b_1 \\ b_2 \\ \vdots \\ b_n
\end{bmatrix}
\tag{A.4}
$$

$\mathbf{A}$ is a square ($n \times n$) matrix while $\mathbf{X}$ and $\mathbf{B}$ are column matrices.

There are several methods for solving Eq. (A.1) or (A.3). These include substitution, Gaussian elimination, Cramer's rule, matrix inversion, and numerical analysis.

A.1 Cramer's Rule

In many cases, Cramer's rule can be used to solve the simultaneous equations we encounter in circuit analysis. Cramer's rule states that the solution to Eq. (A.1) or (A.3) is

$$
\begin{aligned}
x_1 &= \frac{\Delta_1}{\Delta} \\[2mm]
x_2 &= \frac{\Delta_2}{\Delta} \\[2mm]
&\vdots \\[2mm]
x_n &= \frac{\Delta_n}{\Delta}
\end{aligned}
\tag{A.5}
$$

where the Δ's are the determinants given by

$$
\Delta = \begin{vmatrix} a_{11} & a_{12} & \cdots & a_{1n} \\ a_{21} & a_{22} & \cdots & a_{2n} \\ \vdots & \vdots & \cdots & \vdots \\ a_{n1} & a_{n2} & \cdots & a_{nn} \end{vmatrix}, \qquad \Delta_1 = \begin{vmatrix} b_1 & a_{12} & \cdots & a_{1n} \\ b_2 & a_{22} & \cdots & a_{2n} \\ \vdots & \vdots & \cdots & \vdots \\ b_n & a_{n2} & \cdots & a_{nn} \end{vmatrix}
$$

$$
\vdots \qquad\qquad\qquad \vdots \tag{A.6}
$$

$$
\Delta_2 = \begin{vmatrix} a_{11} & b_1 & \cdots & a_{1n} \\ a_{21} & b_2 & \cdots & a_{2n} \\ \vdots & \vdots & \cdots & \vdots \\ a_{n1} & b_n & \cdots & a_{nn} \end{vmatrix}, \ldots, \Delta_n = \begin{vmatrix} a_{11} & a_{12} & \cdots & b_1 \\ a_{21} & a_{22} & \cdots & b_2 \\ \vdots & \vdots & \cdots & \vdots \\ a_{n1} & a_{n2} & \cdots & b_n \end{vmatrix}
$$

Notice that Δ is the determinant of matrix $\mathbf{A}$ and Δ_k is the determinant of the matrix formed by replacing the kth column of $\mathbf{A}$ by $\mathbf{B}$. It is evident from Eq. (A.5) that Cramer's rule applies only when $\Delta \neq 0$. When $\Delta = 0$, the set of equations has no unique solution, because the equations are linearly dependent.

The value of the determinant Δ, for example, can be obtained by expanding along the first row:

$$
\Delta = \begin{vmatrix} a_{11} & a_{12} & a_{13} & \cdots & a_{1n} \\ a_{21} & a_{22} & a_{23} & \cdots & a_{2n} \\ a_{31} & a_{32} & a_{33} & \cdots & a_{3n} \\ \vdots & \vdots & \vdots & \cdots & \vdots \\ a_{n1} & a_{n2} & a_{n3} & \cdots & a_{nn} \end{vmatrix} \tag{A.7}
$$

$$
= a_{11}M_{11} - a_{12}M_{12} + a_{13}M_{13} + \cdots + (-1)^{1+n}a_{1n}M_{1n}
$$

where the minor M_{ij} is an $(n-1) \times (n-1)$ determinant of the matrix formed by striking out the ith row and jth column. The value of Δ may also be obtained by expanding along the first column:

$$
\Delta = a_{11}M_{11} - a_{21}M_{21} + a_{31}M_{31} + \cdots + (-1)^{n+1}a_{n1}M_{n1} \tag{A.8}
$$

We now specifically develop the formulas for calculating the determinants of 2×2 and 3×3 matrices, because of their frequent occurrence in this text. For a 2×2 matrix,

$$
\Delta = \begin{vmatrix} a_{11} & a_{12} \\ a_{21} & a_{22} \end{vmatrix} = a_{11}a_{22} - a_{12}a_{21} \tag{A.9}
$$

For a 3×3 matrix,

$$
\Delta = \begin{vmatrix} a_{11} & a_{12} & a_{13} \\ a_{21} & a_{22} & a_{23} \\ a_{31} & a_{32} & a_{33} \end{vmatrix} = a_{11}(-1)^2 \begin{vmatrix} a_{22} & a_{23} \\ a_{32} & a_{33} \end{vmatrix} + a_{21}(-1)^3 \begin{vmatrix} a_{12} & a_{13} \\ a_{32} & a_{33} \end{vmatrix}
$$

$$
+ a_{31}(-1)^4 \begin{vmatrix} a_{12} & a_{13} \\ a_{22} & a_{23} \end{vmatrix} \tag{A.10}
$$

$$
= a_{11}(a_{22}a_{33} - a_{32}a_{23}) - a_{21}(a_{12}a_{33} - a_{32}a_{13})
$$

$$
+ a_{31}(a_{12}a_{23} - a_{22}a_{13})
$$

An alternative method of obtaining the determinant of a 3×3 matrix is by repeating the first two rows and multiplying the terms diagonally as follows.

$$\Delta = \begin{vmatrix} a_{11} & a_{12} & a_{13} \\ a_{21} & a_{22} & a_{23} \\ a_{31} & a_{32} & a_{33} \\ a_{11} & a_{12} & a_{13} \\ a_{21} & a_{22} & a_{23} \end{vmatrix} \begin{matrix} + \\ + \\ + \end{matrix}$$

$$= a_{11}a_{22}a_{33} + a_{21}a_{32}a_{13} + a_{31}a_{12}a_{23} - a_{13}a_{22}a_{31} - a_{23}a_{32}a_{11} - a_{33}a_{12}a_{21}$$

(A.11)

In summary:

The solution of linear simultaneous equations by Cramer's rule boils down to finding

$$x_k = \frac{\Delta_k}{\Delta}, \qquad k = 1, 2, \ldots, n \qquad \text{(A.12)}$$

where Δ is the determinant of matrix A and Δ_k is the determinant of the matrix formed by replacing the kth column of **A** by **B**.

You may not find much need to use Cramer's method described in this appendix, in view of the availability of calculators, computers, and software packages such as *MATLAB*, which can be used easily to solve a set of linear equations. But in case you need to solve the equations by hand, the material covered in this appendix becomes useful. At any rate, it is important to know the mathematical basis of those calculators and software packages.

One may use other methods, such as matrix inversion and elimination. Only Cramer's method is covered here, because of its simplicity and also because of the availability of powerful calculators.

EXAMPLE A.1

Solve the simultaneous equations

$$4x_1 - 3x_2 = 17, \qquad -3x_1 + 5x_2 = -21$$

Solution:

The given set of equations is cast in matrix form as

$$\begin{bmatrix} 4 & -3 \\ -3 & 5 \end{bmatrix} \begin{bmatrix} x_1 \\ x_2 \end{bmatrix} = \begin{bmatrix} 17 \\ -21 \end{bmatrix}$$

The determinants are evaluated as

$$\Delta = \begin{vmatrix} 4 & -3 \\ -3 & 5 \end{vmatrix} = 4 \times 5 - (-3)(-3) = 11$$

$$\Delta_1 = \begin{vmatrix} 17 & -3 \\ -21 & 5 \end{vmatrix} = 17 \times 5 - (-3)(-21) = 22$$

$$\Delta_2 = \begin{vmatrix} 4 & 17 \\ -3 & -21 \end{vmatrix} = 4 \times (-21) - 17 \times (-3) = -33$$

Hence,

$$x_1 = \frac{\Delta_1}{\Delta} = \frac{22}{11} = 2, \qquad x_2 = \frac{\Delta_2}{\Delta} = \frac{-33}{11} = -3$$

PRACTICE PROBLEM A.1

Find the solution to the following simultaneous equations:

$$3x_1 - x_2 = 4, \qquad -6x_1 + 18x_2 = 16$$

Answer: $x_1 = 1.833, x_2 = 1.5$.

EXAMPLE A.2

Determine x_1, x_2, and x_3 for this set of simultaneous equations:

$$25x_1 - 5x_2 - 20x_3 = 50$$
$$-5x_1 + 10x_2 - 4x_3 = 0$$
$$-5x_1 - 4x_2 + 9x_3 = 0$$

Solution:

In matrix form, the given set of equations becomes

$$\begin{bmatrix} 25 & -5 & -20 \\ -5 & 10 & -4 \\ -5 & -4 & 9 \end{bmatrix} \begin{bmatrix} x_1 \\ x_2 \\ x_3 \end{bmatrix} = \begin{bmatrix} 50 \\ 0 \\ 0 \end{bmatrix}$$

We apply Eq. (A.11) to find the determinants. This requires that we repeat the first two rows of the matrix. Thus,

$$\Delta = \begin{vmatrix} 25 & -5 & -20 \\ -5 & 10 & -4 \\ -5 & -4 & 9 \end{vmatrix} = \begin{matrix} \begin{vmatrix} 25 & -5 & -20 \\ -5 & 10 & -4 \\ -5 & -4 & 9 \\ 25 & -5 & -20 \\ -5 & 10 & -4 \end{vmatrix} \end{matrix}$$

$$= 25(10)9 + (-5)(-4)(-20) + (-5)(-5)(-4)$$
$$- (-20)(10)(-5) - (-4)(-4)25 - 9(-5)(-5)$$
$$= 2250 - 400 - 100 - 1000 - 400 - 225 = 125$$

Similarly,

$$\Delta_1 = \begin{vmatrix} 50 & -5 & -20 \\ 0 & 10 & -4 \\ 0 & -4 & 9 \end{vmatrix} = \begin{matrix} 50 & -5 & -20 \\ 0 & 10 & -4 \\ 0 & -4 & 9 \\ 50 & -5 & -20 \\ 0 & 10 & -4 \end{matrix}$$

$$= 4500 + 0 + 0 - 0 - 800 - 0 = 3700$$

$$\Delta_2 = \begin{vmatrix} 25 & 50 & -20 \\ -5 & 0 & -4 \\ -5 & 0 & 9 \end{vmatrix} = \begin{matrix} 25 & 50 & -20 \\ -5 & 0 & -4 \\ -5 & 0 & 9 \\ 25 & 50 & -20 \\ -5 & 0 & -4 \end{matrix}$$

$$= 0 + 0 + 1000 - 0 - 0 + 2250 = 3250$$

$$\Delta_3 = \begin{vmatrix} 25 & -5 & 50 \\ -5 & 10 & 0 \\ -5 & -4 & 0 \end{vmatrix} = \begin{matrix} 25 & -5 & 50 \\ -5 & 10 & 0 \\ -5 & -4 & 0 \\ 25 & -5 & 50 \\ -5 & 10 & 0 \end{matrix}$$

$$= 0 + 1000 + 0 + 2500 - 0 - 0 = 3500$$

Hence, we now find

$$x_1 = \frac{\Delta_1}{\Delta} = \frac{3700}{125} = 29.6$$

$$x_2 = \frac{\Delta_2}{\Delta} = \frac{3250}{125} = 26$$

$$x_3 = \frac{\Delta_2}{\Delta} = \frac{3500}{125} = 28$$

PRACTICE PROBLEM A.2

Obtain the solution of this set of simultaneous equations

$$3x_1 - x_2 - 2x_3 = 1$$
$$-x_1 + 6x_2 - 3x_3 = 0$$
$$-2x_1 - 3x_2 + 6x_3 = 6$$

Answer: $x_1 = 3 = x_3, x_2 = 2.$

A.2 Matrix Inversion

The linear system of equations in Eq. (A.3) can be solved by matrix inversion. In the matrix equation $\mathbf{AX} = \mathbf{B}$, we may invert $\mathbf{A}$ to get $\mathbf{X}$, i.e.,

$$\mathbf{X} = \mathbf{A}^{-1}\mathbf{B} \tag{A.13}$$

where $\mathbf{A}^{-1}$ is the inverse of $\mathbf{A}$. Matrix inversion is needed in other applications apart from using it to solve a set of equations.

By definition, the inverse of matrix $\mathbf{A}$ satisfies

$$\mathbf{A}^{-1}\mathbf{A} = \mathbf{AA}^{-1} = \mathbf{I} \tag{A.14}$$

where $\mathbf{I}$ is an identity matrix. $\mathbf{A}^{-1}$ is given by

$$\mathbf{A}^{-1} = \frac{\text{adj } \mathbf{A}}{\det \mathbf{A}} \tag{A.15}$$

where adj $\mathbf{A}$ is the adjoint of $\mathbf{A}$ and det $\mathbf{A} = |\mathbf{A}|$ is the determinant of $\mathbf{A}$. The adjoint of $\mathbf{A}$ is the transpose of the cofactors of $\mathbf{A}$. Suppose we are given an $n \times n$ matrix $\mathbf{A}$ as

$$\mathbf{A} = \begin{bmatrix} a_{11} & a_{12} & \cdots & a_{1n} \\ a_{21} & a_{22} & \cdots & a_{2n} \\ \vdots & & & \\ a_{n1} & a_{n2} & \cdots & a_{nn} \end{bmatrix} \tag{A.16}$$

The cofactors of $\mathbf{A}$ are defined as

$$\mathbf{C} = \text{cof}(\mathbf{A}) = \begin{bmatrix} c_{11} & c_{12} & \cdots & c_{1n} \\ c_{21} & c_{22} & \cdots & c_{2n} \\ \vdots & & & \\ c_{n1} & c_{n2} & \cdots & c_{nn} \end{bmatrix} \tag{A.17}$$

where the cofactor c_{ij} is the product of $(-1)^{i+j}$ and the determinant of the $(n-1) \times (n-1)$ submatrix is obtained by deleting the $i$the row and jth column from $\mathbf{A}$. For example, by deleting the first row and the first column of $\mathbf{A}$ in Eq .(A.16), we obtain the cofactor c_{11} as

$$c_{11} = (-1)^2 = \begin{vmatrix} a_{22} & a_{23} & \cdots & a_{2n} \\ a_{32} & a_{33} & \cdots & a_{3n} \\ \vdots & & & \\ a_{n2} & a_{n3} & \cdots & a_{nn} \end{vmatrix} \tag{A.18}$$

Once the cofactors are found, the adjoint of $\mathbf{A}$ is obtained as

$$\text{adj } (\mathbf{A}) = \begin{bmatrix} c_{11} & c_{12} & \cdots & c_{1n} \\ c_{21} & c_{22} & \cdots & c_{2n} \\ \vdots & & & \\ c_{n1} & c_{n2} & \cdots & c_{nn} \end{bmatrix}^{T} = \mathbf{C}^{T} \tag{A.19}$$

where T denotes transpose.

In addition to using the cofactors to find the adjoint of $\mathbf{A}$, they are also used in finding the determinant of $\mathbf{A}$ which is given by

$$|\mathbf{A}| = \sum_{j=1}^{n} a_{ij} c_{ij} \qquad \text{(A.20)}$$

where i is any value from 1 to n. By substituting Eqs. (A.19) and (A.20) into Eq. (A.15), we obtain the inverse of $\mathbf{A}$ as

$$\boxed{\mathbf{A}^{-1} = \frac{\mathbf{C}^T}{|\mathbf{A}|}} \qquad \text{(A.21)}$$

For a 2×2 matrix, if

$$\mathbf{A} = \begin{bmatrix} a & b \\ c & d \end{bmatrix} \qquad \text{(A.22)}$$

its inverse is

$$\mathbf{A}^{-1} = \frac{1}{|\mathbf{A}|} \begin{bmatrix} d & -b \\ -c & a \end{bmatrix} = \frac{1}{ad - bc} \begin{bmatrix} d & -b \\ -c & a \end{bmatrix} \qquad \text{(A.23)}$$

For a 3×3 matrix, if

$$\mathbf{A} = \begin{bmatrix} a_{11} & a_{12} & a_{13} \\ a_{21} & a_{22} & a_{23} \\ a_{31} & a_{32} & a_{33} \end{bmatrix} \qquad \text{(A.24)}$$

we first obtain the cofactors as

$$\mathbf{C} = \begin{bmatrix} c_{11} & c_{12} & c_{13} \\ c_{21} & c_{22} & c_{23} \\ c_{31} & c_{32} & c_{33} \end{bmatrix} \qquad \text{(A.25)}$$

where

$$c_{11} = \begin{vmatrix} a_{22} & a_{23} \\ a_{32} & a_{33} \end{vmatrix}, \qquad c_{12} = -\begin{vmatrix} a_{21} & a_{23} \\ a_{31} & a_{33} \end{vmatrix}, \qquad c_{13} = \begin{vmatrix} a_{21} & a_{22} \\ a_{31} & a_{32} \end{vmatrix},$$

$$c_{21} = -\begin{vmatrix} a_{12} & a_{13} \\ a_{32} & a_{33} \end{vmatrix}, \qquad c_{22} = \begin{vmatrix} a_{11} & a_{13} \\ a_{31} & a_{33} \end{vmatrix}, \qquad c_{23} = -\begin{vmatrix} a_{11} & a_{12} \\ a_{31} & a_{32} \end{vmatrix},$$

$$c_{31} = \begin{vmatrix} a_{12} & a_{13} \\ a_{22} & a_{23} \end{vmatrix}, \qquad c_{32} = -\begin{vmatrix} a_{11} & a_{13} \\ a_{21} & a_{23} \end{vmatrix}, \qquad c_{33} = \begin{vmatrix} a_{11} & a_{12} \\ a_{21} & a_{22} \end{vmatrix}$$

$$\text{(A.26)}$$

The determinant of the 3×3 matrix can be found using Eq. (A.11). Here, we want to use Eq. (A.20), i.e.,

$$|\mathbf{A}| = a_{11} c_{11} + a_{12} c_{12} + a_{13} c_{13} \qquad \text{(A.27)}$$

The idea can be extended $n > 3$, but we deal mainly with 2×2 and 3×3 matrices in this book.

EXAMPLE A.3

Use matrix inversion to solve the simultaneous equations

$$2x_1 + 10x_2 = 2, \qquad -x_1 + 3x_2 = 7$$

Solution:

We first express the two equations in matrix form as

$$\begin{bmatrix} 2 & 10 \\ -1 & 3 \end{bmatrix} \begin{bmatrix} x_1 \\ x_2 \end{bmatrix} = \begin{bmatrix} 2 \\ 7 \end{bmatrix}$$

or

$$\mathbf{AX} = \mathbf{B} \longrightarrow \mathbf{X} = \mathbf{A}^{-1}\mathbf{B}$$

where

$$\mathbf{A} = \begin{bmatrix} 2 & 10 \\ -1 & 3 \end{bmatrix}, \qquad \mathbf{X} = \begin{bmatrix} x_1 \\ x_2 \end{bmatrix}, \qquad \mathbf{B} = \begin{bmatrix} 2 \\ 7 \end{bmatrix}$$

The determinant of $\mathbf{A}$ is $|\mathbf{A}| = 2 \times 3 - 10(-1) = 16$, so the inverse of $\mathbf{A}$ is

$$\mathbf{A}^{-1} = \frac{1}{16} \begin{bmatrix} 3 & -10 \\ 1 & 2 \end{bmatrix}$$

Hence,

$$\mathbf{X} = \mathbf{A}^{-1}\mathbf{B} = \frac{1}{16} \begin{bmatrix} 3 & -10 \\ 1 & 2 \end{bmatrix} \begin{bmatrix} 2 \\ 7 \end{bmatrix} = \frac{1}{16} \begin{bmatrix} -64 \\ 16 \end{bmatrix} = \begin{bmatrix} -4 \\ 1 \end{bmatrix}$$

i.e., $x_1 = -4$ and $x_2 = 1$.

PRACTICE PROBLEM A.3

Solve the following two equations by matrix inversion.

$$2y_1 - y_2 = 4, \quad y_1 + 3y_2 = 9$$

Answer: $y_1 = 3, y_2 = 2$.

EXAMPLE A.4

Determine x_1, x_2, and x_3 for the following simultaneous equations using matrix inversion.

$$x_1 + x_2 + x_3 = 5$$
$$-x_1 + 2x_2 = 9$$
$$4x_1 + x_2 - x_3 = -2$$

Solution:

In matrix form, the equations become

$$\begin{bmatrix} 1 & 1 & 1 \\ -1 & 2 & 0 \\ 4 & 1 & -1 \end{bmatrix} \begin{bmatrix} x_1 \\ x_2 \\ x_3 \end{bmatrix} = \begin{bmatrix} 5 \\ 9 \\ -2 \end{bmatrix}$$

or

$$\mathbf{AX} = \mathbf{B} \longrightarrow \mathbf{X} = \mathbf{A}^{-1}\mathbf{B}$$

where

$$\mathbf{A} = \begin{bmatrix} 1 & 1 & 1 \\ -1 & 2 & 0 \\ 4 & 1 & -1 \end{bmatrix}, \qquad \mathbf{X} = \begin{bmatrix} x_1 \\ x_2 \\ x_3 \end{bmatrix}, \qquad \mathbf{B} = \begin{bmatrix} 5 \\ 9 \\ -2 \end{bmatrix}$$

We now find the cofactors

$$c_{11} = \begin{vmatrix} 2 & 0 \\ 1 & -1 \end{vmatrix} = -2, \qquad c_{12} = -\begin{vmatrix} -1 & 0 \\ 4 & -1 \end{vmatrix} = -1, \qquad c_{13} = \begin{vmatrix} -1 & 2 \\ 4 & 1 \end{vmatrix} = -9$$

$$c_{21} = -\begin{vmatrix} 1 & 1 \\ 1 & -1 \end{vmatrix} = 2, \qquad c_{22} = \begin{vmatrix} 1 & 1 \\ 4 & -1 \end{vmatrix} = -5, \qquad c_{23} = -\begin{vmatrix} 1 & 1 \\ 4 & 1 \end{vmatrix} = 3$$

$$c_{31} = \begin{vmatrix} 1 & 1 \\ 2 & 0 \end{vmatrix} = -2, \qquad c_{32} = -\begin{vmatrix} 1 & 1 \\ -1 & 0 \end{vmatrix} = -1, \qquad c_{33} = \begin{vmatrix} 1 & 1 \\ -1 & 2 \end{vmatrix} = 3$$

The adjoint of matrix $\mathbf{A}$ is

$$\text{adj } \mathbf{A} = \begin{bmatrix} -2 & -1 & -9 \\ 2 & -5 & 3 \\ -2 & -1 & 3 \end{bmatrix}^T = \begin{bmatrix} -2 & 2 & -2 \\ -1 & -5 & -1 \\ -9 & 3 & 3 \end{bmatrix}$$

We can find the determinant of $\mathbf{A}$ using any row or column of $\mathbf{A}$. Since one element of the second row is 0, we can take advantage of this to find the determinant as

$$|\mathbf{A}| = -1c_{21} + 2c_{22} + (0)c_{23} = -1(2) + 2(-5) = -12$$

Hence, the inverse of $\mathbf{A}$ is

$$\mathbf{A}^{-1} = \frac{1}{-12} \begin{bmatrix} -2 & 2 & -2 \\ -1 & -5 & -1 \\ -9 & 3 & 3 \end{bmatrix}$$

$$\mathbf{X} = \mathbf{A}^{-1}\mathbf{B} = \frac{1}{-12} \begin{bmatrix} -2 & 2 & -2 \\ -1 & -5 & -1 \\ -9 & 3 & 3 \end{bmatrix} \begin{bmatrix} 5 \\ 9 \\ -2 \end{bmatrix} = \begin{bmatrix} -1 \\ 4 \\ 2 \end{bmatrix}$$

i.e., $x_1 = -1$, $x_2 = 4$, $x_3 = 2$.

PRACTICE PROBLEM A.4

Solve the following equations using matrix inversion.

$$y_1 - y_3 = 1$$
$$2y_1 + 3y_2 - y_3 = 1$$
$$y_1 - y_2 - y_3 = 3$$

Answer: $y_1 = 6$, $y_2 = -2$, $y_3 = 5$.

Appendix B

Complex Numbers

The ability to manipulate complex numbers is very handy in circuit analysis and in electrical engineering in general. Complex numbers are particularly useful in the analysis of ac circuits. Again, although calculators and computer software packages are now available to manipulate complex numbers, it is still advisable for a student to be familiar with how to handle them by hand.

B.1 Representations of Complex Numbers

A complex number z may be written in *rectangular form* as

$$z = x + jy \tag{B.1}$$

where $j = \sqrt{-1}$; x is the *real part* of z while y is the *imaginary part* of z; that is,

$$x = \text{Re}(z), \qquad y = \text{Im}(z) \tag{B.2}$$

The complex number z is shown plotted in the complex plane in Fig. B.1. Since $j = \sqrt{-1}$,

$$
\begin{aligned}
\frac{1}{j} &= -j \\
j^2 &= -1 \\
j^3 &= j \cdot j^2 = -j \\
j^4 &= j^2 \cdot j^2 = 1 \\
j^5 &= j \cdot j^4 = j \\
&\vdots \\
j^{n+4} &= j^n
\end{aligned} \tag{B.3}
$$

A second way of representing the complex number z is by specifying its magnitude r and the angle θ it makes with the real axis, as Fig. B.1 shows. This is known as the *polar form*. It is given by

$$z = |z|\underline{/\theta} = r\underline{/\theta} \tag{B.4}$$

where

$$r = \sqrt{x^2 + y^2}, \qquad \theta = \tan^{-1}\frac{y}{x} \tag{B.5a}$$

or

$$x = r\cos\theta, \qquad y = r\sin\theta \tag{B.5b}$$

that is,

$$z = x + jy = r\underline{/\theta} = r\cos\theta + jr\sin\theta \tag{B.6}$$

In converting from rectangular to polar form using Eq. (B.5), we must exercise care in determining the correct value of θ. These are the four possibilities:

$$z = x + jy, \qquad \theta = \tan^{-1}\frac{y}{x} \qquad \text{(1st Quadrant)}$$

$$z = -x + jy, \qquad \theta = 180° - \tan^{-1}\frac{y}{x} \qquad \text{(2nd Quadrant)}$$

The complex plane looks like the two-dimensional curvilinear coordinate space, but it is not.

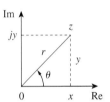

Figure B.I Graphical representation of a complex number.

$$z = -x - jy, \qquad \theta = 180° + \tan^{-1} \frac{y}{x} \qquad \text{(3rd Quadrant)}$$

(B.7)

$$z = x - jy, \qquad \theta = 360° - \tan^{-1} \frac{y}{x} \qquad \text{(4th Quadrant)}$$

assuming that x and y are positive.

The third way of representing the complex z is the *exponential form*:

$$z = re^{j\theta}$$

(B.8)

This is almost the same as the polar form, because we use the same magnitude r and the angle θ.

The three forms of representing a complex number are summarized as follows.

$z = x + jy$,	$(x = r\cos\theta, \; y = r\sin\theta)$	Rectangular form
$z = r\angle\theta$,	$\left(r = \sqrt{x^2 + y^2}, \theta = \tan^{-1}\dfrac{y}{x}\right)$	Polar form
$z = re^{j\theta}$,	$\left(r = \sqrt{x^2 + y^2}, \theta = \tan^{-1}\dfrac{y}{x}\right)$	Exponential form

(B.9)

> In the exponential form, $z = re^{j\theta}$ so that $dz/d\theta = jre^{j\theta} = jz$.

The first two forms are related by Eqs. (B.5) and (B.6). In Section B.3 we will derive Euler's formula, which proves that the third form is also equivalent to the first two.

E X A M P L E B . I

Express the following complex numbers in polar and exponential form: (a) $z_1 = 6 + j8$, (b) $z_2 = 6 - j8$, (c) $z_3 = -6 + j8$, (d) $z_4 = -6 - j8$.

Solution:

Notice that we have deliberately chosen these complex numbers to fall in the four quadrants, as shown in Fig. B.2.
(a) For $z_1 = 6 + j8$ (1st quadrant),

$$r_1 = \sqrt{6^2 + 8^2} = 10, \qquad \theta_1 = \tan^{-1}\frac{8}{6} = 53.13°$$

Hence, the polar form is $10\angle 53.13°$ and the exponential form is $10e^{j53.13°}$.
(b) For $z_2 = 6 - j8$ (4th quadrant),

$$r_2 = \sqrt{6^2 + (-8)^2} = 10, \qquad \theta_2 = 360° - \tan^{-1}\frac{8}{6} = 306.87°$$

so that the polar form is $10\angle 306.87°$ and the exponential form is $10e^{j306.87°}$. The angle θ_2 may also be taken as $-53.13°$, as shown in Fig. B.2, so that the polar form becomes $10\angle -53.13°$ and the exponential form becomes $10e^{-j53.13°}$.
(c) For $z_3 = -6 + j8$ (2nd quadrant),

$$r_3 = \sqrt{(-6)^2 + 8^2} = 10, \qquad \theta_3 = 180° - \tan^{-1}\frac{8}{6} = 126.87°$$

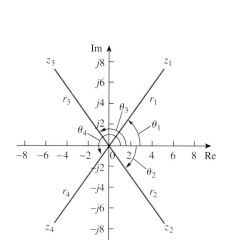

Figure B.2   For Example B.1.

Hence, the polar form is $10\underline{/126.87°}$ and the exponential form is $10e^{j126.87°}$.

(d) For $z_4 = -6 - j8$ (3rd quadrant),

$$r_4 = \sqrt{(-6)^2 + (-8)^2} = 10, \qquad \theta_4 = 180° + \tan^{-1}\frac{8}{6} = 233.13°$$

so that the polar form is $10\underline{/233.13°}$ and the exponential form is $10e^{j233.13°}$.

PRACTICE PROBLEM B.1

Convert the following complex numbers to polar and exponential forms:
(a) $z_1 = 3 - j4$, (b) $z_2 = 5 + j12$, (c) $z_3 = -3 - j9$, (d) $z_4 = -7 + j$.

Answer: (a) $5\underline{/306.9°}$, $5e^{j306.9°}$, (b) $13\underline{/67.38°}$, $13e^{j67.38°}$,

(c) $9.487\underline{/251.6°}$, $9.487e^{j251.6°}$, (d) $7.071\underline{/171.9°}$, $7.071e^{j171.9°}$.

EXAMPLE B.2

Convert the following complex numbers into rectangular form:
(a) $12\underline{/-60°}$, (b) $-50\underline{/285°}$, (c) $8e^{j10°}$, (d) $20e^{-j\pi/3}$.

Solution:

(a) Using Eq. (B.6),

$$12\underline{/-60°} = 12\cos(-60°) + j12\sin(-60°) = 6 - j10.39$$

Note that $\theta = -60°$ is the same as $\theta = 360° - 60° = 300°$.

(b) We can write

$$-50\underline{/285°} = -50\cos 285° - j50\sin 285° = -12.94 + j48.3$$

(c) Similarly,

$$8e^{j10°} = 8\cos 10° + j8\sin 10° = 7.878 + j1.389$$

(d) Finally,

$$20e^{-j\pi/3} = 20\cos(-\pi/3) + j20\sin(-\pi/3) = 10 - j17.32$$

PRACTICE PROBLEM B.2

Find the rectangular form of the following complex numbers:
(a) $-8\underline{/210°}$, (b) $40\underline{/305°}$, (c) $10e^{-j30°}$, (d) $50e^{j\pi/2}$.

Answer: (a) $6.928 + j4$, (b) $22.94 - j32.77$, (c) $8.66 - j5$, (d) $j50$.

B.2 Mathematical Operations

Two complex numbers $z_1 = x_1 + jy_1$ and $z_2 = x_2 + jy_2$ are equal if and only if their real parts are equal and their imaginary parts are equal,

$$x_1 = x_2, \qquad y_1 = y_2 \tag{B.10}$$

We have used lightface notation for complex numbers—since they are not time- or frequency-dependent—whereas we use boldface notation for phasors.

The *complex conjugate* of the complex number $z = x + jy$ is

$$z^* = x - jy = r\underline{/-\theta} = re^{-j\theta} \tag{B.11}$$

Thus the complex conjugate of a complex number is found by replacing every j by $-j$.

Given two complex numbers $z_1 = x_1 + jy_1 = r_1\underline{/\theta_1}$ and $z_2 = x_2 + jy_2 = r_2\underline{/\theta_2}$, their sum is

$$z_1 + z_2 = (x_1 + x_2) + j(y_1 + y_2) \tag{B.12}$$

and their difference is

$$z_1 - z_2 = (x_1 - x_2) + j(y_1 - y_2) \tag{B.13}$$

While it is more convenient to perform addition and subtraction of complex numbers in rectangular form, the product and quotient of the two complex numbers are best done in polar or exponential form. For their product,

$$z_1 z_2 = r_1 r_2 \underline{/\theta_1 + \theta_2} \tag{B.14}$$

Alternatively, using the rectangular form,

$$
\begin{aligned}
z_1 z_2 &= (x_1 + jy_1)(x_2 + jy_2) \\
&= (x_1 x_2 - y_1 y_2) + j(x_1 y_2 + x_2 y_1)
\end{aligned} \tag{B.15}
$$

For their quotient,

$$\frac{z_1}{z_2} = \frac{r_1}{r_2}\underline{/\theta_1 - \theta_2} \tag{B.16}$$

Alternatively, using the rectangular form,

$$\frac{z_1}{z_2} = \frac{x_1 + jy_1}{x_2 + jy_2} \tag{B.17}$$

We rationalize the denominator by multiplying both the numerator and denominator by z_2^*.

$$\frac{z_1}{z_2} = \frac{(x_1 + jy_1)(x_2 - jy_2)}{(x_2 + jy_2)(x_2 - jy_2)} = \frac{x_1 x_2 + y_1 y_2}{x_2^2 + y_2^2} + j\frac{x_2 y_1 - x_1 y_2}{x_2^2 + y_2^2} \tag{B.18}$$

EXAMPLE B.3

If $A = 2 + j5$, $B = 4 - j6$, find: (a) $A^*(A + B)$, (b) $(A + B)/(A - B)$.

Solution:

(a) If $A = 2 + j5$, then $A^* = 2 - j5$ and

$$A + B = (2 + 4) + j(5 - 6) = 6 - j$$

so that

$$A^*(A + B) = (2 - j5)(6 - j) = 12 - j2 - j30 - 5 = 7 - j32$$

(b) Similarly,

$$A - B = (2 - 4) + j(5 - -6) = -2 + j11$$

Hence,

$$\frac{A + B}{A - B} = \frac{6 - j}{-2 + j11} = \frac{(6 - j)(-2 - j11)}{(-2 + j11)(-2 - j11)}$$

$$= \frac{-12 - j66 + j2 - 11}{(-2)^2 + 11^2} = \frac{-23 - j64}{125} = -0.184 - j0.512$$

PRACTICE PROBLEM B.3

Given that $C = -3 + j7$ and $D = 8 + j$, calculate:
(a) $(C - D^*)(C + D^*)$, (b) D^2/C^*, (c) $2CD/(C + D)$.

Answer: (a) $-103 - j26$, (b) $-5.19 + j6.776$, (c) $6.054 + j11.53$.

EXAMPLE B.4

Evaluate:

(a) $\dfrac{(2 + j5)(8e^{j10^\circ})}{2 + j4 + 2\underline{/-40^\circ}}$ (b) $\dfrac{j(3 - j4)^*}{(-1 + j6)(2 + j)^2}$

Solution:

(a) Since there are terms in polar and exponential forms, it may be best to express all terms in polar form:

$$2 + j5 = \sqrt{2^2 + 5^2}\underline{/\tan^{-1}5/2} = 5.385\underline{/68.2^\circ}$$

$$(2 + j5)(8e^{j10^\circ}) = (5.385\underline{/68.2^\circ})(8\underline{/10^\circ}) = 43.08\underline{/78.2^\circ}$$

$$2 + j4 + 2\underline{/-40^\circ} = 2 + j4 + 2\cos(-40^\circ) + j2\sin(-40^\circ)$$

$$= 3.532 + j2.714 = 4.454\underline{/37.54^\circ}$$

Thus,

$$\frac{(2 + j5)(8e^{j10^\circ})}{2 + j4 + 2\underline{/-40^\circ}} = \frac{43.08\underline{/78.2^\circ}}{4.454\underline{/37.54^\circ}} = 9.672\underline{/40.66^\circ}$$

(b) We can evaluate this in rectangular form, since all terms are in that form. But

$$j(3 - j4)^* = j(3 + j4) = -4 + j3$$
$$(2 + j)^2 = 4 + j4 - 1 = 3 + j4$$
$$(-1 + j6)(2 + j)^2 = (-1 + j6)(3 + j4) = -3 - 4j + j18 - 24$$
$$= -27 + j14$$

Hence,

$$\frac{j(3 - j4)^*}{(-1 + j6)(2 + j)^2} = \frac{-4 + j3}{-27 + j14} = \frac{(-4 + j3)(-27 - j14)}{27^2 + 14^2}$$

$$= \frac{108 + j56 - j81 + 42}{925} = 0.1622 - j0.027$$

PRACTICE PROBLEM B.4

Evaluate these complex fractions:

(a) $\dfrac{6\underline{/30°} + j5 - 3}{-1 + j + 2e^{j45°}}$ (b) $\left[\dfrac{(15 - j7)(3 + j2)^*}{(4 + j6)^*(3\underline{/70°})}\right]^*$

Answer: (a) $3.387\underline{/-5.615°}$, (b) $2.759\underline{/-287.6°}$.

B.3 Euler's Formula

Euler's formula is an important result in complex variables. We derive it from the series expansion of e^x, $\cos\theta$, and $\sin\theta$. We know that

$$e^x = 1 + x + \frac{x^2}{2!} + \frac{x^3}{3!} + \frac{x^4}{4!} + \cdots \qquad (B.19)$$

Replacing x by $j\theta$ gives

$$e^{j\theta} = 1 + j\theta - \frac{\theta^2}{2!} - j\frac{\theta^3}{3!} + \frac{\theta^4}{4!} + \cdots \qquad (B.20)$$

Also,

$$\cos\theta = 1 - \frac{\theta^2}{2!} + \frac{\theta^4}{4!} - \frac{\theta^6}{6!} + \cdots$$

$$\sin\theta = \theta - \frac{\theta^3}{3!} + \frac{\theta^5}{5!} - \frac{\theta^7}{7!} + \cdots \qquad (B.21)$$

so that

$$\cos\theta + j\sin\theta = 1 + j\theta - \frac{\theta^2}{2!} - j\frac{\theta^3}{3!} + \frac{\theta^4}{4!} + j\frac{\theta^5}{5!} - \cdots \qquad (B.22)$$

Comparing Eqs. (B.20) and (B.22), we conclude that

$$\boxed{e^{j\theta} = \cos\theta + j\sin\theta} \qquad (B.23)$$

This is known as *Euler's formula*. The exponential form of representing a complex number as in Eq. (B.8) is based on Euler's formula. From Eq. (B.23), notice that

$$\boxed{\cos\theta = \text{Re}(e^{j\theta}), \qquad \sin\theta = \text{Im}(e^{j\theta})} \qquad (B.24)$$

and that

$$|e^{j\theta}| = \sqrt{\cos^2\theta + \sin^2\theta} = 1$$

Replacing θ by $-\theta$ in Eq. (B.23) gives

$$e^{-j\theta} = \cos\theta - j\sin\theta \qquad \text{(B.25)}$$

Adding Eqs. (B.23) and (B.25) yields

$$\cos\theta = \frac{1}{2}(e^{j\theta} + e^{-j\theta}) \qquad \text{(B.26)}$$

Subtracting Eq. (B.25) from Eq. (B.23) yields

$$\sin\theta = \frac{1}{2j}(e^{j\theta} - e^{-j\theta}) \qquad \text{(B.27)}$$

Useful Identities

The following identities are useful in dealing with complex numbers. If $z = x + jy = r\underline{/\theta}$, then

$$zz^* = x^2 + y^2 = r^2 \qquad \text{(B.28)}$$

$$\sqrt{z} = \sqrt{x + jy} = \sqrt{r}e^{j\theta/2} = \sqrt{r}\,\underline{/\theta/2} \qquad \text{(B.29)}$$

$$z^n = (x + jy)^n = r^n\underline{/n\theta} = r^n e^{jn\theta} = r^n(\cos n\theta + j\sin n\theta) \qquad \text{(B.30)}$$

$$z^{1/n} = (x + jy)^{1/n} = r^{1/n}\underline{/\theta/n + 2\pi k/n} \qquad \text{(B.31)}$$
$$k = 0, 1, 2, \ldots, n - 1$$

$$\ln(re^{j\theta}) = \ln r + \ln e^{j\theta} = \ln r + j\theta + j2k\pi \qquad \text{(B.32)}$$
$$(k = \text{integer})$$

$$\frac{1}{j} = -j$$
$$e^{\pm j\pi} = -1$$
$$e^{\pm j2\pi} = 1 \qquad \text{(B.33)}$$
$$e^{j\pi/2} = j$$
$$e^{-j\pi/2} = -j$$

$$\text{Re}(e^{(\alpha + j\omega)t}) = \text{Re}(e^{\alpha t}e^{j\omega t}) = e^{\alpha t}\cos\omega t \qquad \text{(B.34)}$$
$$\text{Im}(e^{(\alpha + j\omega)t}) = \text{Im}(e^{\alpha t}e^{j\omega t}) = e^{\alpha t}\sin\omega t$$

EXAMPLE B.5

If $A = 6 + j8$, find: (a) $\sqrt{A}$, (b) A^4.

Solution:

(a) First, convert A to polar form:

$$r = \sqrt{6^2 + 8^2} = 10, \qquad \theta = \tan^{-1}\frac{8}{6} = 53.13°, \qquad A = 10\underline{/53.13°}$$

Then

$$\sqrt{A} = \sqrt{10}\,\underline{/53.13°/2} = 3.162\underline{/26.56°}$$

(b) Since $A = 10\underline{/53.13°}$,

$$A^4 = r^4\underline{/4\theta} = 10^4\underline{/4 \times 53.13°} = 10{,}000\underline{/212.52°}$$

PRACTICE PROBLEM B.5

If $A = 3 - j4$, find: (a) $A^{1/3}$ (3 roots), and (b) $\ln A$.

Answer: (a) $1.71\underline{/102.3°}$, $1.71\underline{/222.3°}$, $1.71\underline{/342.3°}$,
(b) $1.609 + j5.356$.

Appendix C

Mathematical Formulas

This appendix—by no means exhaustive—serves as a handy reference. It does contain all the formulas needed to solve circuit problems in this book.

C.1 Quadratic Formula

The roots of the quadratic equation $ax^2 + bx + c = 0$ are

$$x_1, x_2 = \frac{-b \pm \sqrt{b^2 - 4ac}}{2a}$$

C.2 Trigonometric Identities

$$\sin(-x) = -\sin x$$
$$\cos(-x) = \cos x$$
$$\sec x = \frac{1}{\cos x}, \qquad \csc x = \frac{1}{\sin x}$$
$$\tan x = \frac{\sin x}{\cos x}, \qquad \cot x = \frac{1}{\tan x}$$
$$\sin(x \pm 90°) = \pm \cos x$$
$$\cos(x \pm 90°) = \mp \sin x$$
$$\sin(x \pm 180°) = -\sin x$$
$$\cos(x \pm 180°) = -\cos x$$
$$\cos^2 x + \sin^2 x = 1$$

$$\frac{a}{\sin A} = \frac{b}{\sin B} = \frac{c}{\sin C} \qquad \text{(law of sines)}$$

$$a^2 = b^2 + c^2 - 2bc \cos A \qquad \text{(law of cosines)}$$

$$\frac{\tan \frac{1}{2}(A - B)}{\tan \frac{1}{2}(A + B)} = \frac{a - b}{a + b} \qquad \text{(law of tangents)}$$

$$\sin(x \pm y) = \sin x \cos y \pm \cos x \sin y$$
$$\cos(x \pm y) = \cos x \cos y \mp \sin x \sin y$$
$$\tan(x \pm y) = \frac{\tan x \pm \tan y}{1 \mp \tan x \tan y}$$
$$2 \sin x \sin y = \cos(x - y) - \cos(x + y)$$
$$2 \sin x \cos y = \sin(x + y) + \sin(x - y)$$
$$2 \cos x \cos y = \cos(x + y) + \cos(x - y)$$
$$\sin 2x = 2 \sin x \cos x$$

$$\cos 2x = \cos^2 x - \sin^2 x = 2\cos^2 x - 1 = 1 - 2\sin^2 x$$

$$\tan 2x = \frac{2\tan x}{1 - \tan^2 x}$$

$$\sin^2 x = \frac{1}{2}(1 - \cos 2x)$$

$$\cos^2 x = \frac{1}{2}(1 + \cos 2x)$$

$$K_1 \cos x + K_2 \sin x = \sqrt{K_1^2 + K_2^2} \cos\left(x + \tan^{-1}\frac{-K_2}{K_1}\right)$$

$$e^{jx} = \cos x + j \sin x \qquad \text{(Euler's formula)}$$

$$\cos x = \frac{e^{jx} + e^{-jx}}{2}$$

$$\sin x = \frac{e^{jx} - e^{-jx}}{2j}$$

$$1 \text{ rad} = 57.296°$$

C.3 Hyperbolic Functions

$$\sinh x = \frac{1}{2}(e^x - e^{-x})$$

$$\cosh x = \frac{1}{2}(e^x + e^{-x})$$

$$\tanh x = \frac{\sinh x}{\cosh x}$$

$$\coth x = \frac{1}{\tanh x}$$

$$\operatorname{csch} x = \frac{1}{\sinh x}$$

$$\operatorname{sech} x = \frac{1}{\cosh x}$$

$$\sinh(x \pm y) = \sinh x \cosh y \pm \cosh x \sinh y$$

$$\cosh(x \pm y) = \cosh x \cosh y \pm \sinh x \sinh y$$

C.4   Derivatives

If $U = U(x)$, $V = V(x)$, and $a = $ constant,

$$\frac{d}{dx}(aU) = a\frac{dU}{dx}$$

$$\frac{d}{dx}(UV) = U\frac{dV}{dx} + V\frac{dU}{dx}$$

$$\frac{d}{dx}\left(\frac{U}{V}\right) = \frac{V\dfrac{dU}{dx} - U\dfrac{dV}{dx}}{V^2}$$

$$\frac{d}{dx}(aU^n) = naU^{n-1}$$

$$\frac{d}{dx}(a^U) = a^U \ln a \frac{dU}{dx}$$

$$\frac{d}{dx}(e^U) = e^U \frac{dU}{dx}$$

$$\frac{d}{dx}(\sin U) = \cos U \frac{dU}{dx}$$

$$\frac{d}{dx}(\cos U) = -\sin U \frac{dU}{dx}$$

C.5   Indefinite Integrals

If $U = U(x)$, $V = V(x)$, and $a = $ constant,

$$\int a\, dx = ax + C$$

$$\int U\, dV = UV - \int V\, dU \qquad \text{(integration by parts)}$$

$$\int U^n\, dU = \frac{U^{n+1}}{n+1} + C, \qquad n \neq 1$$

$$\int \frac{dU}{U} = \ln U + C$$

$$\int a^U\, dU = \frac{a^U}{\ln a} + C, \qquad a > 0, a \neq 1$$

$$\int e^{ax}\, dx = \frac{1}{a}e^{ax} + C$$

$$\int xe^{ax}\, dx = \frac{e^{ax}}{a^2}(ax - 1) + C$$

$$\int x^2 e^{ax}\, dx = \frac{e^{ax}}{a^3}(a^2 x^2 - 2ax + 2) + C$$

$$\int \ln x \, dx = x \ln x - x + C$$

$$\int \sin ax \, dx = -\frac{1}{a} \cos ax + C$$

$$\int \cos ax \, dx = \frac{1}{a} \sin ax + C$$

$$\int \sin^2 ax \, dx = \frac{x}{2} - \frac{\sin 2ax}{4a} + C$$

$$\int \cos^2 ax \, dx = \frac{x}{2} + \frac{\sin 2ax}{4a} + C$$

$$\int x \sin ax \, dx = \frac{1}{a^2} (\sin ax - ax \cos ax) + C$$

$$\int x \cos ax \, dx = \frac{1}{a^2} (\cos ax + ax \sin ax) + C$$

$$\int x^2 \sin ax \, dx = \frac{1}{a^3} (2ax \sin ax + 2 \cos ax - a^2 x^2 \cos ax) + C$$

$$\int x^2 \cos ax \, dx = \frac{1}{a^3} (2ax \cos ax - 2 \sin ax + a^2 x^2 \sin ax) + C$$

$$\int e^{ax} \sin bx \, dx = \frac{e^{ax}}{a^2 + b^2} (a \sin bx - b \cos bx) + C$$

$$\int e^{ax} \cos bx \, dx = \frac{e^{ax}}{a^2 + b^2} (a \cos bx + b \sin bx) + C$$

$$\int \sin ax \sin bx \, dx = \frac{\sin(a - b)x}{2(a - b)} - \frac{\sin(a + b)x}{2(a + b)} + C, \qquad a^2 \neq b^2$$

$$\int \sin ax \cos bx \, dx = -\frac{\cos(a - b)x}{2(a - b)} - \frac{\cos(a + b)x}{2(a + b)} + C, \quad a^2 \neq b^2$$

$$\int \cos ax \cos bx \, dx = \frac{\sin(a - b)x}{2(a - b)} + \frac{\sin(a + b)x}{2(a + b)} + C, \qquad a^2 \neq b^2$$

$$\int \frac{dx}{a^2 + x^2} = \frac{1}{a} \tan^{-1} \frac{x}{a} + C$$

$$\int \frac{x^2 \, dx}{a^2 + x^2} = x - a \tan^{-1} \frac{x}{a} + C$$

$$\int \frac{dx}{(a^2 + x^2)^2} = \frac{1}{2a^2} \left(\frac{x}{x^2 + a^2} + \frac{1}{a} \tan^{-1} \frac{x}{a} \right) + C$$

C.6   Definite Integrals

If m and n are integers,

$$\int_0^{2\pi} \sin ax \, dx = 0$$

$$\int_0^{2\pi} \cos ax \, dx = 0$$

$$\int_0^{\pi} \sin^2 ax \, dx = \int_0^{\pi} \cos^2 ax \, dx = \frac{\pi}{2}$$

$$\int_0^{\pi} \sin mx \sin nx \, dx = \int_0^{\pi} \cos mx \cos nx \, dx = 0, \quad m \neq n$$

$$\int_0^{\pi} \sin mx \cos nx \, dx = \begin{cases} 0, & m+n = \text{even} \\ \dfrac{2m}{m^2 - n^2}, & m+n = \text{odd} \end{cases}$$

$$\int_0^{2\pi} \sin mx \sin nx \, dx = \int_{-\pi}^{\pi} \sin mx \sin nx \, dx = \begin{cases} 0, & m \neq n \\ \pi, & m = n \end{cases}$$

$$\int_0^{\infty} \frac{\sin ax}{x} \, dx = \begin{cases} \dfrac{\pi}{2}, & a > 0 \\ 0, & a = 0 \\ -\dfrac{\pi}{2}, & a < 0 \end{cases}$$

C.7   L'Hopital's Rule

If $f(0) = 0 = h(0)$, then

$$\lim_{x \to 0} \frac{f(x)}{h(x)} = \lim_{x \to 0} \frac{f'(x)}{h'(x)}$$

where the prime indicates differentiation.

Appendix D

PSpice for Windows

There are several computer software packages, such as *Spice*, *Mathcad*, *Quattro*, *MATLAB*, and *Maple*, which can be used for circuit analysis. The most popular is *Spice*, which stands for *Simulation Program with Integrated-Circuit Emphasis*. *Spice* was developed at the Department of Electrical and Computer Engineering at the University of California at Berkeley in the 1970s for mainframe computers. Since then about 20 versions have been developed. *PSpice*, a version of *Spice* for personal computers, was developed by MicroSim Corporation in California and made available in 1984 and later by OrCAD and cadence. *PSpice* has been made available in different operating systems (DOS, Windows, Unix, etc.).

The student version of *PSpice* can be obtained free of charge.

You can download *PSpice* from the Cadence website or obtain a hard copy from:

Cadence PCB Systems Division
13221 SW 68th Parkway, Suite 200
Portland, OR 97223
Phone: (503) 671-9500 or (800) CADENC2
Website: www.pcb.cadence.com or www.pspice.com

Since the Windows version of *PSpice* is becoming more and more popular, this is the version used throughout the text. Specifically, student version 9.1 of *PSpice for Windows* is used throughout this book. Assuming that you are using Windows 95 and have the *PSpice* software installed in your computer, you can access *PSpice* by clicking the Start icon on the left-hand corner of your PC; drag the cursor to Programs, to *PSpice* students and to Schematics, and then click as shown in Fig. D.1.[1]

The objective of this appendix is to provide a short tutorial on using the Windows-based *PSpice* on an IBM PC or equivalent.

PSpice can analyze up to roughly 130 elements and 100 nodes. It is capable of performing three major types of circuit analysis: dc analysis, transient analysis, and ac analysis. In addition, it can also perform transfer function analysis, Fourier analysis, and operating point analysis. The circuit can contain resistors, inductors, capacitors, independent and dependent voltage and current sources, op amps, transformers, transmission lines, and semiconductor devices.

We will assume that you are familiar with using the Microsoft Windows operating system and that *PSpice for Windows* is already installed in your computer. As with any standard Windows application, *PSpice* provides an on-line help system.

> If you need help on any topic at any level, click Help, click Help Topics, click Search, and type in the topic.

---

[1] We assume that the reader is familiar with using windows and dialog boxes. If this is not the case, one can easily learn how to use them with this appendix.

D.1 Design Center for Windows

In earlier versions of *PSpice* prior to Windows 95, *PSpice for Windows* is formally known as the *MicroSim Design Center*, which is a computer environment for simulating electric circuits. The *Design Center for Windows* includes the following programs:

Schematics: This program is a graphical editor used to draw the circuit to be simulated on the screen. It allows the user to enter the components, wire the components together to form the circuit, and specify the type of analysis to be performed.

PSpice: This program simulates the circuit created using Schematics. By simulation, we mean a method of analysis described in a program by which a circuit is represented by mathematical models of the components comprising the circuit.

Orcad PSpice: This program provides a graphic display of the output generated by the *PSpice* program. It can be used to observe any voltage or current in the circuit.

Figure D.I   Accessing *PSpice* on Windows 95.

One may think of Schematics as the computer breadboard for setting up the circuit topology, *PSpice* as the simulator (performing the computation), and *Orcad PSpice* as the oscilloscope. Using the Schematics program is perhaps the hardest part of circuit simulation using *PSpice*. The next section covers the essential skills needed to operate the Schematics.

D.2   Creating a Circuit

For a circuit to be analyzed by *PSpice*, we must take three steps: (1) create the circuit, (2) simulate it, and (3) print or plot the results. In this section, we learn how to create the circuit using the Schematics program.

Before we discuss how to use the Schematics capture, we need to know how to use the mouse to select an object and perform an action. One uses the mouse in Schematics in conjunction with the keyboard to carry out various instructions. Throughout this text, we will use the following terms to represent actions to be performed by the mouse:

- **CLICKL** : click the left button once to select an item.
- **CLICKR** : click the right button once to abort a mode.
- **DCLICKL** : double-click the left button to edit a selection or end a mode.
- **DCLICKR** : double-click the right button to repeat an action.
- **CLICKLH** : click the left button, hold down, and move the mouse to drag a selected item. Release the left button after the item has been placed.
- **DRAG** : drag the mouse (without clicking) to move an item.

When the term "click" is used, it means that you quickly press and release the **left** mouse button. To select an item requires **CLICKL**, while to perform an action requires **DCLICKL**. Also, to avoid writing "click" several times, the menu to be clicked will be highlighted in bold. For example, "click **Draw**, click **Get New Part**" will be written as **Draw/Get New Part**. Of course, we can always press the <Esc> key to abort any action.

Assuming that you are using Windows 95, you can access *PSpice* by clicking the Start icon on the left-hand corner of your PC, drag the cursor to Programs, *PSpice* student; and to Schematics, as shown in Fig. D.1. Alternatively, you have the *PSpice* icon on your screen. **DCLICK** on it. Either way, a blank screen will appear as shown in Fig. D.2. The file name [**Schematic1 p.1**] next to *PSpice* **Schematics** is assigned to a circuit which is yet to be saved. You can change it by pulling down the *File* menu.

To create a circuit using Schematics requires three steps: (1) placing the parts or components of the circuit, (2) wiring the parts together to form the circuit, and (3) changing attributes of the parts.

Step 1: Placing the Parts

Each circuit part is retrieved by following this procedure:

- Select **Draw/Get New Part** to pull down the Draw menu (or type <Ctrl-G>).
- Use scroll bar to select the part (or type the part name, e.g., R for resistor, in the *PartName* box). Figures D.3 to D.5 show some part

Figure D.2   Schematics window.

Figure D.3   Part symbols and attributes for circuit elements: (a) a resistor, (b) a capacitor, (c) an inductor.

names and symbols for circuit elements and independent voltage and current sources.

• Click **Place & Close** (or press <Enter>).

• **DRAG** part to the desired location on the screen.

• **CLICKR** to terminate the placement mode.

Sometimes, we want to rotate a part 90°. To rotate a resistor, for example, select the part R and click **Edit/Rotate** (or type <Ctrl R>). To delete a part, **CLICKL** to select (highlight red) the part, then click **Edit/Cut** (or press <Delete>).

Figure D.4   Part symbols and attributes for independent voltage sources.

Step 2: Wiring Parts Together

We complete the circuit by wiring the parts together. We first select **Draw/Wire** (or type <Ctrl-W>) to be in wiring mode. A pencil cursor will appear in place of an arrow cursor. **DRAG** the pencil cursor to the first point you want to connect and **CLICKL**. Next, **DRAG** the pencil cursor to the second point and **CLICKL** to change the dashed line to a solid line. (Only solid lines are wires.) **CLICKR** to end the wiring mode. To resume the wiring mode, press the <Space bar>. Repeat the above procedure for each connection in the circuit until all the parts are wired. The wiring is not complete without adding a ground connection (part AGND) to a schematic; *PSpice* will not operate without it. To verify that the parts are actually connected together, the *Junctions* option available in the **Options/Set Display Level** menu should be in the on position when wiring the parts. By default, the *Junctions* option is marked with a checksign (✓) in the dialog box, indicating that it is on.

Some of the connections have a black dot indicating a connection. Although it is not necessary to have a dot where a wire joins a pin, having the dot shows the presence of a connection. To be sure a dot appears, make sure the wire overlaps the pin.

If you make a mistake, you can delete the part or wire by highlighting it (select **CLICKL**) and pressing the <Delete> key. Typing <Ctrl-L> will erase the fragments that are not really on the schematic.

Step 3: Changing Attributes of Parts

As shown in Figs. D.3 to D.5, each component has an attribute in addition to its symbol. Attributes are the labels for parts. Each attribute consists of a *name* and its designated *value*. For example, R and VSRC are the names of resistor and voltage source (dc, ac, or transient source), while 2k and DC = +10V are the designated values of the resistor and voltage source, respectively.

As parts are placed on the screen, they are automatically assigned names by successive numbers (R1, R2, R3, etc.). Also, some parts are assigned some predetermined values. For example, all resistors are placed horizontally and assigned a value of 1 kΩ. We may need to change the attributes (names and values) of a part. Although there are several ways of changing the attributes, the following is one simple way.

To change the name R3 to RX, for example, **DCLICKL** on the text R3 to bring up the *Edit Reference Designator* dialog box of Fig. D.6(a). Type the new name RX and click the **OK** button to accept the change. The same procedure can be used to change VDC to V1 or whatever.

To change the value 1k to 10Meg, for example, **DCLICKL** on the 1k attribute (not the symbol) to open up the *Set Attribute Value* dialog box of Fig. D.6(b). Type the new value 10Meg (no space between 10 and Meg) and click the **OK** button to accept the change. Similarly, to change the default value 0V to 15kV for voltage source VDC, **DCLICKL** the symbol for VDC to bring up the *PartName* dialog box. **DCLICKL** on the $DC =$ attribute and type 15kV in the value box. For convenience, one can express numbers with the scale factors in Table D.1. For example, 6.6×10^{-8} can be written as 66N or 0.066U.

OA   IDC

(a) A dc only source

OA   IAC

(b) An ac only source

ISIN

(c) An ac or dc source

ISRC

(d) An ac, dc, or transient source

Figure D.5   Part symbols and attributes for independent current sources.

A component may have several attributes; some are displayed by default. If need be, we may add more attributes for display, but we should hide unimportant attributes to avoid clutter.

(a)

(b)

Figure D.6   (a) Changing name R3 to RX, (b) changing 1k to 10Meg.

TABLE D.1	Scale factors.	
Symbol	Value	Name of suffix
T	10^{12}	tera
G	10^{9}	giga
MEG	10^{6}	mega
K	10^{3}	kilo
M	10^{-3}	milli
U	10^{-6}	micro
N	10^{-9}	nano
P	10^{-12}	pico
F	10^{-15}	femto

It is always expedient to number the nodes by numbering the wires. Otherwise, Schematics will label the nodes its own way, and one may not understand which node is which in the output results.

Except for the ground, which is automatically assigned node 0, every node is either given a name (or number) or is assigned one in the netlist. A node is labeled by giving a name to a wire connected to that node. **DCLICKL** the wire to open up the *Set Attribute Value* dialog box, and type the label.

To obtain a hard copy of the screen/schematic, click **File/Print/OK**. To save the schematic created, select **File/Save As** and type Filename. Click **OK** or press <Enter>. This creates a file named "filename" and saves it with extension .sch.

EXAMPLE D.1

Figure D.7   For Example D.1.

Draw the circuit in Fig. D.7 using Schematics.

Solution:

We will follow the three steps mentioned above. We begin by double-clicking the **Schematics** icon. This provides us with a blank screen as a worksheet to draw the circuit on. We now take the following steps to create the circuit in Fig. D.7.

To place the voltage source, we need to:

1. Click **Draw/Get New Part** (or type < Ctrl-G >).
2. Type VSRC in the *Part Browser Basic* box.
3. Click **OK** (or type <Enter>).
4. **DRAG** the part to the desired location on the screen.
5. **CLICKL** to place VSRC and **CLICKR** to terminate placement mode.

At this point, only the voltage source V1 in Fig. D.8(a) is shown on the screen, highlighted red. To place the resistors, we need to:

1. Click **Draw/Get New Part**.
2. Type R in the *Part Browser Basic* box.
3. Click **OK**.
4. **DRAG** resistor to R1's location on the screen.
5. **CLICKL** to place R1.

6. **CLICKL** to place R2 and **CLICKR** to terminate placement mode.

7. **DRAG** R2 to its location.

8. **Edit/Rotate** (or type <Ctrl-R>) to rotate R2.

At this point, the three parts have been created as shown in Fig. D.8(a). The next step is to connect the parts by wiring. To do this:

1. Click **Draw/Wire** to be in wiring mode, indicated by the pencil cursor.

2. **DRAG** the pencil cursor to the top of V1.

3. **CLICKL** to join the wire to the top of V1.

4. **DRAG** the dotted wire to the top corner.

5. **CLICKL** to turn wire segment solid, and anchor at corner.

6. **DRAG** dotted wire to left of R1.

7. **CLICKL** to turn wire segment solid and anchor to left of R1.

8. **CLICKR** to end placement mode.

Follow the same steps to connect R1 with R2 and V1 with R2. (You can resume the wiring mode by pressing <Space bar>.) At this point, we have the circuit in Fig. D.8(b), except that the ground symbol is missing. We insert the ground by taking the following steps:

1. Click **Draw/Get New Part**.

2. Type AGND in the *Part Browser Basic* box.

3. Click **OK**.

4. **DRAG** the part to the desired location on the screen.

5. **CLICKL** to place AGND and **CLICKR** to terminate placement mode.

The last thing to be done is to change or assign values to the attributes. To assign the attribute 12V to V1, we take these steps:

1. **DCLICKL** on the V1 symbol to open up the *PartName* dialog box.

2. **DCLICKL** on the *DC =* attribute.

3. Type +12V (or simply 12) in the *Value* box.

4. Click **Save Attr**.

5. Click **OK**.

To assign 5k to R1, we follow these steps:

1. **DCLICKL** on 1k attribute of R1 to bring up the *Set Attribute Value* dialog box.

2. Type 5k in the *Value* box.

3. Click **OK**.

Use the same procedure in assigning value 2k to R2. Figure D.8(c) shows the final circuit.

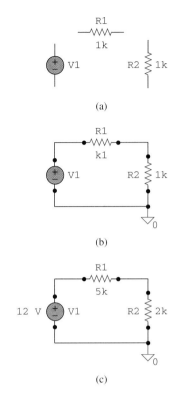

Figure D.8   Creating the circuit in Fig. D.7: (a) placing the parts, (b) wiring the parts together, (c) changing the attributes.

PRACTICE PROBLEM D.1

Construct the circuit in Fig. D.9 with Schematics.

Answer: See the schematic Fig. D.10.

Figure D.9   For Practice Prob. D.1.

Figure D.10   For Practice Prob. D.1.

D.3   DC Analysis

DC analysis is one of the standard analyses that we can perform using *PSpice*. Other standard analyses include transient, AC, and Fourier. Under DC analysis, there are two kinds of simulation that *PSpice* can execute: DC nodal analysis and DC sweep.

1. DC Nodal Analysis

PSpice allows dc nodal analysis to be performed on sources with an attribute of the form DC = value and provides the dc voltage at each node of the circuit and dc branch currents if required. To view dc node voltages and branch currents requires adding two kinds of additional parts, shown in Fig. D.11. The symbol VIEWPOINT is connected to each node at which the voltage is to be viewed, while the symbol IPROBE is connected in the branch where the current is to be displayed. This necessitates modifying the schematic. For example, let us consider placing voltage VIEWPOINTS and current IPROBES to the schematic in Fig. D.8(c). To add VIEWPOINTS, we take the following steps:

   (a)   (b)

Figure D.11   Symbols for:
(a) voltage VIEWPOINT,
(b) current IPROBE.

1. Click **Draw/Get New Part** (or type <Ctrl-G>).
2. Type VIEWPOINT in the *Part Browser Basic* box.
3. Click **OK** (or type <Enter>).
4. **DRAG** to locate VIEWPOINT above V1 and **CLICKL**.
5. **DRAG** to locate VIEWPOINT above R2 and **CLICKL**.
6. **CLICKR** to end placement mode.

Figure D.12 shows the two voltage VIEWPOINTS. Since the IPROBE symbol must be connected in series with a branch element, we need to move R2 down by clicking and dragging R2 and the wires. Once this is done, we add IPROBE as follows:

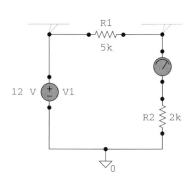

Figure D.12   Placing VIEWPOINTS
and IPROBES.

1. Click **Draw/Get New Part** (or type <Ctrl-G>).
2. Type IPROBE in the *Part Browser Basic* box.
3. Click **OK** (or type <Enter>).
4. **DRAG** to locate IPROBE above R2 and **CLICKL**.

5. **CLICKR** to end placement mode.

6. Use wiring to join all gaps.

The schematic becomes that shown in Fig. D.12. We are ready to simulate the circuit. At this point, we must save the schematic—*PSpice* will not run without first saving the schematic to be simulated. Before learning how to run *PSpice*, note the following points:

1. There must be a reference node or ground connection (part AGND) in the schematic. Any node can be used as ground, and the voltages at other nodes will be with respect to the selected ground.

2. Dependent sources are found in the Parts library. Obtain them by selecting **Draw/Get New Part** and typing the part name. Figure D.13 shows the part name for each type, with the gain. *E* is a voltage-controlled voltage source with gain *e*; *F* is a current-controlled current source with gain *f*; *G* is a voltage-controlled current source with a transconductance gain *g*; and *H* is a current-controlled voltage source with transresistance gain *h*.

3. By convention, we assume in dc analysis that all capacitors are open circuits and all inductors are short circuits.

We run *PSpice* by clicking **Analysis/Simulate**. This invokes the *electric rule check* (ERC), which generates the *netlist*. The ERC performs a connectivity check on the schematic before creating the netlist. The netlist is a list describing the operational behavior of each component in the circuit and its connections. Each line in the netlist represents a single component of the circuit. The netlist can be examined by clicking **Analysis/Examine Netlist** from the Schematics window. If there are errors in the schematic, an *error* window will appear. Click **OK** (or type <Enter>) to display the error list. After noting the errors, exit from the error list and go back to Schematics to correct the errors. If no errors are found, the system automatically enters *PSpice* and performs the simulation (nodal analysis). When the analysis is complete, the program displays **Bias point calculated**, and creates the result/output file with extension .out.

To examine the output file, click **Analysis/Examine Output** from the Schematics window (or click **File/Examine Output** from the *PSpice* window). To print the output file, click **File/Print**, and to exit the output file, click **File/Exit**.

We can also examine the results of the simulation by looking at the values displayed on the VIEWPOINTS and IPROBES parts of the schematics after the simulation is complete. The values displayed with VIEWPOINTS and IPROBES should be the same as those in the output file.

2. DC Sweep

DC nodal analysis allows simulation for DC sources with fixed voltages or currents. DC sweep provides more flexibility in that it allows the calculation of node voltages and branch currents of a circuit when a source is

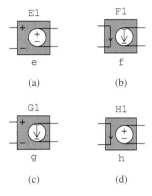

Figure D.13   Dependent sources:
(a) voltage-controlled voltage source (VCVS),
(b) current-controlled current source (CCCS),
(c) voltage-controlled current source (VCCS),
(d) current-controlled voltage source (CCVS).

A netlist can be generated manually or automatically by Schematics.

There are two kinds of common errors in *PSpice*: (1) errors involving wiring of the circuit, and (2) errors that occur during simulation.

swept over a range of values. As in nodal analysis, we assume capacitors to be open circuits and inductors to be short circuits.

Suppose we desire to perform a DC sweep of voltage source V1 in Fig. D.12 from 0 to 20 volts in 1-volt increments. We proceed as follows:

1. Click **Analysis/Setup**.
2. **CLICKL DC Sweep** button.
3. Click *Name* box and type *V*1.
4. Click *Start Value* box and type 0.
5. Click *End Value* box and type 20.
6. Click *Increment* box and type 1.
7. Click **OK** to end the *DC Sweep* dialog box and save parameters.
8. Click **Close** to end the *Analysis Setup* menu.

Figure D.14 shows the *DC Sweep* dialog box. Notice that the default setting is *Voltage Source* for the *Swept Var. Type*, while it is *Linear* for *Sweep Type*. If needed, other options can be selected by clicking the appropriate buttons.

Figure D.14   DC sweep analysis dialog box.

To run DC sweep analysis, click **Analysis/Simulate**. Schematics will create a netlist and then run *PSpice* if no errors are found. If errors are found in the schematic, check for them in the *Error List* and correct them as usual. If no errors are found, the data generated by *PSpice* is passed to *Orcad PSpice*. The *Orcad PSpice* window will appear, displaying a graph in which the X axis is by default set to the DC sweep variable and range, and the Y axis is blank for now. To display some specific plots, click **Trace/Add** in the *Orcad PSpice* menu to open the *Add Traces* dialog box. The box contains traces, which are the output variables (node voltages and branch currents) in the data file available for display. Select the traces to be displayed by clicking or typing them, and click **OK**. The selected traces will be plotted and displayed on the screen. As many traces as you want may be added to the same plot or on different windows. Select a new window by clicking **Window/New**. To delete a trace, click the trace name in the legend of the plot to highlight it and click **Edit/Delete** (or press <Delete>).

It is important to understand how to interpret the traces. We must interpret the voltage and current variables according to the passive sign convention. As parts are initially placed horizontally in a schematic as shown typically in Fig. D.3, the left-hand terminal is named pin 1 while the right-hand terminal is pin 2. When a component (say R1) is rotated counterclockwise once, pin 2 would be on the top, since rotation is about pin 1. Therefore, if current enters through pin 2, the current I(R1) through R1 would be negative. In other words, positive current implies that the current enters through pin 1, and negative current means that the current enters through pin 2. As for voltage variables, they are always with respect to the ground. For example, V(R1:2) is the voltage (with respect to the ground) at pin 2 of resistor R1; V(V1:+) is the voltage (with respect to the positive terminal of voltage source V1; and V(E2:1) is the voltage at pin 1 of component E2 with respect to ground, regardless of the polarity.

EXAMPLE D.2

For the circuit in Fig. D.15, find the dc node voltages and the current i_o.

Figure D.15   For Example D.2.

Solution:

We use *Schematics* to create the circuit. After saving the circuit, click **Analysis/Simulate** to simulate the circuit. We obtain the results of the dc analysis from the output file or from the VIEWPOINT AND IPROBE parts, as shown in Fig. D.16. The netlist file is shown in Fig. D.17. Notice that the netlist contains the name, value, and connection for each element in the circuit. First example, the first line shows that the voltage source V1

Figure D.16   For Example D.2; schematic for the circuit in Fig. D.15.

```
*  Schematics  Netlist  *

V_V1       1 0 28
R_R1       0 4 4k
R_R2       1 2 12k
R_R3       2 3 1k
R_R4       0 3 3k
I_I1       0 3 DC  7mA
v_V2       2 4 0
```

Figure D.17   The Netlist file for Example D.2.

has a value of 28 V and is connected between nodes 0 and 1. Figure D.18 shows the edited version of the output file. The output file also contains the Netlist file, but this was removed from Fig. D.18. From IPROBE or the output file, we obtain i_o as 3.25 mA.

```
**** 11/26/99 20:56:05 ********* NT Evaluation PSpice (Nov. 1999) *********

* C:\ MSIMEV63\ examd2.sch

**** CIRCUIT DESCRIPTION

********************************************************************************

* Schematics Version 6.3 - April 1996
* Sat Jul 26 20:56:04 1997

**** INCLUDING examd2.als ****
* Schematics Aliases *

.ALIASES
V_V1        V1(+=1 -=0 )
R_R1        R1(1=0 2=4 )
R_R2        R2(1=1 2=2 )
R_R3        R3(1=2 2=3 )
R_R4        R4(1=0 2=3 )
I_I1        I1(+=0 -=3 )
v_V2        V2(+-2 -=4 )
_ _(1=1)
_ _(2=2)
_ _(3=3)
.ENDALIASES

.probe

.END

NODE VOLTAGE        NODE VOLTAGE        NODE VOLTAGE        NODE VOLTAGE

( 1) 28.0000      ( 2) 13.0000      ( 3) 15.0000      ( 4) 13.0000

VOLTAGE SOURCE CURRENTS
NAME     CURRENT

V_V1       -1.250E-03
v_V2        3.250E-03

TOTAL POWER DISSIPATION 3.50E-02 WATTS
```

Figure D.18   Output file (edited version) for Example D.2.

PRACTICE PROBLEM D.2

Use *PSpice* to determine the node voltages and the current i_x in the circuit of Fig. D.19.

Figure D.19   For Practice Prob. D.2.

Answer: $V_1 = 50$, $V_2 = 37.2$, $V_3 = 27.9$, $i_x = 3.1$ mA.

EXAMPLE D.3

Plot I_1 and I_2 if the dc voltage source in Fig. D.20 is swept from 2 V to 10 V.

Figure D.20   For Example D.3.

Solution:

We draw the schematic of the circuit and set the attributes as shown in Fig. D.21. Notice how the voltage-controlled voltage source E1 is connected. After completing the schematic, we select **Analysis/Setup** and

Figure D.21   The schematic for the circuit in Fig. D.20.

input the start, end, and increment values as 2, 10, and 0.5, respectively. By selecting **Analysis/Simulate**, we bring up the Orcad *PSpice* window. We select **Trace/Add** and click I(R1) and −I(R3) to be displayed. (The negative sign is needed to make the current through R3 positive.) Figure D.22 shows the result.

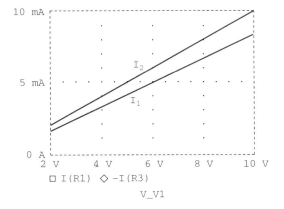

Figure D.22   Plots of I_1 and I_2 against V1.

PRACTICE PROBLEM D.3

Use *PSpice* to obtain the plots of i_x and i_o if the dc voltage source in Fig. D.23 is swept from 2 V to 10 V.

Answer: The plots of i_x and i_o are displayed in Fig. D.24.

Figure D.23   For Practice Prob. D.3.

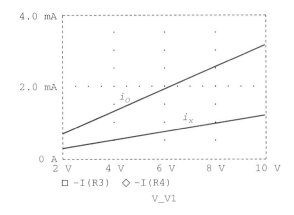

Figure D.24   Plots of i_x and i_o versus V1.

D.4   Transient Analysis

In *PSpice*, transient analysis is generally used to examine the behavior of a waveform (voltage or current) as time varies. Transient analysis solves some differential equations describing a circuit and obtains voltages and currents versus time. Transient analysis is also used to obtain Fourier analysis. To perform transient analysis on a circuit using *PSpice* usually involves these steps: (1) drawing the circuit, (2) providing specifications, and (3) simulating the circuit.

1. Drawing the Circuit

In order to run a transient analysis on a circuit, the circuit must first be created using Schematics and the source must be specified. *PSpice* has several time-varying functions or sources that enhance the performance of transient analysis. Sources used in the transient analysis include:

- VSIN, ISIN: damped sinusoidal voltage or current source, e.g., $v(t) = 10e^{-0.2t}\sin(120\pi t - 60°)$.
- VPULSE, IPULSE: voltage or current pulse.
- VEXP, IEXP: voltage or current exponential source, e.g., $i(t) = 6[1 - \exp(-0.5t)]$.
- VPWL, IPWL: piecewise linear voltage or current function, which can be used to create an arbitrary waveform.

It is expedient to take a close look at these functions.

VSIN is the exponentially damped sinusoidal voltage source, for example,

$$v(t) = V_o + V_m e^{-\alpha(t-t_d)} \sin[2\pi f(t - t_d) + \phi] \tag{D.1}$$

The VSIN source has the following attributes, which are illustrated in Fig. D.25 and compared with Eq. (D.1).

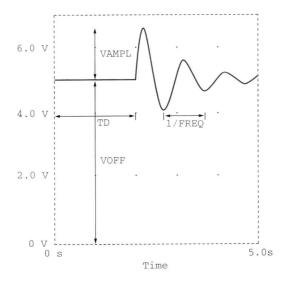

Figure D.25   Sinusoidal voltage source VSIN.

$$\text{VOFF} = \text{Offset voltage}, V_o$$
$$\text{VAMPL} = \text{Amplitude}, V_m$$
$$\text{TD} = \text{Time delay in seconds}, t_d$$
$$\text{FREQ} = \text{Frequency in Hz}, f \qquad \text{(D.2)}$$
$$\text{DF} = \text{Damping factor (dimensionless)}, \alpha$$
$$\text{PHASE} = \text{Phase in degrees}, \phi$$

Attributes TD, DF, and PHASE are set to 0 by default but can be assigned other values if necessary. What has been said about VSIN is also true for ISIN.

The VPULSE source has the following attributes, which are portrayed in Fig. D.26.

$$\text{V1} = \text{Low voltage}$$
$$\text{V2} = \text{High voltage}$$
$$\text{TD} = \text{Initial time delay in seconds}$$
$$\text{TR} = \text{Rise time in seconds} \qquad \text{(D.3)}$$
$$\text{TF} = \text{Fall time in seconds}$$
$$\text{PW} = \text{Pulse width in seconds}$$
$$\text{PER} = \text{Period in seconds}$$

Attributes V1 and V2 must be assigned values. By default, attribute TD is assigned 0; TR and TF are assigned the *print step* value; and PW and PER are assigned the *final time* value. The values of the *print time* and *final time* are obtained as default values from the specifications provided by the user in the **Transient Analysis/Setup**, to be discussed a little later.

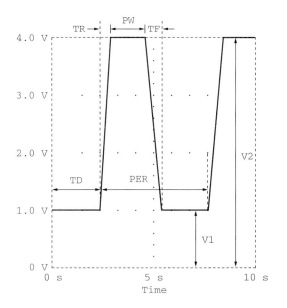

Figure D.26   Pulse voltage source VPULSE.

The exponential voltage source VEXP has the following attributes, typically illustrated in Fig. D.27.

$$
\begin{aligned}
V1 &= \text{Initial voltage} \\
V2 &= \text{Final voltage} \\
TD1 &= \text{Rise delay in seconds} \\
TC1 &= \text{Rise time constant in seconds} \\
TD2 &= \text{Fall delay in seconds} \\
TC2 &= \text{Fall time in seconds}
\end{aligned}
\qquad (\text{D.4})
$$

Figure D.27   Exponential voltage source VEXP.

The piecewise linear voltage source VPWL, such as shown in Fig. D.28, requires specifying pairs of TN, VN, where VN is the voltage at time TN for $N = 1, 2, \ldots, 10$. For example, for the function in Fig. D.29, we will need to specify the attributes $T1 = 0$, $V1 = 0$, $T2 = 2$, $V2 = 4$, $T3 = 6$, $V3 = 4$, and $T4 = 8$, $V4 = -2$.

To obtain information about other sources, click **Help/Search for Help on** ... and type in the name of the source. To add a source to the schematic, take the following steps:

1. Select **Draw/Get New Part**.

2. Type the name of the source.

3. Click **OK** and **DRAG** the symbol to the desired location.

4. **DCLICKL** the symbol of the source to open up the *PartName* dialog box.

5. For each attribute, **DCLICKL** on the attribute, enter the value, and click **Save Attr** to accept changes.

6. Click **OK** to accept new attributes.

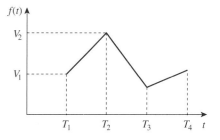

Figure D.28   Piecewise linear voltage source VPWL.

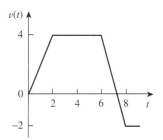

Figure D.29   An example of a piecewise linear voltage source VPWL.

In step 5, the attributes may not be shown on the schematic after entering their values. To display an attribute, select **Change Display/Both Name and Value** in the *PartName* dialog box.

In addition to specifying the source to be used in transient analysis, there may be need to set initial conditions on capacitors and inductors in the circuit. To do so, **DCLICKL** the part symbol to bring up the *PartName* dialog box, click **IC =** and type in the initial condition. The IC attribute allows for setting the initial conditions on a capacitor or inductor. The default value of IC is 0. The attributes of open/close switches (with part names Sw_tClose and Sw_tOpen) can be changed in a similar manner.

2. Providing Specifications

After the circuit is drawn and the source is specified with its attributes, we need to add some specifications for the transient analysis. For example, suppose we want the analysis to run the simulation from 0 to 10 ms with a print interval of 2 ns; we enter these specifications as follows:

1. Select **Analysis/Setup/Transient** to open up the *Transient Analysis* dialog box.
2. **CLICKL** *Print Step* and type 2 ns.
3. **CLICKL** *Final Time* and type 10 ms.
4. **CLICKL** *Step Ceiling* and type 5 us.
5. **CLICKL OK/Close** to accept specifications.

To obtain the Fourier component of a signal, we enable the Fourier option in the *Transient Analysis* dialog box. Chapter 17 has more on this.

These specifications control the simulation and the display of output variables. *Final Time* specifies how long the simulation should run. In other words, the simulation runs from $t = 0$ to $t = $ Final Time. *Print Step* refers to the time interval the print part will print out; it controls how often simulation results are written to the output file. The value of *Print Step* can be any value less than the *Final Time*, but it cannot be zero. *Step Ceiling* is the maximum time between simulation points; specifying its value is optional. By selecting 10 ms as *Final Time* and 5 μs as *Step Ceiling*, the simulation will have a minimum of 10 ms/5 μs = 2000 points. When *Step Ceiling* is unspecified, *PSpice* selects its own internal time step—the time between simulation points. The time step is selected as large as possible to reduce simulation time. If the user has no idea of what the plot may look like, it is recommended that the value of *Step Ceiling* be unspecified. If the plot is jagged as a result of a large time step assumed by *PSpice*, the user may now specify a *Step Ceiling* that will smooth the plot. Keep in mind that a smaller value gives more points in the simulation but takes more time.

3. Simulating the Circuit

After the circuit is drawn, the specifications for the transient analysis are given, and the circuit is saved, we are ready to simulate it. To perform transient analysis, we select **Analysis/Simulate**. If there are no errors, the *Orcad PSpice* window will automatically appear. As usual, the time axis (or X axis) is drawn but no curves are drawn yet. Select **Trace/Add** and click on the variables to be displayed.

An alternative way of displaying the results is to use *markers*. Although there are many types of markers, we will discuss only voltage and current markers. A voltage marker is used to display voltage at a node relative to ground; a current marker is for displaying current through a component pin. To place a voltage marker at a node, take the following steps while in the Schematics window:

1. Select **Markers/Mark Voltage/Level**.
2. **DRAG** the voltage marker to the desired node.
3. **CLICKL** to place the marker and **CLICKR** to end the placement mode.

This will cause two things to happen immediately. The voltage marker becomes part of the circuit and the appropriate node voltage is automatically displayed by Orcad *PSpice* window when the Schematics is run. To place a current marker at a component pin, take the following steps in the Schematics window:

1. Select **Markers/Mark current into pin**.
2. **DRAG** the current marker to the desired pin.
3. **CLICKL** to place the marker and **CLICKR** to end the placement mode.

This will automatically add the current through the pin to your graph. It is important that the current marker be placed at the pin of the component; otherwise the system would reject the marker. You can place as many voltage and current markers as you want on a circuit. To remove the markers from the circuit as well as the plots from the *Orcad PSpice* window, select **Markers/Clear All** from Schematics window.

EXAMPLE D.4

Assuming that $i(0) = 10$ A, plot the zero-input response $i(t)$ in the circuit of Fig. D.30 for $0 < t < 4$ s using *PSpice*.

Solution:

The circuit is the same as the one for Example 7.3, where we obtained the solution as

$$i(t) = 10e^{(-2/3)t}$$

For *PSpice* analysis, the schematic is in Fig. D.31, where the current-controlled source H1 has been wired to agree with the circuit in Fig. D.30. The voltage of H1 is 3 times the current through inductor L1. Therefore, for H1, we set GAIN $= 3$ and for the inductor L1, we set the initial condition IC $= 10$. Using the **Analysis/Setup/Transient** dialog box, we set *Print Step* $= 0.25$ s and *Final Time* $= 4$ s. After simulating the circuit, the output is taken as the inductor current $i(t)$, which is plotted in Fig. D.32.

Figure D.30   For Example D.4.

Figure D.31   The schematic of
the circuit in Fig. D.30.

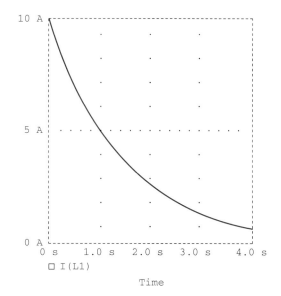

□ I(L1)

Time

Figure D.32   Output plot for Example D.4.

PRACTICE PROBLEM D.4

Figure D.33   For
Practice Prob. D.4.

Using *PSpice*, plot the source-free response $v(t)$ in the circuit of
Fig. D.33, assuming that $v(0) = 10$ V.

Answer: Figure D.34 shows the plot. Note that
$v(t) = 10e^{-0.25t} \cos 0.5t + 5e^{-0.25t} \sin 0.5t$ V.

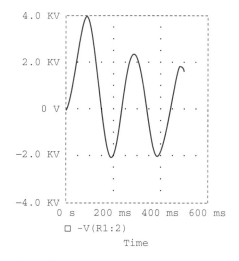

□ -V(R1:2)

Time

Figure D.34   Output plot for Practice Prob. D.4.

EXAMPLE D.5

Plot the forced response $v_o(t)$ in the circuit of Fig. D.35(a) for $0 < t < 5$ s
if the source voltage is shown in Fig. D.35(b).

Figure D.35   For Example D.5.

Solution:

We draw the circuit and set the attributes as shown in Fig. D.36. We enter in the data in Fig. D.35(b) by double-clicking the symbol of the voltage source V1 and typing in T1 = 0, V1 = 0, T2 = 1 ns, V2 = 12, T3 = 1 s, V3 = 12, T4 = 1.001 s, V4 = 0, T5 = 2 s, V5 = 0, T6 = 2.001 s, V6 = 12, T7 = 3 s, V7 = 12, T8 = 3.001 s, V8 = 0. In the **Analysis/Setup/Transient** dialog box, we set *Print Step* = 0.2 s and *Final Time* = 5 s. When the circuit is simulated and we are in the Orcad *PSpice* window, we close or minimize the window to go back to the Schematics window. We place two voltage markers as shown in Fig. D.36 to get the plots of input v_s and output v_o. We press <Alt-Esc> to get into the Orcad *PSpice* window and obtain the plots shown in Fig. D.37.

Figure D.36   The schematic of the circuit in Fig. D.35.

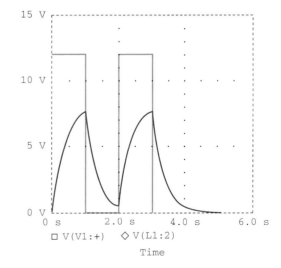

Figure D.37   Output plot for Example D.5.

PRACTICE PROBLEM D.5

Obtain the plot of $v(t)$ in the circuit in Fig. D.38 for $0 < t < 0.5$ s if $i_s = 2e^{-t} \sin 2\pi(5)t$ A.

Answer: See Fig. D.39.

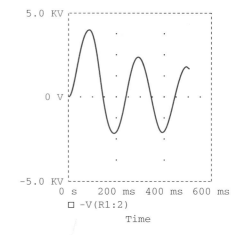

Figure D.38   For Practice Prob. D.5.

Figure D.39   Output plot for Practice Prob. D.5.

D.5 AC Analysis/Frequency Response

Using AC sweep, *PSpice* can perform AC analysis of a circuit for a single frequency or over a range of frequencies in increments that can vary linearly, by decade, or by octave. In AC sweep, one or more sources are swept over a range of frequencies while the voltages and currents of the circuit are calculated. Thus, we use AC sweep both for phasor analysis and for frequency response analysis: it will output Bode gain and phase plots. (Keep in mind that a phasor is a complex quantity with real and imaginary parts or with magnitude and phase.)

While transient analysis is done in the time domain, AC analysis is performed in the frequency domain. For example, if $v_s = 10\cos(377t + 40°)$, transient analysis can be used to display v_s as a function of time, whereas AC sweep will give the magnitude as 10 and phase as 40°. To perform AC sweep requires taking three steps similar to those for transient analysis: (1) drawing the circuit, (2) providing specifications, and (3) simulating the circuit.

1. Drawing the Circuit

We first draw the circuit using Schematics and specify the source(s). Sources used in AC sweep are AC sources VAC and IAC. The sources and attributes are entered into the Schematics as stated in the previous section. For each independent source, we must specify its magnitude and phase.

2. Providing Specifications

Before simulating the circuit, we need to add some specifications for AC sweep. For example, suppose we want a linear sweep at frequencies 50, 100, and 150 Hz. We enter these parameters as follows:

1. Select **Analysis/Setup/AC Sweep** to open up the dialog box for AC Sweep.
2. **CLICKL** *Linear* for the *X* axis to have a linear scale.
3. Type 3 in the *Total Pts* box.

4. Type 50 in the *Start Freq* box.

5. Type 150 in the *End Freq* box.

6. **CLICKL OK/Close** to accept specifications.

A linear sweep implies that simulation points are spread uniformly between the starting and ending frequencies. Note that the *Start Freq* cannot be zero because 0 Hz corresponds to DC analysis. If we want the simulation to be done at a single frequency, we enter 1 in step 3 and the same frequency in steps 4 and 5. If we want the AC sweep to simulate the circuit from 1 Hz to 10 MHz at 10 points per decade, we **CLICKL** on *Decade* in step 2 to make the *X* axis logarithmic, enter 10 in the *Total Pts* box in step 3, enter 1 in the *Start Freq* box, and enter 10Meg in the *End Freq* box. Keep in mind that a decade is a factor of 10. In this case, a decade is from 1 Hz to 10 Hz, from 10 Hz to 100, from 100 to 1 kHz, and so forth.

3. Simulating the Circuit

After providing the necessary specifications and saving the circuit, we perform the AC sweep by selecting **Analysis/Simulate**. If no errors are encountered, the circuit is simulated. At the end of the simulation, the system displays **AC analysis finished** and creates an output file with extension .out. Also, the Orcad *PSpice* program will automatically run if there are no errors. The frequency axis (or *X* axis) is drawn but no curves are shown yet. Select **Trace/Add** from the Orcad *PSpice* menu bar and click on the variables to be displayed. We may also use current or voltage markers to display the traces as explained in the previous section. To use advanced markers such as *vdb, idb, vphase, iphase, vreal,* and *ireal,* select **Markers/Mark Advanced**.

In case the resolution of the trace is not good enough, we may need to check the data points to see if they are enough. To do so, select **Tools/Options/Mark Data Points/OK** in the Orcad *PSpice* menu and the data points will be displayed. If necessary, we can improve the resolution by increasing the value of the entry in the **Total Pts** box in the **Analysis/Setup/AC Sweep and Noise Analysis** dialog box for AC sweep.

Bode plots are separate plots of magnitude and phase versus frequency. To obtain Bode plots, it is common to use an AC source, say V1, with 1 volt magnitude and zero phase. After we have selected **Analysis/Simulate** and have the Orcad *PSpice* program running, we can display the magnitude and phase plots as mentioned above. Suppose we want to display a Bode magnitude plot of V(4). We select **Trace/Add** and type **dB(V(4))** in **Trace Command** box. dB(V(4)) is equivalent to 20log(V(4)), and because the magnitude of V1 or V(R1:1) is unity, dB(V(4)) actually corresponds to dB(V(4)/V(R1:1)), which is the gain. Adding the trace dB(V(4)) will give a Bode magnitude/gain plot with the *Y* axis in dB.

Once a plot is obtained in the Orcad *PSpice* window, we can add labels to it for documentation purposes. To add a title to the plot, select **Edit/Modify Title** in the Orcad *PSpice* menu and type the title in the

To generate Bode plots involves using the AC sweep and the dB command in Orcad *PSpice*.

dialog box. To add a label to the *Y* axis, select **Plot/Y Axis Settings**, type the label, and **CLICKL OK**. Add a label to the *X* axis in the same manner.

As an alternative approach, we can avoid running the Orcad *PSpice* program by using *pseudocomponents* to send results to the output file. Pseudocomponents are like parts that can be inserted into a schematic as if they were circuit elements, but they do not correspond to circuit elements. We can add them to the circuit for specifying initial conditions or for output control. In fact, we have already used two pseudocomponents, VIEWPOINT and IPROBE, for DC analysis. Other important pseudocomponents and their usage are shown in Fig. D.40 and listed in Table D.2. The pseudocomponents are added to the schematic. To add a pseudocomponent, select **Draw/Get New Parts** in the Schematics window, select the pseudocomponent, place it at the desired location, and add the appropriate attributes as usual. Once the pseudocomponents are added to the schematic, we select **Analysis/Setup/AC Sweep** and enter the specifications for the AC sweep, and finally, select **Analysis/Simulate** to perform AC sweep. If no errors are encountered, the voltages and currents specified in the pseudocomponents will be saved in the output file. We obtain the output file by selecting **Analysis/Examine Output** in the Schematics window.

VPRINT1	VPRINT2	VPLOT1	VPLOT2
PRINTDGTLCHG	IPRINT		IPLOT

Figure D.40   Print and plot pseudocomponents.

TABLE D.2	Print and plot pseudocomponents.
Symbol	Description
IPLOT	Plot showing branch current; symbol must be placed in series
IPRINT	Table showing branch current; symbol must be placed in series
VPLOT1	Plot showing voltages at the node to which the symbol is connected
VPLOT2	Plot showing voltage differentials between two points to which the symbol is connected
VPRINT1	Table showing voltages at the node to which the symbol is connected
VPRINT2	Table showing voltage differentials between two points to which the symbol is connected

EXAMPLE D.6

Find current *i* in the circuit in Fig. D.41.

Figure D.41   For Example D.6.

Solution:

Recall that $20 \sin 2t = 20 \cos(2t - 90°)$ and that $f = \omega/2\pi = 2/2\pi = 0.31831$. The schematic is shown in Fig. D.42. The attributes of V1 are set as $ACMAG = 20, ACPHASE = -90$; while the attributes of IAC are set as $AC = 5$. The current-controlled current source is connected in such a way as to conform with the original circuit in Fig. D.41; its gain is set equal to 2. The attributes of the pseudocomponent IPRINT are set as $AC = $ yes, $MAG = $ yes, $PHASE = $ ok, $REAL =$, and $IMAG =$. Since this is a single-frequency ac analysis, we select **Analysis/Setup/AC Sweep** and enter *Total Pts* $= 1$, *Start Freq* $= 0.31831$, and *Final Freq* $= 0.31831$. We save the circuit and select **Analysis/Simulate** for simulation. The output file includes

```
FREQ            IM(V_PRINT3)      IP(V_PRINT3)

3.183E-01       7.906E+00         4.349E+01
```

Figure D.42   The schematic of the circuit in Fig. D.41.

From the output file, we obtain $I = 7.906\,\underline{/43.49°}$ A or $i(t) = 7.906\cos(2t + 43.49°)$ A. This example is for a single-frequency ac analysis; Example D.7 is for AC sweep over a range of frequencies.

PRACTICE PROBLEM D.6

Find $i_x(t)$ in the circuit in Fig. D.43.

Figure D.43   For Practice Prob. D.6.

Answer: From the output file, $I_x = 7.59\,\underline{/108.43°}$ or $i_x = 7.59\cos(4t + 108.43°)$ A.

EXAMPLE D.7

For the RC circuit shown in Fig. D.44, obtain the magnitude plot of the output voltage v_o for frequencies from 1 Hz to 10 kHz. Let $R = 1\ k\Omega$ and $C = 4\ \mu F$.

Solution:

The schematic is shown in Fig. D.45. We assume that the magnitude of V1 is 1 and its phase is zero; we enter these as the attributes of V1. We also assume 10 points per decade. For the AC sweep specifications, we select **Analysis/Setup/AC Sweep** and enter 10 in the *Total Pts* box, 1 in the *Start Freq* box, and 10k in the *Final Freq* box. After saving the circuit, we select **Analysis/Simulate**. From the *Orcad PSpice* menu, we obtain the plot in Fig. D.46(a) by selecting **Traces/Add** and clicking V(2). Also, by selecting **Trace/Add** and typing dB(V(2)) in the *Trace Command* box, we obtain the Bode plot in Fig. D.46(b). The two plots in Fig. D.46 indicate that the circuit is a lowpass filter: low frequencies are passed while high frequencies are blocked by the circuit.

Figure D.44   For Example D.7.

Figure D.45   The schematic of the circuit in Fig. D.44.

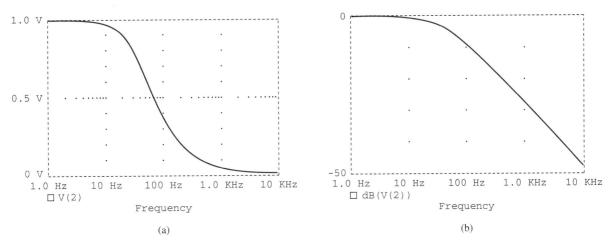

Figure D.46   Result of Example D.7: (a) linear, (b) Bode plot.

PRACTICE PROBLEM D.7

For the circuit in Fig. D.44, replace the capacitor C with an inductor $L = 4$ mH and obtain the magnitude plot (both linear and Bode) for v_o for $10 < f < 100$ MHz.

Answer: See the plots in Fig. D.47.

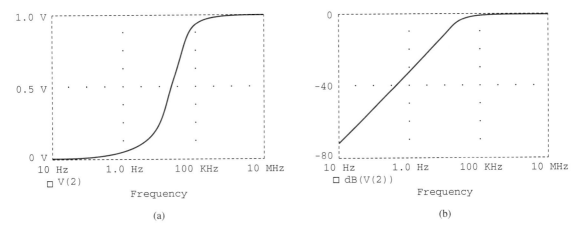

Figure D.47   Result of Practice Prob. D.7: (a) linear plot, (b) Bode plot.

Appendix E

MATLAB

MATLAB has become a powerful tool of technical professionals worldwide. The term *MATLAB* is an abbreviation for *MAT*rix *LAB*oratory, implying that *MATLAB* is a computational tool that uses matrices and vectors (or arrays) to carry out numerical analysis, signal processing, and scientific visualization tasks. Because *MATLAB* uses matrices as its fundamental building blocks, one can write mathematical expressions involving matrices just as easily as one would on paper. *MATLAB* is available for Macintosh, Unix, and Windows operating systems. A student version of *MATLAB* is available for personal computers (PCs). A copy of *MATLAB* can be obtained from

The Mathworks, Inc.
3 Apple Hill Drive
Natick, MA 01760-2098
Phone:(508) 647-7000
Website: http://www.mathworks.com

A brief introduction to *MATLAB* is presented in this appendix. What is presented is sufficient for solving problems in this book. More about *MATLAB* can be found in *MATLAB* books and from on-line help. The best way to learn *MATLAB* is to work with it after having learned the basics.

E.1 *MATLAB* Fundamentals

The Command window is the primary area where you interact with *MATLAB*. A little later, we will learn how to use the text editor to create M-files, which allow for execution of sequences of commands. For now, we focus on how to work in the Command window. We will first learn how to use *MATLAB* as a calculator.

Using MATLAB as a Calculator

The following are algebraic operators used in *MATLAB*:

- $+$ Addition
- $-$ Subtraction
- $*$ Multiplication
- $\hat{}$ Exponentiation
- $/$ Right division (a/b means $a \div b$)
- $\backslash$ Left division ($a \backslash b$ means $b \div a$)

To begin to use *MATLAB*, we use these operators. Type commands to the *MATLAB* prompt ">>" in the Command window (correct any mistakes by backspacing) and press the Enter key. For example,

```
>> a = 2; b = 4; c = -6;
>> dat = b^2 - 4*a*c
dat =
    64
```

```
>> e = sqrt(dat)/10
e =
   0.8000
```

The first command assigns the values 2, 4, and −6 to the variables `a`, `b`, and `c`, respectively. *MATLAB* does not respond because this line ends with a colon. The second command sets `dat` to $b^2 - 4ac$ and *MATLAB* returns the answer as 64. Finally, the third line sets `e` equal to the square root of `dat` and divides by 10. *MATLAB* prints the answer as 0.8. Other mathematical functions, listed in Table E.1, can be used similarly to how the function `sqrt` is used here. Table E.1 provides just a tiny sample of *MATLAB* functions. Others can be obtained from the on-line help. To get help, type

```
>> help
```

A long list of topics will come up. For a specific topic, type the command name. For example, to get help on "log to base 2", type

```
>> help log2
```

A help message on the log function will be displayed. Note that *MATLAB* is case sensitive, so `sin(a)` is not the same as `sin(A)`.

Try the following examples:

```
>> 3^(log10(25.6))
>> y = 2* sin(pi/3)
>> exp(y+4−1)
```

TABLE E.1   Typical elementary math functions.

Function	Remark
`abs(x)`	Absolute value or complex magnitude of `x`
`acos, acosh(x)`	Inverse cosine and inverse hyperbolic cosine of `x` in radians
`acot, acoth(x)`	Inverse cotangent and inverse hyperbolic cotangent of `x` in radians
`angle(x)`	Phase angle (in radian) of a complex number `x`
`asin, asinh(x)`	Inverse sine and inverse hyperbolic sine of `x` in radians
`atan, atanh(x)`	Inverse tangent and inverse hyperbolic tangent of `x` in radians
`conj(x)`	Complex conjugate of `x`
`cos, cosh(x)`	Cosine and hyperbolic cosine of `x` in radians
`cot, coth(x)`	Cotangent and hyperbolic cotangent of `x` in radians
`exp(x)`	Exponential of `x`
`fix`	Round toward zero
`imag(x)`	Imaginary part of a complex number `x`
`log(x)`	Natural logarithm of `x`
`log2(x)`	Logarithm of `x` to base 2
`log10(x)`	Common logarithms (base 10) of `x`
`real(x)`	Real part of a complex number `x`
`sin, sinh(x)`	Sine and hyperbolic sine of `x` in radians
`sqrt(x)`	Square root of `x`
`tan, tanh`	Tangent and hyperbolic tangent of `x` in radians

In addition to operating on mathematical functions, *MATLAB* allows one to work easily with vectors and matrices. A vector (or array) is a special matrix with one row or one column. For example,

```
>> a = [ 1 -3 6 10 -8 11 14];
```

is a row vector. Defining a matrix is similar to defining a vector. For example, a 3×3 matrix can be entered as

```
>> A = [ 1 2 3; 4 5 6; 7 8 9]
```

or as

```
>>   A = [ 1 2 3
           4 5 6
           7 8 9]
```

In addition to the arithmetic operations that can be performed on a matrix, the operations in Table E.2 can be implemented.

Using the operations in Table E.2, we can manipulate matrices as follows.

```
>> B = A'
B =
     1    4    7
     2    5    8
     3    6    9
>> C = A + B
C =
     2    6   10
     6   10   14
    10   14   18
>> D = A^3 - B*C
D =
   372    432    492
   948   1131   1314
  1524   1830   2136
>> e = [1 2; 3 4]
e =
   1    2
   3    4
>> f = det(e)
f =
  -2
>> g = inv(e)
g =
  -2.0000    1.0000
   1.5000   -0.5000
>> H = eig(g)
H =
  -2.6861
   0.1861
```

TABLE E.2   Matrix operations.

Operation	Remark
A'	Finds the transpose of matrix A
det(A)	Evaluates the determinant of matrix A
inv(A)	Calculates the inverse of matrix A
eig(A)	Determines the eigenvalues of matrix A
diag(A)	Finds the diagonal elements of matrix A

TABLE E.3   Special matrices, variables, and constants.

Matrix, Variable, Constant	Remark
eye	Identity matrix
ones	An array of 1s
zeros	An array of 0s
i or j	Imaginary unit or `sqrt(-1)`
pi	3.142
NaN	Not a number
inf	Infinity
eps	A very small number, `2.2e-16`
rand	Random element

Note that not all matrices can be inverted. A matrix can be inverted if and only if its determinant is nonzero. Special matrices, variables, and constants are listed in Table E.3. For example, type

```
>> eye(3)
ans =
    1 0 0
    0 1 0
    0 0 1
```

to get a 3×3 identity matrix.

Plotting

To plot using *MATLAB* is easy. For a two-dimensional plot, use the plot command with two arguments as follows:

```
>> plot(xdata,ydata)
```

where `xdata` and `ydata` are vectors of the same length containing the data to be plotted.

For example, suppose we want to plot `y = 10*sin(2*pi*x)` from 0 to `5*pi`. We will proceed with the following commands:

```
>> x = 0:pi/100:5*pi;      % x is a vector, 0 <= x <= 5*pi, increments of pi/100
>> y = 10*sin(2*pi*x);     % creates a vector y
>> plot(x,y);              % creates the plot
```

With this, *MATLAB* responds with the plot in Fig. E.1.

MATLAB will let you graph multiple plots together and distinguish them with different colors. This is obtained with the format `plot(xdata, ydata, 'color')`, where the color is indicated by using a character string from the options listed in Table E.4.

For example,

```
>> plot(x1,y1, 'r', x2,y2, 'b', x3,y3, '--');
```

will graph data `(x1,y1)` in red, data `(x2,y2)` in blue, and data `(x3,y3)` in dashed line all on the same plot.

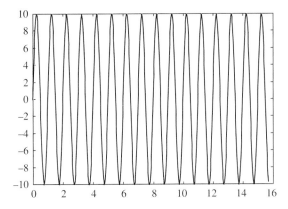

Figure E.1   *MATLAB* plot of `y = 10*sin(2*pi*x)`.

TABLE E.4   Various color and line types.

y	Yellow	.	Point
m	Magenta	o	Circle
c	Cyan	x	x mark
r	Red	+	Plus
g	Green	–	Solid
b	Blue	*	Star
w	White	:	Dotted
k	Black	–.	Dashdot
		– –	Dashed

MATLAB also allows for logarithm scaling. Rather than using the plot command, we use

`loglog`   `log(y)` versus `log(x)`

`semilogx`   `y` versus `log(x)`

`semilogy`   `log(y)` versus `x`

Three-dimensional plots are drawn using the functions `mesh` and `meshdom` (mesh domain). For example, to draw the graph of `z = x*exp( - x^2 - y^2)` over the domain $-1 < x,\ y < 1$, we type the following commands:

```
>> xx = -1:.1:1;
>> yy = xx;
>> [x,y] = meshgrid(xx,yy);
>> z = x.*exp(-x.^2 -y.^2);
>> mesh(z);
```

(The dot symbol used in `x.` and `y.` allows element-by-element multiplication.) The result is shown in Fig. E.2.

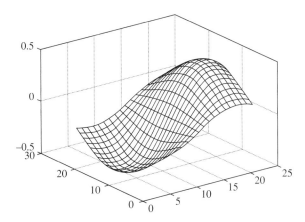

Figure E.2   A three-dimensional plot.

Programming *MATLAB*

So far we have used *MATLAB* as a calculator. You can also use *MATLAB* to create your own program. The command line editing in *MATLAB* can be inconvenient if one has several lines to execute. To avoid this problem, you can create a program that is a sequence of statements to be executed. If you are in the Command window, click File/New/M-files to open a new file in the *MATLAB* Editor/Debugger or simple text editor. Type the program and save it in a file with an extension .m, say filename.m; it is for this reason that it is called an M-file. Once the program is saved as an M-file, exit the Debugger window. You are now back in the Command window. Type the file without the extension .m to get results. For example, the plot that was made in Fig. E.2 can be improved by adding title and labels and being typed as an M-file called example1.m.

```
x = 0:pi/100:5*pi;          % x is a vector, 0 <= x <= 5*pi, increments of pi/100
y = 10*sin(2*pi*x);         % creates a vector y
plot(x,y);                  % create the plot
xlabel('x  (in radians)');  % label the x axis
ylabel('10*sin(2*pi*x)');   % label the y axis
title('A sine functions');  % title the plot
grid                        % add grid
```

Once the file is saved as example1.m and you exit the text editor, type

```
>> example1
```

in the Command window and hit Enter to obtain the result shown in Fig. E.3.

To allow flow control in a program, certain relational and logical operators are necessary. They are shown in Table E.5. Perhaps the most commonly used flow control statements are for and if. The for

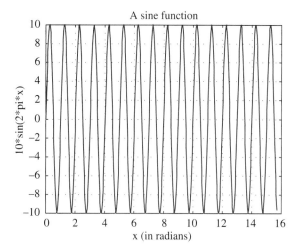

Figure E.3   *MATLAB* plot of y = 10*sin(2*pi*x) with title and labels.

statement is used to create a loop or a repetitive procedure and has the general form

```
for x = array
   [commands]
end
```

The if statement is used when certain conditions need be met before an expression is executed. It has the general form

```
if expression
   [commands if expression is True]
else
  [commands if expression is False]
end
```

TABLE E.5   Relational and logical operators.

Operator	Remark
<	less than
<=	less than or equal
>	greater than
>=	greater than or equal
==	equal
~=	not equal
&	and
|	or
~	not

For example, suppose we have an array $y(x)$ and we want to determine the minimum value of y and its corresponding index x. This can be done by creating an M-file as shown here.

```
% example2.m
% This program finds the minimum y value and its corresponding x index
x = [1 2 3 4 5 6 7 8 9 10]; %the nth term in y
y = [3 9 15 8 1 0 −2 4 12 5];
min1 = y(1); for k = 1:10
   min2 = y(k);
   if(min2 < min1)
      min1 = min2;
      xo = x(k);
   else
      min1 = min1;
   end
end
diary
min1, xo
diary off
```

Note the use of the for and if statements. When this program is saved as example2.m, we execute it in the Command window and obtain the minimum value of y as -2 and the corresponding value of x as 7, as expected.

```
>> example2
min1 =
  -2
xo =
   7
```

If we are not interested in the corresponding index, we could do the same thing using the command

```
>> min(y)
```

The following tips are helpful in working effectively with *MATLAB*:

- Comment your M-file by adding lines beginning with a % character.
- To suppress output, end each command with a semicolon (;); you may remove the semicolon when debugging the file.
- Press the up and down arrow keys to retrieve previously executed commands.
- If your expression does not fit on one line, use an ellipse (. . .) at the end of the line and continue on the next line. For example, *MATLAB* considers

```
y = sin (x + log10(2x + 3)) + cos(x + ...
log10(2x+3));
```

  as one line of expression.
- Keep in mind that variable and function names are case sensitive.

Solving Equations

Consider the general system of n simultaneous equations:

$$a_{11}x_1 + a_{12}x_2 + \cdots + a_{1n}x_n = b_1$$
$$a_{21}x_1 + a_{22}x_2 + \cdots + a_{2n}x_n = b_2$$
$$\vdots$$
$$a_{n1}x_1 + a_{n2}x_2 + \cdots + a_{nn}x_n = b_n$$

or in matrix form

$$\mathbf{AX} = \mathbf{B}$$

where

$$\mathbf{A} = \begin{bmatrix} a_{11} & a_{12} & \cdots & a_{1n} \\ a_{21} & a_{22} & \cdots & a_{2n} \\ \cdots & \cdots & \cdots & \cdots \\ a_{n1} & a_{n2} & a_{n3} & a_{n4} \end{bmatrix} \qquad \mathbf{X} = \begin{bmatrix} x_1 \\ x_2 \\ \cdots \\ x_n \end{bmatrix} \qquad \mathbf{B} = \begin{bmatrix} b_1 \\ b_2 \\ \cdots \\ b_n \end{bmatrix}$$

$\mathbf{A}$ is a square matrix and is known as the coefficient matrix, while $\mathbf{X}$ and $\mathbf{B}$ are vectors. $\mathbf{X}$ is the solution vector we are seeking to get. There are two ways to solve for $\mathbf{X}$ in *MATLAB*. First, we can use the backslash operator (\ ) so that

```
X = A\B
```

Second, we can solve for $\mathbf{X}$ as

$$\mathbf{X} = \mathbf{A}^{-1}\mathbf{B}$$

which in *MATLAB* is the same as

```
X = inv(A) * B
```

EXAMPLE E.1

Use *MATLAB* to solve Example A.2.

Solution:

From Example A.2, we obtain matrix **A** and vector **B** and enter them in *MATLAB* as follows.

```
>> A = [ 25 -5  -20; -5  10  -4; -5  -4  9]
A =
   25    -5    -20
   -5    10    -4
   -5    -4     9
>> B = [50  0  0]'
B =
   50
    0
    0
>> X = inv(A)*B
X =
   29.6000
   26.0000
   28.0000
>> X = A\B
X =
   29.6000
   26.0000
   28.0000
```

Thus, $x_1 = 29.6$, $x_2 = 26$, and $x_3 = 28$.

PRACTICE PROBLEM E.1

Solve the problem in Practice Prob. A.2 using *MATLAB*.

Answer: $x_1 = 3 = x_3$, $x_2 = 2$.

E.2   DC Circuit Analysis

There is nothing special in applying *MATLAB* to resistive dc circuits. We apply mesh and nodal analysis as usual and solve the resulting simultaneous equations using *MATLAB* as is described in Section E.1. Examples E.2 to E.5 illustrate.

EXAMPLE E.2

Use nodal analysis to solve for the nodal voltages in the circuit of Fig. E.4.

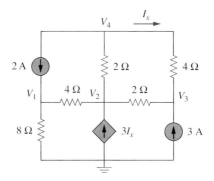

Figure E.4   For Example E.2.

Solution:

At node 1,

$$2 = \frac{V_1 - V_2}{4} + \frac{V_1 - 0}{8} \rightarrow 16 = 3V_1 - 2V_2 \qquad \text{(E.2.1)}$$

At node 2,

$$3I_x = \frac{V_2 - V_1}{4} + \frac{V_2 - V_3}{2} + \frac{V_2 - V_4}{2}$$

But

$$I_x = \frac{V_4 - V_3}{4}$$

so that

$$3\left(\frac{V_4 - V_3}{4}\right) = \frac{V_2 - V_1}{4} + \frac{V_2 - V_3}{2} + \frac{V_2 - V_4}{2} \rightarrow$$
$$0 = -V_1 + 5V_2 + V_3 - 5V_4 \qquad \text{(E.2.2)}$$

At node 3,

$$3 = \frac{V_3 - V_2}{2} + \frac{V_3 - V_4}{4} \rightarrow 12 = -2V_2 + 3V_3 - V_4 \qquad \text{(E.2.3)}$$

At node 4,

$$0 = 2 + \frac{V_4 - V_2}{2} + \frac{V_4 - V_3}{4} \rightarrow -8 = -2V_2 - V_3 + 3V_4 \qquad \text{(E.2.4)}$$

Combining Eqs. (E.2.1) to (E.2.4) gives

$$\begin{bmatrix} 3 & -2 & 0 & 0 \\ -1 & 5 & 1 & -5 \\ 0 & -2 & 3 & -1 \\ 0 & -2 & -1 & 3 \end{bmatrix} \begin{bmatrix} V_1 \\ V_2 \\ V_3 \\ V_4 \end{bmatrix} = \begin{bmatrix} 16 \\ 0 \\ 12 \\ -8 \end{bmatrix}$$

or

$$\mathbf{AV} = \mathbf{B}$$

We now use *MATLAB* to determine the nodal voltages contained in vector **V**.

```
>> A = [ 3 -2   0   0;
        -1   5   1 -5;
         0 -2   3 -1;
         0 -2 -1   3];
>> B = [16   0 12 -8]';
>> V = inv(A)*B
V =
   -6.0000
  -17.0000
  -13.5000
  -18.5000
```

Hence $V_1 = -6.0$, $V_2 = -17$, $V_3 = -13.5$, and $V_4 = -18.5$V.

PRACTICE PROBLEM E.2

Find the nodal voltages in the circuit in Fig. E.5 using *MATLAB*.

Figure E.5   For Practice Prob. E.2.

Answer:
$V_1 = 14.55$, $V_2 = 38.18$, $V_3 = -34.55$, and $V_4 = -3.636$ V.

EXAMPLE E.3

Use *MATLAB* to solve for the mesh currents in the circuit in Fig. E.6.

Solution:

For the four meshes,

$$-6 + 9I_1 - 4I_2 - 2I_4 = 0 \longrightarrow 6 = 9I_1 - 4I_2 - 2I_4 \qquad \text{(E.3.1)}$$

$$12 + 15I_2 - 4I_1 - 4I_3 - 6I_4 = 0 \longrightarrow -12 = -4I_1 + 15I_2 - 4I_3 - 6I_4$$
$$\text{(E.3.2)}$$

$$-12 + 10I_3 - 4I_2 - 2I_4 = 0 \longrightarrow 12 = -4I_2 + 10I_3 - 2I_4 \quad \text{(E.3.3)}$$

$$20I_4 - 2I_1 - 6I_2 - 2I_3 = 0 \longrightarrow 0 = -2I_1 - 6I_2 - 2I_3 + 20I_4$$
$$\text{(E.3.4)}$$

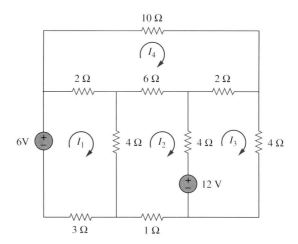

Figure E.6   For Example E.3.

Putting Eqs. (E.3.1) to (E.3.4) together in matrix form, we have

$$\begin{bmatrix} 9 & -4 & 0 & -2 \\ -4 & 15 & -4 & -6 \\ 0 & -4 & 10 & -2 \\ -2 & -6 & -2 & 20 \end{bmatrix} \begin{bmatrix} I_1 \\ I_2 \\ I_3 \\ I_4 \end{bmatrix} = \begin{bmatrix} 6 \\ -12 \\ 12 \\ 0 \end{bmatrix}$$

or $\mathbf{AI} = \mathbf{B}$, where the vector $\mathbf{I}$ contains the unknown mesh currents. We now use *MATLAB* to determine $\mathbf{I}$ as follows.

```
>> A = [9 -4   0 -2; -4   15 -4   -6;
        0 -4 10 -2; -2   -6 -2   20]
A =
    9   -4    0   -2
   -4   15   -4   -6
    0   -4   10   -2
   -2   -6   -2   20
>> B = [6 -12 12 0]'
B =
    6
  -12
   12
    0
>> I = inv(A)*B
  I =
    0.5203
   -0.3555
    1.0682
    0.0522
```

Thus, $I_1 = 0.5203$, $I_2 = -0.3555$, $I_3 = 1.0682$, and $I_4 = 0.0522$ A.

PRACTICE PROBLEM E.3

Find the mesh currents in the circuit in Fig. E.7 using *MATLAB*.

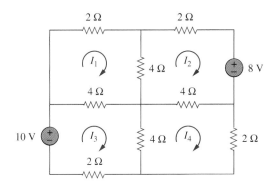

Figure E.7   For Practice Prob. E.3.

Answer: $I_1 = 0.2222$, $I_2 = -0.6222$, $I_3 = 1.1778$, and $I_4 = 0.2222$ A.

E.3 AC Circuit Analysis

Using *MATLAB* in ac circuit analysis is similar to how *MATLAB* is used for dc circuit analysis. We must first apply nodal or mesh analysis to the circuit and then use *MATLAB* to solve the resulting system of equations. However, the circuit is in the frequency domain, and we are dealing with phasors or complex numbers. So in addition to what we learned in Section E.2, we need to understand how *MATLAB* handles complex numbers.

MATLAB expresses complex numbers in the usual manner, except that the imaginary part can be either j or i representing $\sqrt{-1}$. Thus, $3 - j4$ can be written in *MATLAB* as `3 - j4`, `3 - j*4`, `3 - i4`, or `3 - i*4`. Here are the other complex functions:

`abs(A)`	Absolute value of magnitude of `A`
`angle(A)`	Angle of `A` in radians
`conj(A)`	Complex conjugate of `A`
`imag(A)`	Imaginary part of `A`
`real(A)`	Real part of `A`

Keep in mind that an angle in radians must be multiplied by $180/\pi$ to convert it to degrees, and vice versa. Also, the transpose operator (`'`) gives the complex conjugate transpose, whereas the dot-transpose (`.'`) transposes an array without conjugating it.

EXAMPLE E.4

In the circuit of Fig. E.8, let $v = 4\cos(5t - 30°)$ V and $i = 0.8\cos 5t$ A. Find v_1 and v_2.

Figure E.8   For Example E.4.

Figure E.9   The frequency-domain equivalent circuit of the circuit Fig. E.8.

Solution:

As usual, we convert the circuit in the time-domain to its frequency-domain equivalent.

$$v = 4\cos(5t - 30°) \longrightarrow \mathbf{V} = 4\underline{/-30°}, \quad \omega = 5$$

$$i = 0.8\cos 5t \longrightarrow \mathbf{I} = 8\underline{/0°}$$

$$2\,\text{H} \longrightarrow j\omega L = j5 \times 2 = j10$$

$$20\,\text{mF} \longrightarrow \frac{1}{j\omega C} = \frac{1}{j10\,\Omega \times 10^{-3}} = -j10$$

Thus, the frequency-domain equivalent circuit is shown in Fig. E.9. We now apply nodal analysis to this.

At node 1,

$$\frac{4\underline{/-30°} - V_1}{-j10} = \frac{V_1}{10} + \frac{V_1 - V_2}{j10} \longrightarrow 4\underline{/-30°} = 3.468 - j2 \tag{E.4.1}$$
$$= -jV_1 + V_2$$

At node 2,

$$0.8 = \frac{V_2}{20} + \frac{V_2 - V_1}{j10} \longrightarrow j16 = -2V_1 + (2 + j)V_2 \tag{E.4.2}$$

Equations (E.4.1) and (E.4.2) can be cast in matrix form as

$$\begin{bmatrix} -j & 1 \\ -2 & (2+j) \end{bmatrix} \begin{bmatrix} V_1 \\ V_2 \end{bmatrix} = \begin{bmatrix} 3.468 - j2 \\ j16 \end{bmatrix}$$

or $\mathbf{AV} = \mathbf{B}$. We use *MATLAB* to invert $\mathbf{A}$ and multiply the inverse by $\mathbf{B}$ to get $\mathbf{V}$.

```
>> A = [-j 1; -2 (2+j)]
A =
   0 - 1.0000i   1.000
   -2.0000 2.0000 + 1.0000i
>> B=[(3.468 - 2j) 16j].'  %note the dot-transpose
B =
   3.4680 - 2.0000i
   0 + 16.0000i
>> V = inv(A)*B
```

```
V =
   4.6055 - 2.4403i
   5.9083 + 2.6055i
>> abs(V(1))
ans =
   5.2121
>> angle(V(1))*180/pi  %converts angle from radians to degrees
ans =
  -27.9175
>> abs(V(2))
ans =
   6.4573
>> angle(V(2))*180/pi
ans =
   23.7973
```

Thus

$$V_1 = 4.6055 - j2.4403 = 5.212\underline{/-27.92^\circ} \qquad V_2 = 5.908 + j2.605 = 6.457\underline{/23.8^\circ}$$

In the time domain,

$$v_1 = 4.605\cos(5t - 27.92^\circ)\ \text{V} \qquad v_2 = 6.457\cos(5t + 23.8^\circ)\ \text{V}$$

PRACTICE PROBLEM E.4

Calculate v_1 and v_2 in the circuit in Fig. E.10 given $i = 4\cos(10t + 40^\circ)$ A and $v = 12\cos 10t$ V.

Figure E.10   For Practice Prob. E.4.

Answer: $63.58\cos(10t - 10.68^\circ)$ V, $40\cos(10t - 50^\circ)$ V.

EXAMPLE E.5

In the unbalanced three-phase system shown in Fig. E.11, find currents I_1, I_2, I_3, and I_{Bb}. Let

$$Z_A = 12 + j10\ \Omega, \qquad Z_B = 10 - j8\ \Omega, \qquad Z_C = 15 + j6\ \Omega$$

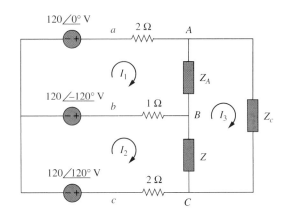

Figure E.11   For Example E.5.

Solution:

For mesh 1,

$$120\underline{/-120^\circ} - 120\underline{/0^\circ} + I_1(2 + 1 + 12 + j10) - I_2 - I_3(12 + j10) = 0$$

or

$$I_1(15 + j10) - I_2 - I_3(12 + j10) = 120\underline{/0^\circ} - 120\underline{/-120^\circ} \quad \text{(E.5.1)}$$

For mesh 2,

$$120\underline{/120^\circ} - 120\underline{/-120^\circ} + I_2(2 + 1 + 10 - j8) - I_1 - I_3(10 - j8) = 0$$

or

$$-I_1 + I_2(13 - j8) - I_3(10 - j8) = 120\underline{/-120^\circ} - 120\underline{/120^\circ} \quad \text{(E.5.2)}$$

For mesh 3,

$$I_3(12 + j10 + 10 - j8 + 15 + j6) - I_1(12 + j10) - I_2(10 - j8) = 0$$

or

$$-I_1(12 + j10) - I_2(10 - j8) - I_3(37 + j8) = 0 \quad \text{(E.5.3)}$$

In matrix form, we can express Eqs. (E.5.1) to (E.5.3) as

$$\begin{bmatrix} 15 + j10 & -1 & -12 - j10 \\ -1 & 13 - j8 & -10 + j8 \\ -12 - j10 & -10 + j8 & 37 + j8 \end{bmatrix} \begin{bmatrix} I_1 \\ I_2 \\ I_3 \end{bmatrix}$$

$$= \begin{bmatrix} 120\underline{/0^\circ} - 120\underline{/-120^\circ} \\ 120\underline{/-120^\circ} - 120\underline{/120^\circ} \\ 0 \end{bmatrix}$$

or

$$\mathbf{ZI} = \mathbf{V}$$

We input matrices $\mathbf{Z}$ and $\mathbf{V}$ into *MATLAB* to get $\mathbf{I}$.

```
>> Z =[(15 + 10j) −1   (−12 − 10j);
       −1  (13 − 8j)  (−10 + 8j);
       (−12 − 10j) (−10 + 8j)  (37 + 8j)];
```

```
>> c1=120*exp(j*pi*(−120)/180);
>> c2=120*exp(j*pi*(120)/180);
>> a1=120 − c1; a2=c1 − c2;
>> V = [a1; a2; 0]
>> I = inv(Z)*V
I =
   16.9910 − 6.5953i
   12.4023 −16.9993i
    5.6621 − 6.0471i
>> IbB = I(2) − I(1)
IbB =
   −4.5887 − 10.4039i
>> abs(I(1))
ans =
   18.2261
>> angle(I(1))*180/pi
ans =
  −21.2146
>> abs(I(2))
ans =
   21.0426
>> angle(I(2))*180/pi
ans =
  −53.8864
>> abs(I(3))
ans =
    8.2841
>> angle(I(3))*180/pi
ans =
  −46.8833
>> abs(IbB)
ans =
   11.3709
>> angle(IbB)*180/pi
ans =
 −113.8001
```

Thus, $I_1 = 18.23\underline{/-21.21°}$, $I_2 = 21.04\underline{/-58.89°}$, $I_3 = 8.284\underline{/-46.88°}$, and $\mathbf{I}_{bB} = 11.37\underline{/-113.8°}$A.

PRACTICE PROBLEM E.5

In the unbalanced wye-wye three-phase system in Fig. E.12, find the line currents I_1, I_2, and I_3 and the phase voltage V_{CN}.

Answer: $22.66\underline{/-26.54°}A$, $6.036\underline{/-150.48°}A$, $19.93\underline{/138.9°}A$, $94.29\underline{/159.3°}V$.

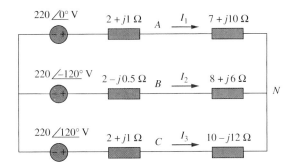

Figure E.12   For Practice Prob. E.5.

E.4 Frequency Response

Frequency response involves plotting the magnitude and phase of the transfer function $H(s) = D(s)/N(s)$ or obtaining the Bode magnitude and phase plots of $H(s)$. One hard way to obtain the plots is to generate data using the `for` loop for each value of $s = j\omega$ for a given range of ω and then plot the data as we did in Section E.1. However, there is an easy way that allows us to use one of two *MATLAB* commands: `freqs` and `bode`. For each command, we must first specify `H(s)` as `num` and `den`, where `num` and `den` are the vectors of coefficients of the numerator `N(s)` and denominator `D(s)` in descending powers of s, i.e., from the highest power to the constant term. The general form of the `bode` function is

```
bode(num, den, range);
```

where `range` is a specified frequency interval for the plot. If `range` is omitted, *MATLAB* automatically selects the frequency range. The `range` could be linear or logarithmic. For example, for $1 < \omega < 1000$ rad/s with 50 plot points, we can specify a linear `range` as

```
range = linspace(1,1000,50);
```

For a logarithmic `range` with $10^{-2} < \omega < 10^4$ rad/s and 100 plot points in between, we specify `range` as

```
range = logspace(-2,4,100);
```

For the `freqs` function, the general form is

```
hs = freqs(num, den, range);
```

where `hs` is the frequency response (generally complex). We still need to calculate the magnitude in decibels as

```
mag = 20*log10(abs(hs))
```

and phase in degrees as

```
phase = angle(hs)*180/pi
```

and plot them. Whereas the `bode` function does it all at once. We illustrate with an example.

EXAMPLE E.6

Use *MATLAB* to obtain the Bode plots of

$$G(s) = \frac{s^3}{s^3 + 14.8s^2 + 38.1s + 2554}$$

Solution:

With the explanation previously given, we develop the *MATLAB* code as shown here.

```
% for example e.6
num=[1 0 0 0];
den = [1  14.8 38.1  2554];
w = logspace(-1,3);
bode(num, den, w);
title('Bode plot for a highpass filter')
```

Running the program produces the Bode plots in Fig. E.13. It is evident from the magnitude plot that $G(s)$ represents a highpass filter.

Figure E.13   For Example E.6.

PRACTICE PROBLEM E.6

Use *MATLAB* to determine the frequency response of

$$H(s) = \frac{10(s + 1)}{s^2 + 6s + 100}$$

Answer: See Fig. E.14

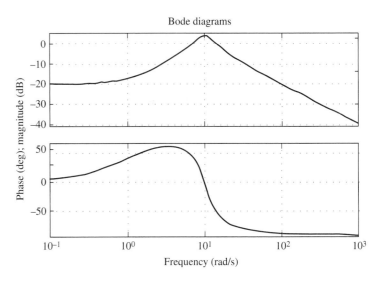

Figure E.14   For Practice Prob. E.6.

AppendixF

Answers to Odd-Numbered Problems

Chapter 1

1.1 (a) -0.1038 C, (b) -0.19865 C, (c) -3.941 C, (d) -26.08 C

1.3 (a) $3t + 1$ C, (b) $t^2 + 5t$ mC,
(c) $2\sin(10t + \pi/6) + 1$ μC,
(d) $-e^{-30t}[0.16\cos 40t + 0.12\sin 40t]$ C

1.5 490 μC

1.7 $i = \begin{cases} 25 \text{ A}, & 0 < t < 2 \\ -25 \text{ A}, & 2 < t < 6 \\ 25 \text{ A}, & 6 < t < 8 \end{cases}$
See the sketch in Fig. F.1.

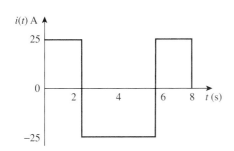

Figure F.1 For Prob. 1.7.

1.9 (a) 10 C, (b) 22.5 C, (c) 30 C

1.11 3.672 kC, 4.406 kJ

1.13 1.1784 kJ

1.15 (a) 1.297 C, (b)$-90e^{-4t}$ W, (c) -22.5 J

1.17 70 W

1.19 3 A

1.21 8 nA

1.23 (a) 12.5 A, (b) 1.125 kWh, (c) 11.25 cents

1.25 21.6 cents

1.27 (a) 43.2 kC, (b) 475.2 kJ, (c) 1.188

1.29 39.6 cents

1.31 $42.05

1.33 6 C

1.35 2.333 MWh

1.37 961.2 J

1.39 16.667 A

Chapter 2

2.1 3.2 mA

2.3 20.8 μS

2.5 $n = 9, b = 15, l = 7$

2.7 7 branches and 4 nodes

2.9 11 A, 4 A, 1 A

2.11 -4 V, -6 V, 4 V, -2 V

2.13 12 A, -10 A, 5 A, -2 A

2.15 -6 V, 4 V, -18 V

2.17 2 V, -22 V, 10 V

2.19 -2 A, 12 W, -24 W, 20 W, 16 W

2.21 45 W

2.23 2 V, 1.92 W

2.25 0.1 A, 2 kV, 0.2 kW

2.27 6 V, 18 V

2.29 12 V, 3 A, 0 A, 0 V

2.31 10 V, 1 A, 4 W

2.33 3 V, 6 A

2.35 8 V, 0.2 A

2.37 12 Ω

2.39 (a) 0 Ω, (b) R, (c) R, (d) R, (e) $\frac{6}{11} R$

2.41 16 Ω

2.43 (a) 12 Ω, (b) 16 Ω

2.45 (a) 59.8 Ω, (b) 32.5 Ω

2.47 24 Ω

2.49 (a) 4 Ω, (b) $R_1 = 18$ Ω, $R_2 = 6$ Ω, $R_3 = 3$ Ω

2.51 (a) 9.231 Ω, (b) 36.25 Ω

2.53 (a) 142.32 Ω, (b) 33.33 Ω

2.55 0.9974 A

2.57 12.21 Ω, 1.64 A

2.59 1.2 A

2.61 Use R_1 and R_3 bulbs

2.63 $\cong 1$ W

2.65 4 kΩ

2.67 (a) 4 V, (b) 2.857 V, (c) 28.57%, (d) 6.25%

2.69 (a) 1.278 V (with), 1.29 V (without) (b) 9.30 V (with), 10 V (without) (c) 25 V (with), 30.77 V (without)

2.71 10Ω

2.73 45 Ω

2.75 (a) 19.9 kΩ, (b) 20 kΩ

2.77 (a) Four 20-Ω resistors in parallel

(b) One 300-Ω resistor in series with a 1.8-Ω resistor and a parallel combination of two 20-Ω resistors

(c) Two 24-kΩ resistors in parallel connected in series with two 56-kΩ resistors in parallel

(d) A series combination of a 20-Ω resistor, 300-Ω resistor, 24-kΩ resistor and a parallel combination of two 56-kΩ resistors

2.79 75 Ω

2.81 38 kΩ, 3.33 kΩ

2.83 375 Ω, 257.1 Ω

Chapter 3

3.1 9.143 V, -10.286 V, $p_{8\Omega} = 10.45$ W, $p_{4\Omega} = 94.37$ W, $p_{2\Omega} = 52.9$ W

3.3 4 A, 2 A, 1.333 A, 0.667 A, 40 V

3.5 20 V

3.7 -0.0556 V, -3.444 V

3.9 3.652 V

3.11 -2 A, -5 A

3.13 8 V, 8 V

3.15 29.45 A, 144.6 W, 129.6 W, 12 W

3.17 1.73 A

3.19 10 V, 4.933 V, 12.267 V

3.21 1 V, 3 V

3.23 18 V, 26 V

3.25 20 V, 0 A

3.27 625 mV, 375 mV, 1.625 V

3.29 -0.7708 V, 1.209 V, 2.309 V, 0.7076 V

3.31 4.97 V, 4.85 V, -0.12 V

3.33 (a) planar, (b) planar, redrawn as shown in Fig. F.2.

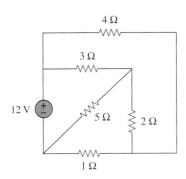

Figure F.2   For Prob. 3.33(b).

3.35 20 V

3.37 1.111 V

3.39 0.8 A, −0.9 A

3.41 1.188 A

3.43 1.778 A, 53.33 V

3.45 8.561 A

3.47 10 V, 4.933 V, 12.267 V

3.49 33.78 V, 10.67 A

3.51 20 V

3.53 1.072 A, 2.041 A

3.55 −1 A, 0 A, 2 A

3.57 3.23 kΩ, 28 V, 72 V

3.59 −1.344 kV, −5.6 A

3.61 −0.3

3.63 −4 V, 2.105 A

3.65 1.673 A, 1.824 A, 1.733 A, 1.864 A, 2.411 A

3.67 $\begin{bmatrix} 1.25 & -1 \\ -1 & 1.5 \end{bmatrix} \begin{bmatrix} V_1 \\ V_2 \end{bmatrix} = \begin{bmatrix} 3 \\ -1 \end{bmatrix}$
$V_1 = 4$ V, $V_2 = 2$ V

3.69 $\begin{bmatrix} 1.75 & -0.25 & -1 \\ -0.25 & 1 & -0.25 \\ -1 & -0.25 & 1.25 \end{bmatrix} \begin{bmatrix} V_1 \\ V_2 \\ V_3 \end{bmatrix} = \begin{bmatrix} 20 \\ 5 \\ 5 \end{bmatrix}$

3.71 $\begin{bmatrix} 6 & -2 & 0 \\ -2 & 12 & -2 \\ 0 & -2 & 7 \end{bmatrix} \begin{bmatrix} i_1 \\ i_2 \\ i_3 \end{bmatrix} = \begin{bmatrix} 12 \\ -8 \\ -20 \end{bmatrix}$, 6.52 W

3.73 $\begin{bmatrix} 9 & -3 & -4 & 0 \\ -3 & 8 & 0 & 0 \\ -4 & 0 & 6 & -1 \\ 0 & 0 & -1 & 2 \end{bmatrix} \begin{bmatrix} i_1 \\ i_2 \\ i_3 \\ i_4 \end{bmatrix} = \begin{bmatrix} 6 \\ 4 \\ 2 \\ -3 \end{bmatrix}$

3.75 −3 A, 0 A, 3 A

3.77 4 V, 2 V

3.79 −10.14 V, 7.847 V, −1.736 V, −29.17 V

3.81 26.667 V, 6.667 V, 173.3 V, −46.67 V

3.83 See Fig. F.3; −12.5 V

Figure F.3   For Prob. 3.83.

3.85 9 Ω

3.87 −8

3.89 1.5 V

3.91 0.61 μA, 8.641 V, 49 mV

Chapter 4

4.1 0.1, 1 A

4.3 (a) 0.5 V, 0.5 A, (b) 5 V, 5 A, (c) 5 V, 0.5 A

4.5 4.5 V

4.7 2 A

4.9 −1.32 A, 17.43 W

4.11 3 A

4.13 4.058 mA

4.15 1.875 A, 10.55 W

4.17 −8.571 V

4.19 −13.333 A

4.21 8 V, 666.7 mA

4.23 1 A, 8 W

4.25 −6.6 V

4.27 −48 V

4.29 3 V

4.31 3.652 V

4.33 (a) 8 Ω, 16 V, (b) 20 Ω, 50 V

4.35 −0.125 V

4.37 10 Ω, 666.7 mA

4.39 2.5 Ω, 6 V

4.41 4 Ω, −8 V, −2 A

4.43 10 Ω, 0 V

4.45 3 Ω, 2 A

4.47 0.4762 Ω, 1.19 V, 2.5 A

4.49 28 Ω, 3.286 A

4.51 (a) 2 Ω, 7 A, (b) 1.5 Ω, 12.67 A

4.53 3 Ω, 1 A

4.55 100 kΩ, −20 mA

4.57 10 Ω, 166.67 V, 16.667 A

4.59 22.5 Ω, 40 V, 1.7778 A

4.61 1.2 Ω, 9.6 V, 8 A

4.63 −3.333 Ω, 0 A

4.65 $V_0 = 24 - 5I_0$

4.67 7.2 Ω, 1.25 W

4.69 ∞ (theoretically)

4.71 8 kΩ, 1.152 W

4.73 20.77 W

4.75 1 kΩ

4.77 (a) 3.8 Ω, 4 V, (b) 3.2 Ω, 15 V

4.79 10 Ω, 167 V

4.81 3.333 Ω, 10 V

4.83 8 Ω, 12 V

4.85 (a) 24 V, 30 kΩ, (b) 9.6 V

4.87 (a) 10 mA, 8 kΩ, (b) 9.926 mA

4.89 (a) 30 kΩ, 24 V, (b) 9.6 V

4.91 (a) 100 Ω, 20 Ω, (b) 100 Ω, 200 Ω

4.93 $\dfrac{V_s}{R_s + (1 + \beta)R_o}$

4.95 5.333 V, 66.67 kΩ

4.97 2.4 kΩ, 4.8 V

Chapter 5

5.1 (a) 1.5 MΩ, (b) 60 Ω, (c) 98.06 dB

5.3 10 V

5.5 0.9999990

5.7 −100 nV, −10 mV

5.9 (a) 2 V, (b) 2 V

5.11 −2 V, −1 mA

5.13 2.7 V, 288 μA

5.15 (a) $-\left(R_1 + R_3 + \dfrac{R_1 R_3}{R_2}\right)$, (b) −92 kΩ

5.17 (a) −2.4, (b) −16, (c) −400

5.19 −0.375 mA

5.21 1.909 V

5.23 $-\dfrac{R_f}{R_1}$

5.25 5 V, 2 V

5.27 (a) 10.2, (b) 1.471 cos 120πt

5.29 $\dfrac{R_2}{R_1}$

5.31 0.7272 mA

5.33 −2 mA, 12 mW

5.35 If $R_1 = 10$ kΩ, then $R_f = 90$ kΩ.

5.37 3 V

5.39 3 V

5.41 See Fig. F.4.

Figure F.4   For Prob. 5.41.

5.43 3 kΩ

5.45 See Fig. F.5, where $R \leq 100$ kΩ.

Figure F.5   For Prob. 5.45.

5.47 −2 V, −2.4 mA

5.49 $R_1 = R_3 = 10$ kΩ, $R_2 = R_4 = 20$ kΩ

5.51 See Fig. F.6.

Figure F.6   For Prob. 5.51.

5.53 Proof.

5.55 7.956, 7.956, 1.989

5.57 120 kΩ

5.59 −1.333

5.61 $\dfrac{R_2 R_4}{R_1 R_5} v_1 - \dfrac{R_4}{R_3} v_2$

5.63 $\dfrac{R_2 R_4 / R_1 R_5 - R_4 / R_6}{1 - R_2 R_4 / R_3 R_5}$

5.65 -21.6 mV

5.67   2.4 V

5.69 -17.14 mV

5.71   10 V

5.73   10.8 V

5.75 $-2,\ 200\ \mu\text{A}$

5.77 -2.726 mV

5.79 -4.99

5.81   343.4 mV, 24.51 μA

5.83   The result depends on your design. Hence, let
$R_G = 10$ k ohms, $R_1 = 10$ k ohms,
$R_2 = 20$ k ohms, $R_3 = 40$ k ohms,
$R_4 = 80$ k ohms, $R_5 = 160$ k ohms,
$R_6 = 320$ k ohms, then,

$$-v_o = (R_f/R_1)v_1 + \text{———} + (R_f/R_6)v_6$$
$$= v_1 + 0.5v_2 + 0.25v_3 + 0.125v_4$$
$$+ 0.0625v_5 + 0.03125v_6$$

(a) $|v_o| = 1.1875 = 1 + 0.125 + 0.0625 = 1 + (1/8) + (1/16)$, which implies,
$[v_1\ v_2\ v_3\ v_4\ v_5\ v_6] = [\textbf{100110}]$

(b) $|v_o| = 0 + (1/2) + (1/4) + 0 + (1/16) + (1/32) = (27/32) = \textbf{843.75 mV}$

(c) This corresponds to [111111].

$$|v_o| = 1 + (1/2) + (1/4) + (1/8) + (1/16)$$
$$+ (1/32)$$
$$= 63/32 = \textbf{1.96875 V}$$

5.85   401

5.87 $\left(1 + \dfrac{R_4}{R_3}\right) v_2 - \left[\dfrac{R_4}{R_3} + \left(\dfrac{R_2 R_4}{R_1 R_3}\right)\right] v_1$

Let $R_4 = R_1$ and $R_3 = R_2$;

then $v_0 = \left(1 + \dfrac{R_4}{R_3}\right)(v_2 - v_1)$

a subtractor with a gain of $\left(1 + \dfrac{R_4}{R_3}\right)$.

5.89   If we use an inverter, $R_1 = 2$ k ohms,

$$(v_o/v_i) = -R_2/R_1 = -6$$
$$R_2 = 6R_1 = 12 \text{ k ohms}$$

Hence the op amp circuit is as shown below.

Figure F.7   For Prob. 5.89.

5.91   9

5.93 $A = \dfrac{1}{\left(1 + \frac{R_1}{R_3}\right) R_L - R_1 \left(\frac{R_2 + R_L}{R_2 R_3}\right)\left(R_4 + \frac{R_2 R_L}{R_2 + R_L}\right)}$

Chapter 6

6.1 $10(1 - 3t)e^{-3t}$ A, $20t(1 - 3t)e^{-6t}$ W

6.3   0.48 A

6.5 $v = \begin{cases} 100t^2 \text{ kV}, & 0 < t < 1 \\ 100(4t - t^2 - 2) \text{ kV}, & 1 < t < 2 \end{cases}$

6.7 $0.04t^2 + 10$ V

6.9   13.624 V, 70.66 W

6.11 $v(t) = \begin{bmatrix} 10t \text{ kV}, & 0 < t < 1 \\ 10 \text{ kV}, & 1 < t < 2 \\ -10t + 30 \text{ kV}, & 2 < t < 3 \end{bmatrix}$

6.13   30 V, 40 V

6.15 (a) 0.1 J, 0.15 J, (b) 36 mJ, 24 mJ

6.17 (a) 3 F, (b) 8 F, (c) 1 F

6.19 10 μF

6.21 2.5 μF

6.23 (a) $v_{4\mu F} = 60$ V, $v_{2\mu F} = 60$ V, $v_{6\mu F} = 20$ V, $v_{3\mu F} = 40$ V, (b) $w_{4\mu F} = 7.2$ mJ, $w_{2\mu F} = 3.6$ mJ, $w_{6\mu F} = 1.2$ mJ, $w_{3\mu F} = 2.4$ mJ

6.25 (a) For the capacitors in series,

$$Q_1 = Q_2 \rightarrow C_1 v_1 = C_2 v_2 \rightarrow \frac{v_1}{v_2} = \frac{C_2}{C_1}$$

$$v_s = v_1 + v_2 = \frac{C_2}{C_1} v_2 + v_2 = \frac{C_1 + C_2}{C_1} v_2$$

$$\rightarrow v_2 = \frac{C_1}{C_1 + C_2} v_s$$

Similarly, $v_1 = \dfrac{C_2}{C_1 + C_2} v_s$

(b) For capacitors in parallel,

$$v_1 = v_2 = \frac{Q_1}{C_1} = \frac{Q_2}{C_2}$$

$$Q_s = Q_1 + Q_2 = \frac{C_1}{C_2} Q_2 + Q_2 = \frac{C_1 + C_2}{C_2} Q_2$$

or

$$Q_2 = \frac{C_2}{C_1 + C_2}$$

$$Q_1 = \frac{C_1}{C_1 + C_2} Q_s$$

$$i = \frac{dQ}{dt} \rightarrow i_1 = \frac{C_1}{C_1 + C_2} i_s,$$

$$i_2 = \frac{C_2}{C_1 + C_2} i_s$$

6.27 (a) 2.857 μF, (b) 0.5714 mC, (c) 57.14 mJ

6.29 (a) 1.6 C, (b) C

6.31 $v(t) = \begin{bmatrix} t^2 \text{ kV}, & 0 < t < 1 \\ 2t - 1 \text{ kV}, & 1 < t < 3 \\ 0.5t^2 - 5t + 15.5 \text{ kV}, & 3 < t < 5 \end{bmatrix}$

$i_1(t) = \begin{bmatrix} 12t \text{ mA}, & 0 < t < 1 \\ 12 \text{ mA}, & 1 < t < 3 \\ 6t - 30 \text{ mA}, & 3 < t < 5 \end{bmatrix}$

$i_2(t) = \begin{bmatrix} 8t \text{ mA}, & 0 < t < 1 \\ 8 \text{ mA}, & 1 < t < 3 \\ 4t - 20 \text{ mA}, & 3 < t < 5 \end{bmatrix}$

6.33 2.5 F, 7.5 V

6.35 0.2 H

6.37 $4.8 \cos 100t$, 96 mJ

6.39 $(5t^3 + 5t^2 + 20t + 1)$ A

6.41 5.977 A, 35.72 J

6.43 144 μJ

6.45 $i(t) = \begin{cases} 0.25t^2 \text{ kA}, & 0 < t < 1 \\ 1 - t + 0.25t^2 \text{ kA}, & 1 < t < 2 \end{cases}$

6.47 5 Ω

6.49 (a) 7 H, (b) 3 H, (c) 2 H

6.51 7.778 H

6.53 20 mH

6.55 (a) 1.4 L, (b) 0.5 L

6.57 6.625 H

6.59 Proof.

6.61 (a) 2 mA, (b) $2.4e^{-2t} + 1.6$ mA, $3.6e^{-2t} - 1.6$ mA, (c) $-0.12e^{-2t}$ mV, $-0.144e^{-2t}$ mV, (d) $W_{10} = 24.36$ nJ, $W_{30} = 92.47$ nJ, $W_{20} = 0.7597$ nJ

6.63   See Fig. F.8.

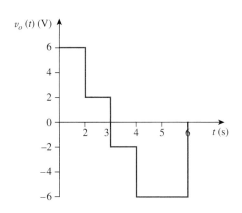

Figure F.8   For Prob. 6.63.

6.65   (a) 40 J, 40 J, (b) 80 J, (c) $5 \times 10^{-5}(e^{-200t} - 1)$
$+4$ A, $1.25 \times 10^{-5}(e^{-200t} - 1) - 2$ A
(d) $6.25 \times 10^{-5}(e^{-200t} - 1) + 2$ A

6.67 $100 \cos 50t$ mV

6.69   See Fig. F.9.

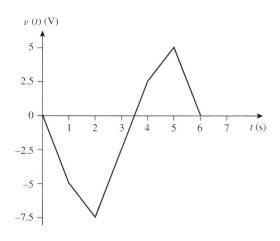

Figure F.9   For Prob. 6.69.

6.71   By combining a summer with an integrator, we
have the circuit shown in Fig. F.10.

Figure F.10   For Prob. 6.71.

$$v_o = -\frac{1}{R_1 C} \int v_1 \, dt - \frac{1}{R_2 C} \int v_2 \, dt - \frac{1}{R_2 C} \int v_2 \, dt$$

For the given problem, $C = 2\mu$F : $R_1 =$
500 kΩ, $R_2 = 125$ kΩ, $R_3 = 50$ kΩ.

6.73   Consider the op amp as shown in Fig. F.11.

Figure F.11   For Prob. 6.73.

Let $v_a = v_b = v$. At node a,

$$\frac{0 - v}{R} = \frac{v - v_0}{R} \rightarrow 2v - v_0 = 0 \qquad (1)$$

At node b, $\dfrac{v_i - v}{R} = \dfrac{v - v_0}{R} + C\dfrac{dv}{dt}$

$$v_i = 2v - v_o + RC\frac{dv}{dt} \qquad (2)$$

Combining Eqs. (1) and (2),

$$v_i = v_o - v_o + \frac{RC}{2}\frac{dv_o}{dt} \qquad \text{or} \qquad v_o = \frac{2}{RC}\int v_i \, dt$$

showing that the circuit is a noninverting
integrator.

6.75 -30 mV

6.77   See Fig. F.12.

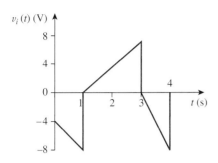

Figure F.12   For Prob. 6.77.

6.79   See Fig. F.13.

6.81   See Fig. F.14.

6.83   Eight groups in parallel with each group made up of two capacitors in series

6.85   1.25 mH inductor

Chapter 7

7.1   Proof

7.3   (a) 10 ms, (b) 6 s

7.5   1.195 V

7.7 $20e^{-\frac{13t}{8}}$ V

7.9 $20e^{-t/2}$ V

7.11   Applying KCL to the RL circuit,

$$\frac{1}{L} \int v \, dt + \frac{v}{R} = 0$$

Differentiating both sides,

$$\frac{v}{L} + \frac{1}{R}\frac{dv}{dt} = 0 \quad \longrightarrow \quad \frac{dv}{dt} + \frac{R}{L}v = 0$$

$$v = A \, e^{-Rt/L}$$

Figure F.13   For Prob. 6.79.

Figure F.14   For Prob. 6.81.

If the initial current is I_0, then

$$v(0) = I_0 R = A$$

$$v = I_0 R e^{-t/\tau}, \tau = \frac{L}{R}$$

$$i = \frac{1}{L} \int_{-\infty}^{t} v(t)\, dt$$

$$= \frac{-\tau I_0 R}{L} e^{-t/\tau} \Big|_{\infty}^{t} = -I_0 e^{-t/\tau}$$

$$i(t) = I_0 e^{-t/\tau}$$

7.13 $54.05\ \mu$s

7.15   (a) 0.25 s, (b) 0.5 ms

7.17 $-2e^{-16t}$ V

7.19 $2e^{-5t}$ A

7.21   13.33 Ω

7.23 $2e^{-4t}$ V, $t > 0$, $0.5e^{-4t}$ V, $t > 0$

7.25 $[u(t) + r(t-1) - r(t-2) - 2u(t-2)]$ V

7.27   See Fig. F.15.

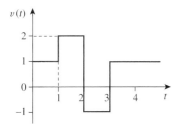

Figure F.15   For Prob. 7.27.

7.29   (a) See Fig. F.16(a).
     (b) See Fig. F.16(b).
     (c) $z(t) = \cos 4t\, \delta(t-1) = \cos 4\delta(t-1) =$
          $-0.6536\delta(t-1)$, which is sketched in
          Fig. F.16(c).

(a)

(b)

(c)

Figure F.16   For Prob. 7.29.

7.31   (a) 112×10^{-9}, (b) 7

7.33 $2u(t-2)$ A

7.35   (a) $-2e^{-3t/5}$ V, (b) $5e^{3t/2}$ V

7.37   (a) 4 s, (b) 10 V, (c) $(10 - 8e^{-t/4})$ V

7.39   (a) 4 V, $t < 0$, $20 - 16e^{-t/8}$, $t > 0$,
     (b) 4 V, $t < 0$, $12 - 8e^{-t/6}$ V

7.41 $10(1 - e^{-0.2t})$ V

7.43   0.8 A, $0.8e^{-t/480}$ A

7.45 $1.25(1 - e^{-t/5})$ V, $0.125e^{-t/5}$ A

7.47 $\begin{cases} 24(1 - e^{-t})\text{V}, & 0 < t < 1 \\ 30 - 14.83e^{-(t-1)}\text{V}, & t > 1 \end{cases}$

7.49 $\begin{cases} 8(1 - e^{-t/5})\text{V}, & 0 < t < 1 \\ 1.45e^{-(t-1)/5}\text{V}, & t > 1 \end{cases}$

7.51 $V_S = Ri + L\dfrac{di}{dt}$

or $L\dfrac{di}{dt} = -R\left(i - \dfrac{V_S}{R}\right)$

$\dfrac{di}{i - V_S/R} = \dfrac{-R}{L}dt$

Integrating both sides,

$\ln\left(i - \dfrac{V_S}{R}\right)\Big|_{I_0}^{i(t)} = \dfrac{-R}{L}t$

$\ln\left(\dfrac{i - V_S/R}{I_0 - V_S/R}\right) = \dfrac{-t}{\tau}$

or $\dfrac{i - V_S/R}{I_0 - V_S/R} = e^{-t/\tau}$

$i(t) = \dfrac{V_S}{R} + \left(I_0 - \dfrac{V_S}{R}\right)e^{-t/\tau}$

which is the same as Eq. (7.60).

7.53 (a) 5 A, $5e^{-t/2}$ A, (b) 6 A, $6e^{-2t/3}$ A

7.55 96 V, $96e^{-4t}$ V

7.57 $2.4e^{-2t}$ A, $0.6e^{-5t}$ A

7.59 $6e^{-4t}u(t)$ V

7.61 $20e^{-8t}$ V, $(10 - 5e^{-8t})$ A

7.63 $-8e^{-8t}$ V, $2e^{-8t}$ A

7.65 $\begin{cases} 2(1 - e^{-2t})\text{A} & 0 < t < 1 \\ 1.729e^{-2(t-1)}\text{A} & t > 1 \end{cases}$

7.67 $5e^{-100t/3}$ A

7.69 $48(e^{-t/3000} - 1)$ V

7.71 $-0.16667e^{-(t-2)/2000}$ mA

7.73 $-6e^{-5t}u(t)$ A

7.75 $(6 - 3e^{-50t})$V, -0.2 mA

7.77 See Fig. F.17.

7.79 $(-0.5 + 4.5e^{-80t/3})$ A

7.81 See Fig. F.18.

7.83 6.278 m/s

7.85 (a) 659.7 μs, (b) 16.636 s

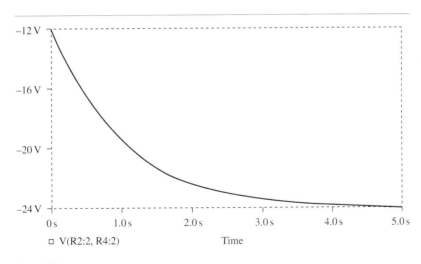

Figure F.17   For Prob. 7.77.

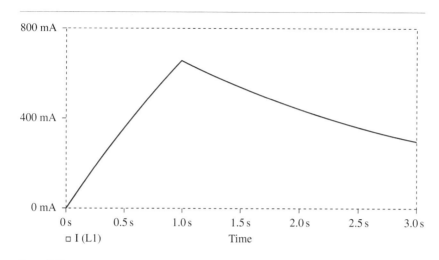

Figure F.18   For Prob. 7.81.

7.87   0.441 A

7.89 $L < 200$ mH

7.91   1.271 Ω

Chapter 8

8.1   (a) 2 A, 12 V, (b) −4 A/s, −5 V/s, (c) 0 A, 0 V

8.3   (a) 0 A, −10 V, 0 V, (b) 0 A/s, 0 V/s, 0 V/s,
(c) 0.4 A, 6 V, 16 V

8.5   (a) 0 A, 0 V, (b) 0.25 A/s, 0 V/s, (c) 2.4 A, 9.6 V

8.7 $s^2 + 4s + 4 = 0, (1 + t)e^{-2t}$

8.9 $(10 + 50t)e^{-5t}$ A

8.11 $10(1 + t)e^{-t}$ V

8.13   120 Ω

8.15   750 Ω, 200 μF, 25 H

8.17 $(60 + 64.53e^{-2.68t} - 4.641e^{-37.32t})$ V

8.19 $24 \sin 0.5t$ V

8.21 $18e^{-t} - 2e^{-9t}$ V

8.23   40 mF

8.25 $(24 \cos 1.984t + 3.024 \sin 1.984t)e^{-t/4}$ V

8.27 $3 - 3(\cos 2t + \sin 2t)e^{-2t}$ V

8.29   (a) $3 - 3 \cos 2t + \sin 2t$ V,
(b) $2 - 4e^{-t} + 4e^{-4t}$ A,
(c) $3 + (2 + 3t)e^{-t}$ V, (d) $2 + 2 \cos 2te^{-t}$ A

8.31   80 V, 40 V

8.33 $(20 - 10e^{-0.05t})$ V

8.35 $[12 - (4 \cos 2t + 2 \sin 2t)e^{-t}]$ V

8.37 $[(5 - 40t)e^{-4t}]$ A

8.39 $\left[30 + (0.021 \, e^{-47.33t} - 6.021e^{-0.167t})\right]$ V

8.41 $[0.7275 \sin(4.583t)e^{-2t}]$ A

8.43   8 Ω, 2.392 mF

8.45 $[4 - [3 \cos(1.3229t)$
$+ 1.1339 \sin(1.3229t)e^{-t/2}]$ A,
$[4.536 \sin(1.3229t)e^{-t/2}]$ V

8.47 $(200te^{-10t})$ V

8.49 $[3 + (3 + 6t)e^{-2t}]$ A

8.51 $\left[-\dfrac{i_0}{\omega_o C} \sin(\omega_o t)\right]$ V where $\omega_o = \sqrt{LC}$

8.53 $R_1C_1R_2C_2\dfrac{d^2v_o}{dt^2} + (R_1C_1 + R_2C_2 + R_1C_2)$
$\dfrac{dv_o}{dt} = R_1C_1\dfrac{dv_s}{dt}$

8.55 $7.45 - 3.45e^{-7.25t}$ V, $t > 0$

8.57 (a) $s^2 + 20s + 36 = 0$, (b) $-\dfrac{3}{4}e^{-2t} - \dfrac{5}{4}e^{-18t}$ A,
$6e^{-2t} + 10e^{-18t}$ V

8.59 $32te^{-t}$ V

8.61 $2.4 - 2.667e^{-2t} + 0.2667e^{-5t}$ A, $9.6 - 16e^{-2t} + 6.4e^{-5t}$ V

8.63 $R^2C^2\dfrac{d^2v_o}{dt^2} + 2RC\dfrac{dv_o}{dt} + v_o = v_s$

8.65 $\dfrac{d^2v_o}{dt^2} + \dfrac{v_o}{R^2C^2} = 0$, $2\sin 10t$

8.67 $-te^{-t}u(t)$ V

8.69 See Fig. F.19.

Figure F.19   For Prob. 8.69.

8.71 See Fig. F.20.

8.73 See Fig. F.21.

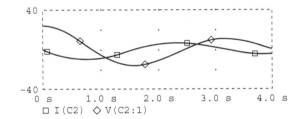

Figure F.21   For Prob. 8.73.

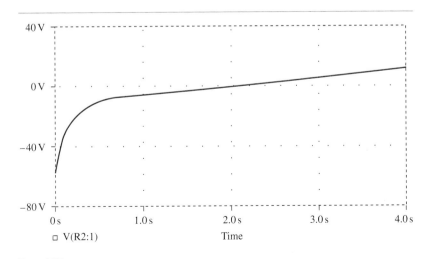

Figure F.20   For Prob. 8.71.

8.75   See Fig. F.22.

Figure F.22   For Prob. 8.75.

8.77   See Fig. F.23.

Figure F.23   For Prob. 8.77.

8.79   434 μF

8.81   2.5 μH, 625 μF

8.83 $\dfrac{d^2v}{dt^2} + \dfrac{R}{L}\dfrac{dv}{dt} + \dfrac{R}{LC}i_D + \dfrac{1}{C}\dfrac{di_D}{dt} = \dfrac{v_s}{LC}$

Chapter 9

9.1   (a) 10^3 rad/s, (b) 159.2 Hz, (c) 6.283 ms,
(d) $12\cos(10^3 t - 66°)$ V, (e) 2.65 V

9.3   (a) $4\cos(\omega t - 120°)$, (b) $2\cos(6t + 90°)$,
(c) $10\cos(\omega t + 110°)$

9.5 $20°$, v_1 lags v_2

9.7   Proof

9.9   (a) $1.809 + j0.4944$, (b) $4.201 - j1.392$,
(c) $-0.5042 - j2.243$

9.11   (a) $-56 + j33$, (b) $-0.3314 + j0.1953$,
(c) $-0.6372 - j0.5575$

9.13   (a) $-1.2749 + j0.1520$, (b) -2.083,
(c) $35 + j14$

9.15   (a) $-6 - j11$, (b) $120.99 + j4.415$, (c) -1

9.17   (a) $13.533\cos(5t + 342.81°)$,
(b) $42.51\cos(120\pi t + 84.76°)$,
(c) $6.974\cos(8t + 265.72°)$

9.19   (a) $3.32\cos(20t + 114.49°)$,
(b) $64.78\cos(50t - 70.89°)$,
(c) $9.44\cos(400t - 44.7°)$

9.21   (a) $f(t) = 8.324\cos(30t + 34.86°)$,
(b) $g(t) = 5.565\cos(t - 62.49°)$,
(c) $h(t) = 1.2748\cos(40t - 168.69°)$

9.23   (a) $40\cos(\omega t - 60°)$, (b) $38.36\cos(\omega t + 96.8°)$,
(c) $6\cos(\omega t + 80°)$, (d) $11.5\cos(\omega t - 52.06°)$

9.25   (a) $0.8\cos(2t - 98.13°)$,
(b) $0.745\cos(5t - 4.56°)$

9.27 $0.289\cos(377t - 92.45°)$ V

9.29 $2\sin(10^6 t - 65°)$

9.31   6.5-Ω resistor

9.33   69.82 V

9.35 $-5\sin 2t$ V

9.37 $2.12\sin(5t + 32°)$ A

9.39 $6.248\cos(120\pi t - 51.34°)$ A,
$3.124\cos(120\pi t + 128.66°)$ A

9.41 $6.325\cos(t - 18.43°)$ V

9.43 $3.328\cos(2t + 33.69°)$ A

9.45 -5 A

9.47 $0.4607\cos(2,000t + 52.63°)$ A

9.49 $1.414\sin(200t - 45°)$ V

9.51 $25\cos(2t - 53.13°)$ A

9.53 $8.873\underline{/-21.67}$ A

9.55 $2.798 - j16.403$ Ω

9.57 $0.3171 - j0.1463$ S

9.59 $8.308 - j1.5385$ Ω

9.61 $1 + j0.5$ Ω

9.63 $34.69 - j6.93$ Ω

9.65 $17.35\underline{/0.9°}$ A, $6.83 + j1.094$ Ω

9.67 (a) $0.0148\underline{/-20.22°}$ S, (b) $0.0197\underline{/74.57°}$ S

9.69 $1.661 + j0.6647$ S

9.71 $1.058 - j2.235$ Ω

9.73 $0.3796 + j1.46$ Ω

9.75 Can be achieved by the RL circuit shown in Fig. F.24.

Figure F.24   For Prob. 9.75.

9.77 (a) 51.49° lagging, (b) 1.5915 MHz

9.79 (a) 140.2°, (b) leading, (c) 18.43 V

9.81 1.8 kΩ, 0.1 μF

9.83 104.2 mH

9.85 Proof

9.87 $38.21\underline{/-8.98°}$ Ω

9.89 2 mH

9.91 235 pF

9.93 $3.592\underline{/-38.66°}$ A

Chapter 10

10.1 $15.73\cos(t + 247.9°)$ V

10.3 $3.835\cos(4t - 35.02°)$ V

10.5 $4.615\underline{/97.38°}$ A

10.7 $124.08\underline{/-154°}$ V

10.9 $6.154\cos(10^3 t + 70.26°)$ V

10.11 $5.024\cos(2t - 46.55°)$ A

10.13 $29.36\underline{/62.88°}$ V

10.15 $7.906\underline{/43.49°}$ A

10.17 $9.25\underline{/-162.12°}$ A

10.19 $7.682\underline{/50.19°}$ V

10.21 (a) $1, 0, -\dfrac{j}{R}\sqrt{\dfrac{L}{C}}$, (b) $0, 1, \dfrac{j}{R}\sqrt{\dfrac{L}{C}}$

10.23 $\dfrac{(1 - \omega^2 LC)V_s}{1 - \omega^2 LC + j\omega RC(2 - \omega^2 LC)}$

10.25 $1.414\cos(2t + 45°)$ A

10.27 $4.698\underline{/95.24°}$ A, $0.9928\underline{/37.71°}$ A

10.29 $4.67\underline{/-20.17°}$ A, $1.79\underline{/37.35°}$ A

10.31 $2.179\underline{/61.44°}$ A

10.33 $7.906\underline{/43.49°}$ A

10.35 $1.971\underline{/-2.1°}$ A

10.37 $2.38\underline{/-96.37°}$ A, $2.38\underline{/143.63°}$ A, $2.38\underline{/23.63°}$ A

10.39 $0.3814\underline{/109.6°}$ A, $0.3443\underline{/124.4°}$ A, $0.1455\underline{/-60.42°}$ A, $0.1005\underline{/48.5°}$ A

10.41 $[5 + 2.56\sin(500t - 39.8°)]$ V

10.43 $9.902\cos(2t - 129.17°)$ A

10.45 $2.816 \cos(10t + 150.98°)$ A

10.47 $\left[4 + 0.504 \sin(t + 19.1°) \right.$
$\left. + 0.3352 \cos(3t - 76.43°) \right]$ A

10.49 $4.472 \sin(200t + 56.56°)$ A

10.51 $4.698\underline{/95.24°}$ A, $0.9928\underline{/37.7°}$ A

10.53 $(3.529 - j5.883)$ V

10.55 (a) $Z_N = Z_{Th} = 22.63\underline{/-63.43°}$ Ω,
$\mathbf{V}_{Th} = -50\underline{/30°}$ V,
$\mathbf{I}_N = 2.236\underline{/273.4°}$ A, (b)
$Z_N = Z_{Th} = 10\underline{/26°}$ Ω,
$\mathbf{V}_{Th} = 33.92\underline{/58°}$ V, $\mathbf{I}_N = 3.392\underline{/32°}$ A

10.57 $Z_N = Z_{Th} = 21.63\underline{/-33.7°}$ Ω,
$\mathbf{V}_{Th} = 107.3\underline{/146.56°}$ V,
$\mathbf{I}_N = 4.961\underline{/-179.7°}$ A

10.59 $15.73 \cos(t + 247.9°)$ V

10.61 $3.855 \cos(4t - 35.02°)$ V

10.63 1 kΩ, $5.657 \cos(200t + 75°)$ A

10.65 $0.542 \cos(2t - 77.47°)$ A

10.67 $4.945\underline{/-69.76°}$ V, $0.4378\underline{/-75.24°}$ A,
$11.243 + j1.079$ Ω

10.69 $-j\omega RC$, $-V_m \cos \omega t$

10.71 $48 \cos(2t + 29.53°)$ V

10.73 $21.21\underline{/-45°}$ kΩ

10.75 $0.08157\underline{/168.23°}$

10.77 $\dfrac{R_2 + R_3 + j\omega C_2 R_2 R_3}{(1 + j\omega R_1 C_1)(R_3 + j\omega C_2 R_2 R_3)}$

10.79 $35.78 \cos(1{,}000t + 26.56°)$ V

10.81 $1.465\underline{/79.59°}$ A

10.83 $6.611 \cos(1{,}000t - 159.2°)$ V

10.85 $2.228\underline{/-167.5°}$ V

10.87 $15.91\underline{/169.6°}$, $5.172\underline{/-138.6°}$, $2.27\underline{/-152.4°}$ V

10.89 Proof

10.91 (a) 180 kHz, (b) 40 kΩ

10.93 Proof

10.95 Proof

Chapter 11

11.1 $800 + 1{,}600 \cos(100t + 60°)$, 800 W

11.3 -7.5 W, 5 W, 0 W, 2.5 W, 0 W

11.5 $P_{1\Omega} = 1.416$ W, $P_{2\Omega} = 5.097$ W,
$P_{3H} = P_{0.25F} = 0$

11.7 160 W

11.9 $P_{10} = 6.4$ mW, $P_2 = 2$ mW, $P_6 = 6$ mW

11.11 12.751 mW

11.13 (a) $12.798 + j49.6$ Ω, (b) 90.08 W

11.15 $0.5 - j0.5$ Ω, 90 W

11.17 20 Ω, 31.25 W

11.19 2.576 Ω, 3.798 W

11.21 19.58 Ω

11.23 9.574 V

11.25 3.266

11.27 2.887 A

11.29 5.773 A, 400 W

11.31 2.944 V

11.33 6.667 A

11.35 21.6 V

11.37 9.487 A

11.39 0.2631 (lagging)

11.41 (a) 0.5547 (leading), (b) 0.9304 (lagging)

11.43 5.477 V, 3 W

11.45 (a) 46.9 V, 1.061 A, (b) 20 W

11.47 (a) $S = 112 + j194$ VA,
average power = 112 W,
reactive power = 194 VAR
(b) $S = 226.3 - j226.3$ VA,
average power = 226.3 W,
reactive power = -226.3 VAR
(c) $S = 110.85 + j64$ VA, average power =
110.85 W, reactive power = 64 VAR
(d) $S = 7.071 + j7.071$ kVA, average power =
7.071 kW, reactive power = 7.071 kVAR

11.49 (a) $4 + j2.373$ kVA, (b) $1.6 - j1.2$ kVA,
(c) $0.4624 + j1.2705$ kVA,
(d) $110.77 + j166.16$ VA

11.51 (a) 0.9956 (lagging), (b) 15.56 W,
(c) 1.466 VAR, (d) 15.63 VA,
(e) $15.56 + j1.466$ VA

11.53 (a) $93.97\underline{/29.8°}$ A, (b) 1.0 (lagging)

11.55 For the 40-V source, $-140 + j20$ VA; for the
capacitor, $-j250$ VA; for the resistor, 290 VA;
for the inductor, $j130\ VA$; for the $j50$-V
source, $-150 + j100$ VA

11.57 $25.23 - j16.82$ VA

11.59 $j169.65$ VAR, $-j707.3$ VAR

11.61 $132.4\underline{/92.4°}$ A, $6.62\underline{/-2.4}$ kVA

11.63 $443.3\underline{/-28.13°}$ A

11.65 80 μW

11.67 $18\underline{/36.86°}$ mVA, 2.904 mW

11.69 (a) 0.6402 (lagging), (b) 295.1 W, (c) 130.4 μF

11.71 10.33 μF

11.73 (a) 12.21 kVA, (b) $50.86\underline{/-35°}$ A,
(c) 4.083 kVAR, 188.03 μF,
(d) $43.4\underline{/-16.26°}$ A

11.75 (a) $1,835.9 - j114.68$ VA, (b) 0.998 (leading),
(c) no correction is necessary

11.77 157.69 W

11.79 50 mW

11.81 \$76.26

11.83 (a) 688.1 W, (b) 840 VA, (c) 481.8 VAR,
(d) 0.8191 (lagging)

11.85 (a) 20 A, $17.85\underline{/163.26°}$ A, $5.907\underline{/-119.5°}$ A,
(b) $2,225 + j308.5$ VA, (c) 0.9905 (lagging)

11.87 0.5333

11.89 (a) 12 kVA, $9.36 + j7.51$ kVA,
(b) $2.866 + j2.3$ Ω

11.91 104 μF

11.93 (a) 7.328 kW, 1.196 kVAR, (b) 0.987

11.95 (a) 2.814 kHz, (b) 431.8 mW

11.97 547.3 W

Chapter 12

12.1 (a) $231\underline{/-30°}$, $231\underline{/-150°}$, $231\underline{/-270°}$ V,
(b) $231\underline{/30°}$, $231\underline{/150°}$, $231\underline{/-90°}$ V

12.3 *acb* sequence, $208\underline{/250°}$ V

12.5 $242.5\underline{/-30°}$, $242.5\underline{/-150°}$, $242.5\underline{/90°}$ V

12.7 $44\underline{/53.13°}$, $44\underline{/-66.87°}$, $44\underline{/173.13°}$ A

12.9 $4.8\underline{/-36.87°}$, $4.8\underline{/-156.87°}$, $4.8\underline{/83.13°}$ A

12.11 $127\underline{/100°}$ V, $220\underline{/130°}$ V, $17.32\underline{/150°}$ A,
$12.7\underline{/-80°}$ Ω

12.13 $6.471\underline{/-61.93°}$ A, $6.471\underline{/-181.93°}$ A,
$6.471\underline{/58.07°}$ A

12.15 13.66 A

12.17 172.6$\underline{/34.76°}$, 172.6$\underline{/-85.24°}$,
172.6$\underline{/154.76°}$ V, 11.51$\underline{/-18.37°}$,
11.51$\underline{/-138.37°}$, 11.51$\underline{/101.63°}$ A

12.19 5.47$\underline{/-18.43°}$, 5.47$\underline{/-138.43°}$,
5.47$\underline{/101.57°}$ A, 9.474$\underline{/-48.43°}$,
9.474$\underline{/-168.43°}$, 9.474$\underline{/71.57°}$ A

12.21 $-17.95\underline{/81.34°}$ A rms, 31.1$\underline{/-8.66°}$ A rms

12.23 (a) 14.41 A, (b) 2.596 kW

12.25 17.74$\underline{/4.78°}$, 17.74$\underline{/-115.22°}$,
17.74$\underline{/124.78°}$ A

12.27 5.081$\underline{/-46.87°}$, 5.081$\underline{/-166.87°}$,
5.081$\underline{/73.13°}$ A

12.29 $4.15 - j5.53$ Ω, $5,000 - j6,667$ VA

12.31 (a) $6.144 + j4.608$ Ω, (b) 18.04 A, (c) 207.2 μF

12.33 7.69 A, 360.3 V

12.35 (a) $14.61 - j5.953$ A, (b) $3.361 + j1.368$ kVA,
(c) 0.9261

12.37 55.51 A, $1.298 - j1.731$ Ω

12.39 423.1 W

12.41 9.021 A

12.43 $4.373 - j1.145$ kVA

12.45 6346$\underline{/28.92°}$ V

12.47 40.42 A (rms), 0.9677 (lagging)

12.49 (a) 6.943$\underline{/26.56°}$ kVA, (b) 2.164$\underline{/26.56°}$ kVA

12.51 12.56$\underline{/47.2°}$ A, 13.6$\underline{/239.17°}$ A,
2.919$\underline{/122.34°}$ A

12.53 3.608$\underline{/-60°}$ A, 2.406$\underline{/-75°}$ A, 7.217$\underline{/120°}$ A,
1.428$\underline{/-34.12°}$ A

12.55 $1,167.5 + j318.2$ VA

12.57 $I_a = 1.9585\underline{/-18.1°}$ A,
$I_b = 1.4656\underline{/-130.55°}$ A, $I_c = 1.947\underline{/117.8°}$ A

12.59 220.6$\underline{/-34.56°}$, 214.1$\underline{/-81.49°}$,
49.91$\underline{/-50.59°}$ V, assuming that N is
grounded.

12.61 11.15$\underline{/37°}$ A, 230.8$\underline{/-133.4°}$ V, assuming N is
grounded.

12.63 18.67$\underline{/158.9°}$ A, 12.38$\underline{/144.1°}$ A

12.65 6.581$\underline{/98.66°}$ A, 11.4$\underline{/-111.3°}$ A,
6.581$\underline{/38.66°}$ A

12.67 (a) 97.67 kW, 88.67 kW, 83.67 kW, (b) 132.3 A

12.69 28 mF

12.71 (a) 2,590 W, 4,808 W, (b) 8,335 VA

12.73 $-2,995$ W, 2,995 W

12.75 (a) 20 mA, (b) 200 mA

12.77 320 W

12.79 17.15$\underline{/-19.65°}$, 17.15$\underline{/-139.65°}$,
17.15$\underline{/100.3°}$ A, 223$\underline{/2.97°}$, 223$\underline{/-117.03°}$,
223$\underline{/122.97°}$ V

12.81 516 V

12.83 183.42 A

12.85 $Z_Y = 2.133$ Ω

12.87 1.448$\underline{/-176.6°}$ A, $1,252 + j711.6$ VA,
$1,085 + j721.2$ VA

Chapter 13

13.1 10 H

13.3 150 mH, 50 mH, 25 mH, 0.2887

13.5 (a) 123.7 mH, (b) 24.31 mH

13.7 $22\underline{/37.66°}$ V

13.9 $2.074\underline{/21.12°}$ V

13.11 For mesh 1,
$V_1 = I_1(R_1 + 1/j\omega C) - I_2(1/j\omega C) - R_1 I_3$
For mesh 2,
$0 = -I_1(1/j\omega C) + (j\omega L_1 + j\omega L_2 + 1/j\omega C$
$\quad - j2\omega M)I_2 - j\omega L_1 I_3 + j\omega M I_3$
For mesh 3,
$V_2 = R_1 I_1 + j\omega(L_1 - M)I_2 - (R_1 + R_2 + j\omega L_1)I_3$

13.13 $13.195 + j11.244$ Ω

13.15 $3 + j16$ Ω

13.17 $0.1989 - j9.7$ Ω

13.19 See Fig. F.25.

Figure F.25   For Prob. 13.19.

13.21 $4.254\underline{/-8.51°}$ A, $1.5637\underline{/27.52°}$ A, 4.89 W

13.23 $5.068 \cos(10t + 52.54°)$ A,
$2.719 \cos(10t - 100.89°)$ A

13.25 $2.2 \sin(2t - 4.88°)$ A

13.27 $13\underline{/-49.4°}$ A

13.29 0.984, 130.5 mJ

13.31 (a) $L_a = 10$ H, $L_b = 15$ H, $L_c = 5$ H,
(b) $L_A = 18.33$ H, $L_B = 27.5$ H, $L_C = 55$ H

13.33 $12.77 + j7.15$ Ω

13.35 $1.4754\underline{/-21.4°}$ A, $0.0775\underline{/-134.85°}$ A,
$0.077\underline{/-110.41°}$ A

13.37 (a) 5, (b) 104.17 A, (c) 20.83 A

13.39 $15.7\underline{/20.31°}$ A, $78.5\underline{/20.31°}$ A

13.41 0.5 A, -1.5 A

13.43 4.186 V, 16.744 V

13.45 36.7 mW

13.47 $2.963\underline{/32.9°}$ V, $2.963\underline{/-147.1°}$ V

13.49 $0.937 \cos(2t + 51.34°)$ A

13.51 $8 - j1.5$ Ω, $2.95\underline{/10.62°}$ A

13.53 (a) 5, (b) 8 W

13.55 1054 W

13.57 (a) $25.9\underline{/69.96°}$, $12.95\underline{/69.96°}$ A (rms),
(b) $21.06\underline{/147.4°}$, $42.12\underline{/147.4°}$,
$42.12\underline{/147.4°}$ V(rms), (c) $1554\underline{/20.04°}$ VA

13.59 $P_{8\Omega} = 2.778$ W, $P_{2\Omega} = 11.11$ W,
$P_{4\Omega} = 5.556$ W

13.61 6 A, 0.36 A, -60 V

13.63 $3.795\underline{/18.43°}$, $1.897\underline{/18.43°}$, $0.6325\underline{/161.6°}$

13.65 11.05 W

13.67 (a) 160 V, (b) 31.25 A, (c) 12.5 A

13.69 $(1.2 - j2)$ kΩ, 5.333 W

13.71 $[1 + (N_1/N_2)]^2 Z_L$

13.73 (a) three-phase Δ-Y transformer,
(b) $8.66\underline{/156.87°}$ A, $5\underline{/-83.13°}$ A, (c) 1.8 kW

13.75 (a) 2.887, (b) 76.98 A, 15.395 A

13.77 (a) a single-phase transformer, 110,
(b) 7.576 mA

13.79 $1.306\underline{/-68.01°}$ A, $406.8\underline{/-77.86°}$ mA,
$1.336\underline{/-54.92°}$ A

13.81 $104.5\underline{/13.96°}$ mA, $29.54\underline{/-143.8°}$ mA,
$208.8\underline{/24.4°}$ mA

13.83 $1.08\underline{/33.91°}$ A, $15.14\underline{/-34.21°}$ V

13.85 100 turns

13.87 0.5

13.89 0.5, 41.67 A, 83.33 A

13.91 (a) 1,875 kVA, (b) 7,812 A

13.93 (a) See Fig. F.26(a).
(b) See Fig. F.26(b).

(a)

(b)

Figure F.26   For Prob. 13.93.

13.95 (a) 1/60, (b) 139 mA

Chapter 14

14.1 $\dfrac{j\omega/\omega_o}{1 + j\omega/\omega_o}$, $\omega_o = \dfrac{1}{RC}$

14.3 (a) $\dfrac{1}{s^2 R^2 C^2 + 3sRC + 1}$, (b) No zeros; poles at
-4.775, -32.72

14.5 (a) $\dfrac{1}{1 + j\omega RC - \omega^2 LC}$,

(b) $\dfrac{j\omega L - \omega^2 RLC}{R + j\omega L - \omega^2 RLC}$

14.7 (a) 1.005773, (b) 0.4898, (c) 1.718×10^5

14.9 See Fig. F.27.

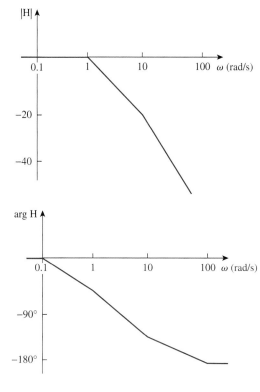

Figure F.27   For Prob. 14.9.

14.11 See Fig. F.28.

(a)

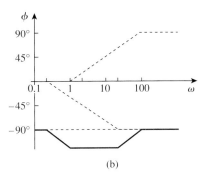

Figure F.28   For Prob. 14.11.

14.13 See Fig. F.29.

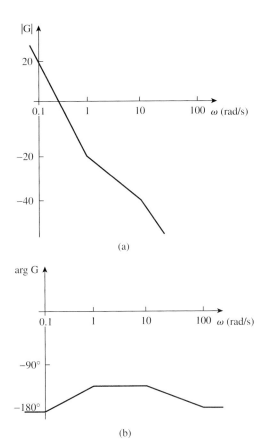

Figure F.29   For Prob. 14.13.

14.15 See Fig. F.30.

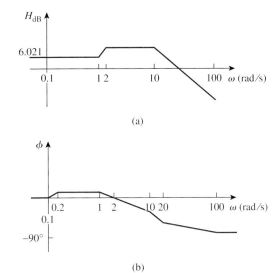

Figure F.30   For Prob. 14.15: (a) magnitude plot, (b) phase plot.

14.17 See Fig. F.31.

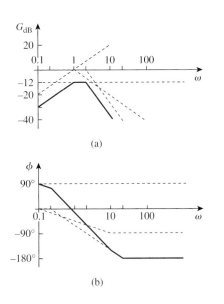

Figure F.31   For Prob. 14.17.

14.19   See Fig. F.32.

(a)

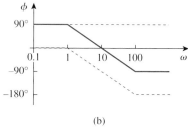

(b)

Figure F.32   For Prob. 14.19.

14.21   See Fig. F.33.

(a)

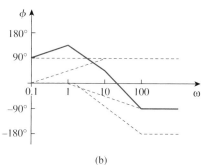

(b)

Figure F.33   For Prob. 14.21.

14.23 $\dfrac{100j\omega}{(1 + j\omega)(10 + j\omega)^2}$

14.25   2 kΩ, $2 - j0.75$ kΩ,
$2 - j0.3$ kΩ, $2 + j0.3$ kΩ, $2 + j0.75$ kΩ

14.27 $R = 10$ Ω, $L = 16$ H, $C = 25$ μF, 0.625 rad/s

14.29   0.7861 rad/s

14.31 8.796×10^6 rad/s,

14.33   14.21 μH, 56.84 pF

14.35   40 Ω, 2.5 μH, 10 μF, 2.5 krad/s, 197.5 krad/s,
202.5 krad/s

14.37 $\dfrac{1}{\sqrt{LC - R^2C^2}}$

14.39   (a) 19.89 nF, (b) 164.45 μH, (c) 552.9 krad/s,
(d) 25.13 krad/s, (e) 22

14.41   (a) 1.5811 rad/s, 0.1976, 8 rad/s,
(b) 5 krad/s, 20, 250 rad/s

14.43   (a) 2.357 krad/s, (b) 1 Ω

14.45   (a) $\dfrac{j\omega}{2(1 + j\omega)^2}$, (b) 0.25

14.47   796 kHz

14.49   0.2 rad/s, -14.023, $-84.3°$

14.51   1.256 kΩ

14.53   18.045 kΩ, 2.872 H, 11.5

14.55   1.56 kHz $< f <$ 1.62 kHz, 25

14.57   (a) 1 rad/s, 3 rad/s, (b) 1 rad/s, 3 rad/s

14.59   9.6 krad/s, 5 krad/s

14.61   (a) $\dfrac{1}{1 + j\omega RC}$, (b) $\dfrac{j\omega RC}{1 + j\omega RC}$

14.63   10 MΩ, 100 kΩ

14.65 $\left(1 + \dfrac{R_f}{R_i}\right), \dfrac{1}{RC}$

14.67 If $R_f = 20$ kΩ, then $R_i = 80$ kΩ and $C = 31.83$ nF.

14.69 Let $R = 10$ kΩ, then $R_f = 25$ kΩ, $C = 7.96$ nF.

14.71 $K_f = 2 \times 10^{-4}, K_m = 5 \times 10^{-3}$

14.73 9.6 MΩ, 32 μH, 0.375 pF

14.75 200 Ω, 400 μH, 1 μF

14.77 (a) 1,200 H, 0.5208 μF, (b) 312.5 nF, (c) 8 mH, 7.81 pF

14.79 (a) $8s + 5 + \frac{10}{s}$, (b) $0.8\,s + 50 + \frac{10^4}{s}$, 111.8 rad/s

14.81 (a) 0.4 Ω, 0.4 H, 1 mF, 1 mS, (b) 0.4 Ω, 0.4 mH, 1 μF, 1 mS

14.83 0.1 pF, 0.5 pF, 1 MΩ, 2 MΩ

14.85 See Fig. F.34.

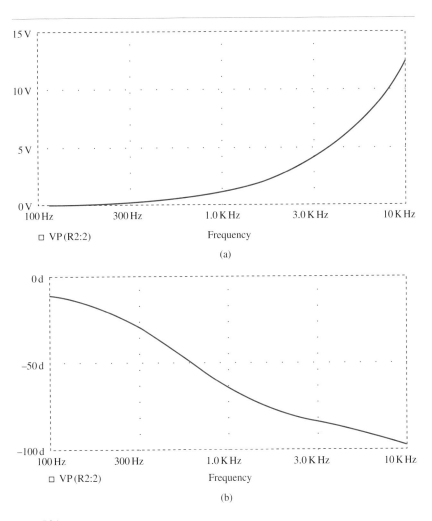

Figure F.34   For Prob. 14.85.

14.87 See Fig. F.35; highpass filter, $f_o = 1.2$ Hz.

14.89 See Fig. F.36.

14.91 See Fig. F.37; $f_o = 800$ Hz.

14.93 938 kHz, remains the same

14.95 (a) 0.541 MHz $< f_o <$ 1.264 MHz, (b) 67.98, 204.1

14.97 $\dfrac{s^3 L R_L C_1 C_2}{(s R_i C_1 + 1)(s^2 L C_2 + s R_L C_2 + 1) + s^2 L C_1 (s R_L C_2 + 1)}$

14.99 1.826 MHz, 4.188×10^6 rad/s

14.101 1.061 kΩ

14.103 $\dfrac{R_2(1 + sCR_1)}{R_1 + sCR_2}$

Chapter 15

15.1   (a) $\dfrac{s}{s^2 - a^2}$, (b) $\dfrac{a}{s^2 - a^2}$

15.3   (a) $\dfrac{s + 2}{(s + 2)^2 + 9}$, (b) $\dfrac{4}{(s + 2)^2 + 16}$,
(c) $\dfrac{s + 3}{(s + 3)^2 - 4}$
(d) $\dfrac{1}{(s + 4)^2 - 1}$, (e) $\dfrac{4(s + 1)}{[(s + 1)^2 - 4]^4}$

Figure F.35   For Prob. 14.87.

Figure F.36   For Prob. 14.89.

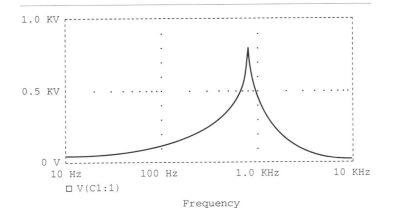

Figure F.37   For Prob. 14.91.

15.5 (a) $\dfrac{8 - 12\sqrt{3}s - 6s^2 + \sqrt{3}s^3}{(s^2 + 4)^3}$, (b) $\dfrac{72}{(s + 2)^5}$,

(c) $\dfrac{2}{s^2} - 4\,s$,

(d) $\dfrac{2e}{s + 1}$, (e) $\dfrac{5}{s}$, (f) $\dfrac{18}{3s + 1}$, (g) s^n

15.7 (a) $\dfrac{10se^{-s}}{s^2 + 16}$, (b) $\dfrac{2}{(s + 2)^3} + \dfrac{e^{-3s}}{s}$

15.9 (a) $\dfrac{e^{-2s}}{s^2} - \dfrac{2e^{-2s}}{s^2}$, (b) $\dfrac{2e^{-s}}{e^4(s + 4)}$,

(c) $\dfrac{2.702s}{s^2 + 4} + \dfrac{8.415}{s^2 + 4}$,

(d) $\dfrac{6}{s}e^{-2s} - \dfrac{6}{s}e^{-4s}$

15.11 (a) $\dfrac{6(s + 1)}{s^2 + 2s - 3}$, (b) $\dfrac{24(s + 2)}{(s^2 + 4s - 12)^2}$,

(c) $\dfrac{e^{-(2s+6)}\left[(4e^2 + 4e^{-2})s + (16e^2 + 8e^{-2})\right]}{s^2 + 6s + 8}$

15.13 (a) $\dfrac{s^2 + s - 1}{(s^2 + 1)^2}$, (b) $\dfrac{2(s + 1)}{(s^2 + 2s + 2)^2}$, (c) $\tan^{-1}\dfrac{\beta}{s}$

15.15 $\dfrac{10}{s}(1 - e^{-s})^2$

15.17 $\dfrac{2}{s^3}(1 - e^{-s}) - \dfrac{2}{s^2}e^{-s} - \dfrac{e^{-3s}}{s}$

15.19 $\dfrac{1}{1 - e^{-2s}}$

15.21 $\dfrac{(2\pi s - 1 + e^{-2\pi s})}{2\pi s^2(1 - e^{-2\pi s})}$

15.23 (a) $\dfrac{(1 - e^{-s})^2}{s(1 - e^{-2s})}$,

(b) $\dfrac{2(1 - e^{-2s}) - 4se^{-2s}(s + s^2)}{s^3(1 - e^{-2s})}$

15.25 (a) 8, 3, (b) 0, does not exist

15.27 (a) $u(t) + 2e^{-t}$, (b) $3\delta(t) - 11e^{-4t}$,

(c) $2e^{-t} - 2e^{-3t}$, (d) $3e^{-4t} - 3e^{-2t} + 6te^{-2t}$

15.29 $2u(t) - 2e^{-2t}\cos 3t - \frac{2}{3}e^{-2t}\sin 3t, t \geq 0$

15.31 (a) $-5e^{-t} + 20e^{-2t} - 15e^{-3t}$

(b) $-e^{-t} + \left(1 + 3t - \dfrac{t^2}{2}\right)e^{-2t}$,

(c) $e^{-t}(-0.2 + 0.2\cos 2t + 0.4\sin 2t)$

15.33 (a) $3\sin t - \cos t + 3e^{-t}$,

(b) $\cos(t - \pi)u(t - \pi)$,

(c) $8u(t)[1 - e^{-t} - te^{-t} - 0.5t^2e^{-t}]$

15.35 (a) $[2e^{-(t-6)} - e^{-2(t-6)}]u(t - 6)$,

(b) $\dfrac{4}{3}u(t)[e^{-t} - e^{-4t}] - \dfrac{1}{3}u(t - 2)[e^{-(t-2)}$

$- e^{-4(t-2)}]$,

(c) $\dfrac{1}{13}u(t)[-3e^{-3(t-1)} + 3\cos 2(t - 1)$

$+ 2\sin 2(t - 1)]$

15.37 (a) $3[1 - \cos 2(t - 2)]u(t - 2)$,

(b) $\dfrac{1}{4}\cos t + \dfrac{1}{8}\sin t - \dfrac{1}{4}\cos 3t - \dfrac{1}{24}\sin 3t$,

(c) $4e^{-2t}(-1 + t + \cos 3t - 5\sin 3t)$

15.39 (a) $-3.138e^{-t}\cos 4t - 2.358e^{-t}\sin 4t$
$+ 5.138e^{-2t}\cos 4t + 1.142e^{-2t}\sin 4t$,

(b) $\left[\dfrac{1}{4}\cos 3t + \dfrac{1}{12}\sin 4t - \dfrac{1}{8}e^{-0.551t}\right.$
$\left. + \dfrac{1}{8}e^{-5.449t}\right]u(t)$

15.41 $y(t) = \begin{cases} 2t^2, & 0 < t < 1 \\ 8t - 2t^2 - 4, & 1 < t < 3 \\ 32 - 16t + 2t^2, & 3 < t < 4 \\ 0, & \text{otherwise} \end{cases}$

15.43 (a) $y(t) = \begin{cases} \dfrac{1}{2}t^2, & 0 < t < 1 \\ -\dfrac{1}{2}t^2 + 2t - 1, & 1 < t < 2 \\ 1, & t > 2 \\ 0, & \text{otherwise} \end{cases}$

(b) $y(t) = 2(1 - e^{-t})$, $t > 0$,

(c) $y(t) = \begin{cases} \dfrac{1}{2}t^2 + t + \dfrac{1}{2}, & -1 < t < 0 \\ \dfrac{1}{2}t^2 - 3t + \dfrac{9}{2}, & 2 < t < 3 \\ 0, & \text{otherwise} \end{cases}$

15.45 Proof

15.47 $\dfrac{1}{2}t\cos t + \dfrac{1}{2}\sin t$

15.49 $2[1 - e^{-2t}]u(t) - 4[1 - e^{-2(t-1)}]u(t - 1)$

15.51 $(5e^{-t} - 3e^{-3t})u(t)$

15.53 $\dfrac{27}{4}e^{-2t} - \dfrac{75}{13}e^{-3t} + \dfrac{1}{52}\cos 2t + \dfrac{5}{52}\sin 2t$

15.55 $\left[\dfrac{1}{10}e^{-2t} + \dfrac{1}{26}e^{-4t} - \dfrac{4}{65}e^{-t}\cos 2t\right.$
$\left. - \dfrac{1}{130}e^{-t}\sin 2t\right]u(t)$

15.57 $-0.4\sin 2t + \cos 3t + 0.6\sin 3t$

15.59 $2.5e^{-t} + 6e^{-2t} - 10.5e^{-3t}$

Chapter 16

16.1 $1.155e^{-0.5t}\sin(0.866t)$A

16.3 $0.5(1 - e^{-2.5t})u(t)$V

16.5 $e^{-2t} - \dfrac{2}{\sqrt{7}}e^{-t/2}\sin\left(\dfrac{\sqrt{3}}{2}t\right)$, $t > 0$

16.7 $\left[6 - 4e^{-0.5t}\cos 0.866t\right]u(t)$A

16.9 (a) $\dfrac{2(s^2 + 1)}{s^2 + 2s + 1}$, (b) $\dfrac{s(5s + 6)}{3s^2 + 7s + 6}$

16.11 $(0.5 + 2.887e^{-t}\sin 1.732t)u(t)$ A,
$-1.732e^{-t}\sin 1.732tu(t)$ A

16.13 $[2e^{-2t} - e^{-t}]u(t)$ A

16.15 $-\dfrac{5s(s^2 + 20)}{s(s + 2)(s^2 + 0.5s + 40)}$

16.17 $(2 - e^{-t})u(t)$A

16.19 $(3.333e^{-t/2} - 1.3333e^{-2t})u(t)$ V

16.21 $v_o(t) = \dfrac{20}{3}[1 - e^{-t}\cos 0.7071t$
$- 1.414e^{-t}\sin 0.7071t]u(t)$V

16.23 $(5e^{-4t}\cos 2t + 230e^{-4t}\sin 2t)u(t)$ V,
$(6 - 6e^{-4t}\cos 2t - 11.37e^{-4t}\sin 2t)\,u(t)$ A, $t > 0$

16.25 $\left[2.202e^{-3t} + 3.84te^{-3t} - 0.202\cos(4t) + \right.$
$\left. 0.6915\sin(4t)\right]u(t)$ V

16.27 $\dfrac{20(s + 1)}{(s + 3)(3s^2 + 4s + 1)}$, $\dfrac{10(s + 1)}{(s + 3)(3s^2 + 4s + 1)}$

16.29 $10\left[2e^{-1.5t} - e^{-t}\right]u(t)$A

16.31 $\dfrac{10s^2}{s^2 + 4}$

16.33 $4 + \dfrac{s}{2(s + 3)} - \dfrac{2s^2}{s^2 + 4s + 20} - \dfrac{12s}{s^2 + 4s + 20}$

16.35 $\dfrac{9s}{3s^2 + 9s + 2}$

16.37 (a) $\dfrac{s^2 - 3}{3s^2 + 2s - 9}$, (b) $\dfrac{-3}{2s}$

16.39 $sRC + 1$

16.41 $10(1 - e^{-t})u(t)$

16.43 $\begin{bmatrix} v_C' \\ i' \end{bmatrix} = \begin{bmatrix} 0 & 1 \\ -1 & -1 \end{bmatrix} \begin{bmatrix} v_C \\ i \end{bmatrix} + \begin{bmatrix} 0 \\ 1 \end{bmatrix} u(t);$

$i(t) = \begin{bmatrix} 0 & 1 \end{bmatrix} \begin{bmatrix} v_C \\ i \end{bmatrix} + [0]u(t)$

16.45 $\begin{bmatrix} i_L' \\ v_C' \end{bmatrix} = \begin{bmatrix} 0 & -1 \\ 4 & -2 \end{bmatrix} \begin{bmatrix} i_L \\ v_C \end{bmatrix} + \begin{bmatrix} 1 & -1 \\ 2 & 0 \end{bmatrix} \begin{bmatrix} v_1(t) \\ v_2(t) \end{bmatrix};$

$v_o(t) = \begin{bmatrix} 0 & -1 \end{bmatrix} \begin{bmatrix} i_L \\ v_C \end{bmatrix} + \begin{bmatrix} 1 & 0 \end{bmatrix} \begin{bmatrix} v_1(t) \\ v_C \end{bmatrix}$

16.47 $\begin{bmatrix} i_L' \\ v_C' \end{bmatrix} = \begin{bmatrix} 0 & -1 \\ 4 & -2 \end{bmatrix} \begin{bmatrix} i_L \\ v_C \end{bmatrix} + \begin{bmatrix} 1 & -1 \\ 2 & 0 \end{bmatrix} \begin{bmatrix} v_1(t) \\ v_2(t) \end{bmatrix};$

$\begin{bmatrix} i_1(t) \\ i_2(t) \end{bmatrix} = \begin{bmatrix} 1 & -0.5 \\ 1 & 0 \end{bmatrix} \begin{bmatrix} i_L \\ v_C \end{bmatrix} + \begin{bmatrix} 0.5 & 0 \end{bmatrix} \begin{bmatrix} v_1(t) \\ v_2(t) \end{bmatrix}$

16.49 $\begin{bmatrix} 0 & 1 \\ -6 & -5 \end{bmatrix}, \begin{bmatrix} 1 \\ -3 \end{bmatrix}, \begin{bmatrix} 1 & 0 \end{bmatrix}, [0]$

16.51 $\left[1 - e^{-2t}(\cos 2t + \sin 2t) \right] u(t)$

16.53 $s_{1,2} = \dfrac{-1}{2RC} \pm \sqrt{\dfrac{1}{(2RC)^2} - \dfrac{1}{LC}}$. Note that both roots lie in the left half-plane since R, L, and C are positive quantities; thus the circuit is stable.

16.55 The circuit is unstable.

16.57 There are two possible solutions:
(1) $C = 0.25$ F, $L = 0.2$ H or
(2) $C = 0.05$ F, $L = 1$ H

16.59 We have three equations and four unknowns. Thus, there is a family of solutions. One such solution is
$R_2 = 1$ kΩ, $C_1 = 50$ nF, $C_2 = 20$ μF

16.61 See Fig. F.38.

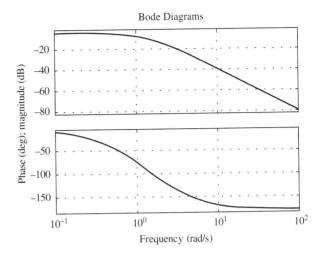

Figure F.38   For Prob. 16.61.

16.63 $\left(\dfrac{2}{3} - \dfrac{1}{2}e^{-t} - \dfrac{1}{6}e^{-3t} \right) u(t)$

16.65 $\left(-e^{-t} - 4e^{-2t} + 6te^{-2t} + 5e^{-3t} \right) u(t)$

16.67 $a = -100, b = 400, c = 20,000$

16.69 Proof

Chapter 17

17.1 (a) periodic, 2, (b) not periodic, (c) periodic, 2, (d) periodic, π, (e) periodic, 10, (f) not periodic, (g) not periodic

17.3 $a_0 = 3, 75,$
$a_n = \begin{cases} -\dfrac{5}{n\pi}(-1)^{n-1/2}, & n = \text{odd}, \\ 0, & n = \text{even} \end{cases}$
$b_n = \dfrac{5}{n\pi}\left[3 - 2\cos n\pi - \cos\dfrac{n\pi}{2} \right]$

17.5 $-0.5 + \displaystyle\sum_{\substack{n=1 \\ n=\text{odd}}}^{\infty} \dfrac{6}{n\pi}\sin nt$

17.7 $a_n = \dfrac{10}{n\pi}(2\sin 2n\pi/3 + \sin n\pi/3 - \sin 5n\pi/3),$
$b_n = \dfrac{10}{n\pi}(\cos 5n\pi/3 + \cos n\pi/3 - 2\sin 2n\pi/3),$
$f(t) = \displaystyle\sum_{n=1}^{\infty}(a_n\cos n\pi t/6 + b_n\sin n\pi t/6)$

17.9 $a_0 = 3.183, \quad a_1 = 10, \quad a_2 = 6.362,$
$a_3 = 0, \quad b_1 = 0 = b_2 = b_3$

17.11 $\displaystyle\sum_{n=-\infty}^{\infty} \frac{1}{n^2\pi^2}\big[1 + j(jn\pi/2 - 1)\sin n\pi/2$
$+ n\pi \sin n\pi/2\big]e^{jn\pi t/2}$

17.13 $\dfrac{30}{\pi} - \dfrac{60}{\pi}\displaystyle\sum_{k=1}^{\infty} \dfrac{\cos(2kt)}{(4k^2 - 1)}$

17.15 (a) $10 + \displaystyle\sum_{n=1}^{\infty} \sqrt{\dfrac{16}{(n^2 + 1)^2} + \dfrac{1}{n^6}}$
$\cos\left(10nt - \tan^{-1}\dfrac{n^2 + 1}{4n^3}\right),$

  (b) $10 + \displaystyle\sum_{n=1}^{\infty} \sqrt{\dfrac{16}{(n^2 + 1)^2} + \dfrac{1}{n^6}}$
$\sin\left(10nt + \tan^{-1}\dfrac{4n^3}{n^2 + 1}\right)$

17.17 (a) neither odd nor even, (b) even, (c) odd,
(d) even, (e) neither odd nor even

17.19 $\dfrac{8}{\pi^2}\displaystyle\sum_{n=\text{odd}}^{\infty} \dfrac{1}{n^2}\cos\left(\dfrac{n\pi t}{2}\right)$

17.21 $\dfrac{1}{2} + \displaystyle\sum_{n=1}^{\infty} \dfrac{8}{n^2\pi^2}\left[1 - \cos\left(\dfrac{n\pi}{2}\right)\right]\cos\left(\dfrac{n\pi t}{2}\right)$

17.23 $\dfrac{2}{\pi}\displaystyle\sum_{n=1}^{\infty} \dfrac{(-1)^{n+1}}{n}\sin(n\pi t)$

17.25 $\displaystyle\sum_{n=1}^{\infty}\left[\dfrac{3}{\pi^2 n^2}\sin\left(\dfrac{2\pi n}{3}\right) - \dfrac{2}{n\pi}\cos\left(\dfrac{2\pi n}{3}\right)\right]$
$\times \sin\left(\dfrac{2\pi nt}{3}\right)$

17.27 (a) odd, (b) -0.045, (c) 0.3829

17.29 $2\displaystyle\sum_{k=1}^{\infty}\left[\dfrac{2}{n^2\pi}\cos(nt) - \dfrac{1}{n}\sin(nt)\right], n = 2k - 1$

17.31 $\omega_o' = \frac{2\pi}{T'} = \frac{2\pi}{T/\alpha} = \alpha\omega_o$
$a_n' = \frac{2}{T'}\int_0^{T'} f(\alpha t)\cos n\omega_o' t\, dt$

Let $\alpha t = \lambda$, $dt = d\lambda/\alpha$, and $\alpha T' = T$. Then
$$a_n' = \frac{2\alpha}{T}\int_0^{T} f(\lambda)\cos n\omega_o\lambda\, d\lambda/\alpha = a_n$$
Similarly, $b_n' = b_n$

17.33 $v_o(t) = \displaystyle\sum_{n=1}^{\infty} A_n \sin(n\pi t - \theta_n),$
$A_n = \dfrac{8(4 - 2n^2\pi^2)}{\sqrt{(20 - 10n^2\pi^2)^2 - 64n^2\pi^2}}, \theta_n =$
$90° - \tan^{-1}\left(\dfrac{8n\pi}{20 - 10n^2\pi^2}\right)$

17.35 $\dfrac{3}{8} + \displaystyle\sum_{n=\text{odd}}^{\infty} A_n \cos\left(\dfrac{2\pi n}{3} + \theta_n\right),$ where
$A_n = \dfrac{\dfrac{6}{n\pi}\sin\dfrac{2n\pi}{3}}{\sqrt{9\pi^2 n^2 + (2\pi^2 n^2/3 - 3)^2}},$
$\theta_n = \dfrac{\pi}{2} - \tan^{-1}\left(\dfrac{2n\pi}{9} - \dfrac{1}{n\pi}\right)$

17.37 $\dfrac{100}{\pi}\displaystyle\sum_{k=1}^{\infty} \dfrac{\sin(n\pi t - 90° + \tan^{-1} 5/n\pi)}{n\sqrt{25 + n^2\pi^2}},$
$n = 2k - 1$ V

17.39 $\dfrac{1}{20} + \dfrac{200}{\pi}\displaystyle\sum_{k=1}^{\infty} I_n \sin(n\pi t - \theta_n), n = 2k - 1,$
$\theta_n = 90° + \tan^{-1}\dfrac{2n^2\pi^2 - 1,200}{802n\pi},$
$I_n = \dfrac{1}{n\sqrt{(804n\pi)^2 + (2n^2\pi^2 - 1,200)}}$

17.41 $\dfrac{2}{\pi} + \displaystyle\sum_{n=1}^{\infty} A_n \cos(2nt + \theta_n),$
$A_n = \dfrac{20}{\pi(4n^2 - 1)\sqrt{16n^2 - 40n + 29}},$
$\theta_n = 90° - \tan^{-1}(2n - 2.5)$

17.43 (a) 33.91 V, (b) 6.782 A, (c) 203.1 W

17.45 3.014 A, 157.54 W

17.47 11.838 W

17.49 (a) 1.581, (b) 1.7086, (c) 8.071%

17.51 $\displaystyle\sum_{n=-\infty}^{\infty} \dfrac{2}{n^2\pi^2}(1 + jn\pi)e^{jn\pi t}$

17.53 $\displaystyle\sum_{n=-\infty}^{\infty} \frac{0.6321 e^{j2n\pi t}}{1 + j2n\pi}$

17.55 $\displaystyle\sum_{n=-\infty}^{\infty} \frac{1 + e^{-jn\pi}}{2\pi(1 - n^2)} e^{jnt}$

17.57 $\displaystyle -3 + \sum_{n=-\infty, n\neq 0}^{\infty} \frac{3}{n^3 - 2} e^{j50nt}$

17.59 $\displaystyle \frac{1}{2} - \sum_{n=-\infty, n\neq 0}^{\infty} \frac{j5 e^{j(2n+1)\pi t}}{(2n + 1)\pi}$

17.61 (a) $6 + 2.571\cos t - 3.83\sin t + 1.638\cos 2t - 1.147\sin 2t + 0.906\cos 3t - 0.423\sin 3t + 0.47\cos 4t - 0.171\sin 4t$, (b) 6.828

17.63 See Fig. F.39.

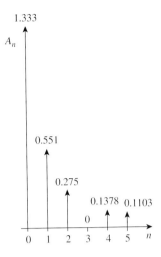

Figure F.39   For Prob. 17.63.

17.65 See Fig. F.40.

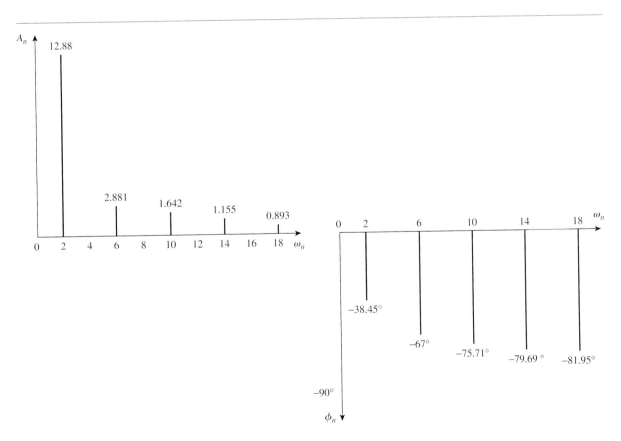

Figure F.40   For Prob. 17.65.

17.67 DC COMPONENT = 4.950000E-01

HARMONIC NO	FREQUENCY (HZ)	FOURIER COMPONENT	NORMALIZED COMPONENT	PHASE (DEG)	NORMALIZED PHASE (DEG)
1	1.667E-01	2.432E+00	1.000E+00	-8.996E+01	0.000E+00
2	3.334E-01	6.576E-04	2.705E-04	-8.932E+01	6.467E-01
3	5.001E-01	5.403E-01	2.222E-01	9.011E+01	1.801E+02
4	6.668E+00	3.343E-04	1.375E-04	9.134E+01	1.813E+02
5	8.335E-01	9.716E-02	3.996E-02	-8.982E+01	1.433E-01
6	1.000E+00	7.481E-06	3.076E-06	-9.000E+01	-3.581E-02
7	1.167E+00	4.968E-02	2.043E-01	-8.975E+01	2.173E-01
8	1.334E+00	1.613E-04	6.634E-05	-8.722E+01	2.748E+00
9	1.500E+00	6.002E-02	2.468E-02	-9.032E+01	1.803E+02

17.69

HARMONIC NO	FREQUENCY (HZ)	FOURIER COMPONENT	NORMALIZED COMPONENT	PHASE (DEG)	NORMALIZED PHASE (DEG)
1	5.000E-01	4.056E-01	1.000E+00	-9.090E+01	0.000E+00
2	1.000E+00	2.977E-04	7.341E-04	-8.707E+01	3.833E+00
3	1.500E+00	4.531E-02	1.117E-01	-9.266E+01	-1.761E+00
4	2.000E+00	2.969E-04	7.320E-04	-8.414E+01	6.757E+00
5	2.500E+00	1.648E-02	4.064E-02	-9.432E+01	-3.417E+00
6	3.000E+00	2.955E-04	7.285E-04	-8.124E+01	9.659E+00
7	3.500E+00	8.535E-03	2.104E-02	-9.581E+01	-4.911E+00
8	4.000E+00	2.935E-04	7.238E-04	-7.836E+01	1.254E+01
9	4.500E+00	5.258E-03	1.296E-02	-9.710E+01	-6.197E+00

TOTAL HARMONIC DISTORTION =   1.214285E+01 PERCENT

17.71 See Fig. F.41.

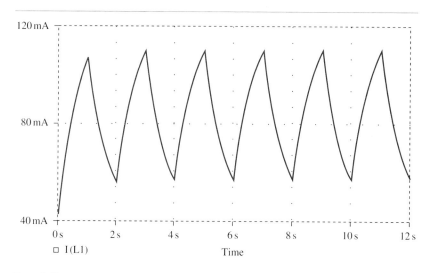

Figure F.41   For Prob. 17.71.

17.73 300 mW

17.75 24.59 mF

17.77 (a) π, (b) 2 V, (c) 11.02 V

17.79 See below for the program in *MATLAB* and the results.

```
% for problem 17.79
a = 10;
c = 4.*a/pi
for n = 1:10
  b(n) = c/(2*n-1);
end
diary
n, b
diary off
```

n	b_n
1	12.7307
2	4.2430
3	2.5461
4	1.8187
5	1.414
6	1.1573
7	0.9793
8	0.8487
9	0.7488
10	0.6700

17.81 (a) $\dfrac{A^2}{2}$, (b) $c_1 = \dfrac{8A^2}{9\pi^2}$, $c_2 = \dfrac{2A^2}{225\pi^2}$, $c_3 = \dfrac{8A^2}{1225\pi^2}$, $c_4 = \dfrac{8A^2}{3969\pi^2}$, (c) 81.1%, (d) 0.72%

Chapter 18

18.1 $\dfrac{2(\cos 2\omega - \cos \omega)}{j\omega}$

18.3 $\dfrac{j}{\omega^2}(\sin 2\omega - 2\omega \cos 2\omega)$

18.5 $\dfrac{2j}{\omega} - \dfrac{2j}{\omega^2}\sin \omega$

18.7 (a) $\dfrac{2e^{-j\omega}(\cos \omega - 1)}{j\omega}$, (b) $\dfrac{4(1 - \cos \omega)}{\omega^2}$

18.9 (a) $\dfrac{2}{\omega}\sin 2\omega + \dfrac{4}{\omega}\sin \omega$, (b) $\dfrac{2}{\omega^2} - \dfrac{2e^{-j\omega}}{\omega^2}(1 + j\omega)$

18.11 $\dfrac{\pi}{\omega^2 - \pi^2}(e^{-j\omega 2} - 1)$

18.13 (a) $\pi e^{-j\pi/3}\delta(\omega - a) + \pi e^{j\pi/3}\delta(\omega + a)$, (b) $\dfrac{e^{j\omega}}{\omega^2 - 1}$, (c) $\pi\left[\delta(\omega + b) + \delta(\omega - b)\right] + \dfrac{j\pi A}{2}[\delta(\omega + a + b) - \delta(\omega - a + b) + \delta(\omega + a - b) - \delta(\omega - a - b)]$, (d) $\dfrac{1}{\omega^2} - \dfrac{e^{-j4\omega}}{j\omega} - \dfrac{e^{-j4\omega}}{\omega^2}(j4\omega + 1)$

18.15 (a) $2j\sin 3\omega$, (b) $\dfrac{2e^{-j\omega}}{j\omega}$, (c) $\dfrac{1}{3} - \dfrac{j\omega}{2}$

18.17 (a) $\dfrac{\pi}{2}[\delta(\omega + 2) + \delta(\omega - 2)] - \dfrac{j\omega}{\omega^2 - 4}$, (b) $\dfrac{j\pi}{2}[\delta(\omega + 10) - \delta(\omega - 10)] - \dfrac{10}{\omega^2 - 100}$

18.19 $\dfrac{j\omega}{\omega^2 - 4\pi^2}(e^{-j\omega} - 1)$

18.21 Proof

18.23 (a) $\dfrac{30}{(6 - j\omega)(15 - j\omega)}$, (b) $\dfrac{20e^{-j\omega/2}}{(4 + j\omega)(10 + j\omega)}$, (c) $\dfrac{5}{[2 + j(\omega + 2)][5 + j(\omega + 2)]} + \dfrac{5}{[2 + j(\omega - 2)][5 + j(\omega - 2)]}$, (d) $\dfrac{j\omega 10}{(2 + j\omega)(5 + j\omega)}$, (e) $\dfrac{10}{j\omega(2 + j\omega)(5 + j\omega)} + \pi\delta(\omega)$

18.25 (a) $\frac{5}{2}\,\text{sgn}(t) - 5e^{-2t}u(t)$,

(b) $(-5e^{-t} + 6e^{-2t})u(t)$

18.27 (a) $5\,\text{sgn}(t) - 10e^{-10t}u(t)$,
(b) $4e^{2t}u(-t) - 6e^{-3t}u(t)$,
(c) $2e^{-20t}\sin(30t)u(t)$, (d) $\frac{1}{4}\pi$

18.29 (a) $\frac{1}{2\pi}(1 + 8\cos 3t)$, (b) $\frac{4\sin 2t}{\pi t}$,
(c) $3\delta(t + 2) + 3\delta(t - 2)$

18.31 (a) $x(t) = e^{-at}u(t)$,
(b) $y(t) = u(t + 1) - u(t - 1)$,
(c) $x(t) = \frac{1}{2}\delta(t) - \frac{a}{2}e^{-at}u(t)$

18.33 (a) $\frac{2j\sin t}{t^2 - \pi^2}$, (b) $u(t - 1) - u(t - 2)$

18.35 (a) $\frac{e^{-j\omega/3}}{6 + j\omega}$, (b) $\frac{1}{2}\left[\frac{1}{j\omega + 7} + \frac{1}{j\omega - 3}\right]$,
(c) $\frac{j\omega}{2 + j\omega}$, (d) $\frac{1}{(2 + j\omega)^2}$, (e) $\frac{1}{(2 + j\omega)^2}$

18.37 $\frac{j\omega}{4 + j3\omega}$

18.39 $\frac{10^3}{10^6 + j\omega}\left(\frac{1}{j\omega} + \frac{1}{\omega^2} - \frac{1}{\omega^2}e^{-j\omega}\right)$

18.41 $\frac{2j\omega(4.5 + j2\omega)}{(2 + j\omega)(4 - 2\omega^2 + j\omega)}$

18.43 $\frac{40}{3}(e^{-1.25t} - e^{-5t})u(t)$

18.45 $v_o(t) = 2te^{-t}u(t)$

18.47 $\frac{8(2 + j\omega)}{2 + j\omega5 - 3\omega^2}$

18.49 $0.542\cos(t + 13.64°)$ V

18.51 0.1332 J

18.53 π

18.55 682.5 J

18.57 2 J, 87.43%

18.59 $(16e^{-t} - 20e^{-2t} + 4e^{-4t})u(t)$

18.61 7.995 MHz, 8.005 MHz

18.63 106 stations

18.65 6.8 kHz

18.67 200 Hz, 5 ms

18.69 35.24%

Chapter 19

19.1 $\begin{bmatrix} 4 & 1 \\ 1 & 1.667 \end{bmatrix}\ \Omega$

19.3 (a) $\begin{bmatrix} 1 + j & j \\ j & 0 \end{bmatrix}\ \Omega$,

(b) $\begin{bmatrix} 1.5 + j0.5 & 1.5 - j0.5 \\ 1.5 - j0.5 & 1.5 - j1.5 \end{bmatrix}\ \Omega$

19.5 $\begin{bmatrix} \dfrac{s^2 + s + 1}{s^3 + 2s^2 + 3s + 1} & \dfrac{1}{s^3 + 2s^2 + 3s + 1} \\[3mm] \dfrac{1}{s^3 + 2s^2 + 3s + 1} & \dfrac{s^2 + 2s + 2}{s^3 + 2s^2 + 3s + 1} \end{bmatrix}\ \Omega$

19.7 $\begin{bmatrix} 29.88 & 3.704 \\ -70.37 & 11.11 \end{bmatrix}\ \Omega$

19.9 $6\ \Omega, 2\ \Omega, 4\ \Omega$

19.11 See Fig. F.42.

Figure F.42   For Prob. 19.11.

19.13 5.877 kW

19.15 24 Ω, 192 W

19.17 $\begin{bmatrix} 4.8 & -0.4 \\ -0.4 & 4.2 \end{bmatrix} \Omega, \begin{bmatrix} 0.21 & 0.02 \\ 0.02 & 0.24 \end{bmatrix} S$

19.19 $\begin{bmatrix} s+0.5 & -0.5 \\ -0.5 & 0.5+1/s \end{bmatrix} S$

19.21 See Fig. F.43.

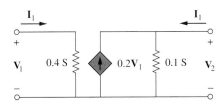

Figure F.43   For Prob. 19.21.

19.23 (a) $\begin{bmatrix} \dfrac{s+2}{s+1} & \dfrac{-1}{s+1} \\ \dfrac{-1}{s+1} & \dfrac{s^2+s+1}{s+1} \end{bmatrix}$,

(b) $\dfrac{2(s+1)}{s(2s^3+6s^2+7.5s+3.5)}$

19.25 See Fig. F.44.

Figure F.44   For Prob. 19.25.

19.27 $\begin{bmatrix} 0.25 & 0.25 \\ 5 & 0.6 \end{bmatrix} \Omega$

19.29 (a) 8 V, 22 V, (b) same

19.31 $\begin{bmatrix} 3.8\ \Omega & 0.4 \\ -3.6 & 0.2\ S \end{bmatrix}$

19.33 $\begin{bmatrix} 3.0769+j1.2821 & 0.3846-j0.2564 \\ -0.3846+j0.2564 & 0.0769+j0.2821 \end{bmatrix}$

19.35 $\begin{bmatrix} 2\ \Omega & 0.5 \\ -0.5 & 0 \end{bmatrix}$

19.37 1.19 V

19.39 $\begin{bmatrix} 0.06757 & -0.8919 \\ 0.8919 & 3.027 \end{bmatrix}$

19.41 Proof

19.43 (a) $\begin{bmatrix} 1 & \mathbf{Z} \\ 0 & 1 \end{bmatrix}$, (b) $\begin{bmatrix} 1 & 0 \\ \dfrac{1}{\mathbf{Y}} & 1 \end{bmatrix}$

19.45 $\dfrac{R_1+R_2+sL}{R_1}, \dfrac{1}{sR_1C}[R_1+(1+sR_1C)$

$(R_2+sL)], \dfrac{1}{R_1}, \dfrac{1+sR_1C}{sR_1C}$

19.47 $\begin{bmatrix} 0.3235 & 1.176 \\ 0.02941 & 0.4706 \end{bmatrix}$

19.49 $\begin{bmatrix} \dfrac{2}{2s+1} & \dfrac{1}{s} \\ \dfrac{(s+1)(3s+1)}{s} & 2+\dfrac{1}{s} \end{bmatrix}$

19.51 $\begin{bmatrix} 2 & 2+j5 \\ j & -2+j \end{bmatrix}$

19.53 $z_{11}=\dfrac{A}{C}, z_{12}=\dfrac{AD-BC}{C}, z_{21}=\dfrac{1}{C}, z_{22}=\dfrac{D}{C}$

19.55 Proof

19.57 $\begin{bmatrix} 3 & 1 \\ 1 & 7 \end{bmatrix} \Omega, \begin{bmatrix} \dfrac{7}{20} & \dfrac{-1}{20} \\ \dfrac{-1}{20} & \dfrac{3}{20} \end{bmatrix} S, \begin{bmatrix} \dfrac{20}{7}\ \Omega & \dfrac{1}{7} \\ \dfrac{-1}{7} & \dfrac{1}{7}\ S \end{bmatrix},$

$\begin{bmatrix} \dfrac{1}{3}\ S & \dfrac{-1}{3} \\ \dfrac{1}{3} & \dfrac{20}{3}\ \Omega \end{bmatrix}, \begin{bmatrix} 7 & 20\ \Omega \\ 1\ S & 3 \end{bmatrix}$

19.59 $\begin{bmatrix} 16.667 & 6.667 \\ 3.333 & 3.333 \end{bmatrix} \Omega, \begin{bmatrix} 0.1 & -0.2 \\ -0.1 & 0.5 \end{bmatrix} S,$

$\begin{bmatrix} 10\ \Omega & 2 \\ -1 & 0.3\ S \end{bmatrix}, \begin{bmatrix} 5 & 10\ \Omega \\ 0.3\ S & 1 \end{bmatrix}$

19.61 $\begin{bmatrix} \dfrac{5}{3} & \dfrac{4}{3} \\ \dfrac{4}{3} & \dfrac{5}{3} \end{bmatrix} \Omega, \begin{bmatrix} \dfrac{3}{5}\,\Omega & \dfrac{4}{5} \\ \dfrac{-4}{5} & \dfrac{3}{5}\,S \end{bmatrix}, \begin{bmatrix} \dfrac{5}{4} & \dfrac{3}{4}\,\Omega \\ \dfrac{3}{4}\,S & \dfrac{5}{4} \end{bmatrix}$

19.63 $\begin{bmatrix} 0.8 & 2.4 \\ 2.4 & 7.2 \end{bmatrix} \Omega$

19.65 $\begin{bmatrix} \dfrac{1}{3} & -\dfrac{1}{3} \\ -\dfrac{1}{3} & \dfrac{2}{3} \end{bmatrix} S$

19.67 $\begin{bmatrix} 1.25 & 0.75\,\Omega \\ 0.75\,S & 1.25 \end{bmatrix}$

19.69 $\begin{bmatrix} \dfrac{s+1}{s+2} & \dfrac{-(3s+2)}{2(s+2)} \\ \dfrac{-(3s+2)}{2(s+2)} & \dfrac{5s^2+4s+4}{2s(s+2)} \end{bmatrix}$

19.71 $\begin{bmatrix} 2 & -3.3341 \\ 3.3341 & 20.2239 \end{bmatrix} \Omega$

19.73 $\begin{bmatrix} 7 & 12\,\Omega \\ 4\,S & 7 \end{bmatrix}, \dfrac{12}{7}\,\Omega$

19.75 (a) $\begin{bmatrix} 0.3015 & -0.1765 \\ 0.0588 & 10.94 \end{bmatrix}$, (b) -0.0051

19.77 $\begin{bmatrix} 0.9488\underline{/-161.6^\circ} & 0.3163\underline{/18.42^\circ} \\ 0.3163\underline{/-161.6^\circ} & 0.9488\underline{/-161.6^\circ} \end{bmatrix}$

19.79 $\begin{bmatrix} 4.669\underline{/-136.7^\circ} & 2.53\underline{/-108.4^\circ} \\ 2.53\underline{/-108.4^\circ} & 1.789\underline{/-153.4^\circ} \end{bmatrix} \Omega$

19.81 $\begin{bmatrix} 1.5 & -0.5 \\ 3.5 & 1.5 \end{bmatrix} S$

19.83 $\begin{bmatrix} 0.3235 & 1.176 \\ 0.02941 & 0.4706 \end{bmatrix}$

19.85 $\begin{bmatrix} 1.581\underline{/71.59^\circ} & -j \\ j & 5.661 \times 10^{-4} \end{bmatrix}$

19.87 $\begin{bmatrix} -j1,765 & -j1,765 \\ j888.2 & j888.2 \end{bmatrix}$

19.89 $-1,613,\ 64.15$ dB

19.91 (a) -25.64, (b) 74.07, (c) 1.2 kΩ
(d) 51.28 kΩ

19.93 $-17.74,\ 144.5,\ 31.17\ \Omega,$
-6.148 MΩ

19.95 See Fig. F.45.

Figure F.45　　For Prob. 19.95.

19.97 0.25 F, 0.3333 H, 0.5 F

19.99 Proof

Bibliography

Aidala, J. B., and L. Katz. *Transients in Electric Circuits.* Englewood Cliffs, NJ: Prentice Hall, 1980.

Angerbaur, G. J. *Principles of DC and AC Circuits.* 3rd ed. Albany, NY: Delman Publishers, 1989.

Attia, J. O. *Electronics and Circuit Analysis Using MATLAB.* Boca Raton, FL: CRC Press, 1999.

Balabanian, N. *Electric Circuits.* New York: McGraw-Hill, 1994.

Bartkowiak, R. A. *Electric Circuit Analysis.* New York: Harper & Row, 1985.

Blackwell, W. A., and L. L. Grigsby. *Introductory Network Theory.* Boston, MA: PWS Engineering, 1985.

Bobrow, L. S. *Elementary Linear Circuit Analysis.* 2nd ed. New York: Holt, Rinehart & Winston, 1987.

Boctor, S. A. *Electric Circuit Analysis.* 2nd ed. Englewood Cliffs, NJ: Prentice Hall, 1992.

Boylestad, R. L. *Introduction to Circuit Analysis.* 10th ed. Columbus, OH: Merrill, 2000.

Budak, A. *Circuit Theory Fundamentals and Applications.* 2nd ed. Englewood Cliffs, NJ: Prentice Hall, 1987.

Carlson, B. A. *Circuit: Engineering Concepts and Analysis of Linear Electric Circuits.* Boston, MA: PWS Publishing, 1999.

Chattergy, R. *Spicey Circuits: Elements of Computer-Aided Circuit Analysis.* Boca Raton, FL: CRC Press, 1992.

Chen, W. K. *The Circuit and Filters Handbook.* Boca Raton, FL: CRC Press, 1995.

Choudhury, D. R. *Networks and Systems.* New York: John Wiley & Sons, 1988.

Ciletti, M. D. *Introduction to Circuit Analysis and Design.* New York: Oxford Univ. Press, 1995.

Cogdeil, J. R. *Foundations of Electric Circuits.* Upper Saddle River, NJ: Prentice Hall, 1998.

Cunningham, D. R., and J. A. Stuller. *Circuit Analysis.* 2nd ed. New York: John Wiley & Sons, 1999.

Davis, A., (ed.). *Circuit Analysis Exam File.* San Jose, CA: Engineering Press, 1986.

Davis, A. M. *Linear Electric Circuit Analysis.* Washington, DC: Thomson Publishing, 1998.

DeCarlo, R. A., and P. M. Lin. *Linear Circuit Analysis.* 2nd ed. New York: Oxford Univ. Press, 2001.

Del Toro, V. *Engineering Circuits.* Englewood Cliffs, NJ: Prentice Hall, 1987.

Dorf, R. C., and J. A. Svoboda. *Introduction to Electric Circuits.* 4th ed. New York: John Wiley & Sons, 1999.

Edminister, J. *Schaum's Outline of Electric Circuits.* 3rd ed. New York: McGraw-Hill, 1996.

Floyd, T. L. *Principles of Electric Circuits.* 7th ed. Upper Saddle River, NJ: Prentice Hall, 2002.

Franco, S. *Electric Circuits Fundamentals.* Fort Worth, FL: Saunders College Publishing, 1995.

Goody, R. W. *Microsim PSpice for Windows.* Vol. 1. 2nd ed. Upper Saddle River, NJ: Prentice Hall, 1998.

Harrison, C. A. *Transform Methods in Circuit Analysis.* Philadelphia, PA: Saunders, 1990.

Harter, J. J., and P. Y. Lin. *Essentials of Electric Circuits.* 2nd ed. Englewood Cliffs, NJ: Prentice Hall, 1986.

Hayt, W. H., and J. E. Kemmerly. *Engineering Circuit Analysis.* 6th ed. New York: McGraw-Hill, 2001.

Hazen, M. E. *Fundamentals of DC and AC Circuits.* Philadelphia, PA: Saunders, 1990.

Hostetter, G. H. *Engineering Network Analysis.* New York: Harper & Row, 1984.

Huelsman, L. P. *Basic Circuit Theory.* 3rd ed. Englewood Cliffs, NJ: Prentice Hall, 1991.

Irwin, J. D. *Basic Engineering Circuit Analysis.* 7th ed. New York: John Wiley & Sons, 2001.

Jackson, H. W., and P. A. White. *Introduction to Electric Circuits.* 7th ed. Englewood Cliffs, NJ: Prentice Hall, 1997.

Johnson, D. E. et al. *Electric Circuit Analysis.* 3rd ed. Upper Saddle River, NJ: Prentice Hall, 1997.

Karni, S. *Applied Circuit Analysis.* New York: John Wiley & Sons, 1988.

Kraus, A. D. *Circuit Analysis.* St. Paul, MN: West Publishing, 1991.

Madhu, S. *Linear Circuit Analysis.* 2nd ed. Englewood Cliffs, NJ: Prentice Hall, 1988.

Mayergoyz, I. D., and W. Lawson. *Basic Electric Circuits Theory.* San Diego, CA: Academic Press, 1997.

Mottershead, A. *Introduction to Electricity and Electronics: Conventional and Current Version.* 3rd ed. Englewood Cliffs, NJ: Prentice Hall, 1990.

Nasar, S. A. *3000 Solved Problems in Electric Circuits.* (*Schaum's Outline*) New York: McGraw-Hill, 1988.

Neudorfer, P. O., and M. Hassul. *Introduction to Circuit Analysis.* Englewood Cliffs, NJ: Prentice Hall, 1990.

Nilsson, J. W., and S. A. Riedel. *Electric Circuits.* 5th ed. Reading, MA: Addison-Wesley, 1996.

O'Malley, J. R. *Basic Circuit Analysis.* (*Schaum's Outline*) New York: McGraw-Hill, 2nd ed., 1992.

Parrett, R. *DC-AC Circuits: Concepts and Applications.* Englewood Cliffs, NJ: Prentice Hall, 1991.

Paul, C. R. *Analysis of Linear Circuits.* New York: McGraw-Hill, 1989.

Poularikas, A. D., (ed.). *The Transforms and Applications Handbook*. Boca Raton, FL: CRC Press, 2nd ed., 1999.

Ridsdale, R. E. *Electric Circuits*. 2nd ed. New York: McGraw-Hill, 1984.

Sander, K. F. *Electric Circuit Analysis: Principles and Applications*. Reading, MA: Addison-Wesley, 1992.

Scott, D. *Introduction to Circuit Analysis: A Systems Approach*. New York: McGraw-Hill, 1987.

Smith, K. C., and R. E. Alley. *Electrical Circuits: An Introduction*. New York: Cambridge Univ. Press, 1992.

Stanley, W. D. *Transform Circuit Analysis for Engineering and Technology*. 3rd ed. Upper Saddle River, NJ: Prentice Hall, 1997.

Strum, R. D., and J. R. Ward. *Electric Circuits and Networks*. 2nd ed. Englewood Cliffs, NJ: Prentice Hall, 1985.

Su, K. L. *Fundamentals of Circuit Analysis*. Prospect Heights, IL: Waveland Press, 1993.

Thomas, R. E., and A. J. Rosa. *The Analysis and Design of Linear Circuits*. 3rd ed. New York: John Wiley & Sons, 2000.

Tocci, R. J. *Introduction to Electric Circuit Analysis*. 2nd ed. Englewood Cliffs, NJ: Prentice Hall, 1990.

Tuinenga, P. W. *SPICE: A Guide to Circuit Simulation*. Englewood Cliffs, NJ: Prentice Hall, 1992.

Whitehouse, J. E. *Principles of Network Analysis*. Chichester, U.K.: Ellis Horwood, 1991.

Yorke, R. *Electric Circuit Theory*. 2nd ed. Oxford, U.K.: Pergamon Press, 1986.

Index

A

ABCD parameters, 867–871
Abc sequence, 506, 525
Acb sequence, 506–507, 527
Active elements, 13–14
Admittance, 387, 390, 401
  hybrid parameters and, 862–867
  matrices, 570
  transfer function and, 726–731; *see also* Transfer
    function
  two-port networks and, 859–862
Air-core transformers, 568
Alexander, Charles K., xvi, 369
Algebra, 694–695
Alternating current (AC) circuits, 7, 370
  applications of, 395–400, 409–410
  bridges and, 398–400
  exercises for, 401–411
  frequency response and, A70–A72
  generator for, 505
  impedance and, 385–395, 404–409
  Kirchhoff's laws and, 388–389
  MATLAB and, A65–A69
  maximum average power transfer and, 464–467
  nodal analysis and, 414–417
  oscillators and, 439–441
  phase-shifters and, 395–398
  phasors and, 375–395, 402–404
  power conservation and, 478–481
  PSpice analysis and, 434–437, A46–A51
  sinusoids and, 371–375, 400, 402, 413–455
  Thevenin/Norton circuits and, 426–431
Alternating current (AC) power analysis, 457, 489
  apparent power and, 471–473
  average power and, 458–468
  complex power and, 473–478
  conservation and, 478–481
  effective value and, 468–470
  electricity consumption cost and, 486–488
  exercises for, 490–501
  importance of, 458
  instantaneous power and, 458–461
  measurement and, 484–486
  power factor and, 471–473, 481–483
Alternator, 505
American Institute of Electrical Engineers, 369
Ammeters, 58–60, 156
Amperage, 6–8; *see also* Current
  inductors and, 222–230
  open circuit, 30
Ampère, André-Marie, 3
Amplifiers; *see* Operational amplifiers
Amplitude modulation (AM)
  carrier and, 839
  complex numbers and, A11
  defined, 840
  Fourier transform and, 823, 839–842, 844
  radio and, 656–658
  sinusoids and, 371–375
Amplitude-phase form, 761
Amplitude spectrum, 761, 785, 815
Analog DC meters, 58–60
Analysis methods; *see also* Laplace transforms;
    MATLAB; Phasors; PSpice
  AC power analysis and, 457–489
  first-order circuits and, 280–285
  Fourier series and, 758–811; *see also* Fourier series
  Fourier transform and, 814–820; *see also* Fourier
    transform
  inspection, 98–103

B

Balance, 156–158
  capacitance and, 520–526
Bandpass filters, 640–641, 645–646
Bandreject filter, 646–647
Bandstop filter, 641–642
Bandwidth, 632
  filters and, 638–649
Barkhausen criteria, 439–440
Batteries, 13
Bell, Alexander Graham, 757
Binary weighted ladder, 193
Bipolar junction transistors (BJTs), 106–107
Bode, Hendrik W., 619
Bode plots, 614
  complex numbers and, 620
  constant terms and, 620
  construction of, 620–630
  description of, 619
  MATLAB and, 745–747
  phase and, 623–630
  pole/zero at origin and, 621
  quadratic pole/zero, 622–623, 628
  simple pole/zero, 621–622
  straight-line magnitude and, 623–624
Boundary conditions, 36–37
Branches, 33–35
  mesh analysis and, 90–103
  nodal analysis and, 78–90, 98–103
Break frequency, 621
Breaking points, 350
Bridges, 398–400
Buffer amplifiers, 644
Burbank, Luther, 27

Analysis methods—*Cont.*
  ladder method, 727, 888–891
  linearity and, 126–128
  mesh, 90–103; *see also* Mesh analysis
  nodal, 78–90, 98–103, 280–285; *see also* Nodal
    analysis
  Norton's theorem and, 143–148
  operational amplifiers and, 174–177; *see also*
    Operational amplifiers
  sinusoidal steady-state, 413–455
  source transformation and, 133–137
  superposition and, 128–133
  synthesis and, 741–745
  Thevenin's theorem and, 137–143, 146–148
  transistors and, 106–110
  two-port networks and, 854–859; *see also* Networks
Angular frequency, 371–375
Apparent power, 471–473
  complex power and, 474
  three-phase circuits and, 521
Argument, 371–375
Automobile ignitions, 293–294, 350–352
Autotransformers, 580–584
Average power, 535
  AC power analysis and, 458–462
  calculation of, 459–464
  Fourier series and, 780–784, 800
  maximum transfer of, 464–467
  measurement of, 484–485
  Parseval's theorem and, 785
  phasors for, 460
  resonance and, 630–638

C

Cadence.com, A25
Calibration circuits, 193
Capacitance, 216–217
  alternating current, 434–437
  apparent power and, 471–473
  applications of, 230–236
  automobile ignitions and, 350–352
  balanced systems and, 520–526
  bridges and, 398–400
  circuit element modeling and, 717–722
  complex power and, 473–477
  coupled circuit energy and, 563–567
  description of, 212–213
  duality principle and, 346–349
  energy storage and, 214–215
  equivalence and, 218–222
  exercises for, 237–248
  filters and, 638–649
  Fourier transform and, 833–835; *see also* Fourier
    transform
  impedance and, 385–395; *see also* Impedance
  instantaneous power and, 459
  integrators and, 231–233
  Kirchhoff's laws and, 221
  Laplace transform for, 717–718
  nonlinear, 214
  parallel, 218–219
  phase-shifters and, 395–398
  power factor correction and, 481–483
  PSpice analysis and, 434–437
  RC circuits and, 250–255, 269–275; *see also RC*
    circuits
  resonance and, 630–638
  RLC circuits and, 310–336; *see also RLC* circuits
  series, 219–222
  sinusoidal steady-state analysis and, 434–437
  step response and, 269–275
  transfer function and, 726–731; *see also* Transfer
    function
  types of, 213–214
  unbalanced systems and, 526–530
Capacitance multipliers, 437–439
Career enhancement, 309
  communication skills and, 125, 715
  communications systems and, 813
  computer engineering and, 249
  control systems and, 613
  education and, 853
  electromagnetics and, 555
  electronics, 77, 173
  power systems and, 457
  software engineering and, 413
Carriers, 839
Cascaded networks, 877
Cascaded op amp circuits, 189–191
  analog computers and, 233–236
Cathode-ray tube (CRT), 15–16
Celestial Mechanics (Laplace), 675
Characteristic equation, 316, 322, 325, 335
Charge, 6–8
Circuit element models, 716–722
Circuit response, 250
  AC operational amplifiers and, 431–433
  capacitance multiplier and, 437–439
  complete, 271–272, 337
  damping and, 254, 317–329, 351
  effective value and, 468–470
  forced response, 271–272, 328, 336, 343
  Fourier series and, 777–780; *see also* Fourier series

Circuit response—*Cont.*
  Fourier transform and, 833–835; *see also* Fourier transform
  maximum power transfer and, 464–467
  natural, 251
  power triangle and, 475–476
  RC circuits and, 269–275
  RLC circuits and, 328–333
  RL circuits and, 276–280
  stability and, 738–741
  steady-state, 271–272, 464–467, 614
  step response and, 261–262, 268–280, 328–336, 703
  superposition theorem and, 421–424
  synthesis and, 741–745
  Thevenin/Norton equivalence and, 426–431
  transient, 271–272, 285–288, 352–353, A38–A46
  two-port networks and, 854–893; *see also* Two-port networks
Clippers, 193
Closed-loop voltage gain, 176
Coefficient of coupling, 565
Coils, 222, 505, 509, 597; *see also* Magnetically-coupled circuits
  coupling conditions and, 565–566
  mutual inductance and, 556–562
  primary winding and, 567
  reactances of, 574
  secondary winding and, 567
  T-equivalent circuits and, 572–573
  transformers and, 567–587
  turns ratio and, 574, 585
Common-base current gain, 107
Common-emitter current gain, 107
Communication skills, 125, 715
Communication systems, 813
Compact discs, 194
Comparators, 193
Complete response, 271–272, 337
Completing-the-square method, 692
Complex amplitude spectrum, 785
Complex Fourier series; *see* Exponential Fourier series
Complex numbers
  Bode plots and, 619–630
  bridges and, 399–400
  complex power and, 474
  Euler's formula and, 377, A16–A17
  exercises for, 380–381
  forms of, 375–376
  imaginary part, 377
  Laplace transforms and, 676–677
  mathematical operations with, A13–A15
  operations on, 376
  phasors and, 377–380
  real part, 377
  representations of, A11–A13
  sinor plot and, 377
  sinusoids and, 377–380
  useful identities for, A17–A18
Complex phase spectrum, 785
Complex poles, 693
Complex power, 489
  in balanced systems, 523, 525
  capacitance and, 473–477
  conservation of, 478–481
  three-phase circuits and, 521
  transformers and, 576
Computers, 19, 106, 173, 193; *see also* MATLAB; PSpice
  analog, 233–236
  careers in, 249
  Maple and, 759
  Mathcad and, 759
  software engineering and, 413
Condensers, 350

Conductance, 31
  equivalent, 44
  inspection of, 98–103
  matrix, 99
  parallel resistors and, 44
Conservation, 478–481
Controlled source, 14
Convolution function
  commutative property of, 697
  defined, 697
  evaluation of, 699–700
  exercises for, 700–706
  Fourier transform and, 826–829
  graphical techniques and, 699–706
  linearity and, 698
  properties of, 697–698
  unit step function and, 703
Corner frequency, 621
Coulomb, 6–7, 9
Coupled conduction; *see* Magnetically-coupled circuits
  Cramer's rule, A1–A3
  DC circuits and, 78, 81, 83–84
  matrix form and, 81, 83–84
  mesh analysis and, 93, 95
  nodal analysis and, 90
Critically damped case, 317–318, 323, 329
Crossover networks and, 660–661
Current, 6–8
  ammeters and, 58–60, 156
  apparent power and, 471–473
  average power and, 458–467
  in balanced systems, 520–526
  capacitance multiplier and, 437–439
  capacitors and, 212–222
  circuit analysis and, 722–726
  circuit element modeling and, 717–722
  common-base gain, 107
  common-emitter gain, 107
  delta-delta system and, 514–516
  delta-Y system and, 516–520
  division, 43–50, 390
  duality principle and, 346–349
  effective value and, 468–470
  filters and, 638–649
  Fourier series and, 780–784; *see also* Fourier series
  gain and, 618–630
  impedance and, 385–388
  inductance and, 222–230, 556–562
  instantaneous power and, 458–461
  Kirchhoff's laws and, 35–37, 61
  labeling of, 80
  line, 510, 526
  linearity and, 126–128
  maximum power theorem and, 148–150
  maximum power transfer and, 464–467
  network parameters and, 854–875
  neutral line equation, 526
  nodal analysis and, 78–90, 98–103, 414–417
  Norton's theorem and, 143–148
  Ohm's law and, 28–33, 542
  oscillators and, 439–441
  parallel resistors and, 43–50
  phase and, 395–398, 510
  phasors and, 383–389
  potentiometers and, 57–61
  power and, 10–13, 481–483
  series resistors and, 42–43
  source transformation and, 133–137, 425–426
  step response and, 269–280
  superposition and, 128–133, 421–424
  Thevenin's theorem and, 137–143, 146–148, 426–431
  transfer function and, 614–617
  transformers and, 567–587

Current—*Cont.*
  transistors and, 106–110, 884–888
  two-port networks and, 854–875; *see also* Two-port networks
  unbalanced systems and, 526–530
  voltage and, 9, 193; *see also* Voltage
  Y-delta system and, 512–514
  Y-Y system and, 508–512
Current-controlled current source (CCCS), 14
Current-controlled voltage source (CCVS), 14
Cutoff frequency, 639–640

D

Damping, 254, 320–321
  automobile ignitions and, 351
  frequency, 318–319
  RLC circuits and, 317–319, 323–329
d'Arsonval movement, 156
Datum node, 78–79
Decaying exponential, 276
Decibel scale, 618
  Bode plots and, 619–630
Definite integrals, A23
Delay circuits, 230, 289–290
Delta systems, 543
  delta-delta, 514–516, 585
  delta-Y systems, 516–520, 585
  power measurement and, 534–540
Derivatives, A21
Difference amplifiers, 185–188
Differentiators, 193
Digital meters, 60
Digital photography, 194
Digital-to-analog converters, 193–195, 352–353
Direct current (DC) circuits, 3, 27, 77, 211
  analog computer and, 233–236
  analog meters and, 58–60
  applications for, 15–18, 106–110, 153–158, 288–294
  automobile ignitions and, 293–294
  capacitors and, 212–222, 230–237
  defined, 7
  delay circuits and, 289–290
  electric charge and, 6–8
  elements of, 13–15
  energy and, 10–13
  exercises for, 22–26, 62–75, 111–124, 159–171, 237–248, 295–307
  inductors and, 222–237
  integrators and, 231–233
  Kirchhoff's laws and, 35–42
  linearity and, 126–128
  MATLAB and, A61–A65
  maximum power transfer and, 148–150
  mesh analysis and, 90–103
  meter design and, 57–61
  network topology, 33–35
  nodal analysis and, 78–90, 98–103
  Norton's theorem and, 143–148
  Ohm's law and, 28–33
  operational amplifiers and, 173–210, 280–285
  parallel resistors and, 43–50
  photoflash units and, 290–292
  power and, 10–13
  problem solving and, 18–21
  PSpice analysis and, 103–106, 150–153, 285–288, A32–A38
  RC circuit and, 250–255, 269–275
  relays and, 292–293
  resistance and, 55–61, 156–158; *see also* Resistance
  RL circuit and, 255–261, 276–280
  second-order circuits and, 309–310; *see also* Second-order circuits
  series resistors and, 42–43

Direct current (DC) circuits—*Cont.*
  singularity functions and, 261–269
  source modeling and, 153–156
  source transformation and, 133–137
  superposition and, 128–133
  systems of units for, 4–5
  Thevenin's theorem and, 137–143, 146–148
  transistor circuits and, 106–110
  voltage and, 9, 42–43
  Y-delta transformations and, 51–55
Dirichlet, P. G. L., 759
Dirichlet conditions, 759, 814
Discrete Fourier transform (DFT), 791–795
Driving-point impedances, 856
Dual in-line package (DIP), 174
Duality, 346–349, 825
Dykes, A., 309

E

Edison, Thomas Alva, 503
Effective value, 468–470, 474
Einstein, Albert, 77, 613, 757
Electrical engineering, 4, 413
Electrical isolation, 581
Electric charge, 6–8
Electric consumption cost, 486–488
Electric distribution, 594–597
Electric isolation, 592–593
Electricity, residential, 540–542
Electric motors, 222, 230
Electric shock, 542
Electromagnetism, 4, 6–8, 555; *see also* Magnetically-coupled circuits
Electromotive force (emf); *see* Voltage
Electronic instrumentation, 173
Elements, 15
  active *versus* passive, 13–14
  branches and, 33–35
  circuit models and, 716–722
  loops and, 33–35
  nodes and, 33–35
Elimination technique, 81, 83
Energy, 4, 10–13
  capacitors and, 212–222
  conservation law of, 11, 37
  in coupled circuit, 563–567
  defined, 11
  dissipation of, 633
  Fourier transform and, 814–820; *see also* Fourier transform
  inductors and, 222–230
  kilowatt-hours and, 17–18
  magnetically-coupled circuits and, 563–567
  Parseval's theorem and, 835–838
  resistor applications and, 55–61
  resonance and, 630–638
  source-free circuits and, 250–261
  transfer function and, 726–731; *see also* Transfer function
  transformers and, 567–587
  transistors and, 106–110
Engineering
  creed of, 853
  problem solving and, 18–21
Equations
  AC bridges, 398–399
  active filters, 644–647
  admittance, 387, 859
  amperage, 7, 30, 59
  amplitude modulation, 823, 840
  analog computer, 234–235
  apparent power, 471, 521

Equations—*Cont.*
  average power, 459–461, 465–466, 468, 535, 780–782
  balanced power, 520–524
  balanced voltage, 506–507
  bandwidth B, 632
  Bode plots, 619–622
  branches, 31
  capacitance in time, 717
  capacitance multiplication, 437–438
  capacitors, 212–215, 219–220, 311
  cascaded circuits, 189
  characteristic, 316, 322, 325, 335
  circuit analysis, 723–724
  circuit element models, 717–719, 721–722
  complex numbers, 375–377, 379, A11–A18
  complex power, 474–475, 478, 521
  convolution, 697–705, 826–829
  coupled circuit energy, 563–566
  Cramer's rule, A1–A3
  current through load, 139
  cutoff frequency, 639
  decibel scale, 618–619
  definite integrals, A23
  delta-Y system, 51–52, 516–518
  demand charge, 486
  derivatives, A21
  difference amplifier, 185–188
  differential, 234, 251, 316
  duality, 825
  effective value, 468–469
  electric charge, 7
  energy, 11
  Euler's identity, 377
  exponential Fourier series, 784–786, 788–789
  Faraday's law, 556
  Fourier/Laplace transform relationship, 839
  Fourier series, 777–778, 790, 796; *see also* Fourier series
  Fourier transform and, 815–818, 820–828; *see also* Fourier transform
  frequency differentiation, 684
  frequency shift, 681, 823
  hybrid parameters, 863–866
  hyperbolic functions, A20
  ideal autotransformers, 581–582
  ideal transformers, 573–577, 579–580
  impedance, 385–391, 649, 855–856, 858
  indefinite integrals, A21–A22
  inductors, 222–224, 226–228, 311, 717
  instantaneous power, 458–459
  integrator, 231–232
  internal resistance, 59
  inverse Laplace transform, 690–694, 696–697
  inverting amplifiers, 179–180
  Kirchhoff's laws, 36–38, 41–42, 415–417, 432, 478; *see also* Kirchhoff's laws
  ladder network synthesis, 889–891
  Laplace transform, 676–686, 690–694, 696–706; *see also* Laplace transforms
  L'Hopital's rule, A23
  linear, 820–821
  linearity, 126
  linear resistance, 60
  linear transformers, 568–570, 572
  MATLAB and, A60–A61
  maximum power transfer, 148–149, 465–466
  mesh analysis, 92–94, 96–99, 417–420, 719, 721
  mutual inductance, 556–562
  network interconnection, 876–878
  network stability, 738–740
  network synthesis, 743
  network topology, 34
  neutral line current, 526
  nodal analysis, 79–83, 85–89, 98–99, 415–417

Equations—*Cont.*
  noninverting amplifiers, 182
  Norton's theorem, 143–144, 147–148
  Ohm's law, 28–31, 40, 42, 526, 542, 833
  open circuit, 30
  operational amplifiers, 175–180, 182, 184–189, 193, 195, 281–283, 342–343
  oscillation, 440
  parallel resistance, 43–45
  parallel resonance, 635–636
  Parseval's theorem, 836–837
  passive filters, 639–642
  phase-shifters, 395–397
  phase voltage, 520
  phasors, 375–377, 379, 383–384, 484
  potentiometer, 57
  power factor, 10–11, 471, 482–483
  quadratic formula, A19
  quality factor of resonance, 633
  RC circuit, 250–253, 270–272
  reactance, 386
  reactive power, 521
  reflected load, 594
  resistance, 42–45, 156, 717
  reversal, 825
  RLC circuits, 315–319, 321–336
  RL circuits, 255–258, 276–277
  rms phasors, 484
  rms value, 780–782
  sampling, 842
  scaling, 649–651, 679–680, 821
  second-order circuits, 311–319, 321–343, 351–352
  series resistance, 42–43
  series resonance, 631–634
  simultaneous, A1–A9
  singularity functions, 262–267
  sinusoids, 371–374
  source modeling, 154–155
  source transformation, 134, 136, 425
  state variables, 732–737
  summing amplifier, 184
  superposition, 130–132, 421–422, 424
  symmetry, 767–772
  Thevenin/Norton equivalence, 426, 430
  Thevenin's theorem, 138–139, 141–142, 147–148
  three-phase power measurement, 535–536
  three-phase transformers, 584–585
  time differentiation, 681–682, 823–824
  time integration, 682–683, 824
  time periodicity, 684–685
  time scaling, 821
  time shift, 680–681, 822–823
  total electrical cost, 486–487
  total real power, 535
  total supplied power, 478
  transfer function, 614–615, 619–620, 660, 726–727, 729–730, 746, 833–834
  transformation ratio, 574
  transistor circuits, 106–107, 109, 885–887
  transmission parameters, 867–871
  trigonometric Fourier series, 758–764, 766
  trigonometric identities, 520, A19–A20
  two-port networks, 872–874; *see also* Two-part networks
  unbalanced three-phase systems, 526, 528
  voltage, 9, 57
  Wien-bridge oscillation, 440
  Y-delta system, 52–53, 512–513, 515
  Y-Y system, 509–510
Equivalence
  admittance and, 390
  capacitors and, 218–222
  impedance and, 389–395
  inductors and, 226–230

Equivalence—*Cont.*
 maximum power theorem and, 148–150
 Norton's theorem and, 143–148
 op amps and, 175
 resistance measurement and, 156–158
 RLC circuits and, 321
 RL circuits and, 257–258
 Thevenin/Norton circuits and, 426–431
 Thevenin's theorem and, 137–143, 146–148
Euler's identity, 377, 784, A16–A17
Even symmetry, 767–768, 774–775
Excitation, 126
 step response and, 269–280
 Fourier series, 777, 780–784; *see also* Fourier series
Exercises
 AC current, 402–411, 442–455, 490–501, 543–554,
   598–612, 663–673
 analysis methods, 111–124, 490–501, 709–714,
   748–756, 801–811, 844–851, 893–904
 capacitors and, 237–248
 circuit theorems, 159–171
 DC current, 22–26, 62–75, 111–124, 159–171,
   198–210, 238–248, 297–308, 354–367
 frequency and, 661–672
 inductors and, 237–248
 Laplace transforms, 709–714
 magnetically-coupled circuits and, 599–612
 operational amplifiers and, 198–210
 resistors, 62–75
 sinusoidal steady-state analysis and, 442–455
 three-phase circuits and, 544–554
Exponential form, 376
Exponential Fourier series, 787–790
 complex amplitude spectrum and, 785
 complex phase spectrum and, 785
 Euler's identity and, 784
 L'Hopital's rule, 786
 line spectra and, 786
 Parseval's theorem, 785
 power spectrum and, 785–786
 sinc function, 786

F

Faraday, Michael, 211–212, 457
Farads, 212
Fast Fourier transform (FFT), 791–795
Feedback, 175–176
 capacitance multiplier and, 437–439
 transistor circuits and, 884–888
Feedforward matrix, 732–733
Field-effect transistors (FETs), 106
Filters, 193
 active, 643–649
 bandpass, 640–641, 645–646
 bandreject, 646–647
 bandstop, 641–642
 buffer amplifiers and, 644
 crossover networks and, 660–661
 defined, 638
 Fourier series and, 796–799, 801
 highpass, 640, 644–645
 ladder network synthesis and, 888–891
 lowpass, 639–640, 644
 notch, 646–647
 passive, 638–643
 radios and, 656–658
 telephones and, 658–660
 transfer function and, 642–643
Final values, 310–315, 685–686

First-order circuits
 applications of, 288–294
 automobile ignitions, 293–294
 delay circuits, 288–290
 exercises for, 295–307
 Laplace transform and, 717; *see also* Laplace
   transforms
 op amps and, 280–285
 photoflash units, 290–292
 PSpice analysis and, 285–288
 RC circuit, 250–255, 269–275
 relays, 291–293
 RL circuit, 255–261, 276–280
 singularity functions, 261–269
 types of, 250
First-order differential equation, 251
Flux, 505
 coupling conditions and, 565
 mutual inductance and, 556–562
Forced response, 271–272, 328, 336, 343
Fourier, Jean Baptiste Joseph, 757–758
Fourier analysis, 759–761
Fourier cosine series, 767
Fourier series, 757
 amplitude-phase form, 761, 800
 application steps, 777
 average power and, 780–784, 800
 circuit analysis and, 777–780
 coefficient determination, 758–762, 799–800
 Euler's identity, 784
 excitation expansion and, 777, 780–784
 exercises for, 801–811
 exponential, 784–790
 filters and, 796–799, 801
 Gibbs phenomenon, 763
 hand calculation of, 763
 L'Hopital's rule, 786
 Parseval's theorem, 785
 phasors and, 761, 800
 power spectrum and, 785–786
 principle of superposition and, 778
 PSpice and, 790–795
 rms values, 780–784
 sinc function, 786
 software for, 759
 spectrum analyzers and, 796, 801
 symmetry, 767–776
 term response and, 777–778
 trigonometric, 758–767
Fourier theorem, 758
Fourier transform
 amplitude modulation and, 823, 839–842, 844
 circuit applications and, 833–835
 convolution and, 826–829
 defined, 814–820
 Dirichlet conditions, 814
 discrete, 791–795
 duality and, 825
 exercises for, 844–851
 fast, 791–795
 frequency shifting and, 823
 gate function and, 818, 831
 impulse function and, 817–818
 as integral transform, 814
 inverse, 816, 832–833
 Laplace transform and, 838–839
 linearity and, 820–821
 pair, 829
 Parseval's theorem, 835–838
 property summary for, 828–829
 reversal, 825
 sampling, 842–843
 signum function, 830–831

Fourier transform—*Cont.*
 sinc function, 830
 time differentiation, 823–824
 time integration, 824
 time scaling, 821–822
 time shifting, 822–823
 transfer function and, 833–835
 unit step function and, 828
Franklin, Benjamin, 6
Frequency, 317–319, 613
 active filters and, 643–649
 angular, 371–375
 bandwidth and, 632
 Bode plots and, 619–630
 break, 621
 corner, 621
 crossover networks and, 660–661
 cutoff, 639–640
 decibel scale and, 618–619
 differentiation, 684
 exercises for, 661–672
 Fourier series and, 758; *see also* Fourier series
 Fourier transform and, 814–820; *see also* Fourier
   transform
 half-power, 632
 high-Q circuits and, 633–634
 impedance and, 385–395
 instantaneous power and, 458–461
 intermediate, 656
 Kirchhoff's laws and, 388–389
 Laplace transform and, 676–706
 MATLAB and, A70–A72
 mixers, 657
 natural, 317
 neper, 317
 Nyquist, 842
 parallel resonance and, 635–638
 passive filters and, 638–643
 phasors and, 379–380
 PSpice and, 652–656
 quality factor and, 632–633
 radio receivers and, 656–658
 sampling, 842–843
 scaling, 649–652
 selectivity and, 633
 series resonance and, 630–635
 shift, 681, 823
 sinusoids and, 371–375
 source transformation and, 425–426
 spectrum, 761
 superposition theorem and, 421–424
 Thevenin/Norton circuits and, 426–431
 touch-tone telephones and, 658–660
 transfer function and, 614–617
 transformers and, 567–587
 translation, 681
 tuning of, 657–658
Frequency modulated (FM) radio, 657
Functions
 convolution, 697–706, 826–829
 exponential, 678
 Fourier series and, 758–811; *see also* Fourier series
 Fourier transform and, 814–820; *see also* Fourier
   transform
 gate, 265–266, 818, 831
 hyperbolic, A20
 ladder network synthesis and, 888–891
 Laplace transform and, 689–697; *see also* Laplace
   transforms
 overlapping of, 703
 quadratic, 127
 ramp, 264–265, 268–269, 295, 678
 sawtooth, 266–268
 signum, 830–831
 sinc, 786, 830
 singularity, 261–269, 274, 295
 transfer, 614–617; *see also* Transfer function
 unit impulse, 263–264, 678, 727, 817–818
 unit step, 261–262, 268–280, 328–336, 678, 703, 828

G

Gain; *see also* Voltage
  Bode plots and, 619–630
  common-base, 107
  common-emitter, 107
  closed-loop, 176
  decibel scale and, 618–619
  filters and, 638–649
  open-loop, 175
  transistor circuits and, 884–888
Galvanometers, 156–158
Ganged tuning, 657
Gate function, 265–266, 818, 831
General Conference on Weights and Measures, 4
Generalized node, 86–87
Generators, 13
Gibbs phenomenon, 763
G parameters, 863–864
Gries, David, 249
Gyrators, 193

H

Half-power frequency, 632
Half-wave symmetry, 770–774
Harmonics; *see* Fourier series
Heaviside's theorem, 691
Henry, Joseph, 211, 222
Henrys (H), 222, 558
Hertz, Heinrich Rudolf, 369
Heterodyne circuit, 657
Highpass filters, 640, 644–645, 659, 779
High-Q circuits, 633–634
Hoover, Herbert, 211
Household wiring, 540–542
Humming, Richard W., 173
Hybrid parameters, 862–867

I

Iconoscope tube, 16
Ideal autotransformers, 580–584
Ideal dependent source, 14
Ideal operational amplifiers, 178–179
Ideal transformers, 573–580, 598
Immittance parameters, 859
Impedance, 386, 401
  admittance and, 385–389
  apparent power and, 471–473
  bridges and, 398–400
  circuit analysis and, 722–726
  circuit element models and, 717–722
  combinations, 389–395
  complex power and, 473–477
  delta-delta system and, 514–516
  delta-Y system and, 516–520
  driving-point, 856
  equivalence and, 389–395
  Fourier series and, 780–784; *see also* Fourier series
  Fourier transform and, 833–835; *see also* Fourier transform
  hybrid parameters and, 862–867
  Kirchhoff's laws and, 389
  matching, 576, 594
  maximum average power transfer and, 464–467
  open circuit, 855–856
  oscillators and, 440
  phase-shifters and, 395–398
  power conservation and, 478–481
  power measurement and, 534–540
  power triangle and, 475–476
  reactance and, 386–387

Impedance—*Cont.*
  reciprocal, 856
  reflected, 569, 576–577
  scaling and, 649–652
  series, 389
  source transformation and, 425–426
  superposition and, 421–424
  symmetry and, 856
  Thevenin/Norton equivalence and, 426–431
  transfer function and, 614–617, 726–731, 856; *see also* Transfer function
  transformers and, 567–587
  transistor circuits and, 884–888
  two-port networks and, 854–875; *see also* Two-port networks
  unbalanced systems and, 526–530
  Y-delta system and, 512–514
  Y-Y system and, 508–512
Impulse function, 817–818
Indefinite integrals, A21–A22
Inductance, 225
  applications of, 230–236
  bridges and, 398–400
  circuit analysis and, 722–726
  circuit element models and, 717–722
  complex power and, 473–477
  coupled circuit energy and, 563–567
  description of, 222–223
  duality principle and, 346–349
  energy storage and, 223–224
  equivalence and, 226–230
  exercises for, 237–248
  Faraday's law and, 556
  filters and, 638–649
  Fourier transform and, 833–835; *see also* Fourier transform
  instantaneous power and, 458–461
  Kirchhoff's laws and, 227–228
  ladder network and, 229
  Laplace transform for, 717–718
  magnetically-coupled circuits and, 556–563
  mutual, 556–563, 567–587
  nonlinear, 223
  parallel, 227–230
  relays and, 292–293
  resonance and, 630–638
  RLC circuits and, 310–336
  RL circuits and, 255–261, 276–280
  second-order circuits and, 311–312
  self, 557
  series, 226–227, 559
  step response and, 276–280
  transformers and, 567–587
  two-port networks and, 854–875; *see also* Two-port networks
  types of, 223
Initial values, 254, 310–315, 685–686
Instantaneous power, 10, 458–461
  in balanced systems, 520–526
  phasors for, 460
  three-phase circuits and, 504–505; *see also* Three-phase circuits
  two parts of, 459
Institute of Electrical and Electronics Engineers (IEEE), 77
Instrumentation amplifiers, 185, 187–188, 195–196
Integral transform, 814
Integrated circuits (ICs), 14, 230
Integrators, 193, 231–232
  analog computers and, 233–236
Intermediate frequency (IF), 656
Internal resistance, 154
  International System of Units (SI), 4–5
  amperes, 7

Internal resistance—*Cont.*
  coulombs, 6
  farads, 212
  henrys, 222, 558
  hertz, 369
  joules, 9–10
  megavolt-amperes (MVA), 595
  mhos, 31
  ohms, 29
  siemens, 31
  volts, 9
  volt-amperes (VA), 474–475
Inverse hybrid parameters, 863–864
Inverse Laplace transforms, 677, 689, 693–697
  complex poles, 692
  repeated poles, 691
  simple poles, 690–691
Inverting amplifiers, 179–181
Inverting input, 174–176
Isolation transformers, 575, 592–593

J

Joules, 9–10

K

Kilowatt-hours (kWh), 17–18, 486–488
Kirchhoff, Gustav Robert, 27
Kirchhoff's laws, 61, 110
  AC conservation and, 478
  AC operational amplifiers and, 432–433
  automobile ignitions and, 351
  boundary conditions and, 36–37
  capacitors and, 221
  current, 35–37, 61
  difference amplifier and, 185–186
  frequency domain and, 388–389
  impedance and, 389
  inductors and, 227–228
  inverting amplifiers and, 179–180
  linear transformers and, 568
  loops and, 37
  mesh analysis and, 90–103, 417–421
  mutual inductance and, 560, 562
  nodal analysis and, 78–90, 98–103, 414–417
  noninverting amplifiers and, 182–183
  Norton's theorem and, 146
  ohmmeters and, 60
  op amps and, 176–177
  parallel resistors and, 43
  power conservation and, 478
  RC circuits and, 251, 342
  resistance measurement and, 157–158
  RLC circuits and, 315–316, 322, 328, 333–334, 337, 339–340
  RL circuits and, 256–258
  second-order circuits and, 312–314, 351
  source transformation and, 136–137
  state variables and, 734–736
  step response and, 279
  supernode and, 87
  Thevenin/Norton equivalence and, 428–429
  Thevenin's theorem and, 141
  transformers and, 583
  transistors and, 106–110
  transmission parameters and, 870
  unbalanced systems and, 526–527
  voltage, 35–41, 62
  Y-delta systems and, 513
  Y-Y systems and, 510

L

Ladder method, 727
Ladder networks, 888–891
Lagging power, 472, 481–483
Laplace, Pierre Simon, 675
Laplace transforms, 675
  algebraic method, 694–697
  application steps for, 716
  bilateral, 677
  circuit analysis and, 722–726
  circuit element models and, 716–722
  completing the square, 692
  complex numbers and, 676–677
  complex poles, 692
  convergence of integral, 677
  convolution integral, 697–706
  definition of, 676–679
  exercises for, 709–714, 748–756
  exponential function, 678
  final value and, 685–686
  Fourier transform and, 838–839
  frequency differentiation and, 684
  frequency shift and, 681
  Heaviside's theorem, 691
  importance of, 676
  initial value and, 685–686
  integrodifferential equations, 706–708
  inverse, 677, 689–697
  linearity and, 679, 716, 718
  MATLAB and, 745–747
  mesh analysis and, 719, 721
  network stability and, 738–741
  network synthesis and, 741–745
  partial fraction expansion, 690
  properties of, 679–689
  ramp function, 678
  repeated poles, 691
  residue method, 690, 694–695
  scaling and, 679–680
  simple poles, 690–691
  sine function, 679
  state variables and, 731–738
  systems and, 716
  time differentiation and, 681–682
  time integration and, 682–683
  time periodicity and, 684–685
  time shift and, 680–681
  transfer function and, 726–731
  unilateral, 677
  unit impulse response and, 678, 727
  unit step function, 678
Law of conservation of charge, 6
Law of conservation of energy, 11, 37
Leading power, 472
  power factor correction and, 481–483
  sinusoids and, 371–375
Level shifters, 193
L'Hopital's rule, 786, A23
Lighting systems, 56–57
Linearity, 126–127, 159
  capacitors and, 212–222
  convolution integral and, 698
  Fourier transform and, 820–821
  inductors and, 222–230
  Laplace transforms and, 679, 716, 718
  Norton's theorem and, 143–148
  source modeling and, 153–156
  superposition and, 128–133
  Thevenin's theorem and, 137–143, 146–148
Linear resistors, 30–31, 55–61
Linear transformers, 567–573
Line spectra, 786
Line-to-line voltage, 509–510

Load, 58
  apparent power and, 471–473
  average power and, 458–467
  balanced, 507, 520–526
  complex power and, 473–477
  delta-delta system and, 514–516
  delta-Y system and, 516–520
  effective value and, 468–470
  instantaneous power and, 458–461
  maximum power transfer and, 464–467
  op amps and, 174–183; see also Operational
    amplifiers
  parallel, 473–478
  power conservation and, 478–481
  power factor and, 481–483
  power measurement and, 534–540
  power triangle and, 475–476
  reflected, 594
  series, 478
  Thevenin's theorem and, 137–143, 146–148
  three-phase circuits and, 504–505; see also
    Three-phase circuits
  transformers and, 567–587
  wattmeter and, 484–485
  Y-delta system and, 512–514
  Y-Y system and, 508–512
Logarithmic amplifiers, 193
Logarithms
  Bode plots and, 619–630, 745–747
  decibel scale and, 618–619
  MATLAB and, 745–747, A56
  resonance and, 631–632
Long, Lazarus, 125
Loops, 33–35
  closed voltage gain, 176
  first-order circuits and, 280–285
  Kirchhoff's laws and, 37
  mesh analysis and, 98–103
  op amps and, 174–179; see also Operational
    amplifiers
  open voltage gain and, 175
  series resistors and, 42–43
Loosely coupled condition, 565
Loudspeakers, 230
Lowpass filters, 639–640, 644, 651

M

Magnetically-coupled circuits, 555
  energy in, 563–567
  exercises for, 599–612
  ideal autotransformers and, 580–584
  ideal transformers and, 573–580
  isolation devices and, 592–593
  linear transformers and, 567–573
  matching devices and, 594–595
  mutual inductance and, 556–563
  power distribution and, 595–597
  PSpice analysis of, 587–591
  three-phase transformers and, 584–587
Magnitude scaling, 649–652
Maple, 759
Matching devices, 594–595
Mathcad, 759
Mathematics
  algebra, 694–695
  analog computers, 233–236
  Bode plots, 619–630
  completing the square, 692
  complex numbers, 375–380, 399–400, A11–A18;
    see also Complex numbers
  convolution integral, 697–706
  Cramer's rule, 78, 81, 83–84, 90, 93, 95, A1–A3
  definite integrals, A23
  derivatives, A21
  differential equations, 233–234
  discrete Fourier transform (DFT), 791–795

Mathematics—Cont.
  Euler's identity, 377, 784, A16–A17
  fast Fourier transform (FFT), 791–795
  final-value theorem, 685–686
  Fourier series, 757–811; see also Fourier series
  Fourier transform, 823; see also Fourier transform
  Heaviside's theorem, 691
  hyperbolic functions, A20
  indefinite integrals, A21–A22
  initial-value theorem, 685–686
  integration, 231
  Kirchhoff's laws, 35–41
  Laplace transforms, 676–706
  L'Hopital's rule, 786, A23
  logarithms, 618–630
  matrices, 80–81, 83–84, 89–90, A1–A9
  mesh analysis, 90–103
  nodal analysis, 78–90, 98–103
  Ohm's law, 28–33
  Parseval's theorem, 785, 835–838
  partial fraction expansion, 690
  quadratic formula, A19
  residue method, 690, 694–695
  resistance measurement, 156–158
  scaling, 649–652
  simultaneous equations, A1–A9
  singularity functions, 261–269
  sinusoids and, 371–375
  source modeling, 153–156
  stability, 738–741
  synthesis, 716, 741–745
  systems, 716
  time constant, 252
  transfer function and, 614–617, 620; see also
    Transfer function
  trigonometry, 371–375, 758–767, A19–A20
Mathworks, Inc., A53
MATLAB, 19, 78
  AC analysis and, A65–A69
  Bode plots and, 745–747
  as calculator, A53–A54
  Cramer's rule and, A3
  DC analysis and, A61–A65
  Laplace transforms and, 745–747
  logarithmic scaling and, A57
  matrices and, A55–A56
  mesh analysis and, 420–421
  nodal analysis and, 80, 84–85, 89
  plotting and, A56–A57
  programming, A58–A60
  solving equations and, A60–A61
Matrices
  admittance, 570
  conductance, 99
  Cramer's rule, 78, 81, 83–84, 90, 93, 95, A1–A3
  feedforward, 732–733
  input coupling, 732–733
  inspection, 98–103
  inversion, A6–A9
  MATLAB and, A55–A56
  mesh analysis and, 93, 95, 418, 420
  mutual inductance and, 562–563
  network parameters and, 854–875
  nodal analysis and, 80, 89–90, 415
  output, 732–733
  resistance, 99
  state variables and, 732–733
  system, 732–733
  transformers and, 569
  two-port networks and, 854–881; see also Two-port
    networks
Maximum average power transfer, 464–467
Maximum power theorem, 148–150
Megavolt-amperes (MVA), 595
Megger tester, 156

Mesh analysis, 94
  Cramer's rule and, 93, 95
  current sources and, 92, 95–98
  duality principle and, 347
  by inspection, 98–103
  Laplace transforms and, 718, 721
  MATLAB and, 420–421
  nodal analysis and, 102–103
  planar *versus* nonplanar circuits and, 90–91
  sinusoidal steady-state analysis and, 417–421
  source transformation and, 134
  supermesh, 96–97
  Thevenin/Norton equivalence and, 430
  transfer function and, 727; *see also* Transfer function
  transformers and, 568
  unbalanced systems and, 526–530
Mho, 31
Microphones, 230
Milliohmmeters, 156
Mixers, 657
Modeling; *see also* Analysis methods
  circuit elements, 716–722
  ladder method, 727
Modulating signal, 839–841
Morse, Samuel F. B., 156, 675
Mutual inductance, 556–563
  transformers and, 567–587
Mutual voltage, 557–562

N

National Electrical Code (NEC), 541–542
Natural frequencies, 317
Natural response, 251, 254, 271–272, 328–329, 351
Negative sequence, 506–507
Neper frequency, 317
Network function; *see* Transfer function
Networks; *see also* Laplace transforms
  cascaded, 877
  circuit analysis and, 722–726
  Fourier series and, 780–784; *see also* Fourier series
  ladder, 888–891
  parameters, 854–875, 881–884
  stability and, 738–741
  state variables and, 731–738
  synthesis and, 741–745
  transfer function and, 726–731; *see also* Transfer function
  two-port, 854–859; *see also* Two-port networks
  unit impulse response and, 727
  voltage/current parameters and, 854–875
Network topology, 33–35
  inductive ladders and, 229
  Norton's theorem and, 143–148
  Thevenin's theorem and, 137–143, 146–148
  Y-delta transformations and, 51–55
Nodal analysis, 33–35, 111
  Cramer's rule, 81, 83–84
  duality principle and, 347
  elimination technique, 81, 83
  first-order circuits and, 280–285
  by inspection, 98–103
  Kirchhoff's laws and, 414–417
  MATLAB and, 80, 84–85, 89
  mesh analysis and, 102–103
  Ohm's law and, 79–80
  PSpice and, A32–A35
  reference node and, 78–79
  sinusoidal steady-state analysis and, 414–417

Nodal analysis—*Cont.*
  source transformation and, 134
  supernode and, 86–87
  synthesis and, 743
  transfer function and, 727; *see also* Transfer function
  transformers and, 570
  transistors and, 106–110
  unbalanced systems and, 526–530
  voltage and, 78–90
Noninverting amplifiers, 182–183
Noninverting input, 174–176
Nonlinear capacitor, 214
Nonlinear inductors, 223
Norton circuits, 426–427, 430–431
Norton's theorem, 159
  defined, 143
  derivation of, 146–148
  network topology and, 144–146
  source modeling and, 153–156
Notch filters, 646–647
NPN transistors, 106
Nyquist frequency, 842

O

Odd symmetry, 769–770
Ohm, Georg Simon, 27
Ohmmeters, 60, 156–158
Ohm's law, 28–29, 32–33, 40–41, 61
  conductance and, 31
  Fourier transform and, 833
  linearity and, 126
  linear resistors and, 30–31
  nodal analysis and, 79–80
  parallel resistors and, 43–50
  phasors and, 383
  series resistors and, 42–43
  three-phase circuits and, 526, 542
One-sided Laplace transform, 677
Open-circuit impedance parameters, 855–856
Open-loop voltage gain, 175
Operational amplifiers, 173, 197
  AC circuits and, 431–433
  analog computers and, 233–236
  applications of, 193–196
  cascaded circuits and, 189–191
  description of, 174–177
  difference, 185–188
  digital-to-analog converter and, 193–195
  exercises for, 198–210
  feedback and, 175–176
  filters and, 638–649
  first-order circuits and, 280–285
  ideal, 178–179
  instrumentation, 185, 187–188, 195–196
  inverting, 179–181
  Kirchhoff's laws and, 176–177, 432–433
  noninverting, 182–183
  PSpice analysis and, 191–192
  saturation and, 176
  second-order circuits and, 341–343
  sinusoidal steady-state analysis and, 431–433
  summing, 184–185
  transresistance amplifiers and, 181
Oscillation, 193; *see also* Fourier series
  Barkhausen criteria and, 439–440
  Laplace transforms and, 685–686; *see also* Laplace transforms
  local, 657
  radio and, 656–658
  resonance and, 630–638
  Wien-bridge, 439–441
Overdamped case, 317, 323, 329

P

Parameters, network
  admittance, 859–862
  g, 863–864
  hybrid, 862–867
  immittance, 859
  impedance, 854–858
  PSpice analysis and, 881–884
  relationships between, 871–875
  transmission, 867–871
  two-port conversion, 873
  y, 859–862
Parseval's theorem, 785
  Fourier transform and, 835–838
Partial fraction expansion, 690, 726
Passive elements, 13–14
Perfectly coupled condition, 565
Periodic time, 371–375
Petroski, Henry, 457
Phase
  Bode plots and, 619–630
  current, 510
  sequence, 506–507
  sinusoids and, 371–375
Phase-shifters, 395–398
Phase spectrum, 761, 765–766, 785, 815
Phase voltage, 505–507; *see also* Three-phase circuits
  in balanced systems, 520–526
  delta-delta systems and, 514–516
  delta-Y systems and, 516–520
  power measurement and, 534–540
  unbalanced systems and, 526–530
  Y-delta systems and, 512–514
  Y-Y system and, 508–512
Phasors, 400–401
  average power and, 460
  circuit elements and, 383–385
  complex numbers and, 375–377, 380–381
  complex power and, 473–477
  diagrams of, 378
  Fourier series and, 761, 800
  Fourier transform and, 833
  frequency domain and, 379–380
  impedance and, 385–395
  instantaneous power and, 460
  Kirchhoff's laws and, 388–389
  Ohm's law and, 383
  rms, 484
  sinusoid argument and, 382
  time factor and, 377–380, 382–383
  transfer function and, 614–617
Photoflash units, 290–292
Photography, 194
Pick-up heads, 230
PNP transistors, 106
Poincaré, Jules Henri, 555
Poisson, Simeon, 675
Polarity, 6, 376
  inverting amplifiers and, 179–180
  mutual voltage and, 558–559
Poles
  completing the square and, 692
  complex, 692
  Laplace transforms and, 690–697; *see also* Laplace transforms
  repeated, 691–700
  simple, 690–691
  stability and, 738–741
  zero origin plot, 621
Polyphase circuit, 504
Ports; *see* Two-port networks
Positive sequence, 506
Potential difference; *see* Voltage
Potentiometers, 30, 57–61

Power, 4, 12–13
    amplitude modulation and, 839–841
    apparent, 471–474, 521
    average, 458–467, 785; *see also* Average power
    in balanced systems, 520–526
    capacitors and, 212–222
    complex, 473–481, 489, 521, 523, 525
    conservation of, 478–481
    decibel scale and, 618–619
    defined, 10
    distribution of, 595–597
    effective value and, 468–470
    electrical cost and, 486–488
    factor, 471–473, 481–484
    Fourier series and, 780–784; *see also* Fourier series
    grids, 596
    inductors and, 222–230
    instantaneous, 10, 458–461
    kilowatt-hours and, 17–18
    leading/lagging of, 371–375, 472, 481–483
    loss in wire, 521–522
    magnetically-coupled circuits and, 595–597
    maximum transfer of, 148–150, 464–467
    measurement of, 484–485
    op amps and, 174–177
    Parseval's theorem and, 785
    Quadrature, 474
    reactive, 474
    resonance and, 630–638
    sign convention for, 10–11
    spectrum, 785–786
    Thevenin's theorem and, 137–143, 146–148
    transformers and, 567–587
    transistors and, 106–110
    triangle, 475–476, 481–483
Principle of current division, 45
Principle of superposition; *see* Superposition
Principle of voltage division, 42–43
Problem solving, 18–21
PSpice, 19, 103–105, 159, 254, 295
    AC analysis and, 434–437, A46–A51
    changing attributes and, A29–A30
    circuit creation and, A27–A32
    circuit theorem verification and, 150–153
    DC analysis and, A32–A38
    design center for, A26–A27
    Fourier series and, 790–795
    frequency response and, 652–656
    magnetically-coupled circuits and, 587–591
    nodal analysis and, A32–A35
    op amp circuit analysis and, 191–192
    part placement and, A27–A28
    RLC circuits and, 344–346
    sinusoidal steady-state analysis and, 434–437
    three-phase circuits and, 530–534
    transient analysis and, 285–288, A38–A45
    two-port networks and, 881–884
    Windows tutorial for, A25–A51
    wiring and, A29

Q

Quadratic equation, 316
Quadratic formula, A19
Quadratic functions, 127
Quadratic pole/zero plot, 622–623
Quadrature power, 474
Quality factor, 632–633

R

Radar, 222
Radio, 222, 230, 555, 813
    AM, 656–658, 839–841
    FM, 657

Radio—*Cont.*
    frequency response and, 656–658
    resonance and, 631
    transformers and, 568
Ramp function, 264–265, 268–269, 295, 678
RC circuits
    delay circuits and, 289–290
    dissipation and, 253
    energy storage and, 250–255
    Kirchhoff's laws and, 251, 342
    natural response and, 251
    phase-shifters and, 395–398
    photoflash units and, 290–292
    second-order circuits and, 341–343
    source-free, 250–255
    step response of, 269–275
    time constant and, 251–253
Reactance, 386–387
Reactive power, 474, 479
    power measurement and, 538
    resonance and, 632–633
    three-phase circuits and, 521
Rectangular form, 375–376
Rectifiers, 193
Reference node, 78–79
Reflected impedance, 569, 576–577
Regulators, 193
Relays, 230, 292–293
Repeated poles, 691–700
Residential wiring, 540–542
Residue method, 690, 694–695
Resistance
    apparent power and, 471–473
    applications of, 55–61
    balanced systems and, 520–526
    bridges and, 398–400
    capacitance multiplier and, 437–439
    circuit analysis and, 722–726
    circuit element modeling and, 717–722
    complex power and, 473–477
    conductance and, 31
    DC meter design and, 57–61
    duality principle and, 346–349
    effective value and, 468–470
    exercises for, 62–75
    filters and, 638–649
    fixed, 30
    Fourier transform and, 833–835; *see also* Fourier transform
    human body and, 542
    inspection methods and, 98–103
    internal resistance and, 154
    Laplace transform for, 717–718
    lighting systems and, 56–57
    linear, 60, 126–128
    matrices for, 99
    maximum power theorem and, 148–150
    maximum power transfer and, 464–467
    measurement of, 156–158
    mesh analysis and, 98–103
    multipliers, 438
    nodal analysis and, 78–90, 98–103
    nonlinear, 30–31
    Norton's theorem and, 143–148
    Ohm's law, 28–33
    op amps and, 179; *see also* Operational amplifiers
    open circuit and, 30
    oscillators and, 439–441
    parallel, 43–50
    Parseval's theorem and, 785, 835–838
    phasors and, 383–385
    potentiometers and, 57–61
    power loss in wires and, 521–522
    RC circuits and, 250–255, 269–275
    relays and, 291–293
    residential wiring and, 540–542
    RLC circuits and, 310–336

Resistance—*Cont.*
    RL circuits and, 255–261, 275–280
    scaling and, 649–652
    series, 42–43
    source modeling and, 153–156
    source transformation and, 133–137
    step response and, 269–280
    superposition and, 128–133
    Thevenin's theorem and, 137–143, 146–148
    time domain and, 717
    transfer function and, 726–731; *see also* Transfer function
    transistors and, 106–110, 884–888
    transresistance amplifiers and, 181
    unbalanced systems and, 526–530
    variable, 30
    Wheatstone bridge and, 156–158
    winding resistance and, 224
    Y-delta transformations and, 51–55
Resonance, 317
    admittance and, 635, 638
    bandwidth and, 632
    circuit duality and, 635–636
    defined, 631
    half-power frequency and, 632; *see also* Frequency
    high-Q circuits and, 633–634
    logarithms for, 631–632
    parallel, 635–638
    quality factor and, 632–633
    radios and, 631, 656–658
    reactive energy and, 632–633
    RLC circuits and, 631–638
    series, 630–635
    sharpness of, 632–633
    symmetry and, 632
    television and, 631
    touch-tone telephones and, 658–660
Reversal, 825
Ringing, 319
RLC circuits, 254
    filters and, 638–649
    initial/final values for, 310–315
    Kirchhoff's laws and, 315–316, 322, 333–334, 339–340
    parallel, 322–328
    PSpice analysis of, 344–346
    resonance and, 631–638
    second-order circuits and, 350–352
    selectivity of, 633
    series, 315–322
    smoothing circuits and, 352–353
    step response and, 328–336
RL circuits
    automobile ignitions and, 293–294
    energy storage and, 266–271
    equivalence and, 257–258
    Kirchhoff's laws and, 256–258
    relays and, 292–293
    step response and, 276–280
    Thevenin's theorem and, 257–258
    time constant and, 259–261
Rogers, G. F. C., 3
Root mean square (rms) value, 468–470
    in balanced systems, 521
    complex power and, 474
    Fourier series and, 780–784
Rotor, 505

S

Sadiku, Matthew N. O., xvii
Sampling, 842–843

Saturation, 176
  cascaded circuits, 189–191
  integrators and, 231
Sawtooth function, 266–268
Scaling, 649–652
  Laplace transforms and, 679–680
  MATLAB and, A57
  time and, 821–822
S-domain; *see also* Laplace transforms
  circuit analysis and, 722–726
  convolution and, 722
  stability and, 738–741
  synthesis and, 741–745
  transfer function and, 726–731
Second-order circuits
  applications of, 350–353
  automobile ignitions and, 350–352
  duality and, 346–349
  exercises for, 354–365
  general, 336–341
  initial/final values and, 310–315
  Kirchhoff's laws and, 312–313, 351
  Laplace transforms and, 717; *see also* Laplace transforms
  op amp circuits and, 341–344
  PSpice analysis and, 344–346
  RLC circuits and, 310–336
  smoothing circuits and, 352–353
Second-order differential equation, 316
Selectivity, 633
Self-inductance, 557
Siemens, 31
Signals, 9; *see also* Frequency
  AM, 371–375, 656–658, 823, 839–842, 844, A11
  convolution of, 697–706
  crossover networks and, 660–661
  Fourier series and, 758–764; *see also* Fourier series
  Fourier transform and, 814–820; *see also* Fourier transform
  Nyquist interval and, 842
  radio and, 656–658
  sampling and, 842–843
  touch-tone telephones and, 658–660
Sign convention, 10–11, 222
Signum function, 830–831
Simple pole/zero plot, 621–622
Sinc function, 786, 830
Sine wave oscillators, 439–441
Singularity functions
  gate, 265–266
  sawtooth, 266–268
  unit impulse, 263–264
  unit ramp, 264–265, 268–269, 295
  unit step, 261–262, 268–269, 274
Sinor plot, 377–378
Sinusoidal steady-state analysis, 413; *see also* Laplace transforms
  AC circuits and, 431–437
  capacitance multiplier and, 437–439
  exercises for, 442–455
  Fourier series and, 758; *see also* Fourier series
  frequency and, 614; *see also* Frequency
  maximum average power transfer and, 464–467
  mesh analysis and, 417–421
  nodal analysis and, 414–417
  Norton circuits and, 426–427, 430–431
  operational amplifiers and, 431–433
  oscillators and, 439–441
  PSpice and, 434–437
  source transformation and, 425–426
  superposition theorem and, 421–424
  Thevenin circuits and, 426–429
Sinusoids, 370, 382, 400; *see also* Phasors
  argument of, 371–375
  Kirchhoff's laws and, 388–389

Sinusoids—*Cont.*
  periodic time and, 371–375
  voltage and, 371
Smoothing circuits, 352–353
Software; *see also* MATLAB; PSpice
  Maple and, 759
  Mathcad and, 759
Solenoids; *see* Inductance
Source-free circuits
  NRC, 250–255
  RL, 255–261
Source modeling, 153–156
Source transformation, 133–137, 425–426
Spark plugs, 352
Spectra
  analyzers, 796, 801
  Fourier series, 784–790; *see also* Fourier series
  Fourier transform, 815; *see also* Fourier transform
  line, 786
  phase, 761, 765–766, 785
Stability, 738–741
State variables, 737–738
  circuit analysis and, 733
  defined, 731
  identity matrix and, 732
  Kirchhoff's laws and, 734–736
  representation of, 732–733
Stator, 505
Steady-state response, 271
  frequency and, 614; *see also* Frequency
  maximum average power transfer and, 464–467
Steinmetz, Charles Proteus, 369, 375
Step-down transformer, 575
Step response, 261–262, 268
  Kirchhoff's laws and, 279
  RC circuits and, 269–275
  RLC circuits and, 328–336
  RL circuits and, 276–280
Subtractors, 186
Summing amplifier, 184–185
Superheterodyne receiver, 657
Supermesh, 96–97, 430
Supernodes, 86–87
  nodal analysis and, 414–417
Superposition, 128–133, 159, 778
  amplifiers and, 183
  Norton's theorem and, 146–148
  sinusoidal steady-state analysis and, 421–424
  Thevenin's theorem and, 146–148
Switching functions; *see* Singularity functions
Symmetry
  cosine series and, 767
  even, 767–768, 774–775
  Fourier series and, 767–776
  half-wave, 770–774
  impedance and, 856
  odd, 769–770
Synthesis, 741–745
Systems
  balanced, 520–526
  linearity and, 716
  matrices and, 733
  state variables and, 731–738
  transfer function and, 726–731; *see also* Transfer function
  unbalanced, 526–530

T

Tap, 580–581
Telegraphs, 675
Telephones, 230, 658–660

Television, 15–16, 222, 230, 555, 813
  inductance and, 222, 230
  resonance and, 631
  transformers and, 568
Teller, Edward, 813
Tesla, Nikola, 503
Theory and Calculation of AC Phenomena (Steinmetz), 369
Thevenin's theory, 159
  defined, 137
  derivation of, 146–148
  hybrid parameters and, 865, 866
  maximum power theorem and, 148–150
  network topology and, 138–143
  op amps and, 175
  RC circuits and, 275
  resistance measurement and, 156–158
  RL circuits and, 257–258, 278
  sinusoidal steady-state analysis and, 426–429
  source modeling and, 153–156
  step response and, 275, 278–279
  transformers and, 576
  transistor circuits and, 887
  transmission parameters and, 870–871
Three-phase circuits, 503, 543–554
  balanced delta-delta, 514–516
  balanced delta-Y, 516–520
  balanced voltages and, 505–508
  balanced Y-delta, 512–514
  balanced Y-Y, 508–512
  economy of, 504–505
  importance of, 504–505
  load of, 504–505
  power and, 520–526, 534–540
  PSpice analysis and, 530–534
  residential wiring and, 540–542
  unbalanced, 526–530
Three-phase transformers, 584–587
Three-wattmeter method, 534–537
Tightly coupled condition, 565–566
Time
  AC operational amplifiers and, 431–433
  amperage and, 7
  amplitude spectrum and, 761
  average power and, 458–467
  circuit element modeling and, 717–722
  constant, 251–253, 259–261, 269–280, 293
  delay, 680
  differentiation, 681–682, 823–824
  effective value and, 468–470
  energy and, 11
  Fourier series and, 758–811; *see also* Fourier series
  Fourier transform and, 814–820; *see also* Fourier transform
  frequency and, 761; *see also* Frequency
  instantaneous power and, 458–461
  integration, 682–684, 824
  Laplace transforms and, 676–706
  periodicity, 684–685
  phase spectrum of, 761
  phasors and, 377–380, 383–392
  power and, 10
  rms value and, 468–470
  scaling and, 821–822
  shift, 680–681, 822–823
  singularity functions and, 261–269
  sinusoids and, 371–375
  step response and, 269–280
  superposition theorem and, 421–424
  symmetry and, 767–776
  unit impulse response and, 727
Touch-tone telephones, 658–660

Transfer function
  Bode plots and, 619–630
  crossover networks and, 660–661
  defined, 614
  filters and, 638–649
  Fourier transform and, 833–835
  ladder network synthesis and, 888–891
  Laplace transforms and, 726–731; see also Laplace transforms
  notch, 646–647
  obtaining, 615–617
  possible types of, 615
  stability and, 738–741
  synthesis and, 741–745
  unit impulse response and, 727
  zero root and, 615
Transfer impedances, 856
Transformation ratio, 574
Transformers, 222, 352
  air-core, 568
  bank of, 584
  complex power and, 576
  cost of, 591–592
  description of, 556
  ideal, 573–580, 598
  ideal autotransformers and, 580–584
  isolation, 575, 581, 592–593
  Kirchhoff's laws and, 583
  linear, 567–573
  as matching device, 594–595
  materials of, 567–568
  mesh analysis and, 568
  nodal analysis and, 570
  primary winding and, 567
  rating of, 575
  reflecting impedance and, 576–577
  secondary winding and, 567
  step-down, 575
  three-phase, 584–587
Transient response, 271–272
  PSpice and, 285–288, A38–A46
  smoothing circuits and, 352–353
Transistors, 14, 108–110
  bipolar junction, 106–107
  field-effect, 106
  filters and, 638, 643–649
  Kirchhoff's laws and, 568
  npn, 106
  pnp, 106
  two-port networks and, 884–888
Transmission lines, 505
Transmission parameters, 867–871
Transresistance amplifiers, 181
Trigonometry, 371–375
  Fourier series and, 758–767
  hyperbolic functions, A20
  identities for, A19–A20
  Laplace transforms and, 679; see also Laplace transforms
Tuning circuit, 657–658
Turns ratio, 574, 585
Two-port networks, 892
  admittance parameters and, 859–862
  cascading of, 877
  conversion of, 873
  defined, 854
  exercises for, 893–904
  hybrid parameters and, 862–867
  impedance parameters and, 854–858
  interconnection of, 875–881

Two-port networks—Cont.
  ladder synthesis and, 888–891
  parameter relationships and, 871–875
  PSpice and, 881–884
  reciprocal, 856, 860
  transistor circuits and, 884–888
  transmission parameters and, 867–871
Two-sided Laplace transform, 677
Two-wattmeter method, 535–540

U

Unbalanced systems, 526–530
Undamped natural frequency, 317
Underdamped case, 317–319, 323–329
Unit impulse function, 263–264, 678, 727
Unit ramp function, 264–265, 268–269, 295, 678
Unit step function, 678
  Fourier transform and, 828
  step response and, 261–262, 268–280, 328–336, 703
Unity gain amplifier, 182
Utilities, 17–18, 486–488

V

Volta, Alessandro Antonio, 3, 9
Voltage, 4
  AC power conservation and, 478–481
  apparent power and, 471–473
  balanced delta-delta connection and, 514–516
  balanced delta-Y connection and, 516–520
  in balanced systems, 520–526
  balanced three-phase, 505–508
  balanced Y-delta connection and, 512–514
  balanced Y-Y connection and, 508–512
  capacitance multiplier and, 437–439
  capacitors and, 212–222
  circuit analysis and, 722–726
  circuit element modeling and, 717–722
  complex power and, 473–477
  current converters and, 193
  defined, 9
  division, 42–43, 157–158, 389–392, 396
  duality principle and, 346–349
  filters and, 638–649
  follower, 182
  Fourier series and, 780–784; see also Fourier series
  Fourier transform and, 833–835; see also Fourier transform
  gain and, 175, 618–630; see also Gain
  impedance and, 385–392
  inductance and, 222–230, 556–562
  instantaneous power and, 458–461
  Kirchhoff's law and, 35–41, 62
  ladder network synthesis and, 888–891
  linearity and, 126–128
  line-to-line, 509–510
  maximum power theorem and, 148–150
  mesh analysis and, 90–103, 417–421
  network parameters and, 854–875
  nodal analysis and, 78–90, 98–103
  Norton's theorem and, 143–148
  Ohm's law and, 28–33
  op amps and, 174–177, 431–433; see also Operational amplifiers
  oscillators and, 439–441
  Parseval's theorem and, 785
  phase-shifters and, 395–398

Voltage—Cont.
  phasors and, 383–389
  power factor and, 481–483; see also Power
  primary winding and, 567
  RC circuits and, 250–255, 269–275
  reference node and, 78–79
  residential wiring and, 540–542
  resistance measurement and, 156–158
  resonance and, 630–638
  RLC circuits and, 310–336
  RL circuits and, 255–261, 276–280
  secondary winding and, 567
  singularity functions and, 265–269
  smoothing circuits and, 352–353
  source-free circuits and, 250–261
  source modeling and, 153–156
  source transformation and, 133–137, 425–426
  step response and, 269–280
  superposition and, 128–133, 421–424
  Thevenin/Norton equivalence and, 426–431
  Thevenin's theorem and, 137–143, 146–148
  time constant and, 251–252
  transfer function and, 614–617, 726–731; see also Transfer function
  transformers and, 567–587
  transistors and, 106–110, 884–888
  two-port networks and, 854–875; see also Two-port networks
  unbalanced systems and, 526–530
  underdamped case and, 323–324
Voltage-controlled current source (VCCS), 14
Voltage-controlled voltage source (VCVS), 14
Volt-ampere (VA) unit, 474–475

W

Watson, James, 715
Watt-hours, 11, 17–18
Wattmeter, 484–485
  power measurement and, 534–540
Watts, 10, 458–461
Westinghouse, George, 503
Wheatstone bridge, 156–158
Wien-bridge oscillator, 439–441
Winding capacitance, 224
Winding resistance, 224
Wiring, 540–542

Y

Y-delta system
  three-phase circuits and, 512–514
  three-phase transformer and, 585
  transformations, 51–55, 133–137
Y-load, 507, 543
  power measurement and, 534–540
  unbalanced systems and, 526–530
Y parameters, 859–862
Y-Y system
  three-phase circuits and, 508–512
  three-phase transformers and, 584

Z

Zero root, 615
Z parameters, 854–858